BIOCHEMISTRY

BY ABRAHAM CANTAROW, M.D.

PROFESSOR OF BIOCHEMISTRY, JEFFERSON MEDICAL COLLEGE

AND BERNARD SCHEPARTZ, Ph.D.

ASSISTANT PROFESSOR OF BIOCHEMISTRY, JEFFERSON MEDICAL COLLEGE

ILLUSTRATED

W. B. SAUNDERS COMPANY

PHILADELPHIA AND LONDON

PREFACE

This book is designed primarily to meet the needs of the first-year medical student. We feel that this aim requires no apology. However, the addition of another textbook of biochemistry to the several already available does require some explanation.

Long experience with students at every stage of their medical education, both undergraduate and postgraduate, has impressed us with the fact that their comprehension of biochemistry is generally poorer than that of the other medical sciences. Although biochemistry currently occupies a focal position in all of the medical sciences, as well as in clinical medicine, this is the one subject in the medical curriculum that the average student is not adequately equipped to grasp readily in the form in which it is usually presented.

The difficulty in this connection stems mainly from the fact that the enormous progress in this field in recent years has been in highly specialized areas, comprehension of which is impeded by barriers of technical nomenclature and inadequate grounding in such basic disciplines as organic and physical chemistry. The student often becomes discouraged, and acquires a feeling of inadequacy which interferes seriously with his desire and ability to comprehend those phases of the subject which he is really in a position to understand.

Attempts to supply these deficiencies in a textbook of biochemistry for medical students often lead to more confusion than enlightenment, for they can usually be considered only superficially. Moreover, if isolated aspects of fundamental chemistry are discussed in detail, they assume an importance that is out of proportion to the place they occupy in the over-all picture of biochemistry, and the student has difficulty in appreciating their true significance for biochemical phenoma. We feel that elucidation of such matters should be left to textbooks on these subjects and to the classroom.

Emphasis has been placed here on dynamic aspects of biochemistry, rather than on fundamental considerations of structure, reactions, and basic chemical principles, except insofar as these have a direct bearing on the role of the substances in question in mammalian physiology. Admittedly, these distinctions are not always well defined, for many of these relationships are as yet imperfectly understood. We have attempted to provide an adequate description of substances of major biological importance. However, insofar as is feasible, isolated considerations of abstract chemical and physicochemical topics are avoided, and these are introduced into the text and discussed mainly in direct relation to their pertinence to biological phenomena.

The major emphasis throughout is on the integration of biochemical processes and on the mechanisms involved in the regulation and coordination of various aspects of metabolism. The aim is to enable the student to perceive the nature of metabolic interrelations and homeostasis, and thus to place biochemistry in its proper relation to physiology, normal and pathological. It has been our experience that this approach best serves to arouse the student's interest and imagination and to stimulate his desire to grasp the essential features of this subject.

There has been a growing tendency to include in textbooks of biochemistry an increasing volume of material on biochemical abnormalities in disease. Much of this is irrelevant to a consideration of physiological chemistry, and is inadequate for any other purpose. We believe that, whereas every attempt should be made to indicate the possible applications of biochemical facts and principles in his future studies of disease processes, the first-year student is not in a position to appreciate the significance of clinical or pathological biochemistry, except in a very general way. He knows nothing of the causes, nature, or effects of diseases, which, to him, are merely names, without real meaning. Emphasis in this connection should be placed on aberrations of normal mechanisms, rather than on isolated details, appreciation of which requires a background of information concerning disease processes and special organ pathology which he has not yet acquired.

These two major questions, namely, how little material should be included on fundamental aspects of organic and physical chemistry, and how much on biochemical abnormalities in disease, have been answered here rather arbitrarily. The manner in which the former is dealt with has been indicated. The view has been taken that disease states should be introduced into the discussion whenever an understanding of the incident biochemical aberrations aids in an understanding of normal reactions and mechanisms. Diabetes mellitus and disturbances of "acid-base" balance are excellent examples of such conditions.

With few exceptions, the main subject headings are those employed in the majority of current textbooks on this subject. Because we feel that a detailed consideration of dietetics does not fall within the province of biochemistry, data on the composition of foods are not presented in detail, and foodstuffs are discussed only with reference to the general nutritional significance of proteins, carbohydrates, and fats.

Each topic is discussed as an entity, with extensive cross references to more detailed discussions of various aspects in other sections. This permits a logical, comprehensive, presentation of each subject, and consecutive reading of any section without the necessity of referring frequently to others, which disrupts the continuity of thought.

It is our belief that numerous literature references in the text are superfluous, if not indeed undesirable in a book of this nature. We feel that at this educational level the student derives more benefit, and less confusion, from critical reviews than from original contributions in highly specialized fields, which he may not be able to understand fully, and which he is seldom able to evaluate adequately. In the interests of reading continuity, we have omitted virtually all direct references from the text. There is a brief list of selected reading references at the end of each chapter, mainly to monographic discussions and reviews.

The first-year medical student must do a truly enormous amount of reading. He must, therefore, be able to get desired information with a minimum expenditure of time. To this end, no feature of a textbook is more important than its index. We have attempted to index each important item in the text according to the various points of view from which it may be approached in the mind of the student.

A textbook, in which the current status of a subject is surveyed, represents a synthesis of the contributions of all workers in the field. We are particularly indebted to those who have generously permitted reproduction of figures and tabulated data from their original publications. We wish to express our thanks also to the publishers, for their unfailing cooperation at every stage of the preparation of this book.

Philadelphia, Pa.

A. C.
B. S.

CONTENTS

1

CHEMISTRY OF CARBOHYDRATES

INTRODUCTION

DEFINITION AND BIOLOGICAL SIGNIFICANCE. For the purposes of this chapter we may define carbohydrates as polyhydroxylic aldehydes and ketones (monosaccharides), their polymers (oligosaccharides and polysaccharides), reduction products (polyhydric alcohols and cyclitols), oxidation products (aldonic, uronic, and saccharic acids), substitution products (amino sugars), and esters (sulfates and phosphates).

The chief function of carbohydrate in the animal organism is that of a fuel, the degradation of which to carbon dioxide and water represents a major source of energy. In addition, certain products of carbohydrate metabolism, as will be seen later, aid in the breakdown of many foodstuffs, acting as catalysts or promoters of oxidations. When the supply of these carbohydrate metabolites runs low, owing to faulty metabolism, widespread disorders prevail, as in diabetes mellitus. Carbohydrate can also be used as a starting material for the biological synthesis of other types of compounds in the body, such as fatty acids and certain amino acids. A final and more obscure function of carbohydrate is its role in the structure of certain biologically important compounds, such as glycolipids, glycoproteins, heparin, nucleic acids, and other substances which will be mentioned in subsequent discussions.

TYPES FOUND IN NATURE. Quantitatively, starch is the most important carbohydrate in the human diet. It is one of a class of carbohydrates of high molecular weight known as polysaccharides. These materials are characterized by a relatively low solubility in their native state, in keeping with their functions in plants and animals as either storage forms or supporting and protecting structures for the tissues. Some polysaccharides, when freed from other tissue constituents, can be dispersed in colloidal form in water. All are insoluble in aqueous ethanol and organic solvents generally. Starch and cellulose are storage and supporting polysaccharides, respectively, in the plant world, while glycogen represents the storage form of carbohydrate in animals.

Many other carbohydrates of lower molecular weight are found in nature. The mono- and oligosaccharides are crystalline substances, soluble in water and dilute ethanol, insoluble in most organic solvents. Among the oligosaccharides, sucrose, lactose, and maltose are of considerable biological importance. Glucose, fructose, galactose, mannose, ribose, and desoxyribose are examples of monosaccharides which will be discussed in this chapter. It may be appropriate to mention at this point that, regardless of the form in which a carbohydrate happens to be ingested, it must be transformed into a monosaccharide for absorption and metabolism, thus emphasizing the significance of monosaccharides in the animal economy. As food for thought we append the fact that the monosaccharide, glucose, is the chief nutrient of the brain.

The sugar alcohols, acids, and amino sugars are of lesser quantitative importance than the major groups mentioned above. Nevertheless they are involved (either as such, or as constituents of more complex compounds) in metabolic processes.

In recent years it has been shown that phosphorylation of the carbohydrates is a metabolic reaction which must occur before these compounds can be oxidized by the body. The phosphate esters, therefore, represent metabolically active carbohydrates.

CLASSIFICATION AND CONFIGURATION

CLASSIFICATION AND NOMENCLATURE. A monosaccharide is a carbohydrate which cannot be broken down to simpler substances by acid hydrolysis. Oligosaccharides and polysaccharides consist of monosaccharide units, combined by the abstraction of the elements of water from each two monosaccharides in the chain. Although no strict dividing line is possible, the term "oligosaccharide" is usually applied to carbohydrates yielding two to ten monosaccharide units on hydrolysis; beyond this, the compounds are called "polysaccharides." Depending on the number of constituent monosaccharide units, the oligosaccharides are called "disaccharides," "trisaccharides," etc.

The characteristic ending in naming mono- and oligosaccharides (commonly called "sugars") is -ose. The portion of the name preceding this, however, reflects the history and origin of the compound more than it does chemical systematics, e.g., lactose (milk sugar). Polysaccharides are not usually named systematically; their historical names are universally used.

Length of the carbon chain forms one basis for the classification of the monosaccharides. The simplest compound containing a hydroxyl group and a carbonyl function is glycolic aldehyde, or glycolaldehyde. Containing two carbon atoms, this would be called a diose. Monosaccharides of three to six carbon atoms are trioses, tetroses, pentoses, and hexoses, respectively.

Each group of monosaccharides except the diose has the possibility of containing both aldehydic and ketonic members. Thus glyceraldehyde and dihydroxyacetone are an aldotriose and ketotriose in the systematic nomenclature.

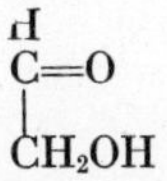

$$
\begin{array}{c}
\overset{\text{H}}{\underset{|}{\text{C}}}=\text{O} \\
| \\
\text{CH}_2\text{OH}
\end{array}
$$

Glycolaldehyde

A final basis for the classification of the monosaccharides and their derivatives is concerned with stereochemical families of compounds. On this basis, which will be discussed in some detail in the following section, compounds are classified as belonging to the D or L series.

An outline of the classification of carbohydrates is given in Table 1. It will be explained in some detail in later discussions.

Table 1. Classification of the Carbohydrates

I. Simple monosaccharides
  A. Diose
  B. Trioses
    1. Aldotriose
    2. Ketotriose
  C. Tetroses
  D. Pentoses
    1. Aldopentoses
    2. Ketopentoses
    3. Desoxypentoses
  E. Hexoses
    1. Aldohexoses
    2. Ketohexoses
    3. Desoxyhexoses
II. Acetal derivatives of I.
  A. Glycosides
  B. Oligosaccharides
    1. Disaccharides
      a. Reducing
      b. Non-reducing
    2. Tri-, tetra-sacch., etc.
  C. Polysaccharides
    1. Homosaccharidic
      a. Pentosans
      b. Hexosans
    2. Heterosaccharidic
      a. Pentosans

      b. Hexosans
      c. Pento-hexosans
III. Substituted, derived, conjugated
    monosaccharides
  A. Amino sugars
  B. Sugar alcohols
    1. Open-chain polyols
    2. Cyclitols
  C. Sugar acids
    1. Aldonic
    2. Uronic
    3. Saccharic
  D. Esters
    1. Sulfuric
    2. Phosphoric
IV. Polymers of III.
  A. Homosaccharidic
    1. Non-nitrogenous
    2. Nitrogenous
  B. Heterosaccharidic
    1. Non-nitrogenous
    2. Nitrogenous
      (mucopolysacch.)
      a. Neutral
      b. Acidic
        (1) Sulfate-free
        (2) Sulfate-containing

ASYMMETRIC CARBON ATOMS AND OPTICAL ISOMERISM. A carbon atom bearing four different groups is spoken of as asymmetric. As can be seen in the accompanying diagram, two different spatial arrangements

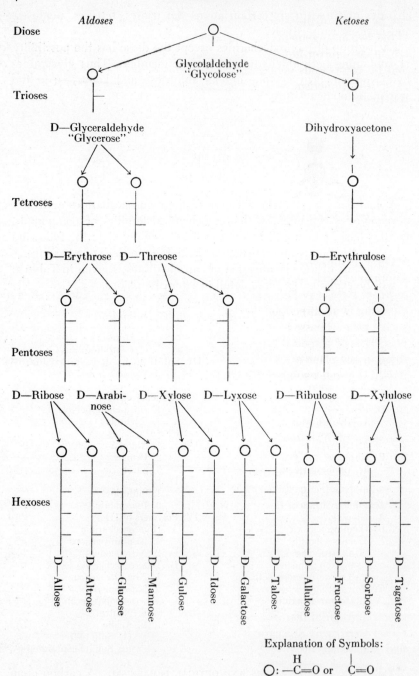

Fig. 1.   D—Family of sugars.

Explanation of Symbols:

$\bigcirc$: $-\overset{\text{H}}{\underset{}{\text{C}}}=\text{O}$ or $\overset{|}{\underset{|}{\text{C}}}=\text{O}$

—:   HO— or —OH

Terminal |: CH_2OH or CH_2OH

can be made of the groups attached to the central atom, and models of the two arrangements will be found to be non-superimposable. They are, in fact, mirror-images of each other (Fig. 2). The isomerism exhibited by compounds containing asymmetric carbon atoms is one type of optical isomerism, and is the only type which will be discussed in this book.

Fig. 2. Mirror images (from Noller: Chemistry of Organic Compounds, W. B. Saunders Company, 1951, p. 324)

Optical isomerism receives its name from the peculiar effect which solutions of such an isomer have on plane polarized light. A beam of ordinary light may be regarded as a bundle of electromagnetic waves vibrating in all directions perpendicular to the axis of the beam. When such a beam is passed through a properly cut crystal of certain minerals or a sheet of a special plastic known as Polaroid, all vibrations except those in one plane are eliminated. If this "plane polarized" light is now passed through a solution of an optical isomer, the plane will be found to be rotated to the left (levorotation) or an equal number of degrees to the right (dextrorotation), depending upon which of the two isomers is under examination. Such rotations are designated $(-)$ and $(+)$, respectively, and represent the only physicochemical difference between optical isomers, or "enantiomorphs," as they are called.

Examination of the formula for glyceraldehyde discloses the presence of an asymmetric carbon atom. The dextrorotatory form is customarily written with the secondary alcoholic hydroxyl extending to the right when the aldehyde group is at the top of the molecule. This isomer is designated "D-glyceraldehyde." Its enantiomorph, the levorotatory L-glyceraldehyde, is written with the corresponding hydroxyl group extending to the left.

Higher sugars contain additional asymmetric carbon atoms. A molecule containing n asymmetric carbon atoms, in the absence of certain special structural features, can exist in 2^n optically isomeric forms. The rather large array of sugars which results from this isomerism is simplified somewhat by dividing the monosaccharides into two families. Sugars whose asymmetric carbon atom farthest from the aldehyde or ketone group has the same spatial arrangement as that of D-glyceraldehyde are called "D sugars"; the corresponding relationship to L-glyceraldehyde places the compound in the L series. The hydroxyl groups involved are then written as for the parent trioses. It must be emphasized that this classification is based upon the spatial arrangement in the molecules, and actually means that the carbohydrates so named can be synthesized chemically from, or degraded chemically to, the proper glyceraldehyde. The optical rotations of the higher sugars, being the resultant of several asymmetric groups in the molecule, need not agree with the direction of rotation of the parent glyceraldehyde. Thus, the naturally occurring glucose and fructose are both members of the D series, but the former is dextrorotatory while the latter is levorotatory. Rotation is expressed, if it is necessary, by the signs + or —, following the designation for configuration, i.e., $D(-)$, $D(+)$, $L(-)$, $L(+)$.

It is a matter of considerable importance that, when a compound which might be expected to contain an asymmetric carbon atom is synthesized by the methods of organic chemistry, an optically inactive product is obtained. In fact, it can be shown that an equimolar mixture of D and L forms, a so-called "racemic mixture," is produced. Nature, however, prefers "asymmetric synthesis," and practically always manufactures only one of the two possible enantiomorphs. This has given rise to the concept that the machinery of biological synthesis, the enzyme system, is itself spatially asymmetric. As is indicated elsewhere (p. 221), the high degree of specificity of enzymes is in agreement with this concept. The carbohydrates found in nature belong, with few exceptions, to the D series, indicating some fundamental optical similarity in most of the enzyme systems having to do with carbohydrate synthesis in the plant and animal kingdoms.

CYCLIC STRUCTURES OF THE SUGARS. Up to this point the sugars have been depicted as open-chain polyhydroxylic aldehydes and ketones. However, there is conclusive evidence that, in the natural state, the aldehyde or ketone group exists in a condensed form, as a hemi-acetal, by combination with one of the alcoholic hydroxyl groups in the same molecule. The formation of a hemi-acetal from a simple aldehyde and simple alcohol occurs as follows:

$$R_1-\overset{\overset{\displaystyle H}{|}}{C}=O + HO-R_2 \;\longrightarrow\; R_1-\overset{\overset{\displaystyle H}{|}}{\underset{\underset{\displaystyle O-R_2}{|}}{C}}-OH$$

If the two reacting groups belong to the same molecule, a cyclic structure must result. If we take the open-chain form of D-glucose, which we may call aldehydo-D-glucose, and condense the aldehyde group on Carbon 1 with the alcohol group on Carbon 5, as shown on page 7, two different forms of glucose may be produced. Carbon 1, after the cyclization, has four different groups attached to it, and is therefore an asymmetric carbon atom. If the hydrogen atom of the participating alcohol group catches the carbonyl oxygen atom of the rotating aldehyde group on one side of the chain, the resulting new hydroxyl group will extend to the right, forming α-glucose. The analogous combination, forming the new hydroxyl group on the other side of the chain, produces β-glucose. The two cyclic compounds will have different optical rotations, but they will not be equal in magnitude and opposite in sign, as is the case with enantiomorphs, because the compounds as a whole are not mirror-images of each other.

| β-D-Glucose | Aldehydo-D-glucose | α-D-Glucose |
| (β-D-Glucopyranose) | | (α-D-Glucopyranose) |

If ordinary, crystalline glucose (which happens to be the α form) is dissolved in water, a gradual change in optical rotation can be observed, finally arriving at a steady value. This change in optical rotation is called "mutarotation," and represents a conversion, in this case, from α-glucose to an equilibrium mixture of the α and β forms. Pure β-glucose can be prepared in the crystalline state, and when dissolved in water undergoes a similar mutarotation, changing from its characteristic optical rotation to a final value exactly the same as that found in the case of mutarotation of α-glucose. The mechanism of mutarotation probably involves opening of the hemi-acetal ring to form traces of the aldehyde form, then recondensation to the cyclic forms. The aldehyde form is extremely unstable and exists only as a transient intermediate in carbohydrate reactions.

The cyclic forms of glucose described thus far have contained six-membered rings. By analogy with the structure of the compound pyran, such rings are called "pyranose forms." In some cases carbohydrates are found to contain five-membered rings. These forms are called "furanose," from the parent structure, furan. Pyranose rings are generally more stable than furanose rings.

Haworth has illustrated the cyclic forms of the sugars by "perspective" formulas. While these formulas are undoubtedly closer to the actual steric shapes of the molecules in nature, they are a source of confusion to the student who is not specializing in organic chemistry and are not considered further in this book.

The student will recall from organic chemistry that a characteristic reaction of aldehydes is the reduction of alkaline copper reagents (Fehling's solution) from the cupric to the cuprous state, with concomitant oxidation of the aldehyde group. Aldose sugars exhibit the same reaction, so that we must assume that the aldehyde group, while apparently blocked in hemi-acetal formation, is still potentially available for certain reactions. There is some evidence that a small amount of the aldehydo sugar is present in solution at all times, in equilibrium with the cyclic forms of the carbohydrate.

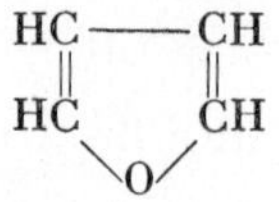

Furan 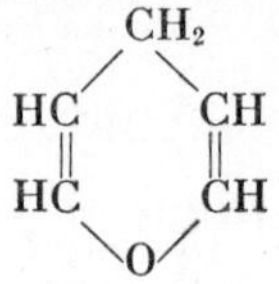   Pyran 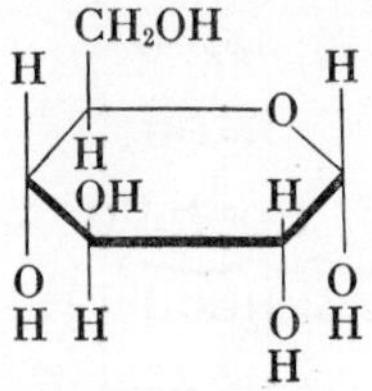   Haworth formula, α-D-Glucopyranose

The ketose sugars also are found to reduce alkaline copper reagents, in contrast to ordinary ketones. It will be noted that, adjacent to the carbonyl group of the ketoses, there are two alcohol groups. A hydroxyl group and ketone group, when existing side by side, form a grouping known as a ketol, and such a combination acts toward many reagents much like an aldehyde. Both aldoses and ketoses, then, so long as their hemi-acetal forms can revert to the open-chain aldehydo and keto sugars, are "reducing sugars."

SIMPLE MONOSACCHARIDES OF BIOLOGICAL IMPORTANCE

DIOSE. Glycolaldehyde, the structure of which has already been given, differs from the higher aldoses in not containing an asymmetric carbon atom, and in not being truly polyhydroxylic. For these reasons some textbooks have not included this compound among the true carbohydrates. However, recent work has implicated glycolaldehyde in the metabolism of pentoses, providing biological, if not chemical, justification for considering it among the carbohydrates.

TRIOSES. Both D-glyceraldehyde and dihydroxyacetone occur, in the form of phosphate esters, as intermediates in the fermentation and glycolysis of carbohydrates. They are also the probable precursors of the glycerol which the organism synthesizes and incorporates into various types of lipids.

PENTOSES. The three most important pentoses from the standpoint of animal biochemistry are shown below. Ribose and desoxyribose are constituents of the nucleic acids, and ribose in addition is a part of the structure of certain coenzymes. These two sugars appear to have the furanose ring in their natural state. When combined in nucleic acids and their derivatives, ribose is of the β configuration. The β form given here for desoxyribose is by analogy; its actual state in the nucleic acids is not known.

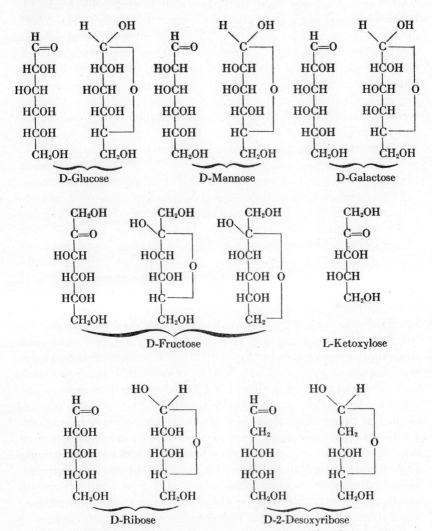

Fig. 3. *Important hexoses and pentoses, open-chain and cyclic formulas*

Ketoxylose is one of the few L sugars found in nature. Its sole importance to the animal economy derives from its excretion in the urine of humans afflicted with a hereditary abnormality in metabolism known as pentosuria.

Arabinose, a pentose closely related to ribose, is of importance only in plants. It is frequently used in the student laboratory as a typical pentose because it is readily available and inexpensive.

HEXOSES.   In addition to glucose, the formulas for which were given previously, other important hexoses are the aldoses, mannose and galactose, and the ketose, fructose.

Glucose and fructose occur in the free state in certain foodstuffs, are found combined with each other in sucrose (ordinary table-sugar), and form the basic units from which many plant and animal polysaccharides are constructed. Older names for these two sugars are dextrose (for glucose) and levulose (for fructose), based on their optical rotations. Fructose is shown with two cyclic forms, fructopyranose being the configuration of the free sugar, while the furanose structure seems to occur whenever fructose exists combined in oligosaccharides and polysaccharides.

D-Galactose is found in the animal organism in the disaccharide, lactose (milk sugar), and in glycolipids known as cerebrosides. Polysaccharides containing mannose are constituents of certain glycoproteins.

Desoxyhexoses have usually been thought of in connection with the plant world. However, the unusual sugar, L-fucose (6-desoxy-L-galactose), has recently been isolated from the blood-group polysaccharides of animals and humans (p. 733).

ACETAL DERIVATIVES OF THE SIMPLE MONOSACCHARIDES

ACETALS.   The formation of hemi-acetals was shown previously. The hydroxyl group resulting from this reaction can react with compounds containing a replaceable hydrogen atom, splitting out water and forming compounds known as acetals. It is obvious that, since the hemi-acetal forms of the parent sugars can be either α or β, two series of acetals are also possible. Since acetalization blocks any possible opening of the ring to form the aldehydo sugar, the sugar acetals show no mutarotation. Other characteristic reactions of carbonyl groups, such as reduction of alkaline copper reagents, are also absent. Acetals are generally stable toward alkali, but easily hydrolyzed by acids. The many biologically important compounds which are acetal derivatives of the simple monosaccharides will be discussed in the following sections.

GLYCOSIDES.   When the group joined to the sugar in acetal linkage is not a carbohydrate, the resulting acetal is called a glycoside, and the non-sugar moiety is known as the aglycon. Glycosides are named from their constituent parts as follows: aglycon—the symbol α or β to indicate the configuration of the original hemi-acetal—the parent sugar, replacing the ending "ose" by "oside," and frequently indicating which cyclic form is involved. The full name for the substance given on page 11, for example, is methyl α-D-glucopyranoside, commonly abbreviated to methyl α-glucoside:

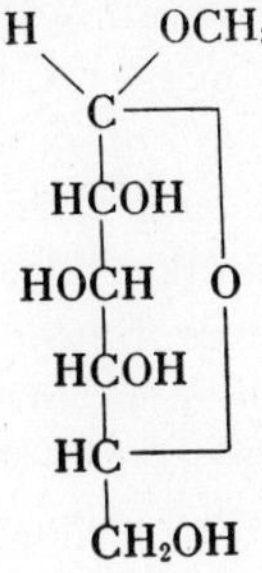

$$
\begin{array}{c}
\text{H} \qquad \text{OCH}_3 \\
\diagdown \qquad \diagup \\
\text{C} \\
| \\
\text{HCOH} \\
| \\
\text{HOCH} \qquad \text{O} \\
| \\
\text{HCOH} \\
| \\
\text{HC} \\
| \\
\text{CH}_2\text{OH}
\end{array}
$$

In contrast to the simple aglycon, methanol, used above, most of those found in biological products are very complex. Many of the red, violet, and blue pigments found in the plant world are present in their natural state as glycosides, the aglycons being rather complex, heterocyclic compounds. Some glycosides of medical interest contain phenanthrene derivatives as aglycons, such as the cardiac glycosides (from the Digitalis plant) and the saponins (hemolytic poisons, widely distributed in plants). The cerebrosides, glycolipids found especially in the nervous system of animals, contain galactose in a glycosidic linkage. Two of the component parts of the antibiotic, streptomycin, are coupled as a glycoside. Finally, many compounds excreted in the urine of animals, including both foreign substances administered experimentally or therapeutically (e.g., menthol) as well as those found or produced naturally within the organism (certain hormones and their breakdown products), are conjugated as glycosides with a glucose derivative, glucuronic acid.

The glycosides mentioned thus far have involved an aglycon linked to the parent sugar through an oxygen atom. A group of glycosides of great biological importance, the nucleosides, contains nitrogenous bases as aglycons, the bond to the sugar being formed through a nitrogen atom. These glycosides occur in the nucleic acids and some related compounds. The carbohydrate portions of the nucleosides are D-ribose and D-2-desoxyribose. Nucleoside structures are considered in detail elsewhere (p. 100).

DISACCHARIDES. If, instead of being coupled in acetal linkage with an aglycon, a monosaccharide is combined with a second monosaccharide, the result is a disaccharide. Continuation of this process leads to trisaccharides, tetrasaccharides, etc., thus giving rise to the group known as oligosaccharides. Of this group only the disaccharides are of importance in animal biochemistry, and only three disaccharides merit discussion in an elementary textbook: maltose, lactose, and sucrose.

Maltose consists of two glucose units, combined in α-glycosidic linkage. As indicated in the figure, disaccharides can be named on the same basis as glycosides, simply substituting the name of the corresponding monosaccharide for the aglycon. For completeness the particular hydroxyl group of the sugar which enters into combination with the glycosidic monosaccharide is indicated by number. Most oligosaccharides form exceptions to certain generalizations made with respect to acetals, in that they are (with few exceptions) reducing sugars and exhibit mutarotation. A glance at the structure of maltose will reveal that, whereas one of the two potential aldehyde groups is blocked in the acetal linkage and cannot possibly revert to the open-chain form, there is nothing to prevent the other hemi-acetal group from displaying all of the reactions of free glucose. Maltose is important, not *per se*, but because it is the product formed when enzymes known as amylases digest starch in the alimentary tract of the animal organism.

Maltose
4-α-D-Glucopyranose-
α-D-glucopyranoside

Lactose
4-α-D-Glucopyranose-
β-D-galactopyranoside

Sucrose
α-D-Glucopyranosido-
β-D-fructofuranoside
or
β-D-Fructofuranosido-α-
D-glucopyranoside

Lactose differs from maltose in several respects. It is a galactoside rather than a glucoside, and the disaccharide linkage is of the β configuration. Like maltose, however, it is a reducing sugar and mutarotates. Lactose is the sugar found in mammalian milk, which is one of the few places where galactose occurs in animals.

Sucrose, a disaccharide obtained from sugar cane, sugar beets, and other sources, forms an important constituent of the human diet, both directly and in combination in various commercially prepared foodstuffs. Its structure is rather unusual. In addition to glucose it contains a fructofuranose residue, and has the interesting peculiarity of being a double glycoside. The inter-saccharide linkage is formed by an α-glucoside on one side coupled to a β-fructoside on the other. Both the potential aldehyde and potential ketone groups are blocked by the manner of linkage, hence sucrose is non-reducing and does not undergo mutarotation. Since either of the two monosaccharide units may be considered the parent glycosidic compound, sucrose may be named in two ways, as indicated in the figure. Upon hydrolysis, sucrose gives rise to a molecule each of glucopyranose and fructopyranose, the fructose reverting to the more stable ring form in the process. If the optical rotation is followed during the course of the hydrolysis, the initial dextrorotation of the sucrose is observed to gradually decrease, the final mixture actually becoming levorotatory. This is caused by the magnitude of the levorotation of fructose, which is greater numerically than the dextrorotation of glucose, with the result that an equimolar mixture of the two monosaccharides is levorotatory. The hydrolysis of sucrose is therefore called "inversion," and the product is called "invert sugar."

POLYMERS OF THE SIMPLE MONOSACCHARIDES. Molecules of the molecular magnitude of polysaccharides can be formed from derived and substituted monosaccharides, but the complexities and problems of classification of these substances are such that it would be best to discuss the simple polysaccharides first, leaving the treatment of the more complex compounds until after the derived and substituted monosaccharides themselves have been considered.

The elucidation of the structures of the polysaccharides is no simple matter, and the problems in this field, as will become evident in the discussions which follow, are far from being completely solved. Identification of the monosaccharide constituents of the polysaccharide can usually be accomplished after complete acid hydrolysis of the large molecule to its simplest units. Partial hydrolysis, stopping at the disaccharide stage, will often reveal the manner in which the units are linked together; e.g., the formation of maltose from starch suggests that this polysaccharide is composed of glucose residues, combined through Carbon atoms 1 and 4 by an α-glucosidic bond.

A technic known as end-group analysis permits an estimate of molecular weight in certain cases; in others it is an indication of the degree of branching in the polysaccharide chain. It will be readily appreciated that a straight chain of monosaccharide units must possess two terminal residues which differ in structure from the "internal" units. One terminus will be formed by a sugar residue with a potential reducing group, while the other will differ from all other sugars in the chain by containing an extra hydroxyl group. Chemical methods are available for determining the ratio of terminal residues to the total number of units in the chain. For a straight chain this makes possible an estimate of the length of the molecule in terms of monosaccharide units, hence the molecular weight can be calculated. In the case of a branched chain, the average number of monosaccharide units per branch can be determined, but the molecular size must then be found by some other method.

Since the polysaccharides are of colloidal dimensions, special physicochemical methods have been developed for the direct determination of their molecular weights. Such technics as measurement of viscosity, osmotic pressure, light-scattering, and ultracentrifugal sedimentation are among those which have been applied. Most of these methods are of considerable importance in protein chemistry also, and are discussed in some detail elsewhere (p. 67).

The polysaccharides of the simple sugars can be divided into two groups, the homosaccharidic and heterosaccharidic, depending upon whether their constituent monosaccharides are all alike, or are of mixed types. Although some heteropolysaccharides of the mixed hexose or hexose-pentose type are found in plants and bacteria, our discussion will be limited to the homosaccharidic group, which includes several familiar and important members.

Polysaccharides may be called "pentosans" or "hexosans," according to the type of monosaccharide unit involved. A more detailed nomenclature specifies the actual sugar, giving rise to terms such as glucosans (dextrans), fructosans (levans), galactans, mannans, etc. Many dextrans are produced by fungi, yeasts, and bacteria. Levans (inulin), mannans, galactans, and pentosans are widely distributed throughout the plant world. Of all the homosaccharidic polymers of the simple sugars, three glucosans are of sufficient economic or biological importance to warrant a more detailed consideration. These are cellulose, starch, and glycogen.

Cellulose acts as a supporting structure for plant tissues. In the human it merely provides bulk when ingested in plant foodstuffs. Ruminants, however, are able to utilize cellulose, since it is digested by the microorganisms which inhabit their alimentary tracts. By the application of the methods mentioned earlier, it has been determined that cellulose consists of unbranched chains of glucopyranose units, combined through Carbon atoms 1 and 4 by a β-glucosidic linkage. Although it is difficult to avoid some degradation of the native cellulose molecules in the course of determining molecular weights, careful studies have indicated that there may be over 10,000 glucose residues per molecule of cellulose, resulting in a molecular weight of over a million. The cellulose fiber consists of bundles of these chains packed side by side, oriented in the direction of the fiber axis. Thus the tensile properties of cellulose, which account for much of the industrial importance of cotton and related materials, are visible manifestations of a type of architecture existing at the molecular level.

Starch differs functionally from cellulose in being a storage form of nutritionally available carbohydrate in plants. Its importance in human nutrition is immeasurably greater than that of cellulose, for the enzymes of the alimentary tract are able to digest starch and convert it into a product which can be absorbed and utilized. As ordinarily found, starch is a mixture of two types of molecules, amylose (linear) and amylopectin (highly branched). The proportions of the two components vary according to the plant source, and there is evidence of variability in structure among the amyloses and amylopectins themselves.

The amylose components of starch consist of a chain of 1,4-linked α-glucopyranose units. Although completely elongated chains of amylose can be prepared, there is evidence that its molecules are usually wound in the form of a helix, with six glucose residues per turn. The molecular weight has been reported to range around 60,000, corresponding to a chain of 300–400 units.

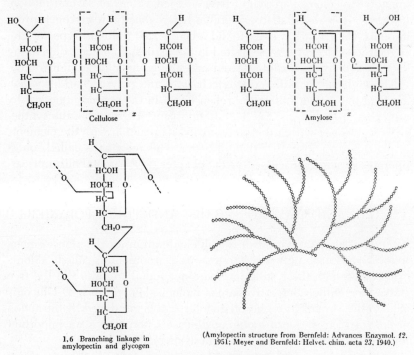

Fig. 4. *Important homopolysaccharides*

1,6 Branching linkage in amylopectin and glycogen

(Amylopectin structure from Bernfeld: Advances Enzymol. *12*, 1951; Meyer and Bernfeld: Helvet. chim. acta *23*, 1940.)

The amylopectins are larger molecules than the amyloses, having molecular weights of 200,000 or more, corresponding to 1300 glucose residues. The molecules are highly branched; it has been estimated that at least 50 branches are present (one for every 24–30 glucose units). While most of the molecule has the same basic unit as the amyloses, 1,4-linked α-glucopyranoses, some other mode of linkage must occur at the points of branching. At the present this is thought to be a 1,6-linkage. The general arrangement of branches within the amylopectin molecule is indicated in Figure 4.

The hydrolysis of starches by enzymes known as amylases proceeds, through a series of lower molecular weight polysaccharides called "dextrins," to maltose as the final product. Reactions of this type occur in the saliva and in the small intestine of animals.

Just as starch is used by the plant as a storage form of carbohydrate, glycogen performs this function in animals. Liver and muscle contain stores of glycogen which are of special importance in intermediary metabolism. The glycogen molecule is similar in many respects to amylopectin (Fig. 4), consisting largely of 1,4-linked α-glycopyranoses, with considerable branching (probably involving 1,6-linkages). Since the average chain length per branch is about 12 glucose units, the glycogen molecule is even more highly ramified than amylopectin. Determinations of molecular weight have yielded values of several million, but there is evidence of considerable heterogeneity in glycogen preparations. In fact, it has been found recently that different types of glycogen molecules may be deposited in the tissues of animals, depending on the carbohydrate administered and the manner of administration.

Although the digestible oligosaccharides and polysaccharides which are ingested as foodstuffs are broken down in the animal organism by a process of hydrolysis, the degradation (and, by reversal, the synthesis) of glycogen within the body involves a reaction with the elements of phosphoric acid, rather than of water. This reaction is called "phosphorolysis," and is discussed in the chapter on the metabolism of carbohydrates (p. 391).

SUGAR ACIDS, AMINO SUGARS, AND THEIR POLYMERS

ALDONIC ACIDS.   Oxidation of the aldehyde group of the aldose sugars to a carboxyl group gives rise to a series of compounds called "aldonic acids." Although these substances are not found in nature in the free state, some of their derivatives are of biological importance. D-Gluconic acid, in the form of its 6-phosphate ester, can be produced by the action of enzymes on the corresponding glucose ester, and is an important intermediate in the biological synthesis of pentoses.

Glyceric acid, in phosphorylated form, is an intermediate in the transformation of carbohydrate to lactic acid in the organism. Ascorbic acid is the anti-scorbutic vitamin C. It is the enol of the γ-lactone formed from the ketoaldonic acid of an L-hexose.

URONIC ACIDS.   If the aldehyde group of an aldose is left intact, but the primary alcohol at the opposite end of the chain is oxidized to a carboxyl group, a uronic acid results. Glucuronic acid is found in the urine, conjugated (as a glucuronide) to foreign substances which may be administered to the organism, or to breakdown products of these substances, or to quite normal metabolites, such as pregnanediol, which arises from the metabolism of the hormone, progesterone (p. 664). In addition, it is a constituent of certain polysaccharides which will be discussed shortly. Galacturonic acid is found in certain plant and bacterial polysaccharides.

SACCHARIC ACIDS. Oxidation at both ends of the monosaccharide molecule produces a saccharic acid, the group taking its name from the acid derived from D-glucose. Mucic acid, from D-galactose, is often used as a derivative for the identification of that sugar. Although tartaric acid, a plant product, is a member of this group of compounds, the saccharic acids are not of importance in animal biochemistry.

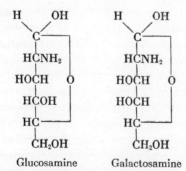

COOH
HCOH
CH₂OH
D-Glyceric Acid

COOH
HCOH
HOCH
HCOH
HCOH
CH₂OH
D-Gluconic acid

Ascorbic acid

D-Glucuronic acid

D-Galacturonic acid   Saccharic acid   Mucic acid

Glucosamine   Galactosamine

Fig. 5. *Sugar acids and amino sugars*

AMINO SUGARS. Two naturally occurring members of this group are derived from glucose and galactose by replacing the hydroxyl group on Carbon atom 2 of each sugar by a primary amino group. Glucosamine, also called "chitosamine," is the basic unit in the polysaccharide, chitin, which forms part of the integument of arthropods. Galactosamine, also known as chondrosamine, is a part of the complex polysaccharides of connective tissue. Both amino sugars are also found in other polysaccharides which are discussed below. The amino groups of both compounds are often present in the acetylated state.

POLYMERS OF THE SUGAR ACIDS AND THE AMINO SUGARS. An example of the non-nitrogenous, homosaccharidic members of this group of polymers is pectin, a substance (really a group of substances) present in fruits, having the economically important property of forming gels with sugar at the proper pH. Pectin is composed of D-galacturonic acid units, connected through a 1,4-linkage, probably as α-glycosides, with many of the carboxyl groups present as methyl esters.

The skeletal material of arthropods contains, in addition to protein, a nitrogenous homopolysaccharide called "chitin." This substance consists of D-glucosamine units, acetylated on the amino group, probably linked by 1,4 β-glucoside bonds.

Among the non-nitrogenous, heterosaccharidic polymers of the substituted and derived sugars are the hemi-celluloses, consisting of hexoses, pentoses, and uronic acids. The plant gums and mucilages have a somewhat similar composition. Some of the pneumococcus polysaccharides and those from the tubercle bacillus also belong to this group.

Although there is no agreement on classification in this field, the nitrogenous heteropolysaccharides would coincide with what are known as mucopolysaccharides in most systems. They may be subdivided into neutral and acidic groups, and the latter further classified as sulfate-free and sulfate-containing. This system omits, for the sake of simplicity, any reference to the protein moiety which may be coupled to the polysaccharide in nature.

Many of the neutral polysaccharides of the various types of pneumococci contain nitrogen, as do the polysaccharides of certain other species of bacteria. Also included in the group of nitrogenous neutral heteropolysaccharides are the blood-group substances, those compounds which account for the immunological reactions between bloods of individuals of the same species. (These substances contain amino acids or peptides as well as carbohydrates.) Of special importance in animal biochemistry are the nitrogenous, neutral polysaccharides found firmly bound to proteins (the combinations called "glycoproteins," p. 46); e.g., ovomucoid, a protein of egg-white, contains mannose, galactose, and N-acetyl-glucosamine. Many protein hormones are united to similar polysaccharides (pp. 698, 699).

Some nitrogenous acidic polysaccharides found in the animal organism occur in the free state, or as dissociable complexes with proteins. These include a number of compounds which are receiving a great deal of attention at the present time. They can be divided into two groups for convenience, depending on the presence or absence of sulfuric acid in the molecule. Hyaluronic acid, a sulfate-free polysaccharide, is found in the vitreous humor, synovial fluid, skin, umbilical cord, and in general (together with protein and other mucopolysaccharides) forms the so-called "ground substance" of the mesenchyme. In connection with the present great interest in diseases of the connective tissues, and the function of hormones of the adrenal cortex in relation to these tissues, investigations of the chemistry of hyaluronic acid and related substances are being pursued intensively. The probable role of hyaluronic acid as an intercellular cement has also focused attention on the possibility that invasion by microorganisms may be facilitated by the secretion of hyaluronidases (enzymes hydrolyzing hyaluronic acids), also called "spreading factors." Hyaluronic acid is known to be composed of alternating units of glucuronic acid and N-acetyl-glucosamine. A recently proposed structure for the repeating unit in this polymer is shown on page 20. It will be noted that the inter-saccharide linkages are β-1,3. As is the case with most mucopolysaccharides, the exact molecular weight of hyaluronic acid in its native state is not known, but it is undoubtedly quite high. Submaxillary (and probably sublingual) glands contain, in addition to neutral mucopolysaccharides, an acidic substance which appears to have gluconic acid in its molecule instead of the usual uronic acid. It contains N-acetyl-glucosamine, and belongs to the sulfate-free class.

A sulfate-containing derivative of hyaluronic acid is found in the cornea. More widely distributed is another mucopolysaccharide (actually a group of related compounds), chondroitin sulfuric acid. As isolated from cartilage, for example, it contains glucuronic acid, N-acetyl-galactosamine, and sulfuric acid.

Gastric mucosa and other sources contain a substance, mucoitin sulfuric acid, differing from chondroitin sulfuric acid in containing glucosamine sulfuric ester instead of the corresponding galactosamine derivative. (Neutral mucopolysaccharides are also found in the gastric mucosa, in combination with proteins.) The "intrinsic factor" involved in the maturation of erythrocytes was formerly believed to be associated with one of the fractions of gastric mucin (p. 262).

The mucopolysaccharides of the various mucous membranes throughout the body, as integral parts of mucoproteins, are thought to have a protective influence on the tissues which secrete them. This protection may be exerted against the action of digestive juices or invading microorganisms; in the latter case the possession of "mucolytic" enzymes by certain bacteria may be a matter of some consequence.

Heparin, a widely distributed mucopolysaccharide with blood anticoagulant properties, contains glucosamine and glucuronic acid residues. It differs from the other compounds thus far discussed in that its sulfuric acid component is present not only as ester sulfate, but also in an amide linkage with the amino group of the glucosamine. Although the structure of heparin is by no means settled, a tentative formula for one of its repeating units is given below.

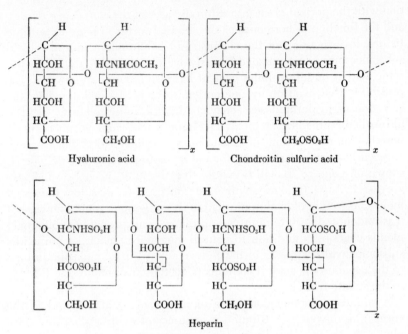

Fig. 6. Mucopolysaccharides

SUGAR ALCOHOLS AND CYCLITOLS

SUGAR ALCOHOLS. Hydrogenation of the aldoses and ketoses reduces the carbonyl groups to alcohol groups, producing a series of compounds known as the sugar alcohols, the acyclic polyols, or the glykitols. Although the alcohols derived from the hexoses (hexitols) have considerable commercial importance as synthetic intermediates, they are not involved in animal biochemistry and will not be considered here. Actually, the only polyols that are significant from the standpoint of mammalian metabolism are two that are derived from the trioses and pentoses.

Glycerol can be considered a derivative of either glyceraldehyde or dihydroxyacetone. Since its metabolism is closely related to that of the lipids, many of which contain glycerol, discussion of the properties of glycerol is best deferred until the glycerides are considered. It should be pointed out, however, that glycerol has its origin in the carbohydrates, and that its ultimate fate, after removal of attached "lipoid" groups, involves a return to the carbohydrate fold.

D-Ribitol is derived from D-ribose. In combination with a heterocyclic moiety known as flavin, it forms the vitamin, riboflavin, a member of the B-complex. The entire riboflavin molecule, in turn, is found combined with other substances in larger molecules which act as coenzymes (p. 361).

Glycerol   D-Ribitol   Meso-inositol

CYCLITOLS. A number of polyhydroxylated cyclohexane derivatives occur in nature. It is possible that they are formed in plants by cyclization of hexoses. One of the group, inositol, is a B vitamin. Humans show no definite dietary requirement for this vitamin, since it is readily synthesized by the microorganisms which inhabit the intestines, and is abundant in most foods, but it must be supplied in one way or another, for it has certain important functions. It is a constituent of certain phospholipids, and has some regulatory influence on fat accumulation in the liver (p. 478). In plants, it is found in the form of phytin, the calcium-magnesium salt of phytic acid, which is a hexa-phosphoric ester of inositol (p. 213).

PHOSPHORIC ESTERS OF THE SUGARS

HEXOSE PHOSPHATES. As mentioned previously, the sugars are phosphorylated by the organism preparatory to their oxidation. The most important of the hexose esters are shown on page 22. Certain derivatives of the hexoses, such as gluconic acid, also form phosphate esters in the course of their metabolism.

TRIOSE PHOSPHATES. It will be shown in the discussion of carbohydrate metabolism (p. 392) that the major pathway of hexose breakdown involves phosphorylation, followed by cleavage into trioses. The triose esters and some of their derivatives which are on this pathway are indicated below. As can be seen, many of the compounds are closely related to glyceric acid. The change from the state of oxidation of glyceraldehyde to that of glyceric acid represents the first oxidation which occurs in the metabolism of carbohydrates.

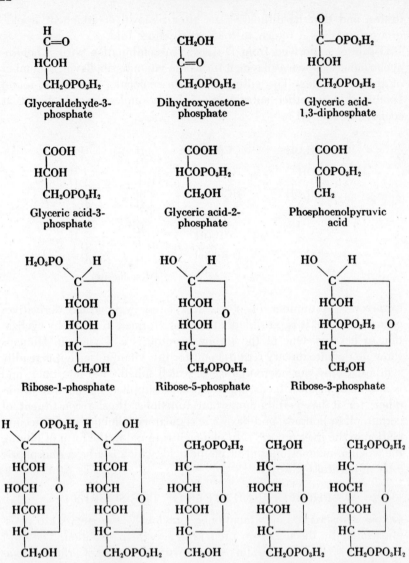

Fig. 7. Phosphate esters of sugars and related compounds

PENTOSE PHOSPHATES. Some esters of D-ribose (and analogous derivatives of desoxyribose) occur as intermediates in pentose metabolism. In addition, such compounds constitute parts of more complex molecules, such as nucleotides, nucleic acids, and coenzymes.

QUALITATIVE AND QUANTITATIVE TESTS FOR CARBOHYDRATES

COPPER REDUCTION TESTS. The most commonly used test for the detection of reducing sugars involves heating the sample with an alkaline reagent containing cupric copper held in solution by some type of complexing agent. Potential aldehyde or *ketol* groups are oxidized, and the copper is reduced to the red cuprous oxide. No equation can be given, since the reaction is not stoichiometric. However, by empirical standardization of the conditions, the reaction can be used for the quantitative determination of reducing sugars. Fehling's solution has been largely replaced by the more convenient Benedict's reagent in clinical laboratories.

$$HC-C-C-C-C=O \xrightarrow{-3H_2O} \quad \begin{array}{c} HC\!-\!-\!-\!CH \\ HC \quad C\!-\!C\!=\!O \\ O \end{array}$$

Pentose   Furfural

$$HOCH_2-C-C-C-C-C=O \xrightarrow{-3H_2O} \quad \begin{array}{c} HC\!-\!-\!-\!CH \\ HOCH_2-C \quad C\!-\!C\!=\!O \\ O \end{array}$$

Hexose   Hydroxymethyl furfural

If a slightly acidic reagent is used (Barfoed's test) and the time of heating carefully controlled, the reducing monosaccharides give a positive reaction, while the reducing disaccharides do not.

FURFURAL-FORMING TESTS. Carbohydrates, in the presence of nonoxidizing acids, undergo dehydration to form furfural or hydroxymethyl furfural. Since these aldehydes will condense with aromatic amines and phenols to give intensely colored compounds, furfural formation can be used as a qualitative or quantitative test for carbohydrates. By employing vigorous conditions all carbohydrates can be made to react; the test then becomes general. Under milder conditions only certain classes of compounds will react, thus giving rise to more specific tests.

In the presence of strong sulfuric acid all of the sugars and their polymers give positive reactions. When α-naphthol is the coupling reagent, the test is known as the Molisch reaction. Orcinol and carbazole give similar reactions, and have been used for quantitative estimations.

Ketoses, when heated with hydrochloric acid and resorcinol, produce a bright red color (Selivanoff test). Under the conditions of this test any ketoses which may be bound in glycosidic linkages will be liberated to give a positive reaction, e.g., the fructose portion of sucrose.

Many tests for pentoses depend upon formation of furfural. Under the usual conditions of the tests, uronic acids are decarboxylated to pentoses, and hence give positive reactions. Galactose is also an interfering factor in many of these tests. Thus, the reaction to Bial's orcinol test is positive for pentoses and galactose, and under certain conditions for uronic acids. Tollen's phloroglucinol reaction yields positive results with pentoses, uronic acids, and galactose, but only the first two groups of substances result in specific absorption bands in the spectrophotometer. Pentoses and uronic acids both react positively toward Tauber's benzidine reagent.

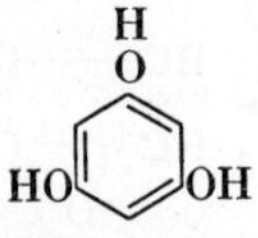

Phloroglucinol 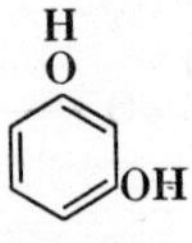 Resorcinol 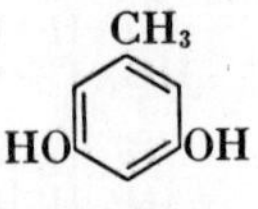 Orcinol

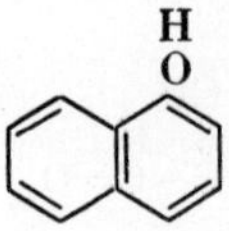

α-Naphthol 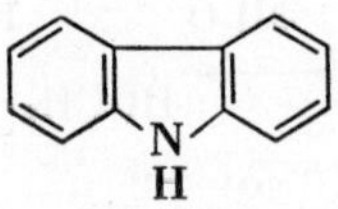 Carbazole 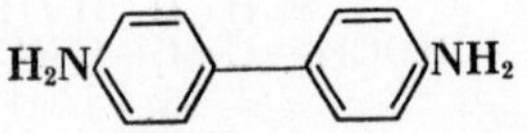 Benzidine

NITRIC ACID OXIDATION. Both the aldehyde and primary alcohol groups of the aldoses are oxidized to carboxyl groups by nitric acid, producing the class of compounds called "saccharic acids" (p. 17). This reaction is often used for the detection and estimation of galactose, because the compound, mucic acid, produced from this sugar, is quite insoluble, in contrast to the other saccharic acids. Under the conditions of the test, galactose-containing glycosides and oligosaccharides (e.g., lactose) are hydrolyzed to give a positive reaction.

PHENYLHYDRAZINE. Aldoses and ketoses, so long as they retain their potential carbonyl groups, react with phenylhydrazine just as do the simple aldehydes and ketones, forming phenylhydrazones. However, in the presence of excess reagent a series of complicated reactions takes place, resulting in the introduction of a second phenylhydrazone group at the primary (for ketoses) or secondary (for aldoses) alcohol group adjacent to the original carbonyl group. These products are called "osazones," and are used for identification of the sugars, since they crystallize in characteristic forms. As shown below, glucose and fructose give the same osazone, since their only structural differences, at Carbon atoms 1 and 2, are obliterated by osazone formation. Mannose would also produce the same osazone as glucose and fructose, except that its phenylhydrazone is so insoluble that the reaction usually stops at that point.

It may be appropriate at this time to point out that reducing properties, mutarotation, and osazone formation all depend upon the presence of a potential aldehyde or ketol group. Blockage of all such groups in a molecule (e.g., sucrose) abolishes all three reactions.

ALKALI. Reducing sugars are profoundly affected by alkaline conditions. Isomerizations occur at the carbonyl end of the molecule, resulting in the formation of a mixture of related aldoses and ketoses. More extensive rearrangements may lead to branched-chain acids. Actual fragmentation of the chain to smaller molecules also takes place, leading to what one of the investigators in this field called a "furchtbares Gemisch." Heating an alkaline solution of a reducing sugar in the presence of air produces a visible change, called "caramelization." The solution turns yellow at first, then brown, probably as a result of the condensation of oxidized and fragmented molecules to higher polymers and tars.

IODINE. Certain polysaccharides give characteristic colors when treated with iodine solutions. The amylose fraction of starch, for example, gives a deep blue color, whereas the reaction with amylopectin is red to purple. Although the usual sample of starch handled in the student laboratory contains more amylopectin than amylose, the latter substance combines with much more iodine and produces such an intense color that the "typical" reaction to the iodine test for starch is the appearance of blue color. Hydrolysis of starch proceeds through a series of dextrins of presumably decreasing molecular weight, reacting in the iodine test to give colors changing from blue through violet to red-brown (erythrodextrins) to colorless (achroodextrins). Glycogen gives a red-brown color with iodine, and cellulose does not react.

FERMENTATION. Of the commonly occurring sugars, ordinary bakers' yeast ferments only glucose, fructose, mannose, maltose, and sucrose. It does not attack galactose, lactose, or pentoses appreciably. Since lactose and pentoses sometimes occur in the urine in conditions which have no serious clinical implication, fermentation tests are used to differentiate these cases from *glucosuria,* which may be indicative of diabetes mellitus.

The explanation for the fermentability of some sugars and the inertness of others involves the enzymatic make-up of the yeast cell and the concept of the specificity of enzymes. These topics will be discussed in the chapters on enzymes and carbohydrate metabolism (pp. 221, 389).

BIBLIOGRAPHY

General

Bell, D. J.: Introduction to Carbohydrate Biochemistry, London, University Tutorial Press, 1952.
Honeyman, J.: An Introduction to the Chemistry of the Carbohydrates, London, Oxford University Press, 1948.
McIlroy, R. J.: The Chemistry of the Polysaccharides, Edward Arnold & Co., London, 1948.
Percival, E. G. V.: Structural Carbohydrate Chemistry, New York, Prentice-Hall, Inc., 1950.
Pigman, W. H., and Goepp, R. M.: Chemistry of the Carbohydrates, New York, Academic Press, Inc., 1948.
Whistler, R. L., and Smart, C. L.: Polysaccharide Chemistry, New York, Academic Press, Inc., 1953.

Glycogen

Meyer, K. H.: Chemistry of Glycogen, Advances in Enzymology 3:109, 1943.

Starch

Meyer, K. H., and Gibbons, G. C.: The present status of starch chemistry, Advances in Enzymology 12:341, 1951.

Mucopolysaccharides

Meyer, K.: The chemistry and biology of mucopolysaccharides and glycoproteins, Cold Spring Harbor Symposia Quant. Biol. 6:91, 1938.
Meyer, K.: Mucoids and glycoproteins, Advances in Protein Chemistry 2:249, 1945.
Stacey, M.: The chemistry of mucopolysaccharides and mucoproteins, Advances in Carbohydrate Chemistry 2:161, 1946.

Blood-Group Polysaccharides

Bray, H. G., and Stacey, M.: Blood group polysaccharides, Advances in Carbohydrate Chemistry 4:37, 1949.

Bacterial Polysaccharides

Burger, M.: Bacterial Polysaccharides, Springfield, Ill., Charles C Thomas, Publisher, 1950.
Evans, T. H., and Hibbert, H.: Bacterial polysaccharides, Advances in Carbohydrate Chemistry 2:203, 1946.
Stacey, M., and Kent, P. W.: The polysaccharides of Mycobacterium tuberculosis, Advances in Carbohydrate Chemistry 3:311, 1948.

2

CHEMISTRY OF THE LIPIDS

INTRODUCTION

DEFINITION AND BIOLOGICAL SIGNIFICANCE. Bloor has defined lipids as "a group of naturally occurring substances consisting of the higher fatty acids, their naturally occurring compounds, and substances found naturally in chemical association with them." Probably the most important role of lipids, from the quantitative viewpoint, is that of fuel. In some respects lipid is even superior to carbohydrate as a raw material for combustion, since it yields more heat per gram when burned, and furthermore can be stored by the body in almost unlimited amount, in contrast to carbohydrate. Some deposits of lipid may exert an insulating effect in the body, while others may provide padding to protect the internal organs. The nervous system is particularly rich in lipids, especially certain types which do not occur normally in such high concentrations elsewhere in the organism, but unfortunately we know little about the functions of these particular substances in the nervous system or other tissues. Some compounds derived from the lipids are important building-blocks of biologically active materials; e.g., acetic acid (a normal breakdown product of the fatty acids, as will be seen later) can be used by the body to synthesize the rather complex compound, cholesterol, which in turn can give rise to certain hormones. One of the important functions of dietary lipid is that of supplying so-called "essential fatty acids," compounds which cannot be synthesized by the animal organism. Compounds of lipids with proteins, lipoproteins, may be important constituents of many natural membranes, such as cell walls, and are involved in a number of other phenomena which will be discussed in the following pages.

FORMS OCCURRING IN NATURE. Most of the lipid material occurring in nature differs from the carbohydrates and the proteins in being insoluble in water and soluble in certain organic solvents (ether, benzene, chloroform, etc.). The fat depots of animals contain mainly neutral fat, by which is meant esters of glycerol with three fatty acid molecules. In contrast, most cells other than adipose tissue contain much less fat; their lipids consist largely of phospholipids and cholesterol. The brain is particularly rich in cholesterol (largely in the free state), phospholipids, and glycolipids. The lipoproteins have been scarcely investigated as a group, but a possible clue to their future importance is given by current researches which have attempted to relate the occurrence of certain lipoproteins in the plasma to atherosclerosis.

CLASSIFICATION

The classification of lipids which we shall follow, a modification of that given by Bloor, is shown in Table 2. Simple lipids contain only fatty

Table 2. Classification of the Lipids

I. Simple lipids
  A. Fats
  B. Waxes
II. Compound lipids
  A. Phospholipids (phosphatides)
    1. Lecithins
    2. Cephalins
      a. Ethanolamine type
      b. Serine type
    3. Lipositols
    4. Plasmalogens
    5. Phosphatidic acids
    6. Sphingomyelins
  B. Glycolipids
    1. Cerebrosides (incl. sulfolipids)
    2. Gangliosides
  C. Lipoproteins

III. Derived lipids
  A. Fatty acids
  B. Alcohols
    1. Acyclic
    2. Sterols (v. infra: IV, D)
    3. Inositol
  C. Bases
    1. Choline
    2. Sphingosine
    3. Ethanolamine
    4. Serine
IV. Substances associated with lipids in nature
  A. Carotenoids
  B. Tocopherols
  C. K vitamins
  D. Steroids

acids and some type of alcoholic compound. In the fats, the alcohol is glycerol; in the waxes, it is some compound of higher molecular weight, such as cholesterol. Compound lipids contain some chemical group in addition to an alcohol and fatty acids. The two subdivisions currently in use are phospholipids and glycolipids, characterized by their content of phosphoric acid and carbohydrate, respectively. Although the lipoproteins are really members of a class known as conjugated proteins, their chief biochemical interest at present resides in the lipid moiety which is attached to the protein, hence they will be discussed in this chapter.

Further subdivisions of the classes of lipids will be discussed in detail in later sections.

FATS, WAXES, AND THEIR COMPONENTS

GLYCERIDES. The storage lipid of animals and a high percentage of the lipid material in their diet consist of triglycerides or neutral fats. Such compounds consist of three molecules of fatty acid esterified to glycerol.

Most of the glycerides found in nature are mixed, that is, R_1, R_2, and R_3 are all different, or only two of the three are the same. Glycerides are named from their constituent fatty acids, beginning at one end of the glycerol molecule, substituting the letter "o" for the acid suffix "-ic," except for the third fatty acid group, which bears the ending "-in." Duplicate or triplicate occurrences of a given fatty acid are also noted. Examples are oleopalmitostearin, oleodipalmitin, and tristearin.

$$
\begin{array}{ccc}
\text{CH}_2-\text{O}-\overset{\overset{\text{O}}{\|}}{\text{C}}-\text{R}_1 & \text{R}_1-\overset{\overset{\text{O}}{\|}}{\text{C}}-\text{OK} & \text{CH}_2\text{OH} \\
& & \\
\text{CH}-\text{O}-\overset{\overset{\text{O}}{\|}}{\text{C}}-\text{R}_2 \xrightarrow{\text{3KOH}} & \text{R}_2-\overset{\overset{\text{O}}{\|}}{\text{C}}-\text{OK} + & \text{CHOH} \\
& & \\
\text{CH}_2-\text{O}-\overset{\overset{\text{O}}{\|}}{\text{C}}-\text{R}_3 & \text{R}_3-\overset{\overset{\text{O}}{\|}}{\text{C}}-\text{OK} & \text{CH}_2\text{OH}
\end{array}
$$

Saponification of a triglyceride

The fats are characterized by their insolubility in water and their solubility in such solvents as benzene, chloroform, ether, and hot alcohol. Their melting points vary with their constituent fatty acids, shorter-chain or more unsaturated fatty acids tending to impart lower melting points. These facts are of some importance, since fats having melting points much above human body temperature ($37°$ C.) may be poorly digested. Fats which are liquid at room temperature are often called "oils," a term which may cause confusion with certain other natural products.

Hydrolysis of the glycerides proceeds by the addition of the elements of water across the ester linkages, producing glycerol and three fatty acid molecules. In the intestine this process is catalyzed by enzymes, while in the test tube it can be catalyzed by acid or base. The alkaline hydrolysis of fats is a reaction of industrial importance, and is called "saponification" (literally, "soap-making"). The metallic salts of the fatty acids which result from this process are the soaps, those of the alkali metals being soluble soaps, while those of the alkaline earths and heavy metals are insoluble.

Given the appropriate conditions of moisture, light, warmth, oxygen, and possibly catalytic substances, fats containing unsaturated fatty acids undergo a reaction known as autoxidation. This is probably the major factor in the complex of changes in fats called "rancidification." A rancid fat not only has a disagreeable odor and taste, but in addition contains groups of the peroxide type which are quite destructive to the fat-soluble vitamins. The vitamin E group (tocopherols) may act as natural antioxidants and protect the other fat-soluble vitamins from oxidation in the food, in the intestine, or in the tissues (p. 157). In addition to the oxidative aspects of rancidity, some hydrolysis of fatty acid may occur, and some new acid groups may be formed by the oxidative scission of the unsaturated fatty acids at the double bonds.

Glycerol, the alcoholic component of the fats, is closely allied chemically and in biological origin to the carbohydrates, as has been pointed out previously. However, in terms of function and occurrence, it is appropriate to consider glycerol along with the lipids. Unesterified glycerol is soluble in water and alcohol, insoluble in the "lipid solvents," but these properties are completely masked when the three hydroxyl groups are attached to fatty acid residues. Stepwise hydrolysis of triglycerides yields diglycerides and monoglycerides, compounds which were assumed to occur only as intermediates in the intestinal digestion of fats until recently, when monopalmitin was found in pancreatic tissue. Molecules such as the monoglycerides, having a "lipid-soluble" group at one end and a water-soluble group at the other, act as detergents and emulsifying agents. This may play a useful role in the digestion of fat. Natural components of this type have served as models for many of the present synthetic detergents.

1. Saturated

Butyric	$CH_3(CH_2)_2COOH$
Caproic	$CH_3(CH_2)_4COOH$
Caprylic	$CH_3(CH_2)_6COOH$
Capric	$CH_3(CH_2)_8COOH$
Lauric	$CH_3(CH_2)_{10}COOH$
Myristic	$CH_3(CH_2)_{12}COOH$
Palmitic	$CH_3(CH_2)_{14}COOH$
Stearic	$CH_3(CH_2)_{16}COOH$
Lignoceric	$CH_3(CH_2)_{22}COOH$

3. Cyclic

$$HC\!\!=\!\!=\!\!CH$$
$$H_2C \quad CH\!-\!(CH_2)_{12}COOH$$
$$CH_2$$

Chaulmoogric

2. Unsaturated

Palmitoleic	$CH_3(CH_2)_5CH\!=\!CH(CH_2)_7COOH$
Oleic	$CH_3(CH_2)_7CH\!=\!CH(CH_2)_7COOH$
Nervonic	$CH_3(CH_2)_7CH\!=\!CH(CH_2)_{13}COOH$
Linoleic	$CH_3(CH_2)_4CH\!=\!CHCH_2CH\!=\!CH(CH_2)_7COOH$
Linolenic	$CH_3CH_2CH\!=\!CHCH_2CH\!=\!CHCH_2CH\!=\!CH(CH_2)_7COOH$
Arachidonic	$CH_3(CH_2)_4CH\!=\!(CHCH_2CH\!=\!)_3CH(CH_2)_3COOH$

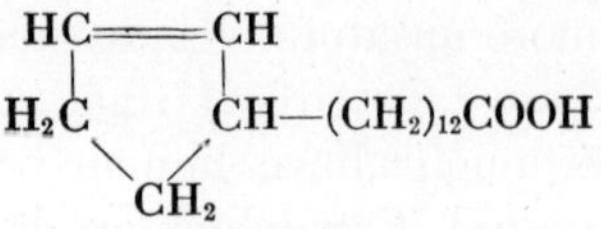

Fig. 8. Typical fatty acids

With few exceptions, the fatty acids found in nature have straight chains and an even number of carbon atoms. The lower fatty acids are soluble in water, but this property decreases with increasing chain-length from caproic acid on, so that, as a generalization, we may say that most of the natural fatty acids are insoluble in water. Hot alcohol and the usual fat solvents dissolve the higher fatty acids. The alkali metal salts (sodium and potassium soaps) are soluble in water but not in the fat solvents. Shorter chain-length and increasing unsaturation result in fatty acids of lower melting point. Palmitic, stearic, and oleic acids make up the bulk of animal depot fat. Milk fat contains a relatively higher percentage of the acids of lower molecular weight, and the glycerides of the liver frequently differ from those of the depots in their greater degree of unsaturation. Chaulmoogric acid, a rather unusual fatty acid of plant origin, is mentioned here because it is one of a group of cyclic fatty acids which are used in the treatment of leprosy. Linoleic, linolenic, and arachidonic acids (poly-unsaturated) are sometimes listed as "essential" fatty acids, since there is some evidence that they cannot be synthesized by the animal and must therefore be provided in the diet.

WAXES. The waxes consist of fatty acids esterified to alcohols other than glycerol. One of the most important of these alcohols is cholesterol, a member of the steroid series. The formula for cholesteryl palmitate, a common wax found in blood plasma, is:

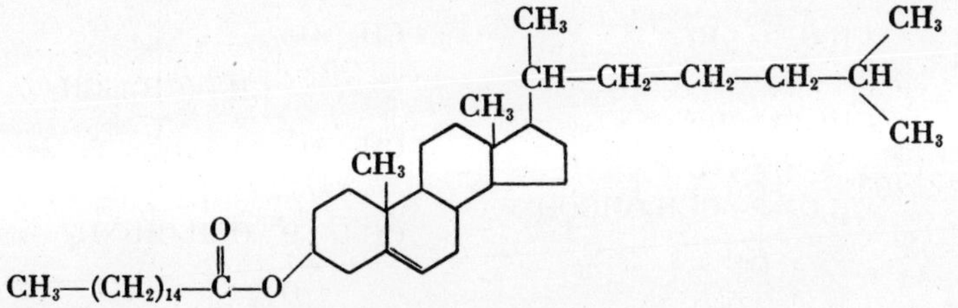

Cholesterol esters occur only in small amounts in animal tissues under normal conditions, except in the adrenal glands. Abnormally high concentrations of cholesterol and its esters are found in the liver, spleen, and other tissues in the condition known as Schüller-Christian disease. Some of the waxes of the skin contain hydroxylated fatty acids esterified with aliphatic alcohols (such as would result from the reduction of the higher fatty acids, e.g., cetyl alcohol from palmitic acid).

PHOSPHOLIPIDS (PHOSPHATIDES)

LECITHINS. A typical lecithin consists of glycerol, to which are esterified two fatty acids (frequently at least one is unsaturated) and phosphoric acid, which in turn is attached to the alcohol group of the organic base, choline. The exact arrangment of the substituent groups on the glycerol is not known, but there is evidence that previous reports of lecithins containing the phosphorylcholine group on the central hydroxyl of glycerol may have been the result of rearrangement during isolation and analysis. Owing to the number of different fatty acids, many lecithins are obviously possible.

The lecithins are soluble in alcohol and the usual fat solvents, with the exception of acetone. Although not truly soluble in water, they have some affinity for that substance and can be dispersed in it in a colloidal state. Owing probably to their high degree of unsaturation, lecithins decompose rapidly on storage in air (some completely saturated lecithins, however, have been found in various tissues).

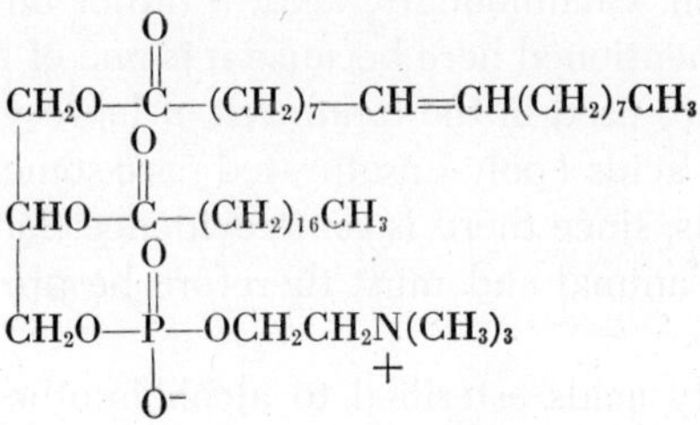

$$CH_2O-\overset{O}{\underset{\|}{C}}-(CH_2)_7-CH=CH(CH_2)_7CH_3$$
$$CHO-\overset{O}{\underset{\|}{C}}-(CH_2)_{16}CH_3$$
$$CH_2O-\underset{\underset{O^-}{|}}{P}-OCH_2CH_2N(CH_3)_3^+$$

A Lecithin

$$CH_2O-\overset{O}{\underset{\|}{C}}-R_1$$
$$CHO-\overset{O}{\underset{\|}{C}}-R_2$$
$$CH_2O-\underset{\underset{O^-}{|}}{P}-OCH_2CH_2NH_3^+$$

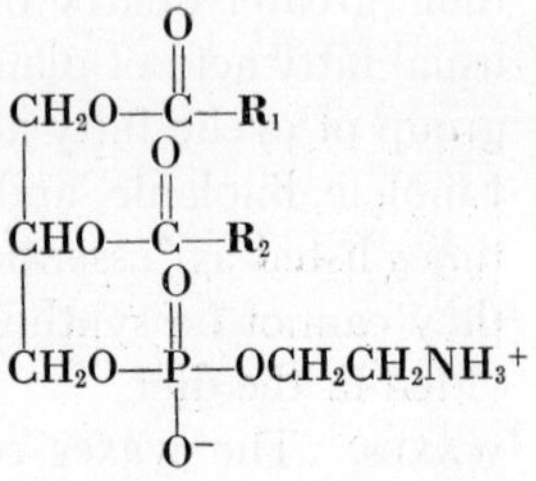

An Ethanolamine-Cephalin

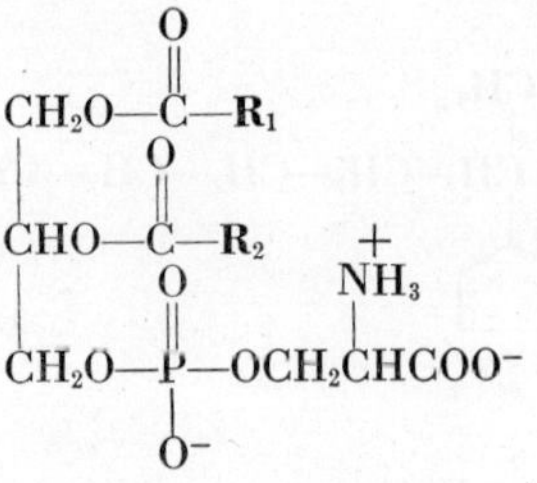

$$CH_2O-\overset{O}{\underset{\|}{C}}-R_1$$
$$CHO-\overset{O}{\underset{\|}{C}}-R_2$$
$$CH_2O-\underset{\underset{O^-}{|}}{P}-OCH_2\overset{NH_3^+}{CHCOO^-}$$

A Serine-Cephalin

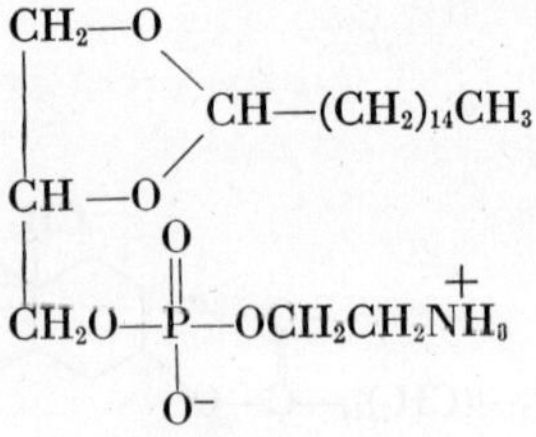

$$CH_2-O$$
$$CH-(CH_2)_{14}CH_3$$
$$CH-O$$
$$CH_2O-\underset{\underset{O^-}{|}}{P}-OCH_2CH_2NH_3^+$$

A Plasmalogen

$$CH_3(CH_2)_{12}CH=CHCHCHCH_2O-\underset{\underset{O^-}{|}}{P}-OCH_2CH_2\overset{+}{N}(CH_3)_3$$
with OH and $NH-\overset{O}{\underset{\|}{C}}-R$

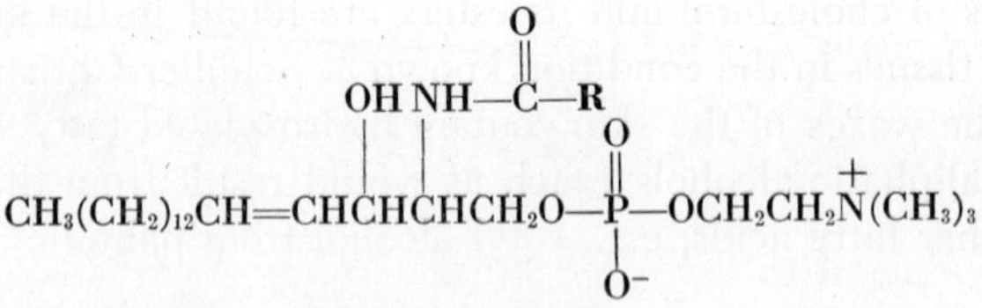

A Sphingomyelin

Fig. 9. Phospholipids

CEPHALINS. The cephalins differ from the lecithins in composition with respect to the base attached to the phosphoric acid. Whether they also differ in the internal arrangement of constituents has not been established. Two types of cephalins are known. In one the base is ethanolamine (phosphatidyl-ethanolamine), in the other the amino acid, serine (phosphatidyl-serine, seryl-phosphatide). Like the lecithins, many cephalins contain one or two unsaturated fatty acids.

Like the lecithins, the cephalins are soluble in most of the fat solvents with the exception of acetone, but differ from the former group by their lower solubility in alcohol. They are unstable in air.

Certain enzymes in snake venoms catalyze the hydrolysis of the unsaturated fatty acid residues from lecithins and cephalins, producing lysolecithins and lysocephalins, compounds with a marked hemolytic action. Certain cephalins may have an accelerating effect on blood coagulation (p. 735).

LIPOSITOLS. These compounds have been obtained from the crude cephalin fractions of tissues, and some systems of classification include them among the cephalins, mainly on the basis of solubility. Chemically, however, they are quite distinct from the compounds which we have discussed as cephalins. They are characterized as a group by containing inositol. Brain lipositol (diphosphoinositide) is composed of one molecule each of inositol, glycerol, and fatty acid, with two phosphoric acid groups esterified to the inositol. A somewhat similar compound from the soybean contains equimolecular proportions of phosphoric acid, inositol, galactose, tartaric acid, ethanolamine, oleic acid, and saturated fatty acid. This material is evidently much more complex than brain lipositol, and the presence of galactose suggests a relationship to the glycolipids. At this time the structures of these compounds cannot be indicated.

PLASMALOGENS. These compounds, to which very little attention has been paid up to now, are similar to the lecithin-cephalin group, except that the two hydroxyl groups of the glycerol which ordinarily would be esterified to fatty acids are instead bound in an acetal linkage to a fatty aldehyde. For this reason these substances are sometimes called "phospholipid acetals."

PHOSPHATIDIC ACIDS AND RELATED COMPOUNDS. In plants, compounds occur which consist of glycerol, two fatty acid molecules, and phosphoric acid. No base is attached to the phosphoric acid group, which is present in the form of a calcium salt. Although these phosphatidic acids are restricted to the plant world, a remotely related compound called "cardiolipin" has been isolated from the heart. This lipid (used in the serological diagnosis of syphilis) contains three molecules of phosphoric acid, four molecules of glycerol, one of oleic, and five of linoleic acid.

SPHINGOMYELINS. This class of phospholipid has been left to the last because it is closely related chemically to the glycolipids, which will be discussed below. The sphingomyelins contain, in addition to phosphorylcholine, a complex base called "sphingosine." A fatty acid is attached to the amino group of the sphingosine in an amide linkage. Some sphingomyelins contain the saturated base, dihydrosphingosine.

Sphingomyelins are much less soluble in ether than are lecithins and cephalins, and precipitate from the cold solution. They can be dissolved in hot alcohol, from which they also separate on cooling. Like the other phospholipids, they are insoluble in acetone, soluble in benzene and chloroform. They form opalescent suspensions in water. Unlike cephalins and lecithins, sphingomyelins are quite stable in air. Greatly increased concentrations of sphingomyelins (and possibly lecithins) occur in the liver, spleen, and other tissues in a condition known as Niemann-Pick disease.

GLYCOLIPIDS

CEREBROSIDES. The general formula accepted at present for a cerebroside is:

$$CH_3-(CH_2)_{12}-CH=CH-CHOH-\underset{\underset{Sphingosine}{}}{\overset{\overset{\displaystyle NH-\overset{\displaystyle O}{\overset{\|}{C}}-R\ \textit{Fatty acid}}{|}}{CH}}-CH_2-O-\underset{\underset{HC-\underset{|}{\overset{|}{}}-}{\underset{CH_2OH}{}}}{\overset{\overset{|}{HCOH}}{\underset{\underset{HOCH}{|}}{\overset{|}{\underset{|}{HOCH}}}}}CH-$$

Sphingosine   O *Galactose*

According to the earlier work in this field, the cerebrosides differed according to the fatty acid attached to the sphingosine: kerasin contained lignoceric acid, phrenosin contained cerebronic acid (an α-hydroxylignoceric acid) and hence was sometimes called "cerebron," nervon contained nervonic acid, and hydroxynervon contained an α-hydroxynervonic acid. The actual identification of these fatty acids has been a matter of considerable controversy, and is not yet entirely settled. The cerebrosides have been called "galactolipids," because of their content of galactose, but a compound resembling kerasin has been isolated (from patients) which contains glucose instead of galactose. The picture has been complicated further by the isolation of dihydrosphingosine from cerebroside fractions, indicating that this saturated base may be a component of still other cerebrosides.

Sulfolipids have been reported in various tissues from time to time. The sulfolipid of brain has been shown to be a sulfuric acid ester of cerebron.

According to some authorities, there are cerebrosides which contain two hexose molecules, glucose and galactose.

Cerebrosides are present in many tissues, but normally in low concentration, except for nervous tissue. Large amounts are found in the white matter of brain and in the myelin sheath of nerves. Abnormally high concentrations occur in the liver, spleen, and other tissues in a condition known as Gaucher's disease.

GANGLIOSIDES. These glycolipids contain, in addition to fatty acids of the C_{24} and C_{22} series, a molecule of sphingosine, three molecules of hexose (glucose and galactose), and a substance called "neuraminic acid," which has not been identified.

GLYCOLIPIDS OF HIGH MOLECULAR WEIGHT. Up to now, the possession of a high molecular weight has been the prerogative of the proteins and some carbohydrates, and has been denied the lipids. These ideas must be revised with the recent isolation from brain of a glycolipid called "strandin." This substance has a molecular weight of about 250,000, contains fatty acids, carbohydrate, probably sphingosine and glucosamine, and some other unidentified fragment.

STEROIDS, STEROLS, AND BILE ACIDS

STEROIDS AS A GROUP. There exists in nature a large group of compounds having in common a structure based on the cyclopentano-perhydrophenanthrene nucleus:

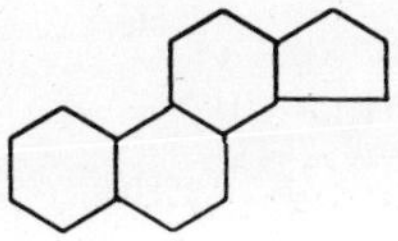

These compounds, the steroids, have greatly diversified physiological properties, despite the basic similarity in chemical structure. The group includes precursors of certain vitamins, hormones of several types, cholesterol (and similar compounds in the plant world), bile acids, certain natural drugs and poisons, and some physiologically inert compounds. Certain of the steroids are found associated with the lipids in nature, either by reason of mutual solubility, or owing to some actual metabolic relationship.

The steroid structure contains many centers of actual or potential asymmetry. The resulting stereoisomerism is of considerable importance, especially in the case of the steroid hormones, since it is closely related to the physiological actions of these compounds. This subject is discussed more fully elsewhere (p. 656).

STEROLS. The sterols are the steroid alcohols, one of which, cholesterol, has already been mentioned in connection with the waxes. Cholesterol can be synthesized by the animal body from small fragments, such as acetic acid. Large amounts of cholesterol occur in the free state in the central nervous system, but its function there is unknown at the present time. In certain endocrine glands (viz., adrenal cortex), cholesterol is the probable parent compound from which steroid hormones are synthesized (p. 458). The participation of cholesterol in gallstone formation has been recognized for many years (p. 269). Cholesterol is an unsaturated alcohol, and in tissues outside of the nervous system (including blood plasma) exists partly in the form of esters with fatty acids. The non-hydroxylic part of the molecule is strictly hydrocarbon in nature, accounting for the solubility characteristics of cholesterol, which are like those of the true lipids.

In the animal body, cholesterol can be converted to 7-dehydrocholesterol. When the latter compound, in the skin, is subjected to ultraviolet radiation (as in sunlight), it is converted to one of the D vitamins, in this case D_3. Ergosterol, a plant sterol differing somewhat in structure from cholesterol, after irradiation acts as a D vitamin in animals. These vitamins and their sterol precursors are discussed more fully elsewhere (p. 148).

Much attention is being directed to cholesterol at the present time, not only because of its close relationship to the other steroids in the body, but also because cholesterol is involved in certain degenerative changes in the arterial wall, known as atherosclerosis, or hardening of the arteries.

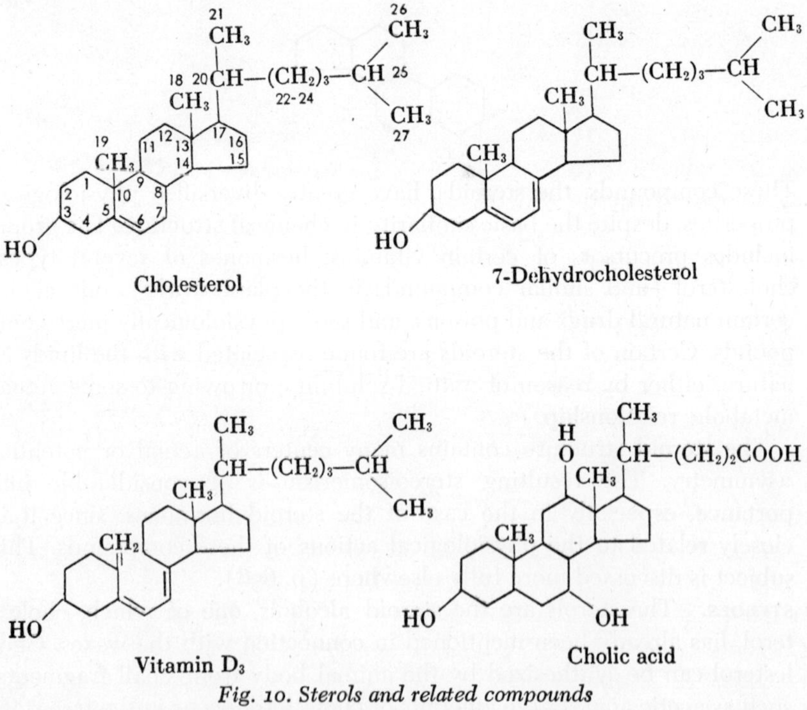

Fig. 10. Sterols and related compounds

BILE ACIDS. In addition to the steroid nucleus and one or more alcoholic hydroxyl groups, bile acids contain a carboxyl group on the side-chain. As found in bile, these compounds are conjugated through their carboxyl groups to an amino acid, glycine, or to a compound called "taurine," which is derived from another amino acid (cysteine). The relationship of bile acids to the lipids is two-fold: on the one hand they are synthesized biologically from cholesterol, hence their ultimate origin is in fragments metabolically derived from fatty acids; on the other, they are important factors in the digestion and absorption of lipids in the intestine. Within the pH range prevailing in the intestine, the bile acids (in their conjugated forms, as stated above) are present as salts. Having an ionic group at one end of the molecule, and a predominantly lipid-soluble nucleus, they are very effective emulsifying agents. This characteristic aids in the digestion of lipids and the subsequent absorption of the less water-soluble products (p. 268).

One of the bile acids, desoxycholic acid, has the unusual property of forming soluble, diffusible complexes with fatty acids. At one time this property was considered important in the absorption of fatty acids from the intestine. However, these complexes (called "choleic acids") are formed only by desoxycholic acid, whereas cholic acid predominates in human bile. Furthermore, *conjugated* desoxycholic acid does not appear to form the choleic acid complexes. At the present time it would appear that the fat-solubilizing action of bile acids, in their natural state, is largely due to their emulsifying abilities.

OTHER SUBSTANCES ASSOCIATED WITH LIPIDS IN NATURE

CAROTENOIDS AND VITAMINS A (P. 128). The carotenoid pigments, as can be deduced from the hydrocarbon type of structure, are lipid-soluble, hence are found associated with lipids in nature. In fact, the yellowish color ascribed to many fats is not due to the fats themselves, but to dissolved carotenoid pigments.

β-Carotene

While the carotenoids themselves are products of the plant world, some of them are important in animal nutrition as precursors of the A-group of vitamins, since the animal organism is able to effect the conversion. Carotenoids and A vitamins are classified as lipids in some systems, and combinations of A vitamins with proteins are consequently regarded as lipoproteins. Regardless of fixed classifications, the complexes of proteins with vitamin A or its derivatives are important in the biochemistry of vision, and for convenience these substances will be mentioned along with the "true" lipoproteins in a later section of this chapter.

VITAMINS K AND E (PP. 161, 157). The K-group of vitamins has little to do with the lipids, aside from solubility considerations. Conditions which prevent proper absorption of lipids from the intestine tend to have a similar effect on the lipid-soluble vitamins. In the case of the K vitamins, at least, a definite state of deficiency can result.

The E vitamins, or tocopherols, are natural antioxidants found dissolved in many vegetable fats, and have the ability to prevent or delay autoxidation of unsaturated fatty acids. These vitamins have no other known connection with the lipids.

LIPOPROTEINS

STATE OF LIPIDS IN NATURE. It is probable that many of the substances described in this chapter do not exist as such in their natural state, and represent what the purists would call artifacts of the laboratory. This is a reflection of the primitive state of intracellular biochemistry (and unfortunately the situation is not confined to the lipids). From the available evidence, it appears that many of the lipids are combined with proteins in the tissues. These combinations are called "lipoproteins." The nature of the linkage between the lipid and protein moieties is not known; it is usually stable toward non-polar solvents, such as ether, but can frequently be disrupted by more highly polar substances, such as alcohol. Despite the evidence for the widespread occurrence of lipoproteins, the technical difficulties in handling these materials have been such that, until the very recent introduction of newer physicochemical methods, few members of this group were characterized as chemical entities.

EXAMPLES OF LIPOPROTEINS. It is widely assumed that the cell membrane is a lipoprotein structure of some type, and, although there is not much direct evidence available, the general properties of cell membranes are at least consistent with this view. Certain of the internal structures of the cell also contain lipids, apparently in combination with proteins. This is the case with visible entities, such as the nucleus and mitochondria, as well as the submicroscopic particles (microsomes).

The thromboplastic protein isolated from lung (p. 735) has been characterized as a lipoprotein. The lipid portion, as in the case of many lipoproteins, consists of more than one type of lipid. Egg yolk contains a lipoprotein known as lipovitellin, the lipid fraction consisting largely of phospholipids. A number of bacteria have been shown to contain firmly bound lipids, although it is not certain in some cases whether the lipids are bound to protein or to polysaccharides. Certain animal viruses appear to contain firmly bound lipids also, but this is not true of the viruses thus far isolated from plant sources. The film which stabilizes the fat droplets in milk appears to be a combination of protein and phospholipid. Most, if not all, of the lipid in blood serum is carried in the form of lipoprotein complexes. The statement also holds for the lipid-soluble vitamins, the carotenoids, and the steroids. Since the presence of lipid causes the lipoprotein molecule to have a lower density than that of ordinary proteins, it is possible, by proper adjustment of the experimental conditions, to force lipoproteins to travel toward the axis instead of toward the periphery of an ultracentrifuge (p. 69). By the use of this "flotation" method, certain cholesterol-containing lipoproteins have been implicated in the development of atherosclerosis in experimental animals. Studies in humans are still in the preliminary stages.

The pigment of the retinal rods, visual purple, is a compound of a protein, opsin, with the aldehyde of vitamin A (retinene), the complex being called "rhodopsin" (p. 134). Owing to the relationship of carotenoids and vitamin A to the lipids, compounds such as rhodopsin are often classed with the lipoproteins.

The lipoproteins have usually been thought of as conjugated proteins, possessing the general properties (e.g., solubility) of proteins. However, a new series of compounds has been isolated from various tissues, having the solubility characteristics of lipids. Probably these substances, which have been named "proteolipids," should be considered primarily as lipids, not as proteins.

QUALITATIVE AND QUANTITATIVE TESTS FOR LIPIDS

SAPONIFICATION NUMBER. This constant, which is of special value in the identification and characterization of neutral fats, is defined as the number of milligrams of KOH required to saponify one gram of fat. Since three equivalents of KOH are consumed in the saponification of the three ester linkages of each mole of triglyceride, the saponification number obviously will depend on the number of mols of fat per gram. This will be an inverse function of the molecular weight of the fat, which in turn is largely determined by the chain length of the fatty acids involved. For triglycerides,

$$\text{Saponification No.} = \frac{168,000}{\text{Molec. wt. of the fat}}.$$

Fats, such as butter, which contain relatively larger amounts of the fatty acids of lower molecular weight, are characterized by higher saponification numbers than are the depot fats.

IODINE NUMBER. This is defined as the number of grams of iodine taken up by 100 grams of fat. Since halogens react by addition to olefinic linkages, the iodine number is a measure of the degree of unsaturation of a fat. For triglycerides consisting largely of C_{18} fatty acids,

Iodine No. $\approx$ 90 X average no. of double bonds per fatty acid residue.

Highly unsaturated fats, such as linseed oil, have characteristically high iodine numbers.

Osmic acid also reacts with the unsaturated fatty acids, giving dark products. This reaction is used by histologists for the microscopic detection of fat.

OTHER "NUMBERS." Additional constants are also used by chemists to characterize lipids, such as the "Reichert-Meissl number" (a measure of the soluble, volatile fatty acids), the "acetyl number" (a measure of hydroxy acids), and others, but they are of no particular importance to non-specialists in this field.

ACROLEIN TEST. Glycerol, when heated in the presence of a dehydrating agent, such as sodium bisulfate, is converted to the unsaturated aldehyde, acrolein, a compound having the characteristic odor of burned fat. This reaction is positive for glycerol whether in the free state or combined in a fat or phospholipid.

$$
\begin{array}{ccc}
\text{H} & & \text{H} \\
\text{HC—O}\,\text{H} & & \text{C}{=}\text{O} \\
| & \text{Heat} & | \\
\text{HC—O}\,\text{H} & \xrightarrow{\qquad} & \text{CH} \\
| & -2\text{H}_2\text{O} & \| \\
\text{HC—OH} & & \text{CH}_2 \\
\text{H} & & \\
\end{array}
$$

Acrolein

CHOLINE TESTS. As a tertiary amine, choline has the property of forming various quaternary salts and addition compounds, such as with Kraut's reagent (a bismuth potassium iodide). These products are frequently brightly colored and serve as tests for the detection of choline. Similar addition compounds are formed by lecithin, owing to the choline contained in the molecule.

LIEBERMANN-BURCHARD TEST. A chloroform solution of cholesterol reacts with acetic anhydride and sulfuric acid to form a succession of colors. The nature of the reaction is not known. It is supposedly specific for sterols unsaturated at C5-C6.

FRACTIONATION OF LIPIDS. Lipids are frequently divided into saponifiable and non-saponifiable fractions. Those substances which, after saponification with alkali, are extractable with ether are called non-saponifiable. Glycerol is not soluble in ether, nor are the sodium or potassium soaps of the fatty acids, hence these substances remain in the saponifiable fraction. Compounds which go into the non-saponifiable fraction are the sterols, carotenoids, and related substances. Of course, acidification of a saponified fat will transform the soaps into free fatty acids, which are ether-soluble, but the term "non-saponifiable" refers only to those substances which are ether-extractable while the saponified mixture is alkaline.

Many schemes of fractionation of lipid mixtures into the several groups of lipids are based upon differences in solubility in various organic solvents. For example, lecithins and cephalins can be separated from other ether-soluble lipids by precipitation with acetone. A complete fractionation of the lipids with the object of producing chemically defined substances is difficult to achieve, if not impossible at the present time.

After the preparation of a presumably pure lipid, the question often arises as to the identity of its constituent fatty acids. The separation and identification of the individual components in a mixture of fatty acids have been approached in a number of ways, such as fractional distillation of the methyl esters, selective solubilities of certain metallic salts of the acids in various solvents, fractional crystallization of the fatty acids from organic solvents at low temperatures, and, recently, chromatography (p. 89).

BIBLIOGRAPHY

General

Bloor, W. R.: Biochemistry of the Fatty Acids, New York, Reinhold Publishing Corporation, 1943.
Bull, H. B.: Biochemistry of the Lipids, New York, John Wiley & Sons, Inc., 1937.
Deuel, H. J., Jr.: The Lipids: Their Chemistry and Biochemistry. Volume I: Chemistry, New York, Interscience Publishers, Inc., 1951.
Hilditch, T. P.: Chemical Constitution of Natural Fats, New York, John Wiley & Sons, Inc., 1947.
Markley, K. S.: Fatty Acids, New York, Interscience Publishers, Inc., 1947.
Ralston, A. W.: Fatty Acids and Their Derivatives, New York, John Wiley & Sons, Inc., 1948.

Phospholipids and Glycolipids

Celmer, W. D. and Carter, H. E.: Chemistry of phosphatides and cerebrosides, Physiol. Rev. 32:167, 1952.
Page, I. H.: Chemistry of the Brain, Springfield, Ill., Charles C Thomas, Publisher, 1937, Chapters 3 and 5.
Thannhauser, S. J. and Schmidt, G.: Lipins and lipidoses, Physiol. Rev. 26:275, 1946.
Wittcoff, H.: The Phosphatides, New York, Reinhold Publishing Corporation, 1951.

Lipoproteins

Chargaff, E.: Lipoproteins, Advances in Protein Chemistry 1:1, 1944.
Tullis, J. L. (ed.): Blood Cells and Plasma Proteins, New York, Academic Press, Inc., 1953, Section VII.

Bile Acids and Sterols

Fieser, L. F. and Fieser, M.: Natural Products Related to Phenanthrene, New York, Reinhold Publishing Corporation, 1949, Chapter 3.

3

CHEMISTRY OF PROTEINS

INTRODUCTION

DEFINITION AND GENERAL PROPERTIES. Proteins may be defined as compounds of high molecular weight, consisting largely (or entirely) of chains of α-amino acids united in peptide linkage. The constituent amino acids can be obtained by hydrolysis of the proteins. While the individual amino acids may be considered analogous to the monosaccharides of carbohydrate chemistry, and the true proteins analogous to the polysaccharides, an important difference must be pointed out. The polysaccharides are polymers of a single sub-unit, or of a few types of sub-units at the most, while the proteins contain, in general, some twenty-odd individual amino acids, present in characteristic proportions and linked in a specific sequence in each protein. Hence, other things being equal, it is possible for nature to concoct many more different proteins than polysaccharides, a fact which lends fascination as well as difficulty to the problems confronting the protein chemist.

The molecular weights of the proteins vary from about 13,000 to many millions. Most proteins, owing to their molecular size, are not diffusible through membranes such as cellophane, and like the polysaccharides are actually of colloidal dimensions and exhibit the properties associated with the colloidal state of matter. Some are soluble in pure water; some require the presence of salts or small amounts of acid or base to dissolve. One group is soluble in certain concentrations of alcohol, although (with the exception of the recently discovered proteolipids) proteins are generally insoluble in organic solvents. The structural proteins known as scleroproteins are dissolved only by reagents which cause considerable alterations in their structure.

The average protein is a very sensitive individual. In reprisal for its exposure to heat, extremes of pH, surface action, or various reagents, the native protein undergoes a series of changes known as denaturation, resulting in alterations in a number of its properties. Heat denaturation, under the proper circumstances, proceeds on to a further stage, coagulation, as can be seen in the familiar example of the fried egg.

As will be shown later (p. 59), proteins possess free ionic or charged groups, so that they migrate in an electrical field. Owing to their charges, proteins combine with ionic reagents, in some cases resulting in insoluble compounds. The reaction of the ionic groups on the protein molecule with both hydrogen and hydroxyl ions indicates that proteins are amphoteric, and the fact that these groups in the protein are weak acids results in the setting-up of buffer systems, a matter of considerable biological importance.

Certain color reactions (p. 84) are given by the unhydrolyzed protein. One of these is due to the peptide linkages possessed by all proteins; the others are given by reactive chemical groups situated in the amino acid residues.

While the immunochemical reactions of proteins (such as the antigen-antibody reactions) are undoubtedly physicochemical phenomena, not enough is known about them to warrant a discussion in chemical terms. They will be considered in connection with other biological aspects of the proteins.

BIOLOGICAL IMPORTANCE. The biochemical significance of proteins cannot be overemphasized. If carbohydrates and lipids, generally speaking, can be considered the fuels of the metabolic furnace, proteins may be regarded as forming not only the structural framework, but also the gears and levers of the operating machinery. Indeed, at the risk of pushing the analogy to extremes, we may regard the protein hormones (which act as regulators of metabolism) as the policy-forming top management of the enterprise.

Such structures as cell walls and various membranes are protein in the main, although frequently coupled or associated with lipids. Connective tissue is composed of chemically rather inert types of proteins, in some cases combined with carbohydrates. The contractile elements of muscle are now thought to be proteins. Aside from such obviously structural substances as those mentioned, the catalysts which permit the reactions of intermediary metabolism to proceed at a reasonable rate under mild conditions, the enzymes, are known to be protein in nature. Finally, as already pointed out, certain proteins in the body act as hormones, or regulators of metabolism.

Protoplasm may be regarded as a colloidal system of proteins, together with some lipids and carbohydrates. With some exceptions, the supply of carbohydrates and lipids may rise or fall, and the cell may flourish or do poorly as a result, but at any rate it survives for some time. If something interferes with the supply of protein, however, the cell inevitably sickens and dies.

CLASSIFICATION OF PROTEINS

BASES FOR CLASSIFICATION. A system for the classification of proteins which differs slightly from that usually presented in textbooks is given in Table 3. It is based on the same characteristics of proteins as the commonly used system, i.e., solubility and composition. That these properties do not provide a perfect system of classification will become evident in what follows.

Table 3. Classification of the Proteins

I. Simple proteins
   A. Albumins
   B. Globulins
   C. Glutelins
   D. Prolamines
   E. Scleroproteins
II. Conjugated proteins
   A. Nucleoproteins
   B. Phosphoproteins
   C. Porphyrinoproteins
     1. Hemoproteins
     2. Chlorophylloproteins
   D. Glycoproteins

   E. Lipoproteins
   F. Flavoproteins
   G. Miscellaneous metalloproteins
III. Derived proteins
   A. Split products of conjugated proteins
     1. Protamines
     2. Histones
     3. Others
   B. Denatured proteins
   C. Hydrolytic products
     1. Proteoses
     2. Peptones
     3. Peptides

The three major classes of proteins are the simple proteins, the conjugated proteins, and the derived proteins. Upon hydrolysis the simple proteins yield only amino acids, while the conjugated proteins yield some substance or substances in addition to amino acids. Derived proteins are the products resulting from various rather deep-seated changes in the structure or composition of the native proteins belonging to the first two classes.

With the advance of biochemical research, the line of demarcation between simple and conjugated proteins has become somewhat obscured. A number of proteins previously classified as simple, in fact some which were used as typical examples of that class, have been shown in recent years to contain carbohydrate groups as integral components of their molecules. Still others are in the process of reclassification to such groups as lipoproteins, metalloproteins, etc. Discrepancies in our present classification will be pointed out in the following sections.

The subdivision of the class of simple proteins is based upon solubility. As will be pointed out later, the division into albumins and globulins is quite arbitrary, as a considerable overlap of properties exists between these groups.

Conjugated proteins are further classified according to the nature of the non-protein group which is attached to the molecule, the so-called "prosthetic group." In some systems of classification all proteins with colored prosthetic groups are collectively designated "chromoproteins." There seems to be no rational chemical or biological basis for this practice, hence no such group is included in Table 3.

Protamines and histones are frequently included among the simple proteins. Since, however, they occur in nature as the protein moieties of conjugated proteins (especially in nucleoproteins and hemoproteins), it seems best to consider them as "derived." This also permits the creation of a class of split-products of the conjugated proteins, which will include any "artificial" proteins that may be produced by the cleavage of prosthetic groups from conjugated proteins. The denatured proteins and the products of partial hydrolysis of proteins will be discussed in subsequent sections.

It is possible to classify proteins on the basis of criteria other than those mentioned above. Alternative systems could be based upon molecular size, shape, numbers of ionic groups, or biological function. However, despite its defects, the system of classifying proteins according to composition and solubility seems to be the most useful at the present time.

SIMPLE PROTEINS. Albumins were originally differentiated from globulins by virtue of the solubility of the former in pure water, since the globulins originally studied required the presence of small quantities of salt for their solution. Later, when it was discovered that proteins could be forced out of solution by high concentrations of salt (salting out), a second criterion was established; globulins were proteins which could be precipitated by ammonium sulfate in concentrations of half-saturation or less, whereas albumins required higher concentrations of the salt. Unfortunately for the system of classification, the two criteria do not lead to the same results in all cases. For instance, among the "globulins," as classified by the salting-out method, are many which are soluble in pure water. These have been called "pseudoglobulins" (to distinguish them from "true globulins," or euglobulins). The opposite type of difficulty also occurs, since there are euglobulins (by the water-solubility criterion) which are salted out with the albumins. It is therefore evident that the terms "albumin" and "globulin" have little significance unless the criterion of classification is stated. Unless indicated otherwise, we shall use the criterion of salting out in our discussions of the albumins and globulins.

Probably the best known proteins of the two groups just discussed are egg albumin, plasma albumin, and the plasma globulins. To the confusion of systematists, highly purified egg albumin as well as some fractions of plasma albumin and of the plasma globulins contain firmly bound carbohydrate. While this fact calls for a classification of these substances as glycoproteins, the change-over has not yet been generally accepted.

The glutelins are simple proteins which are insoluble in pure water and dilute salt solutions, but soluble in dilute acids or bases. Glutenin from wheat is an example of this group. It is probable that these proteins, the best characterized of which have been obtained from plants, actually represent mixtures of closely related individuals. Prolamines are proteins which are insoluble in water and absolute alcohol, but soluble in aqueous ethanol (70 to 80 per cent). Examples are zein from corn and gliadin from wheat. The unusual solubility properties of this group of proteins are accounted for by the predominance of non-polar (hydrocarbon-type) groups in the molecule.

The scleroproteins (sometimes called "albuminoids," a poor choice of terminology) form a group with structural and protective functions, and are appropriately characterized by their insolubility in all of the solvents mentioned thus far. There is evidence that reagents which dissolve scleroproteins do so only as a result of fundamental changes in the protein molecules. Typical scleroproteins are keratin from horn, nails, hoofs, and feathers, collagen from tendon, skin, and bone, and elastin from ligament.

CONJUGATED PROTEINS. Nucleoproteins are characterized by the possession of prosthetic groups known as nucleic acids. Certain nucleic acids are attached to proteins known as protamines, which are water-soluble, basic proteins, of relatively low molecular weight. Other nucleic acids are found in nature combined with histones, which are also basic proteins, differing from the protamines by their higher molecular weight. The protein moieties of some nucleoproteins are less basic, of higher molecular weight, and more complex than the protamines and histones. The nucleic acids and nucleoproteins are substances of such great biological importance that a separate chapter will be devoted to them (p. 94).

Phosphoproteins contain phosphoric acid, linked as an ester to the hydroxyl group of certain amino acids in the protein. Casein of milk is an example of a phosphoprotein.

A number of proteins contain as prosthetic groups certain rather complex heterocyclic compounds known as porphyrins, which in turn are usually combined with a metallic atom. In the case of the chlorophylloproteins, the porphyrin is combined with magnesium to form the familiar green compound, chlorophyll, which is widely distributed in the plant world. The hemoproteins contain iron-porphyrins, known as hemes, attached to the protein portion of the molecule. Hemoglobin and myoglobin are examples of hemoproteins, as are a number of enzymes, such as the catalases, peroxidases, and cytochromes.

The prosthetic groups of the glycoproteins are polysaccharides of the heterosaccharidic, nitrogenous type (mucopolysaccharides). Further subdivision of this group of proteins is based upon the composition of the mucopolysaccharides (p. 18). As indicated earlier, certain of the substances classified as simple proteins are really members of the glycoprotein group, e.g., egg albumin. Other glycoproteins are found in connective tissues and in the mucous membranes which line the digestive tract. Some hormones such as chorionic gonadotrophin and certain of the pituitary hormones (p. 698) are likewise glycoproteins.

Lipoproteins are discussed in some detail in the chapter on lipids (p. 38), and are mentioned again at this point only for completeness of classification.

Riboflavin, a member of the vitamin B complex, forms a part of the prosthetic group of a number of proteins, flavoproteins, which act as enzymes in catalyzing biological oxidations (p. 361). In some cases riboflavin phosphate as such makes up the prosthetic group; in others a compound known as adenylic acid is combined with the riboflavin phosphate to form the prosthetic group.

Many conjugated proteins contain metallic atoms. When these metals are parts of more complex prosthetic groups, the proteins are classified according to the complete group. However, there are metalloproteins which contain, so far as can be ascertained, no special non-protein substances other than the metallic atoms themselves. Among such proteins are ferritin (an iron-containing protein), copper-binding and iron-binding plasma proteins, carbonic anhydrase (the zinc-protein enzyme), insulin (the zinc-containing hormone), and certain metal-activated peptidase enzymes. Hemocyanins, the oxygen-transporting blood pigments of many invertebrates, are copper proteins, although it is not certain whether the copper is combined with some more complex group.

DERIVED PROTEINS. As mentioned earlier, the protein moieties which result from the removal of prosthetic groups from conjugated proteins may be considered one class of derived proteins. In this category are the protamines from the nucleoproteins of spermatozoa, the histones from the nucleoproteins of the thymus, and the familiar histone, globin, from hemoglobin.

The early literature on derived proteins contained such terms as proteans and metaproteins. These substances are now recognized as denatured proteins, and the terms are obsolete. Denaturation is a phenomenon which can be shown to occur in the case of most proteins; it will be discussed in connection with the steric architecture of proteins (p. 81).

The products of partial hydrolysis of proteins are often classified as derived proteins. One class, the proteoses, were differentiated from another class, the peptones, by the precipitability of the former with ammonium sulfate. Actually, these substances are highly heterogeneous mixtures of molecules of varying molecular weight, and it is questionable whether the terms serve any useful purpose at the present time.

Continuation of the process of hydrolysis eventually leads to the production of smaller peptides, many of which have been characterized as chemical individuals.

THE AMINO ACIDS

COMMON STRUCTURAL FEATURES. With the exception of the prolines (which are imino acids), the amino acids which form the building blocks of proteins are characterized by an amino group in a position α to the carboxyl group. The rest of the molecule, represented by "R—," is the source of the variations in structure which differentiate one amino acid from another.

Examination of the formula for an amino acid discloses the fact that the α carbon atom has four different groups attached to it, except for the case where R is H. As a result this carbon atom is asymmetric, with the exception of the simplest amino acid, glycine. In the chapter on carbohydrates it was pointed out that glyceraldehyde was the reference compound for the steric families of sugars. In a similar fashion, serine, an α-amino, β-hydroxy acid, serves as the reference compound for the amino acids. When the carboxyl groups of the amino acids are placed on top of the diagram, the amino group is written to the left for an L amino acid. The opposite arrangement holds for the D compounds.

$$\begin{array}{cc} \text{COOH} & \text{COOH} \\ | & | \\ \text{NH}_2\text{CH} & \text{HCNH}_2 \\ | & | \\ \text{CH}_2\text{OH} & \text{CH}_2\text{OH} \\ \text{L-Serine} & \text{D-Serine} \end{array}$$

If necessary, the direction of optical rotation of the amino acids may be indicated by the symbols $(+)$ or $(-)$, following the designation D or L, viz., D $(+)$, D $(-)$, L $(+)$, L $(-)$. As was emphasized in the case of the carbohydrates, no necessary relation exists between the steric configuration of the amino acids and their optical rotation.

The amino acids which make up the protoplasmic proteins of plants and animals belong to the L stereochemical family. At one time it was thought that only the L amino acids occurred in nature; they were therefore called the "natural" amino acids, and their enantiomorphs were said to be "un-natural." A number of products have been isolated in recent years, however, which are proteins or peptides in structure and contain some D amino acids. Many of these substances, which are liberated by microorganisms into the culture medium, are of medical importance as "antibiotics." Interestingly enough, the intracellular proteins of the microorganisms in question are made up of the L amino acids.

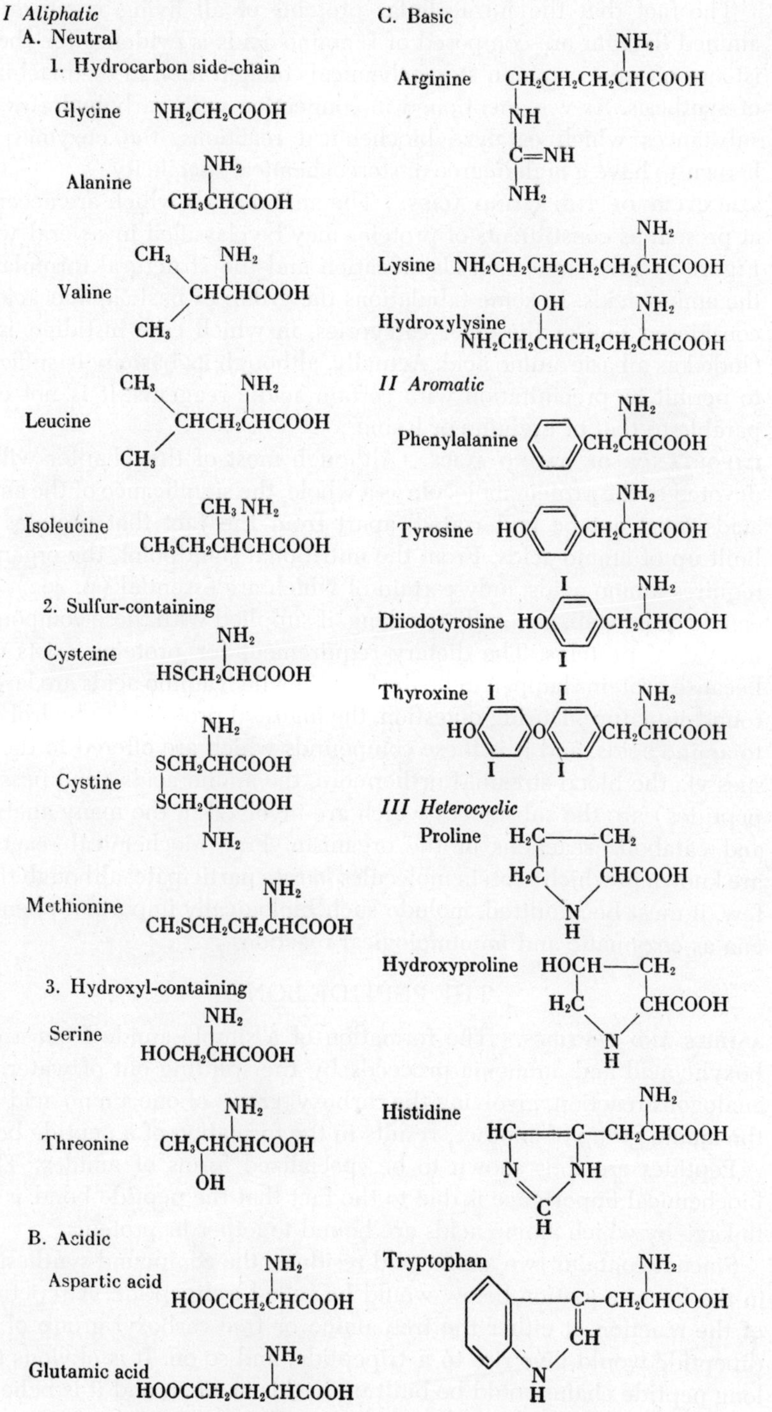

I Aliphatic

A. Neutral

1. Hydrocarbon side-chain

Glycine NH_2CH_2COOH

Alanine $CH_3\overset{\overset{\displaystyle NH_2}{|}}{C}HCOOH$

Valine $\overset{\overset{\displaystyle CH_3}{|}}{C}H\overset{\overset{\displaystyle NH_2}{|}}{C}HCOOH$ with CH_3

Leucine $\overset{\overset{\displaystyle CH_3}{|}}{C}HCH_2\overset{\overset{\displaystyle NH_2}{|}}{C}HCOOH$ with CH_3

Isoleucine $CH_3CH_2\overset{\overset{\displaystyle CH_3}{|}}{C}H\overset{\overset{\displaystyle NH_2}{|}}{C}HCOOH$

2. Sulfur-containing

Cysteine $HSCH_2\overset{\overset{\displaystyle NH_2}{|}}{C}HCOOH$

Cystine $\overset{\overset{\displaystyle NH_2}{|}}{S}CH_2CHCOOH$ / $\overset{\underset{\displaystyle NH_2}{|}}{S}CH_2CHCOOH$

Methionine $CH_3SCH_2CH_2\overset{\overset{\displaystyle NH_2}{|}}{C}HCOOH$

3. Hydroxyl-containing

Serine $HOCH_2\overset{\overset{\displaystyle NH_2}{|}}{C}HCOOH$

Threonine $CH_3\overset{\overset{\displaystyle NH_2}{|}}{\underset{\underset{\displaystyle OH}{|}}{C}}HCHCOOH$

B. Acidic

Aspartic acid $HOOCCH_2\overset{\overset{\displaystyle NH_2}{|}}{C}HCOOH$

Glutamic acid $HOOCCH_2CH_2\overset{\overset{\displaystyle NH_2}{|}}{C}HCOOH$

C. Basic

Arginine $CH_2CH_2CH_2\overset{\overset{\displaystyle NH_2}{|}}{C}HCOOH$
NH
$C=NH$
NH_2

Lysine $NH_2CH_2CH_2CH_2CH_2\overset{\overset{\displaystyle NH_2}{|}}{C}HCOOH$

Hydroxylysine $NH_2CH_2\overset{\overset{\displaystyle OH}{|}}{C}HCH_2CH_2\overset{\overset{\displaystyle NH_2}{|}}{C}HCOOH$

II Aromatic

Phenylalanine ⬡$CH_2\overset{\overset{\displaystyle NH_2}{|}}{C}HCOOH$

Tyrosine HO⬡$CH_2\overset{\overset{\displaystyle NH_2}{|}}{C}HCOOH$

Diiodotyrosine HO⬡$CH_2\overset{\overset{\displaystyle NH_2}{|}}{C}HCOOH$ with I (positions)

Thyroxine HO⬡O⬡$CH_2\overset{\overset{\displaystyle NH_2}{|}}{C}HCOOH$ with I (positions)

III Heterocyclic

Proline
$H_2C\text{——}CH_2$
$H_2C\quad CHCOOH$
$\underset{H}{N}$

Hydroxyproline
$HOCH\text{——}CH_2$
$H_2C\quad CHCOOH$
$\underset{H}{N}$

Histidine
$HC=C\text{—}CH_2\overset{\overset{\displaystyle NH_2}{|}}{C}HCOOH$
$N\quad NH$
$\underset{H}{C}$

Tryptophan
⬡$C\text{—}CH_2\overset{\overset{\displaystyle NH_2}{|}}{C}HCOOH$
CH
$\underset{H}{N}$

Fig. 11. Classification and structures of amino acids

The fact that the intracellular proteins of all living creatures examined thus far are composed of L amino acids is evidence for the existence of some common stereochemical configuration in the machinery of synthesis. As was mentioned in connection with carbohydrates, the substances which catalyze biochemical reactions, the enzymes, are known to have a high degree of stereochemical specificity.

STRUCTURE OF THE AMINO ACIDS. The amino acids which are accepted at present as constituents of proteins may be classified in several ways. Figure 11 gives one such classification and the structural formulas of the amino acids. In some tabulations the group of basic amino acids is considered one of the chief categories, in which case histidine is included as a basic amino acid. Actually, although its basicity is sufficient to permit its precipitation with certain acidic reagents, it is not comparable to that of arginine or lysine.

IMPORTANCE OF AMINO ACIDS. Although most of this chapter will be devoted to the protein molecule as a whole, the significance of the amino acids must not be underrated, apart from the fact that proteins are built up of amino acids. From the nutritional standpoint, the organism requires amino acids, only certain of which are essential (p. 492), and can do quite well, generally speaking, if supplied with these compounds instead of proteins. The dietary requirement for proteins exists only because proteins happen to be the form in which amino acids are largely found in nature. During digestion, the ingested proteins are hydrolyzed to amino acids, and it is these compounds which are offered to the tissues via the blood stream. Furthermore, the amino acids (and possibly peptides) are the substances which are involved in the many anabolic and catabolic reactions of the organism. Few biochemical reactions are known in which protein molecules *in toto* participate, although these few, it must be admitted, include such biologically important phenomena as enzymatic and immunological reactions.

THE PEPTIDE BOND

AMIDES AND PEPTIDES. The formation of a simple amide from a carboxylic acid and ammonia proceeds by the splitting out of water. An analogous reaction, involving the carboxyl group of one amino acid and the amino group of another, results in the formation of a peptide bond.

Peptides are thus shown to be specialized forms of amides. Their biochemical importance is due to the fact that the peptide bond is the linkage by which amino acids are bound together in proteins.

Since it contains two amino acid residues, the compound synthesized in the lower equation below would be called a dipeptide. A repetition of the reaction at either the free amino or free carboxyl group of the dipeptide would give rise to a tripeptide, and so on. It is obvious that long peptide chains could be built up in this manner, and it is believed at the present time that the basic structure of the protein molecule consists of such peptide chains.

Peptides are named by beginning with the amino acid residue which retains its free amino group, substituting the suffix "-yl" for the usual suffix "-ine," and continuing this process through the peptide chain until the amino acid residue containing the free carboxyl group is reached, giving this terminal residue its full chemical name. (If necessary for the particular discussion at hand, the steric families are noted as D or L.)

Glycyl-alanine   Alanyl-glycine

With some twenty-odd amino acids to draw upon, it is evident that a tremendous number of positional isomers is possible in a long peptide chain, and that the situation becomes even more complicated in the case of the proteins, with molecular weights running into the thousands or millions.

NATURALLY OCCURRING PEPTIDES AND PSEUDOPEPTIDES. Before considering the general topic of the peptide structure of the proteins proper, a number of simpler compounds of similar structure may be mentioned. The formulas for some of these are given below and on page 52.

Glutathione   Hippuric acid

Carnosine   Phenylacetyl-glutamine

CH$_3$— here
in anserine

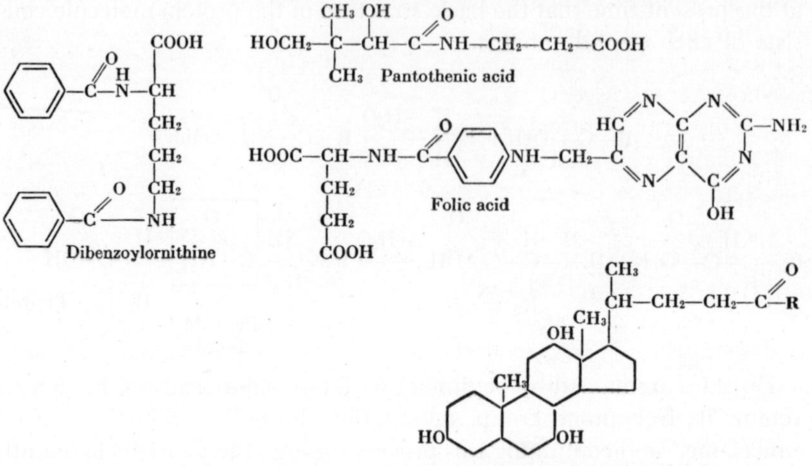

Dibenzoylornithine

Pantothenic acid

Folic acid

Conjugated cholic acid; R = glycine or taurine

Glutathione is a tripeptide of glutamic acid, cysteine, and glycine. Aside from the peculiar mode of attachment of the glutamyl group, which in this case involves the γ instead of the α carboxyl, glutathione may be considered a true peptide. It is distributed widely in living tissues, and has recently been shown to be a prosthetic group of glyceraldehydephosphate dehydrogenase (p. 393).

Carnosine and anserine are found in muscle. Since they contain the compound β-alanine, which does not belong to the class of α-amino acids, they may be called "pseudopeptides." Their biochemical function is not known.

The other compounds, since they contain some residues which are definitely not amino acids, also belong to the category of pseudopeptides. They are more closely related to peptides than to amides, however, because in each case one constituent of the compound is either an amino acid or closely related to an amino acid. Pantothenic and "folic" acids belong to the group of B vitamins. Hippuric acid, phenylacetylglutamine, and dibenzoylornithine are substances which result from the coupling of a foreign substance for excretion from the organism (detoxication). The conjugated bile acids were discussed briefly in the chapter on lipids.

Under proper conditions, carbon dioxide, which may be considered the anhydride of carbonic acid, combines with the amino groups of amino acids or proteins to form "carbamino" compounds:

$$\text{R—NH}_2 + \text{CO}_2 \rightarrow \text{R—N—C—O}^- + \text{H}^+$$

The resulting linkage bears some resemblance to an amide or peptide bond. The carbamino compounds formed by hemoglobin are important in the transport of carbon dioxide in the blood stream (p. 292).

EVIDENCE FOR PEPTIDE LINKAGE IN PROTEINS. Up to this point the formulation of proteins as chains of amino acids united in peptide linkage has been stated as a fact. This formulation should be stated more properly as a hypothesis. Some of the supporting evidence for this hypothesis will now be discussed.

Proteins react positively to the biuret test (p. 88), giving a color reaction mainly characteristic of compounds containing multiple peptide linkages. Most of the chemical groups other than the peptide linkage which give the biuret reaction can be eliminated from consideration, since they do not occur in proteins. The amino acid, histidine, reacts positively to the biuret test in the free state, but it is easily shown that the response as given by proteins is not due to any appreciable extent to their histidine content. Hydrolysis of a protein to the stage of free amino acids or to a mixture of peptides no larger than dipeptides results in the disappearance of the biuret reaction.

By direct chemical or physical chemical methods, proteins can be shown to possess few free carboxyl and amino groups. During hydrolysis of the protein new amino and carboxyl groups appear, and this liberation of the two types of groups occurs at the same rate for each, as though they were linked together in the protein, mol for mol.

Partial hydrolysis of proteins can give rise to small peptides, e.g., of the dipeptide or tripeptide type. These can be isolated and characterized. Identical peptides can be synthesized by chemical methods of such a nature that it is certain that the constituent amino acid residues of the products are joined in peptide linkages. On the reasonable assumption that the peptides isolated from the hydrolyzed proteins represent true fragments of the original molecules, these original molecules must have contained the same peptide linkages.

Proteins are hydrolyzed by enzymes which show a high degree of specificity toward the peptide linkage. Recent demonstrations that proteolytic enzymes also hydrolyze esters of certain types do not invalidate the hypothesis under discussion, since the chemical composition of proteins makes it impossible for ester linkages to constitute any appreciable fraction of the total linkages between amino acids.

The absorption spectra of proteins in the infrared and far ultraviolet also provide evidence for the existence of large numbers of peptide bonds in the protein molecule.

HYDROLYSIS OF THE PEPTIDE LINKAGE. Essentially, hydrolysis of a peptide linkage amounts to the addition of the elements of water across the bond, resulting in the formation of a free amino and carboxyl group for each peptide bond split:

The reaction as written proceeds to completion under physiological conditions; the best available evidence indicates that the biosynthesis of peptide bonds does not proceed by simple reversal of the hydrolytic reaction.

Although the equilibrium point of the hydrolytic reaction lies far toward the side of the products, the rate of the reaction is slow in the absence of catalysts. (For a discussion of the essential nature of catalysis, see Chapter 7.) In the laboratory, the hydrolysis of peptides and proteins is effected by heating in the presence of acids or bases as catalysts. The organism carries out the same reaction at moderate temperatures, using enzymes as catalysts.

Complete cleavage of a protein to its constituent amino acids for analytical purposes is usually accomplished in the laboratory by prolonged boiling with aqueous solutions of mineral acids. This procedure has the advantage in that it results in the retention of the natural stereochemical configurations of the amino acids. However, tryptophan is completely destroyed, and serine and threonine are also decomposed to some extent.

The use of boiling alkali in the hydrolysis avoids the destruction of tryptophan. On the other hand, racemization of the amino acids occurs in alkali, as well as the decomposition of some of these compounds including arginine, cysteine, cystine, and others.

Hydrolysis by proteolytic enzymes is the gentlest of all available methods, but is seldom used as a laboratory procedure except for special purposes. Outside of the body, enzymatic digestion of proteins proceeds at a slow rate and is generally incomplete. Conditions within the digestive tract, however, permit a rapid and quite complete hydrolysis of ingested proteins. In contrast to the action of acidic or basic catalysts, the peptide linkages are not attacked at random by proteolytic enzymes. The nature of the specificity toward certain linkages will be discussed in Chapters 7 and 8.

While there may be variations in the exact course of hydrolysis of a given protein in the presence of a given hydrolytic catalyst, the general succession of events is believed to be the following:

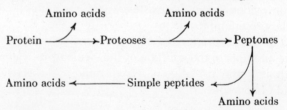

The proteoses and peptones are not chemical individuals, but rather mixtures of ill-defined substances intermediate in molecular weight between the proteins and the smaller peptides. Since terminal as well as central peptide linkages may be hydrolyzed, some free amino acids may be liberated throughout the course of the process, as shown.

Hydrolysates of proteins are currently being used therapeutically. In conditions where digestion is impaired but absorption is satisfactory, the hydrolysate is given orally; should normal intake of food be impossible, intravenous administration of hydrolysates can be used to satisfy the requirements for amino acids for a time.

ARCHITECTURE OF PROTEINS

ELECTROLYTES, pH, AND BUFFERS. Although certain ionic compounds may be encountered among the carbohydrates and lipids, the phenomenon of ionization is the rule rather than the exception among amino acids and proteins. In fact, most of the chemical and many of the biological properties of these substances are explicable only on the basis of their ionic character. In order to provide the necessary background for the consideration of amino acids and proteins as charged particles, a brief summary follows of the elementary principles of electrolytic dissociation and related phenomena.

(a) DISSOCIATION. Many of the chemical compounds encountered in biochemistry exist in solution as undissociated particles. Solutions of these substances have low electrical conductivity, and their colligative properties (those related to the number of particles in solution) can be calculated directly from the molarities of the solutions. As examples, the decrease in the freezing point of water, the increase in the boiling point of water, and the osmotic pressure of such solutions are related to the molar concentration of solute as follows:

$$\Delta^\circ_{fp} = 1.86 \times C \qquad \Delta^\circ_{bp} = 0.52 \times C \qquad P_{osm} = 22.4 \times C \text{ atmospheres}$$
$$\text{(at } 0^\circ \text{ C.)}$$

Examples of such substances are glycerol, glucose, urea, and the proteins (at their isoelectric points only; see p. 64).

Solutions of many other chemical compounds, however, exhibit colligative properties which seem to be far in excess of their indicated molarities; in fact, they are practically integral multiples of the molarities. These solutions have a high electrical conductivity, due to the complete ionization of the compounds into charged particles. Substances of this sort are called "strong electrolytes," and include such common laboratory reagents as the mineral acids (hydrochloric, nitric, and sulfuric), many of the common alkalies (or bases) such as sodium hydroxide, potassium hydroxide, and barium hydroxide, and practically all salts. The colligative properties of solutions of these compounds can be calculated, to a fair degree of approximation in dilute solution, by multiplying the molarity by the number of particles resulting from the ionization, and using this figure (known as the osmolarity, or osmolar concentration) in place of the molarity in the formulas given above. For instance, HCl yields two particles, while $BaCl_2$ produces three, so that the osmolarity of the former will be twice, and that of the latter will be three times the indicated molarity.

In addition to non-electrolytes and strong electrolytes a third group of substances exists, called "weak electrolytes." These compounds are intermediate in properties between the two groups already discussed; they conduct the electric current better than do the non-electrolytes, but not nearly so well as the strong electrolytes. Their solutions have colligative properties which are in excess of those expected from their molar concentrations, but not so much in excess as to indicate complete dissociation. They are, in fact, partly dissociated or ionized. The calculation of the colligative properties of this group of compounds involves a consideration of the degree of dissociation, which in turn varies with the concentration. While not especially complex, this type of calculation is required so seldom in elementary biochemistry that it will not be considered here. Among the weak electrolytes frequently encountered are fatty acids, lactic acid, acetoacetic acid, ammonium hydroxide, carbonic acid, the ionizable groups on amino acid and protein molecules, and water itself.

(*b*) IONIZATION CONSTANTS. In the ionization of weak electrolytes the ionized particles are in equilibrium with the un-ionized molecules, allowing us to set up (according to the law of mass action) an equilibrium constant, or (as it is frequently called in this case) an ionization or dissociation constant:

$$XY \rightleftharpoons X + Y \qquad K_{diss} = \frac{(X)\,(Y)}{(XY)}$$

The quantities in parentheses are concentration units of gram-mols or gram-ions per liter.

Water, as has been mentioned already, is a weak electrolyte. Its dissociation can be represented as follows:

$$H_2O \rightleftharpoons H^+ + OH^- \qquad K_{diss} = \frac{(H^+)\,(OH^-)}{(H_2O)}$$

Since the concentration of water in all ordinary solutions remains practically constant, owing to the very small degree of dissociation, it has been found convenient to incorporate the (H_2O) term into a new constant on the left side of the equation:

$$K_w = (H^+)\,(OH^-) = 10^{-14} \text{ (at room temp.)}$$

In pure water (that is, containing no acidic or basic substances) the concentrations of hydrogen and hydroxyl ions are equal to each other, hence each is present in a concentration of 10^{-7} mols/liter.

(c) HYDROGEN ION CONCENTRATION AND pH. Although the product of the hydrogen and hydroxyl ion concentrations is always 10^{-14}, many solutions contain a large excess of one or the other, so that the expression of the concentration of either ion involves rather unwieldy exponents. A simplified notation has been devised, therefore, which denotes the acidity of all solutions in terms of pH, defined as follows:

$$pH = \log \frac{1}{(H^+)}$$

In this notation a neutral solution will have a pH of 7, a solution containing hydrogen ions in 1 molar concentration will have a pH of 0, while a 1 molar solution of hydroxyl ions (remembering the K_w) will have a pH of 14. An analogous notation for direct expression of hydroxyl ion concentrations would be:

$$pOH = \log \frac{1}{(OH^-)}$$

From the ionization equation for water, the pH and pOH of all solutions are related by:

$$pH + pOH = \log \frac{1}{K_w} = 14$$

In the preceding equation the term "$\log \frac{1}{K_w}$" can be expressed in a notation similar to that used for pH and pOH, namely pK_w ($= 14$). For convenience the dissociation constants of many weak electrolytes are often expressed in this pK notation.

(d) DISSOCIATION OF WEAK ACIDS. Since the weak electrolytes which are of interest in biochemistry are acids or can be formulated as acids (p. 60), the ionization of this class of compounds requires special attention. Taking the general case of the weak acid HA dissociating into H^+ and A^-, the equilibrium can be formulated as follows:

$$HA \rightleftharpoons H^+ + A^-$$

$$K_a = \frac{(H^+)\,(A^-)}{(HA)} \qquad pK_a = \log \frac{1}{K_a}$$

Owing to the reciprocal nature of the mathematical function, the stronger the acid, the smaller the pK_a value.

(e) BUFFERS AND THE HENDERSON-HASSELBALCH EQUATION. A buffer may be defined as a solution which resists the change in pH which might be expected to occur upon the addition of acid or base to the solution. Buffers consist of mixtures of weak acids and their salts or weak bases and their salts. The former type is the more important in biochemistry; its action against added acid or base may be illustrated as shown on page 58.

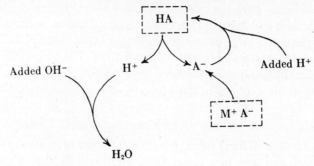

The buffer consists of the weak acid HA and its completely ionized salt M^+A^-. Added hydrogen ions, in the form of a strong acid, combine with anions A^- (largely from the salt component of the buffer) to form the weakly dissociated HA, so that the pH does not become as acid as it would in the absence of the buffer. The capacity to combine with added acid remains so long as there is a supply of the buffer salt in the solution. Added hydroxyl ions, in the form of a strong base, combine with hydrogen ions derived from the acid HA, and form the weakly dissociated water molecule. Hence the pH does not become as alkaline as would otherwise occur. Hydroxyl ions can be buffered as long as some of the acid HA remains to supply hydrogen ions.

The pH of any mixture of a weak acid and its salt can be calculated from the Henderson-Hasselbalch equation, which is readily derived as follows: in any solution of a weak acid, whether its salt is present or not, the usual dissociation constant equation holds true—

$$K_a = \frac{(H^+)\,(A^-)}{(HA)}.$$

The dissociation of the average weak acid is so small that the term (HA) can be replaced with the actual, total molarity of the acid dissolved in the solution. Similarly, when the salt of the acid is present, practically all of the anion A^- in the solution can be regarded as coming from the salt, so that the term (A^-) can be replaced by the molarity of salt added. Making the indicated replacements and rearranging terms,

$$\frac{1}{(H^+)} = \frac{1}{K_a} \times \frac{(salt)}{(acid)}.$$

Taking logarithms of both sides of the equation,

$$pH = pK_a + \log \frac{(salt)}{(acid)},$$

from which one can calculate the pH of any buffer system from the pK of the acid involved and the salt-acid ratio. It may be pointed out that, when the salt and acid are present in equal concentrations, the pH of the solution is numerically equal to the pK of the acid, since the logarithmic term becomes zero. Buffers are most efficient at pH's near their pK's, and their effective range is commonly said to include pH's one (or possibly two) pH units above and below the pK value.

AMINO ACIDS AND PROTEINS AS CHARGED PARTICLES. (a) BIOLOGICAL IM-PORTANCE. The fact that the protein molecule bears electrical charges on its surface is of paramount importance in many biological phenomena. It is probable that the permeability of natural membranes, composed chiefly or entirely of proteins, owes much of its selectivity to the electrical charges in the vicinity of its orifices, especially when the particles approaching the membrane are themselves electrically charged. Interactions between enzyme and substrate, antigen and antibody, and probably hormone and target molecule (an enzyme?) all involve some reactive portion of the surface of a protein. Evidence is accumulating that the degree and specificity of such reactivity is dependent upon the presence and steric placement of electrically charged groups.

(b) TITRATION METHODS. As will be shown later, the electrical charges on amino acid and protein molecules arise from ionizable groups, all of which may be regarded as weak acids. The number and type of each group can be studied by means of titrations with acid and base, acid being used to "back-titrate" those groups which may be in their salt form, while base reacts with those which are present as undissociated acids. The number of groups can be calculated from the stoichiometry of the titration, and the chemical type of each group can be ascertained from the pH range in which it is titrated. A variation of this procedure is the study of the combination with proteins of anions and cations other than H^+ and OH^-, e.g., heavy metal ions and ionic dyestuffs.

(c) ELECTROPHORESIS. Except under special circumstances which will be discussed later, amino acids and proteins in solution carry a net positive or negative charge. They therefore migrate in an electrical field toward one electrode or the other. This migration, called "electrophoresis," may be used not only as a tool in theoretical studies of the numbers of charged groups on protein molecules, but also as an analytical method for the quantitative determination of individual proteins in complex natural mixtures, such as blood plasma.

(d) CHARGED GROUPS ON AMINO ACIDS. The amino acids display, on a simpler and miniature scale, most of the electrical and ionic properties of the proteins. As mentioned earlier, the groups involved may be regarded as weak acids, the term "acid" being defined as any compound or group capable of giving up a hydrogen ion. The form of the group existing after removal of the hydrogen ion will be spoken of as the ionized or "salt" form (called a "base" in certain systems). Two types of acid groups must be considered, the cationic acids and the uncharged acids. Since the student may not be familiar with this sort of formulation, especially with the classification of the ammonium ion as an acid, a detailed outline of the ionization and titration of both types of acids, in the general form and as specific examples (acetic acid and ammonium ion, respectively), is given below.

Cationic Acid, General Formulation

Specific Example

Ionization: $ZH^+ \longleftrightarrow Z^\circ + H^+$ $NH_4^+ \longleftrightarrow NH_3^\circ + H^+$

Titration: $ZH^+ \xrightarrow{Na^+OH^-} Z^\circ + Na^+ + H_2O$ $NH_4^+ \xrightarrow{Na^+OH^-} NH_3^\circ + Na^+ + H_2O$

Back-Titration: $Z^\circ \xrightarrow{H^+Cl^-} ZH^+ + Cl^-$ $NH_3^\circ \xrightarrow{H^+Cl^-} NH_4^+ + Cl^-$

$$K_a = \frac{(H^+)\,(Z^\circ)}{(ZH^+)}$$

Uncharged Acid, General Formulation

Specific Example

Ionization: $ZH \longleftrightarrow Z^- + H^+$ $CH_3COOH \longleftrightarrow CH_3COO^- + H^+$

Titration: $ZH \xrightarrow{Na^+OH^-} Z^-Na^+ + H_2O$ $CH_3COOH \xrightarrow{Na^+OH^-} CH_3COO^-Na^+ + H_2O$

Back-Titration: $Z^-Na^+ \xrightarrow{H^+Cl^-} ZH + Na^+Cl^-$ $CH_3COO^-Na^+ \xrightarrow{H^+Cl^-} CH_3COOH + Na^+Cl^-$

$$K_a = \frac{(H^+)\,(Z^-)}{(ZH)}$$

It will be observed that the uncharged acid becomes negatively charged upon ionization or titration, while the cationic acid loses its positive charge and becomes electrically neutral. For the sake of simplicity the anion which must always accompany the positively charged cationic acid group is omitted from the figure.

(*e*) DISSOCIATION CONSTANTS AND BUFFER SYSTEMS. Since all of the groups under consideration are weak acids, ionization constants can be formulated for them, based on the law of mass action. From each K_a a corresponding pK_a can be derived (cf., p. 57). A tabulation follows on page 61 of the various acid groups found in amino acids and proteins, together with their salt forms and approximate pK's. Under any circumstances in which one of these groups is present partly in its acid form and partly in its salt form, a buffer system will be set up (cf., p. 58), the pH of which will follow the Henderson-Hasselbalch equation for that particular group. As with most buffer systems, the effective buffer range or titration range of each group lies within 1 or 2 pH units above and below its pK.

$$pH = pK_a + \log \frac{\text{(salt form)}}{\text{(acid form)}}$$

(*f*) ZWITTERIONS. From the numerical values given previously, it would be expected that, at pH's around neutrality, carboxyl groups should exist in their salt forms, while ammonium groups should retain

Table 4. Buffer Groups of Proteins

ACID TYPE	GROUP	ACID FORM	SALT FORM	LOCATION	APPROX. PK
Uncharged	Carboxyl	—COOH	—COO⁻	End group	3.5
	Carboxyl	—COOH	—COO⁻	Aspartyl- and glutamyl side-chains	4.0
	Phenol	$\diagdown$C—OH	$\diagdown$C—O⁻	Tyrosine	10.0
	Sulfhydryl	—SH	—S⁻	Cysteine	10.0
Cationic	Imidazolium	HC══C— HN⁺ NH \C/ H	HC══C— N NH \C/ H	Histidine	7.0
	Ammonium	—NH₃⁺	—NH₂	α-Amino end group	8.0
	Ammonium	—NH₃⁺	—NH₂	ε-Amino of lysine	10.0
	Guanidinium	NH | C=NH₂⁺ | NH₂	NH | C=NH | NH₂	Arginine	12.5

their hydrogen ions and exist in cationic form. An amino acid in approximately neutral solution, therefore, cannot have the uncharged structure assigned to it by the classical organic chemists. Instead, it exists as a doubly charged molecule (in the case of those amino acids having only two ionizable groups), containing one positive and one negative charge, and hence is electrically neutral. Such a structure is called a zwitterion (hybrid ion) or dipolar ion.

$$\text{R—C—C—OH (NH}_2\text{, O, H)} \qquad \text{R—C—C—O}^- \text{ (NH}_3^+\text{, O, H)}$$

Classical structure   Zwitterion

The reaction of the zwitterion with acid represents a back-titration of the carboxyl group, leading to the formation of an organic molecule bearing a net positive charge. Bases, on the other hand, react with the ammonium group of the zwitterion, removing its titratable hydrogen and resulting in the formation of an organic molecule bearing a net negative charge. Each of these reactions can be reversed by the use of the appropriate reagent:

$$\left[\begin{array}{c} \mathrm{NH_3^+} \\ | \\ \mathrm{R-C-COOH} \\ | \\ \mathrm{H} \end{array}\right] \mathrm{Cl^-} \quad \underset{\mathrm{Na^+OH^-}}{\overset{\mathrm{H^+Cl^-}}{\longleftarrow \longrightarrow}} \quad \left[\begin{array}{c} \mathrm{NH_3^+} \\ | \\ \mathrm{R-C-COO^-} \\ | \\ \mathrm{H} \end{array}\right] \quad \underset{\mathrm{H^+Cl^-}}{\overset{\mathrm{Na^+OH^-}}{\longleftarrow \longrightarrow}} \quad \left[\begin{array}{c} \mathrm{NH_2} \\ | \\ \mathrm{R-C-COO^-} \\ | \\ \mathrm{H} \end{array}\right] \mathrm{Na^+}$$

The fact that an amino acid (or a protein) can react with both acid and base places it in the category of amphoteric substances.

That pH at which the amino acid molecule bears a net charge of zero is known as the isoelectric point. At that pH the compound will not migrate in an electrical field. The amino acid carries a net positive charge at pH's acid to its isoelectric point, a net negative charge at pH's basic to its isoelectric point, and migrates toward the cathode and anode respectively. The isoelectric pH is frequently symbolized by pI.

From what has been said, it is obvious that even the simplest amino acids contain two potential buffer systems. If the pH of the solution is acid to the pI of the amino acid, but not so acid that all of it is in its positively charged form, then a buffer system will exist in which the (+) form is the acid, and the zwitterion ($\pm$) is the salt. A second buffer system exists on the basic side of the pI, with the zwitterion now acting as the acid (the hydrogen-donor), and the negatively charged form (−) as the salt. Each buffer system can be described by its appropriate Henderson-Hasselbalch equation, using the pK's for the groups involved. The pK's of amino acids are customarily designated by numerical subscripts, taken in the order of decreasing acidity (or increasing pK value). Thus, in the simple amino acids, pK_1 refers to the −COOH group and pK_2 to the −NH_3^+ group. In this case the pI is related to the pK's by:

$$pI = \frac{pK_1 + pK_2}{2}.$$

Taking the case of glycine as an example, $pK_1 = 2$, $pK_2 = 10$, hence $pI = 6$.

(g) PH-TITRATION CURVES. If one gram molecular weight of a simple amino acid in its most positively charged form (i.e., the product of treatment of one mol of the isoelectric form with one equivalent of acid) is titrated with standard base, and equivalents of base used are plotted against the resulting pH at each point, a buffer curve is obtained of the type shown in Figure 12. At the beginning of the curve, all of the amino acid is in the (+) form. As base is added, some of the COOH groups are titrated to the salt form, in this case, the ($\pm$), hence a buffer system is set up. It can be seen that there is a resistance to change in pH, especially around the middle of this part of the titration. When half an equivalent of base has been added, there is as much salt form as acid form present, so that, from the Henderson-Hasselbalch equation describing this part of the curve, $pH = pK_1$. At the end of the addition of the first equivalent of base, all of the amino acid is in the zwitterion form. Here the pH is in the neighborhood of the pI, and practically no buffer action is exerted. Further addition of base converts some of the $-NH_3^+$ groups of the zwitterion (now acting as a H^+ -donor, or acid) to the salt form, $-NH_2$, or $(-)$ for the whole molecule. A second buffer system is thus produced. The mid-point of this part of the titration corresponds to $pH = pK_2$. Upon addition of the complete two equivalents of base to the amino acid, all of it will be present in the $(-)$ form. Any part or all of the titration just described can be reversed by the addition of equivalent amounts of acid.

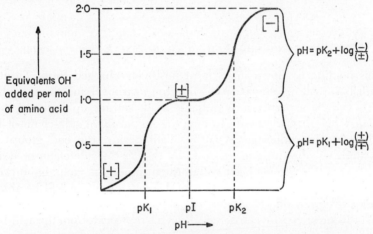

Fig. 12. pH-Titration curve of a monoamino-monocarboxylic acid

Some amino acids contain three titratable groups. They therefore can form three buffer systems operating in three different pH ranges and having three pK values. In all cases the groups can be treated as uncharged acids or cationic acids and their titrations or buffering actions can be described in a manner similar to that used for the simple amino acids. Among the more important compounds of this type are aspartic and glutamic acids, which contain an extra COOH group, and lysine, arginine, and histidine, which contain extra groups of the ammonium or cationic type.

(h) CHARGED GROUPS ON PROTEINS. Since amino acids are united through their amino and carboxyl groups to form the long polypeptide chains of proteins, it follows that most of these groups must be blocked from participation in buffer reactions. This raises the problem of explaining the well-established buffering properties of proteins. Two sources of titratable groups are found in proteins, the end groups and the side-chain groups. Aside from the unusual case of a cyclic structure, each peptide chain, no matter how long, must have a beginning and an end. The few amino and carboxyl groups thus located account for only a minor part of the buffering properties of proteins. More important are the side-chain groups. Those amino acids which contain three titratable groups can be linked to other amino acids in a peptide chain through their α-amino and carboxyl groups, thus tying them up "fore and aft," and still have an unblocked group projecting out to the side, a "side-chain."

A sample peptide containing end groups and typical side-chain groups, with approximate pK values indicated, is given below:

```
   HC—NH                                            NH₂⁺ (12.5)
   ‖       |                                        ╱
   ‖      CH                               COOH (4) C
   C—NH (7)   COOH (4)     NH₃⁺ (10)        |      ╱ ╲
   |          |            |               CH₂   NH  NH₂
   CH₂   O   CH₂   O     (CH₂)₄  O          |      O
(8)| +  ╱    |    ╱       |     ╱          CH₂   ╱ ╲   (CH₂)₃
 NH₃—CH—C—NH—CH—C—NH—CH—C—NH—CH—C—NH—CH—COOH (3.5)
```

This peptide is shown in its most positively charged form. Titration with base will involve first the end group carboxyl and the side-chain carboxyls of aspartic and glutamic acid, setting up buffer systems around pH 4. In the neutral range the imidazolium side-chain of histidine is most important. On the alkaline side, the end group ammonium will be titrated, followed by that in the side-chain of lysine. Finally, at the extreme basic end of the titration, the guanidinium side-chain of arginine is reached. Obviously such a peptide will be able to buffer over a wide pH range.

(*i*) IONIC STATES OF PROTEINS. Proteins represent, from the acid-base standpoint, nothing more than peptides of the above type, but of much higher molecular weight. Their buffering properties are due to the same groups; there are simply more of them. In solutions acid to their isoelectric points, proteins bear a net positive charge. On the basic side of the pI, the net charge is negative. By definition, that pH at which the net charge is zero is the pI. If we regard the ammonium group as characteristic of all the cationic acid groups in the protein, and the carboxyl as representative of the uncharged acids, then a simplified, diagrammatic formulation of the statements just made can be indicated as follows:

$$
\begin{array}{ccc}
\text{NH}_3{}^+ & \text{NH}_3{}^+ & \text{NH}_2 \\
\diagup & \diagup & \diagup \\
\text{Pr} & \text{Pr} & \text{Pr} \\
\diagdown & \diagdown & \diagdown \\
\text{COOH} & \text{COO}^- & \text{COO}^- \\
\text{pH} < \text{pI} & \text{pH} = \text{pI} & \text{pH} > \text{pI}
\end{array}
$$

At the pI of a protein its migration in an electrical field (electrophoresis) will obviously be at a minimum. Other properties of proteins which pass through minima at or near the pI are osmotic pressure, solubility, and viscosity. Since anions will combine most readily with the (+) form of a protein, and cations with the (−) form, the combination of proteins with ions of both types should be at a minimum when the protein is in its isoelectric state.

The numerical value of the pI is characteristic for each individual protein, being the resultant of the number of ionizing groups of each type present and their pK's. Although proteins are known with pI's located throughout the entire pH range, the majority of soluble proteins found in animal tissues and fluids have pI values slightly on the acid side of pH 7. Since most animal tissues and fluids have a slightly alkaline pH (7.4), these proteins are normally found in their negatively charged forms. The foregoing statements mean, in effect, that most proteins have a slight excess of groups with pK values on the acid side.

(j) PROTEINS AS BUFFERS. A survey of the pK's of the various ionizing groups reveals that few will operate as buffers in the physiological pH range. Those few ammonium groups which are located at the ends of peptide chains may contribute to physiological buffer action, but only to a small extent. Actually, the imidazole group of histidine is the most important buffer at pH's around neutrality, a fact which has received insufficient emphasis in the past.

The biological significance of the charged state of proteins was mentioned briefly at the beginning of this section. No less important is the buffer function of proteins. As the result of reactions of intermediary metabolism, various acids are produced in significant amounts normally, and in excessive amounts in certain abnormal conditions. The proteins of the tissues and those of the blood (especially hemoglobin) are as important in buffering these acids as the inorganic buffers such as phosphate and bicarbonate, which are frequently given much more attention (p. 314). Abnormalities in which excessive alkalinity occurs in the body also bring into play the operation of protein buffers along with other types.

(k) ELECTROPHORESIS OF PROTEINS. Since proteins differ in their isoelectric points, they will generally bear net charges of different magnitudes at any given pH. As a result, the individual components of a mixture of proteins will migrate at different velocities in an electrical field. Advantage is taken of this phenomenon in the procedure of electrophoretic analysis, which has many applications. For the purpose of illustration, the analysis of plasma proteins is quite suitable, especially from the viewpoint of its practical application in medical research.

If the pH of plasma is adjusted, by addition of a proper buffer, to a value alkaline to the isoelectric points of all the plasma proteins, they will all carry negative charges, but of different magnitudes. Passage of an electric current through the solution will then cause the proteins to migrate toward the positively charged electrode (anode) at characteristically different rates. If a solution of protein-free buffer is carefully layered over the protein solution before the current is turned on, then the migration of the proteins under the impetus of the electric current can be made to proceed into the protein-free solution, a "moving boundary" of proteins being produced. Examination of this boundary reveals a succession of proteins, traveling at velocities related to their net charges. The actual spatial separation of the proteins in the boundary can be followed by optical scanning methods which take advantage of the fact that solutions of proteins have higher refractive indices than the protein-free solution. Electrophoresis equipment available at present permits visual or photographic scanning diagrams to be produced, resulting in virtual curves of protein concentration (allowing for various refractive index corrections) against linear distance in the boundary. The area under the curve for each migrating component is a measure of the total amount of that particular protein present in the mixture. An electrophoretic diagram of normal plasma is shown in Figure 13.

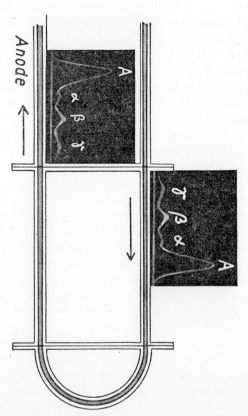

Fig. 13. *Migration of plasma proteins in U-tube of electrophoresis apparatus (from Wuhrmann and Wunderly: Die Bluteiweisskörper des Menschen, Benno Schwabe and Co., Basel, 1952)*

In the recently introduced technic of "paper electrophoresis," proteins or other charged molecules migrate in an electrical field set up across a strip of filter paper saturated with buffer. The results are essentially similar to those described above, differing only in that the migration occurs along a plane rather than in a cylindrical column of solution. Paper electrophoresis has the advantages of being a microtechnic, requiring relatively simple and inexpensive apparatus, and being less time-consuming than the conventional methods.

Although the combination of negatively charged protein molecules with heavy metal ions has been known for many years, the reaction as commonly carried out resulted in alteration of the fine structure of the protein (denaturation), making impossible the regeneration of the protein in its native state. Recent advances in this field, however, utilizing zinc ions under carefully controlled conditions, have resulted in procedures useful in the separation and isolation of plasma proteins. These methods are supplementary to the fractionation of plasma proteins with alcohol at low temperatures, discussed in the next section.

PROTEINS AS GIANT MOLECULES: COLLOIDAL PROPERTIES. (a) IMPORTANCE. To those proteins with an obvious structural purpose in life, large size is an advantage which needs no special explanation. The protein components of fibers, membranes, and other "insoluble" structures are examples of this group. Among the soluble proteins, large size first of all limits diffusibility, thus keeping a protein at its workbench, instead of allowing it to wander throughout the body. (Some proteins, however, are definitely nomadic as part of their function, e.g., the protein hormones.) The really striking advantage of colloidal dimensions is best seen when we consider those proteins which have catalytic functions, such as enzymes, antigens and antibodies, and probably hormones. In order to perform certain operations on smaller molecules, it is necessary for biocatalysts first of all to attract the smaller victims to their surfaces, and one of the chief attributes of colloidal particles is a large surface area, facilitating the phenomenon of adsorption. Also, the particular chemical reaction which is to be catalyzed by the protein, such as cleavage in two of a substrate at some specific linkage, requires an intense electrical field, strong enough to weaken the linkage being attacked, and with its (+) and (−) charges at exactly the proper positions in space. Of all the substances available in nature, none but the proteins can meet these specifications.

(b) OSMOTIC PRESSURE. In order to investigate the molecular sizes of the proteins, it is necessary to use methods of physical chemistry which been developed especially for colloidal systems. One of the simplest of these, in principle, is the measurement of osmotic pressure. A highly diagrammatic representation of an apparatus for this purpose is given in Figure 14. The inverted thistle tube has firmly sealed over

its large end a membrane such as cellophane, which is freely permeable
to water (solvent), but impermeable to the protein being investigated
(solute). A known weight of the protein is dissolved in water and the
solution used to fill the inverted thistle tube to the index mark. The
open end of this tube is then attached to a pressure gage and gas tank,
and the thistle tube is immersed in water. On the solvent side of the
membrane the water molecules are uninhibited and pass through the
orifices of the membrane at the maximum rate fixed by the conditions
of the experiment. On the solution side of the membrane, movements
of the water molecules are inhibited by the presence of the protein
molecules, which by the nature of the membrane must remain on the
inside of the thistle tube. The activity of the water molecules inside

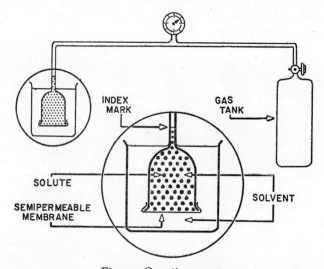

Fig. 14. Osmotic pressure

the tube is thus less than that of the water on the outside, the former
molecules pass through the orifices to the outside at a slower rate than
those coming in, and a net influx of water into the tube tends to occur.
This influx can be prevented by applying pressure to the inner solution from the gas tank, adjusting the pressure so that the solution in
the thistle tube remains at the level of the index mark. The pressure
required to accomplish this, read on the pressure gage, is numerically
equal to the pressure tending to force water into the thistle tube, hence
it is a measure of the osmotic pressure. Under ideal conditions a protein solution of 1 molar concentration will exert an osmotic pressure
of 22.4 atmospheres at 0° C., so that the molecular weight of the protein can be calculated from its osmotic pressure and weight concentration.

(c) ULTRACENTRIFUGATION. Although the proteins are large molecules, their size is not such as to make them settle out under the influence of gravity. By increasing the gravitational force, however, as in an ultracentrifuge, proteins can be forced to sediment at rates related to their molecular weights. By the use of optical scanning devices such as those described in connection with electrophoresis, the migrating boundaries of individual proteins in a mixture can be observed while the ultracentrifuge is in operation (Fig. 15). The results of ultracentrifugal analysis can be used not only for the calculation of molecular weights, but also for the demonstration of the presence of several components in a mixture of proteins. Its use for quantitative analysis of mixtures is limited by its resolution, which is much inferior to that obtained by electrophoresis. One recent analytical application, however, has arisen in connection with the plasma lipoproteins (p. 470), some of which are thought to be related to the occurrence of atherosclerosis.

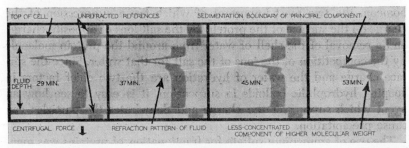

Fig. 15. Ultracentrifugation of commercially prepared gamma-globulin (Specialized Instruments Corp.)

By adjusting the density of plasma samples to the proper value, lipoproteins (which have a rather low density due to the lipid component) can be made to migrate toward the axis of rotation in an ultracentrifuge, this procedure being one of flotation rather than sedimentation.

Other methods which have been used for determination of the molecular weights of proteins include free diffusion, light-scattering, and X-ray diffraction. To some extent the electron microscope also furnishes information on the approximate dimensions of the largest protein molecules.

(d) MOLECULAR WEIGHTS. Table 5 summarizes the currently accepted molecular weights of some typical proteins. Under certain conditions some of the proteins listed appear to have molecular weights higher or lower than those given in the table. The former circumstance is the result of aggregation, the latter of dissociation, both of which are of common enough occurrence to be disturbing factors in any attempt to fix a "true" molecular weight for those proteins subject to such behavior.

Table 5. Molecular Weights of Proteins*

Ribonuclease	13,000	Hemoglobin	67,000
Cytochrome c	13,000	Urease	480,000
Lactalbumin	17,400	Thyroglobulin	630,000
Myoglobin	17,500	Myosin	840,000
Bence-Jones proteins	35,000 and 37,000	Actomyosin	4 million
β-Lactoglobulin	38,000	Tobacco mosaic virus	40 million
Pepsin	39,000	Lung thromboplastin	167 million
Ovalbumin	44,000	Influenza virus	200–322 million
Insulin	48,000		

* Physical data on plasma proteins are tabulated elsewhere (p. 504).

(e) FRACTIONATION BY SALTING OUT. Many of the methods for fractionation of proteins are based primarily on considerations of molecular size. For example, the proteins are forced out of solution by increasing concentrations of salt in an order which, roughly, proceeds from the larger to the smaller protein molecules. This method of "salting out" proteins probably depends upon several physical phenomena, the two most important of which are a suppression of the charge on the surface of the protein by the salt ions of opposite charge, and a removal of the shell of water from around the protein molecule by the competition of the ions of the salt for that water. Since the surface charge and the water of hydration are the two chief factors in keeping hydrophilic colloids in suspension, it is easy to see how an agent which suppresses the charge and dehydrates the particles can cause precipitation.

The use of ammonium sulfate for fractionation of proteins was mentioned earlier in connection with the classification of albumins and globulins. Sodium sulfate is a more suitable salt for the analytical separation of the plasma proteins, since the amount of protein present in the various precipitates or filtrates is often determined by the Kjeldahl nitrogen method, which could not be used in the presence of added ammonium ions. The original sodium sulfate procedure (Howe) gave results which have been found to disagree with those obtained by electrophoretic analysis. Recent modifications of this method have corrected these errors by readjustment of the concentrations of sodium sulfate used in each step (p. 502).

(f) FRACTIONATION BY SOLVENTS. Although salting out is a useful procedure, both for analytical purposes and for the isolation and purification of proteins on a laboratory scale, the subsequent removal of the added salt presents a difficult problem, particularly when it is desired to prepare such materials as plasma protein fractions on a pilot-plant or industrial scale for clinical use. The development of the method of alcohol fractionation at low temperatures, together with the procedure of drying protein precipitates in vacuo from the frozen state (freeze-drying, or lyophilization), has provided a satisfactory solution to this problem.

The addition of alcohol to an aqueous system lowers its dielectric constant, which means, in effect, that the electrical forces between charged particles in the solution are increased, thus reducing the solubilities of substances such as proteins. At high alcohol concentrations the dehydration of the protein molecules also may be a contributing factor. Whatever the underlying phenomena may be, it has been adequately demonstrated that proper adjustment of the pH, alcohol concentration, temperature, protein concentration, and total salt concentration (usually kept at low levels) makes possible a more selective separation of the constituent proteins of a mixture than can be achieved by the older salting-out method. The deleterious effects which alcohol can have on proteins (see under "denaturation," p. 81) are minimized by conducting the fractionations at low temperatures and removing the water and alcohol from the protein fractions in a vacuum while these substances are in a frozen state. In certain of the procedures the dielectric constant is increased, when desired, by the addition of glycine to the system. Some of the more recent fractionations have made use of the insoluble complexes formed by proteins with zinc ions.

While the initial fractionation of plasma, following the above procedures, does not result in homogeneous proteins, it can be supplemented by further separations to secure many of the proteins of each crude fraction in a pure state. Furthermore, the crude fractions have many clinical uses. For instance, one fraction is used for the preparation of fibrin film and fibrin foam, which find application in surgery. Plasma albumin, the most important fraction of the blood in the treatment of shock, nephrosis, and cirrhosis, has been made available in concentrated form. Antibodies are largely found in the γ-globulin fraction, which is used to confer passive immunity to certain infectious diseases (measles and hepatitis). Blood typing has been greatly aided by the preparation of concentrated agglutinins from the plasma of appropriate donors.

(g) DIALYSIS. The colloidal dimensions of proteins, in addition to providing the physical basis for fractionation procedures such as salting out, also make possible certain other technics which are useful in the laboratory and even have their counterparts in biological systems. Dialysis, for example, involves the removal of smaller, crystalloidal particles from proteins (or other colloids) by selective diffusion through a membrane of appropriate permeability (Fig. 16). Thus, the salts used in precipitation of a protein can be removed by suspending the protein and salts in water inside of a cellophane sack, immersing this sack in a large volume of water, and changing the outside water until no more salt ions are detected, having been washed out. This desalting can be accelerated by electrodialysis, in which the protein is placed in the central chamber of a series of three, the compartments being separated by cellophane membranes. Electrodes are placed in the two outer chambers, and a current of electricity is passed through the system, causing rapid migration of diffusible ions (salts only) out of the central chamber. Another variation of dialysis is ultrafiltration, which is dialysis under pressure, the water and crystalloids being forced through the semipermeable membrane (in this case, firmly supported to withstand the pressure) by the application of positive pressure from above the solution or of suction from below, or both simultaneously.

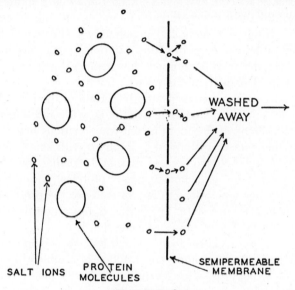

Fig. 16. Dialysis

The non-dialyzability of proteins is of importance in certain biological situations, such as the filtration process across the glomerular membranes of the kidney (p. 754), the formation of lymph by filtration across the capillary wall (p. 309), osmotic equilibration between tissue cells and extracellular fluid, and the Donnan equilibrium which controls the distribution of diffusible ions across the membrane of the red cell (p. 306).

THE SHAPE OF PROTEIN MOLECULES. (*a*) IMPORTANCE. Enough has been said previously concerning the attraction of substrate to the enzyme surface, and hormone molecule to target molecule, to indicate the importance of the shape of protein molecules to their several biological functions. In addition to catalytic proteins of the types mentioned, the structural proteins which form fibers and membranes must also obviously have shapes in keeping with the tasks which they are called upon to perform. As another example, when foreign proteins find their way into the blood stream, the process by which plasma globulins are synthesized (especially the γ-globulins) is modified so as to produce globulins which are altered in shape so that they can combine with the foreign proteins and remove them from circulation. In immunological terms the foreign proteins are antigens, and the altered globulins are antibodies.

(*b*) STREAMING BIREFRINGENCE. One of the methods for determining the shape of proteins depends on a property known as streaming birefringence, or double refraction of flow. If a beam of light is passed through a sheet of Polaroid, a solution of a protein, and a second sheet of Polaroid with an orientation at right angles to the first, the light will be cut off provided that the protein solution has no effect on the plane polarized light coming from the first sheet (see polarimetry of carbohydrates, p. 5). If the protein molecules in question are spherical, they will have no effect* on the polarized light, whether the solution is at rest or in motion. Even elongated molecules do not affect the light while their solution is at rest, since the molecules are distributed in random orientation in space. If the solution is in motion, however, as in streaming through the stem of a funnel, the elongated molecules tend to orient themselves lengthwise in the axis of the stream (Fig. 17). This partial orientation has the effect of adding another

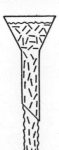

AT REST: RANDOM ORIENTATION

IN FLOW: STREAM–LINE ORIENTATION

Fig. 17. Streaming birefringence

type of polarization to the light passing through the solution, so that now the light is visible even through the second sheet of Polaroid, which has been kept with its axis at right angles to the first. From measurements of this phenomenon of streaming birefringence it is possible to calculate the ratio of the length of the long axis to that of the short axis of the protein molecule, frequently designated as the "axial ratio."

(*c*) VISCOSIMETRY AND DIELECTRIC DISPERSION. Two other methods of determining the axial ratio which also depend on orientation of elongated molecules are viscosimetry and dielectric dispersion. The pres-

---

* This is not strictly true, since proteins are optically active. However, the effects under consideration are above and beyond this optical activity.

ence of rodlike particles in a solution would be expected to interfere with its flow through an orifice to a greater extent than the presence of spherical particles, hence some relation may be expected between the asymmetry of a protein molecule and the viscosity of its solutions, although calculations of the axial ratio from such data are complicated by the degree of hydration of the protein, a factor which is seldom known accurately. The method of dielectric dispersion, on the other hand, depends on the fact that proteins are charged particles and will tend to orient themselves, like electrical dipoles, in an electrical field (Fig. 18). The time taken for the molecule to orient itself is a function of its asymmetry, which frequently can be calculated with considerable precision from measurements of the dielectric properties of protein solutions.

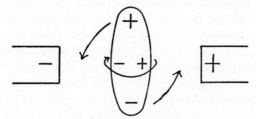

Fig. 18. Dielectric dispersion

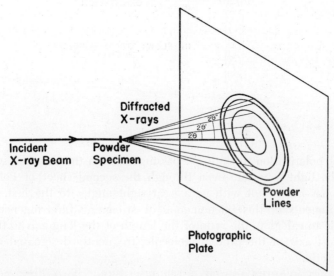

Fig. 19. X-ray diffraction (from Low, in The Proteins, Vol. 1, Part A, edited by H. Neurath and K. Bailey, published by Academic Press, Inc., 1953)

(*d*) X-RAY DIFFRACTION.   The method of X-ray diffraction provides another approach to the problem of the shape of protein molecules. As shown in Figure 19, X-rays are reflected from single crystals of a protein or, in some cases, layers of protein or protein fibers, and the rays, after undergoing some changes in passing through the surface layers of the protein, are allowed to form an image on a photographic plate. Diffraction (deflection from its original course) of a ray occurs when it interacts with the outer electron field of such elements as C, O, or N. Hydrogen is too light an element to have any significant effect. Regions of strong diffraction indicate, therefore, the presence of a heavy atom in the vicinity. The positions and intensities of the spots and lines on the resulting photograph can be analyzed, by a laborious mathematical procedure, to give information on the crystal or fiber structure. Early studies in X-ray diffraction were limited largely to investigations of the "short spacings" in the molecule, such as the periodicity involved in the distance from each peptide linkage to the next. More recently these analyses have included the "long spacings" which are concerned with the over-all structure of the molecule or crystal, leading, in favorable cases, to deductions as to the actual shape of the molecule in space.

(e) ELECTRON MICROSCOPY. What may be considered a direct "picture" of the protein molecule is furnished by the electron microscope. This instrument is analogous to the light microscope, but uses beams of electrons instead of light, and electrical or magnetic fields in place of glass lenses. Magnification of about 100,000x is commonly available, with even greater power possible in some experimental models. Insofar as drying of the specimen and subjecting it to a high vacuum do not produce artifacts, the electron photomicrograph is a true picture of the dimensions and shape of the object under observation. At the present time the resolving power of the instrument unfortunately limits its use to proteins of very high molecular weight, such as viruses (Fig. 20).

(f) SHAPES OF PROTEIN MOLECULES. As a result of investigations using the various methods mentioned, it is possible to classify the proteins found in nature into two groups, the fibrous and the globular. For the purpose of this classification an arbitrary dividing line between the two groups may be set at an axial ratio of 10. Proteins having a length/width ratio under 10 will be considered globular, while those with ratios over 10 will fall into the fibrous class.

(1) Fibrous Proteins. A typical fibrous protein consists of a more or less elongated peptide chain or a group of such chains. Each chain may be spirally coiled along its length. X-ray diffraction studies indicate the presence of amorphous regions in which the chains are distributed in random fashion in space, interspersed with "crystalline" regions in which the adjacent chains are arranged with much the same regularity as that found in the true crystals.

Keratin, a protein found in hair, wool, and skin, has a fibrous structure. As found in nature it is in the form of folded (probably in a spiral fashion) peptide chains, with cross-linkages between adjacent chains of the –S–S– type, formed from the amino acid cystine. Stretching of the keratin fiber causes an unfolding of the natural, or α-keratin configuration, to form the elongated β-keratin. A good deal of the stability of keratin is due to the disulfide linkages, which are cleaved only by vigorous reagents. Silk fibroin and collagen (the major protein of connective tissue) are fibrous proteins having extended chains, causing them to be rather inelastic. Fibrinogen, an elongated molecule found in blood plasma, forms clots of fibrin by first increasing its chain length even further by head-to-tail coupling, followed by formation of a dense network of cross-linkages. The muscle proteins myosin and actin, and their complex, actomyosin, form a fibrous system which represents the mechanical basis of muscle contraction.

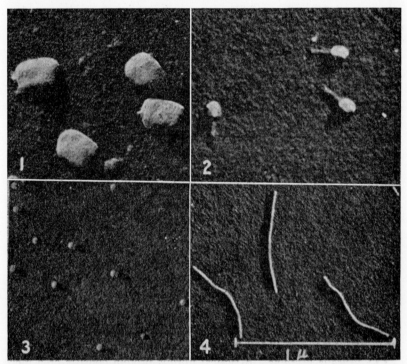

Fig. 20. *Representative shapes of virus particles:* (1) *vaccine virus;* (2) T_2 *bacteriophage;* (3) *bushy-stunt virus;* (4) *orchid mosaic virus. Electron micrographs* ($\times$ 40,000) *by R. C. Williams, Virus Laboratory, University of California (from Rivers (ed.). Viral and Rickettsial Infections of Man, J. B. Lippincott Company, 1952, by permission of the National Foundation for Infantile Paralysis, Inc.)*

(2) *Globular Proteins.* The typical globular protein consists of a rather compactly folded or coiled peptide chain or group of chains. In

these compounds the axial ratios are usually well under 10, and frequently are only about 3 or 4. X-ray diffraction studies indicate a high degree of regularity in the structure of these materials. Most of the easily crystallizable proteins fall into this group, as might be expected from the regularity which is required in true crystal structures.

Insulin, a hormone of the pancreas, belongs to the globular class of proteins. The "sub-unit" of insulin, having a molecular weight of 12,000–13,000, consists of four peptide chains joined by disulfide linkages. As found in the crystalline state or in solution, insulin is an aggregate of three or four of these sub-units. Many of the components of the albumin and globulin fractions of the blood plasma are globular proteins. The structure of hemoglobin is discussed elsewhere (p. 115).

INTERNAL STRUCTURE OF PROTEINS. (*a*) IMPORTANCE. By the internal structure of proteins is meant the over-all quantitative amino acid composition, the sequence of amino acids in the peptide chain or chains, the number of chains per molecule, and the forces involved in holding the chains in specific, folded configurations and in the inter-chain linkages. It is obvious that the gross shapes, sizes, and surface properties of the proteins, which have been discussed thus far, are but reflections of the underlying internal structures. Insofar as the external properties of proteins are important for their specific biological functions, the internal framework upon which these superstructures are based takes on an equal importance.

(*b*) DETERMINATION OF AMINO ACID CONTENT. The methods of investigating the internal structure of proteins are largely those of organic chemistry, although the skill of the physical chemist is called upon in at least one case, that of investigating the forces of configuration and inter-chain linkage mentioned above. Determination of the content of the individual amino acids in a protein involves, usually, hydrolysis, followed by specific analyses for the various amino acids. In many cases, preliminary separation of the amino acids into chemically or physically similar groups or families precedes the final analyses. Some indication of the types of procedures used is given in the section on qualitative and quantitative tests at the end of this chapter.

(*c*) DETERMINATION OF SEQUENCE OF AMINO ACIDS. Although analysis of proteins for their amino acid content has reached a high state of perfection in recent times, this general approach to the problem of protein structure dates back to the earliest years of protein chemistry. Determination of the sequence in which the amino acids occur in the peptide chains of the proteins, however, has been a much more difficult problem to attack, and can be said to be, even now, only in its preliminary phases. Partial hydrolysis of a protein to the stage of small peptides and determination of the amino acid sequence in the peptides represents one technic which has been used to some extent. However, the lack of information on the original location in the protein of the apparent sequences obtained, and the possibility that the peptides may have undergone rearrangement or "resynthesis" during the hydrolysis have been advanced as objections to this method. Chemical procedures are available which make it possible to convert to some identifiable derivative those terminal amino acids which bear free amino or carboxyl groups, following which the converted fragments can be removed and identified, and the procedure repeated on the next amino acid residue in the sequence. Although these methods are laborious, they offer the opportunity of starting at one end of the protein or the other and methodically working one's way into the interior of the molecule. Most investigators in this field have adopted the abbreviated procedure of conversion of terminal amino acids, partial hydrolysis, and identification of those peptides "labeled" by the conversion procedure. A description of this technic belongs more properly in the discussion of end-group analysis.

(*d*) Determination of number of chains per molecule. If the molecular weight of a protein is known, the number of peptide chains per molecule can be determined, theoretically, from the number of terminal amino or carboxyl groups. This technic may be called "end-group analysis," by analogy with the somewhat similar procedure used in the field of carbohydrate chemistry. Complications are caused by the side-chain amino groups of lysine, which behave much like the α-amino groups of terminal amino acids in titrations and chemical reactions, and by the side-chain carboxyl groups of glutamic and aspartic acids, which again are scarcely distinguishable from terminal carboxyl groups. A method which seems to counter these objections, at least in the case of amino groups, is based upon the reaction of dinitrofluorobenzene with free amino groups, yielding N-dinitrophenyl derivatives. After hydrolysis the dinitrophenylamino acids, which were originally at the free amino ends of the protein chains, are isolated, identified, and quantitatively determined. The ϵ-dinitrophenyl derivative of lysine is easily separated from the other derivatives and offers no interference. By the use of partial instead of complete hydrolysis, and identification of the dinitrophenyl peptides, this method has been adapted also to the determination of the sequence of amino acids in the protein molecule, as mentioned in the previous paragraph.

If all of the linkages occurring between peptide chains were known, and methods were available for their accurate determination, a powerful tool would be at hand for the investigation of the number of chains per molecule. At the present time the only known covalent cross-linkage in proteins is the disulfide ($-S-S-$) group of cystine. Other forces which hold peptide chains together seem to be of the non-covalent type, and are furthermore determinable only to a rough degree of approximation. Nevertheless, a consideration of the cystine content of a protein, together with end-group data, often limits the number of possible structures which can be assigned to a protein.

(*e*) DETERMINATION OF INTRA- AND INTER-CHAIN FORCES. Apart from the disulfide linkage, the determination of the forces which hold a peptide chain in its specific steric configuration and also bind it to its fellows is largely a matter of physical chemistry. These studies involve a consideration of the kinetics and thermodynamics of the unfolding process (denaturation), matters which are beyond the scope of this book.

Of all the covalent cross-linkages postulated for the protein molecule, only the disulfide bond has substantial evidence in its favor. This linkage is relatively stable, and as will be seen later, is not cleaved under the usual conditions of denaturation. Among the non-covalent bonds, only the two shown below need be considered.

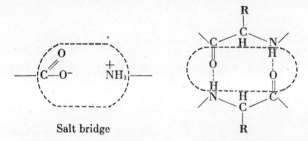

Salt bridge   Hydrogen bonds

The salt bridge is formed between a carboxyl group of one chain and an amino group (or similar cationic group) of another chain. While such a linkage may occur, there is evidence that it cannot be of major quantitative importance. The weight of the data available at the present time indicates that the hydrogen bond is the chief force involved, both in inter-chain linkages (those not accounted for by disulfide bonds, at least) and in preserving the specific spatial configuration of the proteins. Two adjacent peptide chains are shown above. The hydrogen atom attached to the peptide nitrogen of one chain is attracted by the carbonyl oxygen atom belonging to the peptide linkage of the adjacent chain. In effect, the hydrogen atom acts chemically as though it belonged to both groups. While the strength of a single hydrogen bond is not great, the large number of such bonds possible in a protein molecule makes for considerable stability under mild conditions. As will be discussed later, the hydrogen bond is the major linkage which is broken in the unfolding process known as denaturation.

(*f*) COMPOSITION OF TYPICAL PROTEINS. Among the best established results of the various experimental methods discussed are the data on the quantitative amino acid composition of the proteins. Table 6 pre-

Table 6. Amino Acid Composition of Proteins*‡

	FOOD PROTEINS				TISSUE PROTEINS			
	GELATIN†	CASEIN	OVALBUMIN	ZEIN	HORSE HEMOGLOBIN	RABBIT MYOSIN	CALF THYMUS HISTONE	HUMAN SERUM ALBUMIN
Alanine	9.3	3.20	6.72	10.52	7.40	6.5	6.94	0.88
Amide N	0.07	1.6	1.01	2.98	0.87	1.20	0.87	6.20
Arginine	8.55	4.1	5.72	1.71	3.65	7.36	17.4	8.95
Aspartic acid	6.7	7.1	9.30	4.61	10.60	8.9	5.71	0.70
Cysteine	0.0	0.0	1.35		0.56		0.0	5.60
Cystine/2	0.0	0.34	0.51	0.83	0.45	1.40	0.0	
Glutamic acid	11.2	22.4	16.50	26.9	8.50	22.1	4.30	17.0
Glycine	26.9	2.00	3.05	0.0	5.60	1.9	5.07	1.60
Histidine	0.73	3.1	2.35	1.32	8.71	2.41	2.69	3.50
Isoleucine	1.8	6.1	7.00	5.0	0.0	15.6 }	20.5	1.70
Leucine	3.4	9.2	9.20	21.1	15.40	11.92	5.21	11.00
Lysine	4.60	8.2	6.30	0.0	8.51	3.4	10.23	12.30
Methionine	0.9	2.8	5.2	2.41	1.0	4.3	0.0	1.30
Phenylalanine	2.55	5.0	7.66	7.3	7.70	1.9	4.08	7.80
Proline	14.8	10.6	3.60	10.53	3.90	4.33	4.04	5.10
Serine	3.18	6.3	8.15	7.05	5.80	5.1	4.71	3.34
Threonine	2.2	4.9	4.03	3.45	4.36	0.8	4.80	4.60
Tryptophan	0.0	1.2	1.20	0.16	1.70	3.4	0.0	0.2
Tyrosine	1.0	6.3	3.68	5.25	3.03	2.6	3.30	4.70
Valine	3.3	7.20	7.05	3.98	9.10		3.22	7.70

* In grams of amino acid per 100 grams protein.
† Contains in addition 1.2 per cent hydroxylysine and 14.5 per cent hydroxyproline.
‡ Data selected from the compilation by G. R. Tristram, in "The Proteins," edited by Neurath and Bailey, Volume 1, Academic Press, Inc., 1953, Chapter 3.

sents a compilation of these analyses for some of the common proteins. Aside from their importance in the chemical characterization of the proteins, these data have considerable application in the field of nutrition, a matter which is discussed in detail elsewhere (p. 629). Suffice it to say here that some amino acids cannot be synthesized by the animal organism, and therefore must be obtained in the food. The nutritive value of a protein is related to a great extent to its content of these "essential" amino acids.

(g) FINER DETAILS OF STRUCTURE. Information concerning the finer details of protein structure is available in only a few instances. The amino acid sequence has been fairly well established for certain antibiotic substances which have peptide structures. Oxytocin, a cyclic octapeptide hormone of the posterior pituitary (p. 702), has been synthesized following the establishment of the sequence of its constituent amino acids. Pitressin, a closely related hormone (p. 702), is currently being investigated along similar lines. Among the true proteins, the pancreatic hormone, insulin, has been found to consist of four peptide chains, held together by disulfide linkages. There are actually two pairs of peptide chains, the members of each pair being identical in composition. Some of the amino acid sequences in the chains have been determined, and the nature of the end groups at the free amino ends of the chains has been established. In the case of certain other proteins the end groups and a few amino acid sequences are known.

DISRUPTION OF THE ARCHITECTURE: DENATURATION. (a) CHARACTERISTICS. Denaturation may be defined as a change in the chemical, physical, and biological properties of a protein from those of the native state, characterized by an unfolding of the molecule from its previous specific configuration. Figure 21 illustrates the type of change involved in going from the organized structures of globular or fibrous proteins to the dispersed, flexible chains of the denatured state. Although it would seem unlikely that such a change could be reversible, since the native state of most proteins is characterized by a very specific and even unstable organization, it has been found, nevertheless, that conversion of certain denatured proteins into forms practically indistinguishable from their native forms can take place. It may be that this phenomenon is exceptional, and occurs only in the case of proteins that do not have a very specific native organization.

(b) DENATURING AGENTS. Many agents can cause denaturation. Included in the list are physical agents such as heat, surface action, ultraviolet light, and high pressure, and chemical agents such as organic solvents, acids and alkalies, urea and guanidine, and detergents.

(c) CHEMICAL ALTERATIONS. Among the altered chemical properties of the denatured protein is its greatly decreased solubility at its isoelectric point. Many proteins which are quite soluble over the entire pH range, and merely exhibit decreased solubility when isoelectric in their native state, become highly insoluble at that pH upon denaturation. As a result of the unfolding process in denaturation, many chemical groups which were rather inactive owing to shielding in the native state become exposed and more readily detectable. Among these are the sulfhydryl group of cysteine, the disulfide group of cystine, the phenolic group of tyrosine, and several others.

(*d*) PHYSICAL ALTERATIONS.   A further consequence of the conversion of the compact, native structure to the dispersed chains of the denatured proteins is an increase in the viscosity of the solution. Simultaneously, the rate of diffusion of the protein molecules decreases, as might be expected. Many proteins, especially of the globular type, can be crystallized in the native state. Since the formation of a crystal depends upon a high degree of organization of the molecules, it is not surprising that denatured proteins cannot be crystallized.

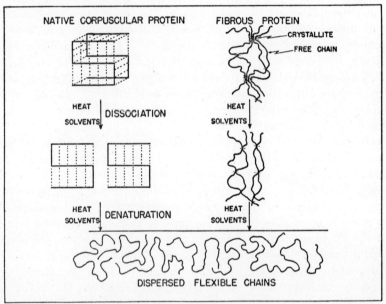

Fig. 21. *Denaturation of globular (corpuscular) and fibrous proteins (adapted from Lundgren: Advances in Protein Chemistry, Vol. 5, Academic Press, Inc., 1949)*

(*e*) BIOLOGICAL ALTERATIONS.   Increased digestibility by proteolytic enzymes has been found in the case of certain denatured proteins. The most marked alterations in biological properties, however, are suffered by those proteins which in the native state had some specific biological function. For instance, enzymatic or hormonal activity is usually destroyed by denaturation. The antigenic or antibody functions of proteins are frequently altered as well.

(*f*) Denaturation, flocculation, coagulation. If a protein is denatured by heat at a pH relatively far removed from its isoelectric point and in the virtual absence of salts, the solution may undergo no very obvious change, although chemical or physical tests will reveal the presence of denatured protein. Adjustment of the pH of the solution to the isoelectric point of the protein will cause it to precipitate, for which process the specific term "flocculation" is used. The flocculation of a denatured protein is reversible in the sense that adjustment of the pH to some value above or below the isoelectric range results in solution of the precipitate. Flocculation is obviously a simple clumping together of the dispersed chains of denatured protein when the forces of mutual repulsion are at a minimum. If a denatured, flocculated protein is heated, the clumped chains become matted together in a mass which is insoluble, not only at the pI, but over the entire pH range. This process is known as coagulation. Heat denaturation of a protein at its pI results in an apparently direct coagulation, but this is only the final, visible manifestation of a series of changes which includes denaturation and flocculation. The relationship between these phenomena can be illustrated as follows:

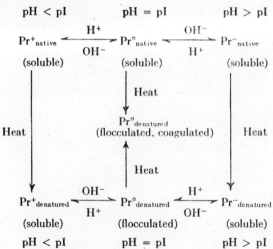

(*g*) Applications and importance. Denaturation is usually something to be avoided. The methods employed by the protein chemist and the enzymologist in the preparation of their materials involve extreme precautions which are designed to subject the protein as little as possible to conditions other than those it encounters in its native environment. Maintenance of low temperatures, avoidance of extremes of pH, elimination of toxic heavy metals from reagents and apparatus, and precautions against shaking and frothing are some of the conditions which come under consideration. Conversely, deproteinization of a solution is frequently achieved by heat coagulation of the proteins, or by precipitation under denaturing conditions with organic solvents or other reagents. A qualitative test for albumin in the urine involves acidification to the pI of the protein and heat coagulation.

QUALITATIVE AND QUANTITATIVE TESTS FOR AMINO ACIDS AND PROTEINS. REACTIONS OF CONSTITUENT GROUPS. (*a*) CARBOXYL GROUPS. (*1*) *Salt Formation.*   Among the many recognized reactions of carboxyl groups, that of forming salts with cations is of considerable importance in the case of amino acids and proteins. The combination of these substances with basic dyes, the precipitation of proteins by cationic detergents, and some of the precipitations of proteins with heavy metal cations (insofar as the —SH group is not involved) are apparently due to direct union of the cationic reagent with the anionic groups of the protein. Carboxylate anions form the majority of such groups in the average protein. Proteins combine best with cationic reagents when the proteins themselves are anionic, i.e., on the basic side of their isoelectric points.

(*2*) *Back-Titration.*   The direct titration of carboxylate anions back to the undissociated acid form is seldom practical, owing to the extremely acidic end-point. Such titrations can be performed, however, by utilizing the considerable increase in pK_1 which occurs upon the addition of certain solvents to the aqueous system.

(*b*) AMINO GROUPS. (*1*) *Formol Titration.*   Free amino groups in amino acids and proteins can be estimated by a technic known as formol titration. The reaction which occurs between amino groups and formaldehyde is:

$$\underset{R-\overset{\overset{\displaystyle NH_3^+}{|}}{C}H-COO^-}{} \longrightarrow \underset{R-\overset{\overset{\displaystyle NH_2}{|}}{C}H-COO^-}{} + H^+$$

$$\downarrow \overset{\displaystyle H}{HC{=}O}$$

$$R-\overset{\overset{\displaystyle NH-CH_2OH}{|}}{C}H-COO^-$$

$$\downarrow \overset{\displaystyle H}{HC{=}O}$$

$$R-\overset{\overset{\displaystyle \overset{.}{N}(CH_2OH)_2}{|}}{C}H-COO^-$$

An equilibrium always exists between the zwitterion form of an amino acid and the anionic form plus a hydrogen ion, this equilibrium representing the ionization of the cationic ammonium group. Formaldehyde reacts with the uncharged amino group, forming N-methylol or N-dimethylol derivatives, thus shifting the ionization equilibrium to the right by removing one of the products of the reaction. In effect, the addition of formaldehyde to a solution of an amino acid or protein decreases the pK_2 of the ammonium groups, making them stronger acids. The formol titration of glycine is shown in Figure 22, superimposed upon the ordinary pH-titration curve for purposes of explanation. An initially isoelectric solution of glycine is titrated with standard base to the phenolphthalein end-point in the presence of formaldehyde. Owing to the decrease of pK_2 from 9.6 to about 7 in the presence of formaldehyde, the ammonium group is completely titrated at pH of 9, instead of at 11. Hence, the effect of formaldehyde is to place the titration of ammonium groups in the convenient range of the usual indicators, and also to avoid the complications due to absorption of atmospheric CO_2 which occurs at a pH as alkaline as 11.

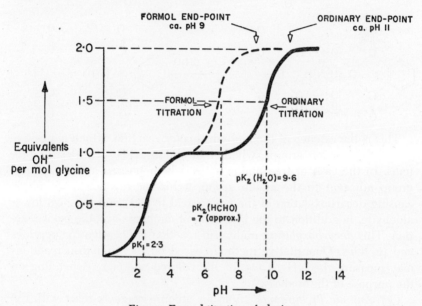

Fig. 22. *Formol titration of glycine*

(2) *Van Slyke Nitrous Acid Method.* Free amino groups react with nitrous acid to form hydroxyl groups and liberate gaseous nitrogen.

$$R—\underset{\underset{NH_2}{|}}{CH}—COOH \xrightarrow{HNO_2} R—\underset{\underset{OH}{|}}{CH}—COOH + N_2$$

Volumetric or manometric measurement of the nitrogen is the basis of the Van Slyke method for the estimation of amino groups. As in the case of formol titration, *free* amino groups are measured, regardless of the attachments of the carboxyl groups, so that both methods can be used to determine the number of such amino groups in peptides and proteins.

(3) *Ninhydrin Reaction.* Ninhydrin (triketohydrindene hydrate) undergoes an oxidation-reduction reaction with free amino groups, oxidatively deaminating them to carbonyl groups and ammonia. The reduced form of the ninhydrin couples with the ammonia and the residual ninhydrin to give rise to a blue-violet dye:

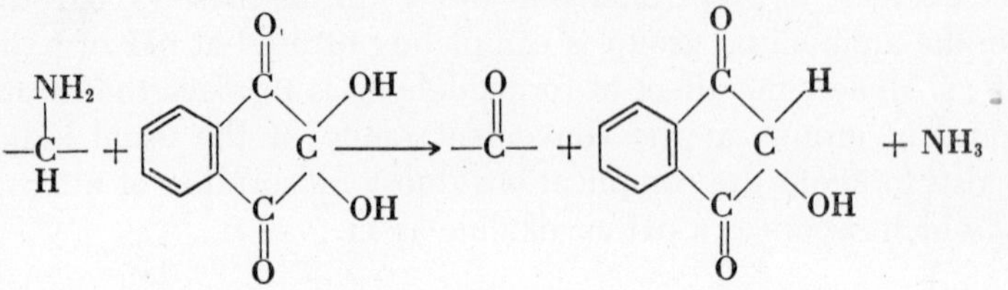

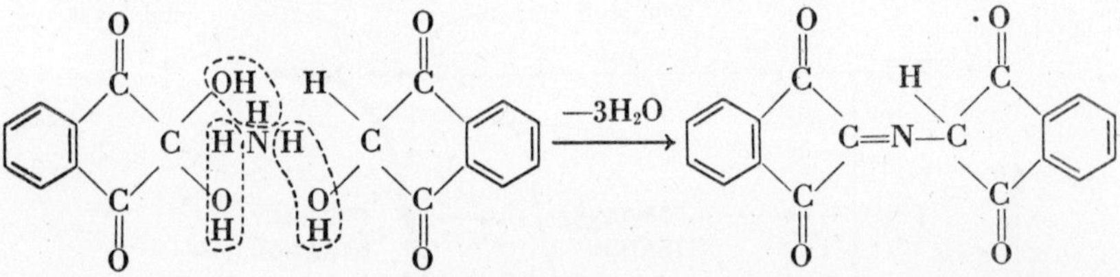

This is the essence of the ninhydrin *color* reaction, which is positive for all free amino groups, whether in amino acids, peptides, or proteins. In the case of free amino acids, which possess a free carboxyl group adjacent to the amino group, a further reaction takes place, causing decarboxylation of the amino acid to CO_2 and the next lower aldehyde, in addition to the liberation of ammonia and the color reaction. This *decarboxylating* ninhydrin reaction is negative for peptides and proteins. Quantitative methods based on the ninhydrin reactions may measure the NH_3, CO_2, or the colored complex, depending on the purpose of the analysis.

(4) *Anionic Precipitants.* Various anionic reagents react with the cationic groups of the protein molecule, such as the ammonium, imidazolium, and guanidinium groups. The precipitation of proteins by anionic detergents, metaphosphate, trichloroacetate, tungstate, picrate, ferrocyanide, and anionic dyes involves such a reaction. Combination of a protein with an anion is best effected when the protein itself is cationic, i.e., on the acid side of its isoelectric point.

(5) *Fluorodinitrobenzene.* Amino groups combine with fluorodinitrobenzene to yield N-dinitrophenyl derivatives. This reaction has already been mentioned as a means of labeling and locating the terminal amino acids of proteins.

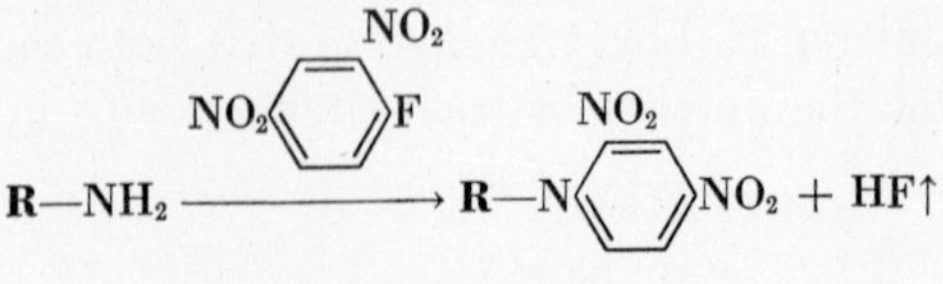

(6) *Carbamino Reaction.* The free amino groups of proteins can condense with carbon dioxide, forming carbamino compounds.

$$R—NH_2 + CO_2 \rightarrow R—NH—C \overset{O}{\diagup} O^- + H^+$$

Such compounds of the plasma proteins and, to an even greater extent, of hemoglobin are concerned in the transport of carbon dioxide in the blood (p. 292).

(c) R— GROUPS. (1) *Millon's Reagent.* Millon's reagent, a mixture of mercuric and mercurous nitrates and nitrites, produces a red color when heated with compounds containing phenolic groups, such as tyrosine. The reaction probably involves mercuration and nitration or nitrosation. It is given by tyrosine whether free or combined in proteins.

(2) *Xanthoproteic Reaction.* In the xanthoproteic reaction the sample is heated with concentrated nitric acid, cooled, and made alkaline. In the presence of either tyrosine or tryptophan, yellowish nitro compounds are formed by the action of the nitric acid on the aromatic or heterocyclic rings. The nitro compounds are converted to orange-colored salts by the alkali. Under the usual conditions of the test the simple benzene ring of phenylalanine is not reactive enough to respond.

(3) *Folin's Phenol Reagent.* Folin's phenol reagent (a phosphomolybdotungstic acid) in alkaline solution undergoes reduction to a blue form in the presence of tyrosine or tryptophan. The reaction is not very specific, since many easily oxidizable substances can interfere.

(4) *Hopkins-Cole Reaction.* In the presence of acid, many aldehydes condense with the indole ring of tryptophan to yield colored products. The original Hopkins-Cole procedure, applied as a qualitative test, calls for mixing the sample with a solution of glyoxylic acid (an aldehyde-acid, its structure being an aldehyde group attached to a carboxyl group), then carefully layering concentrated sulfuric acid under the mixture. The presence of tryptophan is indicated by the appearance of a violet ring at the interface.

(5) *Bromine-Water Reaction.* Free tryptophan in weakly acidic solution produces a pink color with bromine water. The reaction is said to be due to halogenation of the tryptophan. It differs from most of the other color tests for this amino acid in being positive only when the tryptophan is free, not combined in a protein.

(6) *Pauly Reaction.* Histidine and tyrosine couple with diazotized sulfanilic acid in alkaline solution, forming red products which are doubtless azo dyes.

(7) *Sakaguchi Reaction.* In the Sakaguchi reaction, arginine develops a red color when treated with α-naphthol and sodium hypochlorite or hypobromite.

(8) *Alkali-Labile Sulfur.* Protein sulfur which is present as sulfhydryl or disulfide groups (cysteine and cystine) can be detected by

the formation of lead sulfide when alkaline solutions of the protein are heated with lead acetate. The sulfur of methionine is not alkali-labile.

(9) *Nitroprusside Reaction.* Free sulfhydryl groups, as in cysteine, some proteins, and glutathione (in its reduced form), react with sodium nitroprusside in ammoniacal solution to produce a red color. Ammonium sulfate intensifies the reaction. Disulfide groups (as in cystine) give a positive reaction only after reduction to sulfhydryl groups.

(*d*) PEPTIDE LINKAGE. Substances containing two or more peptide linkages produce a blue-violet color with dilute copper solutions in a strong alkali. This is called the biuret reaction, after the compound biuret, which happens to give the test. The color is due to a coordination complex between the cupric ion and four peptide nitrogen atoms, two from each of two adjacent peptide chains.

Although many substances other than peptides and proteins give a positive reaction to the biuret test, these substances, for the most part, do not occur in nature. The amino acid histidine, however, is said to give a positive reaction.

(*e*) TOTAL NITROGEN. All of the nitrogen of a protein, whether in peptide linkage or not, can be determined by the Kjeldahl method. This involves digestion with concentrated sulfuric acid, usually in the presence of certain catalytic substances to hasten the reaction. The carbonaceous matter is entirely oxidized and the nitrogen is left in the form of ammonium sulfate. Alkalinization and distillation of the ammonia into a known excess of standard acid, followed by titration of the residual acid, complete the procedure. In an alternate procedure, the ammonia resulting from the Kjeldahl digestion is allowed to react directly with Nessler's reagent (a potassium mercuric iodide), forming a colored compound which is matched against standards in the colorimeter.

SEPARATION AND DETERMINATION OF AMINO ACIDS. (*a*) METHODS OF FISCHER, DAKIN, VAN SLYKE, AND OTHERS. One of the earliest methods for the determination of the amino acids in the protein hydrolysate was that of Emil Fischer, who fractionally distilled the ethyl esters of the amino acids *in vacuo*. Butyl alcohol was used by Dakin to separate certain groups of amino acids from others. Fractionation of the amino acids into neutral (monoamino, monocarboxylic), basic (diamino), and acidic (dicarboxylic) groups, followed by application of the Van Slyke nitrous acid method, was another of the earlier attempts at separation and estimation of the amino acids arising from the hydrolysis of proteins. These technics are seldom if ever used at the present time.

(b) ELECTRODIALYSIS. By passing an electric current through a mixture of amino acids which is in the central compartment of a three-part apparatus, with each part separated from the others by a semipermeable membrane, it is possible to cause a differential migration of amino acids from one compartment to another. The charges carried by the amino acids can be regulated by proper adjustment of the pH, so that, for instance, diamino acids can be collected in the anodic compartment, dicarboxylic acids at the cathode, while the monoamino monocarboxylic acids remain in the central compartment.

(c) SOLUBILITY PRODUCT. Few reagents are known which specifically precipitate single amino acids quantitatively. However, even semiquantitative precipitations would be expected to follow the solubility-product law, which states that the product of the concentrations of the two substances (amino acid and precipitant) in equilibrium with the precipitate will be a constant. The application of this principle to amino acid determinations involves, essentially, two determinations of this constant on two separate aliquots of the sample containing different quantities of precipitant, resulting in what amounts to two simultaneous equations in two unknowns.

(d) ISOTOPE DILUTION AND ISOTOPE DERIVATIVE METHODS. The amount of any constituent in a mixture can be ascertained by adding to the mixture a known quantity of the compound to be determined, but differing from the normal substance by being labeled with an isotopic atom (see p. 349). Isolation of the compound in a pure state (the isolation need not be quantitative) and determination of the degree of dilution of the original isotopic reagent with non-isotopic compound lead directly to the calculation of the quantity of the latter which must have been present in the sample. Another isotopic technic involves the preparation of labeled derivatives of the amino acids in a mixture, using an isotopic acylating reagent, for example. A known excess of unlabeled derivative of one particular amino acid is then added to the mixture, re-isolated, and the amount of original amino acid in the mixture calculated from the isotope content of the purified derivative.

(e) CHROMATOGRAPHY. Chromatography may be defined as a technic in which the components of a mixture are caused to migrate at different rates through an apparatus which involves equilibration of solutes between a stationary and a moving phase. The three types of chromatography in current use are adsorption, partition, and ion-exchange, to use a classification based upon the physical forces underlying each type. The result obtained in chromatographing a sample is called a chromatogram.

It should be emphasized that, although chromatography is discussed at this point, its application is by no means restricted to the amino acids. In fact, there are few groups of biologically important compounds the fractionation of which has not been facilitated by this technic.

(1) *Adsorption.* In adsorption chromatography a powdered adsorbent, such as charcoal, aluminum oxide, silica, or the like, is packed into a vertical glass tube, usually as a slurry in the solvent to be used later. The mixture to be resolved is added to the top of the column in a small amount of solvent. Larger amounts of pure solvent are then passed through the column by the use of either pressure from above the column or suction from below. The rate of migration of any compound through the column is determined by the balance between its affinity for the solvent and its adsorption by the solid phase. It is possible, by the judicious choice of solvent mixtures and adsorbents, to effect many separations which would be impossible by ordinary chemical means. Figure 23 shows three colored components of a mixture which have separated and are traveling down a column at different rates. By changing receivers, these fractions can be collected separately as they leave the bottom of the column. Colorless substances are frequently separated by collecting many small fractions in succession from the column, testing each fraction chemically or by other means, and combining all fractions containing single components.

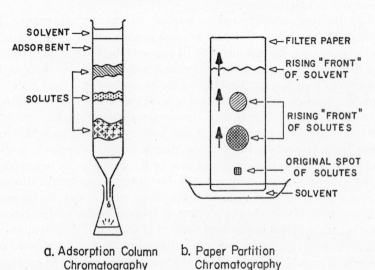

a. Adsorption Column
Chromatography

b. Paper Partition
Chromatography

Fig. 23. *Column and paper chromatography*

(2) *Partition on Column.* In adsorption chromatography the forces of adsorption between the stationary phase and the solutes in the moving phase are of utmost importance. Partition chromatography, on the other hand, uses the solid part of the system as a mere support (in theory, at least) for a stationary liquid phase. One type of partition chromatography makes use of the same columnar arrangement as that discussed for adsorption. The stationary phase may consist of wet starch or wet silica gel, for example, and the solutes, dissolved in the appropriate organic solvent, undergo a series of multiple partitions between the stationary and moving solvent phases as they travel down the column. The over-all effect is that of an infinite number of extractions carried out in a succession of infinitesimal separatory funnels. If side effects are left out of consideration, the major physical basis of this form of chromatography is the partition coefficient of each solute between the stationary solvent (e.g., water) and the moving solvent.

(3) *Partition on Paper.* A very useful form of partition chromatography substitutes a sheet of filter paper for the usual column. The stationary phase consists of water adsorbed to the cellulose fibers of the paper. A small amount of sample is spotted near one end of the strip of paper, the end dipped into an appropriate solvent mixture, and the solvent allowed to travel through the paper by capillarity. At the end of the desired period of time the position of the solvent "front" is marked and the paper is dried. Spraying the paper with the proper reagent (e.g., ninhydrin for amino acids) then reveals the various constituents of the mixture as separate spots. The ratio of the distance traveled by any particular substance to that covered by the solvent is known as the ratio of the "fronts," or R_f, and is usually quite constant for each substance in a particular solvent. At times this simple or "one-dimensional" paper chromatogram is unable to separate some of the constituents of a complex mixture. In that case the sample is placed in one corner of a square sheet of paper which is chromatographed in one direction with one solvent system, then turned and run with another solvent system in a direction at right angles to the first, producing a "two-dimensional" chromatogram.

(4) *Ion-Exchange.* The ion-exchange resins are polymers which contain functional groups that are capable of undergoing exchange reactions with ions. Cation exchangers contain such groups as phenols, carboxyls, or sulfonic acids. Anion exchangers are organic bases, or amines. Amino acids bearing an appropriate charge can be deposited on a column of the proper type of resin by an exchange reaction with the functional groups of the resin, while other amino acids pass through the column. The deposited amino acids can then be displaced from the column by using strong solutions of the proper acids or bases.

(*f*) CHEMICAL REACTIONS.   Many of the color reactions which were discussed in connection with the functional groups of proteins and amino acids have been adapted to the quantitative determination of those amino acids bearing such groups. Some of these reactions are specific enough for one amino acid so as to require no preliminary separation of the amino acid in question from other constituents of natural mixtures.

(*g*) MICROBIOLOGICAL AND ENZYMATIC METHODS.   Some microorganisms require for growth preformed amino acids in their culture media. The extent of growth in a medium complete except for the amino acid being determined can therefore be used for the estimation of that amino acid in a sample added to such a test system.

Specific enzymes which decarboxylate certain amino acids are present in some species of bacteria. The quantity of CO_2 evolved in these reactions can be measured manometrically.

DETECTION AND DETERMINATION OF PROTEIN.   (*a*) HEAT COAGULATION. Albumin is often detected in pathological urine by the appearance of a coagulum on heating. The addition of weak acetic acid to the heated sample will intensify the protein precipitate by moving the pH of the urine closer to the pI of the albumin, while any basic phosphates which may be precipitated by the heat will redissolve when acidified. Heat coagulation is sometimes used for the gravimetric determination of proteins. Complications are introduced by the necessity of removing inorganic salts and all lipids from the coagulum before drying and weighing.

(*b*) PRECIPITATING AGENTS.   In Heller's ring test, protein in urine is detected qualitatively by layering the urine over concentrated nitric acid and observing the ring of acid-denatured protein which appears at the interface of the two liquids. Other reagents, such as sulfosalicylic acid, have been used to determine the degree of proteinuria by turbidimetry, but the methods lack accuracy.

(*c*) SPECIFIC GRAVITY.   The specific gravity of plasma or serum is dependent in large part on its protein content. A method for the determination of plasma proteins has been based on this fact, and involves timing the rate at which a drop of plasma falls through a column of organic solvents of a density slightly less than that of plasma. Both plasma and whole blood proteins have been determined by observing the flotation or sedimentation of a drop of the sample in copper sulfate solutions of graded density.

(*d*) REFRACTIVE INDEX.   The index of refraction of protein solutions is greater than that of water by an amount which is proportional to the concentration of protein. Serum has been analyzed by this method, although it is said to be less sensitive than the falling-drop method mentioned above.

(*e*) ELECTROPHORESIS. This method has been discussed in connection with the properties of proteins as electrically charged particles (p. 65).

(*f*) CHEMICAL DETERMINATION OF CONSTITUENT GROUPS. Protein is widely determined by the Kjeldahl method which was discussed earlier. Assuming a nitrogen content of 16 per cent for the average protein, the percentage of nitrogen in the sample is multiplied by 6.25 to obtain the protein content.

The biuret color reaction has been adapted to the quantitative determination of protein. It is rapid and quite accurate, but requires calibration against some "absolute" method, such as the Kjeldahl.

Folin's phenol reagent has been used for the colorimetric determination of plasma proteins. However, since it is actually a method for the amino acid, tyrosine, it must be standardized against a sample of the same protein as will occur in the samples to be tested. Any variation in the tyrosine content of the samples will invalidate the method.

BIBLIOGRAPHY

Introductory Textbooks

Haurowitz, F.: Chemistry and Biology of Proteins, New York, Academic Press, Inc., 1950.
Sahyun, M. (ed.): Outline of the Amino Acids and Proteins, New York, Reinhold Publishing Corporation, 1944.

Advanced Treatises

Cold Spring Harbor Symposia Quant. Biol. 6, 1938; 14, 1950.
Cohn, E. J. and Edsall, J. T. (eds.): Proteins, Amino Acids and Peptides as Ions and Dipolar Ions, New York, Reinhold Publishing Corporation, 1943.
Greenberg, D. M. (ed.): Amino Acids and Proteins, Springfield, Ill., Charles C Thomas, Publisher, 1951.
Neurath, H. and Bailey, K. (eds.): The Proteins, Volume I, Parts A and B, New York, Academic Press, Inc., 1953.
Schmidt, C. L. A. (ed.): The Chemistry of the Amino Acids and Proteins, ed. 2 (with Addendum), Springfield, Ill., Charles C Thomas, Publisher, 1944.

Reviews of Special Interest

Anson, M. L.: Protein denaturation and the properties of protein groups, Advances in Protein Chemistry 2:361, 1945.
Chargaff, E., Lipoproteins, Advances in Protein Chemistry 1:1, 1944.
Edsall, J. T.: The plasma proteins and their fractionation, Advances in Protein Chemistry 3:384, 1947.
Fox, S. W.: Terminal amino acids in peptides and proteins, Advances in Protein Chemistry 2:156, 1945.
Kirk, P. L.: The chemical determination of proteins, Advances in Protein Chemistry 3:139, 1947.
Martin, A. J. P. and Synge, R. L. M.: Analytical chemistry of the proteins, Advances in Protein Chemistry 2:1, 1945.
Meyer, K.: Mucoids and glycoproteins, Advances in Protein Chemistry 2:249, 1945.
Sanger, F.: The arrangement of amino acids in proteins, Advances in Protein Chemistry 7:1, 1952.
Tristram, G. R.: Amino acid composition of purified proteins, Advances in Protein Chemistry 5:84, 1949.

4

CHEMISTRY OF NUCLEOPROTEINS, NUCLEIC ACIDS, AND NUCLEOTIDES

INTRODUCTION

TERMINOLOGY. From the standpoint of protein chemistry, the nucleo-proteins are a class of conjugated proteins, the prosthetic groups of which are the nucleic acids. As is the case with many other types of conjugated proteins (lipoproteins, glycoproteins, etc.), the chemical and biological properties of the prosthetic groups are at the present time the major objects of attention. While this justifies a consideration of these substances apart from the proteins proper, it may only reflect the current trend and be subject to future revision and reclassification.

Two major chemical types of nucleoproteins have been found in nature, differing from each other in many respects. However, the difference which underlies the current system of nomenclature concerns the nature of the sugar contained in the nucleic acid moiety of the nucleo-protein. In one type of nucleoprotein the sugar is a pentose, which has been shown to be D-ribose in all cases which have been investigated to the point of isolation and final identification. The nucleic acid containing this sugar is called "pentosenucleic acid" (PNA) or "ribonucleic acid" (RNA), and the nucleoprotein is named accordingly. The second type of nucleoprotein contains a desoxypentose. Where this sugar has been identified definitely, it has proved to be D-2-desoxyribose. The corresponding nucleic acid is called "desoxypentosenucleic acid" or "desoxyribonucleic acid" (DNA).

In the early days of nucleic acid chemistry, RNA was isolated from yeast. It was thought to be restricted to the plant world, and was called "yeast nucleic acid" or "plant nucleic acid." DNA was obtained from fish sperm and thymus gland, and was called "thymonucleic acid" or "animal nucleic acid," in accordance with its assumed distribution in nature. Both types of nucleic acid have since been found in all living cells, rendering the older terminology obsolete. The term "nucleic" or "nucleo-" is derived from the early erroneous belief that nucleic acids and nucleoproteins occurred only in the nuclei of cells. At the present time this term refers to a chemically defined class of substances, irrespective of source or location in nature.

BIOLOGICAL IMPORTANCE. The present great interest in the nucleoproteins and nucleic acids, after a period of virtual stagnation, is at least partly the result of the demonstration by research workers in many apparently unrelated fields of biology that these substances are of prime importance in connection with certain of the major problems under investigation in their respective disciplines.

There appears to be a rather direct connection between nucleoproteins and genetics. Several of the intranuclear structures in cells, including the chromosomes, contain or are entirely composed of nucleoproteins. Some authorities have gone so far as to postulate that the genes, the hypothetical determinative units of inheritance which are associated with chromosomes, are desoxyribonucleoproteins. Substances have been discovered in bacterial cells which can transform one genetic type of bacterium into another genetic strain. Chemically, they have proved to be desoxyribonucleic acids.

The participation of the intranuclear nucleoproteins in such processes as mitosis and meiosis seems to be matched by the involvement of the extranuclear nucleoproteins in protein synthesis in the cytoplasm. Evidence that the synthesis of protein in the cytoplasm may be under the eventual control of nuclear events has made the subject of the interrelations between the various nucleoproteins of the cell a matter of concern to workers in the fields of embryology, growth, protein metabolism, and cancer.

The viruses from both the plant and animal worlds contain nucleoproteins. Some of the simplest viruses seem to be purely nucleoprotein, while others are of much more complex composition.

Certain substances which are chemically similar to the sub-units of which the nucleic acids are composed (nucleotides, to be discussed later) exist in the free state in cells. Some of these are important in the energy transfers characteristic of living organisms, while others act as cofactors to the enzymes whose catalytic activities promote the reactions which provide the energy.

NUCLEOPROTEINS

NUCLEOPROTAMINES. These substances are found only in fish sperm. Although they are the most easily prepared nucleoproteins from this source, there is evidence that the sperm nucleus from which they are obtained also contains nucleoproteins of a more complex type.

The nucleic acid components of the nucleoprotamines are of the desoxyribose type. Protamines, the protein moieties of these substances, are proteins by courtesy only, since they are of such low molecular weight (of the order of several thousands) as to cause them to be considered large peptides. Owing to their high content of basic amino acids (such as arginine) the protamines have isoelectric points in the strongly basic pH range, and are therefore positively charged in the usual physiological environment. The protamines contain no tyrosine or tryptophan.

As will be indicated later, the nucleic acids have isoelectric points in the strongly acid range, and are negatively charged at the pH of the cell. The linkage between the anionic nucleic acid and the cationic protamine is salt-like in character. It can be disrupted by mineral acid, which acts as a displacing agent for the nucleic acid, or even by such neutral salts as NaCl, which undergoes a double replacement reaction with the "protamine nucleate."

NUCLEOHISTONES. Certain varieties of fish sperm contain in their nuclei somewhat more complex nucleoproteins than the nucleoprotamines. These are the nucleohistones, which are also found in the sperm of animals, the avian erythrocyte, and somatic cell nuclei in general.

The nucleohistones are combinations of desoxyribonucleic acids with histones, which are basic proteins like the protamines, but of higher molecular weight. The histones also differ from the protamines in containing tyrosine. As in the case of nucleoprotamines, the linkage between nucleic acid and protein in the nucleohistones is of the salt type.

Both nucleoprotamines and nucleohistones are confined in their distribution to the cell nucleus, where they are found in close association with the chromosomes. At one time these desoxyribonucleoproteins were considered the only important constituents of the chromosomes, and were at times thought to be the genes. Recent discoveries have tended to cast some doubt on these interpretations (see following section).

HIGHER NUCLEOPROTEINS. By this term is meant those nucleoproteins in which the nucleic acid is combined with a protein of greater complexity than the protamines or histones. It is a general, but not invariable, rule that such combinations are not cleaved as easily as the salt-like linkages discussed previously. It seems possible that covalent bonds may be involved in these cases.

In addition to the nucleoprotamines and nucleohistones containing DNA, the cell nucleus also contains RNA-proteins. The chromosomes, for instance, contain significant amounts of RNA in combination with an acidic protein called "chromosomin." This latter substance differs from the histones in its content of tryptophan. Outside of the chromosomes, nuclear RNA is found also in the nucleolus, in association with lipids and proteins which are not as yet characterized.

The cytoplasm of the cell, in contrast to the nucleus, contains only RNA-proteins. A large part of the cytoplasmic ribonucleoproteins seems to be incorporated in the particulate fractions which can be isolated by differential centrifugation. RNA is found affiliated with proteins, lipids, and other constituents in both the "large particle" or mitochondrial fraction and the "small particle" or microsomal fraction.

The viruses are submicroscopic particles or "molecules" which are responsible for many infectious diseases of animals and plants. Although they possess many of the properties of "lifeless" matter (e.g., some can be crystallized), they have the peculiar characteristic of reproducing themselves inside the cells of the host. All of the plant viruses isolated thus far contain ribonucleoproteins, and many have been shown to contain no other significant components. Bacteriophages (bacterial viruses) and some animal viruses contain DNA, others RNA, while some appear to have both types of nucleic acids in their make-up. The animal viruses and bacteriophages are generally more complex in composition than the plant viruses. They frequently contain lipids and carbohydrates, and seem to resemble in some ways the particles found in cytoplasm.

NUCLEIC ACIDS

COMPOSITION. The nucleic acids, prosthetic groups of the nucleoproteins, are substances of high molecular weight, containing phosphoric acid, sugars, and purine and pyrimidine bases. The products of complete hydrolysis of the two types of nucleic acids are listed in Table 7.

Table 7. Products of Hydrolysis of Nucleic Acids

RNA	DNA
H_3PO_4	H_3PO_4
Ribose	Desoxyribose
Adenine	Adenine
Guanine	Guanine
Cytosine	Cytosine
Uracil	Thymine (methyl uracil)
	(Methyl cytosine)

In addition to the different sugars, the two types are distinguished by the pyrimidine bases which they contain, for while both contain cytosine, the uracil of RNA is replaced by thymine in DNA. Some samples of DNA also contain methyl cytosine.

The structural formulas for the two sugars of the nucleic acids are shown on page 98. They exist in their furanose forms in the nucleic acids.

Ribose   Desoxyribose

Adenine and guanine are the two purine components of the nucleic acids. The numbering system for the purine skeleton is indicated in the formulas below. While both compounds are capable of undergoing keto-enol tautomerism, they are shown in their enol forms for reasons which will become evident later. The amino groups of adenine and guanine can act as cationic acids in a manner similar to these groups found in amino acids, but the aromatic character of the purine ring causes a shift of the pK values toward the acid side (adenine—3.7, guanine—2.5, as found in the nucleic acids). The enolic hydroxyl group of guanine behaves as an uncharged acid with pK of 9.3.

Adenine   Guanine   Cytosine

Uracil   Thymine   Methyl cytosine

The structural formulas and numbering system for the pyrimidine bases of the nucleic acids are given above. Here again, keto-enol tautomerism is possible. The structures are shown in their enol forms except for positions 2 and 3, since a hydrogen atom is required at position 3 to accommodate a linkage which occurs in the nucleic acids. The amino group of cytosine (and probably methyl cytosine) has a cationic acid pK of 4.2, while the enolic hydroxyl groups of uracil and thymine have pK's of 9.4.

In any nucleic acid structure containing doubly esterified phosphoric acid, the remaining acid group of the phosphoric acid would be expected to have a pK less than 2. Singly esterified phosphoric acid would have one acidic group with a pK less than 2 (the "primary" dissociation), and one with a pK of about 6 (the "secondary" dissociation of phosphoric acid).

The nucleic acids are amphoteric substances which contain a preponderance of acid groups with low pK values, resulting in isoelectric points far on the acid side (probably less than pH 2). At physiological pH's the nucleic acids exist in their anionic forms, thus they can easily combine with the cationic forms of proteins to produce salt-like compounds.

$$
\begin{array}{cccc}
\text{P—OH} & \text{P—O}^- & \text{P—O}^- & \text{P—O}^- \\
\overset{|||}{\boxed{\text{NA}}}\text{—NH}_3^+ \leftarrow\rightarrow & \overset{|||}{\boxed{\text{NA}}}\text{—NH}_3^+ \leftarrow\rightarrow & \overset{|||}{\boxed{\text{NA}}}\text{—NH}_2 \leftarrow\rightarrow & \overset{|||}{\boxed{\text{NA}}}\text{—NH}_2 \\
\underset{|}{\overset{||}{\text{C—OH}}} & \overset{||}{\text{C—OH}} & \overset{||}{\text{C—OH}} & \overset{||}{\text{C—O}}^- \\
\text{(soluble)} & \text{(insoluble)} & \text{(soluble)} & \text{(soluble)}
\end{array}
$$

| ← pH < pI → | ← pH = pI < 2 → | ← pH 2.5–6.3 → | ← pH 8–12 → |

Table 8. Composition of Nucleic Acids

	MOLAR RATIOS OF BASES, ADENINE $= 1.00$					
NUCLEIC ACID	ADENINE	GUANINE	CYTOSINE	URACIL	THYMINE	METHYL-CYTOSINE
RNA:						
Yeast..........	1.00	1.0	0.63	0.7		
Pancreas........	1.00	2.7	0.95	0.45		
Liver nucleus.......	1.00	1.00	0.39	0.45		
Liver cytoplasm.....	1.00	1.83	1.22	1.12		
DNA:						
Thymus.........	1.00	0.76	0.75		0.98	0.046
Sperm..........	1.00	0.77	0.72		0.95	0.045
Wheat germ.....	1.00	0.89	0.65		1.02	0.22
Bacterio-phage (T5)....	1.00	0.9	1.1		1.2	0.0
E. coli..........	1.00	0.6	0.3		1.1	0.0

Table 8 lists some of the more recent determinations of the quantitative composition of typical nucleic acids. Insofar as DNA is concerned, each species seems to synthesize molecules having the same gross composition in all tissues, but differing from the DNA of other organisms. It has been suggested that two general types of DNA exist, one with a preponderance of adenine and thymine (found in animal tissues and yeast), and one with an excess of guanine and cytosine (characteristic of bacteria). In few cases have nucleic acids been found to contain equimolecular proportions of the four bases, a fact of some importance in connection with the internal structures of the nucleic acids. Although the ratios of the various bases in the nucleic acids are different from one source to another, all samples of relatively undegraded nucleic acids contain a mol of phosphoric acid and sugar for every mol of base present.

STRUCTURE. Hydrolysis of the nucleic acids under appropriate conditions liberates a group of compounds known as nucleotides, consisting of purine or pyrimidine bases linked to sugars, which in turn are esterified with phosphoric acid. These nucleotides are thought to be the subunits from which the polymeric nucleic acids are constructed. Further hydrolysis of the nucleotides gives rise to the nucleosides, compounds of sugar and nitrogenous base. The nucleosides and nucleotides, respectively, are named as follows: from adenine, adenosine and adenylic acid (the presence of desoxyribose can be indicated by the prefix "desoxy"); from guanine, guanosine and guanylic acid; from cytosine, cytidine and cytidylic acid; from uracil, uridine and uridylic acid; from thymine and *desoxyribose*, thymidine and thymidylic acid.

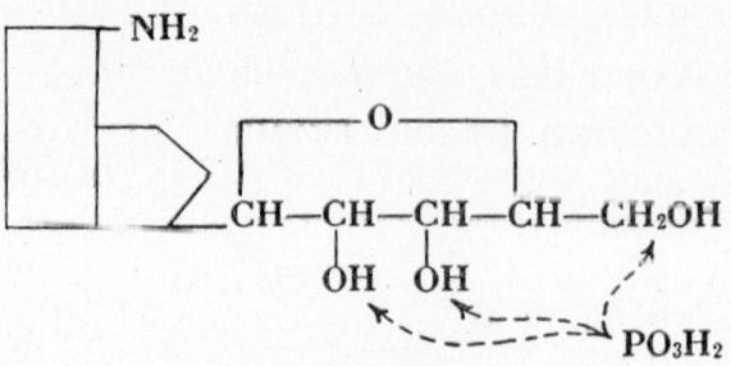

Adenylic acids
Adenosine—2′—phosphate
" —3′— "
" —5′— "

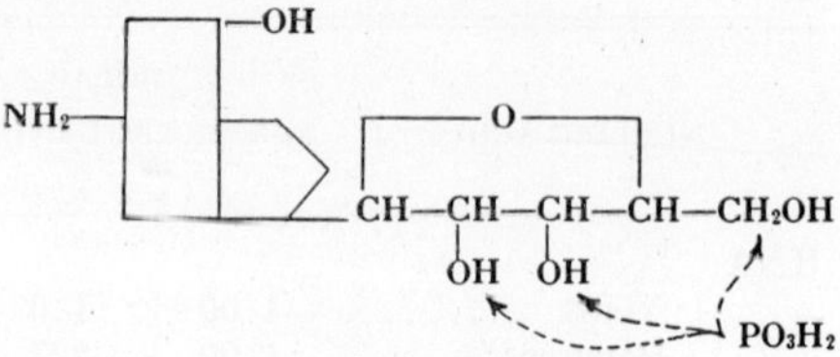

Guanylic acids
Guanosine—2′—phosphate
" —3′— "
" —5′— "

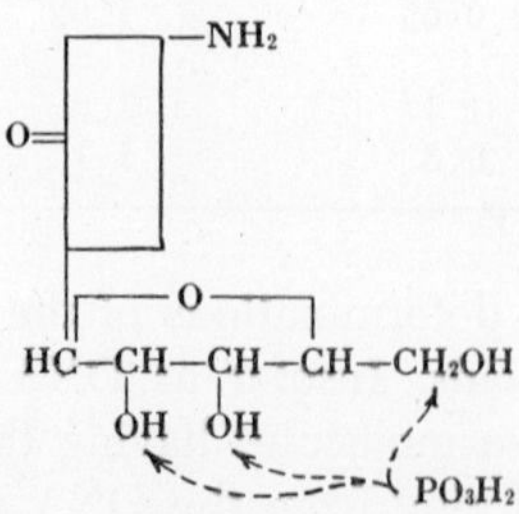

Cytidylic acids
Cytidine—2′—phosphate
" —3′— "
" —5′— "

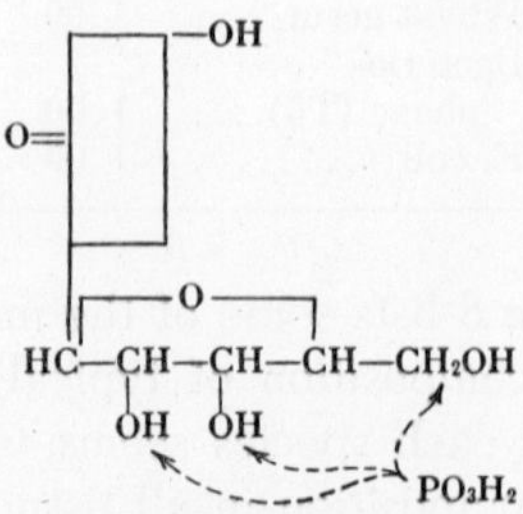

Uridylic acids
Uridine—2′—phosphate
" —3′— "
" —5′— "

Fig. 24. Nucleotides obtained from RNA. Possible position of phosphate group indicated by dotted lines

The nucleotides obtained from RNA are shown in Figure 24. The ribose is attached to the purine nucleus in position 9, to the pyrimidines in position 3, the linkage being a glycosidic one, and in the β configuration. As found in the nucleotides and nucleic acids, ribose exists in its furanose form. Phosphoric acid is esterified on position 2', 3', or 5' of the ribose in the RNA nucleotides.

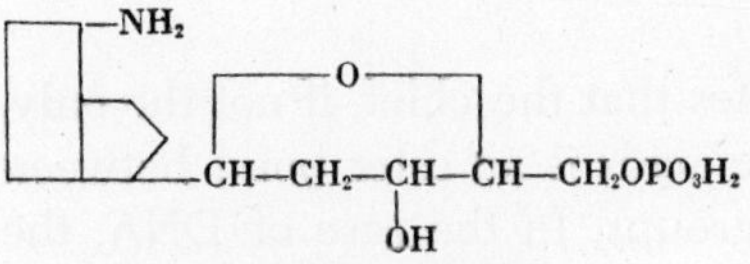

Desoxyadenylic (5') acid
Desoxyadenosine-5'-phosphate

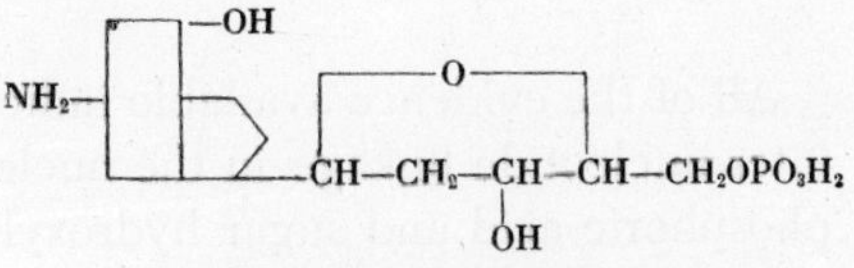

Desoxyguanylic (5') acid
Desoxyguanosine-5'-phosphate

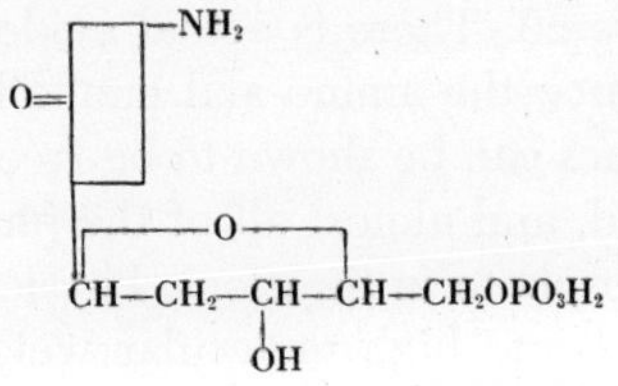

Desoxycytidylic (5') acid
Desoxycytidine-5'-phosphate

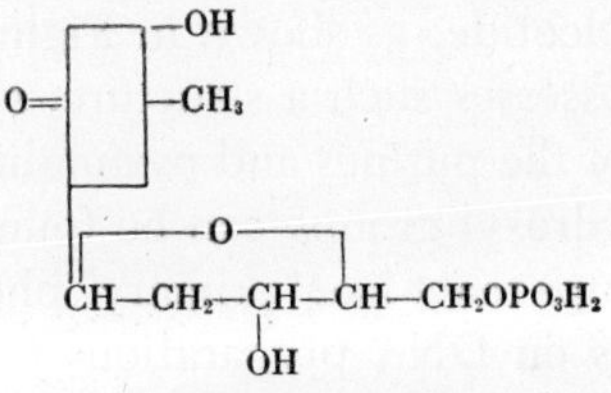

Thymidylic (5') acid
Thymidine-5'-phosphate

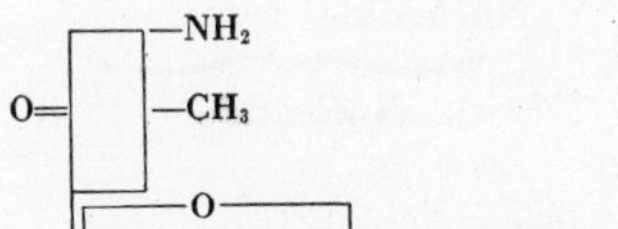

Desoxymethylcytidylic (5') acid
Desoxymethylcytidine-5'-phosphate

Fig. 25. Nucleotides obtained from DNA

The nucleotides isolated from DNA are shown in Figure 25. Desoxyribose, in furanose form, is attached to positions 9 and 3 of the purines and pyrimidines, respectively, in β-glycosidic linkage. Phosphoric acid is esterified at position 5' of the sugar in these compounds. Two interesting di-phosphate esters have been isolated from DNA. By elimination, the phosphate groups are placed at positions 3' and 5' of the desoxyribose.

```
    N=C—OH
    |   ||
O=C   C—CH₃
    |   |
    N—CH
          O—
          |
HC—CH₂—CH—CH—CH₂—O—PO₃H₂
        |
        O
        |
        PO₃H₂
```

Thymidine-3',5'-diphosphate

```
    N=C—NH₂
    |   ||
O=C   CH
    |   ||
    N—CH
          O—
          |
HC—CH₂—CH—CH—CH₂—O—PO₃H₂
        |
        O
        |
        PO₃H₂
```

Desoxycytidine-3',5'-diphosphate

All of the evidence available indicates that the chief, if not the only, inter-nucleotide linkage in the nucleic acids is an ester bond between phosphoric acid and sugar hydroxyl groups. In the case of DNA, the structures of the nucleotides which have been isolated would seem to implicate positions 3' and 5' of the desoxyribose as the sites of esterification. A polynucleotide can be constructed in which the phosphate group of each nucleotide sub-unit is attached to the sugar of the adjacent nucleotide, as shown in Figure 26. There is actual evidence that DNA possesses such a structure, since the amino and enolic hydroxyl groups of the purines and pyrimidines can be shown to be free, no free sugar hydroxyl groups can be found, and almost all of the phosphoric acid groups react like "primary" phosphate in titrations. Physical measurements on DNA preparations indicate high molecular weights and great asymmetry, in agreement with the concept of a long-chain molecule having few branching points.

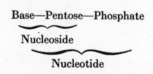

Mononucleotide Structure

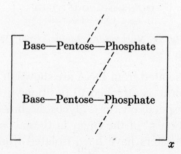

Polynucleotide Structure

Fig. 26. *Structure of mono- and polynucleotides*

The situation is more complex in the case of RNA. From the structures of the nucleotides which have been isolated, the points of attachment of phosphate would seem to be positions 2', 3', and 5' of the sugar. (The 3' and 5' phosphate linkages are probably the major ones in RNA; the 2' linkages probably occur at branching points in the molecule.) Furthermore, only 75 per cent of the phosphate in the ribonucleic acids is titrated as "primary," the remaining 25 per cent behaving like "secondary phosphate." This probably indicates a more complicated structure than the relatively unbranched chain of the desoxyribonucleic acids. Those preparations of RNA which have been isolated in relatively undegraded state have high molecular weights and are asymmetric, although they do not seem to be as highly polymerized as the desoxyribonucleic acids.

In the early days of nucleic acid chemistry, the isolation of approximately equimolecular quantities of four nucleotides gave rise to the theory that the nucleic acids were, in fact, tetranucleotides. When it was realized that these substances were highly polymeric materials, the tetranucleotide hypothesis was modified to mean that a basic subunit of tetranucleotide structure was multiplied many-fold to form the polymer. Modern investigations have necessitated abandonment of the tetranucleotide hypothesis altogether, since the four bases of RNA are not present in equal amounts (Table 8), and, in addition to the inequality in the four bases originally found in DNA, a fifth (methylcytosine) must be reckoned with.

Little is known about the sequence of nucleotides in either type of nucleic acid, except that it cannot be a simple alternation of purine and pyrimidine nucleotides, as was believed by the early proponents of the tetranucleotide hypothesis. Enzymatic degradation of RNA provides some evidence for the existence of chains of purine nucleotides linked to chains of pyrimidine nucleotides. Complex patterns of composition have also been found in similar degradation experiments on DNA preparations.

FREE NUCLEOTIDES OF BIOLOGICAL IMPORTANCE

ADENYLIC SYSTEM.   In addition to the nucleotides which are integral components of the nucleic acids, a number of compounds exist in the free state in tissues, having nucleotide or near-nucleotide structures. These compounds have catalytic functions, act in conjunction with enzyme systems, and probably have no direct metabolic connection with the nucleic acids.

Adenosine monophosphate (also called muscle adenylic acid), adenosine diphosphate, and adenosine triphosphate act as carriers or transfer agents for phosphate groups, a function intimately bound up with the energetics of the living cell (p. 375).

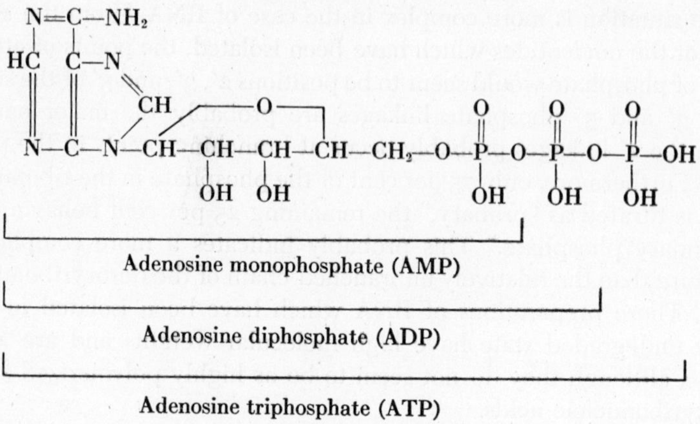

$$
\begin{array}{c}
N{=}C{-}NH_2 \\
HC \quad C{-}N \\
\quad\quad\quad \diagdown \\
\quad\quad\quad CH \quad\quad {-}O{-} \\
N{-}C{-}N{-}CH{-}CH{-}CH{-}CH{-}CH_2{-}O{-}P{-}O{-}P{-}O{-}P{-}OH \\
\quad\quad\quad\quad OH \;\; OH \quad\quad\quad\quad OH \quad OH \quad OH
\end{array}
$$

Adenosine monophosphate (AMP)

Adenosine diphosphate (ADP)

Adenosine triphosphate (ATP)

COENZYMES.   The topic of coenzymes is discussed in detail elsewhere (p. 222). Word formulas of a number of coenzymes which are structurally related to the nucleotides are shown below.

Adenine—ribose—PO_4—PO_4—ribose—nicotinamide
Diphosphopyridine nucleotide (DPN)

Adenine—ribose—PO_4—PO_4—ribose—nicotinamide
PO_4
Triphosphopyridine nucleotide (TPN)

Flavin—ribitol—PO_4—PO_4—ribose—adenine
Flavin—adenine dinucleotide (FAD)

Uracil—ribose—PO_4—PO_4—glucose
Uridine diphosphate—glucose (UDPG)

Adenine—ribose—PO_4—PO_4—pantoic—β-alanine—
PO_4 mercaptoethylamine
Coenzyme A

Diphosphopyridine nucleotide, triphosphopyridine nucleotide, flavin-adenine dinucleotide, and flavin mononucleotide are concerned with biological oxidations (p. 361). Uridine-diphosphate-glucose takes part in the reaction which transforms galactose-1-phosphate to glucose-1-phosphate (p. 395). Trans-acylations (p. 454) of many types involve coenzyme A.

MISCELLANEOUS NUCLEOSIDES AND NUCLEOTIDES.   A nucleoside containing uric acid and ribose is found in the red cells. Its function has not been elucidated, nor has that of the adenine thiomethylriboside of yeast. A portion of the vitamin B_{12} molecule is known to have a nucleotide-like structure (p. 206).

CHEMICAL TESTS ON NUCLEIC ACIDS AND
THEIR COMPONENTS

PURINES AND PYRIMIDINES. In recent investigations the earlier, some-what cumbersome organic procedures for the separation and estima-tion of these nitrogenous bases have been replaced by the methods of paper chromatography and ion-exchange (p. 89). Ultraviolet spectro-photometry is widely used for the quantitative determination of the separated bases. The individual purines and pyrimidines have charac-teristic absorption spectra, the maxima being located in the range, 240–270 mμ. Owing to their content of these bases, nucleic acids ex-hibit an absorption maximum at 260 mμ, which is of such intensity that the nucleic acids can be readily detected even in the presence of protein, which has a maximum around 280 mμ (owing to the amino acids, tyrosine and tryptophan). Use has been made of this intense absorption in the intracellular localization (and estimation) of the nucleic acids by photomicrography in the ultraviolet, employing a quartz microscope.

SUGARS. The usual tests for pentoses can be applied to the detection and determination of ribose. Bial's orcinol reaction is often so used.

Desoxypentoses produce a blue color when heated with diphenylam-ine in a mixture of acetic and sulfuric acids (Dische reaction), a pink color with cysteine and sulfuric acid (Stumpf), a red color with tryptophan and perchloric acid (Cohen). Desoxyribonucleic acids are often located in histological tissue preparations by the Feulgen reac-tion, a test based on the use of the Schiff fuchsin-sulfurous acid re-agent following a preliminary acid treatment of the tissue.

ANALYTICAL SEPARATION OF RNA AND DNA. A frequently used procedure for the estimation of the amounts of the two types of nucleic acids present in tissues involves the removal of acid-soluble phosphorus compounds, followed by removal of phospholipids. The residue is treated with dilute alkali, which degrades RNA to soluble nucleotides without so affecting DNA. Acidification then causes a precipitation of DNA together with degraded proteins. Phosphorus determinations on this precipitate and on the soluble nucleotides from RNA in the filtrate permit a calculation of the amounts of the nucleic acids of each type present in the original tissue.

BIBLIOGRAPHY

Introductory Textbooks

Davidson, J. N.: The Biochemistry of the Nucleic Acids, London, Methuen & Co., Ltd., 1950.

Advanced Treatises, Monographs, and Symposia

Nucleic acids and nucleoproteins, Cold Spring Harbor Symposia Quant. Biol. 12, 1947.

Nucleic acid, Symposia of the Society for Experimental Biology, No. 1, London, Cambridge University Press, 1947.

Symposium on biochemistry of nucleic acids, J. Cell. & Comp. Physiol. *38*, Supplement 1, 1951.

Symposium on the chemistry and physiology of the nucleus, Exper. Cell Research, Supplement 2, 1952.

Significant Reviews

Greenstein, J. P.: Nucleoproteins, Advances in Protein Chemistry *1:*209, 1944.

Gulland, J. M., Barker, G. R. and Jordan, D. O. The chemistry of the nucleic acids and nucleoproteins, Ann. Rev. Biochem. *14:*175, 1945.

Mirsky, A. E.: Chromosomes and nucleoproteins, Advances in Enzymology *3:*1, 1943.

Schlenk, F.: Chemistry and enzymology of nucleic acids, Advances in Enzymology *9:*455, 1949.

Tipson, R. S.: The chemistry of the nucleic acids, Advances in Carbohydrate Chemistry *1:*193, 1945.

5

CHEMISTRY OF HEMOGLOBIN, PORPHYRINS, AND RELATED COMPOUNDS

INTRODUCTION

The compounds to be discussed in this chapter have a unique biochemical significance. Unlike the carbohydrates or lipids, they are not used for fuel by living organisms. Although certain of the substances under consideration are proteins (conjugated), they have no structural significance in the cell, nor do they exert the subtle control over the pattern of metabolism that is attributed to nucleoproteins and their derivatives. Rather, the hemoproteins, i.e., conjugated proteins bearing iron-porphyrin prosthetic groups, are concerned directly or indirectly in facilitating the reaction which is the basis of practically all bioenergetics, the union of oxygen and hydrogen to form water (p. 372).

Hemoglobin is the carrier of atmospheric oxygen from the lungs to the interior of the body. The oxygen may be stored temporarily in muscle attached to another hemoprotein, myoglobin. The combination of the oxygen from the air with hydrogen of metabolic substrates to form water is catalyzed by another group of hemoproteins, the cytochromes and cytochrome oxidase. Ancillary roles in biological oxidations are played by the catalases and peroxidases, enzymes which, like the cytochromes, contain heme prosthetic groups. The vital importance of the hemoproteins is illustrated by the fact that inhibition of the oxygen transport system (hemoglobin) by carbon monoxide, or inhibition of the oxygen utilization system (cytochromes) by cyanide, results in rapid death of the organism.

Detailed consideration of the role of chlorophyll in the photosynthetic reactions of plants lies outside the province of this discussion. However, it may be noted in passing that chlorophyll (a magnesium-porphyrin) is concerned in the catalysis of the cleavage of water into hydrogen and oxygen, whereas the hemoproteins (iron-porphyrin proteins) are involved in the reverse reaction. Evidently the derivatives of porphyrins are of wide significance in comparative biochemistry, from the initial fixation of solar energy in green plants to its eventual utilization by man.

Understanding of the carriage of gases or the catalysis of oxidations by the hemoproteins requires a comprehension of certain aspects of their chemistry. It may be helpful in this regard to consider first the chemistry of the prosthetic groups (porphyrins, hemes) and certain of their metabolic degradation products (bile pigments), and secondly the hemoproteins themselves, primarily hemoglobin.

CHEMISTRY OF PORPHYRINS

STRUCTURES AND NOMENCLATURE. As indicated in Figure 27, porphyrins are cyclic compounds composed of four pyrrole units linked

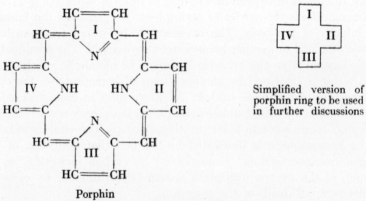

Pyrrole

Hypothetical monopyrrole
precursor of porphyrins

Porphin

Simplified version of porphin ring to be used in further discussions

Fig. 27. Basic pyrrole and porphyrin structures

by methyne ($-CH=$) bridges. All porphyrins may be regarded as derivatives of porphin, a cyclic tetrapyrrole containing no substituent side-chains. The hypothetical biological precursor of the porphyrins is a monopyrrole with acetic and propionic acid side-chains (p. 587).

Other side-chains found in the natural porphyrins are indicated in Figure 28, together with their symbols which will be used hereafter for convenience.

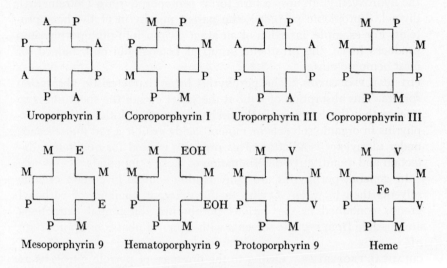

Explanation of Symbols:

Methyl—CH_3 M		Vinyl—$CH{=}CH_2$ V
Ethyl—CH_2CH_3 E		Acetic—CH_2COOH A
Hydroxyethyl—$CHOHCH_3$ EOH		Propionic—CH_2CH_2COOH P

Fig. 28. Naturally occurring porphyrins

The uroporphyrins, so-called because originally discovered in urine (but not restricted to that medium), are tetracetic, tetrapropionic porphins. Of the various possible isomers that can be constructed with such substituents, only two are found in nature, designated uroporphyrins I and III. The Type I uroporphyrin bears its substituents in alternating sequence, whereas this order is reversed in the fourth pyrrole unit of uroporphyrin III.

Decarboxylation of the acetic acid side-chains of the uroporphyrins produces the coproporphyins (so-called because of their original isolation from feces, but also found in urine), tetramethyl, tetrapropionic porphins. Again, only Types I and III are found in nature.

The remaining porphyrins illustrated in Figure 28 contain three rather than two types of substituent groups. Although derived biologically from the Type III porphyrins (p. 588), these latter compounds are designated as Type 9 (or IX), since they are related chemically to one of a series of parent porphins containing three types of substituent groups.

Mesoporphyrin 9 (tetramethyl, diethyl, dipropionic porphin) may be regarded as derived from coproporphyrin III by decarboxylation of two propionic acid groups. Conversion of the two ethyl groups of mesoporphyrin 9 to hydroxyethyl groups produces hematoporphyrin 9 (tetramethyl, bis-hydroxyethyl, dipropionic porphin). Dehydration of the hydroxyethyl groups in turn forms protoporphyrin 9 (tetramethyl, divinyl, dipropionic porphin), the parent porphyrin of the hemoproteins. For example, insertion of an atom of iron into protoporphyrin 9 produces heme, the prosthetic group of hemoglobin and, indeed, of most hemoproteins.

PHYSICAL PROPERTIES. The porphyrins have characteristic absorption spectra. This absorption of light at the violet end of the spectrum is so intense that the compounds themselves are red. Solutions of the porphyrins in organic solvents or mineral acids exhibit a red fluorescence under ultraviolet irradiation. This property is used for qualitative detection and quantitative determination of these compounds.

In general, porphyrins are more readily soluble in certain organic solvents than in water. Owing to the different numbers of carboxyl groups contained in the various porphyrins, differential extractions are possible from organic solvents with aqueous phases of appropriate pH.

CHEMICAL PROPERTIES. Owing to the presence of pyrrole nitrogens as well as carboxyl groups, the natural porphyrins are amphoteric compounds, with isoelectric points (p. 64) at pH 3–4.5. Consequently, at physiological pH's the porphyrins bear negative charges, and may be expected to couple readily to basic proteins (cationic at neutral pH).

The carboxyl groups of porphyrins are readily esterified. Most of the isolations of these substances from natural sources have involved preliminary conversion to methyl esters.

The nitrogen atoms of the pyrrole nuclei are able to form complexes with certain metals, the metal occupying a central position in the porphyrin ring. Although copper, zinc, and possibly other metals are found combined with porphyrins in nature, the complexes with iron are of greatest biological importance. The iron-porphyrins ("hemes") in turn combine with proteins, simpler organic compounds, and, in some cases, gases. These important phenomena are discussed below.

CHEMISTRY OF HEMES

COORDINATION OF IRON. Both ferric and ferrous iron tend to form hexavalent coordination complexes. Insertion of a ferrous ion into the center of protoporphyrin 9 results in ejection of the two protons attached to the pyrrole nitrogen atoms with formation of an uncharged iron-porphyrin complex. Since the iron is coordinated with only the four pyrrole nitrogen atoms, room is available for two additional coordinating groups. The complex of ferrous iron and protoporphyrin ("ferroprotoporphyrin") unites with two electrically neutral groups of the "oxygen" or "nitrogen" type, i.e., H_2O, CO, O_2, NH_3, pyridine, imidazole, HN_3 (azide), NH_2—NH_2 (hydrazine), NH_2OH (hydroxylamine), HCN, NO, CH_3NC.

Insertion of a ferric ion into the protoporphyrin ring ("ferriprotoporphyrin") results in a complex bearing a residual positive charge. Completion of the hexavalent coordination in this case is consequently accomplished by union of ferriprotoporphyrin with one uncharged and one anionic group. Typical of the latter category are OH^-, N_3^-, CN^-, and F^-.

A simplified diagram of the coordination systems under consideration is presented in Figure 29. The four nitrogen atoms of the pyrrole

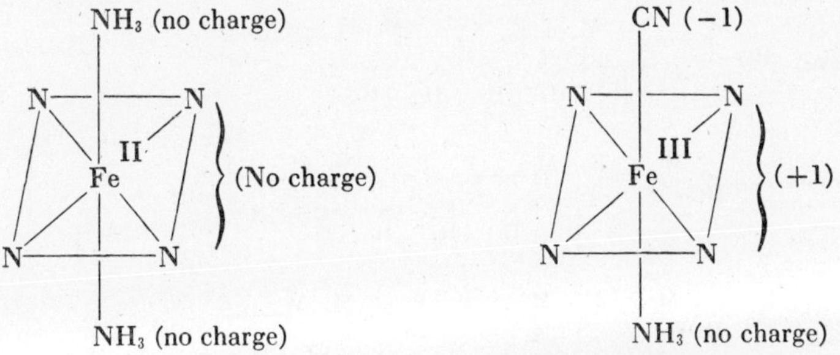

Diammonia ferroprotoporphyrin   Ammonia ferriprotoporphyrin cyanide

Fig. 29. Coordination in ferro- and ferri-hemes

units occupy a plane with the iron; the two additional coordinating groups lie above and below that plane. The bonds between the iron and the pyrrole nitrogen atoms may be covalent or electrovalent, depending on the specific compound involved. This matter is discussed below in connection with hemoglobin and gas transport.

The combination of an iron porphyrin with two nitrogenous groups is sometimes called a hemochromogen or hemochrome. A particularly complex example of this type is the coordination of heme (ferroprotoporphyrin) with two imidazole residues of histidine in the globin moiety of hemoglobin (discussed below).

PSEUDOPEROXIDASE REACTION. Heme compounds, free or combined with protein, catalyze the oxidation of organic substrates (particularly phenols and aromatic amines) by hydrogen peroxide. The reaction is similar to that catalyzed by the true peroxidases (p. 368), differing only in being thermostable. With proper precautions, the pseudoperoxidase reaction may be used as a test for blood, depending in that case on the very high concentration in blood of heme in the form of hemoglobin.

CHEMISTRY OF BILE PIGMENTS

STRUCTURE AND NOMENCLATURE.   The major pathway of catabolism of hemoglobin results in the formation of open-chain tetrapyrroles known as bile pigments (p. 591), the structures of which are indicated in Figure 30. All of the compounds in this group may be regarded as

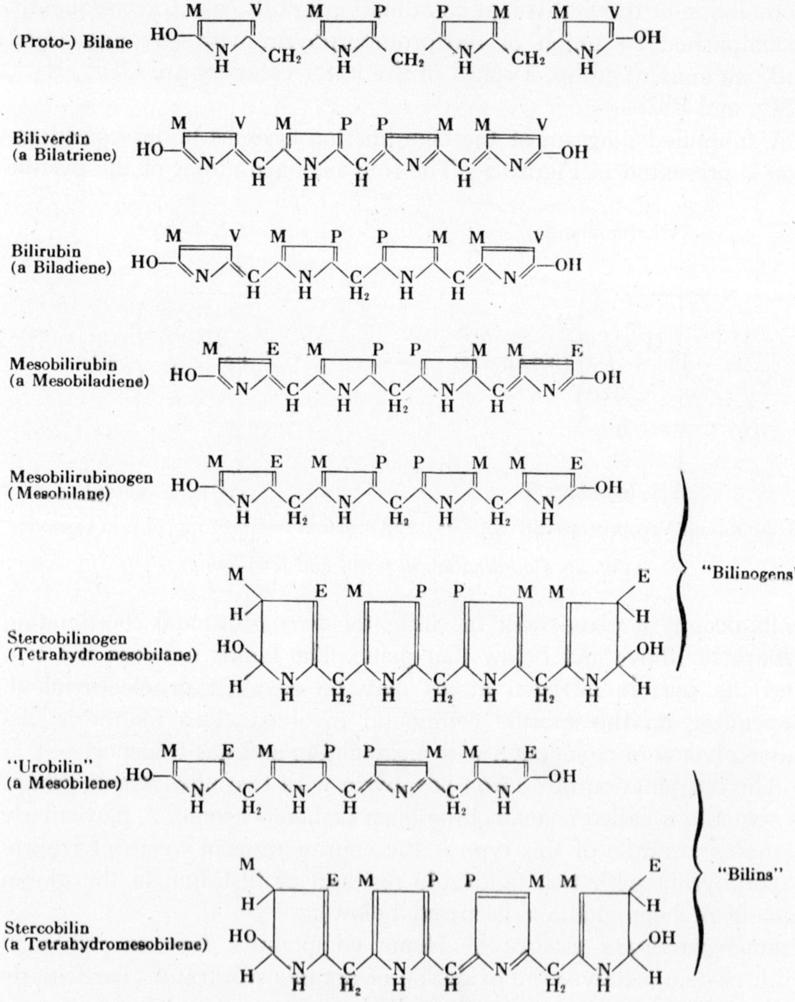

Fig. 30. Bile pigments

derived from a hypothetical parent compound (proto-)bilane. As can be seen from its structure, protobilane could be formed (hypothetically, only) by opening the ring of protoporphyrin 9 between pyrrole units I and II, eliminating the methyne carbon atom at that point by oxidation, and reducing all remaining methyne linkages to methylenes.

Since the substituents on the pyrroles are the same as in protoporphyrin, this parent bilane bears the prefix, "proto-," which is understood if not indicated explicitly. Reduction of the vinyl side-chains to ethyl groups (as in mesoporphyrin) produces mesobilane, the parent of certain of the bile pigments.

Oxidation of a methylene linkage (the central such group in naturally occurring compounds) in a bilane produces a bilene. A similar alteration in two methylene groups (as found in animals, the outer two) forms a biladiene, whereas oxidation of all three results in a bilatriene. Reduction of the outer unsaturated linkages in both external pyrrole rings of a bilane or bilene produces the corresponding tetrahydro derivative.

It is currently believed that the initial bile pigment formed from the degradation of hemoglobin is biliverdin, a (proto-)bilatriene (p. 591). Subsequent reduction of a methyne group produces bilirubin, a biladiene. Conversion of the vinyl groups of bilirubin to ethyl groups places the compound in the "meso" family, the result being mesobilirubin, a mesobiladiene. Further reduction, in this case at the methyne linkages, forms mesobilirubinogen, a mesobilane. Stercobilinogen, a tetrahydromesobilane, is formed by hydrogenation of the two outer pyrrole nuclei. Mesobilirubinogen and stercobilinogen are collectively designated "bilinogens" or "urobilinogens" in clinical biochemistry. By oxidation of the central methyne group of each of these two compounds there are formed, respectively, urobilin (a mesobilene) and stercobilin (a tetrahydromesobilene), which together are known as "bilins" or, confusingly, "urobilins." As in the case of the porphyrins, the prefixes "uro-" and "sterco-" indicate sources originally used in the isolation of these compounds, and do not exclude their occurrence in other tissues, body fluids, or excreta.

PHYSICAL PROPERTIES. The colors of the bile pigments depend on the number of unsaturated linkages and their degree of conjugation. Thus, bilanes and tetrahydrobilanes (mesobilirubinogen, stercobilinogen) are colorless, bilenes and tetrahydrobilenes (urobilin, stercobilin) are yellow, biladienes of the type occurring in animals (bilirubin, mesobilirubin) are orange, and the bilatrienes (biliverdin) are blue-green.

The free acid forms of bilirubin and biliverdin are insoluble in water, as are the Ba and Ca salts (the Ca salt of bilirubin is found in certain types of biliary calculi). The Na and K salts are water-soluble. Certain organic solvents (e.g., ethanol) dissolve the free acids.

CHEMICAL PROPERTIES. (*a*) OXIDATION TESTS. Treatment of certain bile pigments with nitric acid containing nitrous acid results in the formation of a sequence of colors: green, blue, violet, red, and yellow (Gmelin reaction). The mechanism of the reaction involves oxidation of the pigment to the bilatriene (green, blue) stage, followed by conversion of methyne linkages to carbonyl groups with eventual cleavage of the chain. The reaction is given by bilirubin and mesobilirubin. Biliverdin, since it is already a bilatriene, gives only the later stages of the reaction. Other oxidation tests for bile pigment (more specifically, for pigments of the bilirubin type), such as the Huppert-Cole and Fouchet tests, depend on initial isolation or concentration of the pigment as the Ba or Ca salt, followed by oxidation to the biliverdin stage.

(*b*) AZO DYE FORMATION. Bilirubin and mesobilirubin couple with diazotized sulfanilic acid to give an azo dye (van den Bergh reaction, p. 593). The reaction involves initial cleavage of the molecule, and requires the presence of a central methylene ($-CH_2-$) group (i.e., biliverdin does not react), but in addition has other structural requirements, since the reaction is not given by the bilinogens. A suggested mechanism follows:

$$HSO_3-\bigcirc-N=NCl$$

The resulting azo dye is blue-violet in strong acid, red at pH's between 2.0 and 5.5, and green above 5.5.

Production of color within one minute after mixing serum and diazotized sulfanilic acid is known as the "prompt, direct" van den Bergh reaction; and is obtained with bile and with serum in obstructive and hepatocellular jaundice. Rapid formation of the azo dye only upon the addition of alcohol or caffeine characterizes the "indirect" reaction, given by the bilirubin found in serum of normal subjects or those with hemolytic jaundice. The suggested explanations for these phenomena are discussed elsewhere (p. 593).

(*c*) ALDEHYDE CONDENSATION. The bilinogens (mesobilirubinogen, stercobilinogen) condense with Ehrlich's aldehyde reagent (*p*-dimethyl-amino benzaldehyde) in acid solution to give a red color, the chemical nature of which is not certain. The colored product formed from the bilinogens is soluble in organic solvents, in contrast to that formed by "porphobilinogen," a substance (possibly a monopyrrole) excreted in certain abnormal conditions (p. 597).

(*d*) FLUORESCENCE OF ZN COMPLEXES. The bilins (stercobilin, urobilin) exhibit a brilliant green fluorescence when treated with alcoholic zinc acetate (Schlesinger reaction). This fluorescence is easily differentiated from that produced by various drugs which may be excreted in the urine or feces, since the former disappears on acidification.

CHEMISTRY OF HEMOGLOBIN

GENERAL PHYSICAL PROPERTIES. Hemoglobin has a molecular weight of about 68,000, and consists of the protein, globin, to which are attached four heme groups. Recent studies by the method of X-ray diffraction (p. 74) indicate that hemoglobin has a spheroidal shape, of dimensions 55 x 55 x 65 Å. Internally, the molecule appears to consist of five parallel layers of closely packed peptide chains. The four heme groups are oriented parallel to each other and perpendicular to the planes of the peptide chains. Hemoglobin contains a large number of histidine residues, a factor of considerable importance in connection with its buffering properties (p. 315) and the transport of oxygen (p. 288).

Fetal hemoglobin is probably synthesized mainly in the liver rather than in the bone marrow, and consequently contains a globin different from that synthesized by the bone marrow of the adult. Although the molecular weights are similar, fetal hemoglobin differs from the adult pigment in oxygen affinity (p. 289), lability toward alkali denaturation, and electrophoretic mobility (p. 65). It requires about four months of extrauterine life for the fetal type of hemoglobin to be replaced completely by the adult type.

An "abnormal" type of hemoglobin appears to be synthesized in sickle-cell anemia. Although similar to the normal in molecular dimensions, it differs in solubility and isoelectric point (p. 64).

ACID-BASE PROPERTIES. As in the case of other proteins (p. 61), the ionizable groups which are operative in hemoglobin at physiological pH are chiefly the imidazole side-chains of histidine (p. 65), possibly supplemented to a slight extent by certain of the amino end groups (p. 64). The isoelectric point (pI) of hemoglobin is approximately 6.8, varying somewhat with the salt concentration in the solution.

Owing to its large content of histidine and its high concentration in whole blood, hemoglobin is a very effective buffer. It is probable, in fact, that hemoglobin is responsible for most of the buffering efficacy of blood which is not accounted for by bicarbonate (p. 318). Certain special aspects of the acid-base properties of the hemoglobin histidines are discussed below, in connection with gas transport.

TRANSPORT OF GASES BY HEME GROUPS OF HEMOGLOBIN. (*a*) COMBINATION WITH OXYGEN. The physiological importance of hemoglobin derives chiefly from its ability to combine reversibly with oxygen. The gas is taken up readily at high partial pressures (e.g., in the lungs) and is released as readily at low oxygen pressures (e.g., in the tissues), thus providing an effective system for the transport of oxygen from the atmosphere to the cells of the body (p. 288).

Under conditions of constant temperature, salt concentration, and pH, the degree of saturation of hemoglobin with oxygen is a function of the partial pressure of the gas, a plot of one variable versus the other producing a sigmoid curve (Fig. 60, p. 290). At constant partial pressure of oxygen, the extent of combination of the gas with hemoglobin is decreased by (1) increased temperature, (2) increased acidity (decrease in pH), and (3) increased salt concentration.

(*b*) HEME-HEME INTERACTIONS. Each molecule of hemoglobin (m.w. 68,000) contains four heme groups, each of which is capable of combining with a molecule of oxygen. The hemes are apparently not altogether independent; combination of oxygen with one heme group influences the oxygen affinity of the other heme groups. It is believed that these heme-heme interactions are responsible for the sigmoid shape of the oxygenation curve referred to above. In this connection, it is of interest that the oxygenation curve of myoglobin, which contains only one heme group (p. 123), is hyperbolic rather than sigmoid.

(*c*) HEME-LINKED GROUPS. As mentioned previously, the affinity of hemoglobin for oxygen decreases with decrease in pH (in the physiological range). The converse effect occurs also; oxygenation of hemoglobin results in a liberation of hydrogen ions into the solution. The biological significance of these effects is discussed elsewhere (p. 290). We are concerned here with their chemical basis.

The interrelation of oxygenation and ionization suggests the presence in hemoglobin of ionizable groups located in sufficient proximity to the heme rings to be influenced by the state of oxygenation. Such groups are designated "heme-linked," and are currently believed to be imidazole rings of certain of the histidine residues of globin.

The state of affairs existing at a single heme in hemoglobin during oxygenation is illustrated in Figure 31. In the unoxygenated (frequently called "reduced") hemoglobin molecule, bonds between the ferrous iron and the four pyrrole nitrogen atoms, the imidazole, and the sixth coordinating group (shown here as water) are essentially ionic in character. For reasons of simplification, only one of the several possible resonance structures is shown for the imidazole ring, the cationic "inium" group of which ionizes with a pK (p. 57) of 7.93.

Displacement of the water molecule by oxygen results in a number of alterations in the heme and heme-linked group, but it should be noted that, despite its direct attachment to oxygen, the iron of oxygenated hemoglobin ("oxyhemoglobin") remains in the ferrous state. Oxygenation causes the former ionic linkages to become covalent. In addition, the strongly electron-attracting character of oxygen tends to cause certain electron displacements along the lines shown in the figure. Liberation of a proton from the acid group is facilitated as a result, since ionization of a hydrogen amounts to, essentially, stripping a hydrogen atom of its electron. The inium group, therefore, becomes a stronger acid (pK=6.68).

Since the oxygenation-deoxygenation and ionization-deionization reactions are both true equilibria, their relation has a two-sided character. That is to say, not only does oxygenation increase the ionization of the heme-linked group, but also any condition which facilitates the ionization (e.g., higher pH) likewise favors the oxygenation. The physiological applications of these effects are considered in connection with respiration (p. 290).

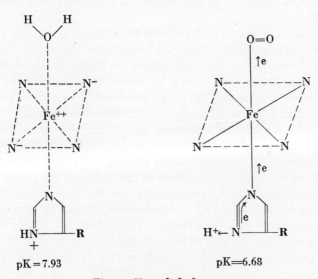

Fig. 31. Heme-linked groups

Evidence has been obtained for the existence of a second heme-linked group in hemoglobin. This group is believed also to be an imidazole, but farther removed from the iron than the group already discussed, and consequently interacting only weakly with the heme group. Oxygenation of the heme group increases the pK of this imidazole from 5.25 to 5.75, hence this effect tends to oppose that previously described, but to only a slight extent. With the aid of the Henderson-Hasselbalch equation (p. 58), it can be calculated that the net result of the changes in the pK's of the two heme-linked imidazoles is the liberation of approximately 0.6 mEq. of H+ at each oxygenated heme (p. 318), assuming a pH of 7.25 within the erythrocyte.

(*d*) COMBINATION WITH CARBON MONOXIDE. Hemoglobin combines with carbon monoxide ("carboxyhemoglobin") much as it does with oxygen, but with several hundred times the affinity. The effects on the character of the linkages and on the heme-linked groups are the same as in the formation of oxyhemoglobin. Sufficiently high partial pressures of oxygen can reversibly displace carbon monoxide from hemoglobin. It has been suggested that the competition of these two gases for hemoglobin may be regarded as an example of biological antagonism (p. 635).

CARBAMINO COMPOUND FORMATION. All proteins bearing free amino groups can combine with carbon dioxide under appropriate conditions, forming carbamino compounds (p. 87). Although small amounts of CO_2 are carried by the plasma proteins in carbamino form, most of the CO_2 transported in this manner is combined with hemoglobin (p. 293).

It is commonly stated that reduced hemoglobin is capable of carrying more carbamino-CO_2 than oxyhemoglobin. However, the amino groups responsible for this combination are probably distributed over the globin molecule, and cannot be considered "heme-linked" as are the histidine imidazoles discussed previously. The phenomenon is probably due, not directly to the oxygenation-deoxygenation reaction, but to the concomitant alteration in intracellular pH. Theoretical analysis of the problem, as a matter of fact, indicates that the extent of carbamino-CO_2 formation varies directly with the partial pressure of CO_2, and inversely as the *square* of the hydrogen ion concentration. Slight alterations in pH, consequently, can account for considerable differences in the amount of carbamino-CO_2 bound by hemoglobin.

REDOX PROPERTIES OF HEMOGLOBIN. Throughout all of the reactions discussed thus far, the iron of hemoglobin has remained in the ferrous form. Treatment of hemoglobin with certain oxidants (e.g., ferricyanide) converts it to methemoglobin, in which the iron is ferric. Traces of methemoglobin may exist normally in the erythrocyte; clinically, significant "methemoglobinemia" is found as a result of the ingestion of or exposure to certain substances, viz., chlorates, nitrites, phenacetin, acetylsalicylic acid, sulfonamides, aromatic amines, and aromatic nitro compounds.

The oxidation of hemoglobin to methemoglobin is reversible. *In vitro*, reducing agents such as $Na_2S_2O_4$ (dithionite) are effective; *in vivo*, it is probable that the glycolytic system (p. 389) of the erythrocyte is responsible for the reduction.

Owing to the valence of the iron, the heme groups of methemoglobin bear unit positive charges. A number of consequences ensue (Fig. 32). The pK of the major heme-linked imidazole discussed previously takes on the value that it has in oxyhemoglobin (6.68), influenced by the positive charge of the iron. (In the figure, this group is shown ionized, as it largely would be at physiological pH.) In addition, the coordinated water molecule (p. 117), also influenced by the positive charge of the iron, is enabled to lose a hydrogen ion, thus becoming a new acid group ($pK = 8.10$). Although the bonds in methemoglobin are ionic, liberation of a hydrogen ion from the water molecule to form the corresponding hydroxide results in partial conversion of the bonds to the covalent form (estimated to be two-thirds covalent in this case). At physiological pH's, a significant fraction of methemoglobin exists as the hydroxide.

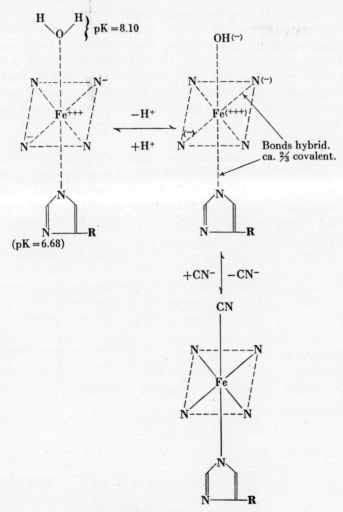

Fig. 32. *Methemoglobin and its cyanide*

In contrast to hemoglobin, methemoglobin cannot combine with O_2 or CO. Having net positive charges, however, the heme groups of methemoglobin can combine with various anions. The combination with cyanide (cyanmethemoglobin; bonds entirely covalent) is of considerable interest (Fig. 32). Methemoglobinemia is sometimes induced clinically in the treatment of cyanide poisoning, since the methemoglobin will compete for the cyanide with the cytochrome system of the tissues (p. 366), which otherwise might be inhibited to the point of causing death; such treatment obviously must be prompt to be effective.

SULFHEMOGLOBIN. This is a pigment of uncertain structure, formed by the action of H_2S on oxyhemoglobin. It is found in the blood after administration of aromatic amines or sulfur, in severe constipation, and in certain types of bacteremia. The formation of sulfhemoglobin involves the production of H_2S in the intestine by bacterial action on protein (p. 274). This H_2S is normally excreted or oxidized after absorption. Sulfhemoglobinemia results from the presence in the blood of either excessive quantities of H_2S or compounds (aromatic amines) which catalyze the formation of sulfhemoglobin from the normal traces of H_2S in the body.

INTERCONVERSIONS OF THE MAJOR HEMOGLOBIN DERIVATIVES. Figure 33 illustrates the interrelations which exist among the more important derivatives of hemoglobin, indicating the common and systematic names of each compound and the means of interconversion. Table 9 lists the absorption bands in the visible range of the major hemo-

Table 9. Absorption of Visible Light by Hemoglobin and Derivatives

	VIOLET	BLUE	GREEN	YELLOW	ORANGE	RED
	400	475	510	575	590	620	700
Hemoglobin	430		555			
Oxyhemoglobin	412–415		540–542	576–578		
Carbon monoxide-hemoglobin	418		538–540 568–572			
Methemoglobin pH $<$ 7	405–407	500				630
pH $>$ 7	411		540	577	600	
Cyanmethemoglobin	412–416		540			
Sulfhemoglobin						620

ABSORPTION BANDS, WAVELENGTHS IN mμ

globin derivatives. The absorption spectra and interconversion reactions are often used for identification of these compounds.

"Reduced" hemoglobin, oxyhemoglobin, and carbon monoxide hemoglobin are readily interconverted by displacement of one gas by another at appropriate partial pressure, or by the use of reagents which combine specifically with one gas. Oxyhemoglobin may react further with H_2S to form sulfhemoglobin.

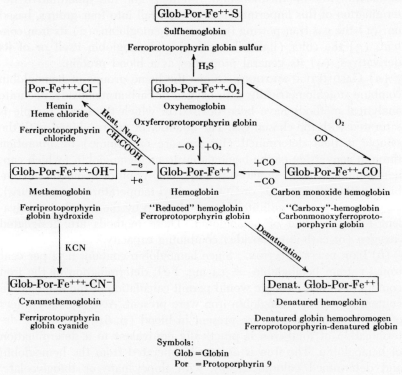

Symbols:
Glob = Globin
Por = Protoporphyrin 9

Fig. 33. Interrelations of hemoglobin derivatives

Oxidation of hemoglobin produces methemoglobin; the reaction can be reversed by reducing agents. Methemoglobin combines with cyanide, forming cyanmethemoglobin.

Denaturation of hemoglobin under proper conditions produces a compound in which ferroprotoporphyrin is united with denatured globin. This compound readily undergoes autoxidation to the ferric derivative.

If hemoglobin is heated with glacial acetic acid in the presence of NaCl, denatured globin is split off from the prosthetic group, which undergoes oxidation to the ferric state, producing ferriprotoporphyrin chloride (heme chloride, or hemin). This product forms characteristic crystals which may be used in the detection of hemoglobin.

The term "hematins" is sometimes used to denote the products obtained by treatment of hemoglobin with acid or alkali, usually for purposes of quantitative determination. "Acid hematin" consists of a colloidal system of hemin (heme chloride) and denatured globin. "Alkaline hematin" solutions contain heme hydroxide (salt formation also occurring on the propionic acid groups of the porphyrin) and probably also denatured globin and its hemochromogen.

DETERMINATION OF HEMOGLOBIN. Methods for the quantitative determination of this important hemoprotein fall into four groups, based on: (1) the gas-transporting function of hemoglobin; (2) its iron content; (3) the color (light absorption) of hemoglobin itself or of its derivatives; (4) its general properties as a blood protein.

(a) GASOMETRIC METHODS. Since the heme groups of hemoglobin combine stoichiometrically with oxygen or carbon monoxide, accurate analytical methods have been devised in which the blood sample is saturated with the chosen gas. The quantity of gas combined with the sample is then determined (by pressure or volume) by liberation through conversion of the hemoglobin to methemoglobin (which cannot combine with these gases, p. 119). One gram of hemoglobin combines with 1.36 ml. of O_2 or CO (standard temperature and pressure), or, conversely, each milliliter of gas taken up by the sample is equivalent to 0.736 gram of hemoglobin. These methods are designated "oxygen (or carbon monoxide) combining capacity."

(b) IRON DETERMINATION. Since hemoglobin contains 0.34 per cent iron (1 gram hemoglobin = 3.4 mg. Fe), determination of the iron content of a blood sample would permit calculation of the hemoglobin content if no non-hemoglobin iron were present. Actually, only traces of non-hemoglobin iron are present in blood (p. 619), so that a determination of total iron is practically equivalent to a determination of hemoglobin. The iron is ordinarily liberated from the hemoglobin and determined colorimetrically with thiocyanate or thioglycolate.

(c) COLORIMETRIC AND SPECTROPHOTOMETRIC METHODS. Direct measurement of light transmission (at 540 or 576 mμ) of blood samples suitably diluted with weak alkali yields results that are satisfactory for clinical purposes. Increased accuracy can be obtained by the use of a spectrophotometer instead of the ordinary photoelectric colorimeter, but the method even then is probably not as accurate as those discussed in groups (a) and (b). Conversion of the hemoglobin to cyanmethemoglobin and determination of the latter by colorimetric or spectrophotometric means has been suggested as a particularly accurate modification of this group of methods. In any case, the colorimetric or spectrophotometric methods require comparison with standard samples or reliance on previous calibrations.

Conversions of the hemoglobin in the blood sample to acid or alkaline "hematin" (p. 122) and measurement of the resulting color against standards is the basis of certain widely used clinical methods (e.g., the Sahli "acid hematin" method). These methods are not very precise.

(*d*) PROTEIN DETERMINATION. Theoretically, the quantity of hemoglobin in blood could be determined by the difference between analyses for total blood protein and plasma protein (since hemoglobin accounts for almost all of the protein within the red cell), using standard methods (p. 92). In practice, such a procedure would be too time-consuming. However, the copper sulfate specific gravity method represents this approach in an abbreviated form.

OTHER HEMOPROTEINS

MYOGLOBIN. Muscle contains an intracellular pigment known as myoglobin. Its prosthetic group is iron protoporphyrin 9; the protein moiety differs chemically from the globin of hemoglobin. In certain respects, myoglobin seems like a quarter of a hemoglobin molecule, i.e., its molecular weight is about 17,000 and it contains only one heme group.

Oxygen combines with the heme group of myoglobin in essentially the same manner as it does with hemoglobin, the iron remaining in the ferrous state. However, myoglobin has a greater affinity for oxygen than has hemoglobin, particularly at lower partial pressures of the gas. This property is well suited to the physiological functions of myoglobin (p. 414). The oxygenation curve of myoglobin is hyperbolic rather than sigmoid; as indicated previously, this is to be expected of a hemoprotein containing a single heme.

CYTOCHROMES. (*a*) CYTOCHROME OXIDASE. All aerobic organisms contain a group of intracellular hemoprotein enzymes which are concerned with the major pathway of biological oxidations. These catalysts are the cytochromes (p. 364). One member of the group, cytochrome oxidase, is the terminal catalyst in the sense that it effects the direct union of oxygen with the electrons initially derived from substrates. The other members of the group are go-betweens, transferring electrons from other enzyme systems (e.g., flavoproteins, p. 366) to the cytochrome oxidase. The cytochrome system is present entirely in the mitochondria of the cell (p. 348).

Since cytochrome oxidase has yet to be isolated in a pure state, little is known of its properties. Its prosthetic group differs from iron protoporphyrin 9 in that one of the vinyl side chains has been converted to a formyl group. In contrast to the hemoproteins discussed previously, cytochrome oxidase and the other members of the cytochrome group undergo repetitive oxidation and reduction of the iron as an integral feature of their function.

The exact nature of the reaction between cytochrome oxidase and oxygen is not known, beyond the fact that the ferrous oxidase reduces the oxygen, becoming ferric in the process (p. 366). The ferrous form of cytochrome oxidase resembles hemoglobin in its ability to combine with carbon monoxide; the ferric form resembles methemoglobin in combining with cyanide. Both types of unions effectively prevent the oxidase from performing its normal function, and, in fact, almost completely inhibit oxidative metabolism in aerobic organisms.

(b) CYTOCHROME C. In contrast to cytochrome oxidase, which clings tenaciously to the particulate matter of the cytoplasm, cytochrome c is readily prepared in a soluble state. It has a molecular weight of ca. 13,000 and contains one heme group, which appears to be iron protoporphyrin 9 to which sulfur is attached. It has been suggested that the prosthetic group is linked to the protein by means of thioether bridges, formed by attachment of sulfhydryl groups of cysteine in the protein to the vinyl groups of the porphyrin.

Cytochrome c does not react with oxygen. Instead, it transfers electrons from other systems to cytochrome oxidase, the iron atoms of both compounds undergoing cycles of oxidation and reduction (p. 364).

(c) OTHER CYTOCHROMES. What was formerly considered cytochrome "a" has since been found to consist of several components. One of these, a_3, is currently believed to be identical with cytochrome oxidase. Other members of the "a" group probably function similarly to cytochrome c.

A group of "b" cytochromes is recognized also. It is thought that the cytochrome b of animal tissues is closely related to the succinic dehydrogenase system (p. 366).

A new factor in biological oxidations, called the "Slater factor" after its discoverer, appears to be involved with the cytochromes in electron transport (p. 366). It also may be a hemoprotein.

CATALASES AND PEROXIDASES. These hemoprotein enzymes, which catalyze either the decomposition of peroxide or its oxidation of secondary substrates (p. 368), contain iron protoporphyrin 9 as prosthetic groups. The biliverdin contaminant found in certain catalase preparations is believed to be either an artifact or possibly a stage in the catabolism of catalase (p. 591). Liver catalase has a molecular weight of 225,000 and contains four heme groups. The plant and animal peroxidases studied thus far contain only single heme groups, but their protein moieties differ widely in molecular weight. All catalases and peroxidases contain trivalent iron, which is believed to remain in the oxidized state during the enzyme reactions. These enzymes are inhibited by cyanide, but not by carbon monoxide.

BIBLIOGRAPHY

Drabkin, D. L.: Animal pigments, Ann. Rev. Biochem. 11:531, 1942.

Fischer, H. and Orth, H.: Die Chemie des Pyrrols, Volume 2, Part I, Leipzig, Akademische Verlagsgesellschaft, 1937.

Granick, S., and Gilder, H.: Distribution, structure, and properties of the tetrapyrroles, Advances in Enzymology 7:305, 1947.

Gray, C. H.: The Bile Pigments, London, Methuen & Co., Ltd., and New York, John Wiley & Sons, Inc., 1953.

Lemberg, R., and Legge, J. W.: Hematin Compounds and Bile Pigments, New York, Interscience Publishers, Inc., 1949.

Roughton, F. J. W. and Kendrew, J. C. (eds.): Haemoglobin (Barcroft Memorial Symposium), London, Butterworth & Co., Ltd., and New York, Interscience Publishers, Inc., 1949.

Theorell, H.: Heme-linked groups and mode of action of some hemoproteins, Advances in Enzymology 7:265, 1947.

Wyman, J., Jr.: Heme proteins, Advances in Protein Chemistry 4:407, 1948.

6

VITAMINS

The fact that normal nutrition cannot be maintained in animals receiving diets containing only purified proteins, carbohydrates, lipids, and minerals was recognized at least thirty years before the existence of substances now known as vitamins was actually demonstrated. Such clinical observations as the prevention and cure of scurvy by citrus fruit juices and of beriberi by rice polishings also strongly suggested the nutritional importance of then unknown dietary factors. The names of Hopkins, Osborne, Mendel, and McCollum are associated with fundamental observations in this field (1912–1913) which resulted in the establishment of this class of substances, originally designated "accessory food factors." Funk (1912) demonstrated the presence of basic nitrogen in a substance extracted from rice polishings and yeast, which was curative for pigeon beriberi. He applied the term "vitamine," i.e., an amine essential for life, to this substance. This designation (minus the terminal "e" to avoid the implication that they are amines, as a class) has since been employed to designate this category of "accessory food factors," which have come to be recognized as playing vital roles in nutrition and in certain fundamental metabolic processes.

Vitamins have been defined as organic compounds, occurring in natural foods, either as such or as utilizable precursors, which are required in minute amounts for normal growth, maintenance, and reproduction, i.e., for normal nutrition and health. They differ from other organic foodstuffs in that they do not enter into the tissue structure and do not undergo degradation for purposes of providing energy. They were originally classified according to their solubility in water or fats, and alphabetically, e.g., fat-soluble A and D, water-soluble B and C. The list of members of the vitamin family has grown considerably; most of them have been identified chemically and many have been synthesized. With establishment of the chemical structure of a vitamin, alphabetical designations have become unnecessary; with elucidation of its specific metabolic functions, even the term "vitamin" becomes superfluous, except as an indication of its occurrence in nature and exogenous requirement. For example, several of the B vitamins are known to serve as coenzymes in fundamentally important metabolic reactions, and the functional activity of others, perhaps of all, may ultimately be found to be due to their influence on or participation in enzyme systems.

Demonstration of their chemical nature led in many instances to the discovery that several structurally related substances may possess similar vitamin activities. The terms "isotels" and "vitamers" have been suggested for such substances; e.g., activated 7-dehydrocholesterol (vitamin D_3) and activated ergosterol (vitamin D_2) are isotels, or D vitamers.

Although procedures are available for quantitative determination of most of the known vitamins, especially in foods, clinical evaluation of nutritional status with respect to vitamins is often difficult and the available methods unsatisfactory. This is particularly true during the usually long latent period of progressing deficiency which precedes the appearance of frank symptoms and signs. Various types of diagnostic procedures may be employed for this purpose:

1. The concentration of the vitamin or one of its metabolites may be determined in the blood or urine.

2. The curve of concentration in the blood or excretion in the urine may be measured after administration of a standard test dose of the vitamin. This is the so-called "saturation test" procedure, based on the assumption that subsaturation of the tissues with the vitamin will result in a subnormal rise in the blood and subnormal excretion in the urine under conditions of the test.

3. Quantitative determinations may be made of the vitamin content of tissues obtained at biopsy (e.g., liver, muscle).

4. Evidence of certain types of deficiency may be obtained by microscopic studies, e.g., of mucosal scrapings in vitamin A deficiency.

5. Certain consequences of specific deficiencies may be demonstrated by biophysical methods, e.g., impaired dark adaptation in vitamin A deficiency and increased capillary fragility in ascorbic acid deficiency.

6. In the case of certain vitamins, deficiency may manifest itself in some characteristic derangement of metabolism which can be measured quantitatively, e.g., elevation of blood pyruvate in thiamine deficiency, and increase in serum alkaline phosphatase, hypophosphatemia and hypocalcemia in vitamin D deficiency.

7. Of great diagnostic value is the prompt relief of clinical manifestations of suspected deficiency upon administration of adequate amounts of the vitamin in question.

The usefulness of each of these procedures for the detection of deficiency varies in the case of different vitamins, and few of them are entirely satisfactory for any vitamin. Biochemical studies in this connection are most valuable when used in conjunction with other types of data, e.g., clinical and dietary.

VITAMINS A

Vitamin A derives its alphabetical designation from the fact that, although not isolated until some years later, it was the first substance to be placed in this category of nutritionally essential factors (in 1913). It was originally recognized as a substance present in egg-yolk and butter fat, in the absence of which from the diet rats could not maintain normal growth. This growth factor was designated "unidentified dietary factor fat-soluble A."

It was found also that rats deprived of this substance developed rather characteristic eye changes, viz., dryness (xerophthalmia) and inflammation of the conjunctiva, ulceration, edema and opacity of the cornea (keratomalacia), eventuating in blindness. These were preventable by administration of small amounts of cod-liver oil. The resemblance of this condition to xerophthalmia and keratomalacia occurring in children (and also adults) on restricted diets (largely vegetable) was noted. It was then shown that this clinical disorder responded promptly to administration of foods rich in vitamin A.

CHEMISTRY. Vitamin A is a derivative of certain carotenoids (p. 37), which are hydrocarbon (polyene) pigments (yellow, red) widely distributed in nature. The most important of these carotenoid precursors, designated provitamins A, are α-, β-, and γ-carotene, which are $C_{40}H_{56}$-hydrocarbons, and a monohydroxy-β-carotene ($C_{40}H_{55}OH$), termed "cryptoxanthin." The structure of β-carotene is indicated in Figure 34. It is a symmetrical molecule, containing two terminal β-ionone rings (A and B), connected by an 18C hydrocarbon chain with eleven conjugated double bonds. The three other provitamins A differ from β-carotene only in the nature of ring B (Fig. 34). Such compounds are subject to cis-trans isomerization and, when considered from a three-dimensional standpoint, there are a large number (148) of possible stereoisomers of the four provitamins named. Only a few of these have been investigated as to their biological activity. In general, the trans-isomers are active and the cis-isomers inactive, although this distinction is not an absolute one. One important exception is encountered in the synthesis of rhodopsin (visual purple), an important function of vitamin A (p. 134), in which apparently only the cis-isomers are active.

The general structural relation of vitamin A to β-carotene may be indicated as follows (Fig. 34): (1) β-carotene contains two β-ionone rings, vitamin A one; (2) β-carotene ($C_{40}H_{56}$) contains forty C atoms, vitamin A twenty ($C_{20}H_{29}OH$); (3) β-carotene has eleven conjugated double bonds in the hydrocarbon chain, vitamin A five; (4) vitamin A has a terminal primary alcoholic group, whereas β-carotene has no such group.

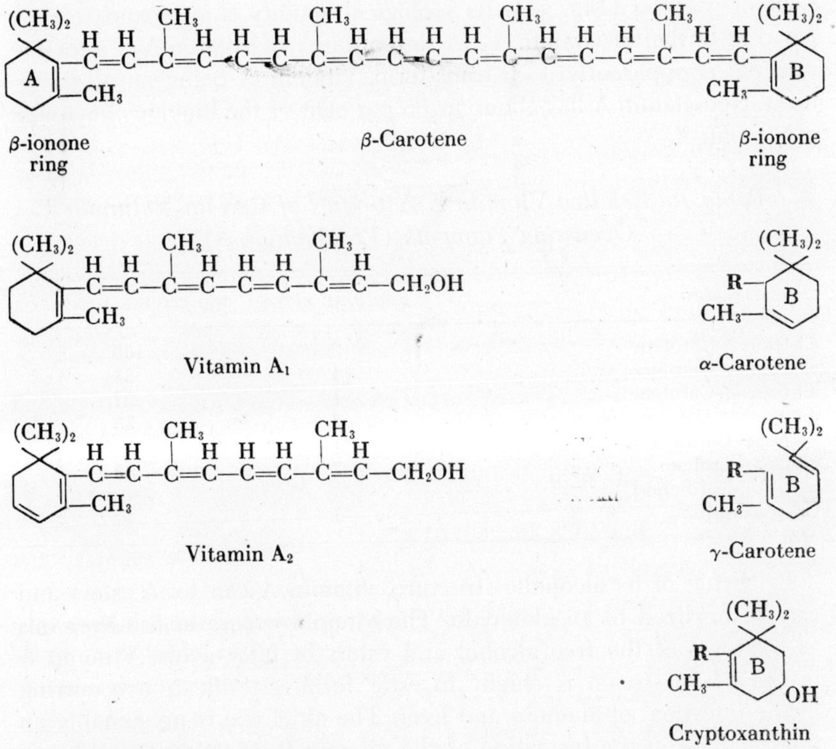

β-ionone ring   β-Carotene   β-ionone ring

Vitamin A₁   α-Carotene

Vitamin A₂   γ-Carotene

Cryptoxanthin

Fig 34. *Structures of provitamins A and vitamins A. The symbol "R" attached to the B rings of the provitamins refers to the remainder of the molecule, which is identical with that of β-carotene*

Two molecules of vitamin A are formed by symmetrical oxidative scission of β-carotene. Oxidation of the central double bond may produce as intermediate an aldehyde, which is subsequently reduced to the alcohol (vitamin A). Similar splitting of α- or γ-carotene, or cryptoxanthin, containing only one β-ionone ring, gives rise to only one molecule of the vitamin, no vitamin A activity being associated with the portion of the molecule which does not contain a β-ionone ring. The approximate relative biological activities of these provitamins are indicated in Table 10.

Vitamin A occurs in nature in different forms. The usual form, vitamin A_1, described above, predominates, except in the livers (and other
tissues) of certain fresh-water fishes; in these, another type predominates, designated "vitamin A_2," which shows an absorption band at
$693m\mu$ when treated with antimony trichloride, whereas A_1 shows a
band at $620m\mu$. Vitamin A_2 differs from A_1 apparently in having an
additional unsaturated linkage in the ring, i.e., a double bond between
carbons 3 and 4 (Fig. 34). Its biological activity is approximately 40
per cent of that of vitamin A_1. A stereoisomer of vitamin A_1, "neovitamin A," is apparently a cis-trans-form, vitamin A being an all-trans-
form. Neovitamin A has about 70–80 per cent of the biological activity
of vitamin A.

Table 10. Relative Vitamin A Activities of Certain Naturally
Occurring Pigments (Provitamins A)

PROVITAMIN	β-IONONE RINGS	RELATIVE A ACTIVITY
all-trans-β-Carotene	2	100
all-trans-α-Carotene	1	53
all-trans-γ-Carotene	1	27
mono-cis-β-Carotene (neo-β-Carotene B)	2	53
di-cis-β-Carotene (neo-β-Carotene U)	2	38
Cryptoxanthin	1	57

By virtue of its alcoholic structure, vitamin A can form esters and
can be oxidized to an aldehyde. The vitamin occurs in fish-liver oils
as mixtures of the free alcohol and esters of fatty acids. Vitamin A
in the blood stream is chiefly in ester form, esterification occurring
in the intestinal epithelium and liver. The aldehyde is presumably an
intermediate in the formation of the vitamin from its carotenoid precursors (p. 134). Moreover, "retinene," an intermediate in the rhodopsin (visual purple) cycle (p. 135), has been identified as vitamin
A aldehyde.
Vitamin A and the provitamins are practically insoluble in water
and are very soluble in most fat solvents. Vitamin A is referred to,
therefore, as a "fat-soluble vitamin." One of the most important of
the physical properties of this vitamin and its precursors is their spec-
tral absorption, which is useful in their identification and quantitative
determination. Individual carotenoids differ in their absorption maxima. β-Carotene (in chloroform) shows two peaks, at 466 and 497 mμ.
Vitamin A, on the other hand, shows absorption bands in the ultraviolet portion of the spectrum, the absorption maximum for A_1 (in
chloroform) being at 328 mμ. It is sensitive to ultraviolet radiation,

biological activity being lost after such treatment. A blue color develops when vitamin A in anhydrous solvents is treated with certain inorganic chlorides. This is the basis for the Carr-Price test (anhydrous chloroform, antimony trichloride). The resulting blue compound has an absorption maximum at 620 mμ for vitamin A$_1$ and at 693 mμ for A$_2$. The test is commonly employed for identification and quantitation of vitamin A.

Both provitamins and vitamins A are destroyed by oxidation and by exposure to light, vitamin A being more stable than carotene. Both are protected by the presence of antioxidants, e.g., α-tocopherol (vitamin E) (p. 157). They are not thermolabile, but heat accelerates their destruction in the presence of oxygen. The vitamin A content of foods is not affected by canning or freezing, but is lowered by dehydration.

OCCURRENCE AND FOOD SOURCES. Whereas carotenoids are present in both plant and animal tissues, vitamin A occurs only in animals. It is generally believed that the carotenoids found in animals are derived from the food, although the possibility of their formation in the animal organism has not been excluded. If true, this is a unique situation, in which a vitamin is formed only by animals from precursors formed only by plants. β-Carotene has been found in the corpus luteum, placenta and adrenals in man.

The provitamin carotenoids are the chief dietary source of vitamin A. They are widely distributed throughout the plant kingdom, in which they represent an important class of pigments (yellow-red). There is a parallelism between greenness, i.e., chlorophyll content, and vitamin A activity in leafy vegetables, but the nature of this relationship is not clear. Yellow-colored vegetables and fruits are also rich in carotenoid provitamins, e.g., corn, sweet potatoes, carrots, tomatoes, apricots, yellow peaches, etc. The most important animal food sources of vitamin A are whole milk, butter, and egg-yolk. The vitamin A potency of butter fat (milk), which contains both β-carotene and vitamin A$_1$, varies in different breeds of cattle and with the carotenoid content of the feed. Colostrum has a higher content (both carotene and vitamin A) than has mature milk. This is true also of human milk, which can be enriched by ingestion of vitamin A.

The livers of certain fish contain higher concentrations of vitamin A than do any other tissues; consequently, fish-liver oil concentrates are commonly used therapeutically. The livers of marine fishes contain vitamin A$_1$ and those of fresh-water fishes A$_2$. The concentration in halibut-liver oil (1.5 per cent) may be 150 times and in tuna-liver oil (4.5 per cent) 450 times that in cod-liver oil (0.01 per cent). However, these ratios vary widely in similar types of fish in different regions. The liver of the polar bear is very rich in vitamin A (p. 139).

ASSAY. The bioassay procedure for vitamin A is based upon the acceleration of growth produced in young rats given a basal diet nutritionally complete except for the absence of vitamin A or its precursors. When β-carotene was found to be a provitamin A, it was adopted as a reference standard. Crystalline vitamin A acetate is also used for this purpose. The International unit (I.U.) (also U.S.P. unit) is defined as the amount of vitamin A equivalent in effect to 0.6 μg. of pure crystalline β-carotene. A satisfactory grade of cod-liver oil (unconcentrated) contains at least 600 I.U./gram.

ABSORPTION. Vitamin A and its carotene precursors are absorbed in the small intestine. It is believed that the simultaneous presence of tocopherols and other antioxidants protects them against destruction in the intestinal lumen. Dietary vitamin A is chiefly in the form of esters, which are hydrolyzed in the lumen to free vitamin A alcohol and fatty acid. The vitamin apparently undergoes re-esterification in the intestinal epithelial cells and in the liver, for it appears in the blood in the ester form promptly, regardless of the form in which it is administered. The maximum blood level is attained four to five hours after a single large dose (130 mg.). The blood carotene level reaches a maximum about seven to eight hours after oral administration of carotene.

Under normal conditions, vitamin A is absorbed chiefly by the lymphatic route and carotene chiefly via the portal blood, but the former can be absorbed satisfactorily after ligation of the thoracic duct. At least in some species (rat, pig), carotene can be converted to the vitamin in the intestinal epithelial cells.

Bile salts are necessary for proper absorption of carotene, but not of vitamin A. Because of its solubility in mineral oil, absorption of carotene is diminished by the presence of this oil, being carried out with it in the feces. Absorption of vitamin A is not affected significantly.

STORAGE AND INTERMEDIARY METABOLISM. Carotenoids which contain a β-ionone ring (α-, β-, γ-carotene, cryptoxanthin) are capable of transformation into vitamin A, as indicated previously. This conversion occurs probably chiefly in the liver, but also, at least in certain species (rat, pig), in the intestinal mucosa. An enzyme ("carotenase") may be involved in this transformation. The Kupffer cells are apparently active in this connection, their carotene content increasing after the absorption of carotenoids, and subsequently decreasing gradually as their vitamin A content increases.

The thyroid is apparently implicated in the utilization of carotene, conversion of which to vitamin A is increased by thyroxine and decreased after thyroidectomy or administration of antithyroid drugs (thiouracil). The level of serum carotene may be elevated (carotenemia) and that of vitamin A decreased in subjects with hypothyroidism. Thyroxine also appears to accelerate mobilization of vitamin A from the liver. There is evidence that vitamin A influences thyroid function, the rate of formation of thyroxine being decreased in vitamin A deficient animals. The results of other experiments suggest that large doses of the vitamin antagonize the action of thyroxine. The nature of this purported antagonism is not clear.

About 95 per cent of the vitamin A reserves of the body is held in the liver, chiefly in ester form (combined with fatty acids), a small amount being present in other tissues, e.g., kidney (not in man), lactating breast, adrenals, lung, intestine. Under normal conditions, vitamin A is stored chiefly in the liver cells; after ingestion of large amounts it enters the Kupffer cells also. In subjects with liver damage, the capacity for storage and formation of vitamin A from carotene is impaired and concentration of this vitamin in the blood is decreased. The hepatic storage capacity is comparatively low in young infants, increasing with age. The quantity stored in the liver varies in different species, but is largely dependent upon the antecedent diet. About 70 per cent of a single large dose of vitamin A may be recovered from the liver of the rat, which can store enough in a few days of adequate intake to satisfy its requirement for months. On the other hand, less than 10 per cent of a similar dose can be recovered from the liver of the guinea pig, which is very sensitive to deficiency in vitamin A. The storage capacity in man is apparently relatively large.

MOBILIZATION AND CIRCULATION. The blood plasma contains both vitamin A and carotenoid pigments. The former is present chiefly in the free state (alcohol) except after ingestion of large amounts of vitamin A or its carotene precursors, when the ester form appears in the blood. Under normal conditions, the levels of both substances in the blood are maintained by transformation of carotene to vitamin A in the liver and mobilization of the latter from the hepatic stores. The mechanism which regulates this mobilization is not clear, but certain factors are known to influence it.

Under conditions of decreased intake the plasma vitamin A concentration is maintained at the expense of the hepatic reserves. Hyperthermia causes depletion of liver vitamin A with a simultaneous decrease in its concentration in the blood. Administration of thyroxine or testosterone accelerates mobilization from the liver, whereas 17-α-hydroxyallopregnane-20-one, an adrenal steroid, produces a decrease in the plasma and a simultaneous increase in the liver. These observations suggest that certain steroid hormones may regulate the equilibria between liver and plasma vitamin A or between the esterified and unesterified forms in the liver. At least in certain species (e.g., the rat), the plasma vitamin A concentration is apparently related more directly to the quantity of free (alcohol) rather than of total (including esterified) vitamin A in the liver.

Reported values for vitamin A and carotenoids in the blood of normal subjects vary widely, owing in part to differences in methods employed, several of which have proved unsatisfactory. The following figures appear to be acceptable: vitamin A, 18–60 μg. (60–200 I.U.) per 100 ml. serum; carotenoids, 100–300 μg. per 100 ml. serum.

EXCRETION.   The urine contains no vitamin A or carotene except after administration of excessive amounts. Under normal conditions only very small quantities are excreted in the feces. Administration of mineral oil, especially in young children, may cause excessive loss of carotene in the feces (p. 132). Considerable amounts of vitamin A and carotene are present in milk, the concentration being greatest in colostrum and decreasing gradually over the period of lactation. Human colostrum possesses about twice as much vitamin A activity as early milk, the latter, providing 2400–4000 I.U. daily, being considerably richer in this factor than cow's milk. The vitamin A content of milk is increased by ingestion of added amounts of vitamin A during pregnancy, but not by similar doses of carotene.

FUNCTIONS.   With the exception of its role in relation to certain visual processes, the functions of vitamin A in the organism are suggested chiefly indirectly, by changes which occur in the presence of deficiency in this factor (p. 138). The mechanism whereby vitamin A operates to prevent these changes in not known.

VITAMIN A AND VISION.   The retina contains two types of receptor cells: (1) cones, which are specialized for color and detail vision in bright light; (2) rods, which are specialized for visual acuity in dim light (night vision). Light waves, striking these receptors, produce chemical changes which, in turn, give rise to nerve impulses that pass to the brain. Vitamin A plays an essential role in the photochemical phase of this process.

Visual acuity of the rod cells (vision in dim light) is dependent upon their content of a photosensitive pigment, rhodopsin or visual purple (in land and marine vertebrates), a dissociable combination of a protein, "opsin," and "retinene$_1$" (vitamin A$_1$ aldehyde). The cones contain a similar pigment, "iodopsin" (visual violet). In fresh-water vertebrates (fishes, lampreys, and certain larval amphibia), rhodopsin is replaced by "porphyropsin," a combination of opsin and retinene$_2$ (vitamin A$_2$ aldehyde).

Under the influence of light, rhodopsin is converted to unstable orange products which undergo chemical change to a yellow mixture of trans-retinene and opsin. Trans-retinene is inactive in the resynthesis of rhodopsin; it must first be converted to the active cis-isomer (Fig. 35). *In vitro*, this can be accomplished by exposure to blue, but not to yellow light, which is not absorbed by retinene, the absorption spectrum of which, maximal at 385 mμ, extends into the violet and blue, but is negligible in and beyond the green. In the eye, however, this isomerization pathway is relatively unimportant, for the trans-retinene is promptly transformed to trans-vitamin A, its carbonyl group being reduced to the primary alcohol by retinene reductase (alcohol dehydrogenase) and DPN·H₂. The trans-vitamin A, which too is inactive in rhodopsin synthesis, is passed into the blood stream.

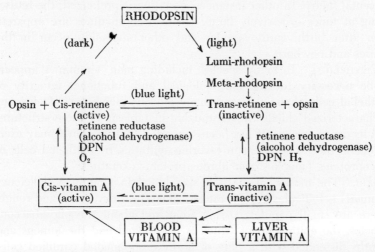

Fig. 35. *Rhodopsin-vitamin A cycle* (*Hubbard and Wald: J. Gen. Physiol. 36:269, 1952*)

In the course of resynthesis of rhodopsin, which occurs in dim light and in the dark, the active cis-vitamin A enters the retina from the blood and is oxidized to cis-retinene by reverse action of retinene reductase (alcohol dehydrogenase) in the presence of DPN. The cis-retinene couples with opsin to form rhodopsin; this reaction is exergonic, thereby serving to drive continuous oxidation of vitamin A to retinene by promptly removing the latter from the reaction mixture.

The visual process therefore involves continual removal of the active vitamin A isomer from the blood by the retina, which returns the inactive isomer to the circulation. Vitamin A isomerizes in the body, the four likely isomers (p. 130) probably being in equilibrium in the organism, ensuring an adequate supply of the active form.

Visual Defects in Deficiency (Nyctalopia). One of the earliest functional defects induced by vitamin A deficiency is impairment of dark adaptation. Bright light causes bleaching of rhodopsin, which must be resynthesized in the dark, chiefly from vitamin A reaching the retinal rods via the blood stream, before normal visual acuity in dim light is possible. Individuals having vitamin A deficiency are consequently unable to see clearly in dim light (nyctalopia). In mild deficiency there may be merely delay in the development of visual acuity in the dark following a period of exposure to bright light (delayed rhodopsin synthesis).

REPRODUCTION. In vitamin A deficient rats, although litters may be produced, fertilization or implantation often fails. Synthesis or release of androgen by the testis may be interfered with. Fetal resorption or growth retardation and death may occur early in pregnancy, owing to placental injury. In other instances, gestation is prolonged, the fetuses being at times excessively large. Dental abnormalities are apparent soon after birth; cardiovascular and other anomalies occur in the fetuses and newborn.

EPITHELIUM. In many species, including man, vitamin A appears to be necessary for the morphological and functional integrity of epithelial cells of the skin and many mucous membranes. Deficiency is characterized chiefly by keratinizing metaplasia of these structures and its consequences. It has been suggested that vitamin A may exert a general metabolic effect in favoring synthesis by epithelial cells of glycoproteins (mucin) over fibrous proteins (keratin).

Skin. The most characteristic skin lesion in vitamin A deficiency (human) is follicular hyperkeratosis. The skin is dry, scaly, and rough. There are small papules, arising from and about the pilosebaceous follicles, the epithelium of which is keratinized and the lumens and mouths distended with a plug of horny desquamated cornified cells. The skin about these papules may show a mild inflammatory reaction and there may be an acne-like non-suppurative eruption. Follicular hyperkeratosis of this type occurs most commonly on the extensor surfaces of the arms and thighs, shoulders, abdomen, back, and buttocks, in frequency in the order named. The specificity of these lesions has not been established, but they appear, in varying degrees, in vitamin A deficiency in several species.

Mucous Membranes. The primary changes appear to involve atrophy of the lining cells, with proliferation of basal cells and formation of a stratified keratinized epithelium, resembling epidermis. This phenomenon may occur in mucous membranes in the eye, certain glands (salivary, lacrimal, sebaceous), and the respiratory, gastrointestinal and genitourinary tracts. Various complications may occur as a result of these lesions in different situations.

Keratinization of the conjunctiva and in the lacrimal glands leads to dryness of the eyes (xerophthalmia), with consequent irritation and photophobia, or follicular conjunctivitis. Keratinized cells may be found in scrapings from the bulbar conjunctiva. Small, triangular, silvery or pearly, foamlike spots (Bitot's spots) appear in the conjunctiva just lateral, at times also medial, to the cornea. These are due to keratinization of the conjunctival epithelium. Vision is impaired as a result of keratinization of the epithelium of the cornea which, in severe deficiency, becomes edematous, infiltrated with leukocytes, cloudy, and softened (keratomalacia). These changes, together with the frequently associated secondary infection resulting from dryness and irritation, may lead to blindness and perforation of the cornea.

Keratinizing metaplasia of the epithelium in the nose, accessory nasal sinuses, pharynx, and tracheobronchial tree may lead to irritation and lowering of local resistance of these structures to infection. This has given rise to the designation of vitamin A as the "anti-infective" vitamin. This term is entirely unwarranted and misleading. Vitamin A exerts no effect upon infectious diseases other than those local infections which may result from tissue changes induced by severe deficiency. In such cases, its administration, by correcting these changes, may restore local tissue resistance to invading organisms.

Keratinization and desquamation of the lining cells of the trachea and bronchi, especially in small animals, may lead to bronchiolar obstruction and areas of atelectasis. Similar changes in the mucosa of the lower urinary passages in the rat lead to calculus formation, the desquamated cells forming a nidus on which calcium salts precipitate out of the urine. There is no evidence that this mechanism operates in urinary lithiasis in man. In certain species, metaplastic changes occur in the lining of the salivary ducts, middle ear, esophagus, and intestines.

Vitamin A deficiency results in keratinization of the vaginal epithelium in rats, with a decrease in leukocytes and eventual replacement of the normal cyclic changes by the phase of complete cornification (diestrus smear). Topical application of vitamin A suppresses the vaginal cornification produced by estrogens, suggesting that, at least in the rat, this effect of estrogen may be due to the induction of local vitamin A inadequacy. However, the histologic changes in the deeper mucosal layers in estrus and in vitamin A deficiency are not identical.

BONES AND TEETH.   In addition to its requirement for normal growth, which it shares with other vitamins, vitamin A plays a role in the construction of normal bone. In several species, vitamin A deficiency results in slowing of endochondral bone formation and decreased osteoblastic activity, the bones becoming cancellous, losing their fine structural details. Vitamin A apparently accelerates the normal growth sequences, including both deposition and resorption processes, required for orderly formation of normal bone structure. Dental defects appear in the newborn rats of vitamin A deficient mothers, the enameloblasts being keratinized, with consequent thinning of the enamel and the appearance of chalky patches (underlying dentin) resembling those seen in fluorosis (p. 716). Odontoblasts may atrophy and tooth growth cease. The normal orange-brown color of the outer layer of the incisors may be lost and the teeth may be deformed.

DEFICIENCY IN MAN. Present understanding of the role of vitamin A in human nutrition is reflected in the following statements (A.M.A. Council on Pharmacy):

1. Vitamin A is specific for the cure and prevention of xerophthalmia, nyctalopia (night blindness), and hemeralopia (day blindness).

2. Vitamin A is essential to the normal structure and behavior of epithelial tissue, e.g., the epithelium covering the skin, and forming the lining of the nasal sinuses and respiratory tract, mouth, pharynx, entire digestive tract, and the genitourinary tract. It prevents folicular hyperkeratosis of the skin.

3. Vitamin A is a growth factor.

VITAMIN INTERRELATIONSHIPS. The occurrence of manifestations of vitamin K deficiency in animals receiving excessive amounts of vitamin A is referred to elsewhere (p. 140), as is the effect of vitamin E (and other antioxidants) in preventing destruction of vitamin A in the intestine (p. 131). It has been reported that rats deficient in vitamin A exhibit certain manifestations which resemble those of vitamin C deficiency (to which the rat is very resistant), viz., red, swollen gums, changes in the molars, joint swelling, and bleeding from the lacrimal glands. These symptoms, which may be accompanied by a drop in the blood vitamin C content, disappear after administration of vitamin C.

DETECTION OF DEFICIENCY IN MAN. The most important clinical manifestations of vitamin A deficiency in man are: (1) xerophthalmia, i.e., thickening and loss of transparency of the bulbar conjunctiva, with yellowish pigmentation and occasionally Bitot's spots; (2) follicular conjunctivitis; (3) keratomalacia, i.e., softening of the cornea with, in advanced cases, ulceration and necrosis; (4) impairment of dark adaptation, progressing to night blindness (nyctalopia); (5) follicular hyperkeratosis of the skin.

The clinical manifestations and their prompt response to administration of adequate amounts of vitamin A constitute the best available means of diagnosis. No reliable procedures are available for detecting subclinical deficiency states. The following objective methods have been investigated: (1) determination of the concentration of vitamin A and carotene in the blood; (2) the dark adaptation test; (3) examination of scrapings of the bulbar conjunctiva and vagina (and other mucous membranes).

VITAMIN A CONTENT OF BLOOD. The concentration of vitamin A in the blood (plasma or serum) is not a reliable index of the status of vitamin A nutrition, although extremely low values (below 40 I.U./100 ml.) may be regarded as indicative of deficiency. One source of difficulty is lack of agreement as to what are the limits of normal concentration. Of greater importance, however, is the fact that a normal plasma vitamin A level may be maintained for many months in previously normal subjects receiving diets containing virtually no carotene or vitamin A. There is considerable individual variation in this connection, due undoubtedly to quantitative differences in the hepatic stores of the vitamin which, in well-nourished, normal subjects may be adequate to meet the body requirements for several months. Fever may be accompanied by a sudden drop in plasma (and liver) vitamin A, and a rise follows administration of large doses of the vitamin. There is no satisfactory consistent correlation between the blood vitamin values and the presence or severity of the various clinical deficiency manifestations. The plasma carotene level is of still less diagnostic value. It reflects the immediate past intake of carotenoids, falling promptly after their exclusion from the diet and rising promptly following their readministration. A zero value is compatible with normal nutrition inasmuch as there is no consistent relationship between the level of plasma carotene and the quantity of vitamin A in the organism.

DARK ADAPTATION TEST. The biophotometer has been employed to test the speed of visual adaptation to dim light after a period of exposure to bright light (p. 134). Although night blindness is an important manifestation of vitamin A deficiency, the general experience has been that the dark adaptation test does not satisfactorily reflect subclinical levels of vitamin A deficiency and that biophotometer readings do not parallel the concentration of the vitamin in the blood. The time of development of significant impairment of dark adaptation in subjects on a diet low in vitamin A and carotenoids varies widely, from several days to many months. Moreover, conditions other than vitamin A deficiency may cause this phenomenon.

EXAMINATION OF SCRAPINGS. In established A-deficiency, keratinized epithelial cells may be demonstrated in scrapings from the bulbar conjunctiva and the vagina. These changes generally occur rather late, being preceded usually by subjective evidence of impaired dark adaptation. This procedure is therefore of little clinical value.

EFFECTS OF EXCESS OF VITAMIN A. Acute symptoms may follow ingestion of very large amounts of vitamin A. These include drowsiness, sluggishness, severe headache, vomiting, and peeling of the skin about the mouth and elsewhere. This syndrome has been recognized by Eskimos as occurring after eating the livers of polar bears and arctic foxes, which are extremely rich in vitamin A.

Continued intake of excessive amounts, especially in children, produces roughening of the skin, irritability, coarsening and falling of the hair, anorexia, loss of weight, headache, vertigo, hyperesthesia, occasionally hepatomegaly, splenomegaly, hyperlipemia and hemorrhages (in some species), and certain rather characteristic skeletal changes. The hemorrhagic manifestations are associated with hypoprothrombinemia, and may be prevented by simultaneous administration of vitamin K (p. 161). This effect may be due to interference with bacterial synthesis of vitamin K in the intestine; it does not occur in chicks.

The skeletal changes are the result chiefly of acceleration of the normal bone growth sequences, with simultaneous increase in the processes of resorption (osteoclasis) and cortical bone deposition (hyperostosis). Young rats and guinea pigs fed large amounts of vitamin A may show a equivalent of a year's growth in a few weeks, the new bone being inadequately mineralized and fracturing easily. Weanling rats fail to grow, have difficulty in walking and pain in the extremities, with fractures and associated hemorrhages.

Infants may tolerate daily doses of about 200,000 I.U. of vitamin A for a year, but develop symptoms with 500,000 I.U. daily for even brief periods. On this basis the toxic daily dose for adults would be between 1,000,000 and 3,000,000 I.U.

CAROTENEMIA. Increase in the plasma carotenoid concentration above a level which varies in different individuals (carotenemia) results in a yellow or yellow-orange discoloration of the skin. Apparently the dermal epithelium is colored by carotene excreted by sebaceous glands. This condition may occur in normal subjects after protracted ingestion of large amounts of carotenoid-rich vegetables and is not uncommon in diabetics, for similar dietary reasons. In contrast with jaundice, the conjunctivae and urine are not discolored. The condition is harmless and disappears promptly when the carotene intake is reduced.

VITAMIN A REQUIREMENT. In subjects receiving diets virtually devoid of vitamin A and carotene, it has been found that the blood vitamin A concentration is maintained by daily doses of 2500 I.U. of vitamin A esters, and that clinical evidences of deficiency did not appear. It was concluded that adequate safety is provided by a daily intake (normal adults) of 2500 I.U. of preformed vitamin A or, in the form of carotene, as 4000 I.U. in oily solution, 7500 I.U. as green vegetables, or 12,000 I.U. as boiled sliced carrots.

It is generally considered that the adult requirement is 25–55 I.U./kg. body weight for preformed vitamin A and about twice these amounts, or more, if the sole source is carotene. Because of the fact that the requirement is increased by an increase in metabolic rate, children require relatively more than adults (Table 54, p. 624). The National Research Council recommendations for normal subjects receiving an otherwise adequate mixed diet are: adults, 5000 I.U.; during pregnancy (latter half), 6000 I.U.; during lactation, 8000 I.U.; children under 1 year, 1500 I.U., increasing to 5000 I.U. at adolescence.

The requirement is increased in hepatic disease, with the possible attendant impairment of storage of vitamin A and of its formation from carotene. An increased supply should also be provided in the presence of increased metabolic rates, as in fever and thyrotoxicosis. Faulty absorption may occur in chronic diarrhea, and specifically in sprue and celiac disease because of defective fat absorption.

VITAMIN C (ASCORBIC ACID)

In the early days of ocean navigation, scurvy was one of the most prevalent and dreaded diseases to which sailors were subject owing to the unavailability of fresh foods for long periods of time. It was also prevalent during wars and famines, and among inmates of prisons, asylums, and almshouses. The curative value of oranges, lemons, and certain herbs ("scurvy grass") was recognized as early as the sixteenth century, but it was not until the middle 1700's that the effectiveness of this method of control was widely publicized.

Upon introduction of the vitamin concept in the early 1900's, suspicion was aroused that scurvy might be a vitamin deficiency disease. Experimental production of this condition in guinea pigs laid the basis for systematic research in this direction, culminating (1927–1933) in the isolation of "hexuronic acid" from adrenal cortex, cabbage, and lemon juice; its identification as the antiscorbutic principle; demonstration of its chemical structure; and its synthesis.

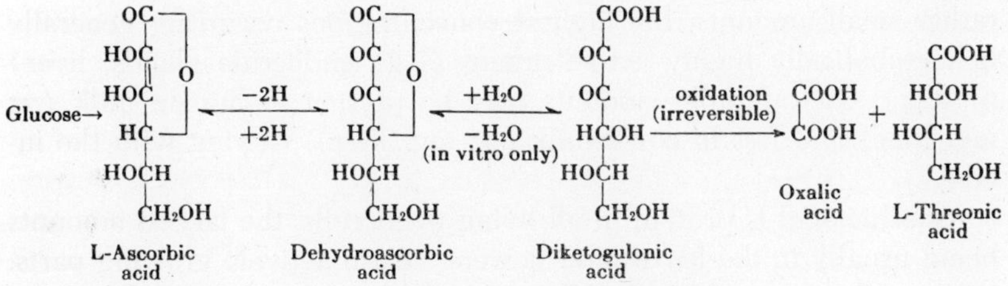

Fig. 36. *Metabolism of ascorbic acid*

CHEMISTRY. Ascorbic acid is an enediol-lactone of an acid with a configuration similar to that of the sugar, L-glucose (Fig. 36). It is a comparatively strong acid (e.g., stronger than acetic acid), owing to dissociation of the enolic hydrogen at C-3, not to the carboxyl group, which is tied up in lactone form. Inasmuch as it contains two asymmetric C-atoms (C-4 and C-5), two pairs of optically active isomers are possible. The D-forms are generally inactive as antiscorbutic agents. Naturally occurring vitamin C is L-ascorbic acid, the biological activity of which is considerably greater than that of several related substances that have been synthesized. It is readily soluble in water (1 gram in 3 ml.), and somewhat in ethyl alcohol (1 gram in 50 ml.), but is insoluble in most organic solvents.

Because of its acid nature, ascorbic acid readily forms metallic salts. Its most important and prominent chemical property is its strong reducing activity. This depends on the liberation of the H atoms from the enediol-hydroxyl groups (on C-2 and C-3), the ascorbic being oxidized to dehydroascorbic acid (Fig. 36) (e.g., by air, H_2O_2, $FeCl_3$, iodine, quinones, methylene blue, silver nitrate, ferricyanide, 2,6-dichlorophenol indophenol). This reaction is readily reversible by reducing agents, *in vitro* (e.g., by H_2S) and *in vivo* (e.g., by HS-compounds, such as glutathione). In alkaline, neutral, or slightly acid solutions (above pH 5), dehydroascorbic acid undergoes hydrolysis, with splitting of the lactone ring, to form diketogulonic acid, which is biologically inactive. This reaction is irreversible *in vivo,* but can be reversed *in vitro* by hydrogen iodide. Diketogulonic acid readily undergoes further irreversible oxidation to oxalic and D-threonic acids (Fig. 36).

Oxidative destruction of ascorbic acid is accelerated by increasing pH (increased tendency toward hydrolysis of the lactone ring), by light (especially in presence of flavins), and by silver and cupric ions (ascorbic acid oxidase is a copper-protein enzyme). These facts are of practical importance in relation to the vitamin C activity of processed foodstuffs (p. 143).

OCCURRENCE AND FOOD SOURCES. Ascorbic acid is distributed widely throughout the plant and animal kingdoms. Animal tissues contain rather small amounts, the highest concentrations occurring generally in metabolically highly active organs (e.g., endocrine glands, liver) (p. 144). Considerable amounts may be present in human milk (75 mg./liter) and less in cow's milk (22 mg./liter), varying with the intake.

Ascorbic acid is present in all living plant cells, the largest amounts being usually in the leaves and flowers, i.e., in actively growing parts. It cannot be demonstrated in dry seeds, but appears immediately upon germination. The pathway of its biosynthesis in plants and animals is not completely known. Glucose and glucuronic acid are precursors; light accelerates but is not essential for this process. In most tissues, ascorbic acid (reduced form) occurs in equilibrium with its oxidized form, dehydroascorbic acid, in varying proportions. As indicated elsewhere (p. 145), both of these forms are biologically active but the products of further degradation (hydrolysis, oxidation) are not. Consequently, provision must undoubtedly be made for maintaining a large proportion of the vitamin in the reduced form e.g., by such reducing agents as HS-compounds, present in all cells (p. 145).

Important dietary sources of ascorbic acid include leafy vegetables, green peas and beans, peppers, certain tubers (potatoes, turnips), tomatoes, and citrus and other fruits (oranges, lemons, limes, grapefruit, cantaloupe, strawberries, bananas). Because of its water-solubility and its susceptibility to irreversible oxidative degradation to inactive compounds, considerable amounts of ascorbic acid may be lost during cooking, processing, and storage procedures. Boiling and heating (in air) involves loss by extraction by the cooking water and oxidation. Activity, which diminishes rapidly during ordinary drying, wilting, chopping, crushing, or storage, may be preserved by (1) low-temperature storage before processing, (2) quick preheating (to destroy oxidative enzymes), and (3) exclusion of oxygen (by N or CO_2) during processing (e.g., canning, drying, freezing). The vitamin C in milk is usually destroyed by pasteurization or evaporation as usually conducted.

ASSAY. Ascorbic acid may be determined by bioassay or by chemical procedures. Although the former are the most specific and accurate, they have been largely replaced by the latter for practical reasons.

BIOASSAY. The guinea pig is the test animal of choice, because of its extreme sensitivity to dietary lack of vitamin C. (The albino rat is unsuitable because of its immunity to the development of scurvy.) The animals are given a vitamin C-free diet, on which they develop scurvy in two to three weeks. Various procedures determine the minimum amount of test material required to (1) protect against or (2) cure gross scorbutic manifestations (e.g., weight-loss, joint-tenderness, edema, hemorrhage, etc.), or (3) prevent characteristic scorbutic changes in dental structure (development of incisor odontoblasts).

One unit of vitamin C (I.U. or U.S.P. unit) is defined as equivalent to 0.05 mg. of pure ascorbic acid, i.e., 1 mg. of ascorbic acid = 20 units.

CHEMICAL METHODS. The procedures in common use are based on one or the other of two principles: (1) measurement of the rate or extent of reduction of certain oxidizing agents, e.g., methylene blue, 2,6-dichlorophenol indophenol; (2) measurement of the colored complex formed by coupling of dehydroascorbic acid with 2,4-dinitrophenylhydrazine and treatment with strong H_2SO_4.

The blue dye, 2,6-dichlorophenol indophenol, undergoes stoichiometric reduction to a colorless compound by ascorbic acid (reduced form). The amount of ascorbic acid is reflected in the rate or extent of this transformation, which may be measured by titration or in a photoelectric colorimeter. Although the reaction is not specific for ascorbic acid, other reducing substances likely to be present react much more slowly, so that, under appropriate conditions, this procedure is satisfactory for clinical purposes (blood and urine assay). Inasmuch as this procedure measures only the reduced form of ascorbic acid, determination of total vitamin C, which is more important, must be preceded by reduction of dehydroascorbic acid by treatment with H_2S.

The 2,4-dinitrophenylhydrazine method measures dehydroascorbic acid. Consequently, the ascorbic acid present in the sample is first oxidized by shaking with activated charcoal. The dehydroascorbic acid is then coupled with the reagent and treated with H_2SO_4, producing a red color which is measured in the photoelectric colorimeter. One of the disadvantages of this procedure is the fact that the reaction is given also by diketogulonic acid, an inactive oxidation product of ascorbic acid. This is particularly serious in determining the vitamin C content of foods but is not particularly important in assaying biological material (blood, urine).

ABSORPTION; DISTRIBUTION; CIRCULATION. Only man, other primates and guinea pigs, of the many species investigated, are unable to synthesize ascorbic acid, the entire human requirement for which must consequently be supplied by the diet. Ascorbic acid is absorbed readily from the small intestine, peritoneum, and subcutaneous tissues. It is widely distributed throughout the body, in local concentrations roughly paralleling the metabolic activity of the tissue, in the following descending order: pituitary, corpus luteum, adrenal cortex, thymus (young), liver, brain, gonads, spleen, thyroid, pancreas, salivary glands, lung, kidney, intestinal wall, heart, skeletal muscle, blood. Ascorbic acid is supplied to the fetus from the maternal circulation, passing the placental barrier readily. The concentration in umbilical cord blood is higher than in the maternal blood, suggesting that the placenta may be able to concentrate the vitamin.

There is no evidence that any particular organ or tissue serves as a storage reservoir. That the body does contain mobilizable reserve stores of ascorbic acid is indicated, however, by the fact that clinical manifestations of scurvy develop in man only after several months on an ascorbic acid-free diet.

Normal human blood plasma contains about 0.6 to 1.5 mg. ascorbic acid per 100 ml. Under adequate dietary conditions the concentration in the erythrocytes is one to two and one-half times and in the white blood cells and platelets ("white layer") twenty to forty times that in the plasma.

METABOLISM; EXCRETION. In the rat, it has been shown that the carbon chain of glucose is utilized for synthesis of ascorbic acid. No synthesis occurs in man, other primates, and the guinea pig.

The vitamin exists in the body largely in the reduced form (ascorbic acid), in reversible equilibrium with a relatively small amount of dehydroascorbic acid (oxidized form) (Fig. 36). Under conditions of normal dietary intake (75–100 mg.), about 50 to 75 per cent of ingested ascorbic acid undergoes metabolic conversion to inactive compounds. The remainder is excreted, as such, in the urine. It is also present in milk in active form. The main catabolic pathway is degradation to CO_2. The other demonstrated important metabolic end-product is oxalic acid, which is eliminated in the urine.

FUNCTIONS.   The fundamental role played by ascorbic acid in metabolic processes is not known. The fact that it is very sensitive to reversible oxidation (ascorbic acid$\rightleftharpoons$dehydroascorbic acid) suggests that it may be involved in cellular oxidation-reduction reactions, perhaps serving as a hydrogen-transport agent.

Inasmuch as the oxidized (dehydro-) form is irreversibly hydrated to the inactive diketoglulonic acid (Fig. 36), preservation of vitamin activity must involve some mechanism which maintains a large proportion of the vitamin in the reduced form (ascorbic acid). Such reducing agents as sulfhydryl compounds, including glutathione, cysteine and HS-proteins, have been suggested as possibly implicated in this connection. Reversible oxidation of ascorbic acid may be accomplished by a number of tissue catalysts, e.g., the cytochrome system, peroxidases, ascorbic acid oxidase (plants), polyphenol oxidases, hemochromogens, and adrenochrome. Evidence against the view that ascorbic acid functions as a major respiratory catalyst is the fact that the tissues of scorbutic animals do not show a decreased respiratory capacity and their O_2 consumption is not increased by addition of the vitamin.

Scorbutic guinea pigs and premature infants given a high-protein (or tyrosine or phenylalanine), ascorbic acid-deficient diet excrete p-hydroxyphenylpyruvic, and p-hydroxyphenyllactic acids in the urine. Administration of ascorbic acid corrects this condition. These compounds are intermediates in the catabolism of tyrosine (p. 551), and there is evidence that ascorbic acid may act as a coenzyme in the oxidation of p-hydroxyphenylpyruvic acid. It also apparently aids in the conversion of pteroylglutamic (folic) acid to the citrovorum factor (p. 204).

Ascorbic acid is essential for the normal regulation of the colloidal condition of intercellular substances, including the fibrils and collagen of connective tissue, osteoid tissue, dentin, and perhaps the intercellular "cement substance" of the capillaries. Many of the important clinical manifestations of vitamin C deficiency are directly dependent upon abnormal development and maintenance of these structures. The capillary defect in scurvy may be related to an inhibitory effect of ascorbic acid on the hyaluronidase-hyaluronic acid system (p. 19).

DEFICIENCY MANIFESTATIONS—SCURVY.   Guinea pigs, the standard species used for demonstrating ascorbic acid deficiency, exhibit characteristic histological abnormalities after about one week and symptoms in about two weeks on a vitamin C-free diet. The essential defect appears to be in the maintenance and formation of the intercellular ground substance, particularly the collagen bundles and fibrils of connective tissue, the osteoid matrix of the bones, and the dentin of the teeth. The earliest histological changes include alteration in osteoblasts and odontoblasts. The animals lose appetite and weight, their joints become swollen and tender (subperiosteal hemorrhage), and they assume the "scurvy" position, lying flat with the hindlegs extended. There may be enlargement of the costochondral junctions, hemorrhages in the gums, and loosening and fracture of the teeth.

Symptoms appear in man only after a much longer period of ascorbic acid privation (four to five months). They include: hyperkeratotic papules over the buttocks and calves (specificity?); petechial, subcutaneous, subperiosteal, and internal hemorrhages; pain on movement; swelling at ends of long bones and at costochondral junctions; hyperemia, swelling, sponginess, tenderness, retraction and bleeding of the gums, leading in severe scurvy to secondary infection and loosening and falling of the teeth; edema, pallor, anemia; delayed wound healing; defective formation of the teeth in children; roentgenographic signs of defective skeletal structure, most of which are not specific.

DETECTION OF DEFICIENCY IN MAN. Advanced scurvy is readily diagnosed, but is rarely seen. Detection of subclinical deficiency is difficult, as is demonstration of ascorbic acid deficiency as a cause of various clinical conditions. As in the case of vitamin deficiencies generally, prompt improvement following administration of ascorbic acid constitutes the most reliable evidence that deficiency in this substance had contributed to the development of the condition in question. Certain objective methods have been proposed for the demonstration of subclinical deficiency states. They include: (1) the concentration of ascorbic acid in the blood; (2) urinary excretion of ascorbic acid; (3) urinary excretion following administration of the vitamin (saturation test); (4) intradermal test for ascorbic acid; (5) capillary fragility test.

BLOOD ASCORBIC ACID. The plasma ascorbic acid concentration falls relatively promptly after removal of the vitamin from the diet, approaching zero in forty to eighty days. Usually, when the plasma values fall below 0.3 mg./100 ml. the concentration in the leukocytes and platelets begins to decrease, and when the former reaches 0.1 mg./100 ml. the latter may be assumed to be seriously reduced. As a rule, recognizable clinical manifestations of scurvy appear only after this degree of depletion has been reached. Consequently, decrease in ascorbic acid of the "white blood cell-platelet layer" or, less significantly, of whole blood, is a more reliable index of the scorbutic nature of clinical signs than is a fall in the plasma ascorbic acid concentration.

URINE ASCORBIC ACID. Urinary excretion of ascorbic acid decreases rather promptly following lowering of the intake and does not therefore reflect the nutritional status of the organism in this regard. Test procedures which embody the "tissue saturation" principle are perhaps more useful clinically. These saturation tests are based upon the principle that if the tissues contain an adequate amount of ascorbic acid, i.e., are "saturated" with the vitamin, a certain proportion of an administered test dose will be excreted in the urine. If the tissues are "undersaturated" they will retain an abnormally large proportion of the test dose, and a subnormal amount will be excreted in the urine. A number of different procedures and dosages have been employed, with rather equivocal results. The chief difficulty has been in the establishment of normal values because of the wide range of individual variation. Such saturation tests may be valuable under carefully controlled conditions.

INTRADERMAL TEST. This consists in the intradermal injection of 2,6-dichlorophenolindophenol and determination of the time required for decolorization (reduction) of this dye. Abnormally long persistence of the blue color in the cutaneous wheal is regarded as indicative of tissue subsaturation with ascorbic acid. This procedure is not very reliable.

CAPILLARY RESISTANCE (FRAGILITY) TEST. This is designed to disclose, by the application of mechanical stress, increased fragility of the capillary walls. This is generally ascribed to defective formation of the intercellular capillary cement substance, but increased activity of the hyaluronidase-hyaluronic acid system may be involved. A positive reaction may be obtained before the defect manifests itself spontaneously by petechial or other hemorrhages. The mechanical stress is applied in the form of either negative (cupping) or positive (tourniquet) pressures.

These procedures are of value in the diagnosis of ascorbic acid deficiency, but, unfortunately, capillary fragility may be increased in other conditions. They are useful chiefly as screening procedures, a normal (negative) response constituting evidence against serious ascorbic acid deficiency.

VITAMIN AND HORMONE INTERRELATIONSHIPS. In rats, vitamin A deficiency is accompanied by a sharp decrease in blood and tissue ascorbic acid, followed by the appearance of rather characteristic scorbutic manifestations (p. 145). The latter disappear after administration of ascorbic acid. The nature of this relationship is not clear; it has been suggested that loss of protection (i.e., by antioxidant action of vitamin A) against oxidative degradation of ascorbic acid may be involved.

Reference is made elsewhere (p. 145) to the possible role of ascorbic acid in the conversion of pteroylglutamic (folic) acid to the citrovorum factor (folinic acid). In this connection, severe deficiency in ascorbic acid in human infants and in monkeys may be accompanied by a megaloblastic type of anemia, relieved by the citrovorum factor or large amounts of folic acid.

The increase in size (and decrease in cholesterol) of the adrenal glands in scorbutic guinea pigs may be due in part to stress, but exceeds that produced by inanition due to other causes. Administration of adrenocorticotrophic hormone (ACTH) results in a prompt decrease in the relatively high concentration of ascorbic acid in the adrenal cortex of normal animals. This response is so striking that it is used as the basis for a sensitive method of bioassay of ACTH (p. 697). The urinary excretion of 11-oxygenated adrenal cortical hormones is increased in scorbutic guinea pigs, but excretion of 17-ketosteroids is decreased. The nature of the relationship between ascorbic acid and adrenal cortical hormones is not understood. The early suggestion that the vitamin is implicated in the synthesis of these hormones has not been substantiated. The decrease in adrenal ascorbic acid in response to administration of ACTH may merely reflect the increase in metabolic activity of the adrenal cells stimulated by ACTH.

EFFECTS OF EXCESS ASCORBIC ACID. Administration of large amounts of ascorbic acid are not known to produce deleterious effects in man. In rats, dehydroascorbic acid, in enormous doses (1.5 grams per kg.), produces permanent diabetes identical with that produced by alloxan (destruction of beta-cells of islands of Langerhans) (p. 432). This action is prevented by immediately antecedent intravenous injection of sulfhydryl compounds (cysteine; glutathione) as in the case of alloxan, which resembles dehydroascorbic acid in chemical structure.

ASCORBIC ACID REQUIREMENT. A daily intake of about 100 mg. is adequate to maintain the plasma ascorbic acid concentration at about 1 mg./100 ml. in normal adults. Official recommended minimal daily intakes are: children, 30 mg. (infants under one year) to 80 mg. (adolescence); adults, 75 mg.; pregnant women, 100 mg.; during lactation, 150 mg. The requirement is increased in the presence of infections, owing apparently to an increased rate of destruction of the vitamin. Increased urinary excretion, with depletion of the tissue reserves, has been seen after prolonged ether anesthesia.

VITAMINS D

The curative value of cod-liver oil in rickets (rachitis) was demonstrated in 1822, and the possible relation of absence of sunlight to the occurrence of this disease was suggested in 1890. However, the demonstration of the true nature of this condition necessarily had to await the development of the vitamin concept. The remedial action of cod-liver oil in rickets was first attributed to the presence of vitamin A, until it was shown that milk, which contains this vitamin, did not prevent rickets in infants. In 1920, this disorder was produced experimentally in rats, by special diets, and shortly thereafter (1922) the antirachitic component of cod-liver oil, later designated "fat-soluble vitamin D," was separated from vitamin A by destroying the latter by heating and oxidation.

In 1924 it was shown that antirachitic activity could be induced in certain foods by ultraviolet irradiation. It was soon demonstrated that this phenomenon occurred in the sterol fraction of the foodstuff, specifically in ergosterol, which has no antirachitic activity prior to irradiation. This discovery was followed, during the next fifteen years, by isolation of this vitamin in pure form, and by demonstration of its chemical structure and of the existence of other forms of vitamin D. The most important of these originates in animal species from 7-dehydrocholesterol, corresponding to that originating in plants from ergosterol.

CHEMISTRY. The inactive natural precursors of the D vitamins, the corresponding provitamins, are cyclopentanophenanthrene derivatives, classified as steroids (p. 35). At least ten such substances are known, differing only in their hydrocarbon side-chain; only two of these have been found to occur in nature, ergosterol (provitamin D_2) and 7-dehydrocholesterol (provitamin D_3), the former in plants, the latter in animals (Fig. 37). Other provitamins D are mainly of chemical rather than biological interest. They include 22-dihydroergosterol (D_2), epi-7-dehydrocholesterol, and 7-dehydrositosterol (D_5). All of the provitamins D possess certain essential structural characteristics: (1) —OH group at C-3; (2) two conjugated double bonds (at C-5, 6; C-7, 8); (3) a hydrocarbon chain at C-17. None has been completely synthesized, but 7-dehydrocholesterol has been prepared from cholesterol and 7-dehydrositosterol from sitosterol (soybean oil).

Each D vitamin has the same empirical formula as its corresponding provitamin, i.e., they are isomers. Transformation from the inactive to the active forms is accomplished physiologically by the ultraviolet rays present in sunlight, or artificially, by ultraviolet irradiation (275–300 mμ), and α, β, γ, and other similar types of radiation. The photochemical activation process results only in an intramolecular rearrangement, not an oxidation, with opening of ring B between C-9 and C-10, conversion of the methyl group (—CH_3) at C-10 to a methylene ($=CH_2$) group, and hydrogenation of C-9 (Fig. 37). Vitamin D activity requires these structural characteristics in addition to those specified above for the provitamins. The alcohol group (—OH at C-3) must be free or, if esterified, capable of being hydrolyzed in the organism. The only forms of importance in human nutrition are activated ergosterol (calciferol: vitamin D_2) and activated 7-dehydrocholesterol (vitamin D_3). Both of these have been isolated in pure form.

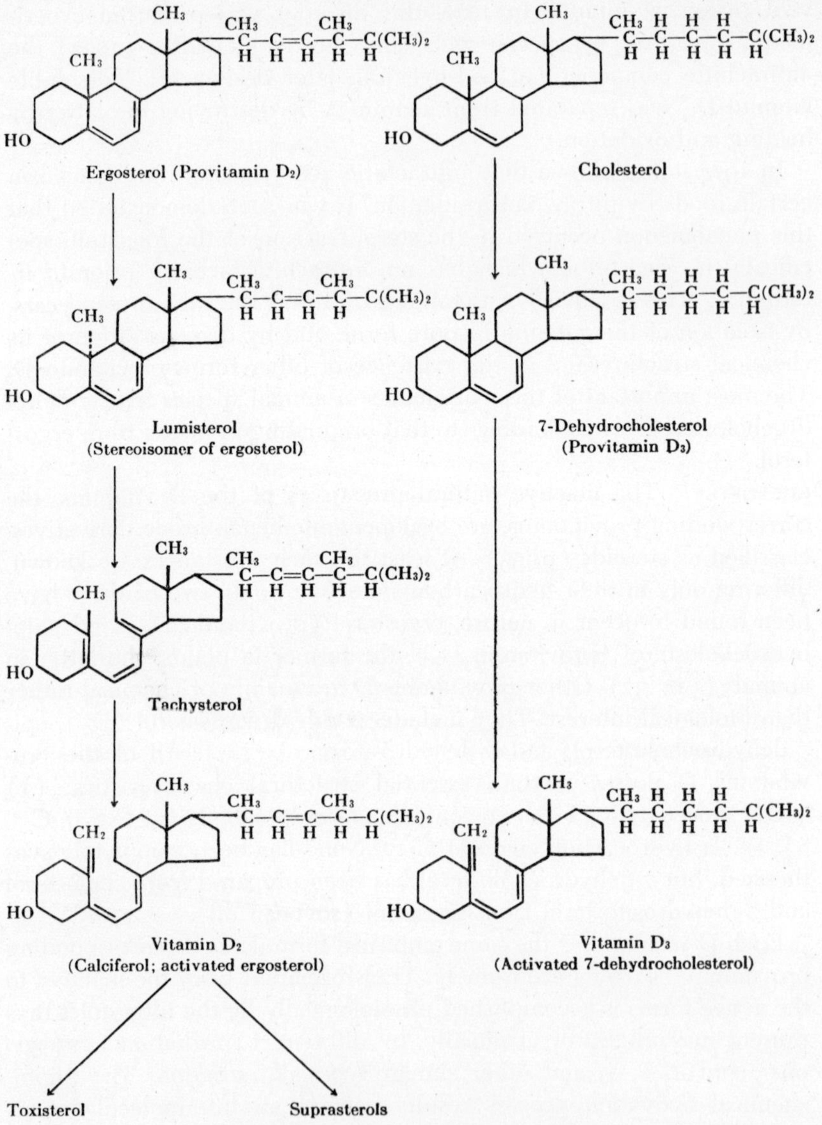

Fig. 37. *Pathways of synthesis of Vitamins* D_2 *and* D_3

The process of photochemical activation involves a series of irreversible reactions with the formation of compounds intermediate between the provitamin and the vitamin. Prolonged irradiation may result in decomposition of the latter. Thus, ergosterol, on irradiation, passes through the stages of "lumisterol$_2$" (a stereoisomer of ergosterol) and "tachysterol$_2$" (opening of ring B) before forming vitamin D_2 (calciferol). Overirradiation of the latter produces toxi-sterol$_2$ and suprasterol$_2$. The other provitamins D yield similar series of photochemical derivatives. The term "vitamin D_1," which is no longer used, was originally applied to what later proved to be a mixture of calciferol and lumisterol$_2$. Apart from the vitamins themselves, these substances have no significant antirachitic activity, with the exception of certain toxisterols, which have toxic, calcifying properties out of proportion to their antirachitic potency. A reduction product of tachysterol, dihydrotachysterol, is of considerable practical interest (Fig. 37). While only slightly antirachitic, it exerts a powerful hyper-calcemic effect on oral administration, its action resembling that of the parathyroid hormone. It is therefore used rather widely in the treatment of hypoparathyroidism (tetany) (p. 694), and is sometimes referred to as A.T. 10 (antitetany compound No. 10).

The vitamins D and their provitamins are soluble in fat solvents and practically insoluble in water. They are therefore included among the "fat-soluble vitamins." The several provitamins have rather characteristic and virtually identical ultraviolet absorption spectra, as have vitamins D_2 and D_3. Vitamin D, crystalline or in vegetable-oil solution, is quite stable if kept anaerobically in the dark. It is resistant to oxidation and to heat (in neutral solution). This relative stability as compared to vitamin A permitted its original identification as an entity separable from the latter in cod-liver oil (p. 131).

OCCURRENCE AND FOOD SOURCES. Ergosterol is widely distributed in plants. It makes up 90 to 100 per cent of the sterols of yeast, which is the most practical source of this provitamin. It has also been found in animal species (snail, earthworm, chicken egg, milk), perhaps of dietary origin. Ergosterol (non-activated) is of no dietary nutritional value to man since it cannot be absorbed from the intestine. It differs in this respect from calciferol (activated ergosterol), which is readily absorbed. 7-Dehydrocholesterol is the characteristic provitamin D in the higher animals and man. It is believed to be formed in the intestinal mucosa from cholesterol, passing to the skin, where it undergoes activation to vitamin D_3 by the action of solar ultraviolet rays.

Vitamin D is present in plants in relatively insignificant amounts. Although distributed widely in various animal species, largely as vitamin D_3, very few natural foods contain enough to provide an adequate amount of vitamin D in the diet. Of common foods, egg-yolks (chicken) are perhaps richest in this factor, averaging about 300 I.U./100 grams. Values for cow's milk range from 5 to 45 I.U./quart, for butter 8 to 60 I.U./100 grams, while human milk contains about 60 I.U./quart (colostrum about 150 I.U./quart). Other foods contain only negligible quantities, with the exception of fish, in which the highest concentrations of vitamin D occur, chiefly in the liver. There is an enormous species difference in this regard: e.g., cod-liver oil contains about 100 I.U./gram, halibut-liver oil about 1200 I.U./gram, blue-fin tuna-liver oil about 40,000 I.U./gram. For practical purposes, however, edible portions of fish, as is true of other foods, cannot be relied upon for an adequate daily supply of this vitamin.

It is advisable to supply the entire requirement (p. 156) as a dietary supplement, unless artificially enriched milk or bread is used. The vitamin D content of milk can be increased by (1) irradiation of the milk, (2) addition of calciferol or of fish-oil oil concentrates, and (3) feeding irradiated yeast to cows. The most useful preparations for dietary supplementation are the highly active fish-liver oil concentrates and solutions of calciferol in oil (viosterol).

ASSAY. Physical and chemical procedures are of limited value in the quantitative determination of vitamin D. These include spectrophotometry, chromatography, and the antimony trichloride reaction, which are of value, however, in distinguishing between various forms of vitamin D and their precursors.

Two types of bioassay procedure are in common use; these involve comparison of the amounts of test material and standard vitamin D preparations required (1) to induce healing of rickets in rats, or (2) to maintain normal bone ash levels in chicks. The former is employed chiefly in determining the potency of materials intended for human use; the latter is applied in assays of poultry feed, because of the relative insensitivity of fowl to vitamin D_2. In the rat, the process of healing (calcification) of the characteristically decalcified zone in the epiphyseal region of the tibia, radius, or ulna (zone of provisional calcification) is followed either histologically ("line test"; U.S.P. procedure) or roentgenographically.

One International unit (I.U.) or U.S.P. unit of vitamin D is defined as represented by the activity of 0.025 μg. of pure crystalline vitamin D_2 (calciferol), which, therefore, has an activity of 40,000 I.U./mg. rat assay). Vitamins D_2 and D_3 apparently are about equally active ($D_3 : D_2 = 1.5$) in man (and other mammals), although vitamin D_3 may have a potency in the chick as much as 100 times that of vitamin D_2. Distinction between the two is therefore important in poultry but not in human nutrition.

ABSORPTION STORAGE; EXCRETION. Athough plant sterols, including ergosterol, are not absorbed from the gastrointestinal tract, irradiated ergosterol is readily absorbed in the small intestine and also from the skin surface. Being fat-soluble, its absorption from the bowel is enhanced by factors which favor fat absorption, including an adequate quantity of bile salts.

Little is known about the intermediary metabolism of vitamin D. Adequate liver function is apparently necessary for optimal antirachitic activity. This may be related to the fact that the liver is the chief site of storage of vitamin D, although significant amounts are stored also in the skin and brain and small amounts in the lungs, spleen, and bones. Administered vitamin D is retained in the body, especially in the liver, with remarkable tenacity, being released very gradually. A small dose exerts an influence for several weeks, a large dose for much longer periods, undergoing very little destruction or excretion under normal conditions. A small amount may be excreted in the bile, but is apparently largely reabsorbed in the intestine. None is eliminated in the urine. The vitamin D content of milk reflects the intake; e.g., ingestion of a single large dose (600,000 I.U.) increased the concentration in the milk (human) from about 10 I.U./liter to 1000 I.U./liter in one day, the level being still elevated (100 I.U./liter) after one month.

FUNCTIONS. The over-all effect of vitamin D is to increase the availability and retention of calcium and phosphorus and their utilization for proper mineralization of the skeleton. Except in a few particulars, the exact manner in which these effects are produced is not known.

1. Vitamin D promotes absorption of calcium from the distal ileum, where absorption is otherwise relatively poor, but not from the upper ileum and jejunum, where calcium is absorbed more readily.

2. Intestinal absorption of phosphate is apparently increased. It is not certain whether this is dependent entirely on increased calcium absorption.

3. Vitamin D is necessary for proper growth, perhaps through its action in promoting endochondral growth of long bones and mineralization of the "zone of provisional calcification" (antirachitic action).

4. It promotes, in some way, mineralization of the skeleton, in both adult and growing organisms, perhaps by providing an adequately balanced supply of available calcium and phosphate in the body fluids.

5. It may aid in mobilizing inorganic phosphate from organic sources in the bones.

6. It lowers the pH in the colon, cecum, and distal ileum, the urinary pH increasing simultaneously. This may be, in part at least, secondary to increased absorption of calcium, decreasing the base of the intestinal contents.

7. It counteracts the inhibitory effect of calcium ions on the hydrolysis of phytate (inositol hexaphosphate). In adequate amounts and in the presence of a high calcium intake, it suppresses the anticalcifying and rachitogenic effect of phytate. The mechanism of action is unknown.

DEFICIENCY MANIFESTATION. RICKETS; OSTEOMALACIA. Vitamin D deficiency during the period of skeletal growth results in rickets (rachitis), with a characteristic defect in endochondral bone growth and mineralization of the "zone of provisional calcification" of long bones (junction of epiphysis and diaphysis) and corresponding areas of flat bones. This lesion cannot occur in fully grown bones, the characteristic skeletal manifestation of deficiency in adults being a type of defective mineralization of osteoid tissue termed "osteomalacia."

Under normal conditions, the narrow plate of epiphyseal cartilage, containing transverse rows of cartilage cells in orderly arrangement, is supported by bone on the epiphyseal side and by marrow capillaries on the diaphyseal side. Growth is accomplished by continual proliferation of the row of cartilage cells bordering the epiphysis and simultaneous degeneration of those bordering the diaphysis, the degenerating cells being absorbed and invaded by capillaries and osteoblasts, which accomplish mineralization of the newly formed osteoid tissue in a narrow, dense, even, transverse line (zone of provisional calcification). In vitamin D deficiency these cells continue to proliferate but do not undergo orderly degeneration. Consequently, capillaries cannot enter this zone in a regular fashion and mineralization is scanty and uneven. The cartilaginous area enlarges unevenly and imperfectly mineralized osteoid tissue and chondro-osteoid trabeculae are formed irregularly. Similar changes occur in all developing bones (defective mineralization of osteoid tissue), as in the cancellous portions of long bones, along the lacunae in the cortex, and in the tables of the skull. In adult, non-growing bones, mineralization of osteoid tissue throughout the skeleton may be impaired. The roentgenographic picture of these lesions is rather characteristic.

The phenomena attending bone growth in vitamin D deficiency result in enlargements at the ends of long bones, which, being abnormally pliable, are rather readily bent by the forces of muscle-pull and weight-bearing, with consequent deformities. The cranial sutures are widened and the fontanelles remain open; other cranial deformities develop as a result of external and internal pressure. Other characteristic deformities include enlargement of the costochondral junctions ("rachitic rosary"), "chicken breast," lateral sternal depressions, kyphosis, bowlegs and other distortions of the legs, pelvic deformities, and "potbelly."

In the rat, the rachitogenic effect of D hypovitaminosis is influenced considerably by the quantities and proportions of calcium and phosphorus in the diet. At any given level of vitamin D deficiency the development of rickets is facilitated by lowering of the intakes of these elements and by increase in the dietary Ca:P ratio above 2:1 (ratio in milk, 1.3:1). The latter effect is apparently related to the fact that, on low phosphorus intakes, large amounts of calcium prevent adequate phosphorus absorption. A similar rachitogenic effect may be produced in the rat by administration of excessive amounts of other cations which form insoluble, and therefore poorly absorbable, phosphates, e.g., beryllium, aluminum, lead, iron, magnesium, strontium.

There can be little question but that vitamin D deficiency alone is responsible for the production of rickets in children. However, there is no precise information as to whether the other dietary features indicated above as influencing the development of this condition in the rat are also operative in man. Clinical experience suggests that factors which promote absorption of calcium or phosphorus from the intestine exert a beneficial influence in rickets, e.g., increased acidity of the intestinal contents (p. 610), and absence of excessive amounts of phytic acid (p. 611).

METABOLIC MANIFESTATIONS OF DEFICIENCY. Vitamin D deficiency results in decreased net retention of calcium and inorganic phosphate in the organism. The mineral content of the bones is diminished, the water and organic matter being correspondingly increased. The bones have a lower calcium, phosphate, and carbonate content and a higher magnesium content. Urinary excretion of calcium and phosphate falls and fecal excretion increases. The serum inorganic phosphate concentration usually falls, whereas the serum calcium usually remains within normal limits for some time; in advanced deficiency it, too, decreases, often to markedly hypocalcemic levels (infantile tetany). The serum alkaline phosphatase activity increases, usually in proportion to the severity of the skeletal defect.

The sequence of events is believed to be as follows:

1. There is decreased intestinal absorption of calcium, resulting in tendency toward decrease in serum calcium and decrease in urine calcium.

2. As soon as the serum calcium tends to fall the parathyroids are stimulated to increased activity (also hyperplasia), maintaining the serum calcium level, now at the expense of the skeleton (p. 695).

3. Increased parathyroid activity results in increased urinary excretion of inorganic phosphate. This may be due also to a direct effect of vitamin D deficiency on renal tubular absorption of phosphate.

4. Increase in fecal phosphate may result, in part at least, from diminished absorption due to the excess of unabsorbed calcium in the bowel (unfavorable Ca:PO$_4$ ratio).

5. As deficiency progresses, the available mobilizable mineral reserves of the skeleton may become depleted to the extent that the serum calcium level cannot be supported adequately, despite the increased parathyroid activity. Hypocalcemia then develops and, if of sufficient degree, is manifested clinically by neuromuscular hyperexcitability (infantile or osteomalacic tetany).

6. Decreased mineralization of the bones, both generalized and, in

growing long bones, also in the zone of provisional calcification, results in softening and deformities. This strain constitutes a stimulus to proliferation of osteoblasts, which form alkaline phosphatase. The local increase in this enzyme is reflected in increased alkaline phosphatase activity in the blood.

All of the above manifestations are reversed promptly after administration of adequate amounts of vitamin D, calcium, and phosphorus. The increased alkaline phosphatase activity is the last abnormality to disappear.

DEMONSTRATION OF VITAMIN D DEFICIENCY. This depends on the presence of (1) suggestive clinical manifestations, (2) characteristic roentgenographic abnormalities, and (3) metabolic aberrations. The most important of the latter are: (1) hypophosphatemia; (2) increased serum alkaline phosphatase activity; (3) normal or decreased serum calcium; (4) decreased urinary and increased fecal excretion of calcium and phosphate. Prompt response to specific therapy, except in cases of so-called "vitamin D-resistant rickets," is of great diagnostic importance.

EFFECTS OF EXCESS VITAMIN D. Vitamin D is well tolerated in doses many times the normal requirement. However, seriously deleterious effects may be produced by extremely large amounts (500–1000 times the normal requirement). The early symptoms are due chiefly perhaps to the induced hypercalcemia (increased intestinal absorption of calcium and possibly increased skeletal mobilization). These include anorexia, thirst, lassitude, constipation, and polyuria, followed later by nausea, vomiting and diarrhea. Hyperphosphatemia may occur.

Increased urinary excretion of calcium and phosphate may lead to urinary lithiasis and the hypercalcemia and hyperphosphatemia may lead to metastatic calcification. The kidneys, arteries, bronchi, pulmonary alveoli, muscles, and gastric mucosa are principally involved. Renal failure may develop, leading to death. In growing children there may be excessive mineralization of the zone of provisional calcification at the expense of the diaphysis, which undergoes demineralization (with extremely large doses).

REQUIREMENT. Exogenous vitamin D is required throughout the period of skeletal growth, i.e., to adult life. The following recommendations have been made (National Research Council): infants (under 1 year) 400–800 I.U. daily; children and adolescents (up to 20 years) 400 I.U. These recommendations presuppose adequate intakes of calcium and phosphorus (milk) and no excess of phytate-containing cereals (oatmeal) (p. 610). The requirement for adults is not known. It is generally believed that, with adequate exposure to sunlight, sufficient amounts of vitamin D are formed in the skin to provide for normal nutrition in this regard if the intake of calcium and phosphorus is satisfactory. Daily supplements of 400–800 I.U. should be provided during the last half of pregnancy and throughout the period of lactation.

VITAMINS E (TOCOPHEROLS)

The presence, in the non-saponifiable fraction of certain fats, of a nutritional essential other than vitamins A and D was demonstrated in 1922. In addition to its requirement for normal growth, male rats and chicks deprived of this factor became sterile; female rats and birds with this dietary deficiency failed to produce normal progeny. Inclusion of the missing principle in the diet prevented these conditions and its administration to females early in pregnancy resulted in normal gestation and normal fetal development. This factor was therefore designated "fat-soluble vitamin E," and the "antisterility" or "fertility" vitamin. It was subsequently found that a rather specific type of muscle dystrophy occurred in certain species rendered deficient in this factor. Subsequently, a group of compounds, designated "tocopherols" (*tokos* = childbirth; *phero* = to bear; *ol* = alcohol or phenol) were shown to possess vitamin E activity and were identified as the active principles in foodstuffs. They were also found to be potent antioxidants. Despite the similarity of several of the deficiency manifestations in experimental animals to conditions occurring in man, there is no evidence that vitamin E deficiency is a factor in the pathogenesis of the latter or that its administration is of therapeutic value.

CHEMISTRY. The vitamins E, or "tocopherols," may be regarded as possessing a hypothetical "tocol" nucleus (Fig. 38). Four naturally occurring tocopherols have been identified, designated α-, β-, γ-, and δ- tocopherols, respectively, differing from one another in the number and/or position of methyl groups on the chroman portion (ring) of the "tocol" nucleus (Fig. 38). The presence of the phenolic hydroxyl group permits the formation of esters. Both the free tocopherols and their esters are insoluble in water and soluble in fat solvents. The vitamins E are therefore designated "fat-soluble vitamins."

The tocopherols have characteristic absorption spectra in the ultraviolet and infrared, which are useful in their detection and determination. They are very susceptible to oxidation, which results in loss of their biological activity. In the absence of oxygen, they are quite resistant to heat (to 200° C.), even in the presence of H_2SO_4 or HCl (to 100° C.). They are fairly stable to visible light but are readily destroyed by ultraviolet light. In general, the esters are more stable than the free phenols.

Perhaps the most striking chemical property of the tocopherols is their antioxidant activity, which is due to the presence of the phenolic hydroxyl group at C-6 in the ring (Fig. 38). Because of their extreme susceptibility to oxidation, they protect less susceptible compounds by breaking up the chain of oxidation reactions. This is the basis for their important commercial use as inhibitors of the oxidation of fats (also carotenes and vitamin A, p. 131), and perhaps for their physiological importance. This stabilizing effect on fats is greatly enhanced by the simultaneous presence of other substances, which act as synergists, such as ascorbic, pyruvic and phosphoric acids, phospholipids, and certain phenols (gallic and tannic acids); most of these are also antioxidants. δ-Tocopherol is the most potent of the four vitamins E, in antioxidant activity, followed in order by γ-, β-, and α-tocopherols. It should be noted that this is the reverse of the order of certain aspects of their biological vitamin E activity in certain species (e.g., antisterility action in the rat). Moreover, esterification abolishes their antioxidant power whereas practically all esters possess vitamin activity equal to or greater than that of the free alcohols.

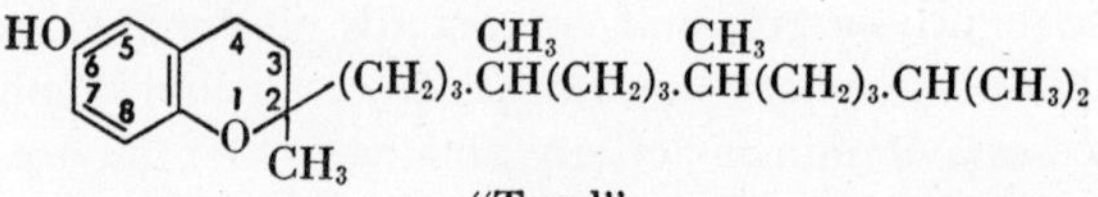

"Tocol"

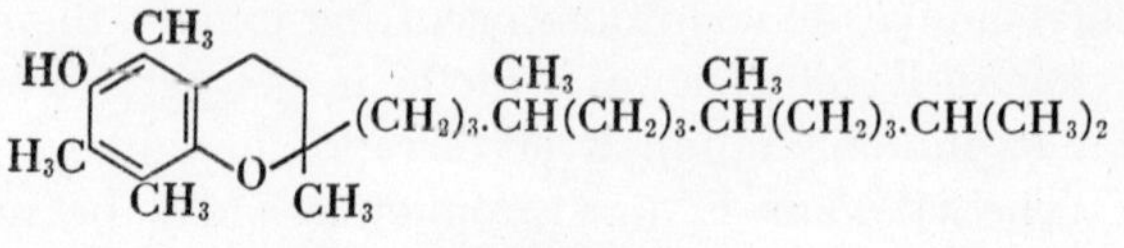

α-Tocopherol
(5,7,8-trimethyltocol)

β-Tocopherol
(5,8-dimethyltocol)

γ-Tocopherol
(7,8-dimethyltocol)

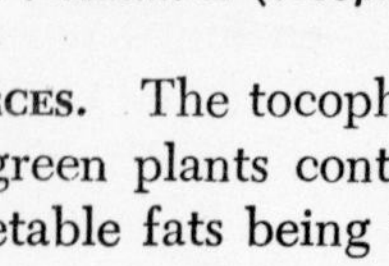

δ-Tocopherol
(8-methyltocol)

Fig. 38. Vitamins E (tocopherols)

OCCURRENCE AND FOOD SOURCES. The tocopherols occur in nature predominantly in plants. All green plants contain considerable amounts (e.g., lettuce, alfalfa), vegetable fats being the richest natural source (e.g., wheat-germ oil and other seed-germ oils). Only small amounts are present in olive and coconut oils. Animal tissues contain relatively small amounts, which vary considerably, however, especially in the liver, in relation to the dietary intake. The same is true of egg-yolk. Milk is generally poor in this factor, human milk containing more than cow's milk and colostrum more than later milk. The tocopherol content of animal fats is quite low, but may be raised somewhat by increasing the intake.

ASSAY. One International unit (I.U.) of vitamin E is defined as the specific activity of 1 mg. of synthetic racemic α-tocopherol acetate. When administered orally, this amount prevents fetal resorption in rats deprived of vitamin E. Several different "rat unit" designations are also employed, based on different bioassay procedures.

The tocopherols can also be determined spectroscopically (in pure systems) or colorimetrically. The chemical methods depend on the ready oxidizability of these substances and are therefore interfered with by reducing substances and also by carotenoids.

ABSORPTION; DISTRIBUTION; EXCRETION. Free tocopherols (and esters) are readily absorbed from the small intestine; bile acids are apparently necessary for absorption. They can be demonstrated in the blood in amounts which vary with the intake (e.g., in rats, 0.04 to 1.0 mg./100 ml. serum). The average level in man is 1.0 mg./100 ml. serum. They are present in practically all tissues, the highest concentrations being found in the pituitary and adrenals, the largest amounts usually in the pelt (rat), skeletal muscle, lungs, mammary tissue, placenta, liver, bowel, and body fat. However, the relatively small amounts in all tissues and in the feces suggest that the tocopherols may undergo rapid and extensive destruction in the gastrointestinal tract and tissues. After administration of large amounts, the extent of the increase in the liver is greatly in excess of that in other tissues. This suggests that this organ may serve as a site of temporary storage of tocopherols, supplying the needs of other tissues during limited periods of low intake. There is no evidence of metabolic interconversion of the several tocopherols. These substances are apparently transferred from the mother to the fetus, since the fetal tissues possess vitamin E activity.

Under ordinary dietary conditions, there is no significant excretion of tocopherols in urine or feces. When large excesses are fed, some appear in the feces, but only traces in the urine. Secretion in milk is referred to elsewhere (above).

FUNCTIONS; DEFICIENCY MANIFESTATIONS. The tocopherols apparently exercise a dual physiological role. (1) They exert a specific, vitamin-like function in certain species. (2) They exert a less specific function, probably based on their antioxidant activity or possibly by participating in oxidation-reduction reactions. There is no evidence that these two types of function are related directly. In fact, the order of activity of the four tocopherols in certain of their vitamin actions (e.g., "anti-sterility") is the reverse of that of their antioxidant potency (p. 158).

Despite the accumulation of considerable information regarding the structure and chemical and biochemical actions of the tocopherols, and the biological consequences of deficiency in these compounds, their physiological role in the animal organism is not known. At the present time, there is no satisfactory evidence that vitamin E is a nutritional requirement for man. Its demonstrated functions and deficiency manifestations in lower animal species will therefore be discussed rather briefly.

FUNCTIONS BASED ON ANTIOXIDANT ACTION. The antioxidant action of the tocopherols is probably responsible for its sparing action on vitamin A and carotene (p. 131), which are particularly sensitive to oxidative destruction in the presence of unsaturated fats. This protective effect of vitamin E, which is enhanced by the presence of other antioxidants, e.g., ascorbic acid, is probably exerted mainly in the intestinal tract, but also perhaps in the tissues. The increased *in vitro* O_2 uptake of the muscles and body fat of vitamin E deficient animals is reduced strikingly by pre-treatment with the vitamin or by its addition *in vitro*.

Highly unsaturated fatty acids, e.g., those in cod-liver oil, cause peroxidation and brown pigmentation of the adipose tissue of rats and chicks; this is prevented by administration of tocopherols. These fatty acids (in enameloblasts) are responsible also for the dental depigmentation of vitamin E deficient rats, normal pigmentation being restored by administration of tocopherols.

Oral administration of tocopherols (or cysteine) prevents the massive hepatic necrosis produced experimentally in rats by feeding certain British brands of yeast as the sole dietary source of protein. It has been suggested that this protection is dependent upon "detoxification" of an unidentified toxic factor produced in the bowel under these circumstances, perhaps of bacterial origin. Vitamin E also prevents the liver injury induced by feeding excessive amounts of cod-liver oil or diets containing artificially purified proteins.

The development of encephalomalacia (cerebellar disorder) and an "exudative diathesis" in chicks maintained on diets containing cod-liver oil and deficient in vitamin E is probably due to the toxic action of abnormal oxidation products of highly unsaturated fatty acids. These conditions are prevented by administration of tocopherols.

VITAMIN FUNCTIONS. The most prominent manifestations of vitamin E deficiency occur in certain rodent species (rat, rabbit, guinea pig) and fall into two general categories: (1) gonadal and reproductive functions; (2) muscle metabolism and structure.

REPRODUCTION. In male rats deprived of vitamin E the seminiferous epithelium (germ cells) undergoes irreversible degenerative changes at the onset of sexual maturity, leading to permanent sterility. Similar changes may occur in the guinea pig, but not in the mouse.

In the female rat, vitamin E deficiency does not affect the ovary, since the processes of estrus, ovulation, conception, and implantation of the fertilized ovum are normal. However, the fetus does not develop normally, dying *in utero* and undergoing resorption. This phenomenon is apparently due to placental abnormalities, chiefly of a vascular nature, which interfere with the nutrition of the fetus. Administration of vitamin E within the first ten days after conception results in normal gestation and fetal development. These effects of vitamin E deficiency in the female rat are, therefore, completely reversible.

There is no satisfactory evidence that vitamin E deficiency is a factor in the production of sterility or spontaneous abortion in man, or that tocopherol therapy exerts a favorable influence in these conditions.

MUSCLES. The most common manifestation of vitamin E deficiency in a number of species (e.g., rat, rabbit, hamster, young guinea pig, duckling) is a degenerative change in the skeletal muscles, leading to necrosis, edema, inflammation, and fibrosis (muscle dystrophy). This is accompanied by weakness or paralysis. Similar changes may occur in smooth muscle (uterus, heart) in certain species. In vitamin E deficient rabbits, creatine is lost from the muscles and increases in the liver, blood, and urine before the appearance of morphological damage. These rather characteristic muscle lesions, with paralysis, occur also in the young born to vitamin E deficient mothers. These metabolic and morphological abnormalities can be prevented or cured by administration of tocopherols.

The muscle lesions of experimental vitamin E deficiency resemble closely those of certain muscular dystrophies in man, the pathogenesis and etiology of which are unknown. However, there is no satisfactory evidence that vitamin E deficiency is a factor in these clinical conditions or that tocopherol therapy exerts a beneficial influence.

REQUIREMENT. Whereas vitamin E is a dietary essential for certain species (e.g., rat, rabbit, guinea pig, dog, chick), there is no conclusive evidence that deprivation of this factor results in any demonstrable abnormality in man. The human requirement, if any, is therefore not known. It has been estimated that the average daily diet should contain about 30 mg. of mixed natural tocopherols.

VITAMINS K

These are the most recently recognized members of the group of fat-soluble vitamins. A hemorrhagic syndrome was observed (1929) in chicks raised on an artificial diet low in lipids, which did not respond to administration of any of the then known vitamins. The hemorrhagic manifestations were associated with a blood-clotting defect (1934) which was shown to be due to deficiency in prothrombin (1935). The term "vitamin K" (Koagulations-Vitamin) was applied to the missing factor, which was later (1939) identified as a naphthoquinone. It was subsequently found that vitamin K activity was exhibited by a number of naturally occurring and synthetic compounds possessing a quinonoid ring structure.

The great practical importance of this vitamin arose out of the observation that certain common hemorrhagic disorders in man are dependent upon hypoprothrombinemia (e.g., in obstructive and hepatocellular jaundice; in the newborn; in certain intestinal disorders). Administration of vitamin K was found to be strikingly effective in controlling the hemorrhagic diathesis in many of these conditions.

CHEMISTRY. The several substances, natural and synthetic, with vitamin K (antihemorrhagic) activity are naphthoquinones (Fig. 39). It has been suggested that the relative effectiveness of these compounds in this connection may be related to their capacity for forming 2-methyl-1,4-naphthoquinone ("menadione") in the body; this is the most potent known substance exerting this effect.

Two naturally occurring vitamins K have been identified. Vitamin K_1, isolated originally from alfalfa, has a phytyl chain attached at position 3 of the menadione nucleus (2-methyl-3-phytyl-1,4-naphthoquinone). Vitamin K_2, isolated originally from putrid fish meal, has a longer, difarnesyl chain attached at position 3 (2-methyl-3-difarnesyl-1,4-naphthoquinone). Phthiocol, a constituent of tubercle bacilli possessing slight vitamin K activity, has an —OH substituent at the 3 position (2-methyl-3-hydroxy-1,4-naphthoquinone). Menadione (2-methyl-1,4-naphthoquinone), because of its high activity, is the most important of the synthetic vitamins K, a number of which have been prepared. Vitamin K_1 has also been synthesized.

Activity is apparently related to the presence of the methyl group at the 2 position in the quinonoid ring. Substitution of the 2-methyl group by other alkyl radicals or by hydrogen results in marked decrease in activity. Less striking alterations are produced by substitutions in the 3 position, activity being favored by branching of the side-chain.

The natural vitamins K are "fat-soluble vitamins," i.e., they are insoluble in water and are quite soluble in most fat solvents. The synthetic forms, lacking the long hydrocarbon chain, are somewhat soluble in water, but not sufficiently so for practical purposes. However, the hydroquinones of the vitamins K form esters (disulfate, diphosphate, diacetate) which are more soluble (water), less irritating, and more stable than the parent compounds, although less active. Certain

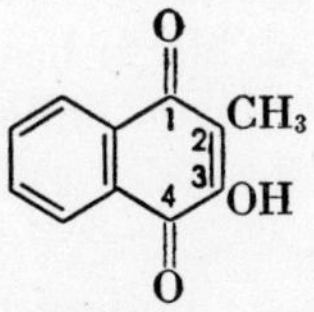

Phthiocol
(2-methyl-3-hydroxy-1,4-naphthoquinone)

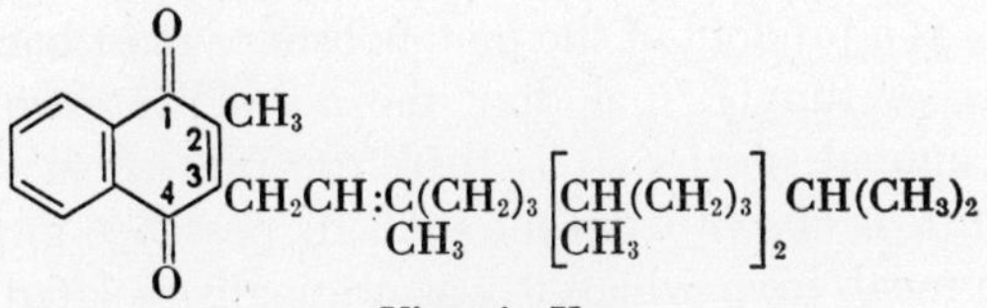

Vitamin K₁
(2-methyl-3-phytyl-1,4-naphthoquinone)

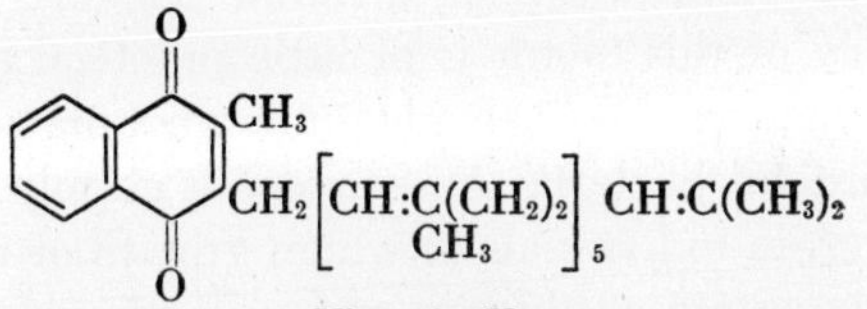

Vitamin K₂
(2-methyl-3-difarnesyl-1,4-naphthoquinone)

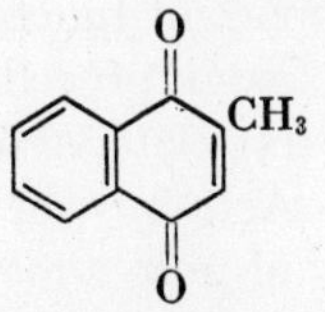

Menadione
(2-methyl-1,4-naphthoquinone)

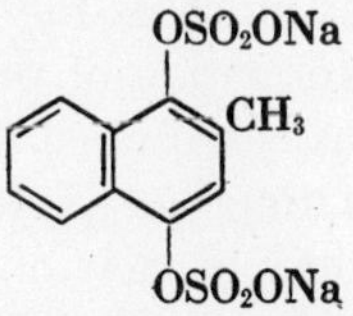

2-Methyl-1,4-naphthoquinone
disulfate, Na salt

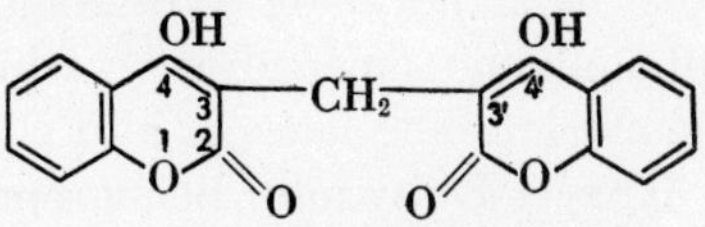

Dicumarol
3,3'-methylene-bis(4-hydroxycoumarin)

Fig. 39. Vitamins K and dicumarol, a vitamin K antagonist

of these are available and satisfactory for parenteral administration, e.g., 2-methyl-1,4-naphthohydroquinone-3-sodium sulfonate; 4-amino-2-methyl-1-naphthol hydrochloride.

The K vitamins are fairly stable to heat, but are readily destroyed by light (including ordinary Mazda bulbs), alkali, and alcohol. They have rather characteristic ultraviolet absorption patterns which are useful in their identification.

OCCURRENCE AND FOOD SOURCES.   Both of the natural vitamins K occur principally in the plant kingdom. Vitamin K_1 is present chiefly in green leafy tissues (e.g., alfalfa, spinach), but has also been found in cauliflower, cabbage, kale, tomatoes, soybeans, rice-bran, and oat-shoots.

Vitamin K_2 is a product of the metabolism of most bacteria (but not yeasts, molds, or fungi), including the normal intestinal bacteria of most higher animal species. It is therefore present in the feces even when vitamin K is absent from the diet. Its presence in large amounts in putrid fish meal, from which it was originally isolated, is due to the luxuriant growth of bacteria in this material. The generally small amounts of vitamin K in animal tissues and products (milk, egg-yolk) are of both dietary and intestinal bacterial origin.

Dietary supply of this factor is of little practical importance under ordinary circumstances, because adequate amounts are synthesized by the normal intestinal bacteria. An exogenous supply may become important, however, in individuals in whom growth of intestinal bacteria is inhibited (by certain antibiotics and sulfonamides) for therapeutic purposes (e.g., preliminary to surgical operations on the gastrointestinal tract).

ASSAY.   In as much as the only known important function of vitamin K is in the formation of prothrombin, the assay procedure employed originally was based upon the effect of the test material on the "plasma prothrombin time" of K-deficient chicks. Activity was expressed as "curative units." In view of the availability of pure 2-methyl-1,4-naphthoquinone, vitamin K activity is expressed most satisfactorily in relation to the biological effect of a given amount of this substance. There are no international or U.S.P. standards for vitamin K. A convenient standard of reference is the activity (on "prothrombin time") of 1 μg. of 2-methyl-1,4-naphthoquinone (menadione), which is about three times as active as vitamin K_1. The latter is also commonly used as a reference standard, a "Thayer-Doisy unit" being represented by the activity of 1 μg. of pure vitamin K_1.

ABSORPTION; METABOLISM; EXCRETION.   A normal diet contains an abundance of vitamin K, which is also formed by intestinal bacteria (chiefly Escherichia coli) in amounts adequate to meet normal requirements. Being fat-soluble, its absorption, which occurs predominantly in the jejunum, by way of the lymphatics, is influenced by factors which affect the absorption of lipids. Adequate amounts of bile salts must be present for optimal absorption, a fact of great importance in relation to the hemorrhagic manifestations of biliary obstruction. Absorption is diminished by large amounts of liquid petrolatum (p. 166).

Vitamin K has not been found consistently in the blood stream in significant amounts. During pregnancy, it apparently passes readily from the mother to the fetus. The capacity of the organism for storing this vitamin is extremely limited, at least in experimental animals, and evidence suggests that this is true also of man. Both vitamin K and prothrombin are utilized or metabolized rather rapidly, so that deficiency manifestations appear after a relatively brief period of deprivation (twenty-four to forty-eight hours in rats).

Vitamin K is apparently not excreted in the urine or bile. It has been found in the milk of women receiving adequate amounts of the vitamin. Rather large quantities may be present in the feces; whereas this may represent actual excretion by the intestinal mucosa, a more probable source is the intestinal bacterial flora.

Administration of excessive amounts of vitamin A results, in certain species, in hypoprothrombinemia and hemorrhagic manifestations which are prevented by simultaneous administration of vitamin K (p. 140). It is believed that this effect may be due to interference with bacterial synthesis of vitamin K in the intestine.

FUNCTION. Vitamin K is apparently essential for the formation of prothrombin by the hepatic polygonal cells. This is its only known function. The mechanism of its action is unknown. Prothrombin does not possess vitamin K activity, nor does the vitamin enter into the prothrombin molecule. It has been suggested that it acts as a coenzyme in the synthesis of prothrombin or as an oxidation-reduction catalyst in this process.

DEFICIENCY. Vitamin K deficiency can be induced by dietary restriction in several species (chick and other birds, rat, mouse, rabbit). In man, because of adequate synthesis of the vitamin by intestinal bacteria, deficiency rarely results from dietary inadequacy. The low plasma prothrombin which occurs consistently in the newborn, during the first few days of life, is attributed to vitamin K deficiency, due in part to inadequacy of the intestinal bacterial flora, and in part perhaps to inadequate bile flow and intestinal hypermotility, with consequent poor absorption.

Deficiency manifestations result usually from conditions which interfere with (1) absorption of the vitamin from the intestine, (2) its utilization in prothrombin formation, or (3) its production by intestinal bacteria. The latter is accomplished by drugs (certain sulfonamides and antibiotics) which inhibit growth of bacteria in the intestinal tract. Inadequate absorption may occur in association with an external bile fistula and biliary obstruction (absence of adequate amount of bile salts in intestine), chronic diarrhea or steatorrhea (ulcerative colitis, tuberculous enteritis, sprue, celiac disease), gastrocolic fistula, intestinal obstruction, etc. Deficient utilization may occur in association with hepatocellular damage, the liver cells being unable to synthesize prothrombin despite an adequate supply of vitamin K. This situation is not one of vitamin K deficiency but rather prothrombin deficiency, due to impaired liver function. Unless the mother is given vitamin K during the last few days of pregnancy or during labor, the plasma prothrombin of the newborn infant is low (first week of life). The characteristic manifestations of vitamin K deficiency are due to inadequate formation of plasma prothrombin, an essential component of the blood-clotting mechanism (p. 735). When the plasma prothrombin falls to 30–40 per cent of normal, clot formation is demonstrably delayed. When it falls below 20 per cent of normal, subcutaneous, intramuscular, and internal hemorrhage may occur as a result of otherwise insignificant trauma, and uncontrollable bleeding may follow minor abrasions and cuts. This was formerly a frequent cause of death following operations on patients with obstructive jaundice. In the absence of serious liver damage, the bleeding can now be effectively prevented or controlled by administration of vitamin K.

Vitamin K deficiency can be induced in rats by inclusion of dihydroxystearic acid in the diet. Although not bacteriostatic or bactericidal, this substance blocks intestinal synthesis of the vitamin, presumably by displacing a precursor from the enzyme system involved. A similar state of hypoprothrombinemia, correctable by administration of vitamin K, can be produced by certain structural analogues of the vitamin, e.g., bishydroxycoumarin (Dicumarol) and α-tocopherol quinone. These apparently are examples of biological antagonism (competition), discussed in detail elsewhere (p. 639).

REQUIREMENT. From what has been said previously, it is obvious that there is no dietary requirement (human) for vitamin K under physiological conditions. An exogenous supplement is required under the circumstances indicated as potential causes of vitamin K deficiency. Only small amounts are required, e.g., 1–2 mg. of menadione or its equivalent, daily.

"VITAMIN P"

The observation was made (1936) that the increased fragility and permeability of capillaries in scurvy (p. 145) are not corrected completely by administration of ascorbic acid. It has been claimed that these residual defects, and also similar capillary defects in other clinical states (e.g., certain types of purpura), respond favorably to certain vegetable pigments present in crude natural vitamin C preparations (e.g., from lemons, paprika, etc.). These substances, originally collectively designated "citrin" (isolated from lemon peel), are regarded by some as possessing vitamin activity, and the term "vitamin P" (P = Permeability) has been applied to them. The validity of this designation has been questioned, mainly on the grounds that the term, as commonly employed, includes a number of substances which are not all closely related chemically, and the actions of which may be pharmacological rather than physiological. Their vitamin status is still in doubt. Much of the existing uncertainty is due to lack of a generally acceptable assay procedure.

CHEMISTRY. When tested critically on the basis of their ability to reverse increased capillary fragility (e.g., in the guinea pig) due to dietary deficiency but not responsive to ascorbic acid, compounds (flavonoids) active in this respect have certain features in common (Fig. 40). All contain: (1) a benzenoid ring (A), fused to (2) a γ-pyrone ring (B), which may be partly or wholly reduced, and (3) a benzenoid ring (C) attached to the carbon atom adjacent to the pyrone ring oxygen. Reduction of the 2:3 double bond of flavones produces flavanones. Introduction of an OH group at C-3 produces flavonols. Activity has been demonstrated in certain but not in all compounds presenting either chromone, chroman, or coumarin structures (Fig. 40). The most active of these is 3,3',4'-trihydroxyflavone (sixteen times as active as rutin).

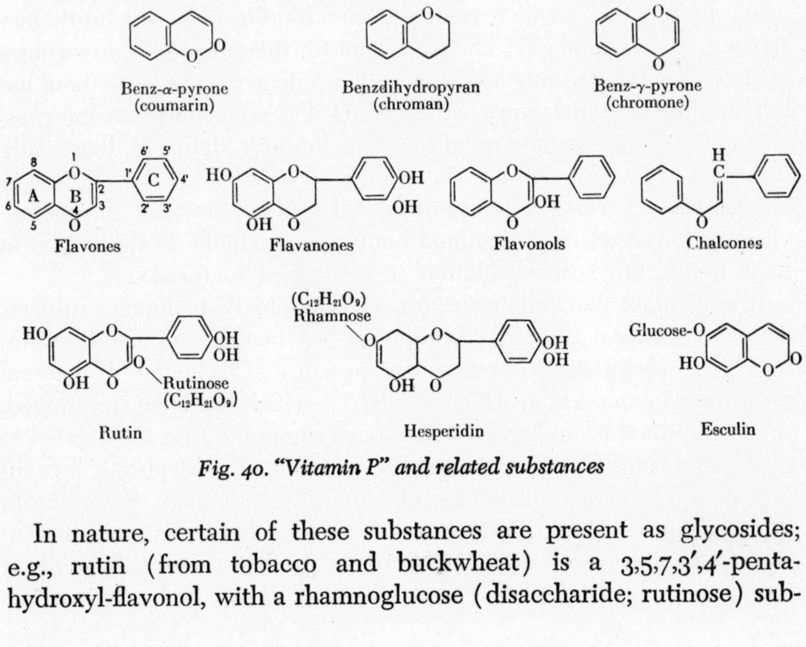

Fig. 40. *"Vitamin P" and related substances*

In nature, certain of these substances are present as glycosides; e.g., rutin (from tobacco and buckwheat) is a 3,5,7,3',4'-pentahydroxyl-flavonol, with a rhamnoglucose (disaccharide; rutinose) substituent on the C-3 hydroxyl group (Fig. 40). Hesperidin (from citrus fruits) is 5,7,3'-trihydroxy-4'-methoxy-flavonol-7-rutinoside (rhamnoglucoside). On the other hand, esculin (from chestnuts) contains only a portion (coumarin) of the flavone structure, being 6,7-dihydroxy-coumarin-6-glucoside. Eriodictyol is 5,7,3',4'-tetrahydro-flavonone. An outstanding chemical characteristic of compounds of this type is the tendency of ring B (pyrone) to split between the ring oxygen (position 1) and the 2-carbon position. This results in the formation of "chalcones," which have strong reducing power and which tend to revert to the original cyclic form. It has been suggested that this is the basis of their physiological activity.

OCCURRENCE. The distribution in nature of this group of plant pigments resembles that of ascorbic acid. However, there is apparently no consistent quantitative relationship between ascorbic acid content and "vitamin P" activity, nor between the latter and plant pigments in general. High activities have been reported for citrus fruits (rind and juice), rose hips, black currants, buckwheat, and tobacco. In general, fruits are more active than vegetable leaves or roots.

ASSAY. A number of color reactions have been used as a basis for chemical assay. These may afford a rough index of total flavonoid content. They cannot, however, be interpreted in terms of "vitamin P" activity for reasons indicated above; i.e., the fact that not all such substances possess this activity and that wide variations exist among the active compounds.

Bioassay procedures are based on measurement of a prophylactic or curative action on increased capillary fragility induced by dietary restriction of "vitamin P." The usual diet for this purpose is a scorbutogenic diet with adequate ascorbic acid supplements. None of these has proved entirely satisfactory, a fact which has contributed to the present state of uncertainty regarding the vitamin status of these substances.

METABOLISM. ACTIONS. REQUIREMENTS. Little is known of the metabolism of flavonoids in the animal body, owing chiefly to difficulties in their quantitative determination in biological material.

It is claimed that administration of "vitamin P" to human subjects and experimental animals is followed by increase in capillary resistance to elevation of intracapillary pressure or reduction of external pressure. The manner in which this effect, which has been questioned, is accomplished is not known. It has been suggested that it is related to the ability of the flavonoids to inhibit oxidation of epinephrine, a property shared by other substances, including ascorbic acid. According to this concept, epinephrine is the substance actually causing the increased capillary resistance. Data are contradictory on this point. It has been proposed also that chalcones may act as hydrogen carriers (prosthetic groups) in enzyme systems involved in cellular oxidations. Data obtained in this connection in *in vitro* studies cannot be assumed to reflect necessarily a similar role *in vivo,* inasmuch as other reversibly oxidizable compounds produce the same effect (e.g., ascorbic acid, glutathione).

It is difficult to demonstrate unequivocally a state of "vitamin P" deficiency in man or in experimental animals. Claims to this effect have been presented, but have been seriously questioned. Similarly, there have been reports of the beneficial therapeutic effects of this group of substances on the abnormal capillary fragility (petechial hemorrhages) in purpura, essential hypertension, radiation injury, and scurvy (beyond that accomplished by ascorbic acid). It is believed by many that if these effects actually are produced they should be regarded as evidence of a pharmacological rather than a physiological action of these agents.

Obviously, in view of the present state of uncertainty regarding its nutritional essentiality, no statement can be made concerning the dietary requirement for "vitamin P."

GUINEA PIG ANTISTIFFNESS FACTOR

Guinea pigs maintained on certain synthetic diets develop stiffness of the joints, with deposition of calcium in various muscles (skeletal, heart, gastrointestinal), the kidneys and the liver, and a peculiar type of arteriosclerosis and deafness (calcification of auditory apparatus). These phenomena are prevented by supplementing the diet with concentrates of raw (but not of pasteurized) cream or of sugar-cane juice. The active factor has been identified, tentatively, as stigmasterol.

VITAMINS B (VITAMIN B COMPLEX)

In the early period of vitamin investigations, the term "water-soluble vitamin B" was applied to the factor, present in rice polishings, bean extracts, yeast and liver, deficiency in which results in beriberi. At that time (before 1920), two other vitamins were recognized, "fat-soluble A" and "water-soluble C," and shortly thereafter another, "fat-soluble D," was identified as distinct from vitamin A. The multiple nature of "vitamin B" soon became obvious, and the numerical designations, B_1, B_2, etc., were applied to the various components of the "vitamin B complex." As soon as their chemical nature or structures were established, they were given more descriptive names, but the numerical designation is still applied to components of undetermined constitution, e.g., vitamin B_{13}.

As information accumulated regarding the occurrence and functions of these substances, it became increasingly evident that, in contrast to other known vitamins (e.g., A, C, D), they are nutritional essentials for all forms of life, from the lowly yeasts, molds and bacteria to man. It has been shown that several are essential components (coenzymes) of fundamentally important intracellular enzyme systems (e.g., thiamine, riboflavin, niacin, pantothenic acid, pyridoxine). The same may prove to be true of other B vitamins. This concept has been emphasized by Williams, who regards them as essential parts of the metabolic machinery of all cells, their strictly nutritional function being of secondary importance. He includes among the B vitamins those organic substances which are present in all living cells, act catalytically, and function nutritionally for at least some of the higher animals. Some of these indispensable factors may be synthesized by man and are therefore not dietary essentials.

Although whether a substance is or is not regarded as a B vitamin is of little consequence, it is desirable that some uniformity be maintained in this connection, if only for purely academic purposes. The following are generally accepted as B vitamins: (1) thiamine; (2) riboflavin; (3) niacin and niacinamide; (4) pantothenic acid; (5) pyridoxine, pyridoxal, pyridoxamine; (6) biotin; (7) the folic acid group (pteroylglutamic acid; "folinic acid," citrovorum factor); (8) vitamin B_{12} (cobalamin; antipernicious anemia [extrinsic] factor); (9) vitamin B_{13}, a growth factor for rats; (10) α-lipoic acid (pyruvate oxidation factor) (acetate factor). There is no agreement about the inclusion in this category of (a) inositol, (b) choline, and (c) p-aminobenzoic acid. Strepogenin and Lactobacillus bulgaricus factor are other principles, of undetermined constitution, which are important growth requirements for certain species and which are regarded by some as B vitamins. We shall concern ourselves here mainly with the significance of these substances in mammalian organisms, particularly in man.

THIAMINE

Beriberi, a disabling condition that was endemic for centuries in the Orient and Pacific islands, was the first disorder to receive the designation of a "deficiency disease." Eijkman (1897) showed that an analogous condition could be produced in hens by feeding polished rice, and could be cured or prevented by adding rice polishings (pericarp and germ) to the diet. It was shortly found that extracts of rice polishings (or of beans) cured beriberi in human subjects and this disease was therefore identified with deficiency in some factor removed from the rice grains in the process of milling. Thirty years later (1926) the factor, thiamine, was isolated from rice polishings, and about ten years thereafter its chemical structure was established and its total synthesis accomplished.

CHEMISTRY. Free thiamine is a basic substance containing a pyrimidine and a thiazole ring. It is generally prepared as a chloride-hydrochloride (Fig. 41), soluble in water (1 gram/1 ml.) and 95 per cent ethanol (1 gram/100 ml.) but not in fat solvents. In this form it is acid in aqueous solution owing to dissociation of the HCl; it is rather resistant to heat (boiling or autoclaving) in solutions below pH 3.5, but loses activity above pH 5.5 (hydrolysis). The relative heat stability of thiamine in foods, under ordinary conditions of preparation, may be due to the fact that much of it is in combined form. However, its high solubility may result in considerable loss in the cooking water. The thiamine content of vegetables is well preserved by freezing and by storage below 0° C. It exhibits absorption bands in the ultraviolet spectrum, varying with the pH, owing probably to its pyrimidine component.

By virtue of its basic characters, it forms a number of salts and esters which possess equal vitamin activity on a molar basis. The most important ester is the pyrophosphate (reacting with the alcoholic –OH on the thiazole ring) (Fig. 41), which serves as the prosthetic group (co-carboxylase) for metabolic reactions involving decarboxylation of certain α-keto-acids (pp. 397–400).

Thiamine and its pyrophosphate undergo both oxidation and reduction. It has been postulated that, under physiological conditions, thiamine exists in reversible equilibrium with an oxidized form, a disulfide (Fig. 41). This has not been demonstrated in enzyme systems. Treatment *in vitro* with mild oxidizing reagents (e.g., potassium ferricyanide) results in the formation of thiochrome (Fig. 41). This reaction forms the basis of one of the methods for quantitative determination of thiamine. Reduction (e.g., by hydrosulfite) results in irreversible loss of vitamin activity.

BIOSYNTHESIS. Thiamine is a nutritional requirement for all plants and animal species. It is synthesized by all higher plants, but to only a limited extent in the dark, and by many bacteria, yeasts, and molds. There may be a certain degree of symbiosis in this connection between plants and soil microorganisms, particularly during the initial stages of growth of seedlings. It is apparently not synthesized in significant amounts in animal tissues. In general, the most important source of this vitamin for man and other animals is dietary. However, certain ruminants (sheep, cattle) may obtain their total requirement from intestinal bacterial synthesis; the extent of the contribution from this source in man is not known, but it is apparently not adequate. This may be due, in part at least, to the possibility that the bulk of this thiamine is within the bacteria as the pyrophosphate, and that neither dephosphorylation, which must precede absorption, nor absorption of free thiamine occurs to a significant extent in the human colon.

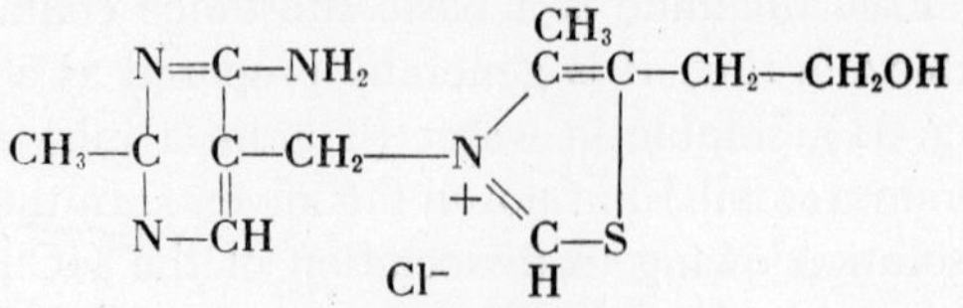

Thiamine (chloride)

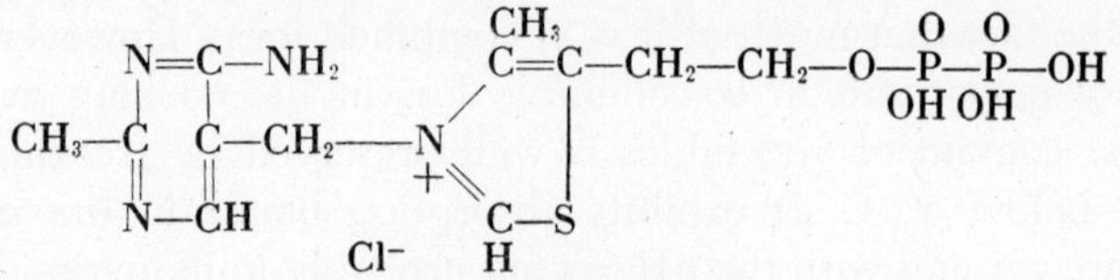

Thiamine pyrophosphate
(cocarboxylase)

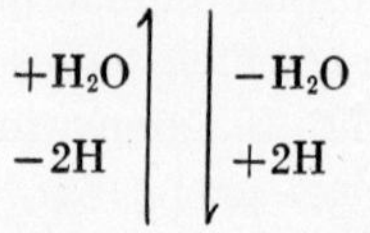

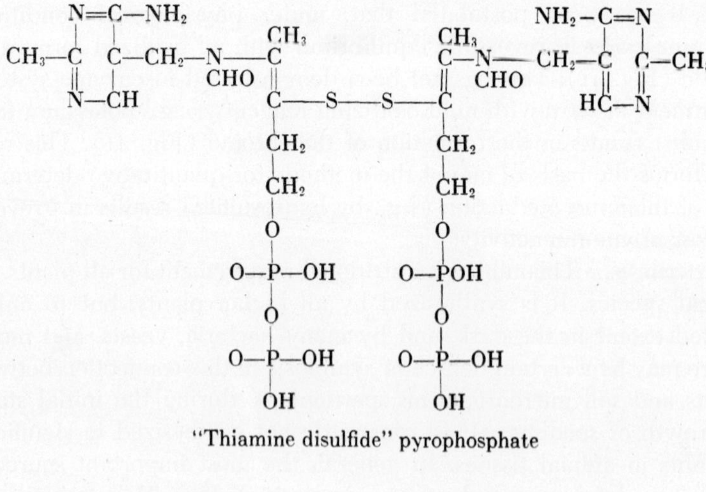

$+H_2O$ $-H_2O$

$-2H$ $+2H$

"Thiamine disulfide" pyrophosphate

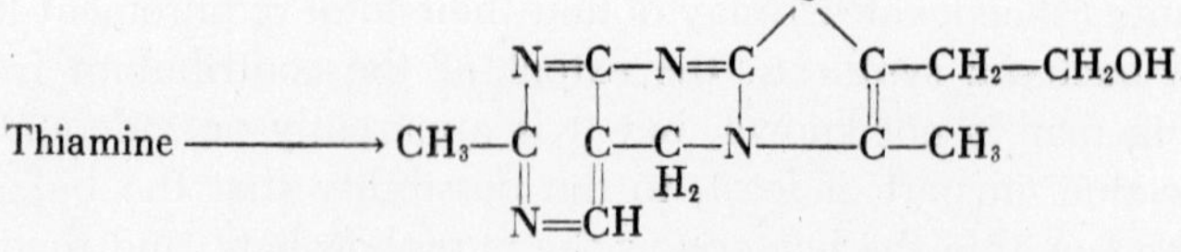

Thiamine ⟶

Thiochrome

Fig. 41. Thiamine and derivatives

Certain plants and microorganisms can synthesize thiamine if the pyrimidine component alone is supplied, others if the thiazole portion alone is supplied, while others require neither of these components in a preformed state. The final step in the synthesis involves coupling of the pyrimidine and thiazole moieties (methylene bridge). Cocarboxylase activity is exhibited by thiamine pyrophosphate, not by the free base. Cells of several tissues contain enzymes capable of phosphorylating thiamine in the presence of ATP, or if coupled with enzymatic reactions in which reactive phosphate compounds are formed (pp. 377–380).

METABOLISM OF THIAMINE. Free thiamine is absorbed readily from the intestine, but the pyrophosphate (cocarboxylase) is not. The bulk of the dietary vegetable thiamine is in the free state. It is very actively phosphorylated to cocarboxylase in the liver and, to a lesser extent, in other tissues (muscle, brain), including nucleated red blood cells.

It is present in the blood plasma and cerebrospinal fluid in the free state (about 1 μg./100 ml.). The largest portion of the blood thiamine, which ranges from 6 to 12 μg./100 ml., is in the blood cells as the pyrophosphate, in protein combination. Since free thiamine (base) is readily diffusible and the pyrophosphate is not, the plasma thiamine probably represents the transport form (inactive) of the vitamin, which undergoes phosphorylation (activation) upon entrance into tissue cells, including nucleated red blood cells in the bone marrow.

The capacity of the organism for storing thiamine in any form is apparently limited. It is present in both free and combined forms, mainly the latter, in the heart, liver, and kidneys, and, in lower concentration, in skeletal muscle and brain. Administration of thiamine may result in an increase in the tissues, within certain limits. However, on a thiamine-free diet, the tissue content is depleted within a short time, emphasizing the desirability of providing an adequate daily supply.

Cocarboxylase, formed within the cell, unites with protein apoenzymes to form carboxylases, one of which (pyruvic carboxylase) contains 0.46 per cent diphosphothiamine and 0.13 per cent magnesium. The pyrophosphate group is apparently involved in this union.

The pyrophosphate linkage in cocarboxylase is readily hydrolyzed by tissue phosphatases, free thiamine being liberated. However, when the coenzyme is combined with the apoenzyme it is quite resistant to such hydrolysis; thiamine is released from this combination through the action of proteolytic enzymes.

If normal amounts of thiamine are ingested (1–2 mg. daily), about 10 per cent is excreted in the urine. The remainder is apparently partly phosphorylated and utilized for carboxylase action and partly degraded to neutral sulfur compounds and inorganic sulfate. If large amounts are given, the excess is largely excreted in the urine. All of the urinary thiamine is in the free form. Normal subjects on an adequate intake excrete at least 50 μg. daily in the urine. That present in the feces is probably largely of bacterial origin (large intestine). It is secreted in the milk as a thiamine-protein complex and, in certain species (e.g., goat), as mono- and diphosphothiamine.

OCCURRENCE AND FOOD SOURCES. Thiamine is distributed widely throughout the plant kingdom, occurring in the highest concentrations usually in the seed, but also being present in the leaf, root, stem, and fruit. In cereal grains, it is concentrated in the outer germ and bran layers (e.g., rice polishings), which are often discarded during milling processes (e.g., of wheat flour and rice). The following are good dietary sources of this vitamin: peas, beans, whole cereal grains, bran, nuts, prunes, gooseberries, killed yeast. Whole-wheat bread is a good source; white bread is now commonly made from thiamine-enriched flour, and is therefore satisfactory from this standpoint.

Thiamine is present in most animal tissues. Of those which are commonly used as foods, ham and pork are particularly rich in this factor, beef, liver, and eggs also supplying considerable amounts. Milk, although containing comparatively low concentrations, is an important dietary source because of the large quantities consumed.

ASSAY. An International unit (I.U.) (also U.S.P. unit) of thiamine is equal to 3 μg. of thiamine hydrochloride.

Thiamine may be determined quantitatively by (1) chemical or (2) biological methods. Although certain of the latter are more sensitive, they have been largely replaced by the former, for practical reasons.

FLUOROMETRIC (THIOCHROME). The most widely employed method is based upon oxidation of thiamine to thiochrome, a yellowish pigment which exhibits a bluish fluorescence in the ultraviolet. This procedure can be used to measure thiamine in foods, urine, blood, and tissues, in concentrations as low as 0.05 μg./100 ml.

COLORIMETRIC. This procedure is based upon the formation of a red pigment when thiamine reacts with a diazotized aromatic amine (*p*-amino acetophenone) in an alkaline medium. It may be superior to the thiochrome method if a sufficiently high concentration of thiamine can be secured (2–3 μg./100 ml.).

YEAST FERMENTATION. This method, which can detect thiamine in amounts as small as 0.005–0.025 μg., is based upon its action in enhancing fermentation by certain yeasts. This is measured by the evolution of CO_2 (Warburg apparatus) under suitable test conditions.

MICROBIOLOGICAL GROWTH METHODS. These are based upon the action of thiamine in stimulating the growth of certain strains of yeasts. Under appropriate standardized conditions, amounts as small as 0.001 μg. (or less) can be demonstrated by this procedure.

CURATIVE TEST. In the U.S.P. bioassay procedure, rats are maintained on a thiamine-free diet until they exhibit signs of acute polyneuritis. Groups are then given a standard dose of thiamine adequate to cause disappearance of symptoms. They are then allowed to regress to their previous state (polyneuritis), when they are given the test material. The therapeutic effectiveness of the latter is compared with that of the standard dose of thiamine (duration of symptomatic relief).

FUNCTIONS. Thiamine pyrophosphate (diphosphothiamine; DPT), the active form of the vitamin, is the cofactor (coenzyme) in reactions involving decarboxylation of the α-keto acids, pyruvic and α-ketoglutaric acids, reactions which result in rupture of the bond between the keto carbon atom and the adjacent carboxyl group. The holoenzymes catalyzing these reactions are termed "carboxylase" and the coenzyme (DPT) "cocarboxylase." It is not involved in decarboxylation of carboxyl groups beta to the keto group. It has been suggested that biotin may be associated with the latter type of reaction (β-decarboxylation) (p. 407).

The metabolic importance of these reactions in the animal organism is reflected in the fact that pyruvic acid occupies a position at the junction between anaerobic and aerobic metabolism of carbohydrate. The several processes in plant and animal tissues which are known to require thiamine pyrophosphate as a coenzyme fall into two categories: (1) simple decarboxylation of pyruvic and α-ketoglutaric acids; (2) oxidative decarboxylation of these substances. In animal tissues, which operate largely under aerobic conditions, oxidative decarboxylation is of primary physiological importance. In the complete sequence of reactions involved in the metabolic utilization of pyruvic and α-ketoglutaric acids in mammalian organisms, the primary reaction catalyzed by DPT-containing enzymes is linked to others involving other vitamin coenzymes (DPN, pantothenic acid) (p. 361), among other factors. The nature of these reactions is considered elsewhere (p. 361). There is evidence that, in the oxidative decarboxylation of pyruvic or α-ketoglutaric acids, thiamine pyrophosphate functions in combination with α-lipoic acid (p. 215). These two factors are joined by an amide bond to form "lipothiamide pyrophosphate," the synthesis being catalyzed by "lipoic acid conjugase."

DEFICIENCY MANIFESTATIONS. In its severe form, formerly endemic in the Orient, and occurring elsewhere during periods of severe malnutrition (post-war), thiamine deficiency results in the condition known as beriberi. This is characterized by cardiovascular and neurological manifestations, and, in some cases, edema ("wet" beriberi).

Cardiovascular manifestations include: palpitation, dyspnea, cardiac hypertrophy and dilatation, progressing to congestive heart failure (hepatic and pulmonary congestion, peripheral edema).

Neurological manifestations are predominantly those of an ascending, symmetrical, peripheral polyneuritis, accompanied, at times, by an acute hemorrhagic polioencephalitis (Wernicke's encephalopathy). They include: tenderness of calf muscles; hyperesthesia of feet or finger tips, followed by painful cramps in muscles of extremities; loss of vibratory sense in toes and over tibia; decreased or absent patellar and achilles tendon reflexes; later, paralysis, with foot drop; muscle atrophy; retrobulbar neuritis; myelin degeneration in peripheral nerves; occasionally Wernicke's disease (hemorrhage into third and fourth ventricles, with lethargy or excitability, nystagmus or ophthalmoplegia).

Edema may occur ("wet" beriberi), due probably in part to congestive heart failure and in part to protein undernutrition (low plasma albumin). Anorexia is an early symptom. There may be gastric atony, with diminished gastric motility and nausea. Fever and vomiting occur in advanced stages.

The fully developed clinical picture of beriberi is seldom encountered in the western world except, at times, in famine areas. Manifestations of thiamine deficiency are usually mild, with anorexia, nausea, cardiovascular symptoms (palpitation, dyspnea, cardiac enlargement), and evidence of early peripheral neuritis (e.g., tenderness of calf muscles, hyperesthesia, diminished reflexes).

In most animals, thiamine deficiency produces symptoms resembling these of beriberi, described above, with certain important additional features. In the rat, after about two weeks on a thiamine-free diet, the heart rate decreases from about 500 beats to about 250–300 beats per minute (bradycardia). This phenomenon has been used as a basis for a bioassay procedure for thiamine. Pigeons develop a rather characteristic, rigid, retraction of the head (opisthotonus), which sign has also been employed in bioassay procedures. A type of spastic paralysis (Chastek paralysis) has been observed in foxes on a raw-fish diet, characterized by extreme, boardlike rigidity, with retraction of the head. This has been attributed to the presence of a thiamine-splitting enzyme (thiaminase) in the raw fish.

The important biochemical features of thiamine deficiency include: decreased levels of thiamine and cocarboxylase in the blood and urine; increased concentrations of pyruvic and lactic acids in the blood; decreased uptake of oxygen by thiamine-deficient brain tissue (in glucose or pyruvate), reversible, *in vitro,* by addition of thiamine ("catatorulin effect"). The decreased oxygen uptake is probably due to blocks in the conversion of pyruvate to acetate (p. 397) and of ketoglutarate to succinate (p. 399), for which cocarboxylase is required.

DEMONSTRATION OF DEFICIENCY IN MAN. The prompt response of symptoms to specific (thiamine) therapy is of great diagnostic significance. Supportive evidence is furnished by the demonstration of subnormal levels of thiamine and cocarboxylase, or increased concentrations of pyruvic and lactic acids in the blood. It has been suggested that the blood pyruvate-lactate levels are of greater diagnostic significance if studied in relation to the blood sugar concentration after administration of glucose. Rather extensive use has been made of saturation tests, a lower urinary excretion of thiamine and cocarboxylase after administration of a test dose occurring in thiamine-deficient than in normal subjects.

REQUIREMENT (TABLE 54, P. 624). The estimated daily thiamine requirement (dietary) for adults is 0.5 mg. for each 1000 Calories, i.e., 1.0 and 1.5 mg. for diets providing 2000 and 3000 Calories, respectively, with a minimum of 1 mg. The actual requirement is probably related more directly to the carbohydrate content than to the caloric value of the diet. Recommended daily intakes for children range from 0.4 mg. for infants to 1.2 for pre-adolescents (10–12 years).

The requirement for thiamine may be increased under the following circumstances: anoxia (shock, hemorrhage); serious illness or injury; during oral administration of antibiotics; during refeeding of markedly undernourished subjects; increased caloric expenditure (e.g., fever, hyperthyroidism).

RIBOFLAVIN

Certain substances exhibiting a strong yellowish-green fluorescence, isolated from egg-white, milk, liver, plants, and other sources, were found (1933) to stimulate the growth of rats. These were called "ovoflavin," "lactoflavin," "hepatoflavin," and "verdoflavin," respectively, until it was found that they were probably the same substance. It was shortly thereafter demonstrated that this pigment was also contained in the "yellow enzyme" discovered (1932) by Warburg and Christian in yeast. Its relation to cellular oxidation mechanisms was thereby established. The original designation, "lactoflavin," was changed to "riboflavin" when its constitution became known. Synthesis of riboflavin was accomplished in 1935.

CHEMISTRY. Riboflavin is an orange-yellow compound containing D-ribitol (a ribose alcohol) and a heterocyclic substance, isoalloxazine (flavin) (Fig. 42). The 1-carbon of the ribityl group is attached at the 9 position of isoalloxazine (6,7-dimethyl-9 (1'-D-ribityl)-isoalloxazine).

In pure crystalline form it is only slightly soluble in water and alcohol, and is insoluble in most fat solvents. Impure preparations and certain esters (phosphate, acetate) are quite soluble in water. Aqueous solutions are greenish-yellow with a yellow-green fluorescence in the ultraviolet.

Riboflavin is quite stable to heat in neutral and acid, but not in alkaline solutions. Aqueous solutions are unstable to visible and ultraviolet light, this instability being increased by heat and alkalinity. On exposure to light, the ribityl residue is split off, with the formation, in alkaline solution, of a yellow, chloroform-soluble pigment, "lumiflavin," and, in acid or neutral solution, of a similar compound, called "lumichrome" (Fig. 42). This reaction is irreversible. Riboflavin readily undergoes reversible reduction to a colorless substance, "leucoriboflavin" (Fig. 42). This phenomenon is probably related to the important function of riboflavin as a component of enzyme systems catalyzing cellular oxidation-reduction reactions (p. 361).

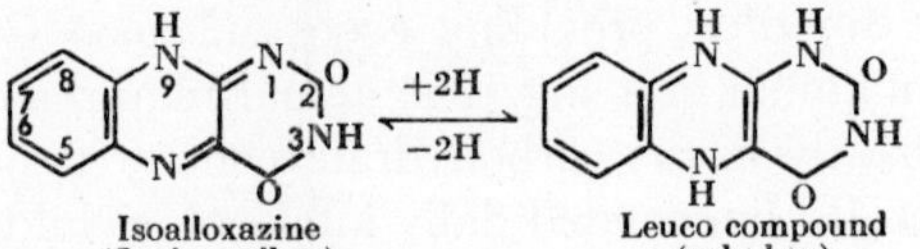

Isoalloxazine (flavin, yellow) — Leuco compound (colorless)

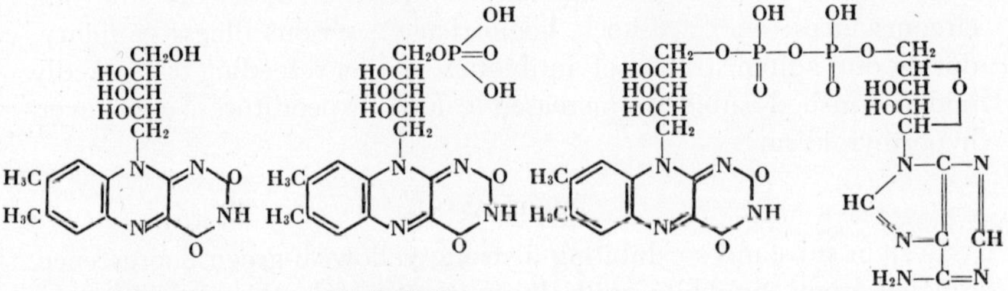

Riboflavin (6,7-dimethyl-1′-D-ribityl-isoalloxazine) — Riboflavin-5′-phosphoric acid — Riboflavin adenine dinucleotide (FAD)

Fig. 42. Riboflavin and related compounds

The biologically active forms in which riboflavin serves as the prosthetic group (coenzyme) of a number of enzymes are phosphorylated derivatives: (1) flavin mononucleotide (riboflavin phosphate), and (2) flavin adenine dinucleotide (FAD) (Fig. 42). These derivatives resemble riboflavin in many important respects, viz., (a) color and fluorescence, (b) reversible reduction, and (c) decomposition on exposure to light. However, the acidic properties imparted by addition of phosphoric acid influence their capacity for combining with the protein apoenzymes. This union apparently occurs through both this acid group and the imide N of the isoalloxazine nucleus, forming linkages with basic and acidic groups of the proteins. These compounds (holoenzymes) are termed "flavoproteins" (p. 47). In most instances they are readily dissociable in acid solution into their apoenzyme (protein) and prosthetic (coenzyme; flavin nucleotide) components; the latter can be removed by dialysis. The two factors readily undergo recombination, with restoration of the original enzyme activity.

BIOSYNTHESIS. All higher plants synthesize riboflavin, the younger portions containing more than the older (e.g., leaves more than stems). Young leaves are richer in this factor than old leaves. Most ungerminated seeds contain little riboflavin, which increases during the process of germination. Riboflavin occurs in nature in the free form and as the mono- and dinucleotides, as such, or as flavoproteins.

It is synthesized also by most yeasts, fungi, and bacteria, but not by animals. Animal tissues are apparently unable to effect the combination of D-ribitol and 6,7-dimethylisoalloxazine, and are therefore completely dependent on extrinsic sources for their riboflavin supply. In certain instances, a variable portion of the requirement may be derived from intestinal bacteria (p. 272), which apparently liberate the vitamin when they disintegrate. Ruminants (cow, goat) can obtain all of their requirement from this source, none being required in the diet. In man, on the other hand, although considerable amounts may be formed by intestinal microorganisms, the quantity absorbed is not adequate to maintain normal nutrition. The fact that the bacteria involved in this synthesis occur predominantly in the large bowel may be an important factor in limiting the availability of this riboflavin to the host organism.

METABOLISM. The flavin nucleotides are readily absorbed in the small intestine. Free riboflavin apparently undergoes phosphorylation as a prerequisite to absorption. The mono- and dinucleotides can apparently be formed in the tissue cells also, since the normal requirements can be met by parenteral administration of free riboflavin.

Human blood plasma contains 2.5 to 4.0 μg. of riboflavin per 100 ml., about two-thirds as the dinucleotide, the bulk of the remainder as the mononucleotide. The concentration in erythrocytes has been reported as 15–30 μg./100 grams, and in leukocytes (plus platelets) as about 250 μg./100 grams. These values remain quite constant even in severe riboflavin deficiency. Determination of riboflavin in the blood is not useful in the clinical evaluation of the state of riboflavin nutrition.

Riboflavin is present in all tissue cells, principally as the nucleotides (coenzymes), a variable proportion of which is bound as flavoprotein (holoenzymes). The retina apparently contains free riboflavin. The animal organism does not appear to have a specialized mechanism for storage of riboflavin. The highest concentrations occur in the liver and kidneys, but the tissue content is not increased significantly by administration of large amounts. Certain tissues (e.g., muscle) may retain considerable quantities in the presence of manifestations of riboflavin deficiency. Riboflavin is secreted in the milk, 40 to 80 per cent being in the free state, increasing with increased intake. It is also present in perspiration (10 μg./hour). The riboflavin content of the feces (free and nucleotides) tends to remain quite constant (500–750 μg. daily), and is presumably largely of bacterial origin. The urinary excretion (mainly free, but up to 50 per cent nucleotide) varies with the intake. Under ordinary dietary conditions (1–2 mg. riboflavin), the daily urinary excretion is about 0.1–0.4 mg. (10–20 per cent of intake). When larger amounts are administered, as much as 50 per cent may be eliminated in the urine. The bulk of the dietary riboflavin is metabolized in the body, largely to unknown compounds; a substance of undetermined constitution, uroflavin (aquoflavin), present in the urine, is believed to be a degradation product of riboflavin.

OCCURRENCE AND FOOD SOURCES. Riboflavin, being an essential component of many biological oxidation-reduction systems, is widely distributed in nature. It is probably present in all plant and animal cells, but very few common foodstuffs contain large amounts. Comparatively high concentrations occur in yeasts and fermenting bacteria. Appreciable amounts are present in liver (2–3 mg./100 grams), kidney, crab meat, whole grain, dry beans and peas, nuts, milk, eggs, meats, and green leafy vegetables. There appears to be a general correspondence between the occurrence of riboflavin and melanin in tissues (but not in higher vertebrates). In tissues, it occurs largely as the mono- (riboflavin phosphate) or dinucleotide (isoalloxazine-adenine-dinucleotide; FAD), usually probably bound to proteins (apoenzymes). Milk contains free riboflavin. The riboflavin of different foodstuffs is not equally available upon ingestion. Drying (e.g., yeast) and cooking may increase its availability.

ASSAY. Riboflavin can be determined quantitatively by (1) biological, (2) microbiological, and (3) chemical procedures.

BIOLOGICAL METHODS. Young rats or chicks are maintained on a riboflavin-free diet until the weight curve reaches a plateau. One group then receives supplements of graded amounts of riboflavin; another group receives the material to be assayed. The riboflavin content of the test material is calculated on the basis of the growth response curves. This procedure has been largely supplanted by the less expensive microbiological procedures.

MICROBIOLOGICAL METHOD. This is the most sensitive and specific available procedure, applicable to all types of material, and is the official U.S.P. method of assay. A number of technics may be employed, all based on the same principle. A stock culture of Lactobacillus casei is grown in a medium deficient only in riboflavin. Measurements are made of the stimulation of growth and of lactic acid production induced by addition of the test material as compared with that induced by graded supplements of riboflavin.

CHEMICAL METHODS. Chromatographic, colorimetric, and fluorometric procedures have been described, none being as accurate or as sensitive as the microbiological method for routine assay of all types

of material. Of the chemical procedures, fluorometry is the one most
frequently employed. Inasmuch as plant and animal tissues contain
substances which fluoresce similarly to riboflavin under the conditions
of the test, measurements of fluorescence must be made before and
after destruction of the vitamin (e.g., by sodium hydrosulfite or alkali).
Another method consists in conversion of the riboflavin, by irradiation in alkaline solution, to lumiflavin, which is extracted by chloroform in acid solution and determined fluorometrically or colorimetrically.

FUNCTIONS. Riboflavin, in the form of the mono- and dinucleotides,
acts as the prosthetic group (coenzyme) of several enzymes (flavoproteins) involved in biological oxidation-reduction reactions. These
enzymes serve as bridges over which hydrogen atoms can pass between two other molecules (p. 359). The flavoprotein enzymes catalyze many fewer reactions and exhibit much more hydrogen-acceptor
specificity than do the pyridinoprotein enzymes (containing nicotinamide as a prosthetic group) (p. 361). Moreover, the redox potential
of riboflavin is intermediate between the relatively low values of its
H-donors (organic metabolites; nicotinamide) and the higher values
of its H-acceptors (cytochromes; oxygen). Consequently, the majority
of biological reactions catalyzed by flavoprotein enzymes proceed effectively only in one direction; i.e., from organic substrates as the
original H-donors to molecular oxygen as the ultimate H-acceptor.
In its reduction and oxidation, riboflavin alternately accepts and
releases two H-atoms, being reversibly transformed to leucoriboflavin
(Fig. 42).

The reactions catalyzed by flavoproteins may be divided into two
groups:

1. Reactions in which the enzyme removes hydrogen directly from
a primary substrate (organic metabolite). The latter include D-amino
acids, L-amino acids, glycine, L-hydroxyacids, aldehydes, purines
(xanthine, hypoxanthine). Oxygen is the common physiological hydrogen acceptor for the oxidases (flavin enzymes) in this group.

2. Reactions in which the enzyme removes hydrogen, not from
the primary substrate, but from an intermediate carrier, either (a)
a reduced pyridine nucleotide system ($DPN \cdot H_2$; $TPN \cdot H_2$) (p. 361),
or perhaps (b) a reduced thiamine system which has catalyzed an
oxidative decarboxylation (p. 397). Cytochrome systems are probably
the physiological hydrogen acceptors for this group of enzymes.

The individual reactions in which the flavin nucleotides function
as H-carriers are considered elsewhere (pp. 362, 363). In a few of
these the mononucleotide (riboflavin phosphate) is involved, and in
the majority the dinucleotide (FAD).

DEFICIENCY MANIFESTATIONS. As is the case with other B vitamins, the effects in man of deficiency in riboflavin are not very well defined, because clinical (i.e., dietary) deficiency in this factor is almost inevitably accompanied by deficiencies in other B vitamins. However, certain symptoms in subjects with multiple deficiencies (e.g., pellagra, beriberi) respond quite specifically to administration of riboflavin, and are presumably due to lack of this factor.

The most important and consistent lesions of riboflavin deficiency in man involve the mouth, tongue, nose, and eyes, with weakness, lassitude and, less consistently, skin lesions. They include: redness and shiny appearance of the lips; lesions at the mucocutaneous juncture at the angles of the mouth, leading to painful fissure (cheilosis); painful glossitis, the tongue assuming a red-purple (magenta) color, with large, flattened papillae, occasionally becoming fissured; seborrheic dermatitis (scaly, greasy desquamation), chiefly about the ears, nose, and nasolabial folds, with a "shark-skin" appearance of the affected areas; vascularization, opacity, and ulceration of the cornea with photophobia, burning of the eyes and scleral congestion; cataract; abnormal pigmentation of the iris. The specific nature of the ocular lesions has been questioned.

Similar lesions occur in experimental animals: dermatitis, with roughening or loss of hair (alopecia) (rat, mouse, pig, dog, monkey); conjunctivitis, vascularization, opacity and ulceration of the cornea (rat, mouse, dog, pig); incoordination and paralysis of the legs (myelin degeneration) (rat, mouse, dog, monkey, pig); lymphopenia (rat); anemia (rat, dog, monkey).

DEMONSTRATION OF DEFICIENCY IN MAN. This depends largely on recognition of characteristic symptoms and the response to adequate specific therapy. Determination of the blood level or urinary excretion of riboflavin is of no diagnostic value. Saturation tests may be useful if adequately standardized. Normal subjects excrete at least 20 per cent of a test dose (3 mg.) during the subsequent twenty-four hours. REQUIREMENT (TABLE 54, P. 624). The human requirement for riboflavin is not known exactly. The recommended daily intake is as follows: adults, 1.5–1.8 mg., depending on weight; women in the latter half of pregnancy, 2.5 mg.; during lactation, 3 mg.; infants, 0.6 mg.; children, 0.9 mg.–1.8 mg., and 2–2.5 mg. during adolescence.

The requirement for riboflavin may be increased under the following circumstances: after severe injury or burn; during acute illness and early convalescence. This is apparently related to the active participation of riboflavin in anabolic processes.

NIACIN (NICOTINIC ACID)

Pellagra is a serious disease which has for centuries occurred in endemic and epidemic forms in various regions and was quite common in the southern United States. It was clearly demonstrated as early as 1912 (Goldberger) that it originated in some dietary inadequacy, the exact nature of which was not clear. It was also shown (1917) that a condition in dogs, called "canine blacktongue," had much in common with human pellagra. In 1937, Elvehjem isolated nicotinic acid and nicotinamide from liver extract and showed that they were highly effective in curing canine blacktongue. Shortly thereafter their curative effect in clinical pellagra was reported.

Nicotinic acid was first derived from nicotine in 1867, and it had been isolated from yeast and rice bran as early as 1912, with no appreciation of its nutritional significance. However, in 1935, Warburg and Christian had demonstrated the participation of nicotinamide in cellular oxidation systems as a hydrogen-transport agent. This observation, together with the development of knowledge regarding ribo-flavin, emphasized the possible role of certain vitamins, at least, as essential components of fundamentally important intracellular enzyme systems. The term "niacin" (and "niacinamide") was adopted officially to avoid the implication of a functional or pharmacological resemblance to the alkaloid nicotine.

CHEMISTRY. Nicotinic acid (niacin) is pyridine 3-carboxylic acid (Fig. 43). It derives its name from the fact that it can be prepared by oxidation of nicotine, although it differs strikingly from the latter in its pharmacological effects. It occurs in tissues principally as the amide (nicotinamide; niacinamide; pyridine 3-carboxylic acid amide), in which form it enters into physiologically active combination.

Nicotinic acid is slightly soluble in water (1 per cent) and more so in alkali (salt formation) and alcohol. It can form metallic salts with the carboxyl group, and salts of the hydrochloride type with the basic nitrogen. It is stable to heat (boiling); the amide undergoes hydrolysis to the acid by heating in acid or alkali.

Both nicotinic acid and nicotinamide react with cyanogen bromide in the presence of a primary amine, forming a yellow-green compound. This reaction, which is also given by other pyridine compounds, is the basis for a chemical method of assay.

In tissues, nicotinamide is present largely as a dinucleotide, the pyridine N being linked to a ribose residue. Two such compounds are known: (1) diphosphopyridine nucleotide (coenzyme I; cozymase; codehydrogenase; DPN) contains nicotinamide, two molecules each of D-ribose and phosphoric acid, and one of adenine (Fig. 43); (2) triphosphopyridine nucleotide (coenzyme II; TPN), differing from DPN in that it contains an additional molecule of phosphoric acid.

These coenzymes are soluble in water, stable in acid but not in alkali, and exhibit characteristic absorption maxima in the ultraviolet which shift upon reduction (e.g., 260 mμ for DPN, 340 mμ for DPN·H$_2$). This fact is of importance in demonstrating participation of this factor in biological oxidation reactions.

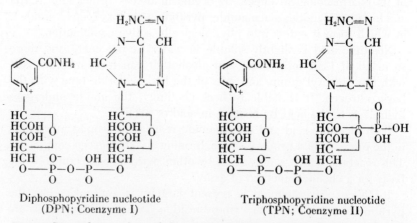

Fig. 43. Biosynthesis and metabolism of nicotinamide and structures of niacin-containing coenzymes

OCCURRENCE AND FOOD SOURCES. Nicotinamide and its combined forms (DPN, TPN) are distributed widely in plant and animal tissues. As is true of other B vitamins, nicotinamide is present in cereal grains in highest concentration in the germ and pericarp (bran), which are often discarded in the milling process (e.g., wheat, rice). Yeast (brewers' and bakers') is particularly rich in this factor (also beer and ale). Important food sources include liver, kidney, meats, fish, legumes (peas, beans, lentils), certain nuts, certain green vegetables, coffee, tea, and whole-wheat, rye, and artificially enriched white bread. Fruits, milk, and eggs are generally poor sources.

BIOSYNTHESIS. Tryptophan is a precursor of nicotinic acid in certain species (c.g., man, dog, pig, rat, rabbit, horse, fowl, certain bacteria, neurospora). Kynurenine and 3-hydroxyanthranilic acid are intermediates in this biosynthetic pathway (Fig. 43). A pyridoxine-containing factor is involved in this reaction sequence (p. 191). In higher animals, tryptophan (also hydroxyanthranilic acid) can substitute nutritionally for nicotinic acid and, in man also, administration of tryptophan is followed by increased urinary excretion of niacin metabolites (viz., N^1-methylnicotinamide) (p. 546).

This synthesis can be accomplished by animal tissues (e.g., rat liver) and also by certain intestinal bacteria. The latter can also apparently form nicotinic acid from other amino acids, i.e., glutamic acid, proline, ornithine, and glycine (Fig. 43). The dietary supply of this vitamin is therefore supplemented by its tissue and intestinal bacterial synthesis in the presence of adequate provision of proteins, especially those rich in tryptophan. The increased niacin requirement incident to a high corn diet is probably due to the low tryptophan content of zein (maize protein).

In higher organisms, the bulk of the intracellular nicotinic acid is in the form of the dinucleotide coenzymes, DPN and TPN. These are synthesized by intracellular enzymes from nicotinamide, ribose, ATP, and adenylic acid.

METABOLISM. Nicotinic acid and its amide are absorbed from the intestine, the concentration in the blood plasma rising promptly after oral administration of large doses (20 mg.). Stated values for human blood are as follows: (1) whole blood, total nicotinic acid activity, 0.2–0.9 (av. 0.6) mg./100 ml. (2–3.5 [av. 3.0] mg. as coenzyme); (2) erythrocytes, total nicotinic acid activity, 1.3 mg./100 ml. (6.5–9.0 [av. 7.0] mg. as coenzyme); free nicotinic acid, 0.135 mg./100 ml.; (3) plasma, total nicotinic acid activity, 0.025–0.15 (av. 0.075) mg./100 ml. Most of the nicotinic acid (or amide) in the blood is in the erythrocytes, mainly in combination, presumably as coenzyme. That in the plasma is apparently largely in the free state. The values in the blood are not altered significantly in severe niacin deficiency (i.c., in pellagra), and their determination is therefore of no value in the detection of clinical deficiency states.

Little is known concerning the metabolic degradation of the niacin coenzymes. Certain tissues (rabbit brain) can split off niacinamide from DPN (nucleosidase action). Others (rabbit kidney) contain a pyrophosphatase which splits DPN into niacin mononucleotide and adenylic acid. Inasmuch as neither the coenzymes (nucleotides) nor their component ribosides are excreted in the urine, enzymatic cleavage of the nicotinamide-ribose bond apparently occurs as a general process in the degradation of these substances.

The bulk of present information on the catabolism of nicotinic acid is derived from studies of its urinary excretion products. Normal adults, on a normal diet, excrete both nicotinic acid and nicotinamide in the urine (0.25–1.25 mg., and 0.5–4 mg. daily, respectively). However, the major urinary metabolite is a methylated derivative, N^1-methylnicotinamide, also referred to as F_2 (3.0–12.5 mg. daily), which exhibits a bluish-white fluorescence in alkaline butanol in the ultraviolet. There may also be variable amounts of an oxidation product of the latter, N^1-methyl-6-pyridone-3-carboxylamide (Fig. 43). Urinary excretion of the latter substance accounts for 40–50 per cent and of F_2 for about 10–20 per cent of administered nicotinamide. A portion of the remainder undergoes decarboxylation, the nature of the resulting compounds being unknown. In the dog, the major urinary metabolite is trigonelline (N^1-methylnicotinic acid) or its betaine (Fig. 43). These processes of methylation and oxidation occur in the liver. In rats, administration of large amounts of nicotinic acid or nicotinamide may produce fatty liver, which is prevented by simultaneous administration of methionine, choline, or betaine (p. 479). This phenomenon is apparently due to diversion of methyl groups for the formation of N^1-methylnicotinamide.

Traces of nicotinamide are present in the sweat. Small amounts are secreted in human milk, increasing from less than 0.05 mg. on the first day postpartum to about 3.0 mg. on the tenth day (intake 16.5 mg. daily). Somewhat larger amounts are present in cow's milk.

ASSAY. Nicotinic acid can be determined by chemical and microbiological methods. There is no satisfactory procedure for its bioassay in animals.

CHEMICAL METHODS. Those in common use involve conversion of all active derivatives to nicotinic acid by acid hydrolysis, and reaction of the latter with cyanogen bromide and an organic base, such as aniline, p-aminophenol or p-aminoacetophenone, to produce a yellow pigment. This is measured colorimetrically. Values obtained compare favorably with the results of microbiological assay.

MICROBIOLOGICAL METHODS. The U.S.P. procedure is based upon determination (titration) of the lactic acid production by standardized pure cultures of Lactobacillus arabinosus grown in a medium containing no niacin or active derivatives but complete in other respects. The amount of acid produced when the test material is added is compared to that produced with added amounts of nicotinic acid.

Other procedures measure the growth (turbidimetric measurements) of Proteus vulgaris under similar conditions.

FUNCTIONS. DPN and TPN function as prosthetic groups (coenzymes) for a large number of dehydrogenases (pyridinoproteins) (p. 361). The respective apoenzymes generally exhibit a distinct preference, if not an absolute requirement, for one or other of these factors. However, at least one (glutamic acid dehydrogenase) can use either with equal efficiency. With the exception of systems catalyzing dehydrogenation of glucose-6-phosphate and isocitrate, which utilize TPN, other pyridinoprotein-containing dehydrogenation systems in animal tissues function most satisfactorily with DPN. The dehydrogenating function of these coenzymes is accomplished by the addition of two hydrogen atoms to one of the $-N=C<$ bonds of the pyridine nucleus (Fig. 43). In most instances, the added hydrogen atoms (DPN·H$_2$; TPN·H$_2$) are transferred to the riboflavin component of flavoprotein enzymes (p. 361), with the regeneration of DPN and TPN (p. 362).

The pyridinoprotein enzymes catalyze many more dehydrogenation reactions and exhibit much less hydrogen-acceptor specificity than do the flavoprotein enzymes (containing riboflavin as a prosthetic group) (p. 366). They differ from the latter also in that the redox potentials of the systems with which they are associated usually fall in the same range as those of the pyridine-coenzymes themselves. Consequently, the reactions catalyzed by these enzymes are frequently reversible under physiological conditions, e.g., with changes in the relative concentrations of reacting metabolites in the cell, or with changes in the ratio between the oxidized and reduced forms of the coenzymes.

PHARMACOLOGICAL ACTION. Unlike most vitamins, niacin and niacinamide, being pyridine derivatives, have rather marked pharmacological actions when given in relatively large doses. Both have a stimulating effect on the central nervous system. In therapeutic doses, nicotinic acid, but not nicotinamide, produces pronounced, transient vasodilatation, with flushing of the face, neck, and arms. This is accompanied by an increase in peripheral blood flow and skin temperature, with a frequently uncomfortable sense of warmth and, at times, burning and itching. There is a wide individual variation in this regard.

DEFICIENCY MANIFESTATIONS. Certain of the most characteristic features of human pellagra (*pelle* = skin; *agra* = rough) are due to niacin deficiency, although the complete picture, as it occurs clinically, is dependent upon a multiple B vitamin deficiency. The cardinal symptoms of this condition have been referred to as the three "D's," i.e., dermatitis, diarrhea, and dementia.

The skin lesions typically occur most consistently bilaterally and symmetrically, involving areas exposed to sunlight and subjected to pressure, heat, chafing, and other types of trauma or irritation. These include the face, neck, dorsal surfaces of the wrists and forearms, the elbows, knees, breasts, and perineum. The skin becomes reddened, later brown, thickened, and scaly.

Gastrointestinal manifestations include: anorexia, nausea, vomiting, abdominal pain, with alternating constipation and diarrhea, the latter becoming intractable later; gingivitis and stomatitis, with reddening of the tip and margin of the tongue, which becomes swollen and cracked; achlorhydria in about 40 per cent of cases; thickening and inflammation of the colon, with cystic lesions of the mucosa, which later becomes atrophic and ulcerated; possible development of fatty liver.

Cerebral manifestations include: headache, irritability, forgetfulness, confusion, insomnia, vertigo, anxiety, depression, and other mental symptoms ranging from those of mild psychoneuroses to severe psychoses (hallucinations, delusions, mania).

General effects include inadequate growth (children), loss of weight and strength, anemia (which may be due to associated deficiency in other B vitamins), and dehydration and its consequences (resulting from diarrhea). Niacin deficiency is aggravated by a low tryptophan intake (p. 185), i.e., by diets low in protein or those in which corn furnishes the bulk of the protein. Subjects with pellagra excrete the red pigments, urorosein and indirubin, in the urine. The former is apparently formed from indolylacetic acid. Although these pigments are not found in normal urine, their presence cannot be correlated with the occurrence of niacin deficiency nor with its correction by proper therapy. They are therefore of little practical significance.

Because of its extensive biosynthesis (p. 185), niacin deficiency can be induced in certain animals only by diets deficient in protein (i.e., in tryptophan) as well as in the vitamin. The most characteristic picture develops in the dog, the outstanding feature being a condition known as "canine blacktongue," in which the mouth is dark red, with necrotic lesions in the mucosa.

DEMONSTRATION OF DEFICIENCY IN MAN.   In its fully developed form the clinical picture is rather characteristic and response to administration of adequate doses of nicotinic acid or nicotinamide is prompt and dramatic. The diagnosis is usually made easily on the basis of clinical features and response to specific therapy.

Available diagnostic laboratory tests, although useful, are not entirely reliable. The most promising are based on the "saturation" principle (p. 127), in which the urinary excretion of N^1-methylnicotinamide is measured following administration of a standard test dose of nicotinic acid or nicotinamide. The amount excreted is subnormal in niacin deficiency. As is true of most "saturation tests," difficulty is encountered chiefly in the establishment of normal standards.

REQUIREMENT (TABLE 54, P. 624).   In view of present knowledge of the influence of dietary tryptophan on the nicotinic acid requirement, previous estimates of the latter must be regarded as provisional. With a completely adequate diet, ranging from 2000 to 4500 Cal., a daily niacin intake (adults) of 10 to 18 mg. has been recommended. Suggested values for children range from 4 mg. for infants to 12 mg. for pre-adolescents (10–12 years).

The requirement for niacin is increased under the following circumstances: increased caloric intake or expenditure; acute illness and early convalescence; after severe injury, infection, and burn.

PYRIDOXINE (VITAMIN B₆)

With the identification of thiamine and riboflavin in the early 1930's, the multiple nature of what had been designated "vitamin B" began to be apparent. A rather characteristic dermatitis in rats, called "acrodynia," had previously been attributed to the pellagra-preventive (P-P) factor. It was soon found, however, that niacin had no preventive or curative effect on this lesion. The missing responsible substance (rat antidermatitis factor) was designated "vitamin B₆" (György). Within a few years (1938, 1939) it was isolated (yeast and liver), its chemical structure established, and its synthesis accomplished. This factor was named "pyridoxine."

CHEMISTRY. Pyridoxine is 2-methyl-3-hydroxy-4,5-di(hydroxymethyl)-pyridine (Fig. 44). It occurs in nature in association, perhaps in equilibrium with an aldehyde (pyridoxal) and an amine (pyridoxamine) form (Fig. 44). All three forms exhibit "vitamin B₆" activity, which, however, actually resides apparently in phosphorylated derivatives, pyridoxal phosphate and pyridoxamine phosphate (Fig. 44). These forms occur in nature largely in combination with protein (apoenzymes). The phosphorylation apparently involves the hydroxymethyl group (position 5 in the pyridine ring).

Pyridoxine is soluble in water and alcohol, as is its hydrochloride, the form in which it is generally used. The three forms of the vitamin give characteristic absorption curves in the ultraviolet. They are rather readily destroyed by exposure to light, but are quite stable to heat, acid, and alkali. They are destroyed by strong oxidizing agents.

Pyridoxine has a phenolic hydroxyl group and reacts with diazonium salts to produce colored compounds. Reacting with ferric chloride, it produces an orange-red compound. It couples with 2,6-dichloroquinone-chloroimide to form a blue dye (probably an indophenol). These reactions form the basis for certain chemical methods for determination of vitamin B₆.

OCCURRENCE AND FOOD SOURCES. In common with other members of the vitamin B group, vitamin B₆ is distributed widely in animal and plant tissues. Foodstuffs containing relatively large amounts include yeast, rice polishings, the germinal portion of various seeds and cereal grains, and egg-yolk. Moderate amounts are present in liver, kidney, muscle, and fish, and relatively low concentrations in milk. The highest concentrations occur in Royal jelly (bee).

Although pyridoxine, pyridoxal, and pyridoxamine are nutritionally interchangeable in animals, this is not the case in all plants and microorganisms, the predominating form varying in different strains, certain of which, for example, cannot convert the base (pyridoxine) to the active aldehyde (pyridoxal). These substances are generally present as phosphorylated derivatives bound to their protein apoenzymes.

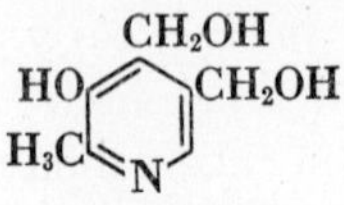

CH₂OH
HO   CH₂OH
H₃C   N
Pyridoxine

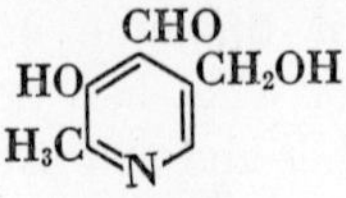

CHO
HO   CH₂OH
H₃C   N
Pyridoxal

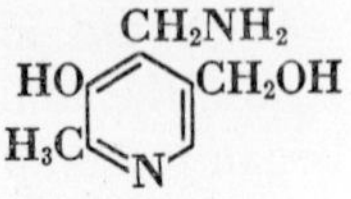

CH₂NH₂
HO   CH₂OH
H₃C   N
Pyridoxamine

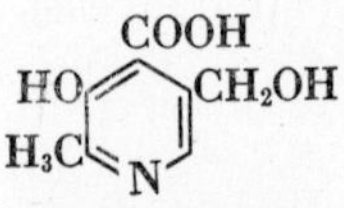

COOH
HO   CH₂OH
H₃C   N
Pyridoxic acid

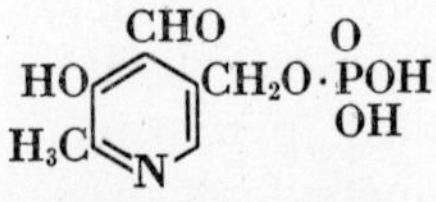

CHO   O
HO   CH₂O·POH
H₃C   N   OH
Pyridoxal phosphate

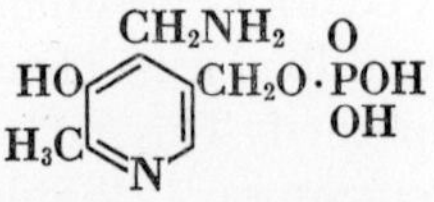

CH₂NH₂   O
HO   CH₂O·POH
H₃C   N   OH
Pyridoxamine phosphate

Fig. 44. Pyridoxine and derivatives

ASSAY. Chemical, biological, and microbiological methods are available, the latter being most satisfactory and most widely employed.

CHEMICAL. These are relatively nonspecific, and are based on the color reactions referred to above (e.g., with ferric chloride, sulfanilamide, 2,6-dichloroquinone-chloroimide). They are useful mainly in pure solutions (pharmaceutical preparations).

BIOLOGICAL. Rats (or chicks) are maintained on a diet deficient in vitamin B_6. After a period of depletion, they are given supplements of the test material and the weight curves are compared with those of other groups receiving standard supplements of pyridoxine. These procedures are time-consuming, expensive, and not very satisfactory.

MICROBIOLOGICAL. These are based upon the stimulation of growth of yeast or bacteria. The growth increment induced by the test material, measured turbidimetrically, is compared to that induced by supplements of standard amounts of pyridoxine or an appropriate active derivative.

Microbioassay procedures are complicated by the fact that different microorganisms do not respond equally to pyridoxine, pyridoxal, and pyridoxamine. This fact has been utilized as a basis for estimating the individual forms of the vitamin. For example, an induced mutant of Neurospora sitophila requires pyridoxine, but does not respond to pyridoxal or pyridoxamine, whereas the latter two are extremely more active (several thousand-fold) than pyridoxine for certain lactic acid bacteria. The yeast, Saccharomyces carlsbergensis, is satisfactory for determination of total vitamin B_6 activity, inasmuch as all three forms exert approximately the same growth-stimulating effect.

BIOSYNTHESIS AND METABOLISM. There is little precise information regarding the biosynthesis of the B_6 vitamins. They are apparently formed by many microorganisms, and probably also plants, but the precursors and pathways are not known. In certain dry seeds, e.g., wheat and rice, which are metabolically inactive, pyridoxine is present as a relatively inactive storage form, whereas pyridoxal and pyridoxamine predominate in metabolically active tissues. Phosphorylation to the functioning forms is apparently accomplished readily (ATP). Pyridoxine is synthesized by intestinal bacteria in several animal species, but the extent to which it is available from this source in man is questionable. Pyridoxine, pyridoxal, and pyridoxamine are nutritionally interchangeable in man, the base being apparently converted to the functionally active phosphorylated aldehyde and amine derivatives.

Although pyridoxal and pyridoxamine are excreted in the urine in small amounts (0.5–0.7 mg. daily), the major urinary metabolite (about 3 mg. daily) is the biologically inactive 4-pyridoxic acid (2-methyl-3-hydroxy-5-hydroxymethylpyridine-4-carboxylic acid) (Fig. 44). When large amounts (70–80 mg.) of either of the three vitamin forms are administered, 30–70 per cent may be excreted unchanged. Pyridoxal and pyridoxamine are also secreted in the milk and sweat.

FUNCTIONS. The demonstrated functions of vitamin B_6 are concerned principally with the metabolism of amino acids. In animals, the three fundamental vitamin forms, pyridoxine, pyridoxal, and pyridoxamine, are equally effective nutritionally, suggesting that they are all readily interconvertible or convertible to some functional form or forms. Available evidence indicates that functional activity is identified chiefly, if not entirely, with pyridoxal phosphate (Fig. 44), produced by phosphorylation (ATP) of pyridoxal. Whether or not pyridoxamine phosphate is functionally active as such is questionable.

Reversible interconversion of pyridoxal and pyridoxamine in the process of transamination has been postulated (p. 246).

Pyridoxal phosphate is the prosthetic group (coenzyme) in mammalian enzyme systems catalyzing the following reactions: (1) transamination (cotransaminase), i.e., the reversible transfer of an α-amino group between an amino acid and an α-keto acid (p. 247); (2) decarboxylation (codecarboxylase) of at least two amino acids, viz., 3,4-dihydroxyphenylalanine (dopa) and glutamic acid (p. 553); (3) in addition, there is evidence that vitamin B_6 is involved in the mechanism of conversion of tryptophan to nicotinic acid (p. 185). There are indications that it may be concerned in the metabolism of unsaturated fatty acids and in enzyme systems involved in the transfer of sulfur from homocysteine, with the formation of cysteine (p. 530). More extensive functions have been demonstrated in mold and bacterial enzyme systems, e.g., in decarboxylation of several α-amino acids and in the synthesis of tryptophan from indole and serine (reversible).

DEFICIENCY MANIFESTATIONS. Epileptiform convulsions in infants have been attributed to pyridoxine deficiency. Reports of symptomatic improvement following its administration in a number of clinical disorders have not been very convincing. These include: multiple B vitamin deficiency states (e.g., pellagra, beriberi), nausea and vomiting of pregnancy, dermatoses, certain types of anemia and neutropenia, epilepsy, X-ray sickness, paralysis agitans, pseudohypertrophic muscular dystrophy, etc. However, there is suggestive evidence that pyridoxine is a nutritional requirement for man, as it has been shown to be for other animals (monkey, dog, rat, mouse, pig, cow, and chicken).

The general manifestations of vitamin B_6 deficiency in those species requiring this vitamin include inadequate growth or failure to maintain weight, anemia, leukopenia, skin lesions, nervous system symptoms, and evidence of interference in tryptophan metabolism. All of these do not occur in every species.

In the rat, the most characteristic feature is a form of dermatitis (acrodynia), involving the paws, tail, nose, mouth, and ears, with scaliness, loss of hair, and swelling. Similar lesions occur in acute deficiency in adult but not in young mice nor in other species.

Epileptiform seizures (excitement, convulsions, coma), with degenerative changes in the nervous system, occur in the dog, rat, pig, and chick. Monkeys exhibit ataxia and pigs a "goose-step" type of gait.

Anemia occurs in the monkey, dog, pig, chick, and duck, but not in the rat. There is evidence of impaired synthesis of protoporphyrin and an increased amount of iron in the blood plasma and tissues. Poikilocytosis is a prominent feature in cattle. Lymphoid tissue (e.g., thymus, spleen) undergoes rapid involution in mice with pyridoxine deficiency.

Interference in tryptophan metabolism is indicated by increased urinary excretion of xanthurenic acid and decreased excretion of kynurenic acid (p. 184) and nicotinic acid metabolites. Manifestations of pyridoxine deficiency are exaggerated by administration of tryptophan or a high protein diet (increased pyridoxine requirement). Atherosclerosis has been reported in the monkey.

REQUIREMENT. In the absence of known manifestations of vitamin B_6 deficiency in man (except infants), no accurate statement can be made regarding the dietary pyridoxine requirement. A daily intake of 2 mg. has been recommended on the basis of animal requirements. This should perhaps be increased when the protein intake is unusually high.

PANTOTHENIC ACID

It had been recognized (1934) that a factor was present in liver and yeast which was necessary for the prevention of a rather characteristic dermatitis in chicks (chick antidermatitis factor), distinct from the rat antidermatitis factor (which proved to be pyridoxine). This unknown substance was referred to as the "filtrate factor," because it could be separated from pyridoxine by adsorbing the latter on fullers' earth.

This factor was found (1939) to resemble pantothenic acid, which had been shown (1933) to be essential for the normal growth of yeast. In a short time (1940) its chemical identity was established and its synthesis accomplished.

CHEMISTRY. Pantothenic acid consists of β-alanine in peptide linkage with a dihydroxydimethylbutyric acid (Fig. 45). The free acid is soluble in water and is destroyed (hydrolyzed) by acid or alkali; it is thermolabile. Its sodium and calcium salts are fairly soluble in water, and are somewhat more stable to heat than the free acid.

In tissues, this vitamin is apparently present almost entirely in the form of coenzyme, designated coenzyme A (CoA), largely perhaps bound to proteins (apoenzymes). It may be released from this combination by certain proteolytic enzymes, certain phosphatase preparations, and a liver enzyme system. The exact structure of coenzyme A (A = acetylation) has not been established, but a tentative formulation, indicated in Figure 45, represents pantothenate, joined on the one hand to adenosine phosphate by a pyrophosphate bridge, and on the other hand in peptide linkage with β-mercaptoethylamine. The terminal thiol group of the latter component is apparently the reactive center of the CoA molecule, e.g., reacting with acetate to form acetyl-CoA (Fig. 45). The naturally occurring forms of the coenzyme probably include the reduced —SH form, oxidized —S—S— forms, and combinations of the —SH form with various metabolites, e.g., acetate, succinate (p. 454).

OCCURRENCE AND FOOD SOURCES. Pantothenic acid, mainly perhaps in bound forms, is present in all living tissues. Yeast, liver, kidney, eggs, wheat and rice bran, peanuts, and peas contain relatively large amounts; milk, beef, pork, lamb, chicken, certain fish, wheat, rye, oats, and sweet potatoes moderate amounts; most vegetables and fruits are rather poor sources. It is interesting that the richest known source of pantothenic acid is Royal jelly (also rich in biotin and pyridoxine), which is responsible for the development of queen bees from bee larvae. The significance of this fact is not clear, since this vitamin alone cannot accomplish this metamorphosis.

ASSAY. No adequate chemical procedure is available for assay of pantothenic acid. Satisfactory microbiological methods are based on

$CH_2OH \cdot C(CH_3)_2 CHOH \cdot CO \cdot NH \cdot CH_2CH_2COOH$
Pantothenic acid

$HOOC \cdot CHNH_2 \cdot CH_2 \cdot COOH \xrightarrow{-CO_2} CH_2NH_2 \cdot CH_2COOH$
Aspartic acid β-Alanine

$CH_2OH \ C(CH_3)_2 CHNH_2 \ COOH$
Pantonine
(α-amino-γ-hydroxy-β-dimethyl-butyric acid)

$CH_2OH \ C(CH_3)_2 \ CHOH \ COOH$
Pantoic acid
(α, γ-dihydroxy-β-dimethyl-butyric acid)

β-Alanine + Pantoic acid $\rightarrow$ Pantothenic acid

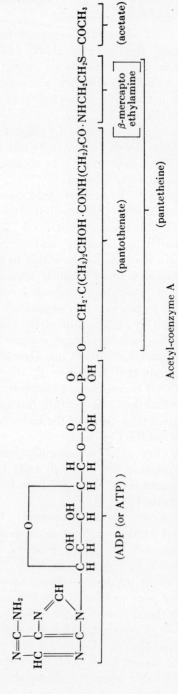

Acetyl-coenzyme A

Fig. 45. *Structures of pantothenic acid and acetyl-CoA, and suggested pathway of biosynthesis of pantothenic acid*

measurement of the degree of stimulation of growth of a strain of Lactobacillus arabinosus, as determined by increase in turbidity of the culture or increase in lactic acid production (titration).

BIOSYNTHESIS AND METABOLISM. In many microorganisms (molds, yeasts, bacteria), pantothenic acid is synthesized by direct coupling of β-alanine and pantoic acid (Fig. 45). β-Alanine is apparently formed by decarboxylation of aspartic acid, and pantoic acid by hydrolytic deamination of an amino acid, "pantonine." This vitamin is synthesized by intestinal bacteria in ruminant animals and in man, but the extent to which it is available (i.e., utilized) from this source in man is not known.

The concentration of pantothenic acid (microbiological assay) in whole blood is 15–45 (av. 30) μg./100 ml.; it is somewhat higher in the cells than in the plasma. It is present in all tissues in small amounts, the highest concentrations occurring in liver (40 μg./gram dry weight) and kidney (30 μg./gram). These values decrease in depleted animals and can be increased above normal by administration of large amounts of the vitamin. It is secreted in the milk (200–300 μg./100 ml.) and sweat (3–4 μg./100 ml.).

The products of catabolism of pantothenic acid are not known. Under ordinary dietary conditions about 2.5–5 mg. are excreted daily in the urine. Normal subjects excrete (urine) about 10 per cent of an orally administered dose of calcium pantothenate within four hours. As much as 60 per cent may be recovered in the urine after intravenous injection.

FUNCTIONS. Pantothenic acid is required by all animal species studied; microorganisms that are not able to effect its synthesis require an exogenous supply.

One of the earliest indications of the fundamental metabolic role of pantothenic acid was the demonstration that coenzyme A is concerned with certain enzymatic processes involving a 2-carbon compound, including (1) acetylation of certain aromatic amines (e.g., sulfonamides) and choline, (2) synthesis of acetoacetate and citrate, and (3) oxidation of pyruvate and acetaldehyde. The 2-carbon intermediate commonly referred to as "active acetate" occupies a key position in intermediary metabolism (p. 454); the term "acetyl-CoA" is regarded as synonymous with "active acetate" in animal systems. The concept of acetyl-CoA as a focal point in mechanisms of acetyl transfer has been extended to acyl groups other than acetate (e.g., succinate, benzoate, propionate, butyrate).

A tentative structure of acetyl-CoA is indicated in Figure 45. In the processes of acetylation of aromatic amines or choline, one must presuppose activation of the carboxyl group of acetate (p. 455), whereas in condensation reactions such as occur in the synthesis of citrate or acetoacetate, activation of the methyl carbon of acetate is required. The nature and mechanisms of the various reactions in which CoA serves as a prosthetic group are considered in detail elsewhere (p. 454). Suffice it here to point out that accumulating evidence emphasizes its important role in several transacylating reactions which occupy strategic positions in intermediary metabolism.

DEFICIENCY MANIFESTATIONS. No manifestations of pantothenic acid deficiency have been recognized in man. This may be due, in part at least, to its widespread distribution in foodstuffs and to its synthesis by intestinal bacteria. However, certain symptoms attributed to deficiency in other members of the vitamin B complex may be due to lack of this factor. The fact that all other animal species investigated require pantothenic acid suggests that it is also a nutritional essential for man.

Apart from such general effects as inadequate growth, failure to maintain weight, decreased reproductive capacity (rat, hen), and fatty liver, the manifestations of pantothenic acid deficiency in experimental animals cannot be correlated readily with its known metabolic functions. Changes in the skin and hair occur in a number of species. These include: dermatitis (rat, chick) and scaling of the paws and tail (rat); loss of hair (alopecia) (rat, mouse, pig), which may be a reflection of a more complicated multiple B vitamin deficiency, e.g., inositol, biotin; circumocular (spectacle) alopecia (also in inositol deficiency); graying of the hair (rat, fox, monkey), due to atrophy of the hair apparatus and cessation of melanin deposition; dipigmentation of feathers in chicks.

Nervous system manifestations include: myelin degeneration of peripheral nerves and degenerative changes in posterior root ganglia and dorsal fibers, leading to paralysis of hind quarters (mouse, dog) and uncoordinated, "goose-stepping" gait (pig); convulsions, coma (dog).

Gastrointestinal manifestations include gastritis and enteritis, with ulceration and bloody diarrhea. Fatty liver occurs in dogs and rats.

Anemia develops (monkey, dog, pig, rat) and, in severe cases, hypoplasia of the bone marrow. Hemorrhages occur beneath the skin and in the kidneys and adrenal cortex (rat). The rather characteristic phenomenon of "blood-caked whiskers" appears in rats, due to deposition of porphyrin, secreted by the Harderian glands and excreted through the nasolacrimal ducts. A similar condition has been induced in rats by severe water restriction. There may also be epistaxis and ocular exudates.

REQUIREMENT. The human requirement for pantothenic acid is not known. Daily intakes of 5 to 12 mg. per 2500 Cal. have been recommended. This should perhaps be increased in the presence of severe stress (e.g., acute illness, burns, severe injury, etc.), especially when antibiotics are being given, because of the possible occurrence of adrenal cortical exhaustion in states of pantothenic acid deficiency.

BIOTIN

Elucidation of the nutritional significance of biotin developed from investigations in different directions. It had been known for some years that diets rich in raw egg-white produced a rather characteristic train of symptoms in the rat and chick. Cooked egg-white was without effect and administration of liver or yeast protected against the toxic action of raw egg-white. This protective substance was called "vitamin H."

It was recognized that yeast extracts, egg-yolk, liver, and other substances contained a factor, distinct from the then known vitamins, which stimulated the growth of certain strains of yeast. This factor was called "biotin." It was also known that a factor, called "coenzyme R," was a growth essential for the nitrogen-fixing organism, Rhizobium, in the root nodules of legumes.

In 1940, it was demonstrated (György) that biotin, vitamin H, and coenzyme R were identical. The toxic factor in raw egg-white was identified as a basic protein, avidin, which combines with and inactivates biotin. The chemical structure of biotin was established in 1942 (du Vigneaud) and its synthesis accomplished in 1943.

CHEMISTRY. Biotin is a heterocyclic, S-containing, monocarboxylic acid (Fig. 46). There are apparently two forms (at least) with essentially identical biological activities, α-biotin (egg-yolk) and β-biotin (liver), differing in the nature of the side-chain. The free acid is sparingly soluble in water; the salts are quite soluble. Biotin is quite stable to heat and light. It is destroyed by heating with strong alkalies and acids and by oxidation (permanganate, peroxide).

Desthiobiotin and oxybiotin (Fig. 46) are biologically active in certain strains of yeast and bacteria, the former probably being converted to biotin (yeast), the latter being utilized as such (also by certain animals, e.g., chick).

By analogy with other B vitamins, biotin might be expected to occur in nature in active combined forms (i.e., coenzymes). There are indications that this is the case. One such form, biocytin, has been identified as ϵ-N-biotinyl-L-lysine (Fig. 46). A considerable portion of the biotin-active material in tissues cannot be extracted with water, suggesting its presence in some firmly bound form, probably to protein apoenzymes. Avidin, a basic protein present in egg-white, forms a very stable, biologically inactive complex with biotin.

OCCURRENCE AND FOOD SOURCES. Biotin is distributed widely in nature in both plant and animal tissues. It occurs chiefly in a water-soluble form in most plant materials (except cereals and nuts), and mainly in a water-insoluble form in animal tissues and products and in yeast. Foodstuffs particularly rich in biotin include egg-yolk, liver, kidney, milk, and yeast. Exceptionally large amounts are present in Royal jelly (bee).

ASSAY. Animal assay methods have been employed (rat, chick), but suffer from the difficulty of producing biotin deficiency by simple dietary restriction. Avidin (egg-white) has been used for this purpose in the rat.

Microbiological assay procedures are employed most extensively. These involve determination of the extent of stimulation of growth of various microorganisms, e.g., Lactobacillus arabinosus or Saccharomyces cerevisiae, measuring increase in turbidity of cultures (yeast) or increase in lactic acid production (bacteria).

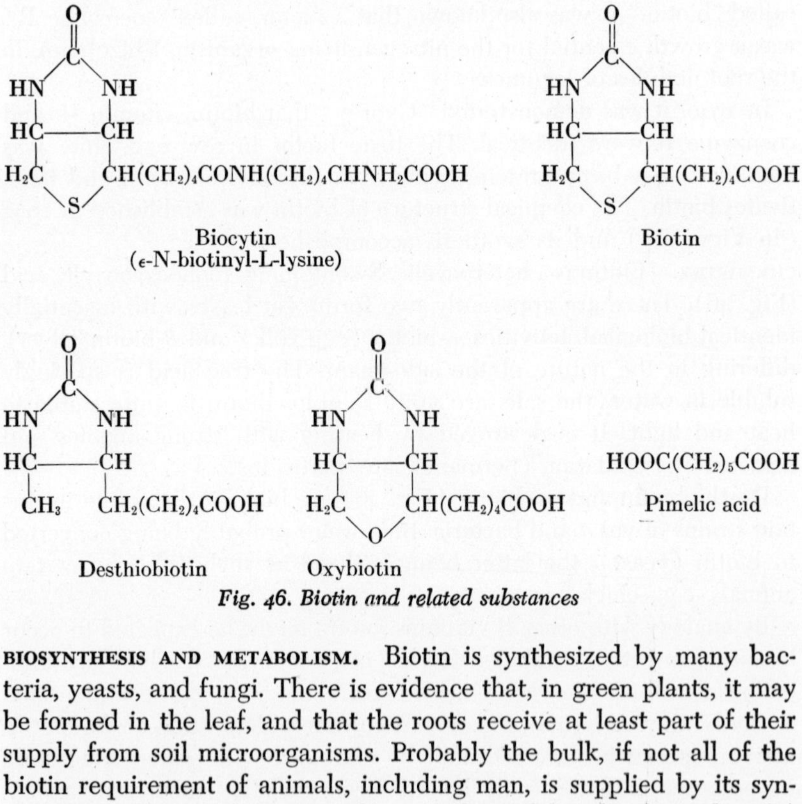

Fig. 46. Biotin and related substances

BIOSYNTHESIS AND METABOLISM. Biotin is synthesized by many bacteria, yeasts, and fungi. There is evidence that, in green plants, it may be formed in the leaf, and that the roots receive at least part of their supply from soil microorganisms. Probably the bulk, if not all of the biotin requirement of animals, including man, is supplied by its synthesis by intestinal bacteria. This is indicated by the facts that (1) animals excrete considerably more biotin than is contained in the diet, and (2) biotin deficiency can be produced only by inhibiting growth of intestinal bacteria (sulfonamides, antibiotics), or by oral administration of avidin (raw egg-white), which inactivates biotin. The pathways of synthesis are not clear. Pimelic acid is a possible precursor, and desthiobiotin a probable intermediate (Fig. 46).

There is little precise information on the metabolism of biotin. It may be stored to a limited extent in the liver and kidneys and is excreted in the urine and feces. It is also secreted in the milk. Normal adults on an adequate diet excrete 10 to 180 μg. daily in the urine and 15 to 200 μg. in the feces. Fecal excretion probably represents unabsorbed material. The amount in the urine increases promptly following administration of biotin. The exact nature of the urinary excretion products has not been determined. At least some of it (biologically active) is in a form which does not combine with avidin.

FUNCTIONS. The physiological importance of biotin is suggested by its virtually universal distribution in plant and animal tissues. Although it has been shown that biotin exerts an important influence in several enzyme systems, perhaps serving as a prosthetic group (coenzyme), its presence in such enzymes has not been established with certainty. With a few exceptions, these influences have been demonstrated only in bacterial systems.

There is evidence that biotin is implicated in enzyme mechanisms involved in the following processes:

1. Reversible decarboxylation (β) of oxaloacetate (to pyruvate), oxalosuccinate (to α-ketoglutarate), and succinate (to propionate).

2. Deamination of aspartic acid, serine, and threonine.

3. Synthesis of aspartic acid and citrulline.

4. Synthesis of oleic acid.

5. Incorporation of CO_2 into carboxyl group of acetoacetate (CO_2 fixation) from pyruvate and certain fatty acids (viz., caproate, caprylate, isovalerate).

6. Oxidation (dehydrogenation) of succinate.

The only processes shown to be influenced by biotin in animal tissues are those of β-decarboxylation, CO_2 fixation, and citrulline synthesis.

DEFICIENCY MANIFESTATIONS. No symptoms attributable to biotin deficiency appear in subjects maintained on diets low in this factor, presumably because it is synthesized in adequate amounts by intestinal bacteria. Human subjects given diets containing a minimal amount of biotin and large amounts of raw egg-white (30 per cent of total calories) developed the following symptoms, beginning after five to seven weeks: dermatitis of the extremities, pallor of skin and mucous membranes, depression, lassitude, somnolence, muscle pains and hyperesthesia, anorexia, and nausea. There were anemia and hypercholesterolemia. All manifestations were relieved within a few days after daily injection of biotin. Whether or not biotin deficiency occurs as a clinical entity is not known; a few suggestive cases have been reported.

Interest in biotin deficiency in experimental animals was stimulated by the discovery that deficiency symptoms may be induced by inclusion of large amounts of raw egg-white in the diet. The active component was found to be a basic protein, "avidin," which combines stoichiometrically with biotin, preventing its absorption from the intestine. This complex is non-dialyzable and the biotin is not released by proteolytic enzymes. Avidin is destroyed by light and heat (i.e., cooked egg-white is inactive).

The physiological significance of avidin is not clear. It is present in the albumen-secreting portion of the oviduct (hen), being increased by administration of estrogen and progesterone. The occurrence of large amounts of biotin in egg-yolk and of avidin in egg-white suggests some metabolic relationship, possibly of importance in reproduction. Biotin is required for normal reproduction in fowl and mice.

Manifestations of biotin deficiency, induced by feeding raw egg-white or intestinal antibiotic agents, include: dermatitis (rat, pig, fowl); "spectacle-eyed" appearance (circumocular alopecia) in rats; thinning or loss of fur (alopecia) (mouse, pig, monkey); graying of black or brown fur (mouse, monkey); perosis (slipped-tendon disease in fowl); paralysis, chiefly of hind quarters (dog, cow, rat).

REQUIREMENT. Because of its abundant supply by intestinal bacteria, a dietary source of biotin is of little nutritional significance except under unusual circumstances. However, it may assume importance during periods of oral administration of therapeutic agents which inhibit growth of intestinal bacteria (certain sulfonamides, antibiotics). Deficiency manifestations induced in human subjects by feeding large amounts of raw egg-white disappeared rapidly when 100 to 300 μg. of biotin were injected daily.

THE FOLIC AND FOLINIC ACID GROUPS AND VITAMINS B_{12}

Substances with vitamin B_{12} activity (cobalamins; antipernicious anemia factor) are apparently related functionally but not structurally to those of the folic acid (pteroylglutamic acid) and folinic acid (citrovorum factor) groups. It seems advisable, therefore, to consider the chemistry and metabolism of these two categories of substances separately, and subsequently to discuss their functions and deficiency manifestations jointly.

Folic Acid and Folinic Acid Group

Early studies in different fields had demonstrated the presence in liver, yeast, and certain green leafy vegetables of substances required for normal growth and nutrition of certain microorganisms and animal species. These received various designations: "fermentation L. casei factor" and "norite eluate factor," required by Lactobacillus casei; "vitamin M," required by the monkey for normal hemopoiesis; "vitamins B_c, B_{10}, and B_{11}," "factors R, S, and U," required by the chick; "factor SLR," required by Streptococcus lactis R.

In 1941, the term "folic acid" (folium = leaf) was applied to the S. lactis R factor, and soon thereafter the similarity of this agent to the factors required by L. casei, the chick, and the monkey became apparent. Isolation of active crystalline materials, chemical identification, and synthesis followed rapidly (1944–1946), and the identity of the several factors as pteroylglutamic acid and its conjugates (Fig. 47) has been established.

A substance in liver, designated "citrovorum factor" (CF), is required for growth of Leuconostoc citrovorum. A formylated reduction product of folic acid (5-formyl-5,6,7,8-tetrahydrofolic acid), prepared synthetically, was found to have CF activity. This synthetic product is designated "folinic acid–SF," and the citrovorum factor, "folinic acid" (p. 203). Subsequent studies suggested the current view that folinic acid is probably the biologically active form of folic acid.

Before the chemical nature of folic acid was established, *p*-aminobenzoic acid (PABA) was regarded as a B vitamin. Recognition of its importance in the nutrition of certain microorganisms arose out of studies of the growth-inhibiting actions of sulfonamides (competitive inhibition) (p. 635). It is now believed that PABA should not be accorded vitamin status and that its sole nutritional significance lies in the fact that it is a component of the pteroic acid molecule (Fig. 47).

CHEMISTRY (FIG. 47). The "folic acid group" includes a number of compounds which contain one or more of the following chemical groups: (1) a pteridine nucleus (pyrimidine and pyrazine rings), (2) *p*-aminobenzoic acid, and (3) glutamic acid.

XANTHOPTERIN. This yellow pigment, present in liver and urine, is 2-amino-4,6-dioxypteridine. It has folic acid activity in certain (rat, monkey) but not in all (e.g., chick) species. It has been regarded as a possible precursor of folic acid, but may act rather as an inhibitor of its inactivation.

p-AMINOBENZOIC ACID (PABA). This substance is only very slightly soluble in water, but is soluble in alcohol, acids, and alkalies. Originally regarded as a B vitamin, it is now believed to exist in nature and to function solely as a component of the folic acid group of compounds. Acetyl-PABA occurs in the blood and urine, presumably a metabolite of folic acid.

PTEROYLGLUTAMIC ACIDS (FOLIC ACID AND FOLIC ACID CONJUGATES). The folic acid compounds are peptide conjugates of L-glutamic acid (Fig. 47). They may exist in nature in equilibrium with reduced, formylated derivatives, i.e., the "folinic acid group" (see below), presumably the functionally active forms of the vitamin. Folic acid exists in nature as such and as two polyglutamic acid conjugates.

(a) *Pteroylglutamic Acid* (*PGA; Folic Acid; Folacin* [*Fig. 47*]). This has been isolated as a yellow crystalline material, very slightly soluble in water, soluble in dilute alcohol. It exhibits characteristic absorption bands in the ultraviolet and infrared ranges of the spec-

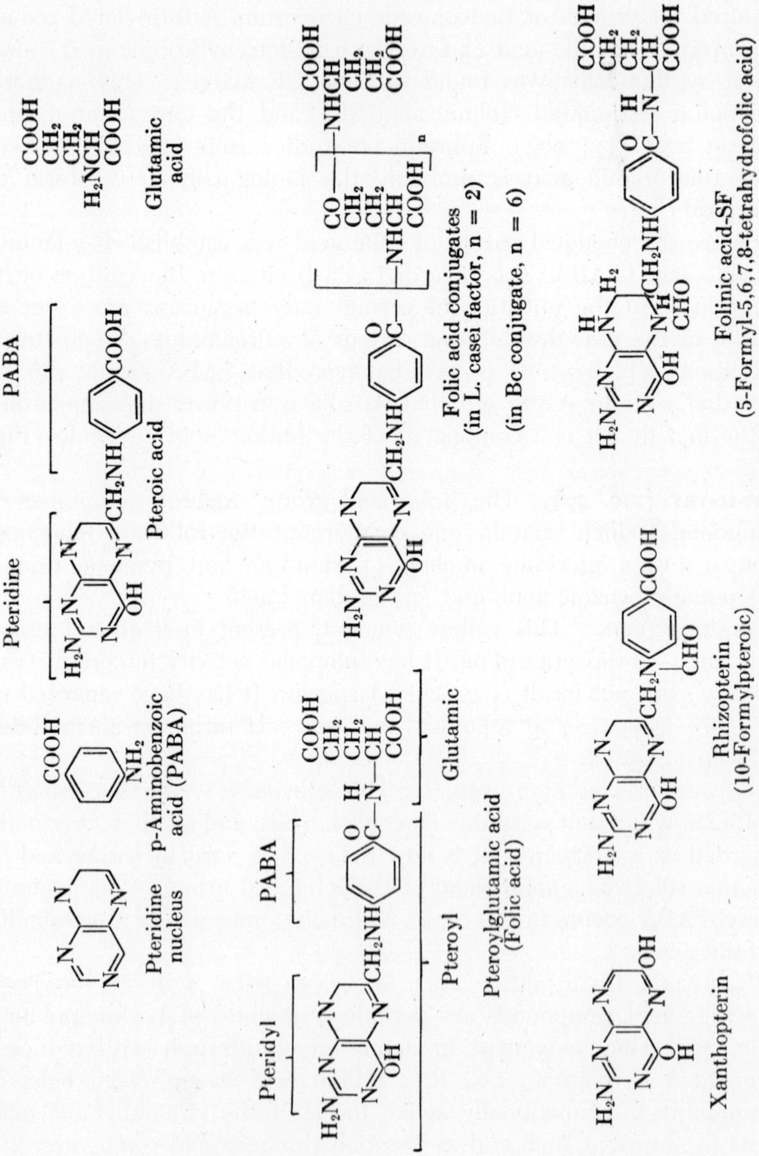

Fig. 47. Folic acid and related substances

trum. It contains a pteridine nucleus joined by a methylene linkage to the amino group of *p*-aminobenzoic acid, which is, in turn, in peptide linkage with L-glutamic acid. The designation "pteroyl" is applied to the "pteridyl-methylene-PABA" moiety.

(*b*) *Folic Acid Conjugates* (*Fig. 47*). These have the general formula, "pteroyl (glutamyl)$_n$ glutamic acid." Two such naturally occurring conjugates have been identified: (1) The fermentation L. casei factor, with three glutamic acid residues in peptide linkage, i.e., pteroyltriglutamic acid (PTG). (2) Vitamin B$_c$ conjugate, with seven glutamic residues, i.e., pteroylheptaglutamic acid (PHG). Folic acid (PGA) is liberated from these conjugates by enzymes called "conjugases."

THE FOLINIC ACID GROUP; CITROVORUM FACTOR (CF). Crude liver and yeast extracts, as well as other biological materials, contain a factor necessary for optimal growth of Leuconostoc citrovorum, which is designated "citrovorum factor" (CF) and also "folinic acid." This exhibits much greater "folic acid" activity than does PGA or its conjugates, and is regarded as the functional form of this group of vitamins (p. 201).

A substance has been prepared by formylation and reduction of folic acid (5-formyl-5,6,7,8-tetrahydro-PGA), which resembles citrovorum factor in its biological actions and is called "folinic acid–SF" (i.e., SF = synthetic factor) and also "leucovorin." The chemical identity of naturally occurring folinic acid (i.e., citrovorum factor) as folinic acid–SF (leucovorin) has not been established. The latter has approximately one-half the biological activity of the former, which has been attributed by some to the possibility that the synthetic factor may be a mixture of two optical isomers, only one of which is biologically active. However, there is evidence that the two compounds may not be identical chemically, although they are probably closely related.

Folinic acid (CF) apparently exists in nature as conjugates of glutamic acid, similar to those of folic acid.

RHIZOPTERIN (FIG. 47). This naturally occurring substance has been identified as N^{10}-formylpteroic acid.

BIOSYNTHESIS AND METABOLISM. Comparatively little is known about the mechanism of biosynthesis of folic and folinic acids, especially in man. What information is available has been derived chiefly from studies on experimental animals and microorganisms employing inhibitory compounds that act as competitive analogs of metabolites (inhibition analysis) (p. 643). Folinic acid, which may be regarded as at least one metabolically active form of the folic acid group of vitamins, can be synthesized by most microorganisms (e.g., intestinal bacteria in man and rat) grown on simple synthetic media.

Folic acid is apparently the immediate precursor of folinic acid, serving therefore as a provitamin. Administration of the former results in increased urinary excretion of the latter. The liver and kidneys are apparently active in this process. This conversion, involving presumably formylation and reduction, is stimulated by ascorbic acid. Conversely, subjects with scurvy (ascorbic acid deficiency) excrete relatively small amounts of CF in the urine, even after administration of folic acid. Moreover, a megaloblastic anemia (p. 209) occurs in scorbutic monkeys, which is corrected by administration of small amounts of folinic acid more readily than by large amounts of folic acid.

It has been claimed that vitamin B_{12} stimulates the transformation of PGA to CF in the chick. This has not been observed in the rat. Furthermore, administration of PGA to subjects with pernicious anemia results in an increase in urinary excretion of CF as in normal subjects, indicating that there is no significant interference with this transformation in the presence of vitamin B_{12} deficiency (p. 209).

Xanthopterin has been regarded as a possible precursor (pteridine nucleus), inasmuch as it has some folic acid activity in certain species (monkey, rat). There is evidence, however, that it may act as an inhibitor of biological inactivation of folic acid rather than as a factor in its synthesis.

Certain microorganisms require p-aminobenzoic acid for the formation of folic acid, synthesis of which may be blocked, under such circumstances, by sulfonamides (p. 636), i.e., by competitive inhibition. This is not the case in animals, including man, which are not known to have an independent requirement for PABA.

Active folinic acid may be liberated from inactive conjugates (polyglutamic acid forms) by enzymes (conjugases) apparently identical with those which liberate folic acid (PGA) from its conjugated forms.

Under average dietary conditions, adults excrete 2.0–6 γ daily in the urine and 130–550 γ in the feces. The total amount excreted is four to seven times that contained in the diet (40–90 γ), the major portion obviously being contributed by intestinal microorganisms.

OCCURRENCE. Compounds exhibiting folic acid activity are distributed widely in nature, being present in many animal and plant tissues and microorganisms. They are particularly abundant in green leafy vegetables, yeast, and liver; other green vegetables, kidney, beef, and wheat are also good sources.

ASSAY. Folic acid activity may be assayed in animals (growth of rat, chick) or microorganisms. The microbiological methods, which are generally preferred, usually employ Lactobacillus casei and Streptococcus fecalis as test organisms. The growth response of S. fecalis may be measured turbidimetrically and that of L. casei by titration of the increment in lactic acid.

REQUIREMENT. Nothing is known regarding human quantitative requirements for folic acid or its derivatives. This is due mainly to the fact that most if not all of our needs in this connection are supplied by synthesis of these factors by intestinal bacteria. The requirement is apparently increased during pregnancy, lactation, and early infancy (active growth).

Vitamins B_{12} (Cobalamins) (Anti-pernicious Anemia Factor)

It has been recognized for many years that certain animal proteins contain a growth factor (or factors) not present in vegetable foods nor in yeasts. This was termed the "animal protein factor" (APF). In 1948, a crystalline substance was isolated from liver which was found to produce clinical remission in patients with pernicious anemia and was apparently the "anti-pernicious anemia factor." The same substance was isolated from cultures of several microorganisms, and the material from both sources was found to possess "animal growth factor" activity in rats and chicks. Shortly thereafter, information was gained concerning certain aspects of its chemical constitution, and the designation "cobalamin" was applied to it; much of the chemical structure, however, is not yet known (Fig. 48).

CHEMISTRY. Substances possessing vitamin B_{12} activity are reported to have an elemental composition expressed by the formula, C_{61-64} $H_{86-92} N_{14} O_{13} PCo$, to which the designation "cobalamin" has been applied. Certain degradation products have been identified: (1) 1-α-D-ribofuranosido-5,6-dimethylbenzimidazole (α-ribazole); (2) D-1-amino-2-propanol; (3) one containing phosphorus. The 5,6-dimethylbenzimidazole is in glycosidic linkage with a molecule of ribose, which is phosphorylated at C_2 or C_3. The benzimidazole nucleus is linked to cobalt by a coordinate bond (Fig. 48). The nature of the remaining, major portion (R) of the molecule is not known.

Vitamin B_{12} occurs in different forms, with similar biological activities. All contain the "cobalamin" nucleus. The designation "B_{12}" is applied to cyanocobalamin, in which CN is bound coordinatively to the Co atom. Accordingly, B_{12a} (same as B_{12b}) is hydroxocobalamin. Chlorocobalamin and sulfatocobalamin have been prepared, also possessing B_{12} activity. It has been suggested that these should more properly be designated "aquocobalamin chloride" and "aquocobalamin sulfate," respectively (i.e., salts of aquocobalamin).

One of the important properties of vitamin B_{12} is its capacity for binding with certain proteins (e.g., "intrinsic factor"). This phenomenon plays an important role in connection with the "anti-pernicious anemia action" of this vitamin (p. 209).

BIOSYNTHESIS AND METABOLISM. Vitamin B_{12} is synthesized in abundance by intestinal bacteria, but largely in the colon, where its absorption is questionable. However, the apparently small amount

(1 γ daily) required may possibly be provided from this source. Although certain degradation products (viz., 5,6-dimethylbenzimidazole; 1,2-diamino-4,5-dimethylbenzene) exhibit B_{12} activity in the rat when given in large doses, there is no evidence that vitamin B_{12} is synthesized *de novo* by animal tissues. Parenteral administration of cobalt is followed by an increased tissue content of a substance that resembles vitamin B_{12} chemically but is biologically inactive.

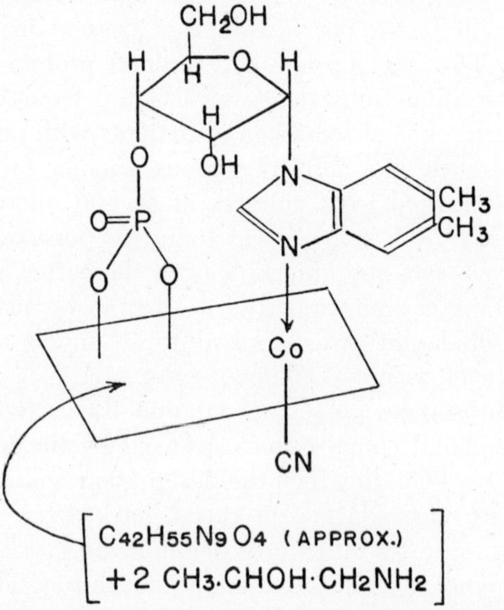

Fig. 48. *Suggested structure of vitamin* B_{12} *(cyanocobalamin). The portion shown in detail has been established, viz., 2' or 3' -phosphoryl-1-α-D-ribofuranosyl-5,6,-dimethylbenzimidazole (α-ribazole phosphate). The remaining (major) portion of the molecule is an unidentified Co-CN complex, the Co being linked to the benzimidazole by a coordinate linkage*

Vitamin B_{12} is not absorbed from the intestine in the absence of the "intrinsic factor," a non-dialyzable, thermolabile substance present in normal gastric juice and saliva, the chemical nature of which is unknown. Pertinent information in this connection is presented elsewhere (p. 209). There is little precise information regarding its intermediary metabolism. After ingestion (man) of even large amounts (10 mg.) no vitamin B_{12} activity is detectable in the urine. This vitamin is excreted in the urine, however, after intravenous injection. It is excreted in the milk under physiological conditions, the quantity increasing with increased intake of the vitamin. The liver is apparently an important storage site.

OCCURRENCE. Substances with vitamin B_{12} activity are present in liver, eggs, milk, meats, and fish. The liver is apparently an important storage site. However, after feeding vitamin B_{12} (chick), the highest concentrations have been found in the kidneys, somewhat less in the liver, pancreas, and heart muscle, and low concentrations in skeletal muscle. Minute amounts are probably present in all animal cells. Peculiarly, vitamin B_{12} is not found in significant quantities in higher plants and yeasts.

ASSAY. Microbiological and chemical assay procedures are available. The former are not entirely satisfactory. The latter are based either on (1) determination of 5,6-dimethylbenzimidazole released by hydrolysis of the vitamin, or (2) determination of CN released from cyanocobalamin. Vitamin B_{12} may also be assayed on the basis of the hematological response of patients with pernicious anemia in relapse.

REQUIREMENT. Parenteral administration of as little as 1 γ of vitamin B_{12} daily can maintain a patient with pernicious anemia in complete remission. Several times this amount should perhaps be provided in order to insure absorption of an adequate quantity from the intestine. As indicated elsewhere (p. 205), although large amounts of vitamin B_{12} are synthesized by intestinal bacteria, probably very little if any is available to man from this source because it is produced largely in the colon, where its absorption is highly questionable.

Functions of Folic Acid, Folinic Acid, Vitamin B_{12}

Although their exact metabolic role has not been established, it is probable that the functional forms of these factors serve as coenzymes in certain important biological mechanisms concerned mainly with growth, development, and hemopoiesis. Evidence available at present suggests that they function specifically in the formation and utilization of single carbon units, related to formate, for synthetic purposes. This subject is considered in detail elsewhere (p. 542). It will suffice here merely to outline the most important types of reaction in which these factors appear to be involved. In many, of these the nature of the interrelationships between folic and folinic acids and vitamin B_{12} is not clear. It has been suggested that the formation or metabolic availability of the single carbon unit may be facilitated by vitamin B_{12} and that folinic acid (formed from folic) may serve as a carrier of this unit (formyl group) in the same manner as nicotinamide serves as a carrier of hydrogen. This plausible hypothesis is not readily applicable to certain of the demonstrated actions of these principles, although many could be explained on this basis.

REACTIONS INVOLVING FOLIC ACID, FOLINIC ACID, VITAMIN B_{12}. These factors are required for the following reactions:

(a) SERINE ⇌ GLYCINE (P. 519). The reductive condensation of glycine and a formic acid derivative to form serine, and also the oxidative cleavage of serine to form glycine and a single carbon unit.

(*b*) FORMATION OF LABILE METHYL GROUPS (P. 540). Utilization of formate, methanol, acetone, and formaldehyde as sources of labile methyl groups (vitamin B_{12} not invariably involved) (p. 541). As a result of this general function, a number of methylation reactions are facilitated, including the following:

1. Homocysteine $\rightarrow$ methionine (p. 537).
2. Formation of choline (p. 538).
3. Synthesis of creatine (p. 539).

(*c*) NUCLEIC ACID SYNTHESIS (P. 566). Animals deficient in folic and folinic acids and/or vitamin B_{12} exhibit a decreased capacity for utilizing CO_2, formate, and glycine for nucleic acid synthesis. The actions of these factors in this connection apparently differ in different microorganisms and in animals, but are probably related to their influence in the formation and utilization of single carbon units. These are known to be the common source of the 2 and 8 carbons of purines and the methyl group of thymine (p. 571).

Incorporation of formate into nucleic acid purines is greatly diminished in folic acid deficient animals. In the case of certain microorganisms, at least, this effect of folic acid is exerted mainly, if not exclusively, in the synthesis of desoxyribonucleosides. In general, folic (folinic) acid is apparently necessary for the formation of purines and pyrimidines from their precursors and for interconversion of purines and pyrimidines or their ribosides (or desoxyribosides) (pp. 567, 571).

The exact role of vitamin B_{12} in purine synthesis is not clear, but it seems to be involved in the conversion of aminoimidazolecarboxamide (or a derivative) to purines. Synthesis of nucleic acid is impaired in B_{12} deficient animals. The most striking defect, however, is apparently in the formation of thymine and particularly its desoxyriboside, thymidine (p. 573). This nucleoside can replace folic and folinic acids and vitamin B_{12} for growth of certain organisms, and is included by some in the category of B vitamins. On the basis of inhibition analysis studies with L. citrovorum and L. leichmannii, it has been suggested that B_{12} is involved in synthesis of the desoxyribosides of adenine, guanine, hypoxanthine, and cytosine, whereas folinic acid is concerned with the transformation of these compounds to thymidine. This scheme is not applicable to all organisms.

(*d*) MAINTENANCE OF SULFHYDRYL GROUPS. A marked decrease in soluble HS-compounds in the blood, mainly glutathione, has been observed in vitamin B_{12} deficiency. In view of the presumed role of such compounds in cell growth, this action of vitamin B_{12} may be involved in its effect in promoting growth and hemopoiesis.

(*e*) TYROSINE OXIDATION (P. 550). Scorbutic guinea pigs given large amounts of tyrosine excrete increased quantities of phenolic metabolites in the urine (hydroxyphenyluria) (pp. 145, 551). This is apparently corrected by administration of folic acid. However, reports of the stimulating effect of PGA (*in vitro*) on tyrosine oxidation in liver homogenates from PGA-deficient animals have not been substantiated. The role of this factor in this connection is therefore questionable at the present time.

ROLE IN HEMOPOIESIS. Vitamins of the folic acid and B_{12} groups exert important effects on hemopoiesis. These are apparently related basically to the functions of these factors in nucleic acid biosynthesis. Their functions in this connection are reflected most clearly in the hematological abnormalities that characterize clinical and experimental states of deficiency in these factors, which are outlined elsewhere (p. 210).

The precise manner in which they act cannot be stated, nor can the functional relation of PGA (or CF) to vitamin B_{12}. Both act to promote development of cells of the erythroid series beyond the megaloblast stage. Inadequacy in vitamin B_{12} results in accumulation of megaloblasts in the bone marrow (arrested development) and a macrocytic type of anemia, accompanied by other features characteristic of pernicious anemia (p. 211). The hematological abnormalities are corrected either by vitamin B_{12} (parenteral) or by PGA (or CF) (but not always completely by the latter). On the other hand, similar hematological manifestations resulting from PGA deficiency are corrected by PGA (or CF) but often not by vitamin B_{12}. The reasons for these similarities and differences in action are not understood.

Vitamin B_{12} stimulates local maturation of megaloblasts when introduced into the bone marrow (or in marrow cultures). Neither PGA nor CF exerts this local effect; presumably they must be converted to an active hemopoietic substance elsewhere in the body.

VITAMIN B_{12} AND "INTRINSIC ANTI-PERNICIOUS ANEMIA FACTOR." According to current concepts, pernicious anemia is due to deficiency in vitamin B_{12}, which, under physiological conditions, is required for normal erythropoiesis beyond the stage of megaloblasts. This factor is therefore termed the "erythrocyte maturation factor," deficiency in which results in a megaloblastic type of bone marrow (p. 210).

Normal gastric juice (also saliva) contains a non-dialyzable (protein ?), thermolabile substance, the "intrinsic factor," also called "apoerythein," which combines stoichiometrically with vitamin B_{12}, the "extrinsic factor," to form a complex, "erythrotin." The nature of the intrinsic factor has not been established. It is unlikely that the gastric glandular mucoprotein is the main carrier of this factor, as has been suggested.

Ingestion of vitamin B_{12} by patients with pernicious anemia results in excretion in the feces (unabsorbed) of 70 to 95 per cent of the amount ingested, as compared to 5 to 30 per cent of that ingested by normal subjects or by those with pernicious anemia given normal gastric juice simultaneously. No hematological effect is produced in the first instance (except with very large doses), whereas a prompt response occurs in the latter case. Vitamin B_{12}, given parenterally in minute doses (1 γ daily), is effective in producing complete remission in patients with pernicious anemia. These observations indicate that a factor present in normal gastric juice, i.e., the intrinsic factor, is required for absorption of vitamin B_{12}, i.e., extrinsic factor, from the intestine. This factor is absent from the gastric juice in pernicious anemia.

The mechanism of action of the intrinsic factor is not understood, although the fact that it is essential for adequate absorption of vitamin B_{12} is firmly established. It had been suggested that binding of cobalamin by this agent may render the former unavailable for utilization by intestinal bacteria, which would otherwise deprive the host (man) of amounts of the vitamin required for normal erythrocyte maturation. This hypothesis is not supported by evidence now available. Possibly the intrinsic factor acts to permit binding of cobalamin (B_{12}) by the intestinal mucosa, facilitating its subsequent penetration into the lining epithelial cells.

Manifestations of Deficiency of Folic Acid, Folinic Acid, Vitamin B_{12}

Vitamins of the folic acid and B_{12} group are essential for normal growth of microorganisms and many animal species (e.g., human, monkey, rat, pig, guinea pig, dog, fowl). Their growth effects are particularly striking in rapidly developing tissues, such as embryonic and hematopoietic, and certain types of neoplasms.

Deficiency in PGA is produced in experimental animals most readily in two ways: (1) by feeding certain sulfonamides, which inhibit growth of intestinal bacteria (by blocking PABA utilization) and, therefore, PGA synthesis; (2) by administration of certain inhibitory analogs of folic acid (e.g., aminopterin) (p. 643). Abnormalities of blood formation are outstanding clinical features of PGA deficiency. Other manifestations include growth retardation, weakness, lethargy, reproduction difficulties (infertility [female], fetal resorption, congenital abnormalities), and inadequate lactation. The bone marrow shows evidences of arrested development of all elements (erythroid, myeloid, thrombocytes). Megaloblasts and myeloblasts accumulate at the expense of more mature cells, viz., erythroblasts, normoblasts, and myelocytes. The number of megakaryocytes decreases. The peripheral blood picture reflects these production defects, being characterized by one or more of the following, depending mainly on the degree of deficiency: a macrocytic type of anemia, at times with normoblasts, erythroblasts, and megaloblasts; granulocytopenia, occasionally with myelocytes; thrombocytopenia.

The general and hematological manifestations reviewed above occur also in experimental and clinical vitamin B_{12} deficiency. In addition, other important features appear, particularly in man: (1) mucosal atrophy and inflammation of the tongue (glossitis), mouth (stomatitis), and pharynx (pharyngitis); (2) degenerative lesions of the posterior and lateral columns of the spinal cord (combined system disease), resulting in peripheral sensory disturbances, hyperactive reflexes, ataxia, and paralysis. These, with the hematological manifestations, comprise the clinical picture of pernicious anemia. In its spontaneously occurring form in man, this is due usually to absence of intrinsic factor in the gastric juice (atrophy of gastric mucosa) and consequent lack of intestinal absorption of adequate amounts of vitamin B_{12}. It may occur also following total gastrectomy.

On the basis chiefly of prompt response to specific replacement therapy, the following clinical conditions have been attributed to folic acid deficiency:

1. Nutritional macrocytic anemia (dietary deficiency in PGA).

2. Megaloblastic anemia of infancy (dietary PGA deficiency).

3. Megaloblastic anemia of pregnancy (mechanism unknown; relative PGA deficiency ?).

4. Macrocytic anemia in liver disease (inadequate storage or conversion ?).

5. Megaloblastic anemia in sprue (inadequate absorption).

6. Macrocytic anemia after extensive intestinal resection (inadequate absorption).

7. Macrocytic anemia in infestation with Diphyllobothrium latum (fish tape worm) (inadequate absorption).

Vitamin B_{12} is usually not very effective in the treatment of these conditions in the majority of cases. On the other hand, folic acid (or CF) produces improvement in the hematological abnormalities of vitamin B_{12} deficiency, although often not completely. It is also apparently required for a full response to vitamin B_{12}. However, folic acid (or CF) has no beneficial effect on the neurological manifestations of B_{12} deficiency, for the prevention or treatment of which this vitamin is specifically required (i.e., in pernicious anemia).

INOSITOL

Inclusion of inositol in the category of vitamins rests mainly on the relatively few manifestations of deficiency that develop in mice (and possibly rats), and on the fact that it is a growth essential for certain strains of yeasts, molds, and fungi. On the other hand, it occurs in animal and plant tissues (phosphatides) in much larger

amounts than do substances classified as vitamins. Moreover, no catalytic function has yet been demonstrated for inositol (p. 170). Its
status as a B vitamin is therefore questionable.

Inositol was originally (1850) isolated from muscle (*inos* = muscle),
and was referred to commonly as "muscle sugar." Its general chemical
structure was suggested in 1887 and was established in 1942 (*i*-inosi-
tol). It was identified as one of the "bios" factors necessary for optimal
growth of certain yeasts in 1928. Subsequent studies in animals revealed the occurrence of alopecia as a specific manifestation of inositol
deficiency in mice (1940) and demonstrated its significant lipotropic
action under certain conditions (1941).

CHEMISTRY.   Inositol is a cyclic compound, hexahydroxycyclohexane
(empirical formula $C_6H_{12}O_6$). It may be regarded as a cyclicized
glucose, the aldehyde group of which has been converted to a secondary alcohol group, with linkage of carbon atoms 1 and 6 (p. 9).
The term is applied to a group of stereoisomers (at least nine), four
of which have been identified in biological materials, and three others
synthesized. These are sometimes referred to as "the inositols." The
form occurring most commonly in nature, the only isomer shown to
have important biological activity, is commonly designated "myo-,"
"meso-," or "*i*-inositol," or simply "inositol." It has two meta-positioned
OH groups in one spatial plane and the other four in a different
plane with respect to the cyclohexane ring.

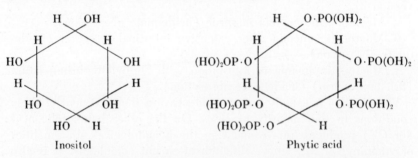

Inositol   Phytic acid

Inositol is a colorless crystalline substance with a high melting point
(225° C.), soluble in water, insoluble in alcohol and ether.

Because of its alcoholic nature it forms esters, the most important
of which, biologically, are the phosphoric acid esters, which are distributed widely in nature. The hexaphosphoric acid ester is "phytic
acid." Mono- and dimethyl ethers are the only other known naturally
occurring derivatives of inositol (e.g., in rubber). One of the important chemical properties of phytic acid is its capacity for forming
highly insoluble salts with calcium and magnesium (phytin) in the
intestine, thus diminishing absorption of these elements (p. 610)
(rachitogenic action).

OCCURRENCE AND FOOD SOURCES. Inositol is present in many plants, microorganisms, and animal tissues, occurring sometimes in free, but mainly in combined, forms. Hexaphosphoric acid esters comprise the bulk of the latter, usually in the form of mixed calcium and magnesium salts (phytin). These may account for as much as 85 per cent of the phosphorus of seeds and cereal grains, in which they occur in high concentrations (also mono-, di-, and triphosphoric acid esters). Inositol occurs in animal tissues, mainly in combination with phosphoric acid, but as esters containing less than six phosphate groups (except avian erythrocytes). Highest concentrations of inositol in man are found, in decreasing order, in brain, stomach, kidney, spleen, and liver; smaller amounts are present in blood, muscle (high in heart muscle), and other tissues.

Inositol is present in plants (e.g., soybeans) as a constituent of phosphatides ("lipositols") (p. 33), replacing glycerol as the poly-alcohol component. Lipositols have been found also in yeasts, tubercle bacilli, brain and spinal cord (cephalins), and liver.

BIOSYNTHESIS AND METABOLISM. The structural relation of inositol to glucose (p. 212) raises the possibility of a metabolic relationship between these substances. This may be of a dual nature: (1) glucose (by cyclization) may serve as a precursor in the synthesis of inositol; (2) inositol may be converted to glucose in the body. Evidence on both of these points is suggestive but inconclusive, at least for animals. Inositol has been found to alleviate ketosis (rat) produced by dietary carbohydrate restriction and to give rise to small amounts of glucose (up to 7 per cent) in phlorizinized rats.

Free inositol is readily absorbed from the intestine, as are inositol-containing phosphatides. Salts of the phosphoric acid esters are also absorbed, the monophosphate apparently more rapidly than free inositol. It is probable that phytates (hexaphosphates) are at least partially hydrolyzed in the intestine, the extent varying in different species and with different diets. Phosphorus from this source is partially utilizable by man. In certain species (e.g., mouse, rat), synthesis by intestinal bacteria provides an adequate and available supply of inositol to the organism. This is possibly the case also in man.

ASSAY. Chemical methods are available but are not as specific nor as satisfactory as microbiological procedures. The most widely used of the latter are based on the growth response of certain strains of yeasts or of Neurospora as compared to that induced by known amounts of inositol.

REQUIREMENT. There are no recognized manifestations of inositol deficiency in man and, therefore, the human requirement is unknown. The daily intake on an average adequate diet has been estimated as approximately 1 gram.

FUNCTIONS; ACTIONS; DEFICIENCY MANIFESTATIONS.   Apart from the fact that inositol is a component of certain phosphatides, there is little precise knowledge of its physiological actions (if any) or functions. Certain aspects of its possible role in nutrition are suggested by the consequences of experimentally induced deficiency and by its influence on cholesterol metabolism and liver fat.

No manifestations attributable to inositol deficiency have been recognized in man. This may be due, in part at least, to its synthesis by intestinal bacteria, which is known to occur, or by body tissues, for which there is no evidence. Much of the literature on experimental inositol deficiency is confused and misleading because of lack of understanding, at the time, of the importance of intestinal bacterial synthesis of this substance and of the influence of other B vitamins on this process. There are apparently striking species differences in this connection; the most definitive data have been obtained in the mouse. In this species, inositol deficiency causes alopecia (loss of hair), growth retardation, and even death. In certain strains, pantothenic acid is necessary, and in other strains p-aminobenzoic acid, in addition to inositol, for prevention of the alopecia. Data obtained in the rat and other species (pig, rabbit, fowl) are contradictory and inconclusive.

LIPOTROPIC ACTION (P. 477).   Rats fed certain fat-free diets containing choline and B vitamins other than inositol develop fatty liver which is prevented or corrected by administration of inositol, but not choline. Addition of fat to the diet prevents this lipotropic effect of inositol, whereas choline is effective under such circumstances. For its lipotropic action, choline apparently requires a supply of unsaturated fatty acids, whereas these inhibit this effect of inositol. However, these two agents apparently act synergistically in this connection, combined therapy producing a greater diminution in liver fat than the sum of the effects of each given singly. Inositol has been found to decrease liver fat in patients with gastrointestinal cancer.

A specialized influence is exerted in cholesterol metabolism. In rats, inositol lowers the cholesterol ester content of the liver and the concentration of both free and esterified cholesterol in the blood plasma. Similar observations have been reported in patients with hypercholesterolemia (diabetes mellitus and other conditions), but such findings are by no means consistent. Studies in this direction have been stimulated considerably by the suggested relationship between hypercholesterolemia and atherosclerosis.

The mechanism underlying the lipotropic action of inositol is not clear. The fact that it is a component of certain phosphatides suggests that this may be an important factor in this connection, as is believed to be the case with choline. However, in contrast to the latter (p. 467), administration of inositol apparently does not increase the rate of turnover of liver phosphatides, which casts doubt on the validity of this hypothesis. It has been suggested that inositol, glycerol, and cholesterol, all of which form esters with fatty acids, may compete with one another for combination with the latter or with certain fatty acids preferentially. The lipotropic ineffectiveness of inositol in the presence of triglycerides, and its inhibition of cholesterol ester formation, might be explicable on this basis, i.e., preferential affinities for certain fatty acids.

α-LIPOIC ACID

The water-insoluble fraction of liver (also yeast) remaining after removal of known B vitamins contains certain bacterial growth factors. One of these was originally designated the "pyruvate oxidation factor" (POF) because it is required for oxidative decarboxylation of pyruvate by Streptococcus fecalis. The term "protogen A" was applied to a factor necessary for the growth of the protozoan, Tetrahymena gelii. A factor that can replace acetate for growth of Lactobacillus casei was called "L. casei acetate factor." The substance apparently responsible for these actions has been isolated and designated "α-lipoic acid." Its chemical structure has been established as 6,8-dithio–octanoic acid (6-thioctic acid) (p. 361).

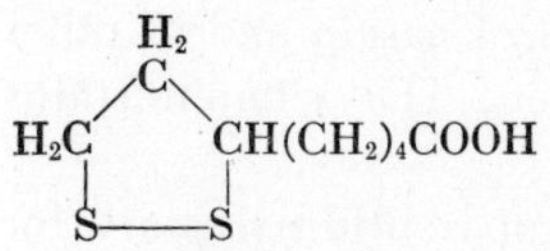

α-Lipoic acid

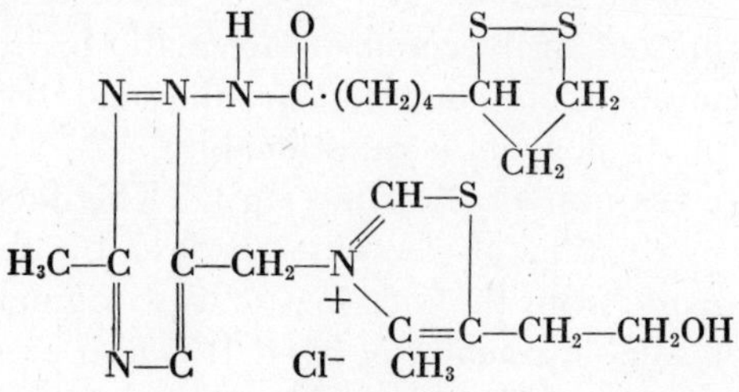

Lipothiamide

In free form it is soluble in fat solvents. It occurs in nature also in combined form, from which the active factor can be released by hydrolysis. This is apparently "lipothiamide pyrophosphate" (p. 175), in which α-lipoic acid is joined to thiamine pyrophosphate by an amide bond (p. 361). A bacterial enzyme capable of effecting synthesis of this compound has been designated "lipoic acid conjugase." This active factor (lipothiamide pyrophosphate) is a necessary cofactor in the oxidative decarboxylation of pyruvate (forming acetyl-CoA) and α-ketoglutarate (forming succinyl-CoA) (p. 397). Transformation of pyruvate to acetate, therefore, is now known to require at least four coenzymes: DPN, thiamine pyrophosphate, CoA, and α-lipoic acid (POF, protogen A, L. casei acetate factor).

POSTULATED VITAMIN-B FACTORS

Certain naturally occurring materials rich in known B vitamins contain additional factors that stimulate growth of certain microorganisms and experimental animals. Their significance in human nutrition is unknown.

VITAMIN B_{13}. This designation has been applied to a principle, prepared in highly concentrated form from liver, yeast (distillers' solubles), and rice polishings, that stimulates growth in rats, pigs, and chicks maintained on purified diets supplemented with sulfonamides. It has been reported to be related chemically to orotic acid (4-carboxy-uracil) (p. 571).

VITAMIN B_T. This factor is a growth requirement for a few insect species; e.g., mealworm (Tenebrio molitor) larvae deficient in this substance die before undergoing metamorphosis. It has been identified as carnitine (betaine of β-hydroxy-γ-aminobutyric acid), a muscle extractive.

$$(CH_3)_3 \cdot \overset{+}{N} \cdot CH_2 \cdot \overset{\overset{\textstyle OH}{|}}{CH} \cdot CH_2 \cdot COO^-$$

STREPOGENIN. This term is applied to a factor of unknown structure, which stimulates growth of certain strains of hemolytic streptococci and lactobacilli and also of mice. It is apparently a peptide and is present in liver and in enzymatic hydrolysates of casein and of other purified proteins, e.g., insulin and trypsinogen. The vitamin status of strepogenin is questionable.

LIVER RESIDUE FACTOR (LRF). This factor is apparently necessary for production of xanthine oxidase by the rat intestine. It derives its name from the fact that it was originally demonstrated in the water-insoluble fraction of liver. It is also present in milk, cream, and yeast.

CHOLINE (P. 479). There seems to be no justification for regarding choline as a vitamin, although it was originally considered a member of the B complex. It serves no catalytic function, and the manifestations associated with choline deficiency are known now to be reflections of deficiency in labile methyl groups (p. 537).

BIBLIOGRAPHY

General

Annual Review of Biochemistry.
Annual Review of Physiology.
Vitamins and Hormones (annual volumes), New York, Academic Press, Inc.
Clark, G. W.: A Vitamin Digest, Springfield, Ill., Charles C Thomas, Publisher, 1953.
Dann, W. J.: The appraisal of nutritional status in humans, Physiol. Rev. 25:326, 1945.
Eddy, W. H. and Dalldorf, G.: The Avitaminoses, Baltimore, Williams & Wilkins Company, 1944.

Follis, R. H., Jr.: The Pathology of Nutritional Disease, Springfield, Ill., Charles C Thomas, Publisher, 1948.
Handbook of Nutrition, American Medical Association, Philadelphia, Blakiston Company, 1951.
Johnson, B. C.: Methods of Vitamin Determination, Minneapolis, Burgess Publishing Company, 1948.
Lowry, O. H.: Biochemical evidence of nutritional status, Physiol. Rev. 32:431, 1952.
Rosenberg, H. R.: Chemistry and Physiology of the Vitamins, New York, Interscience Publishers, Inc., 1942.

Vitamin A

General references.
Deuel, H. J., Jr.: The Lipids. Their Chemistry and Biochemistry. Volume I: Chemistry, New York, Interscience Publishers, Inc., 1951, p. 667.
Wald, G.: Vision, Federation Proc. 12:606, 1953.
Zechmeister, L.: Stereoisomeric provitamins A, Vitamins & Hormones 7:57, 1949.

Vitamin C

General references.
King, C. G.: Vitamin C, J.A.M.A. 142:363, 1950.
Ralli, E. P. and Sherry, S.: Adult scurvy and the metabolism of vitamin C, Medicine 20:251, 1941.

Vitamin D

General references.
Albright, F. and Reifenstein, E. C., Jr.: Parathyroid Glands and Metabolic Bone Disease, Baltimore, Williams & Wilkins Company, 1948.
Deuel, H. J., Jr.: The Lipids: Their Chemistry and Biochemistry. Volume I: Chemistry, New York, Interscience Publishers, Inc., 1951, p. 739.
Jeans, P. C.: Vitamin D, J.A.M.A. 143:177, 1950.
Nicolaysen, R.: Physiology of calcium metabolism, Physiol. Rev. 33:424, 1953.

Vitamin E

General references.
Deuel, H. J., Jr.: The Lipids: Their Chemistry and Biochemistry. Volume I: Chemistry, New York, Interscience Publishers, Inc., 1951, p. 373.
Hickman, K. C. D. and Harris, P. L.: Tocopherol interrelationships, Advances in Enzymology 6:469, 1946.

Vitamin K

General references.
Almquist, H. J.: Vitamin K, Physiol. Rev. 21:194, 1941.
Dam, H.: Vitamin K, Vitamins & Hormones 6:28, 1948.
Deuel, H. J., Jr.: The Lipids: Their Chemistry and Biochemistry. Volume I: Chemistry, New York, Interscience Publishers, Inc., 1951, p. 829.

Vitamin P

General references.
Scarborough, H. and Bacharach, A. L.: Vitamin P, Vitamins & Hormones 7:1, 1949.

B Vitamins (General)

General vitamin references.
Horwitt, M. K., Kreisler, O. and Wittman, P.: Investigations of human requirements for B-complex vitamins, Bull. No. 116, Washington, National Research Council, 1948.
Robinson, F. A.: The Vitamin B Complex, New York, John Wiley & Sons, Inc., 1951.
Williams, R. J., Eakin, R. E., Beerstecher, E., Jr. and Shive, W.: The Biochemistry of B Vitamins, New York, Reinhold Publishing Corporation, 1950.

Thiamine

General B vitamin references.
Jansen, B. C. P.: The physiology of thiamine, Vitamins & Hormones 7:84, 1949.

Riboflavin

General B vitamin references

Niacin (Nicotinic Acid)

General B vitamin references.
Krehl, W. A.: Niacin in amino acid metabolism, Vitamins & Hormones 7:111, 1949.

Pyridoxine

General B vitamin references.

Pantothenic Acid

General B vitamin references.
Lipmann, F.: On chemistry and function of coenzyme A, Bacteriol. Rev. 7:1, 1953.

Biotin

General B vitamin references.
Lichstein, H. C.: Functions of biotin in enzyme systems, Vitamins & Hormones 9:27, 1951.

Folic and Folinic Acid Groups and Vitamin B_{12}

General B vitamin references.
Darby, W. J.: The physiological effects of pteroylglutamates in man, Vitamins & Hormones 5:119, 1947.
Hutchings, B. L. and Mowat, J. H.: The chemistry and biological action of pteroyl-glutamic acid and related compounds, Vitamins & Hormones 6:1, 1948.
Jukes, T. H.: Pteroylglutamic acid and related compounds, Physiol. Rev. 28:51, 1948.
Jukes, T. H.: Folic acid and vitamin B_{12} in the physiology of vertebrates, Federation Proc. 12:633, 1953.
Jukes, T. H. and Stokstad, E. L. R.: The role of vitamin B_{12} in metabolic processes, Vitamins & Hormones 9:1, 1951.
Petering, H. J.: Folic acid antagonists, Physiol. Rev. 32:197, 1952.
Reisner, E. H., Jr.: The present status of vitamin B_{12} in pernicious anemia, Bull. New York Acad. Med. 25:429, 1949.
Shive, W.: The functions of B vitamins in the biosynthesis of purines and pyrimidines, Vitamins & Hormones 9:76, 1951.
Shive, W.: B-vitamins involved in single carbon unit metabolism, Federation Proc. 12:639, 1953.
SubbaRow, Y. et al.: Folic acid, Ann. New York Acad. Sc. 48:255, 1946.

Inositol

General B vitamin references.
Weidlein, E. R., Jr.: The biochemistry of inositol, Bull. No. 6, Mellon Institute Bibliographic Series, 1951.

α-Lipoic Acid

Ann. Rev. Biochem. 22:598, 1953.

Postulated Vitamin-B Factors

General B vitamin references.

7

ENZYMES

INTRODUCTION

The major task of metabolism is to provide energy for the maintenance of life. This is accomplished by degrading chemical compounds of relatively high potential energy to products of low potential energy. The energy evolved in such processes is collected, stored, and utilized by the cell for those functions, the totality of which we call "life."

Certain limitations are placed upon the chemical reactions of the body, owing to the necessity of preserving a "physiological" environment in the tissues. Thus, the pH cannot vary far from neutrality (in many parts of the body a pH of 7.4 is maintained), temperatures cannot exceed 37°–38° C., and corrosive or poisonous reagents must not be used. The oxidation of a fatty acid to carbon dioxide and water in the test tube is not a gentle process; extremes of pH, high temperatures, and corrosive chemicals are required. Yet, in the body, such a reaction goes on smoothly and rapidly under the restricted conditions enumerated above. This remarkable state of affairs is explained by the presence in the body of a group of powerful catalysts, the enzymes.

The phenomenon of catalysis can be explained by referring to the diagram in Figure 49. A represents a molecule which can undergo cleavage to the products C. Since A is at a higher potential energy level than C, the conversion $A \rightarrow C$ should be spontaneous and occur with the liberation of energy. Actually, the fact that a reaction is spontaneous does not guarantee that it will proceed at a significant rate. The conversion of the reactant to the products requires rupture of the bond which connects the two parts of the original molecule. Final cleavage of this bond is preceded by a "loosening" process, involving transformation of the molecule A to the form B, often called the "activated complex." Since the activated molecule B is at a some-what higher potential energy level than A, it is obvious that an initial "push" must be given to A before any reaction can occur.

In any large collection of molecules, some will have higher energies than others, owing to energy transfers between molecules and for other reasons. Hence, at ordinary temperatures and in the absence of other influences, certain molecules of the A type will acquire enough energy to reach the activated state. The conversion to C will proceed, but possibly at a slow rate. The addition of a catalyst to the system will speed up the reaction, facilitating the conversion of A to B by actually lowering the amount of energy required in the initial "push" to reach the activated state.

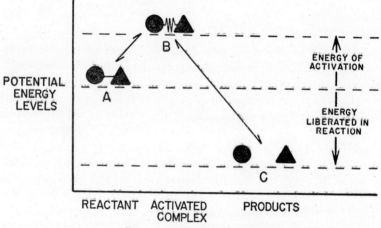

Fig. 49. *Activation of reactants*

As shown in the diagram, it is possible for the products of the reaction to recombine and re-form the reactant. Since this requires an input of energy equal to that liberated in the forward reaction, plus an extra increment of energy for activation, the rate of this reverse reaction will be low. At equilibrium, therefore, the ratio of products to reactant will be high in this particular example. The point of equilibrium is determined by the energy difference between the reactant and the products. Catalysts do not affect the position of this equilibrium; they merely hasten its attainment, since they influence equally the transformation of either reactant or products to the activated complex.

While the catalysts in non-living systems seem to possess a variety of chemical structures (hydrogen ions, spongy platinum, etc.), all enzymes which have been secured in a pure state have proved to be proteins. They therefore exhibit all of the attributes of proteins, such as denaturation and precipitation with salts, solvents, and other reagents, and are of colloidal dimensions. Many enzymes belong to the class of simple proteins, while others contain firmly bound non-protein groups, hence are conjugated proteins. The digestive enzymes are liberated into the digestive tract from the cells which synthesize them, and are called "extracellular enzymes." Most other enzymes are intracellular. The specific nomenclature of enzymes is discussed in a later section.

GENERAL MECHANISMS OF ENZYME ACTION

ENZYME-SUBSTRATE COMBINATION. The substrate is the compound the chemical transformation of which is catalyzed by the enzyme. It seems quite possible that all catalytic reactions involve a temporary union of the substrate with the catalyst. At any rate, there is direct evidence that such combinations occur in the case of enzymatic catalysis. The activated complex referred to in the previous action probably exists as this sort of combination when a catalyst is present. Figure 50 illustrates the concepts involved. The enzyme (a protein)

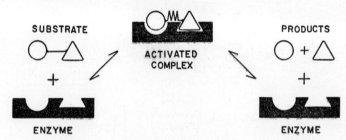

Fig. 50. Enzyme action

has on its surface a reactive site into which the substrate can fit. This fit is either not quite perfect, or else there are very reactive groups in the vicinity; whatever the reason, the bond in the substrate is strained to the point of rupture, liberating the reaction products into the solution and thus regenerating the original enzyme molecule. In this way one enzyme molecule can catalyze the transformation of many substrate molecules.

One characteristic which distinguishes enzymes from the usual catalysts in non-living systems is the high degree of specificity of the former. Hydrogen ions, for instance, will catalyze with complete impartiality the hydrolysis of glycosides and that of peptides, whereas totally different enzymes are required for these two reactions. In addition, the enzymes show considerable specificity toward the groups surrounding the bond which is split or formed, even to the point of requiring a certain stereochemical configuration (e.g., D and L isomerism). It is obvious that this specificity must be due to the chemical nature of the groups at the site of action on the enzyme surface, to their disposition in space, and to the nature of their electrical charges (cf. acetylcholine esterase, p. 644).

COENZYMES AND PROSTHETIC GROUPS. Certain enzymes require for their function the presence of certain organic, dialyzable, thermostable compounds. If such a compound is rather firmly attached to the enzyme protein it is usually called a "prosthetic group," as in the case of other conjugated proteins. The group or compound is called a "coenzyme" if its attachment to the protein is not very firm. Certain coenzymes seem to exist in the free state in solution, contacting the enzyme protein only at the instant of reaction. The distinction between prosthetic groups and coenzymes is therefore quantitative, not qualitative, and is related to the magnitude of the equilibrium constant describing the dissociation of the smaller group from the enzyme protein. This general state of affairs is illustrated in Figure 51. The term "apoenzyme" is sometimes used for the protein portion of the system, which becomes a "holoenzyme" when combined with coenzyme.

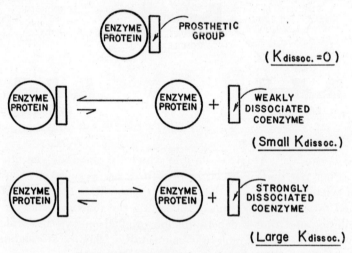

Fig. 51. *Coenzymes and prosthetic groups*

Certain coenzymes of nucleotide structure were described in the chapter on nucleoproteins (p. 104). Many coenzymes, especially those concerned with biological oxidations, contain members of the B-complex group of vitamins in their structures. In any case, they are much smaller molecules than proteins, so that they can be removed from their apoenzymes by dialysis if they are at all dissociable. Their resistance to heat makes it possible to prepare them conveniently, freed from their apoenzymes, by simply heat-denaturing the proteins in the preparation.

The function of the coenzyme in the enzymatic reaction is to assist in the cleavage of the substrate by acting as an acceptor for one of the cleavage products, as shown in Figure 52. The substrate and apoenzyme form an activated complex, but in the presence of the coenzyme. When the bond in the substrate becomes strained, one of the cleavage products (usually a small fragment of the entire substrate molecule) is transferred directly to the coenzyme, which has an appropriate receptor site in its structure. What is left of the substrate now dissociates from the apoenzyme. The fragment which is attached to the coenzyme is either liberated as such or passed on to other enzyme systems for additional changes; in either case the coenzyme is regenerated. Both apoenzyme and coenzyme are then able to repeat the same cycle of events, hence it can be said that both act catalytically. A prosthetic group acts in an analogous fashion, the only difference being that the acceptor of the substrate fragment remains attached to the surface of the apoenzyme.

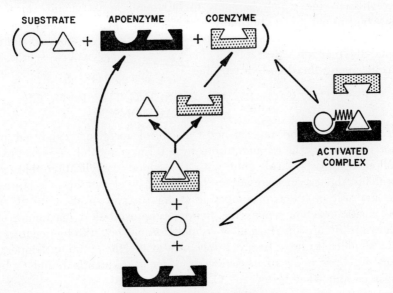

Fig. 52. Function of coenzymes

SPECIFIC ION ACTIVATORS. When the requirement of certain enzyme systems for dialyzable cofactors is examined, it is found that specific inorganic ions are necessary for the reaction to proceed. Thus, many reactions involving phosphorylation seem to require magnesium ions, while cobalt, manganese, magnesium, or zinc ions are necessary for the action of various peptide-splitting enzymes. It is probable that many of the apoenzymes in these cases are actually metalloproteins with rather loosely bound metallic ions.

In those cases in which the function of the metal in an enzyme system has been well established, it seems to be directly concerned in the reaction. The metallic component of certain oxidative enzyme systems (Cu, Fe) may undergo valence changes in accepting electrons from substrates which are being oxidized. In the peptide-splitting systems, the metallic ion joins with groups on the substrate molecule and assists the protein part of the enzyme system in creating a "strain" on that bond of the substrate which is to be cleaved. The requirement of certain enzymes for univalent ions, such as K^+, is difficult to explain.

ZYMOGENS. Certain enzymes are synthesized in an inactive state, in which condition they are known as proenzymes or zymogens. The conversion of these substances to active enzymes is effected by agents which are more or less specific. One zymogen is transformed to an active enzyme by hydrogen ions, another by a specific activating enzyme which is synthesized for that purpose, and a third by a proteolytic enzyme which happens to be found in its vicinity in the gastrointestinal tract. In many instances the active enzyme, once formed, can itself act as an activator of its own zymogen, an autocatalytic reaction. Most of the known cases of zymogen synthesis occur among the digestive enzymes.

PHYSICAL FACTORS INFLUENCING THE RATE OF ENZYMATIC REACTIONS

TEMPERATURE. The rate of most chemical reactions, catalyzed or not, increases as the temperature is raised. Enzyme-catalyzed reactions follow the general rule, but with the added complication that, as proteins, the enzymes are adversely affected by elevated temperatures. As a result of the two competing factors, a plot of the rate of an enzymatic reaction versus the temperature exhibits a maximum, as shown in Figure 53. Since most animal enzymes begin to be denatured at a significant rate at temperatures over 40° C., the optimum temperature in experiments of moderate duration is frequently found to be near or somewhat below 40° C.

pH. Enzymes, being proteins, cannot withstand the action of strong acid or base. However, even over the pH range in which inactivation does not occur, enzymes exhibit optima in their activity (Fig. 54). In the case of an enzyme which attacks non-ionic substrates, the optimum pH is constant for the several substrates. The optimum in the curve, then, must correspond to some particular configuration of electrical charges on the reactive surfaces of the enzyme protein, in which condition the action on the substrate is most efficient. Ionized substrates will themselves vary in electrical properties over the pH range, so that enzymes attacking such substances often show pH optima which differ from one substrate to another. In these examples the peak in the curve must be a resultant, or compromise, between the most efficient, charged states of the enzyme and substrate.

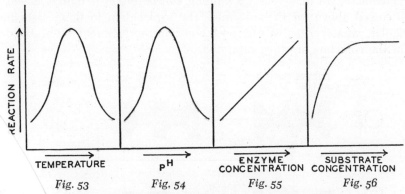

REACTION RATE

TEMPERATURE   pH   ENZYME CONCENTRATION   SUBSTRATE CONCENTRATION

Fig. 53   *Fig. 54*   *Fig. 55*   *Fig. 56*

Figs. 53–56. Effects of various factors on reaction rate

ATION OF ENZYME. The velocity of a catalyzed reaction is proportional to the concentration of catalyst. Figure 55 indicates that this generalization holds true for enzymatic reactions. It is possible that the rates of certain metabolic reactions may be limited by the localization of certain enzyme systems in discrete particles in the cell, as in the mitochondria, allowing the reaction to proceed only to the extent that substrate can diffuse into the region of the enzymes. In this way a reaction can be limited in rate throughout the cell, except in regions of high concentrations of enzyme. This localization is most appropriate if a succession of enzymes is required to effect a given metabolic transformation, and if all such enzymes are localized in the same region. Such a situation actually obtains in nature (p. 254).

CONCENTRATION OF SUBSTRATE. With a fixed amount of enzyme, it would be expected that the reaction rate should be proportional to the substrate concentration. This is true up to a point, but as shown in Figure 56, a limiting concentration is reached, beyond which increase in substrate concentration causes no further increase in the rate of the reaction. The explanation of this situation is illustrated by the diagrams in Figure 57. A hypothetical enzyme with four active sites is shown combining with a substrate at three concentration levels, each double the preceding. At the lowest concentration of substrate, only a fraction of the active sites of the enzyme is occupied by substrate molecules at any instant. Increasing the substrate concentration has the effect of increasing the coverage of active sites, until a concentration is reached which "saturates" these sites. Higher concentrations will permit no greater reaction rate than was possible with the limiting concentration, since the reaction can proceed only as rapidly as active sites become available.

CONCENTRATION OF COFACTORS. If an enzyme requires for its activity the presence of a dissociable cofactor, such as an inorganic ion or a coenzyme, the rate of the reaction will vary with the concentration of the cofactor. In many cases a limiting concentration is found, as was discussed above for the substrate. The explanation in these cases is similar; whatever active sites on the enzyme surface may be reserved for the cofactors are then saturated.

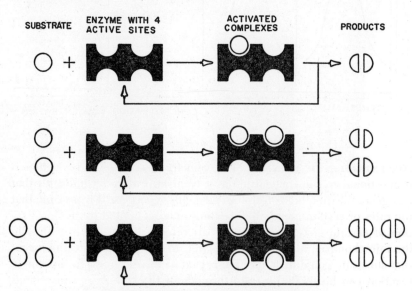

Fig. 57. *Saturation of enzyme with substrate*

CLASSIFICATION OF ENZYMES

INTRODUCTION. When enzymes were first discovered they were given various "unsystematic" names by their discoverers, such as pepsin, trypsin, ptyalin, etc. In more recent times enzymes have been designated by the suffix "-ase," preceded by a term which indicates either the general nature of the substrate, the actual name of the substrate, the type of reaction catalyzed, or a combination of several of these facts.

There is no perfect and generally accepted method for the classification of enzymes. However, a scheme which serves most purposes is presented in Table 11. The enzymes are classified first according to the general type of chemical reaction catalyzed, and, secondly, by the type of bond split or formed, the type of chemical group removed or transferred, or in some cases by a simple sub-classification of the general reaction type.

Table 11. Classification of Enzymes

A. Hydrolases
  1. Esterases
  2. Glycosidases
  3. Peptidases
  4. Amidases
  5. Amidinases
  6. Hydrolytic deaminases

B. Adding and Removing Enzymes
  1. Dehydrases
  2. Desulfhydrases
  3. Non-oxidative decarboxylases
  4. Isomerases
  5. Aldolases

C. Transferring Enzymes
  (excluding hydrogen or electron transfer)
  1. Transglycosidases
  2. Transamidases
  3. Transpeptidases
  4. Transaminases
  5. Transphosphorylases
  6. Transmethylases
  7. Transformylases
  8. Transacylases

D. Oxidizing and Reducing Enzymes
  1. Hydroperoxidases
    a. Peroxidases
    b. Catalase
  2. Aerobic oxidases
  3. Aerobic dehydrogenases
  4. Anaerobic dehydrogenases
  5. Flavoprotein transhydrogenases
  6. Transelectronases (cytochromes)

GENERAL CLASSES OF ENZYMES. The hydrolases are those enzymes which catalyze the reaction of hydrolysis, that is, the direct addition of the elements of water across the bond which is cleaved. A logical subdivision of this group of enzymes then can be made according to the type of linkage which is hydrolyzed.

"Adding and removing enzymes" is a somewhat cumbersome term, but no euphonious Latin or Greek name has as yet been invented for this group. These enzymes catalyze the removal or addition of some chemical group of a substrate, without hydrolysis, oxidation, or reduction. They differ from the transferring enzymes in that the group in question is liberated in the free state (or taken up from the free state), not merely passed on to become a part of another molecule directly. The great variety of enzymes in this group necessitates a subclassification based largely on the types of reactions involved.

The transferring enzymes catalyze the transfer or shift, from one molecule to another, of a chemical group which is not present in the free state during the transfer. The nature of the group transferred forms the basis for the sub-classification of these enzymes. Although, strictly speaking, the transfer of hydrogen atoms or electrons can be included in this group, such reactions have complexities and peculiarities all their own, and for convenience are best classified separately.

Biological oxidations are chiefly dehydrogenations or de-electronations. The enzymes catalyzing such reactions almost all require coenzymes, or contain prosthetic groups or heavy metals. One system of classification is based on the nature of this non-protein substance which is essential to the reaction. However, the relationship of these enzymes to the general reactions of intermediary metabolism is made somewhat clearer if they are classified with reference to their actual position in the sequence of events which constitutes the over-all oxidation of natural substrates. The detailed explanation of this and related matters will be left to the section on biological oxidations (p. 354).

HYDROLASES

Some of the common types of biologically important hydrolytic reactions are shown on the opposite page.

CARBOXYLESTERASES. The hydrolysis of esters is catalyzed by a group of enzymes called "esterases," which are listed in Table 12 with their typical substrates and their occurrence. By carboxylesterases is meant those enzymes which catalyze the hydrolysis of the esters of carboxylic acids. Triglycerides are hydrolyzed by lipases, whereas simple esters, such as ethyl butyrate, are split most readily by another esterase which has a quite different distribution in animal tissues. Acetylcholine, a compound of considerable physiological importance, is hydrolyzed by a number of enzymes. One type has a higher affinity for its natural substrate than for any other ester, and is called "acetylcholine esterase." Other esterases are known which attack choline esters more actively than the non-choline esters, but differ from the previously mentioned enzyme in their affinity for various substrates; these enzymes are designated "choline esterases." Since acetylcholine is concerned in the chemical mediation of the transmission of nervous impulses, the physiological function of acetylcholine esterase is thought to be the rapid destruction of the substrate, thus allowing for single rather than continuous nervous discharges. Specific inhibitors of this enzyme have been used in therapy for many years (parasympathomimetics), but the mechanism of their action has been clarified only recently (cf. also p. 645). Cholesterol esters are split by enzymes which have a rather wide distribution. Lecithinases of Type A remove one fatty acid molecule (probably an unsaturated one) from lecithins and cephalins, producing the lysolecithins and lysocephalins, from which the remaining fatty acid is removed by the lecithinases of Type B.

SULFATASES. Certain natural substrates as well as some of the products

$$R_1-C\overset{O}{\diagup}O-R_2 \xrightarrow{H_2O} R_1COOH + R_2OH \qquad R-C\overset{O}{\diagup}NH_2 \xrightarrow{H_2O} RCOOH + NH_3$$

$$RO\!\mid\!SO_3H \xrightarrow{H_2O} ROH + H_2SO_4 \qquad R-NH\!\mid\!\overset{NH}{\overset{\|}{C}}-NH_2 \xrightarrow{H_2O} RNH_2 + NH_2-\overset{O}{\overset{\|}{C}}-NH_2$$

$$R_1-\overset{NH_2}{\underset{}{CH}}-C\overset{O}{\diagup}NH-\underset{\overset{|}{R_2}}{CH}-COOH \xrightarrow{H_2O} R_1-\overset{NH_2}{\underset{}{CH}}-COOH + R_2-\overset{NH_2}{\underset{}{CH}}-COOH$$

$$R-O\!\mid\!PO_3H_2 \xrightarrow{H_2O} ROH + H_3PO_4 \qquad R-CH_2\,NH_2 \xrightarrow{H_2O} RCH_2OH + NH_3$$

$$R-O-\overset{O}{\overset{\|}{\underset{\underset{OH}{|}}{P}}}-O-R' \xrightarrow{H_2O} R-O-\overset{O}{\overset{\|}{\underset{\underset{OH}{|}}{P}}}-OH + HOR'$$

$$R-C\overset{O}{\diagup}O-PO_3H_2 \xrightarrow{H_2O} RCOOH + H_3PO_4$$

$$R-O-\overset{O}{\overset{\|}{\underset{\underset{OH}{|}}{P}}}-O-\overset{O}{\overset{\|}{\underset{\underset{OH}{|}}{P}}}-O-R' \xrightarrow{H_2O} R-O-\overset{O}{\overset{\|}{\underset{\underset{OH}{|}}{P}}}-OH + HO-\overset{O}{\overset{\|}{\underset{\underset{OH}{|}}{P}}}-O-R'$$

Common types of biologically important hydrolytic reactions

of intestinal putrefaction are coupled with sulfuric acid by the tissues. The hydrolysis of these sulfate esters is catalyzed by the sulfatases, a group of enzymes about which very little is known. The physiological significance of some of the enzymes listed in Table 12 is not at all certain.

PHOSPHATASES. The phosphatases comprise a large group of enzymes, many of which are involved in important phases of digestion or inter-

Table 12. Esterases

CLASS OR INDIVIDUAL ENZYME	TYPICAL SUBSTRATE	OCCURRENCE
I. Carboxylesterases		
Simple esterases	Simple esters	Liver, muscle
Acetylcholine esterases	Acetyl choline	Nervous tissue, muscle, red cell
Choline esterases	Various choline esters	Serum, pancreas
Cholesterol esterases	Cholesterol esters	Blood, pancreas, liver, kidney, spleen, intestinal mucosa
Lecithinase A	Lecithin, cephalin	Pancreas, liver, kidney, heart, muscle, adrenals
Lecithinase B	Lysolecithin, lysocephalin	Pancreas, etc.
Lipase	Fats	Stomach, pancreas
II. Sulfatases		
Phenolsulfatase	Aromatic sulfate esters	Liver, adrenal, kidney
Glycosulfatase	Carbohydrate esters	Mollusc livers
Myrosulfatase	Potassium myronate (sinigrin)	Liver, muscle, kidney
III. Phosphatases		
A. Phosphomonoesterases of low specificity		
Alkaline phosphatase (pH 8.6–9.4)	Many alcoholic or phenolic monoesters	Plasma, bone, kidney, intestinal mucosa, mammary gland
Acid phosphatase (5.0–5.5)	Many alcoholic or phenolic monoesters	Liver, prostate, spleen, kidney
Acid phosphatase (3.4–4.2)	Many alcoholic or phenolic monoesters	Liver, spleen
Acid phosphatase (5.0–6.0)	Many alcoholic or phenolic monoesters	Red cells
B. Phosphomonoesterases of higher specificity		
Hexosemonophosphatase	Glucose-6-phosphate	Liver, kidney
Hexosediphosphatase	Fructose-1,6-diphosphate	Liver, kidney
5-Nucleotidase	5-Nucleotides (adenosine-5-phosphate, inosine-5-phosphate)	Testis, retina, nervous tissue, prostate, sperm
C. Phosphodiesterases, low specificity		
Alkaline phosphodiesterase (8.5–9.0)	Many diesters of orthophosphoric acid	Serum, liver, kidney
Acid phosphodiesterase (5.5)	Many diesters of orthophosphoric acid	Serum, liver, kidney
D. Phosphodiesterases, higher specificity		
1. Simple diesterases cholinephosphatase (lecithinase C)	-Glyceryl-phosphoryl$\frac{\mid}{\mid}$choline	Pancreas, intestinal mucosa, kidney, liver, brain
Glycerophosphatase (lecithinase D)	-Glyceryl$\frac{\mid}{\mid}$phosphoryl-choline	Pancreas, intestinal mucosa, kidney, liver, brain
2. Polynucleotidases		Pancreas, liver, spleen, lungs, leukocytes
Ribonuclease	RNA	
Desoxyribonuclease	DNA	Pancreas, intestinal mucosa

Table 12. Esterases (Continued)

E. Anhydrophosphatases
  1. Polyphosphatases

Pyrophosphatase	$H_4P_2O_7$	Intestinal mucosa, muscle, heart, liver, kidney
Metaphosphatase	$(HPO_3)_n$	Liver, kidney
Triphosphatase	$H_5P_3O_{10}$	Intestinal mucosa
Non-specific "apyrase"	ATP	Muscle, liver, heart
Adenylpyrophosphatase	ATP	Muscle, liver, brain
2. Phosphoacylases	Acyl phosphates	Muscle, liver

mediary metabolism. They can be divided for convenience into the monoesterases and diesterases, the substrates for which are singly or doubly esterified phosphoric acid, respectively. Each of these groups seems to be subdivided into two sub-groups, one of low and one of high specificity. As can be seen in the table, the phosphomonoesterases of low specificity are called "alkaline" or "acid" phosphatases, according to their pH optima. The alkaline phosphatase, in addition to its role in hydrolysis of phosphate monoesters in the digestive tract, probably plays an important part in the absorption of sugars from the intestine, the reabsorption of glucose in the kidney tubules, and the calcification of bones and teeth. Its level in plasma is increased markedly in certain diseases of bone and in obstructive jaundice. Among the various acid phosphatases, that of the prostate is of special medical significance, since metastasizing cancer of the prostate often results in high levels of this enzyme in the plasma, where it is normally found in minimal amounts.

While the phosphatases mentioned thus far show little preference for specific substrates, a few exhibit much more limited activity. The hexosemonophosphatase and hexosediphosphatase of liver and kidney, for instance, are quite specific for glucose-6-phosphate and fructose-1,-6-diphosphate, respectively. They are both important in the anaerobic phase of carbohydrate metabolism (p. 392). Most so-called "nucleotidases," especially those of the intestinal tract, have turned out to be identical with the non-specific phosphomonoesterases on closer investigation. However, a nucleotidase specific for adenosine-5-phosphate (or its deaminated derivative) has been found in certain tissues.

Phosphodiesterases of low specificity are located in several tissues. Their metabolic role has yet to be established. On the other hand, there is evidence that the phosphoryl-choline and the glyceryl-phosphate linkages which occur in some phospholipids are hydrolyzed by more specific diesterases, called "lecithinase C" and "lecithinase D," or "choline phosphatase" and "glycerophosphatase." Specific diesterases attacking the two types of nucleic acids are ribonuclease and desoxyribonuclease. The general term "nuclease" is sometimes used to include all enzymes concerned in the hydrolysis of nucleic acids. The action of these two enzymes is not a simple random attack upon all the diester linkages in the substrates, for recent investigations have shown that pyrimidine-containing fragments are split off preferentially.

Although the anhydrides of phosphoric acid with itself or with other acids are not esters by any means, the enzymes which catalyze their hydrolysis are generally considered together with the true phosphoesterases. Of the polyphosphatases, those which attack inorganic pyrophosphate, metaphosphate, and triphosphate are found in many tissues, but their biological significance is obscure at present. On the other hand, the specific adenylpyrophosphatase (ATP-ase) which produces inorganic orthophosphate and adenosine diphosphate from adenosine triphosphate would seem to play an important role in the regulation of the rate of intermediary metabolism (p. 402). Apyrase is the name given to whatever system or systems catalyze the hydrolysis of adenosine triphosphate to adenylic acid and two molecules of orthophosphate, no difference in specificity being shown between the terminal and the central phosphoric acid group in the substrate.

Mixed anhydrides of phosphoric acid and carboxylic acids exist in plants, animals, and microorganisms, examples being acetyl phosphate and 1,3-diphosphoglyceric acid (the 1-phosphate only). The enzymes which attack such substrates have not been studied extensively, but the one which catalyzes the hydrolysis of acetyl phosphate and its higher homologs (as well as succinyl phosphate) is abundant in liver and muscle.

SIMPLE GLYCOSIDASES AND OLIGOSACCHARIDASES. The second large group of hydrolytic enzymes includes those which attack glycosidic linkages. As indicated in Table 13, they may be divided into two subgroups, the first being those enzymes which are specific for the simple glycosides and the oligosaccharides, the second comprising those enzymes which attack the polysaccharides. Enzymes hydrolyzing carbohydrates are sometimes collectively called "carbohydrases."

α- and β-Glycosidic linkages are hydrolyzed by different groups of enzymes. Among the α-glycosidases are maltase, which hydrolyzes maltose and a few related compounds, and sucrase, also called "invertase," from its catalysis of the inversion of sucrose (p. 13). The invertase of yeast differs from that of animal tissues; the former is a β-fructosidase, whereas the latter has its specificity directed toward the α-glucosidic half of the substrate molecule. Various β-glucosides and β-galactosides are hydrolyzed by enzymes which have been called "β-glucosidases" and "β-galactosidases," but there is still some controversy over the separate existence of these two groups. In any case, the disaccharide lactose is hydrolyzed by whatever system attacks β-galactosides generally, not by a specific lactase.

β-Glucuronidase, an enzyme attacking the glycosidic linkage in natural and synthetic glucuronides, has been implicated in estrogen metabolism and in the process of cell division and multiplication. The level of this enzyme in various tissues is increased by administration of estrogens, a finding which may be correlated with the conjugation of estrogens with glucuronic acid in the body. Increased amounts of the enzyme have also been found in certain tumors.

Table 13. Glycosidases

ENZYME	SUBSTRATE	OCCURRENCE
I. Simple glycosidases and oligosaccharidases		
A. α-Glycosidases		
Maltase	Maltose	Intestinal juice
Sucrase (glucosaccharase, (glucoinvertase)	Sucrose	Intestinal juice
B. β-Glycosidases		
β-Glucosidase	Various β-glucosides	Kidney, liver, intestinal mucosa
β-Galactosidase (lactase)	Various β-galactosides	Kidney, liver, intestinal mucosa
β-Glucuronidase	β-Glucuronides	Spleen, liver, endocrines
II. Polysaccharidases		
A. Homopolysaccharidases		
Exoamylases (β-amylases)	Starch, glycogen	Higher plants
Endoamylases (α-amylases)	Starch, glycogen	Saliva, pancreas, blood muscle, liver
B. Heteropolysaccharidases (Mucopolysaccharidases, mucases)		
Hyaluronidase	Hyaluronic acid	Testis, spleen, skin, cornea
Lysozyme	Polysaccharides of Micrococcus lysodeikticus	Nasal secretions, egg-white
Sulfomucase	Chondroitin sulfate, mucoitin sulfate, heparin	Testis, liver
Mucodextrinases	Partially degraded mucopolysaccharides	?
Oligomucases	Oligosaccharides from mucopolysaccharides	Testis

POLYSACCHARIDASES. Of the various enzymes which catalyze the hydrolysis of the homopolysaccharides, the amylases are most important in mammalian metabolism, since their substrates include the starches and glycogen. In the body, except in the digestive tract, glycogen is broken down by phosphorolysis, not hydrolysis (p. 391). There are two types of amylases, differing considerably in their modes of action. The exoamylases or β-amylases are found chiefly in the higher plants. They produce β-maltose from the substrate, appear to attack the ends of the polysaccharide chains, form no non-fermentable products, and cause only a slow decrease in the viscosity of starch solutions. Amylose is split completely, amylopectin and glycogen only at the end-chains up to the branching points. Salivary and pancreatic amylases belong to the group of endoamylases or α-amylases. These enzymes attack the interior of polysaccharide chains, forming products of the α-configuration. Althought some reducing sugar and fermentable substances are produced throughout the reaction, the main course of events is the breakdown of the polysaccharides first to dextrins (accompanied by marked reduction in the viscosity of the solution), followed by a slower phase of maltose formation. The animal amylases require the presence of chloride or related anions for their activity. Since the action of the amylases is limited to α-1,4-glucosidic linkages, the 1,6-branch-points in amylopectin and glycogen must be hydrolyzed by other enzymes, similar to the amylo-1,6-glucosidase recently discovered in muscle. It is a curious fact that preparations of salivary or pancreatic amylase will not attack raw starch, although this substance is known to be well utilized by the intact organism. It has been suggested that auxiliary enzymes are present in the pancreatic juice, enabling the organism to digest this substrate.

As was pointed out in the chapter on carbohydrate chemistry, the nitrogenous heteropolysaccharides (mucopolysaccharides) are the only members of this group which need be considered in animal metabolism. Hyaluronic acid (p. 19) is said to be hydrolyzed by "hyaluronidase," although it seems probable at the present time that the commonly used enzyme preparations are quite heterogeneous. The general course of hydrolysis of hyaluronic acid is thought to pass through a series of stages which are analogous to those occurring during the hydrolysis of starch by amylase; i.e., a series of dextrins (mucodextrins in this case), followed by a stage of muco-oligo-saccharides, leading finally to glucuronic acid and acetylglucosamine. There is some evidence that these intermediate stages involve the action of separate enzymes, as indicated in Table 13. Since hyaluronic acid acts as an intercellular cement, the fact that certain pathogenic microorganisms possess hyaluronidases has been thought to be related to their invasiveness. Attempts have also been made to relate hyaluronidase to the fertilization of the ovum and to the invasiveness of malignant cells, but these hypotheses are not widely held at the present time. Nevertheless, with the present interest in hyaluronic acid and disorders of the mesenchyme, an important role for hyaluronidase will probably be established eventually.

Micrococcus lysodeikticus contains, in its cell wall, a mucopolysaccharide which is hydrolyzed by lysozyme, an enzyme found in egg-white and in the nasal secretions. No metabolic role has as yet been shown for this enzyme.

The name "sulfomucase" has been given to enzymes hydrolyzing the sulfate-containing mucopolysaccharides, such as chondroitin sulfate, mucoitin sulfate, and heparin. These enzymes are presumably distinct from the hyaluronidases, although their number, identity, and characteristics are not established. A partially purified heparinase has been prepared from liver.

EXOPEPTIDASES. Peptide linkages are hydrolyzed by a large group of enzymes, sometimes called "proteases," listed in Table 14. There are

Table 14. Peptidases

ENZYME	SUBSTRATE	OCCURRENCE
I. Exopeptidases		
Carboxypeptidase	—NH—CHR—CO⊹NH—CHR′—COOH phenylalanine tyrosine tryptophan leucine	Pancreas
Folic acid conjugases	Pteroyl-glutamyl⊹glutamyl⊹glutamic acid	Various tissues
Leucine aminopeptidase	NH₂CHR⊹CO—NH—CHR′—CO leucine	Intestinal mucoa
Aminotripep-tidase	NH₂CHR—CO⊹NH—CHR′—CO—NH—CHR′—COOH	Intestinal mucosa, thymus, muscle
Glycylglycine dipeptidase	Glycyl⊹glycine	Muscle, uterus
Glycylleucine dipeptidase	Glycyl⊹leucine	Muscle, intestinal mucosa, uterus
Prolidase	Glycyl⊹proline	Intestinal mucosa, muscle
Prolinase	Prolyl⊹glycine	Intestinal mucosa
Carnosinase	β-alanyl⊹L-histidine (carnosine) glycyl⊹L-histidine -L-alanyl⊹L-histidine -D-alanyl⊹L-histidine	Kidney
Dehydropeptidase I	$$NH_2—CH_2—CO⊹NH—\overset{\overset{CH_2}{\|\|}}{C}—COOH$$	All tissues
Dehydropeptidase II	$$Cl—CH_2—CO⊹NH—\overset{\overset{CH_2}{\|\|}}{C}—COOH$$	Kidney, liver, pancreas
Alanine peptidases	Glycyl⊹alanine	Intestinal mucosa
	Alanyl⊹glycine	Intestinal mucosa
Glutathione peptidases	γ-Glutamyl⊹cysteinyl-glycine	Kidney
	γ-Glutamyl-cysteinyl⊹glycine	Liver, muscle, kidney
II. Endopeptidases		
Pepsin	-glutamyl⊹tyrosyl- -glutamyl⊹phenylalanyl- -cysteinyl⊹tyrosyl- -tyrosyl⊹cysteinyl-	Gastric mucosa
Rennin	Casein	Gastric mucosa
Trypsin	-arginyl⊹ -lysyl⊹	Pancreas
Chymotrypsin	-tyrosyl⊹ -phenylalanyl⊹ -tryptophanyl⊹ -methionyl⊹	Pancreas
Cathepsin I	Carbobenzoxy-glutamyl⊹tyrosine	Spleen, liver, kidney
Cathepsin II	Benzoyl-arginyl⊹amide	Spleen, liver, kidney
Cathepsin III	Leucyl⊹amide	Spleen, liver, kidney
Cathepsin IV	Carbobenzoxy-glycyl⊹phenylalanine	Spleen, liver, kidney
Cathepsin V-a	Glycyl-phenylalanyl⊹amide	Spleen, liver, kidney
Cathepsin V-b	Phenylalanyl⊹amide	Spleen, liver, kidney

two subdivisions of the peptidases: the exopeptidases are limited in their action to terminal peptide bonds, whereas the endopeptidases can hydrolyze peptide linkages whether terminal or in the interior of the peptide chain. The specificity of the peptidases is further determined by the nature of the side-chain groups in the amino acid residues on either side of the peptide linkage.

Carboxypeptidase, an exopeptidase, is synthesized by the pancreas in the form of a zymogen which is converted to the active enzyme on standing or by the action of trypsin. The highly purified, crystallized enzyme contains magnesium in firm combination. As indicated by its name, it requires the presence of a free carboxyl group on the amino acid residue which contributes its amino group to the peptide linkage being attacked. Peptides containing the amino acid termini indicated in the table are hydrolyzed with the greatest speed; others are attacked more slowly.

The vitamin, folic acid (pteroylglutamic acid), occurs in nature in a number of polyglutamyl conjugate forms. These are hydrolyzed by conjugases, probably types of carboxypeptidases.

Leucine aminopeptidase is found in the intestinal mucosa and many other tissues. The naturally occurring enzyme exists as a dissociable complex with magnesium, although manganese can also play the role of ion activator. Leucyl peptides are hydrolyzed more readily, but not exclusively. In contrast to the preceding enzymes, leucine aminopeptidase requires a free amino group for its action.

Aminotripeptidase hydrolyzes the peptide linkage adjacent to the free amino group of a number of tripeptides, although it is necessary that the distal carboxyl group also be free. This enzyme has little or no action on dipeptides or tetrapeptides. It is not certain at present whether it requires any metallic ion for activation.

The existence of a general dipeptidase was assumed for many years, but the evidence accumulated in recent times makes it probable that a multiplicity of dipeptidases exists, each characterized by its own specificity. Thus, glycylglycine dipeptidase hydrolyzes the peptide named and practically no other. It requires cobalt ions. Glycylleucine dipeptidases are found in several tissues, that from rabbit muscle and hog intestinal mucosa being activated by manganese, whereas the corresponding enzymes from rat muscle or human uterus require zinc. Prolidase and prolinase (see Table 14) are apparently distinct enzymes, although both are activated by manganese. Carnosinase is the name given to the enzyme which hydrolyzes carnosine, a peptide occurring in rather large quantities in animal tissues. As indicated in the table, the action is not entirely specific. Either zinc or manganese can serve as activator, but the former is probably the one involved in nature. Enzymes attacking certain alanine dipeptides are shown in the table, although they have not been well characterized as yet.

"Dehydropeptides," formed by the linkage of various residues to the amino group of dehydroalanine or dehydrophenylalanine, are hydrolyzed to the acylating compound, an α-keto acid, and ammonia by enzymes known as dehydropeptidases. There are two types of dehydropeptidases, differing in their distribution in tissues and in their specificity toward special test substrates, as shown in the table. Since there is some evidence against the occurrence of dehydropeptides as metabolic intermediates, the biological significance of these enzymes remains to be established.

The naturally occurring tripeptide, glutathione, is hydrolyzed in two steps. Glutaminase, a kidney enzyme responsible for the hydrolysis of the γ-amide linkage of glutamine, also removes the γ-glutamyl residue from glutathione. Magnesium is required. The cysteinyl-glycine linkage is cleaved by a second enzyme.

ENDOPEPTIDASES. Pepsin is the most thoroughly studied of all the endopeptidases. It is secreted by the gastric mucosa in the form of the inactive pepsinogen, which is converted to pepsin under the influence of hydrogen ions, and also by the autocatalytic action of pepsin itself. The conversion involves the splitting off of an inhibitor, a basic peptide of 5000 molecular weight. It is of interest that pepsinogen has an isoelectric point of pH 3.7, while pepsin is anionic even at pH 1.0. This difference is probably accounted for by the nature of the inhibitor. Pepsin also has a lower molecular weight than pepsinogen, the difference again being explained by the removal of the inhibitory peptide. Pepsin contains no special prosthetic groups other than a molecule of phosphoric acid. Its specificity is directed toward those peptide linkages formed by the amino groups of phenylalanine or tyrosine, the action being accelerated by the presence of a carboxyl group (glutamic acid) in the immediate vicinity. Recently such combinations as cysteinyl-tyrosyl- and tyrosyl-cysteinyl- have been shown to be suitable substrates also. The hydrolysis of proteins by pepsin exhibits a pH optimum in the range 1.5–2.5. Pepsin also possesses a milk-clotting action (see rennin, below), with an optimal pH of about 5.

Rennin is an enzyme found in the stomach of the young mammal, formed by the activation by hydrogen ions of the zymogen, prorennin. Although pure rennin has definite proteolytic activity, with an optimum pH of 3.7 when hemoglobin is the substrate, the chief interest in this enzyme centers about its milk-clotting activity. Under the influence of rennin, casein is converted to paracasein (pH optimum for this reaction, 5.4), which in the presence of calcium ions flocculates out of solution as a curd. Despite much effort extending over many years, the exact nature of the casein-paracasein conversion is not known.

The proenzyme trypsinogen, secreted by the pancreas, is converted to trypsin by another enzyme, enterokinase, which is found in the small intestine. The optimal pH range for this conversion extends from 6.0 to 9.0. Trypsin can also be formed autocatalytically from trypsinogen. In this case the reaction proceeds optimally at pH 7–8, and is greatly accelerated by calcium salts. The pH optimum for the hydrolysis of proteins by typsin varies somewhat with different substrates, but is usually found around pH 8. It is of interest that denatured proteins are hydrolyzed much more readily than those in the native state. Trypsin specifically attacks those peptide linkages containing the amino groups of arginine or lysine. Pancreatic extracts, soybeans, egg-white, and blood contain trypsin inhibitors which are proteins or polypeptides.

A second proteolytic enzyme originating in the pancreas is chymotrypsin, so named from its powerful milk-clotting action. Its proenzyme, chymotrypsinogen, is converted to the active enzyme by trypsin, a process thought to involve the opening of internal peptide bonds in the zymogen molecule. Chymotrypsin is rather unique among enzymes, in that six different forms have been shown to exist (thus far). The optimum pH for proteolysis by chymotrypsin is about the same as that for trypsin. There is considerable difference in specificity, however, the action of chymotrypsin being directed toward peptide linkages containing the carboxyl groups of aromatic amino acids, tryptophan, or methionine.

Intracellular proteolytic enzymes known as cathepsins are widely distributed throughout animal tissues. They are presumably responsible for the autolysis undergone by the tissues after death. In life, the cathepsins may function in the continual breakdown of tissue protein which is known to occur, and which, together with the counterbalancing synthetic reactions, forms the mechanism underlying the "dynamic state" of body proteins (p. 500). The cathepsins exhibit a range of individual specificities comparable to that of the extracellular proteinases.

AMIDASES, AMIDINASES, IMIDAZOLASES. Some of the more important amidases and related enzymes are shown in Table 15. Under the influence of urease, urea, the diamide of carbonic acid, is hydrolyzed to a molecule of carbon dioxide and two molecules of ammonia, these products forming ammonium carbonate in solution. Although it occurs in certain animal tissues, urease is predominantly a member of the plant world. The physiological significance of its presence in gastric mucosa is unknown at present. Urease was the first enzyme to be crystallized; its current importance in biochemistry derives largely from its use as an analytical reagent in the determination of blood urea.

The amides asparagine and glutamine are ubiquitous in both plant and animal kingdoms. Much of the glutamic and aspartic acid found in proteins is actually present in the form of the amides. In addition, both amides appear to function as temporary stores of ammonia, which is quite toxic to the cells and cannot be allowed to remain in the free state. When required, the ammonia is set free by the appropriate hydrolytic enzyme. In the kidney, for example, the hydrolysis of glutamine by glutaminase provides much of the urinary ammonia which plays an important role in the regulation of "acid-base" balance (p. 323).

Table 15. Amidases and Related Enzymes

ENZYME	SUBSTRATE	OCCURRENCE
Amidases		
Urease	H_2N—CO—NH_2	Bacteria, yeasts, molds, plants, mollusks, gastric mucosa
Asparaginase	$HOOC$—$CHNH_2$—CH_2—CO—NH_2	Plants, liver, kidney, spleen, pancreas, muscle
Glutaminase	$HOOC$—$CHNH_2$—CH_2—CH_2—CO—NH_2	Plants, liver, kidney, retina, brain, spleen, lung, muscle
Phosphoamidases	R—NH—$PO(OH)_2$	Liver, kidney, small intestine
Amidinases		
Arginase	NH_2—$C{:}NH$—NH—CH_2—CH_2—CH_2—$CHNH_2$—$COOH$	Liver, mammary gland, testis, kidney
Imidazolases		
Histidase	? HC══C—CH_2—CH(NH$_2$)—COOH / HN N \ CH	Liver
Urocanase	? HC══C—CH=CH—COOH / HN N \ CH	Liver

Amides of phosphoric acid, e.g., phosphocreatine, are hydrolyzed by enzymes which have not been studied extensively. The most important pathway for the dephosphorylation of phosphocreatine and related compounds is transphosphorylation (p. 377), not hydrolysis.

The amidine group of arginine is split off under the influence of arginase to yield (after a spontaneous rearrangement) urea and ornithine. This reaction is the final step in the ornithine cycle, a metabolic mechanism used by many organisms for the synthesis of urea from the nitrogen derived from the catabolism of protein (p. 513).

Histidine and the related α, β-unsaturated acid, urocanic acid, are hydrolyzed by enzymes which cleave the imidazole ring. The exact mechanism of these reactions is not known, but the end-products of histidine breakdown appear to be ammonia, formic acid, and glutamic acid. Possibly more than one enzyme is involved in the over-all reaction.

HYDROLYTIC DEAMINASES. Although deamination of amino acids in animal tissues proceeds via an oxidative route, or by a special mechan-

Table 16. Hydrolytic Deaminases

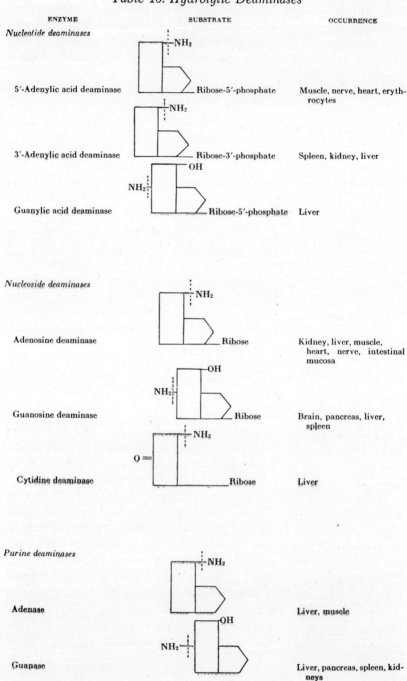

ENZYME	SUBSTRATE	OCCURRENCE
Nucleotide deaminases		
5'-Adenylic acid deaminase	Ribose-5'-phosphate	Muscle, nerve, heart, erythrocytes
3'-Adenylic acid deaminase	Ribose-3'-phosphate	Spleen, kidney, liver
Guanylic acid deaminase	Ribose-5'-phosphate	Liver
Nucleoside deaminases		
Adenosine deaminase	Ribose	Kidney, liver, muscle, heart, nerve, intestinal mucosa
Guanosine deaminase	Ribose	Brain, pancreas, liver, spleen
Cytidine deaminase	Ribose	Liver
Purine deaminases		
Adenase		Liver, muscle
Guanase		Liver, pancreas, spleen, kidneys

ism known as transamination, removal of the amino group from purines and pyrimidines and their derivatives is catalyzed by hydrolytic enzymes (Table 16). Thus, adenine (as the free purine, the nucleoside, or nucleotide) is converted to the corresponding hydroxy-compound, hypoxanthine, while guanine and cytosine form xanthine and uracil, respectively. The deaminated nucleotide formed from 5'-adenylic acid is known as inosinic acid, and may be produced in some of the side reactions of muscle contraction. It is probable that hydrolytic deaminases exist for all purines and pyrimidines bearing amino groups, but this group of enzymes has not been studied in detail in animal tissues.

ADDING AND REMOVING ENZYMES

DEHYDRASES. The dehydrases and other adding and removing enzymes are listed in Table 17. Enolase is an enzyme of importance in the anaerobic metabolism of carbohydrate, while fumarase is involved in the aerobic phases of the oxidation of carbohydrate as well as other foodstuffs. Both enzymes catalyze the reversible removal or addition of a molecule of water from or to their respective substrates. The enolase reaction is of special importance in bioenergetics, since it results in the formation of a "high-energy" phosphate bond (p. 376). Enolase requires magnesium for its action, and is inhibited by fluoride.

The over-all glyoxalase reaction shown in the table actually occurs in two steps; in the first, methyl glyoxal is condensed with glutathione (a coenzyme for this reaction) under the influence of an enzyme; in the second step, the complex is broken down in a slow spontaneous reaction, or more rapidly in the presence of a second enzyme, forming the hydroxy acid and regenerating the glutathione. It is of interest that the lactic acid thus produced is of the D configuration, whereas L-lactic acid is formed in the normal anaerobic metabolism of carbohydrate. Although methyl glyoxal is in all probability not a normal intermediate, it may be formed in small quantities by the spontaneous decomposition of triose phosphates (p. 392); the glyoxalase reaction may then have a "mopping up" function.

Serine and threonine are deaminated by a rather unusual reaction. A molecule of water is removed from the β-hydroxyl group and a hydrogen atom on the α-carbon. The resulting amino-acrylic acid derivative spontaneously hydrolyzes to yield a molecule of ammonia and the keto acid.

Carbonic anhydrase is a zinc-containing enzyme, inhibited by rather low concentrations of the sulfa drugs. Its catalysis of the reversible hydration of CO_2 is of great importance in gas transport in the blood (p. 293) and secretion of acid by the kidney (p. 322).

DESULFHYDRASES. Reactions analogous to the dehydrations of serine and threonine are undergone by cysteine and homocysteine (the amino

Table 17. Adding and Removing Enzymes

ENZYME	REACTION	OCCURRENCE
Dehydrases		
Enolase	Phosphoglyceric acid $\overset{-H_2O}{\underset{+H_2O}{\rightleftharpoons}}$ phosphoenolpyruvic acid	All tissues
Fumarase	Fumaric acid $\overset{+H_2O}{\underset{-H_2O}{\rightleftharpoons}}$ malic acid	All tissues
Glyoxalase	Methyl glyoxal $\overset{+H_2O}{\longrightarrow}$ lactic acid	Yeast, liver, kidney, muscle
Serine dehydrase	Serine $\overset{-H_2O}{\longrightarrow}$ pyruvic acid + ammonia	Liver
Threonine dehydrase	Threonine $\overset{-H_2O}{\longrightarrow}$ α-ketobutyric acid + ammonia	Liver
Carbonic anhydrase	$CO_2 + H_2O \rightleftharpoons H_2CO_3$	Red cells, gastric mucosa, renal tubules
Desulfhydrases		
Cysteine desulfhydrase	Cysteine → pyruvic acid + H_2S + ammonia	Bacteria, liver, pancreas, kidney
Homocysteine desulfhydrase	Homocysteine → α-ketobutyric acid + H_2S + ammonia	Liver, kidney, pancreas
Exocystine desulfhydrase	Cystine peptides	Most normal, but not cancer tissues
Non-oxidative decarboxylases		
Dopa decarboxylase	Dopa → dopamine + CO_2	Kidney (man); liver, intestine, pancreas (in some species)
Glutamic acid decarboxylase	Glutamic acid → γ-aminobutyric acid + CO_2	Brain, bacteria
Tyrosine decarboxylase	Tyrosine → tyramine + CO_2	Kidney
Histidine decarboxylase	Histidine → histamine + CO_2	Intestine (man); liver, kidney, intestine (in other species)
Tryptophan decarboxylase	Tryptophan → tryptamine + CO_2	Kidney
Cysteic acid decarboxylase	Cysteic acid → taurine + CO_2	Liver
Pyruvic acid decarboxylase	Pyruvic acid → acetaldehyde + CO_2	Plants
Oxalacetic acid decarboxylase	Oxalacetic acid → pyruvic acid + CO_2	Liver, plants
Oxalosuccinic acid decarboxylase	Oxalosuccinic acid → α-ketoglutaric acid + CO_2	All tissues
Ketoglutaric acid decarboxylase	α-Ketoglutaric acid → succinic semialdehyde + CO_2	All tissues
Isomerases		
Aconitase	Citric acid $\overset{-H_2O}{\underset{+H_2O}{\rightleftharpoons}}$ cis-aconitic acid $\overset{+H_2O}{\underset{-H_2O}{\rightleftharpoons}}$ isocitric acid	All tissues
Phosphotriose isomerase	Phosphoglyceraldehyde ⇌ phosphodihydroxyacetone	All tissues
Phosphohexose isomerase	Glucose-6-phosphate ⇌ fructose-6-phosphate	All tissues
Phosphoribose isomerase	Ribose-5-phosphate ⇌ ribulose-5-phosphate	Liver
Phosphomannose isomerase	Glucose-6-phosphate ⇌ mannose-6-phosphate	Muscle
Phosphogalactose isomerase (Galactowaldenase)	Galactose-1-phosphate $\underset{?}{\rightleftharpoons}$ glucose-1-phosphate	Liver
Aldolases		
Hexose diphosphate aldolase	Fructose-1,6-diphosphate ⇌ glyceraldehyde-3-phosphate + dihydroxyacetone-3-phosphate	All tissues
Pentose phosphate aldolase	Ribose-5-phosphate ⇌ glyceraldehyde-3-phosphate + glycolaldehyde (?)	Liver
Desoxypentose phosphate aldolase	Desoxyribose-5-phosphate ⇌ glyceraldehyde-3-phosphate + acetaldehyde	Liver

acid resulting from the demethylation of methionine), except that H_2S is removed instead of H_2O. Certain cystine peptides are treated similarly in a complicated reaction which involves the dehydropeptidases and, probably, reduction to the cysteine peptides.

NON-OXIDATIVE DECARBOXYLASES. Many decarboxylations of amino acids to the corresponding amines occur in the intestine as the result of bacterial action (p. 272). A few such reactions are also catalyzed by enzymes in the tissues. The coenzyme for many bacterial and mammalian amino acid decarboxylases is pyridoxal phosphate.

Tyrosine and glutamic acid are decarboxylated in reactions the metabolic importance of which remains to be seen. 3,4-Dihydroxy-phenylalanine (abbreviated "dopa") decarboxylase is probably involved in the synthesis of adrenaline (epinephrine) from tyrosine (p. 553). Decarboxylation of histidine gives rise to the potent pharmacological agent, histamine. A serum vasoconstrictor, serotonin, is formed from a derivative of tryptamine, the amine corresponding to tryptophan. Cysteic acid, an oxidation product of cysteine, decarboxylates to taurine, a compound found conjugated to certain bile acids (p. 268).

A number of keto acids are decarboxylated non-oxidatively, oxalacetic and oxalosuccinic acids being among the most important (p. 407). The usual decarboxylation of ketoglutaric acid is oxidative; the reaction shown in the table may have no great significance. The pyruvic acid decarboxylase of plants is included in the table for the sake of contrast; the normal decarboxylation of this substrate in animal tissues is oxidative. Thiamine pyrophosphate ("cocarboxylase") acts as a coenzyme for both systems, in the free state for the non-oxidative, as the amide of lipoic acid (p. 360) for the oxidative reaction.

ISOMERASES. The isomerases are included among the adding and removing enzymes because the action of several has been shown to consist in the successive removal and addition of the elements of water, in the course of which the original compound is transformed to an isomer. In one instance (aconitase) the intermediate compound is stable enough to be isolated.

Phosphohexose and phosphotriose isomerases are involved in the anaerobic metabolism of carbohydrate (p. 392), whereas aconitase plays a role in aerobic reactions (p. 399). Isomerases have also been described for the phosphorylated derivatives of ribose, mannose, and galactose. The phosphogalactose isomerase ("galactowaldenase," from the presumed Walden inversion occurring at carbon 4) requires the unusual coenzyme, uridine-diphosphate-glucose.

ALDOLASES. This group of enzymes derives its name from the type of reaction catalyzed, which is, superficially at least, a reversible aldol condensation. Until recently only one aldolase was known, namely, the enzyme catalyzing the reversible cleavage of hexose diphosphate into triose phosphates, a reaction of great importance in the anaerobic metabolism of carbohydrate (p. 392). To this original aldolase must now be added similar enzymes which catalyze the breakdown of various pentose phosphates into triose phosphates and "dioses."

TRANSFERRING ENZYMES

TRANSGLYCOSIDASES. These enzymes are also known as phosphorylases, because until very recently it was believed that the reaction which they catalyzed could be considered a "phosphorolysis," that is, the addition of the elements of phosphoric acid across the attacked bond, by analogy to hydrolysis. However, it has been shown for some of these enzymes (and generalized to the remainder) that the actual reaction mechanism consists of the transfer of the glycosidic portion of the substrate from its linkage thereon to some sort of linkage with the enzyme, from which location it is passed on to form another glycosidic linkage with an acceptor molecule.

In the case of the amylophosphorylases (frequently designated simply as "phosphorylases," since they were the first enzymes of this class to be investigated), as shown in Table 18, a terminal glycosidically linked glucose molecule is detached from a linear polysaccharide chain (1–4 bonds) and transferred to phosphate to form glucose-1-phosphate. This type of reaction is the major pathway in the reversible synthesis and breakdown of glycogen in the animal body. It is of interest that, in the synthesis of a polysaccharide from glucose-1-phosphate, a small amount of polysaccharide must be present to act as a primer, a fact which is in accord with the transglycosidation mechanism. Since the formation of glycogen requires branching of the chains, and since the phosphorylases synthesize only molecules of the amylose type, the cooperation of various "branching enzymes" is required. These transform 1–4 linkages to 1–6 linkages, yielding the necessary branching points for a molecule of the amylopectin or glycogen type.

Phosphorylases operating in much the same way as the amylophosphorylases are known which have as substrates the nucleosides of various purines, pyrimidines, and nicotinamide. It is quite probable that the hydrolytic breakdown of nucleosides described in the older literature was in reality due to the phosphorylases of this group, especially since many of the experiments were performed in phosphate buffers.

Table 18. Transglycosidases

ENZYME	REACTION	OCCURRENCE
(Amylo) phosphorylases	$(-G-G-G-G)_n + H_3PO_4 \rightleftharpoons$ $(-G-G-G)_{n-1} + G-1-PO_4$	Muscle, liver, heart, brain, plants
Various "branching" enzymes	1,4-linkages → 1,6-linkages	Muscle, liver, heart, brain, plants
Purine nucleoside phosphorylases	Purine nucleoside $+ H_3PO_4 \rightleftharpoons$ purine $+$ ribose-1-PO_4 Purine "desoxy"-nucleoside $+ H_3PO_4 \rightleftharpoons$ purine $+$ desoxyribose-1-PO_4	Liver, thymus
Pyrimidine nucleoside phosphorylases	Pyrimidine nucleoside $+ H_3PO_4 \rightleftharpoons$ pyrimidine $+$ ribose-1-PO_4 Pyrimidine desoxynucleoside $+ H_3PO \rightleftharpoons$ pyrimidine $+$ desoxyribose-1-PO_4	Kidney, bone marrow, liver
Nicotinamide riboside phosphorylase	Nicotinamide-riboside $+ H_3PO_4 \rightleftharpoons$ nicotinamide $+$ ribose-1-PO_4	Liver

TRANSAMIDASES AND TRANSPEPTIDASES. In recent years a number of enzymes have been found to catalyze the transfer of amide and peptide moieties from one locus to another (Table 19). Glutamotransferase catalyzes the transfer of the γ-glutamyl residue of glutamine from ammonia to hydroxylamine and other amines. A similar aspartotransferase is found in bacteria. Of more physiological interest at the moment is the glutathione glutamotransferase, which can pass the glutamyl radical from the tripeptide to various natural amino acid acceptors. Although the resulting compounds retain the γ-peptide linkage, this sort of reaction may be a model for the redistribution of amino acid residues in α-peptide linkages during protein synthesis. In this connection it is of interest that endopeptidases (trypsin, chymotrypsin, etc.), in addition to their strictly hydrolytic functions, have also been shown to catalyze transfers of amino acid residues into and out of true α-peptide bonds.

Table 19. Transamidases and Transpeptidases

ENZYME	REACTION	OCCURRENCE
Glutamotransferase	γ-Glutamyl-NH$_2$ + NH$_2$-R $\rightleftarrows$ γ-glutamyl-NH-R + NH$_3$ (glutamine)	Brain, liver, kidney, muscle, bacteria, plants
Glutathione glutamotransferase	γ-Glutamyl-cysteinyl-glycine + $\begin{cases} \text{leucine} \\ \text{valine} \\ \text{phenylalanine} \end{cases} \rightleftarrows \gamma$-glutamyl $\begin{cases} \text{leucine} \\ \text{valine} \\ \text{phenylalanine} \end{cases}$ + cysteinyl-glycine	Kidney, pancreas
Various endopeptidases	Acyl-amino acid amide + NH$_2$-R $\rightleftarrows$ acyl-amino acid-NH-R + NH$_3$ (R = amino acid amide or dipeptide residue) Amino acid$_1$ + amino acid$_2$—peptide $\rightleftarrows$ amino acid$_1$—peptide + amino acid$_2$	

TRANSAMINASES. The transfer of an amino group from an amino acid to a keto acid, forming a new amino and keto acid in the process, is one of the more important general reactions of protein metabolism (p. 510). The two enzymes listed first in Table 20 are the most widespread and active of the transaminases, but a large number of keto acids other than pyruvic and oxalacetic are known to react with glutamic acid in various tissues. Until very recently it was thought that one member of each transaminating system must be dicarboxylic, but enzyme systems are now known which can catalyze transaminations between alanine and several monocarboxylic keto acids.

In those cases in which a coenzyme has been shown to participate in a transaminase system, it has proved to be pyridoxal phosphate. A suggested mechanism for the role of this coenzyme in the reaction is shown below:

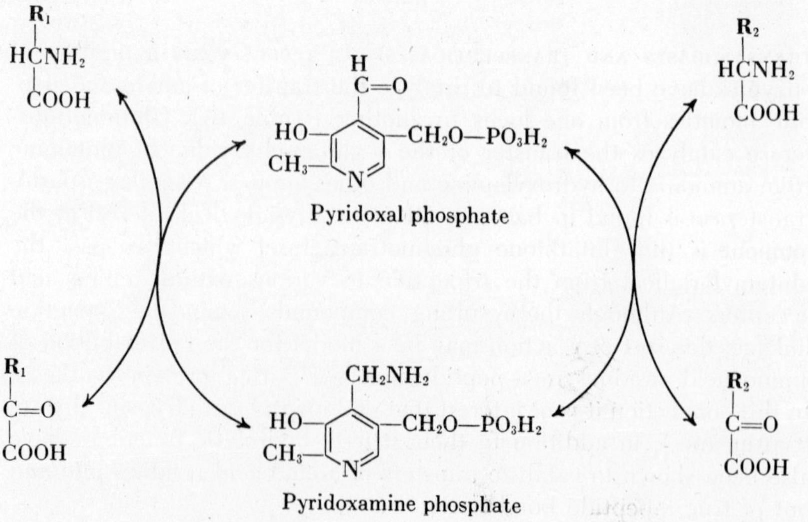

Pyridoxal phosphate

Pyridoxamine phosphate

Most transaminations are reversible; indeed, their chief importance in protein metabolism resides in that fact. However, an irreversible transamination has been described, involving the simultaneous removal of the amide group and the transfer of the α-amino group of glutamine.

Table 20. Transaminases

ENZYME	REACTION	OCCURRENCE
Glutamic-pyruvic transaminase	Glutamic + pyruvic $\rightleftharpoons$ ketoglutaric + alanine	Muscle, liver
Glutamic-oxalacetic transaminase	Glutamic + oxalacetic $\rightleftharpoons$ ketoglutaric + aspartic	Heart, muscle, brain, liver, kidney, testis
Various glutamic transaminases	Glutamic + keto acid $\rightleftharpoons$ ketoglutaric + amino acid	Liver, heart, kidney
Various alanine transaminases	Alanine + keto acid $\rightleftharpoons$ pyruvic + amino acid	Liver
Glutamine transaminase	Glutamine + keto acid $\rightarrow$ ketoglutaric + amino acid + NH_3	Liver

TRANSPHOSPHORYLASES. Transfers of phosphate groups from one molecule to another are of great metabolic importance, especially in the case of carbohydrates. The transphosphorylases are listed in Table 21.

Table 21. Transphosphorylases

ENZYME	REACTION	OCCURRENCE
Phosphomutases		
Phosphoglucomutase	$G\text{-}1\text{-}PO_4 \rightleftharpoons G\text{-}6\text{-}PO_4$	All tissues
Phosphoglyceromutase	$Glyc\text{-}COOH\text{-}3\text{-}PO_4 \rightleftharpoons Glyc\text{-}COOH\text{-}2\text{-}PO_4$	All tissues
Phosphofructomutase	$F\text{-}1\text{-}PO_4 \rightleftharpoons F\text{-}6\text{-}PO_4$	Liver
Phosphoribomutase	$R\text{-}1\text{-}PO_4 \rightleftharpoons R\text{-}5\text{-}PO_4$	Liver
Phosphodesoxyribomutase	$Desoxy\text{-}R\text{-}1\text{-}PO_4 \rightleftharpoons Desoxy\text{-}R\text{-}5\text{-}PO_4$	Liver
"Reversible" phosphokinases		
3-Phosphoglycerate kinase	$Gylc\text{-}COOH\text{-}3\text{-}PO_4 + ATP \rightleftharpoons Glyc\text{-}COOH\text{-}1.3\text{-}PO_4 + ADP$	All tissues
Pyruvate kinase	$Pyruvate + ATP \rightleftharpoons Pyruvate\text{-}PO_4 + ADP$	All tissues
Adenylate kinase (myokinase)	$AMP + ATP \rightleftharpoons ADP + ADP$	Muscle, heart, brain, liver
Creatine kinase	$Creatine + ATP \rightleftharpoons Creatine\text{-}PO_4 + ADP$	Muscle
"Irreversible" phosphokinases		
Hexokinase	$\left.\begin{array}{l}Glucose\\Fructose\\Mannose\end{array}\right\} + ATP \rightarrow \left.\begin{array}{l}G\text{-}\\F\text{-}\\M\text{-}\end{array}\right\}6\text{-}PO_4 + ADP$	Brain
Glucokinase	$G + ATP \rightarrow G\text{-}6\text{-}PO_4 + ADP$	Muscle
Fructokinase	$F + ATP \rightarrow F\text{-}1\text{-}PO_4 (?) + ADP$	Muscle
Glucokinase	$G + ATP \rightarrow G\text{-}6\text{-}PO_4 (?) + ADP$	Liver
Fructokinase	$F + ATP \rightarrow F\text{-}1\text{-}PO_4 + ADP$	Liver
Galactokinase	$Gal + ATP \rightarrow Gal\text{-}1\text{-}PO_4 + ADP$	Liver
Phosphofructokinase (1)	$F\text{-}1\text{-}PO_4 + ATP \rightarrow F\text{-}1,6\text{-}PO_4 + ADP$	Muscle
Phosphofructokinase (2)	$F\text{-}6\text{-}PO_4 + ATP \rightarrow F\text{-}1,6\text{-}PO_4 + ADP$	Muscle
Phosphoglucokinase	$G\text{-}1\text{-}PO_4 + ATP \rightarrow G\text{-}1,6\text{-}PO_4 + ADP$	Muscle
Adenosine kinase	$Adenosine + ATP \rightarrow Adenylic\text{-}5' \ acid + ADP$	Kidney, liver

The phosphomutases catalyze what would appear on the surface to be a series of intramolecular migrations of phosphate groups. Actually, these reactions are intermolecular and involve a group of rather unusual coenzymes. The mechanisms of two of these systems are shown below:

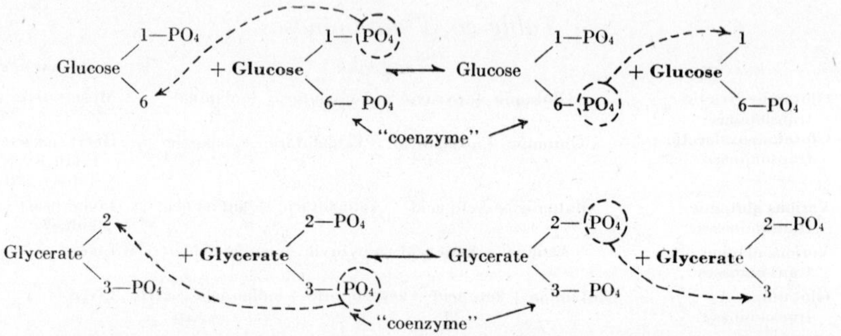

Glucose $1-PO_4$ 6 $+$ **Glucose** $6-PO_4$ $\longleftrightarrow$ $1-(PO_4)$ Glucose $6-PO_4$ "coenzyme" Glucose $1-PO_4$ $+$ **Glucose** $6-(PO_4)$ $\longrightarrow$ 1 Glucose $6-PO_4$

Glycerate 2 $3-PO_4$ $+$ **Glycerate** $2-PO_4$ $3-(PO_4)$ $\longleftrightarrow$ Glycerate $2-(PO_4)$ $3-PO_4$ "coenzyme" $+$ **Glycerate** Glycerate $2-PO_4$ 3

Transfers of phosphate groups between the adenylic system of compounds (p. 377) and other molecules are catalyzed by the phosphokinases, a group of enzymes which may be subdivided on the basis of reversibility of reaction. The sub-group of reversible phosphokinases is of importance in the production and storage of energy from the anaerobic breakdown of carbohydrate, while the irreversible group functions largely in the preparation of the carbohydrate substrates for this breakdown, which requires phosphorylated intermediates.

Enzymes of the hexokinase type, in addition to their role as initiators of carbohydrate catabolism, are also believed to participate in the transfer of hexoses across membranes and cell walls. Thus, glucose may be phosphorylated by a hexokinase or glucokinase on one side of a membrane, then dephosphorylated by a phosphatase on the other side. Such processes may take place during the absorption of glucose in the intestine, in the reabsorption of glucose in the kidney tubules, and in the passage of blood glucose into the tissues.

Table 22. Transacylases

ENZYME	REACTION	OCCURRENCE
β-Ketoacyl-CoA transacetylase	β-Ketoacyl-CoA + CoA ⇌ Acyl(-C₂)-CoA + Acetyl-CoA	Liver
Acetoacetic transacetylase	Acetyl-CoA + Acetyl-CoA ⇌ Acetoacetyl-CoA + CoA	Liver
Citric transacetylase ("condensing enzyme")	Acetyl-CoA + oxalacetate → Citrate + CoA	Muscle, heart, liver, kidney, brain
Choline acetylase	Acetyl-CoA + choline → Acetyl-choline + CoA	Nervous tissue
Aromatic amine acetylase	Acetyl-CoA + sulfonamide → Acetyl-sulfonamide + CoA	Liver
Amino acid acylase	Benzoyl-CoA + glycine → Hippurate + CoA	Liver, kidney
Phosphotransacetylase	Acetyl-CoA + phosphate ⇌ Acetyl-phosphate + CoA	Bacteria

TRANSACYLASES. One of the most rapidly developing phases of current biochemical research concerns the metabolism of 1-carbon and 2-carbon "fragments." Consequently, statements made and reactions depicted in this and the next section are to be regarded as provisional.

The transfer of acetyl fragments from one molecule to another is a reaction which, to some extent at least, is involved in the metabolism of all classes of foodstuffs. Recently it has been found that all trans-acetylations follow a common pattern. In a "donor" reaction, such as the first one shown in Table 22, an acetyl group is transferred from the donor molecule to a coenzyme of acetylations.

Acetyl-CoA

(A major source of acetyl groups, in addition to the β-keto acids from fatty acids, is provided by the oxidation of pyruvic acid derived from carbohydrate catabolism; this reaction is rather complex and is not included in this section.) In a second reaction an acceptor molecule takes up the acetyl fragment, regenerating the free coenzyme. A variety of acceptor reactions is shown in Table 22.

The participation of coenzyme A in the transfer of acyl groups other than acetyl has been demonstrated recently, viz., butyryl, succinyl, and benzoyl. It seems, therefore, that acetylation is but one special instance of a more general reaction, acylation, and that coenzyme A is involved in all cases. It is probable that each donor reaction is preceded by an activation reaction, wherein coenzyme A is phosphorylated by ATP, and that this phosphorylated form of the coenzyme accepts acetyl groups from donor molecules.

TRANSFERS OF 1-CARBON UNITS. Transmethylation (Table 23) is a reaction which is of special concern in the fields of lipid and amino acid metabolism. Although the reaction has been studied for many years in intact animals, only recently has much effort been expended on the strictly enzymatic aspects. Even at present, there is much that is still unknown. For example, certain transmethylations used to be formulated with choline as methyl donor, although it has been shown in several instances that choline *per se* is inactive, and that it must be oxidized to betaine which is the true methylating agent. Also, methionine as such is not a methylating agent. Methylations by methionine have been shown to occur in two phases, the first of which is an "activation" of methionine by ATP. The residue left after the activated methionine parts with its methyl group has not been identified. These matters are discussed in greater detail elsewhere (p. 536).

Table 23. Transfer of 1-Carbon Units

Enzyme

Transmethylases:
  Group I

S-Adenosyl-methionine +

(noradrenaline)*		(adrenaline)
guanidoacetic acid		creatine
nicotinamide	→	N^1-methylnicotinamide + (?)
ethanolamine		methylethanolamine
(methylethanolamine)*		(dimethylethanolamine)
dimethylethanolamine		choline

  Group II   Betaine + homocysteine → methionine + dimethylglycine

Transformylases:

"CoF" + serine ⇌ "formyl-CoF"† + glycine

Inosinic acid + "CoF" ↔ aminoimidazolecarboxamide-ribotide
(hypoxanthine ribotide)   + "formyl-CoF"†

* Nature of methyl donor not established, but probably as indicated.
† Nature of C_1 fragment and coenzyme not established.

The transfer of "formate" groups is a reaction, the study of which is still in its infancy (p. 540). Little can be said of the enzymes involved. There seems to be a general coenzyme of transformylations, as there is of transacylations. The exact structure of this coenzyme is not established, but it is related to the folinic acid group of vitamins (p. 200). Vitamin B_{12} also has some connection with the metabolism of "formyl" groups, but the nature of this relationship has not been elucidated. In the absence of such information, only two donor and acceptor reactions are shown in Table 23. Other sources of "formyl" groups and examples of their utilization will be indicated in connection with various phases of the metabolism of amino acids, purines, and pyrimidines.

OTHER TRANSFER REACTIONS. It seems probable that other group-transfer reactions will be discovered in the future. At present, the reactions discussed previously are the best substantiated in this category. At one time, transthiolation (p. 531), transamidination (p. 521), and transimination (p. 514) were listed as group-transfer reactions. One of these has not been studied sufficiently to be accurately classified; the others have resolved themselves into complex series of reactions, including condensations and cleavages, and scarcely fit into the same scheme as the true transfer reactions.

It has been suggested that hemoglobin and myoglobin can be regarded as "transoxygenases." Although these compounds are conjugated proteins, the prosthetic groups of which are identical with those of other proteins which are definitely classified as enzymes, the mere transport of oxygen (the "substrate") without changing it in any way, and the completely non-specific release of the gas in response to low environmental partial pressures of oxygen, all militate against such a classification.

As was mentioned earlier in this chapter, the transfer of hydrogen atoms or electrons is certainly a true transfer reaction, and the enzymes mediating such transfers rightly belong in this section. However, for reasons already given, they will be discussed in the chapter on biological oxidation.

INHIBITION OF ENZYME REACTIONS

TYPES OF INHIBITORS. Since enzymes are proteins, any agents which denature proteins will inactivate enzymes. Such inactivations are quite non-specific and reveal nothing concerning the nature of enzyme action. Certain chemical agents block specific groups in the enzyme protein. This type of inhibition is still considered non-specific, inasmuch as the groups being blocked are common to many enzymes. However, it frequently does indicate that particular chemical groups in the protein fabric are concerned in the action of the enzyme.

Specific inhibitors differ from the foregoing in that they exert their action on only one enzyme, or a small group of related enzymes. The mechanism of the inhibition is specifically related to the structure and action of the enzyme involved, not to some group or property common to all proteins. The target of action of this type of inhibitor may be the coenzyme or prosthetic group, the specific ion activator, the site of combination of substrate and enzyme on the enzyme surface, or some adjacent site otherwise necessary for the action of the enzyme.

SULFHYDRYL INHIBITORS. Among the non-specific inhibitions, those which involve sulfhydryl groups of the enzymes are perhaps the most thoroughly studied. Many, but not all, enzymes contain sulfhydryl groups derived from the side-chains of cysteine residues. Blockage or chemical transformation of these groups results in inhibition of the enzymes. In several cases there is definite evidence that the sulfhydryl groups take part in the combination of enzyme and substrate, accounting for their essentiality.

Several types of sulfhydryl inhibitors are shown on page 252.

Oxidants such as ferricyanide convert sulfhydryl groups to disulfides, iodoacetate and similar agents block the groups by alkylation, while mercury and other heavy metal ions form mercaptides with them. The vesicant war gas, Lewisite, and the arsenical drugs exert their characteristic actions by combination with sulfhydryl groups. Poisoning by heavy metals or arsenicals has been treated successfully with 2,3-dimercaptopropanol (British Anti-Lewisite, or BAL), the sulfhydryl groups of which compete with the protein's sulfhydryl groups for the toxic substance.

Triose phosphate dehydrogenase (p. 392) is an example of an enzyme which is especially sensitive to sulfhydryl reagents.

$$2RSH \xrightarrow[-2H]{\text{Ferricyanide}} R-S-S-R$$

$$RSH \xrightarrow[-HI]{ICH_2COOH} R-S-CH_2COOH$$

$$2RSH \xrightarrow[-2H^+]{Hg^{++}} R-S-Hg-S-R$$

$$2RSH \xrightarrow[-2HCl]{\substack{Cl \\ \diagdown \\ As-CH=CHCl \\ Cl \diagup \\ (\text{Lewisite})}} \begin{array}{c} R \\ \diagdown \\ S \\ \diagdown \\ \quad As-CH=CHCl \\ \diagup \\ S \\ \diagup \\ R \end{array}$$

$$\begin{array}{l} CH_2-SH \\ | \\ CH-SH \\ | \\ CH_2OH \\ (\text{BAL}) \end{array} \xrightarrow[-2HCl]{\text{Lewisite}} \begin{array}{l} CH_2-S \diagdown \\ | \qquad\qquad As-CH=CHCl \\ CH-S \diagup \\ | \\ CH_2OH \end{array}$$

Sulfhydryl inhibitors

INHIBITORS ACTING ON COENZYME, PROSTHETIC GROUP, OR ION ACTIVATOR. Reagents blocking essential groups of coenzymes are relatively specific. As was mentioned earlier, pyridoxal phosphate is the coenzyme (among other functions) for a number of amino acid decarboxylases of bacterial and animal origin. The aldehyde group of this coenzyme would be expected to combine with various carbonyl reagents, an expectation which is fulfilled by the finding that these decarboxylases are inhibited by cyanide, hydrazine, hydroxylamine, and semicarbazide. (The lack of effect of most of these inhibitors on the transaminases remains to be explained.)

Cytochrome oxidase (p. 366), an important oxidative enzyme containing an iron-porphyrin prosthetic group, is inhibited by cyanide, azide, and carbon monoxide, all of which prevent the reaction of the metal in the prosthetic group with molecular oxygen.

Enolase, a magnesium-activated enzyme, in the presence of phosphate buffer is inhibited by fluoride. The inhibition has been shown to be due to the formation of a magnesium fluorophosphate.

INHIBITION DUE TO METABOLIC ANTAGONISM. In addition to the specific inhibitions mentioned in the preceding section, a special variety of specific inhibition has been studied intensively in recent years, which is due to the structural similarity of certain inhibitors to normal substrates. The classic example of this type is the inhibition of succinic dehydrogenase by malonic acid.

$$
\begin{array}{ll}
\begin{array}{l}
\text{COOH} \\
| \\
\text{CH}_2 \\
| \\
\text{CH}_2 \\
| \\
\text{COOH}
\end{array}
&
\begin{array}{l}
\text{COOH} \\
| \\
\text{CH}_2 \\
| \\
\text{COOH}
\end{array}
\\
\quad\text{Succinic acid} & \quad\text{Malonic acid}
\end{array}
$$

The structural similarity of malonic acid to the normal substrate misleads the enzyme into accepting the inhibitor at the active sites on its surface, thus displacing succinic acid and retarding the rate of conversion of succinic to fumaric acid. Inhibitors such as malonic acid are known as metabolic antagonists or substrate analogs. In many cases the reaction of the enzyme with both analog and substrate is freely reversible, both substances compete for the active sites on the enzyme, and the degree of inhibition depends solely on the ratio of the concentrations of inhibitor to substrate, and not on the absolute concentration of either. Under such conditions the inhibition is said to be competitive. Owing to the importance attached to the phenomenon of metabolic antagonism in recent years, it is discussed in greater detail elsewhere (p. 635).

ENZYMES AND DRUG ACTION. In order that drugs may alter the metabolism of an animal or a microorganism, it is almost certain that their action must concern enzymes directly or indirectly. Narcotics, for example, are known to depress the activity of dehydrogenase systems (p. 358). Many other drugs are known to be metabolic antagonists, sulfhydryl inhibitors, or metal-complexing agents. Considerable effort is being expended at the present time by workers in the fields of chemotherapy and pharmacology in relating their empirical findings to a rational enzymological basis.

THE INTRACELLULAR LOCALIZATION OF ENZYMES

CYTOCHEMICAL STUDIES. In the technics of histo- or cytochemistry a section of tissue is incubated with a substrate and the reaction products are located by microscopic observation, usually after conversion to some easily detectable precipitate. Alkaline phosphatase, for example, is detected by allowing a tissue section to incubate in buffered glycerophosphate containing lead salts. The liberated phosphate is precipitated *in situ* as lead phosphate, which is then converted to lead sulfide for easy visualization. Using this technic with duodenal epithelium, alkaline phosphatase was found to be concentrated in the cuticular border, with significant amounts also apparently in the nuclei and in the region of the Golgi apparatus.

DIFFERENTIAL CENTRIFUGATION. By the application of special grinding procedures to tissues it is possible to prepare "homogenates" which consist of nuclei, cytoplasmic particles, the soluble portion of the cytoplasm and some debris composed of cell membrane fragments and a few intact or partially disrupted cells. Individual fractions of this mixture can then be isolated by the technic of differential centrifugation. Many studies at the present time are concerned with the distribution of enzymes among the following fractions: a nuclear fraction, isolated by low-speed centrifugation; the "large granules" or mitochondria of the cytoplasm, spun down at intermediate speeds; the "small granules" or microsomes, requiring very high speeds for their isolation; the "supernatant" fraction, containing what is assumed to be the clear ground-substance of the cytoplasm.

Using these technics, nuclei of liver and kidney cells have been found to contain few enzymes. Both liver and kidney nuclei appear to be lacking in succinic dehydrogenase, a key enzyme in the oxidative catabolism of many foodstuffs.

Percentagewise speaking, most of the glycolytic system of liver is found in the "supernatant" fraction. Cytochrome oxidase and the enzymes associated with the tricarboxylic acid cycle (p. 397) are largely concentrated in the mitochondria of liver cells. The microsomes, in addition to a number of phosphatases and other enzymes, have recently been shown to have a high rate of turnover of amino acids.

The present tendency is to regard the mitochondria as the aerobic "powerhouse" of the cell, containing the enzymes required for energy production in a closely knit organization, so set up that the substrate is efficiently passed on from one stage of catabolism to the next. The more primitive, anaerobic production of energy by glycolysis is left to the unorganized soluble phase of the cytoplasm. Of the functions of the microsomes but little is known; their main concern may be the synthesis of protein. Since most enzymes which are found in the nucleus are present in relatively small amounts, it is believed that the nucleus contributes little to the total metabolic activities of the cell, its chief function probably being the regulation of metabolic patterns.

INFLUENCE OF HORMONES ON ENZYMES

The facts that hormones act in very low concentrations and that their action amounts to a rather specific type of control over metabolic events have led to the hypothesis that the targets of hormonal action are the enzymes. Actually, it has been very difficult to obtain definite evidence on this point. The injection of a hormone into an intact animal is frequently followed by a change in the activity of one or more enzyme systems, as assayed in the excised tissues of the animal. In such experiments the action of the hormone could be the result of increased synthesis or destruction of the enzyme, removal or addition of inhibitory substances or cofactors, or simply changes in tissue permeability, all of which are rather far removed from the enzymatic reaction proper (although it is entirely possible that the action of hormones proceeds by just such mechanisms). The same general ambiguities attend experiments performed with tissue slices. On the other hand, attempts to demonstrate hormonal action in cell-free enzyme systems have been largely unsuccessful. One of the few encouraging investigations along these lines demonstrated that the hexokinase (or glucokinase) reaction in muscle extracts was inhibited by hormones of the anterior pituitary and adrenal cortex, this inhibition being counteracted by insulin. This effect, which is by no means unanimously accepted at the present time, will, if substantiated, provide at least a partial explanation for certain of the metabolic disorders attending the diabetic state (p. 430). Another line of approach which is being pursued at the present time is the attempt to demonstrate that thyroxine acts as an "uncoupling agent" for aerobic phosphorylations (p. 381).

ENZYMES AND GENETICS

There is abundant evidence that the general enzymatic pattern of the cell is under genetic control. Whereas much of the modern evidence on this score is provided by studies on bacteria and fungi, relevant data from "inborn errors of metabolism" in man (p. 346) have been available since the beginning of this century.

In many cases there seems to be rather strict "nuclear" control of the enzyme content of the cell, and the offspring of a given cell appear to inherit enzyme patterns in precise, Mendelian fashion. This has led to the "one gene–one enzyme" hypothesis, according to which the elaboration of each enzyme is under the control of a single, corresponding gene. An organism lacking a given gene will be deficient in the corresponding enzyme and will exhibit a block at the point in the sequence of metabolic events at which that enzyme operated. This metabolic block frequently results in the accumulation and excretion of an unmetabolized compound, as occurs in man in the condition known as "alcaptonuria" (p. 552).

In other cases, however, the enzymatic pattern of a cell seems to be influenced by factors outside the nucleus. The very presence of a substrate, for instance, sometimes elicits the synthesis of an enzyme which can attack that substrate. The existence of these "adaptive enzymes" has led to the theory that there is a sort of cytoplasmic inheritance, perhaps due to actual entities (plasmagenes) which are more or less under the control of the nuclear genes, but are also responsive to environmental factors, such as the presence or absence of substrates. The present consensus seems to be that, although the enzymatic potentialities of the cell are determined in Mendelian fashion by the nuclear genes, determination of the fruition of these potentialities is under considerable cytoplasmic (and environmental) influence.

BIBLIOGRAPHY

Introductory Textbooks

Baldwin, E.: Dynamic Aspects of Biochemistry, London, Cambridge University Press, 1952, especially Chapters 1, 2, 4, and 5.
Sumner, J. B. and Somers, G. F.: Chemistry and Methods of Enzymes, New York, Academic Press, Inc., 1953.
Tauber, H.: Enzyme Chemistry and Technology, New York, John Wiley & Sons, Inc., 1949.

Advanced Treatises

Northrup, J. H., Kunitz, M. and Herriott, R. M.: Cystalline Enzymes, New York, Columbia University Press, 1948.
Sumner, J. B. and Myrbäck, K. (eds.): The Enzymes (2 volumes in 4 parts), New York, Academic Press, Inc., 1950–52.

Annual General Reviews

Nord, F. F. and Werkman, C. H. (eds.): Advances in Enzymology, Volumes 1 through 14, New York, Interscience Publishers, Inc., 1941–1953.

8

CHANGES IN FOODSTUFFS IN THE ALIMENTARY TRACT

DIGESTION

Digestion is the term applied to processes which convert relatively large organic molecules into smaller molecules capable of being absorbed by the gastrointestinal tract and utilized by the organism. With the exception of water, inorganic salts, vitamins, monosaccharides, and certain lipids, practically all common foodstuffs must undergo certain changes in the digestive tract preliminary to absorption and utilization. These digestive processes are hydrolytic in nature and are accomplished by enzymes in the various digestive fluids (salivary, gastric, pancreatic, and intestinal).

The manner in which food is prepared for ingestion influences its digestibility. Cooking causes disruption of the cellulose shell of starch granules, and softening of the connective tissue of meats, permitting more ready access to digestive enzymes. Digestibility of egg proteins is increased by their coagulation. Favorable chemical changes also occur during ripening of fruits (dextrinization) and aging of meats (hydrolysis).

Foodstuffs entering the mouth are subjected to mastication and the digestive and lubricating actions of saliva, which is secreted by the salivary and buccal glands in response to psychic, mechanical, and chemical stimuli. The bolus of food passes through the pharynx and esophagus into the stomach, where it is exposed to the digestive action of gastric juice, stimulated by psychic, gastric (nervous and hormonal), and intestinal (hormonal) factors. After an interval which varies with the nature of the ingested foodstuffs, portions of the gastric digestive mixture are periodically ejected into the duodenum, where they encounter a mixture of bile, pancreatic juice, and duodenal secretion. Secretion of pancreatic juice is stimulated by vagal impulses and by secretin and pancreozymin, hormones formed by the duodenal mucosa in response to the presence of acid in the duodenum. Secretion also apparently stimulates the flow of bile from the liver. Relaxation of the sphincter of Oddi and simultaneous contraction and evacuation of the gallbladder result from the presence of emulsified fats in the duodenum; a hormonal influence (cholecystokinin, formed in the intestinal mucosa) may also be involved. The food mixture passes down the intestine, subjected to the digestive action of the intestinal secretions. The end-products of digestion are absorbed, chiefly in the small intestine, as are certain of the products of bacterial action on the foodstuffs. The unabsorbed residuum passes into the colon, where it is largely concentrated by absorption of water, to be excreted ultimately, together with intestinal bacteria and products of their activity, as the feces.

DIGESTIVE ENZYMES. The enzymes concerned with fragmentation of large molecules of organic foodstuffs to smaller molecules suitable for absorption are all hydrolases (p. 228). The most important of these may be classified as follows:

(a) PEPTIDASES (PROTEASES). These protein-digesting enzymes include pepsin, rennin, trypsin, chymotrypsin, carboxypeptidases, aminopeptidases, and tri- and dipeptidases.

(b) GLYCOSIDASES (CARBOHYDRASES). These carbohydrate-splitting enzymes include salivary amylase, pancreatic amylase, maltase, sucrase (invertase), and lactase.

(c) LIPASES. These enzymes include gastric lipase and pancreatic lipase and lipases in intestinal secretions. They are esterases which act preferentially on glycerides of long-chain fatty acids.

(d) NUCLEASES. The nucleolytic enzymes hydrolyze nucleic acids and are subdivided as follows: (1) Phosphodiesterases (nucleodepolymerases), which do not liberate free phosphate. (2) Phosphatases (nucleotidases), which liberate free phosphate. (3) Nucleosidases, which liberate free bases. There is evidence that the action of certain, if not all, nucleosidases is phosphorolytic and not hydrolytic. These should therefore properly be designated "nucleoside phosphorylases" and should not be included in the category of nucleolytic enzymes as here defined. (4) The nucleodeaminases, which liberate free ammonia, are not found in the digestive secretions.

(e) ESTERASES (CARBOXYLESTERASES OTHER THAN LIPASES). This group of enzymes act preferentially on glycerides of short-chain fatty acids (e.g., tributyrin) and other fatty acid esters (e.g., cholesterol esters).

(f) PHOSPHATASES. These include a variety of enzymes which liberate phosphoric acid from organic phosphate compounds, such as lecithin and other phospholipids and phytic acid.

SALIVA

Saliva, as it is found in the mouth, is a mixture of secretions of the three pairs of salivary glands, the parotid, submaxillary, and sublingual, and to a lesser extent, of the buccal glands. It is a colorless, slightly opalescent, viscous fluid, the composition of which varies with the conditions of stimulation, depending chiefly upon the relative proportions of secretion from the several glands involved. The twenty-four-hour volume varies widely, but has been calculated to average about 1500 cc. It is influenced by the water and food intake, the character of the food, and by chewing.

Under average conditions, mixed saliva is 99.42 per cent water and 0.58 per cent solid. Inorganic substances comprise about one-third of the total solids, and organic substances the remainder. The specific gravity is about 1.003 and the reaction of freshly collected saliva is usually slightly acid, pH 6.35–6.85, if care is taken to prevent loss of CO_2. The inorganic components include principally chloride, bicarbonate, and sodium, but also potassium and calcium, with relatively small amounts of sulfate and phosphate. There are traces of thiocyanate and, after administration of iodides, these are excreted by the salivary glands in relatively high concentration. The most important organic constituents of saliva are the amylolytic enzyme, ptyalin (salivary amylase), and mucin. Other organic components include other proteins, the exact nature of which is not known, and small amounts of such substances as urea, glucose, lactic acid, and certain enzymes, e.g., phosphatase and carbonic anhydrase (which probably enter the saliva from desquamated glandular epithelium and surface cells). The mucin, a glycoprotein, is largely responsible for the viscosity of saliva, and is secreted chiefly by the sublingual but also by the submaxillary glands. Salivary amylase is secreted principally by the parotid glands, which secrete little or no mucin.

The urea content of saliva varies directly with that of the blood plasma. The pH of saliva depends primarily on the $BHCO_3:H_2CO_3$ ratio, which varies roughly with that in the blood plasma.

FUNCTIONS OF SALIVA. The principal functions of saliva are probably not due to its direct digestive actions, which consist chiefly of a relatively unimportant degree of digestion of starches and dextrins to maltose by the action of salivary amylase. More important, perhaps, are the facts that it serves to moisten foods and to reduce them to a consistency suitable for swallowing, and to lubricate the bolus of food for its passage through the esophagus. Its solubilizing action on dry foods aids in stimulating taste nerves which, in turn, plays a role in the secretion of gastric juice.

SALIVARY AMYLASE (PTYALIN). This carbohydrase acts on the polysaccharides, starch and glycogen, and certain of their derivatives (dextrins), hydrolyzing them to the disaccharide maltose in a manner similar to pancreatic amylase (p. 263). Certain anions serve as activators, particularly Cl^- and Br^-, but also, to a lesser degree, I^-, NO_3^-, and others. Its optimum pH in NaCl solution is 6.9, but varies from 5.5 to 6.5 with different substrates.

It is not stable below pH 4–5, and is inactivated by pepsin. Consequently, the amylolytic action of this enzyme can be exerted only during its relatively brief contact with substrate material in the mouth and before the bolus of food, mixed with saliva by chewing, has been thoroughly permeated by the acid gastric juice in the stomach (fifteen to twenty minutes).

Amylase acts more rapidly and vigorously on cooked than on raw starch *in vitro,* but this difference is not so striking *in vivo.* It is probable that contact of the enzyme with the starch molecule is facilitated by mechanical damage of the dense lattice structure of the starch granule. The polysaccharide is initially rapidly converted to lower molecular weight, non-fermentable, soluble dextrins (liquefaction). The latter then undergo slower hydrolysis, terminal molecules of maltose being successively split off, with gradual, more or less complete degradation of the intermediate dextrins to maltose and a small amount of glucose.

GASTRIC JUICE

Normal gastric juice is a rather watery, usually colorless liquid with a specific gravity of about 1.003, containing about 99.4 per cent water and 0.6 per cent solids. In the average young normal adult the chief inorganic constituent is HCl, with small amounts of NaCl and KCl and phosphate. The chief organic constituents are mucin, a glycoprotein, the proteolytic enzyme pepsin, and small amounts of a lipase. The gastric juice of newborn infants contains rennin, a milk-clotting enzyme, and little or no pepsin or HCl. There is no HCl in approximately 4 per cent of otherwise apparently normal young adults (achlorhydria), the incidence of this condition increasing in older age groups.

The gastric juice is contributed to by three types of cells with different secretory functions: (1) the parietal cells of the gastric tubules secrete the HCl; (2) the chief cells secrete pepsin; (3) columnar cells of the necks of the gastric glands (mucous cells) secrete the gastric mucus. The acidity and peptic activity of the mixed gastric secretion depend upon the relative proportions of these component secretions, each of which is affected quantitatively rather specifically by certain stimuli. For example, the parietal cells are stimulated by histamine, producing a highly acid gastric juice; the peptic cells are stimulated by the vagus, producing a juice rich in pepsin.

HYDROCHLORIC ACID. The gastric parietal cells secrete a fluid of constant composition, which is practically a pure solution of HCl, about 170 mEq./liter (0.17 N), the pH being about 0.87. This is the source of the free acid of gastric juice, which varies within wide limits, depending upon the rate (volume) of parietal cell secretion, the extent of its dilution by other gastric secretions (chief cells, mucous cells), and the buffering action of mucin. The maximum attainable acidity of gastric juice, e.g., by histamine stimulation, is consequently that of pure parietal-cell secretion. The infant stomach secretes but little HCl. The chief function of gastric HCl is to provide a satisfactory pH for digestion of protein in the stomach (by pepsin). Other effects include: (1) slight preliminary action on proteins (swelling, denaturation, possible hydrolysis); (2) activation of pepsinogen; (3) facilitation of absorption of iron (p. 618); (4) possibly hydrolysis of disaccharides; (5) stimulation of secretion of secretin (or activation of prosecretin) in duodenum; (6) germicidal action restricting fermentation by microorganisms in the stomach.

PEPSIN. This proteolytic enzyme, the principal digestive component of gastric juice, is secreted by the chief cells as pepsinogen (inactive). The latter is activated by H^+ ions and also, autocatalytically, by pepsin at pH 5 or lower. Pepsin acts optimally at pH 1.5–2.5, depending on the substrate. It is almost completely inactive at neutral or alkaline pH levels. Gastric juice in the infant contains but little pepsin (little HCl).

Pepsin is an endopeptidase, catalyzing hydrolysis of peptide linkages at all points in the protein molecule. There is evidence that it acts preferentially on linkages involving the amino group of tyrosine and of phenylalanine. It attacks practically all native proteins, except certain keratins, protamines, histones, and mucoproteins, but exerts a more pronounced effect on denatured proteins which possess free SH groups. Depending upon the pH, rate of gastric emptying, and nature of the protein, the latter is broken down into smaller peptide units ("proteoses," "peptones"), shorter peptide chains, and perhaps a few amino acids. Pepsin also has a milk-clotting action similar to that of rennin, converting casein by hydrolysis, first to soluble paracasein, then to insoluble paracasein in the presence of Ca^{++} ions. Milk clotting in the stomach probably involves also precipitation of isoelectric casein by HCl.

GASTRIC LIPASE. This fat-hydrolyzing enzyme is relatively unimportant physiologically because its optimum pH, about 5.5 for lower glycerides and 7.5 for higher glycerides, is above that usually present following ingestion of a mixed meal. However, it is stable in an acid medium, and may exert a lipolytic effect in the intestine, where the pH is more favorable. The products of its action *in vitro* are identical with those of pancreatic lipase (p. 264).

RENNIN. This is a powerful milk-clotting enzyme, secreted as pro-rennin, which is activated by H^+ ions. It is not present in the gastric juice of human adults, but is present in infants (before pepsin formation) and, most abundantly, in the calf and other young ruminants.

$$\text{Casein} \xrightarrow[\text{Ca}^{++}]{\text{Rennin}} \text{Insoluble Paracasein (curd) (p. 261)}.$$

In the adult, this function is assumed by pepsin and chymotrypsin. The paracasein then undergoes the digestive fate of all digestible proteins.

GASTRIC "MUCUS." This appears to be a mixture of substances secreted by cells of the necks of the gastric glands and the surface epithelium, containing certain glycoproteins ("mucin," "mucoprotein"), some soluble and some undissolved. Gastric mucus is not digested by pepsin. It is believed to exert an important protective influence on the mucous membrane of the stomach and to buffer the HCl secreted by the parietal cells. There is some questionable evidence that the soluble mucoprotein fraction of gastric "mucin" is, contains, or carries the so-called "intrinsic anti-pernicious anemia factor" (p. 209), which, in conjunction with certain B vitamins (B_{12}, folinic acid, folic acid), is essential for normal erythrocyte maturation. Its function seems to be to promote intestinal absorption of vitamin B_{12} (extrinsic anti-pernicious anemia factor).

PANCREATIC JUICE

Pancreatic juice is a clear fluid, secreted by the acinar cells of the pancreas, containing about 98.7 per cent water and 1.3 per cent solids (specific gravity about 1.007). It has the highest consistent alkalinity of the normal body fluids, with a pH of about 7.5–8.2, owing to its relatively high bicarbonate content (Fig. 68, p. 328). The most important organic constituents are powerful proteolytic, lipolytic, amylolytic, and nucleolytic enzymes, which comprise virtually its entire protein content. The average daily output is about 500 cc. Vagal stimulation produces a fluid rich in enzymes, but of comparatively low volume. Secretin, a hormone produced by the duodenal mucosa by the action of acid, causes secretion of a fluid of high volume and bicarbonate content, but low enzyme concentration. Another hormone, pancreozymin, secreted by the duodenal mucosa, has an effect similar to that produced by vagal stimulation but not mediated by the vagus.

TRYPSIN. Trypsin, a protease, is secreted by the pancreatic acinar cells as an inactive proenzyme, trypsinogen. In the intestine, this is activated (to trypsin) by the enzyme enterokinase (optimum pH 6–9), subsequent activation proceeding autocatalytically (i.e., by trypsin) at pH 7–8, acclerated by Ca^{++} and other alkaline earth

ions. Trypsin acts maximally at pH 8–9 as an endopeptidase, hydrolyzing practically all types of protein, including several not attacked by
pepsin. Like the latter, it digests denatured and partially digested
proteins more rapidly than native proteins, breaking them down to
polypeptides of various weights and some amino acids. A preferential
action on peptide linkages involving the carboxyl group of either
arginine or lysine has been suggested.

Extracts of the pancreas contain a trypsin inhibitor, a polypeptide,
which may be identical with an inhibitor present in blood. The ovomucoid of egg-white is also a potent trypsin inhibitor, as is a component of soybean.

CHYMOTRYPSIN. This is an endopeptidase, secreted by the pancreatic
acinar cells as an inactive proenzyme, chymotrypsinogen, which, in
the intestine, is activated by trypsin, but not by enterokinase. Its
optimum pH (8–9) and actions are similar to those of trypsin, but, in
addition, it possesses a powerful milk-clotting action identical with
that of rennin and pepsin (p. 261). A preferential attack on peptide
linkages involving the carboxyl group of tyrosine and phenylalanine
has been suggested.

CARBOXYPEPTIDASE. This is an exopeptidase (optimum pH 7.4), the
peptide linkage attacked being that of a terminal amino acid possessing a free carboxyl group. It apparently contains —SH groups and
Mg, and is inhibited by iodoacetate, cyanide, sulfide, cysteine, citrate,
phosphate, and oxalate. It acts on peptide chains of various lengths,
splitting off single terminal amino acids.

$$H_2N-\underset{\underset{O}{\overset{\|}{C}}}{\overset{R}{\underset{H}{C}}}-C \;\;\Big|\underset{HO\;\Big|\;H}{}\;\; N-\underset{\underset{O}{\overset{\|}{C}}}{\overset{R}{\underset{H}{C}}}-C -N-\underset{\underset{O}{\overset{\|}{C}}}{\overset{R}{\underset{H}{C}}}-C-N-\underset{\underset{O}{\overset{\|}{C}}}{\overset{R}{\underset{H}{C}}}-C\;\;\Big|\underset{HO\;\Big|\;H}{}\;\; N-\underset{H}{\overset{R}{\underset{}{C}}}-COOH$$

      Aminopeptidase   Carboxypeptidase

PANCREATIC AMYLASE (DIASTASE; AMYLOPSIN). The action of this carbohydrase is qualitatively identical with but more potent than that
of salivary amylase. It digests cooked more actively than raw starch
in vitro, but the latter is well digested *in vivo* (see salivary amylase,
p. 260). It requires Cl⁻ ions for normal activity. Its optimum pH is
6.9, but it acts well between pH 6.5 and 7.2, varying somewhat with
different substrates. In the intestine, hydrolysis of starch and dextrins
by pancreatic amylase proceeds rapidly because of prompt removal
of the end-product, maltose, which is hydrolyzed to glucose by the
intestinal enzyme, maltase.

PANCREATIC LIPASE (STEAPSIN). This is a glyceride-hydrolyzing (lipolytic) enzyme, secreted by the pancreas in weakly active form. In
the duodenum, its activity is potentiated by a number of substances,
including bile salts, Ca, and certain peptides. Its optimum pH is 7–8.

The activity of hydrolysis of glycerides by pancreatic lipase increases with (1) the molecular weight of the constituent fatty acids, (2) the extent of their unsaturation, and (3) the number of fatty acids in the glyceride molecule. Hence, triglycerides of such acids as oleic and linoleic are hydrolyzed more rapidly than diglycerides and triglycerides of short-chain acids such as butyric. Fats, in general, are attacked more actively than other esters of fatty acids (p. 28).

$$
\begin{array}{l}
\text{H}_2\text{C}-\text{O}-\overset{\displaystyle O}{\overset{\|}{\text{C}}}-\textbf{R} \\
\quad \\
\text{HC}-\text{O}-\overset{\displaystyle O}{\overset{\|}{\text{C}}}-\textbf{R} \xrightarrow[\text{Lipase}]{3\text{H}_2\text{O}} \text{C}_3\text{H}_5(\text{OH})_3 + 3\textbf{RCOOH} \\
\quad \\
\text{H}_2\text{C}-\text{O}-\overset{\displaystyle O}{\overset{\|}{\text{C}}}-\textbf{R} \\
\end{array}
$$

Triglyceride   Glycerol   Fatty acids

Because of the insolubility of fats in aqueous media, their hydrolysis by lipase is facilitated by emulsification, which increases enormously the surface area of the substrate exposed to the enzyme. Emulsification is favored by mechanical action of the stomach and intestine but especially by the surface tension-lowering action of the bile salts, which enter the duodenum in the bile. As fatty acids are split off, the resulting monoglycerides, and perhaps also the soaps (i.e., Na and K salts) of the fatty acids, being surface-active substances, favor further emulsification and, consequently, digestion. Soaps are probably not present at the usual pH of the intestinal contents.

Conditions in the intestine are usually not optimal for complete hydrolysis of ingested fats to glycerol and fatty acids. The digestive mixture usually consists of undigested fat (triglycerides), diglycerides, monoglycerides and fatty acids, in varying proportions, depending upon a number of circumstances, including the quantity of fat, its nature, the pH, and the motility of the bowel.

NUCLEODEPOLYMERASES. Pancreatic juice contains ribonuclease and desoxyribonuclease, which partially hydrolyze the corresponding nucleic acids into mononucleotides. Completion of this action depends upon the presence of other enzymes. No free phosphoric acid is liberated. The actions of these enzymes have not been clearly characterized. The optimum pH for desoxyribonuclease is apparently about 7.0.

INTESTINAL JUICE (SUCCUS ENTERICUS)

The cells of the mucosal glands of the small intestine at different levels (duodenum, jejunum, ileum) secrete fluids of different composition, which are collectively designated "succus entericus" (intestinal juice). These secretions are apparently under nervous and hormonal (enterocrinin, secretin) control. As ordinarily collected, intestinal fluid is rather viscous and turbid, owing to the presence of mucus, and of leukocytes and desquamated mucosal epithelial cells. The solid content is about 1.5 per cent, about half of which is inorganic (chiefly bicarbonate, chloride, phosphate, Na, K, Ca). The chief organic components are mucin, enzymes, and various lipids (cholesterol, phospholipids, fat), but it also contains various metabolites, such as urea.

Certain of the enzymes are undoubtedly truly extracellular, secreted into the lumen of the bowel, but others (e. g., phosphatases, nucleotidases, nucleosidases) are probably intracellular, entering the bowel lumen in disintegrating, desquamated mucosal cells. This circumstance, and functional and anatomical factors resulting in mixtures of secretions of variable constitution from different portions of the intestine, contribute to the lack of uniformity of composition of succus entericus, which is therefore not a distinct entity as are the gastric and pancreatic secretions.

The pH varies considerably at different levels of the small intestine, depending upon the acidity of the gastric contents entering the duodenum, and the volume and conditions of stimulation of pancreatic juice and bile flow. However, under average normal conditions, the pH in the duodenum in the fasting state is about 5.5–6.0, falling somewhat after taking food. It increases gradually at lower levels to about 6.0–6.5 in the terminal ileum. The pH may vary within rather wide limits with variation in composition of the diet and bacterial action, e.g., with variable production of organic acids such as lactic acid (fermentation).

CARBOHYDRASES. Maltase splits maltose into two molecules of glucose. Sucrase (invertase) splits sucrose into glucose and fructose. Lactase splits lactose into glucose and galactose.

PEPTIDASES. Two main types are found in intestinal juices: (1) aminopeptidases, which are exopeptidases acting on the peptide linkage of terminal amino acids possessing a free amino group; (2) tripeptidases and dipeptidases, which split tri-and dipeptides into their two constituent amino acids.

NUCLEOPHOSPHATASES (NUCLEOTIDASES). These are apparently nonspecific phosphatases. They split the nucleotides into phosphoric acid and nucleosides. There is some question as to whether these enzymes are secreted into the intestine (extracellular enzymes) or whether they are intracellular enzymes shed into the lumen with exfoliated mucosal cells.

NUCLEOSIDASES (GLUCOSIDASES OR PHOSPHORYLASES). These are intracellular enzymes of two varieties, (1) purine nucleosidases and (2) pyrimidine nucleosidases. The former, but not the latter, have been found in the intestinal lumen, presumably as a result of desquamation of mucosal epithelium. They split the corresponding nucleosides into the constituent bases (purines or pyrimidines) and sugars (ribose or desoxyribose). As indicated previously, there is evidence that the action of at least some nucleosidases is phosphorolytic rather than hydrolytic. This would be expected to be a strictly intracellular reaction.

ENTEROKINASE. This enzyme, secreted by the duodenal mucosal cells, has no direct digestive action; it converts (activates) trypsinogen to trypsin.

BILE

Human bile, as freshly secreted by the liver, is a clear, golden-yellow, slightly viscous, bitter-tasting fluid, with a pH of about 7.0–8.5 and a daily volume of about 500–700 cc. It has a solid content of about 1–4 per cent, approximately one-fourth of which is inorganic (chiefly HCO_3, Cl, Na, K), the remainder organic. The most distinctive of the latter are bile acids (salts), bilirubin, and cholesterol, but there are also smaller amounts of phospholipid (lecithin), mucin, and other substances, e.g. urea, alkaline phosphatase. The inorganic substances and bilirubin (p. 112) are removed by the liver cells from the blood stream for biliary excretion. The bile acids (p. 36) and biliary cholesterol orginate in the hepatic polygonal cells; the bile phosphatase probably is formed in these cells or in the epithelial cells of the terminal bile-duct radicals. Mucin is a product of the bile-duct epithelium and gallbladder mucosa. The bile is the most important channel of excretion of other substances preferentially removed from the blood by the liver. These include iron and certain halogenated organic compounds, such as iodinated, chlorinated, and brominated phenolphthaleins, which are used clinically for testing liver and gallbladder function and bile duct patency.

Bile is probably secreted continually by the liver, but is prevented from entering the duodenum by the state of tonicity of the sphincter of Oddi. It accumulates and is stored in the gallbladder, where it undergoes concentration (reabsorption of water) and is periodically discharged into the bowel by relaxation of the duodenal sphincter and simultaneous contraction of the gallbladder.

Gallbladder bile is more viscous than hepatic bile, and is dark yellow, brown, or green, the color depending on the duration of its storage (oxidation of bilirubin to biliverdin) and extent of concentration. A large amount of water, and certain of the inorganic components, principally HCO_3, but also Cl and Na, are reabsorbed in the gallbladder, the solid content increasing to 4–17 per cent and the pH falling to as low as 5.5. The concentration of bile salts and pigment may at times reach ten times that in hepatic bile (Table 24).

Table 24. Composition of Human Liver and Gallbladder Bile

	LIVER BILE	BLADDER BILE
Sp. gr.	1.009–1.013	1.026–1.032
pH	7.1–8.5	5.5–7.7
Total solids (%)	1–3.5	4–17
Mucin (%)	0.1–0.9	1–4
Bile acids (%)	0.2–2	1.5–10
Bile pigment (%)	0.05–0.17	0.2–1.5
Total lipid (%)	0.1–0.5	1.8–4.7
Cholesterol (%)	0.05–0.17	0.2–0.9
Phosphatide (%)	0.05–0.08	0.2–0.5
Inorganic (%)	0.2–0.9	0.5–1.1
Total base (mEq./liter)	150–180	
Chloride (mEq./liter)	75–110	15–30
Calcium (mg. %)	4–9	10–14
Iron (mg. %)	0.03–7	

BILE ACIDS (BILE SALTS) (FIG. 58, P. 268). The bile acids are present chiefly as salts (Na). It is generally stated that the most abundant in human bile are cholic (3,7,12-trihydroxycholanic) and desoxycholic (3,12-dihydroxycholanic) acids, in the proportion of three to one. By improved technics, there is evidence of the presence, also, of chenodesoxycholic (3,7-dihydroxycholanic) acids, formerly believed to occur mainly in the dog. The relative amounts of these three bile acids in human bile are approximately as follows: cholic, 25–60 per cent of the total; chenodesoxycholic, 30–50 per cent; desoxycholic, 5–25 per cent. These exist apparently exclusively as conjugates with glycine or taurine, i.e., glycocholic acid, taurocholic acid, etc. (Fig. 58), the glyco- usually predominating over the tauro- forms. The latter are apparently conjugated first, the amounts of the glyco- conjugates being determined by the excess of bile acid (i.e., cholic acid, etc.), which is usually large, except in the presence of excessive protein catabolism (i.e., excessive taurine formation).

Cholic acid is apparently formed in the liver from cholesterol (p. 459). Conjugation with glycine and taurine (from cysteine) also occurs in the liver, apparently by peptide linkage, which may be broken by hydrolysis.

The quantity of bile acids formed and excreted varies within wide limits, depending presumably upon the intensity of stimulation of this

function by the digestive mixture in the intestine, the capacity of the
liver in this regard being very large. Their concentration in hepatic
bile has been found to vary from 0.4–2.0 grams/100 ml. and the total
daily excretion from 5–10 grams. In the intestine, the bile salts are
absorbed into the portal circulation, from which they are largely removed by the liver and re-excreted in the bile (enterohepatic circulation). A small amount escapes removal by the liver, passing into the
systemic circulation, in which cholate is present in concentrations of
0.2–3.0 mg./100 ml.

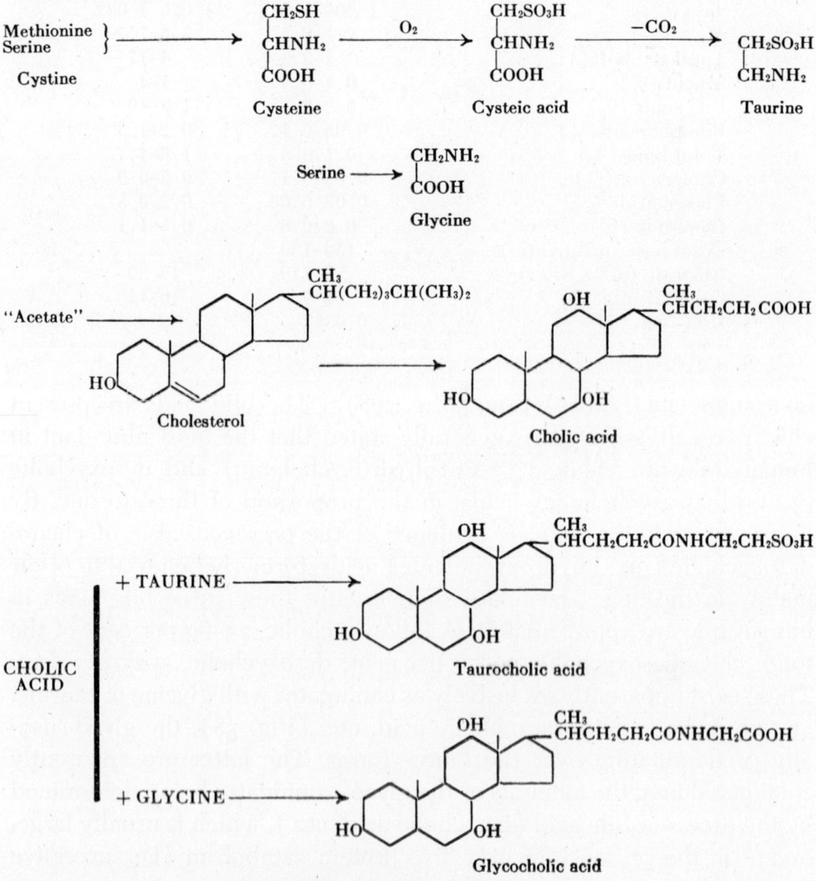

Fig. 58. Biosynthesis of bile acids

The most important functions of the bile salts are:

1. They facilitate digestion of fats by their emulsifying action (lowering surface tension), thus increasing enormously the surface area of
the substrate exposed to pancreatic lipase.

2. They aid in absorption of fatty acids, cholesterol, and the fat-

soluble vitamins D and K, and of carotene, presumably by forming complexes more soluble in water ("hydrotropic" action).

3. They are the most potent natural stimulus to hepatic bile flow, increasing several-fold the volume flow of bile (choleretic action), the output of solids being, however, not affected.

4. They aid in keeping cholesterol in solution in the bile. When the bile acid : cholesterol concentration ratio falls below a critical level, cholesterol may precipitate; this may be a factor in the pathogenesis of biliary calculi (gallstones).

BILE PIGMENTS. The yellow-brown color of freshly secreted human bile (hepatic) is due mainly to bilirubin. On standing (in air or, at times, in the gallbladder) this undergoes oxidation to biliverdin (green). In certain species (e.g., rabbit), biliverdin is the chief pigment of bile. Normal bile may also contain a trace of urobilinogen, which has escaped removal from the portal blood by the liver after its absorption from the bowel. These pigments are waste products of the degradation of heme; their chemistry and metabolism are discussed in detail elsewhere (p. 591). Suffice it here to state that bilirubin, carried in the blood plasma in combination with an α-globulin (pp. 504, 593), is separated from the protein and removed from the blood by the liver cells, which subsequently excrete the "free" pigment in the bile. A portion of the bilirubin is formed in the Kupffer (reticuloendothelial) cells of the liver; however, in man, the bone marrow and spleen are the main sites of normal erythrocyte destruction and heme degradation.

The bile pigments serve no known function, but abnormalities in their formation, excretion, and concentration in the blood plasma are of considerable clinical significance in the diagnosis of diseases of the liver and bile passages and conditions of excessive hemolysis. The quantity excreted daily in the bile (Table 24), normally averaging about 300 mg., is a reflection of the amount of heme undergoing degradation (about 300 mg.), the latter being derived from the approximately 7.5 grams of hemoglobin liberated from destroyed erythrocytes.

CHOLESTEROL. By virtue of the relatively large amounts present (Table 24), and its participation in the formation of gallstones, cholesterol is one of the most important constituents of bile. However, what function it serves in this fluid is conjecturable. It was formerly believed that the bile is an important medium of excretion of the cholesterol circulating in the blood plasma. It appears, however, that this is not the case. Whereas the liver cells actively remove cholesterol from the blood stream, this is largely (at least 60 per cent in the rat) converted here to bile acids, which are excreted in the bile (p. 462). Probably little if any of the cholesterol of the plasma is transferred as such to the bile, and its concentration in the latter medium bears no consistent relation to that in the former. Recent observations indicate that the biliary cholesterol is largely, if not entirely, synthesized in the liver, as is the plasma cholesterol (p. 458).

SUMMARY OF DIGESTION

CARBOHYDRATES. Hydrolysis of polysaccharides (starch, glycogen, dextrins) is begun by salivary amylase in the mouth and continues for a short time in the stomach, until this enzyme is inactivated by the increasing acidity and pepsin. Digestion products are dextrins and maltose. The unchanged polysaccharides and the dextrins are split to maltose by pancreatic amylase. The maltose and ingested lactose and sucrose are ultimately hydrolyzed to glucose, galactose, and fructose by the intestinal enzymes, maltase, lactase, and sucrase (invertase). Monosaccharides are the end-products of carbohydrate digestion.

PROTEINS. Proteins are denatured to a certain extent by the gastric HCl. Gastric pepsin and pancreatic trypsin and chymotrypsin act on native and denatured proteins to form polypeptides and simpler peptides of varying size and a small amount of amino acids. The peptides are attacked further by carboxypeptidase (pancreas), aminopeptidases (intestine), and tri- and dipeptidases (intestine), the end-products of protein digestion being largely amino acids and, probably, a small amount of short peptide chains.

Casein is converted to insoluble paracasein, in the presence of Ca^{++}, by rennin (infants), pepsin, and chymotrypsin. The paracasein is then attacked by proteolytic enzymes as indicated above. Casein is also denatured and precipitated by gastric HCl.

NUCLEOPROTEINS. The proteolytic enzymes apparently split nucleoproteins into their protein and nucleic acid components, digesting the former as outlined above. The nucleic acids are hydrolyzed by nucleodepolymerases (pancreas) to mononucleotides. The latter are split by phosphatases (nucleotidases) into phosphoric acid and nucleosides. There is some question as to the extent to which this and subsequent changes occur in the intestinal lumen. The action of nucleotidases and nucleosidases is probably exerted predominantly within the intestinal mucosal cells, during the process of absorption. Nucleosidases split the nucleosides into their constituent bases (purine and pyrimidine) and sugars (ribose and desoxyribose).

LIPIDS. Digestion of fats is facilitated by the emulsifying action of bile salts, which lower surface tension. When their digestion has begun, it is further aided by the emulsifying effect of fat-digestion products. There is little fat digestion in the stomach (gastric lipase), pancreatic lipase being the most important lipolytic enzyme in the digestive tract (there are also lipases in intestinal secretions). Hydrolysis of fats does not proceed to completion in the intestine under physiological conditions. The final products to be absorbed include the original triglycerides, di- and monoglycerides, fatty acids, and glycerol. Triglycerides of short-chain fatty acids, e.g., tributyrin, are not attacked effectively by lipase, nor are other fatty acid esters. Various esterases and phosphatases are present in the intestine, which may hydrolyze such compounds as tributyrin, phospholipids, and cholesterol esters prior to their absorption. In certain instances, e.g., cholesterol esters and phospholipids, this process may be reversed, these substances being synthesized either in the lumen or, more probably, in the mucosal cells during the process of absorption.

ABSORPTION

Nutrient materials are not ordinarily absorbed from the mouth, although certain therapeutically administered substances may be under specialized conditions. Alcohol and relatively small amounts of water, iron, amino acids, monosaccharides, other simple organic compounds and inorganic salts may be absorbed from the stomach. However, the small intestine is the major site of entrance of nutrient and other materials into the organism, via the intestinal lymphatics and portal circulation. Substances absorbed by the former route are transported in the thoracic duct to the subclavian vein, and hence enter the systemic circulation directly; those absorbed into the portal blood pass to the liver, where many of them undergo metabolic transformations before they pass into the systemic circulation. Absorptive functions of the colon are normally restricted almost exclusively to water, although certain inorganic elements and simple organic compounds may be absorbed here.

Water, inorganic substances, end-products of digestion of carbohydrates, lipids and proteins, and other essential nutrient materials, e.g., vitamins, are generally absorbed readily from the small intestine. Individual peculiarities of absorption of various foodstuffs and digestive products are considered in the discussions of the metabolism of these substances.

The contents of the terminal ileum pass through the ileocecal valve into the colon. Here the final changes occur prior to expulsion of unabsorbed material (feces) from the bowel.

ACTION OF BACTERIA IN THE INTESTINES

After the first few hours of life, microorganisms gain entrance to the alimentary tract and multiply, chiefly in the colon, but also to a relatively limited extent in the small intestine. Most of them do not survive exposure to a highly acid gastric juice, but may flourish in the presence of achlorhydria; some are attacked by digestive enzymes in the small intestine. In some species, these organisms serve important digestive functions, e.g., in cattle, rendering nutritionally available such substances as cellulose, which the host cannot digest. In man, the normal intestinal microorganisms, acting chiefly on products of enzymatic digestion of organic foodstuffs, produce substances some of which are potentially harmful (e.g., toxic amines, phenols), others beneficial (certain vitamins), others neither harmful or beneficial (e.g., urobilinogen). These are products of metabolic activity of the bacteria, involving processes similar to many operating in animal tissues, e.g., oxidation, decarboxylation, deamination, reduction and hydrolysis, catalyzed by enzymes often similar to those encountered in mammalian cells.

The important matter of synthesis of vitamins by intestinal bacteria is considered in the discussion of individual vitamins. We are concerned here with their primary action on digestive products of organic foodstuffs.

CARBOHYDRATES AND LIPIDS. The action of intestinal bacteria on carbohydrates is commonly referred to as intestinal fermentation. The products include chiefly (1) organic acids, such as formic, acetic, propionic, butyric, lactic, oxalic, and succinic, and (2) gases, such as methane, carbon dioxide, and hydrogen. Fats may be hydrolyzed to glycerol and fatty acids, but little is known about the action of microorganisms on lipids in the intestine.

PROTEINS. Bacterial enzymes act on proteins to form polypeptides (proteoses, peptones), smaller peptides, amino acids, and ammonia. Aromatic amino acids are converted to phenol, cresol, indole, and skatole. Cystine yields H_2S, mercaptans, and methane. Certain amino acids form amines (tyramine, putrescine, cadaverine, histamine). These changes are commonly included under the designation "putrefaction."

Certain of the simpler amino acids undergo (1) decarboxylation, to amines, or (2) deamination, to short-chain fatty acids, by the action of bacterial enzymes.

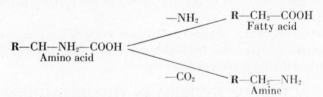

TYROSINE. Tyrosine may undergo (1) decarboxylation to tyramine, which may be converted to cresol and phenol, or (2) deamination, oxidation, and decarboxylation to phenol.

Tyramine is a "pressor base," having an action similar to but weaker than that of epinephrine and norepinephrine, to which it is closely related structurally. As indicated on page 273, it may in part be reduced in the bowel to cresol. If absorbed, it is metabolized in the liver, in part at least undergoing deamination (oxidative) to form hydroxy-

Tyrosine → (—CO_2) → Tyramine → (+2H, Methylamine CH_3—NH_2) → Cresol → Phenol

Tyrosine (—NH_2) → p-Hydroxyphenylpropionic acid → p-Hydroxyphenylacetic acid (—CO_2) → Cresol

phenylacetic acid. Absorbed phenols are largely conjugated in the liver with sulfate and glucuronic acid (p. 281), to be excreted ultimately in the urine.

TRYPTOPHAN. This may also undergo primary (1) decarboxylation to indole-ethylamine (tryptamine) or (2) deamination to indolepropionic acid. The subsequent changes are indicated below, eventuating in skatole and indole, which contribute the characteristic foul odor to the feces. These substances are relatively non-toxic in quantities ordinarily produced, but may be toxic in very large amounts.

Tryptophan → (—NH_2, +H) → Indolepropionic acid → (—CO_2) → Ethylindole

Indolepropionic acid → Indoleacetic acid → (—CO_2) → Skatole

Ethylindole → Skatole

Tryptophan → (CO_2) → Indole ethylamine → (+2H) → Indole + Ethylamine ($C_2H_5NH_2$)

Indoleacetic acid → (—$CH_3\cdot NH_2$, +2H) → Skatole

A small portion of the indole is absorbed and, in the liver, is conjugated with sulfate and excreted in the urine as indican (indoxyl sulfate). Increased amounts of indole may be absorbed and increased amounts of indican formed in constipation and lower intestinal obstruction.

HISTIDINE. Histidine undergoes decarboxylation to histamine, a powerful vasodepressor substance with additional important actions when introduced into the organism. Many tissues, including the intestines, contain histamine, and also the enzyme histaminase (diamine oxidase), which effects its oxidative degradation to innocuous metabolites.

Histidine $\xrightarrow{-CO_2}$ Histamine

$$\downarrow -NH_2$$

Imidazolepropionic acid $\xrightarrow[O_2]{-CO_2}$ Imidazoleacetic acid $\xrightarrow[O_2]{-CO_2}$ Imidazoleformic acid

CYSTINE AND CYSTEINE. Cystine undergoes primary reduction to cysteine, which may in turn be (1) deaminated or (2) decarboxylated, with the eventual production of mercaptans, H_2S and CH_4. These are largely eliminated in the feces, although mercaptans may be absorbed and excreted in the urine. (See formula on page 275.)

LYSINE, ARGININE. These amino acids may undergo decarboxylation to the diamines, cadaverine and putrescine, respectively, which are largely excreted in the feces, but are essentially non-toxic in amounts ordinarily formed. (See formula on page 275.)

MISCELLANEOUS. Bacteria undoubtedly act on numerous other substances in the intestine. Among these is bilirubin, which is reduced by bacterial enzymes to mesobilirubinogen and stercobilinogen (urobilinogen), these being subsequently oxidized to urobilin and stercobilin. The major, unabsorbed portion of the "bilinogens" and "bilins" is excreted by the bowel, contributing the normal brown color to the feces (p. 276). A portion of the fecal coprosterol may be produced by bacterial reduction of cholesterol, although this transformation perhaps occurs largely in the intestinal mucous membrane, during the process of excretion.

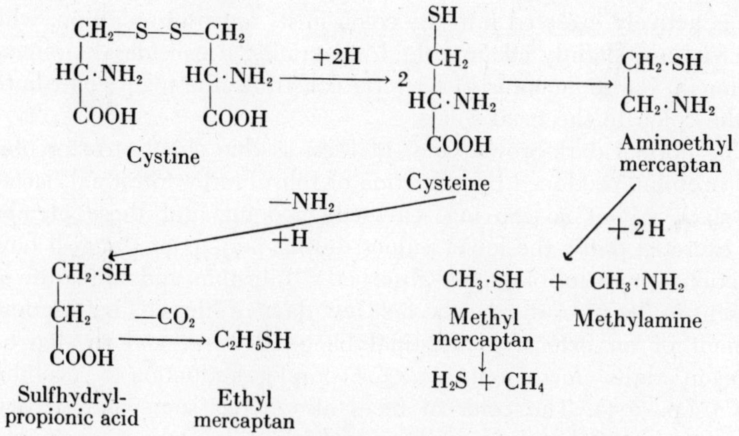

$$CH_2-S-S-CH_2$$
$$HC \cdot NH_2 \quad HC \cdot NH_2 \xrightarrow{+2H} 2$$
$$COOH \quad COOH$$

Cystine

$$SH$$
$$CH_2$$
$$HC \cdot NH_2 \longrightarrow$$
$$COOH$$

Cysteine

$$CH_2 \cdot SH$$
$$CH_2 \cdot NH_2$$

Aminoethyl mercaptan

$$\xrightarrow[+H]{-NH_2}$$

$$CH_2 \cdot SH$$
$$CH_2 \quad \xrightarrow{-CO_2} C_2H_5SH$$
$$COOH$$

Sulfhydryl-propionic acid

Ethyl mercaptan

$$CH_3 \cdot SH + CH_3 \cdot NH_2$$

Methyl mercaptan   Methylamine

$$+2H$$

$$H_2S + CH_4$$

Reduction of Cystine

$$CH_2 \cdot NH_2 \cdot (CH_2)_3 \cdot CH \cdot NH_2 \cdot COOH \rightarrow CH_2 \cdot NH_2 \cdot (CH_2)_3 \cdot CH_2 \cdot NH_2$$

Lysine   Cadaverine

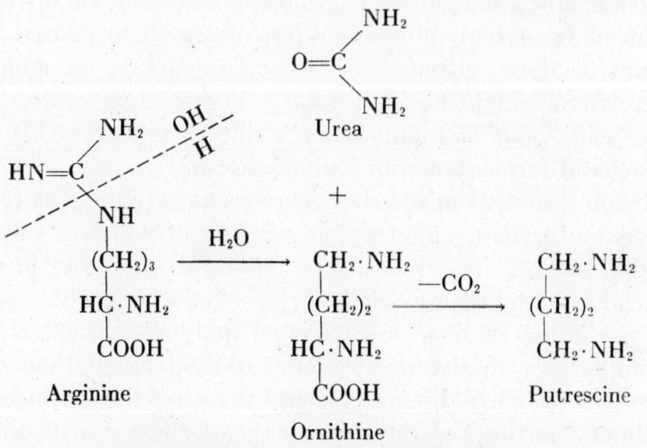

$$NH_2$$
$$O=C$$
$$NH_2$$

Urea

$$NH_2 \quad OH$$
$$HN=C \qquad H$$
$$NH$$
$$(CH_2)_3 \xrightarrow{H_2O}$$
$$HC \cdot NH_2$$
$$COOH$$

Arginine

$$+$$

$$CH_2 \cdot NH_2$$
$$(CH_2)_2 \xrightarrow{-CO_2}$$
$$HC \cdot NH_2$$
$$COOH$$

Ornithine

$$CH_2 \cdot NH_2$$
$$(CH_2)_2$$
$$CH_2 \cdot NH_2$$

Putrescine

Decarboxylation of Lysine and Arginine

FORMATION AND COMPOSITION OF FECES

The contents of the terminal ileum enter the colon in a semiliquid state. The solid material includes indigestible food residues (e.g., cellulose), small amounts of undigested and unabsorbed foodstuffs, remains of desquamated mucosal cells and digestive fluids, together with bacteria and unabsorbed products of their activity. The function of the colon consists chiefly in absorption of water, converting its contents to a semisolid state. What chemical changes occur here are almost exclusively due to bacterial action. Comparatively little material is actively excreted into the colon in its mucosal secretion, which is a viscous, slightly alkaline fluid, containing a considerable amount of mucin. Large amounts of bacteria constitute the main contribution of the colon to the fecal solids.

The normal dark-brown color of feces is due chiefly to stercobilin and urobilin, produced by reduction of bilirubin by intestinal bacteria (p. 594). About 40–280 mg. (average 200 mg.) of these pigments are excreted daily, the lower values during periods of sluggish bowel function (more urobilinogen absorbed). Bilirubin and biliverdin are present in the feces during the first few days of life, i.e., before development of an extensive intestinal bacterial flora, and in diarrheal states in adults (inadequate time for complete reduction to "urobilinogen") (p. 595). The color of feces also varies somewhat with the character of the diet, being paler on a high milk intake. Certain drugs and pigmented vegetables may influence the color, e.g., black after Fe and Bi (sulfides and oxides formed), yellowish after senna, santonin and rhubarb, etc.

The characteristic foul odor is due largely to indole and skatole, but is contributed to also by H_2S and methyl mercaptan. It is more pronounced on a high protein intake, owing to formation of larger quantities of these substances by bacterial action on amino acids, and is relatively slight on high milk or high carbohydrate diets. The slightly "sour" odor of infant feces is due to organic acids resulting from bacterial fermentation of carbohydrates.

Adults on a normal mixed diet excrete 75–170 grams of feces daily (average 100 grams), about 25–30 per cent of which is solid (25–45 grams dry weight). The quantity (total and dry weight) increases on diets rich in vegetables, especially if uncooked (indigestible cellulose). About 7–8 grams of feces are excreted daily if no food is ingested, consisting largely of bacteria, remnants of desquamated mucosal cells, and residues of mucosal secretions and digestive fluids. Bacteria comprise about one-third of the dry weight of the feces under average dietary conditions. The pH, 7.0–7.5, is relatively uninfluenced by wide variations in composition of the diet, but may be lowered by ingestion of large amounts of lactose (fermentation acids).

The inorganic components are mainly substances poorly soluble in alkaline pH ranges, such as calcium phosphate and oxalate, iron phosphate, etc., but also small amounts of magnesium, potassium, and sodium. The organic constituents include carbohydrate (chiefly cellulose), proteins, and lipids.

PROTEIN. On an average diet, the daily nitrogen excretion in the feces is 0.5–1.5 grams (average 1.3 grams). About half of it is of bacterial origin, the remainder representing nitrogenous components of (1) unabsorbed intestinal secretions and digestive fluids, (2) mucus, (3) desquamated mucosal epithelial cells, and a small amount of (4) food residues and (5) intestinal enzymes. Under normal conditions, protein digestion and amino acid absorption are so nearly complete that only small amounts of food protein nitrogen (5–10 per cent) escape in the feces. Enzymes are also present in very small quantities, including pancreatic amylase, trypsin, nucleases, maltase, sucrase, lipase, and lysozyme. These are increased in diarrhea. The term "metabolic N" is used to indicate the fecal N originating from sources other than bacteria and food residues. This factor is employed in quantitative studies of protein utilization and N balance.

LIPIDS. Lipids comprise 5–25 per cent (average 17) of the dry weight of normal feces. They include neutral fats, free fatty acids, soaps, and sterols. Approximately one-third of the fecal lipid is unsaponifiable, consisting mainly of phytosterols, and cholesterol and its reduction products, coprosterol and dihydrocholesterol. Cholesterol enters the bowel in the food, bile, and intestinal secretions. The only quantitatively important sterols and their derivatives absorbed by the human intestine are cholesterol and vitamin D. The remainder of the lipids are largely of endogenous origin, secreted into the bowel, and resemble the plasma lipids in their fatty acid composition. Their nature and amount are altered but little, under normal conditions, by wide variations in dietary fat, which is almost completely utilized unless given in excessive amounts, causing diarrhea. The average normal distribution of saponifiable fecal lipids is as follows: (1) neutral fat, 7.3 per cent of dry weight; (2) free fatty acid, 5.6 per cent; (3) soaps, 4.6 per cent.

BIBLIOGRAPHY

Annual Review of Physiology.

Babkin, B. P.: Secretory Mechanism of the Digestive Glands, ed. 2, New York, Paul B. Hoeber, Inc., 1950.

Bockus, H. L.: Gastro-enterology, Philadelphia, W. B. Saunders Company, 1946.

Conway, E. J.: The Biochemistry of Gastric Acid Secretion, Springfield, Ill., Charles C Thomas, Publisher, 1953.

Davies, R. E.: The mechanism of hydrochloric acid production by the stomach, Biol. Rev. 26:87, 1951.

Florey, H. W., Wright, R. D. and Jennings, M. A.: The secretions of the intestine, Physiol. Rev. 21:36, 1941.

Frazer, A. C.: The absorption of triglyceride fat from the intestine, Physiol. Rev. 26: 103, 1946.

Hollander, F.: The composition and mechanism of formation of gastric acid secretion, Science 110:57, 1949.
Sobotka, H.: Physiological Chemistry of the Bile, Baltimore, Williams & Wilkins Company, 1937.
Sumner, J. B. and Myrbäck, K.: The Enzymes. Chemistry and Mechanism of Action, New York, Academic Press, Inc., 1950–1952.
Wolf, S. and Wolff, H. G.: Human Gastric Function, London, Oxford University Press, 1944.
Verzar, F. and McDougall, E. J.: Absorption from the Intestine, London, Longmans, Green & Co., Inc., 1936.

9

DETOXICATION MECHANISMS

In its broadest sense the term "detoxication" is applied to chemical changes undergone in the body by foreign organic compounds, i.e., substances not ordinarily ingested or utilized by the organism. Employed in this manner, the term is frequently inaccurate and misleading, for many of the compounds in question are originally non-toxic and, in certain instances, the chemical changes result in increased rather than reduced toxicity. In certain cases the metabolites are excreted more readily in the urine than are the original compounds. The reactions involved in these detoxication processes are (1) oxidation, (2) reduction, (3) hydrolysis, and (4) conjugation (synthesis). The type of reaction depends primarily on the chemical nature of the compound, but occasionally the metabolism of a given substance follows different pathways in different species. In man, oxidation and conjugation are most widely employed in this connection, occuring almost exclusively in the liver and, to a minor extent, in the kidney.

OXIDATION. Many foreign organic compounds undergo oxidation in the body. The most important types of these may be classified as follows:

(*a*) PRIMARY ALCOHOLS. Aliphatic (e.g., methyl) and aromatic (e.g., benzyl) primary alcohols are oxidized to the corresponding acids, perhaps via aldehydes as intermediates.

$$CH_3OH \longrightarrow HCOOH$$

Methanol Formic acid

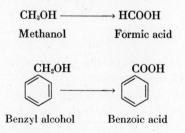

Benzyl alcohol Benzoic acid

(*b*) Aromatic hydrocarbons. Mono- or polycyclic aromatic hydrocarbons (e.g., benzene) are frequently oxidized to phenols. In rare instances the aromatic ring may open, but only to a slight extent.

Benzene   Phenol   Catechol   Muconic acid

(*c*) Methyl groups. Methyl groups are largely oxidized to carboxyl groups, via alcohols and aldehydes as intermediates.

$$-CH_3 \longrightarrow -CH_2OH \longrightarrow -CHO \longrightarrow -COOH$$

(*d*) Oxidation preliminary to conjugation. Oxidation may occur as a necessary preliminary to conjugation; e.g., benzene is oxidized to phenol, which then combines with sulfuric or glucuronic acid (p. 282).

reduction. This does not occur extensively in man as a detoxication mechanism. Certain of the reduced metabolites are more toxic than the original compounds. Illustrative examples of this mechanism are as follows:

1. Certain aldehydes (e.g., chloral) may be reduced to the corresponding alcohol, usually as a preliminary to conjugation of the latter.

$$CCl_3CHO \xrightarrow{\ 2H\ } CCl_3CH_2OH \xrightarrow[\text{acid}]{\text{Glucuronic}} CCl_3CH_2OC_6H_9O_6$$

Trichloroethyl
glucuronide

2. Aromatic nitro compounds (e.g., *p*-nitrobenzaldehyde) may be reduced to the corresponding amines.

p-Nitrobenzaldehyde   *p*-Aminobenzoic acid

In this instance, reduction of the nitro group is accompanied by oxidation of the aldehyde group.

hydrolysis. Certain compounds which are used for therapeutic purposes undergo hydrolysis in the body. Acetylsalicylic acid is hydrolyzed to salicylic and acetic acids; many glucosides, e.g., digitalis, are hydrolyzed to sugars and aglucones.

CONJUGATION. This term, as applied specifically to detoxication processes, refers to the coupling of the foreign substance or one of its metabolites (see Oxidation and Reduction, pp. 279, 280) with a compound occurring normally in the body. The latter is referred to as the conjugating agent. In man, this important type of reaction occurs virtually only in the liver; the kidney participates to only a minor extent in certain instances, although it plays a more important role in this connection in other species.

In man, eight types of conjugation have been established, the conjugating agents being as follows: (1) glucuronic acid, (2) sulfuric acid, (3) glycine, (4) cysteine, (5) glutamine, (6) acetic acid (or "active acetate"), (7) "active" methyl groups, and (8) thiosulfate, involved in the conversion of cyanide to thiocyanate. In birds, ornithine (forming ornithinuric acid) also is employed as a conjugating agent (for benzoic acid). As is true of oxidation, reduction, and hydrolysis, these conjugation reactions are employed also in the metabolism of compounds produced normally in the body. It is of interest that, under experimental conditions, administration of excessive amounts of foreign substances may result in the diversion of excessive quantities of conjugating agent from normal metabolic reactions to "detoxication" processes, to the possible detriment of the organism.

(*a*) GLUCURONIC ACID. Glucuronic acid, formed in the body from carbohydrate (p. 17), is the conjugating agent most commonly involved in this type of detoxication process in man. Two varieties of glucuronides may be formed: (1) an ether (glucosidic) linkage (e.g., phenyl glucuronide); (2) an ester linkage (e.g., benzoyl glucuronide). Glucuronic acid is conjugated commonly with the following types of compound:

1. Aromatic acids (e.g., benzoic acid), in which it couples with the carboxyl group.

Benzoic acid + Glucuronic acid ⟶ Benzoylglucuronic acid

2. Phenols, and secondary and tertiary aliphatic alcohols, in which coupling occurs with the hydroxyl group.

Glucuronic acid
$(C_6H_{10}O_7)$

Phenol + Glucuronic acid → Phenyl glucuronide (glucosidic)

(*b*) SULFURIC ACID. Phenolic hydroxyl groups (e.g., phenol, indole) combine with sulfuric acid to form esters, referred to as ethereal sulfates (p. 534).

Phenol + H_2SO_4 → Phenylsulfuric acid

Indole → Indoxyl → Indoxylsulfuric acid (Indican = K salt)

(*c*) GLYCINE. In man, this amino acid couples chiefly with certain aromatic acids to form aroylglycine compounds. Although aliphatic carboxyl groups as a rule do not combine with glycine, those of cholic and desoxycholic acids do so, glycine conjugates of these bile acids being important normal constituents of bile (p. 267). The following types of carboxyl groups undergo this reaction:

1. Nuclear carboxyl groups in benzene (e.g., benzoic acid), pyridine (e.g., nicotinic acid), naphthalene, thiophene, and furan rings. In man, benzoic acid, when given in relatively small doses, is excreted almost quantitatively as hippuric acid. (See formula on page 283.) When large amounts are given, a portion is excreted also as the glucuronide (p. 281).

2. Carboxyl groups separated from an aromatic ring by a vinyl group (e.g., cinnamic acid). (See formula on page 283.)

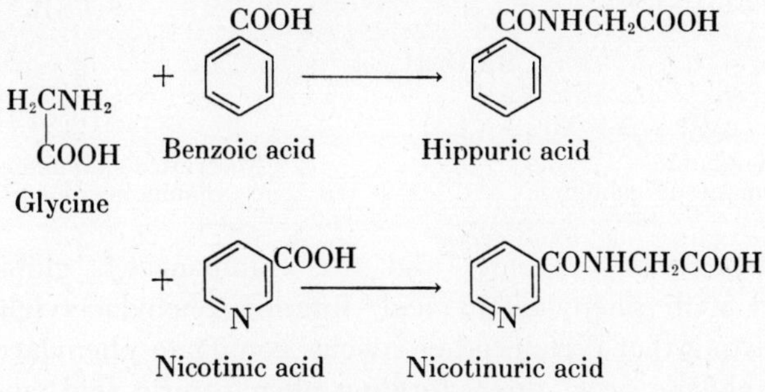

$$\begin{array}{ccc}
\text{H}_2\text{CNH}_2 & & \\
| & + \quad \text{C}_6\text{H}_5\text{COOH} & \longrightarrow \quad \text{C}_6\text{H}_5\text{CONHCH}_2\text{COOH} \\
\text{COOH} & \text{Benzoic acid} & \text{Hippuric acid} \\
\text{Glycine} & &
\end{array}$$

COOH — Benzoic acid → CONHCH$_2$COOH — Hippuric acid

$$+ \quad \text{(pyridine)COOH} \longrightarrow \text{(pyridine)CONHCH}_2\text{COOH}$$

Nicotinic acid   Nicotinuric acid

Nuclear carboxyl groups

CH=CHCOOH (Cinnamic acid) + CH$_2$NH$_2$COOH (Glycine) ⟶ CH=CHCONHCH$_2$COOH

Carboxyl groups

(*d*) CYSTEINE. This amino acid is involved in detoxication reactions to a limited extent in man. It undergoes acetylation (at the amino group) to form N-acetylcysteine, which then may form mercapturic acids with certain aromatic compounds. These include benzene, polycyclic hydrocarbons (e.g., naphthalene), and ring-halogenated hydrocarbons (e.g., brombenzene). In this type of conjugation the —S of the cysteine is usually linked to a nuclear carbon atom.

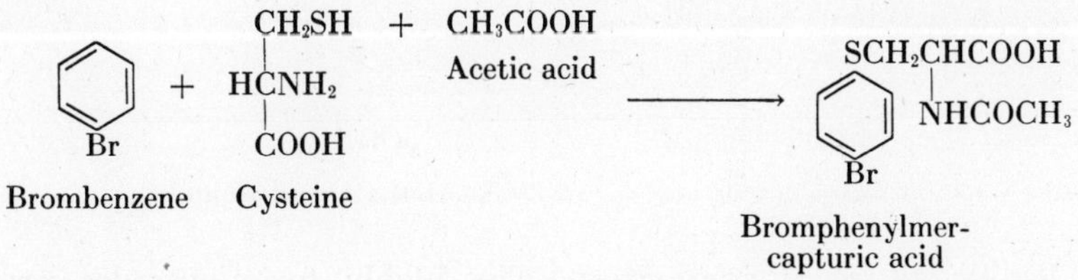

(Brombenzene) + CH$_2$SH | HCNH$_2$ | COOH (Cysteine) + CH$_3$COOH (Acetic acid) ⟶ SCH$_2$CHCHCOOH | NHCOCH$_3$ (on brombenzene ring, Br) — Bromphenylmercapturic acid

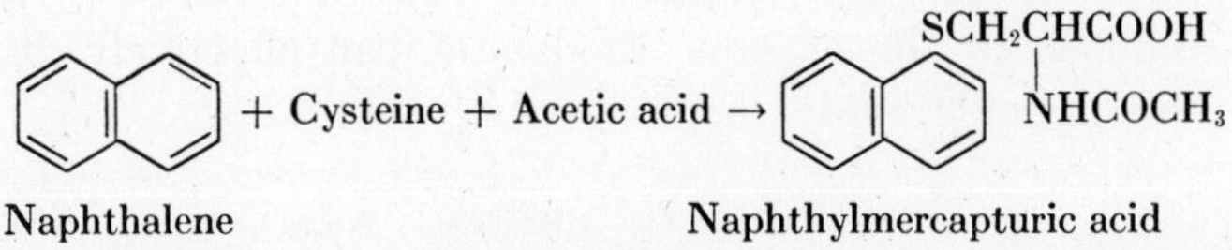

(Naphthalene) + Cysteine + Acetic acid → (Naphthalene) SCH$_2$CHCOOH | NHCOCH$_3$ — Naphthylmercapturic acid

(*e*) ACETIC ACID. As a "detoxication" reaction, acetylation apparently involves only the amino group, although acetylation of hydroxyl groups occurs commonly in the course of metabolism of physiological compounds (e.g., formation of acetylcholine). Aromatic amino groups are involved most commonly (e.g., sulfanilamide; *p*-aminobenzoic acid), but not exclusively. Acetylation of cysteine in the synthesis of mercapturic acids was referred to above.

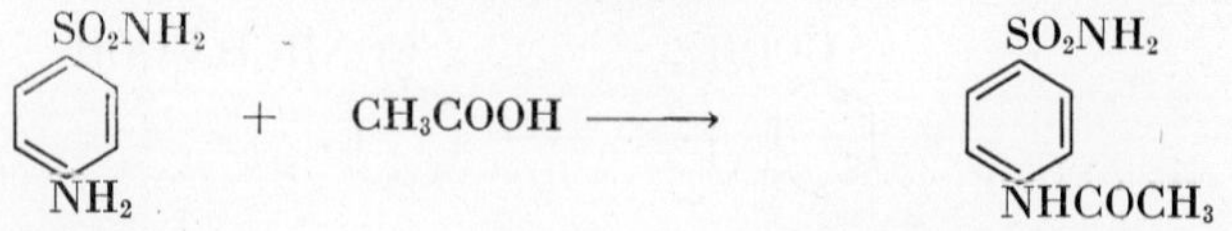

Sulfanilamide
(p-Aminobenzenesulfonamide)

Acetylated sulfanilamide
(p-N-acetylaminobenzenesulfonamide)

(f) GLUTAMINE. In man (and the chimpanzee), glutamine is conjugated with phenylacetic acid, forming phenylacetylglutamine. It is interesting that certain other species conjugate phenylacetic acid only with glycine (e.g., dog), forming phenaceturic acid, and others only with ornithine (fowl).

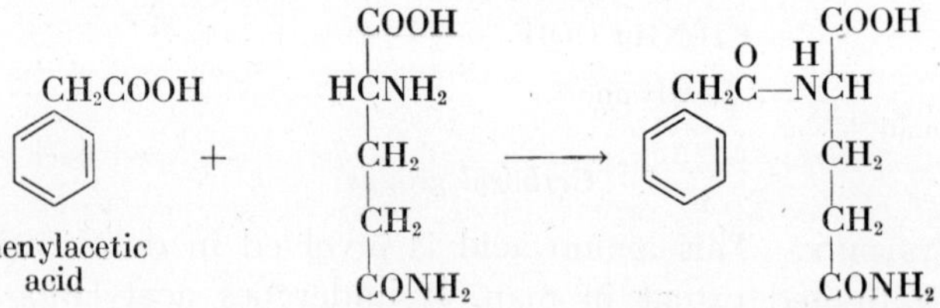

Phenylacetic
acid

Glutamine

Phenylacetylglutamine

(g) METHYLATION. In detoxication reactions, the process of methylation is apparently restricted to the N atom of compounds of the pyridine and quinoline types.

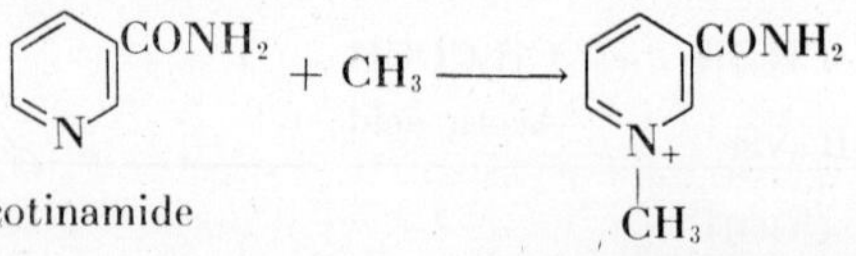

Nicotinamide

N^1-Methylnicotinamide

(h) THIOCYANATE FORMATION. The highly toxic cyanides react with thiosulfate to form relatively non-toxic thiocyanates. This reaction, catalyzed by the enzyme, rhodanese, can effectively dispose of small amounts of cyanide.

$$HCN + Na_2S_2O_3 \rightarrow HCNS + Na_2SO_3$$

BIBLIOGRAPHY

Annual Review of Biochemistry.
Annual Review of Physiology.
Williams, R. T.: Detoxication Mechanisms, New York, John Wiley & Sons, Inc., 1947.

10

RESPIRATION

The maintenance of cell functions and of life is dependent upon the continuous supply of adequate amounts of oxygen to the tissues. In the course of metabolic activities of the cells, large quantities of CO_2 are produced, the bulk of which must be removed from the body. Both substances being gases, these exchanges of O_2 and CO_2 between the organism and the environment are accomplished by way of the lungs, comprising the beginning and end, respectively, of the process of respiration. Proper understanding of some of the fundamental aspects of these exchanges requires an understanding of certain of the so-called "gas laws."

1. At the same pressure and temperature, equal volumes of all gases contain the same number of mols.

2. In the absence of chemical reaction between gas and solvent, the amount of a gas which dissolves in a liquid is directly proportional to the pressure of the gas.

3. The pressure exerted by a gas at a given temperature depends upon the number of mols of gas in a given volume (molar concentration). This is referred to as the "partial pressure" or "tension" (p) of the gas, e.g., pO_2, pCO_2, pN_2.

4. The total pressure of a mixture of gases is equal to the sum of their partial pressures. Thus, the atmospheric (barometric) pressure (BP) is represented by $pO_2 + pCO_2 + pN_2$. This applies only to dry atmospheric air. The partial pressure of water vapor is a function only of temperature and is independent of the presence of other gases. Consequently, in calculating pO_2 and pCO_2, the following equation is applicable:

$$BP - pH_2O \text{ vapor} = pO_2 + pCO_2 + pN_2.$$

Inasmuch as the pressure exerted by a gas is determined by the number of mols of gas, and since the same number of mols of gases, under the same pressure, occupy equal volumes, it follows that the partial pressure of each component of a mixture of gases will be determined by the fraction which it occupies of the total volume of the mixture. In air, therefore,

$$pO_2 = \frac{(BP - pH_2O\ vapor) \times \%\ O_2}{100}$$

$$pCO_2 = \frac{(BP - pH_2O\ vapor) \times \%\ CO_2}{100}$$

$$pN_2 = \frac{(BP - pH_2O\ vapor) \times \%\ N_2}{100}$$

In dry atmospheric air at a barometric pressure of 760 mm. Hg, the partial pressures of the constituent gases would be: $pO_2 = 20.9\%$ of 760, or 158 mm.; $pCO_2 = 0.04\%$ of 760, or 0.3 mm.; $pN_2 = 79\%$ of 760, or 600 mm. (Table 25).

The air in the pulmonary alveoli similarly contains O_2, CO_2, and N_2, but is also saturated with water vapor, which evaporates from the surface of the lining membranes at body temperature, exerting a partial pressure of about 48 mm. Hg. Inasmuch as the total gas pressure in alveolar air is the same as in the inspired (atmospheric) air, the partial pressure of each of the dry gases is exerted in a total of 760 minus 48 mm., or 712 mm. Hg. The same is true of the expired air. The percentage composition of, and pO_2 and pCO_2, in alveolar and expired air in a normal subject at rest are indicated in Table 25.

Table 25. Percentage Composition of, and pO_2 and pCO_2 in Inspired, Expired, and Alveolar Air in Normal Subject at Rest

	BARO- METRIC PRESSURE (mm. Hg)	H₂O VAPOR (mm. Hg)	OXYGEN CONTENT (vol. %)	OXYGEN pO₂ (mm. Hg)	CARBON DIOXIDE CONTENT (vol. %)	CARBON DIOXIDE pCO₂ (mm. Hg)
Inspired air (dry)	760	0	20.9	158	0.04	0.3
Expired air	760	48	16.1	115	4.4	31
Alveolar air	760	48	14.2	101	5.6	40

In the lungs the blood gases come into approximate equilibrium with those of alveolar air. The separating membrane is very thin (1–2 μ), permitting ready diffusion of gases, and its surface area is very large (50–100 sq. m.). Blood passes through the lungs in about 0.75 second in a resting subject and in about 0.3 second during severe exercise, gas equilibrium being approximated more closely in the former state, which provides longer exposure of the blood to alveolar air. Under normal resting conditions, therefore, the pO_2 and pCO_2 of blood leaving the lungs (arterial blood) are about 100 mm. Hg and 40 mm. Hg, respectively.

In the tissue cells, where oxygen is being utilized and carbon dioxide produced, the pO_2 is relatively low (< 30 mm. Hg) and the pCO_2 high (50–70 mm. Hg).

Inasmuch as a gas flows from a higher to a lower pressure (diffusion gradient), O_2 passes from the arterial blood to the tissue cells and CO_2 passes in the opposite direction. Under ordinary conditions of blood flow in a normal resting subject, the pO_2 of the blood leaving the tissues (venous blood) is thereby lowered to about 40 mm. Hg and the pCO_2 increased to about 46 mm. Hg. The venous blood is then returned to the lungs, where it is arterialized, drawing O_2 from and losing CO_2 to the alveolar air, with which it comes into approximate equilibrium. These pressure relationships are illustrated in Figure 59.

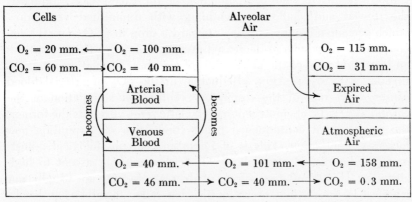

Fig. 59. *Pressure relationships and direction of flow of oxygen and carbon dioxide between tissue cells, blood, lungs, and atmosphere*

At rest, a normal man absorbs about 250 cc. O_2 and eliminates about 200 cc. CO_2 per minute. During severe exercise, the volume exchange of these gases may increase more than ten-fold. The mechanisms of control of pulmonary ventilation are discussed in detail in texts on physiology, and the chemical aspects are summarized here only briefly.

CHEMICAL CONTROL OF RESPIRATION

The respiratory movements and pulmonary ventilation are controlled by nerve impulses arising in the respiratory center in the medulla. The activity of the latter is influenced, directly or indirectly, by changes in: (1) pCO_2, (2) pH, (3) pO_2, (4) blood flow, and (5) temperature. The indirect influences are mediated through chemo-receptors in the carotid and aortic bodies, which are stimulated chiefly by a decrease in pO_2 but also by an increase in pCO_2 and in H^+ ion concentration. Activity of the respiratory center is stimulated directly by an increase in pCO_2, and in H^+ ion concentration, the pCO_2 being the most important chemical factor in the regulation of respiration.

INFLUENCE OF CO_2 TENSION AND pH.   Increase in the pCO_2 or acidity, either in the blood or locally in the respiratory center or aortic and carotid body chemoreceptors, results in stimulation of respiration and increased pulmonary ventilation. The reverse occurs with decrease in pCO_2 and H^+ ion concentration. The pCO_2 apparently exerts an influence in this connection beyond that which can be accounted for by the associated change in pH alone.

Under normal conditions, the extreme sensitivity of the respiratory center to minute changes in pCO_2 in the blood serves to maintain the latter within very narrow limits. The increased ventilation which accompanies any tendency toward a rise in pCO_2 (or H^+ ion concentration) results in prompt elimination of the excess CO_2. Similarly, the slowed and shallower breathing, with diminished ventilation, which accompanies any tendency toward a drop in pCO_2 (or H^+ ion concentration) results in decreased excretion of CO_2. This constitutes an important part of the mechanism of acid-base regulation (p. 320).

INFLUENCE OF O_2 TENSION.   Reduction in the pO_2 of arterial blood causes depression of the respiratory center, but stimulation of the carotid and aortic chemoreceptors. The latter effect exceeds the former, the predominant consequence being stimulation of respiration and increased ventilation. This is of importance in physiological adjust-ment to diminished atmospheric O_2 tensions during ascent to high altitudes. The stimulating effects of decrease in pO_2 are usually not manifest in the resting subject until it has fallen to rather low levels, but are more pronounced at higher levels during exercise.

TRANSPORT OF OXYGEN

The tissue cells of a normal man utilize about 250 ml. of oxygen per minute in the resting state and may consume over ten times that amount during strenuous exercise. At the pO_2 of alveolar air, a liter of blood is able to take up in physical solution only about 2 ml. O_2. Inasmuch as the maximum attainable blood flow is about 25 liters per minute, the maximum amount of O_2 that can be supplied to the tissue cells in this form is about 50 ml./minute, less than 2 per cent of the maximum requirement. Obviously, the oxygen must be transported in the blood chiefly in some form other than physical solution. This is accomplished by its combination with hemoglobin, the nature of which is considered in detail elsewhere (pp. 110, 115).

Under conditions of complete saturation, the blood of a normal man (16 grams Hb/100 ml.) holds a little more than 21 ml. of O_2, only about 0.3 ml. of which is in physical solution. Although of small magnitude, the latter factor is of considerable significance because, being a reflection of the pO_2, it comes into equilibrium in the lungs with the alveolar air O_2, and in the tissues with the interstitial fluid O_2. It is therefore one of the determinants of the amount of O_2 taken up and liberated by Hb, according to the equation,

$$O_2 + Hb \rightleftharpoons HbO_2.$$

Table 26. Oxygen and Carbon Dioxide Contents and Pressures in Blood

| | OXYGEN | | CARBON DIOXIDE | |
	CONTENT (ml./100 ml.)	pO_2 (mm. Hg)	CONTENT (ml./100 ml.)	pCO_2 (mm. Hg)
Arterial	17–22	(100)	44–50	(40)
blood	(20)*		(48)	
Venous	11–16	(40)	51–58	(46)
blood	(13)		(55)	
A-V	4–8		4–8	
difference	(6.5)		(6.5)	

* Mean values indicated in parenthesis.

One mol of oxygen combines with 16,700 grams of Hb. Inasmuch as a mol of O_2 (at 0° C. and 760 mm. Hg) occupies 22,400 ml., 1 gram of Hb can combine with 22,400/16,700 or 1.34 ml. of O_2 (Hüfner factor). Consequently, the 16 grams of Hb in 100 ml. of blood, when fully saturated, can carry 21.4 ml. of O_2. However, under the conditions existing in the circulating blood, the Hb is not completely saturated with O_2, the amounts present in normal arterial and venous blood being indicated in Table 26. The degree of saturation depends upon the pO_2, this relationship being expressed in the dissociation curve of oxyhemoglobin (Fig. 60).

DISSOCIATION OF OXYHEMOGLOBIN. The equation $O_2 + Hb \rightleftharpoons HbO_2$ is shifted to the right or left as the pO_2 increases or decreases, with corresponding increasing saturation of Hb with oxygen (HbO_2) and increasing dissociation of HbO_2, respectively. However, the degree of saturation (or dissociation) is not directly proportional to the pO_2. If blood is equilibrated with air containing O_2 at different partial pressures, and the quantity of O_2 (or HbO_2) in the blood is plotted against the pO_2, an S-shaped curve is obtained (Fig. 60). This is referred to as the dissociation curve of oxyhemoglobin and indicates the relative amounts of oxyhemoglobin (HbO_2) and reduced hemoglobin (Hb) present at different levels of oxygen tension.

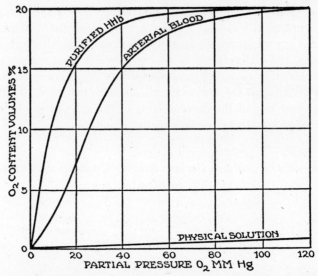

Fig. 60. Dissociation curve of oxyhemoglobin. The O_2 contents of arterial blood and plasma (physical solution) and a solution of purified HHb at various partial pressures of O_2. (After Barcroft. From Fulton: Howell's Textbook of Physiology, ed. 16, W. B. Saunders Company, 1950.)

Certain features of this curve are of great physiological significance.

(a) INFLUENCE OF pO_2. At a pO_2 of 100 mm. Hg, as in arterial blood (at pCO_2 40 mm. Hg and pH 7.4), Hb is 95–98 per cent saturated with O_2, i.e., 95–98 per cent is in the form of HbO_2 and 2–5 per cent in the reduced form. At a pO_2 of 70 mm. Hg, Hb is still 90 per cent saturated. The ability of the blood to carry oxygen therefore varies relatively slightly with variations in pO_2 above 70 mm. Hg. In fact, there is comparatively little reduction in Hb saturation, i.e., comparatively little dissociation of HbO_2, until the pO_2 falls below 50 mm. Hg, dissociation of HbO_2 increasing greatly, i.e., Hb saturation decreasing greatly, as the pO_2 falls below this level (Fig. 61; Table 27).

Because of this peculiar behavior of Hb in relation to the pO_2, adequate uptake of oxygen by the blood in the lungs is assured as long as the alveolar air pO_2 is above 80 mm. Hg. Adequate liberation of oxygen from the blood is assured in the tissues, where the pO_2 is usually below 30 mm. Hg.

(b) INFLUENCE OF pCO_2 AND pH. With increasing CO_2 tension in the blood the affinity of Hb for O_2 decreases (i.e., increasing dissociation of HbO_2 or decreasing saturation of Hb), the equation, $O_2 + Hb \rightleftharpoons HbO_2$, being shifted to the left. This effect is more pronounced at relatively low than at high levels of pO_2, because of the shape of the dissociation curve (Fig. 61; Table 27). Thus, at 90 to 100 mm. Hg pO_2 (alveolar air), variations in pCO_2 from 20 to 80 mm. Hg have comparatively little effect on HbO_2 dissociation (95–100 per cent saturation of Hb). On the other hand, at a pO_2 of 20 mm. Hg (tissues), increasing the pCO_2 from 20 mm. to 80 mm. Hg causes the percentage saturation of Hb to fall from about 40 to less than 20.

*Table 27. Effect of Oxygen and Carbon Dioxide Tensions on Oxygenation of Hemoglobin**

O_2 TENSION	PROPORTION OF HEMOGLOBIN COMBINING WITH OXYGEN AT FOLLOWING CO_2 TENSIONS			
mm.	$CO_2 = 3$ mm.	$CO_2 = 20$ mm.	$CO_2 = 40$ mm.	$CO_2 = 80$ mm.
	(%)	(%)	(%)	(%)
0	0	0	0	0
5	13.5	6.8	5.5	3.0
10	38.0	19.5	15.0	8.0
20	77.6	50.0	39.0	26.0
30	92.0	72.2	60.6	49.8
40	96.7	87.0	76.0	63.5
50	98.5	93.3	85.5	76.9
60	100	96.3	90.5	85.0
70	100	98.0	94.0	90.3
80	100	99.0	96.0	93.7
90	100	100	97.5	95.7
100	100	100	98.6	97.1

*(Henderson, Bock, Field, and Stoddard: J. Biol. Chem. *59*:379, 1924)

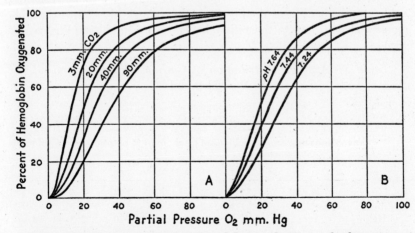

Fig. 61. *The effects of increased pCO_2 and decreased pH upon the dissociation of oxyhemoglobin. Increased temperature also shifts the curve in the same direction as increased pCO_2. (After Peters and Van Slyke. From Fulton: Howell's Textbook of Physiology, ed. 16, W. B. Saunders Company, 1950.)*

Acids other than H_2CO_3, e.g., lactic acid, exert a similar effect, i.e., increase in the H^+ ion concentration of the blood increases dissociation of HbO_2. As in the case of the pCO_2, this influence is more pronounced at relatively low than at high pO_2 levels (Fig. 61).

Rise in temperature also increases dissociation of HbO_2, shifting the curve in the same direction as do increases in pCO_2 and acidity.

As a result of these phenomena, adequate uptake of oxygen from the alveolar air is assured, despite the presence of CO_2, and its delivery to the tissue cells, facilitated primarily by the relatively low pO_2, is enhanced by the relatively high pCO_2, acidity and temperature in the actively metabolizing tissues.

TRANSPORT OF CARBON DIOXIDE

In the resting state, about 200 ml. of CO_2 are produced per minute in the course of oxidative processes in the tissues, and are carried in the blood to the lungs, where they are excreted. During strenuous exercise, the quantity produced and transported increases enormously. The manner in which this relatively large amount of acid ($CO_2 + H_2O \rightleftharpoons H_2CO_3$) is carried in the blood with only slight change in pH is discussed elsewhere (p. 318). Attention will be directed here chiefly to the various forms in which CO_2 exists in the blood and their quantitative distribution.

The direction of flow of CO_2 is determined by the pCO_2, which is 50–70 mm. Hg in the tissues, about 40 mm. in the arterial blood, rises to 46 mm. during passage of blood through the tissues (venous), and is 40 mm. in the alveolar air. The diffusion constant for CO_2 is much higher than for O_2 because of its greater solubility in body fluids; consequently it diffuses readily from the venous blood into the pulmonary alveoli despite the rather low pressure gradient (Fig. 59, p. 287).

Table 28. Average Distribution of Carbon Dioxide in 100 ml. Normal Blood

CARBON DIOXIDE	ARTERIAL ml.	% of total	VENOUS ml.	% of total	DIFFERENCE ml.	% of total
Total	48.2		51.9		3.7	
Total in plasma (600 ml.)	35.6	74	38.0	73	2.4	65
as dissolved CO_2	1.6	3	1.8	3	0.2	5
as HCO_3^-	34.0	71	36.2	70	2.2	60
Total in erythrocytes (400 ml.)	12.6	26	13.9	27	1.3	35
as dissolved CO_2	0.8	1.5	0.9	1	0.1	3
as carbamino-CO_2	2.2	4.5	3.1	6	0.9	24
as HCO_3^-	9.6	20	9.9	20	0.3	8

CO_2 IN ARTERIAL BLOOD (TABLE 28). At rest, 100 ml. of arterial blood contains 45–55 ml. of CO_2 (volumes per cent), about 75 per cent of which is in the plasma and 25 per cent in the erythrocytes.

The 35.6 ml. (average) in the plasma are present in three forms: (1) physical solution (1.6 ml.); (2) HCO_3^- ions (34 ml.); (3) carbamino compounds of plasma proteins (R-NHCOOH), in very small amounts (less than 0.7 ml.) because the plasma proteins contain relatively few NH_2 groups capable of combining with CO_2 under conditions existing in the blood. The 12.6 ml. (average) in the erythrocytes are present in the same forms: (1) physical solution (0.8 ml.); (2) HCO_3^- ions (9.6 ml.); carbamino compounds of Hb (2.2 ml.). About 90 per cent of the CO_2 in arterial blood is in the form of HCO_3^- ions (bicarbonate).

ENTRANCE OF CO_2 IN TISSUES (TABLE 28). At rest, 3.5–4.5 ml. (average 3.7) of CO_2 enter each 100 ml. of blood in the tissues, diffusing across the capillary walls in consequence of the tissue:blood CO_2 diffusion gradient. It enters the blood plasma in physical solution and diffuses readily from the plasma into the erythrocytes.

Carbon dioxide reacts with water as follows:

$$CO_2 + H_2O \rightleftharpoons H_2CO_3 \rightleftharpoons H^+ + HCO_3^-$$

In the plasma, this reaction proceeds very slowly, the equilibrium being far to the left. Consequently, the increment in CO_2 occurring in passing through the tissues drives the reaction to the right only slightly.

Within the erythrocytes, the reaction,

$$CO_2 + H_2O \rightarrow H_2CO_3 \rightarrow H^+ + HCO_3^-,$$

proceeds very rapidly, owing to the presence of carbonic anhydrase, an enzyme which catalyzes this reaction. Because of prompt removal of the ion end-products (H^+ and HCO_3^-), as indicated below (also p. 294), the fraction of the added CO_2 which diffuses into the erythrocytes is much larger than that which remains in the plasma (Fig. 63).

The relatively small capacity of plasma proteins for forming carbamino compounds is not influenced significantly by changes which occur in the blood during its passage through the tissues. Consequently, virtually none of the added CO_2 is transported in this manner (i.e., plasma carbamino–CO_2 is unaltered). Within the erythrocytes, however, a considerable fraction of the added CO_2 is held in this form because of the fact that the capacity of reduced hemoglobin for forming carbamino compounds is more than three times that of oxyhemoglobin. Moreover, this capacity increases with increasing levels of pCO_2. In consequence, therefore, of the liberation of O_2 and addition of CO_2 in the tissues, about 20–25 per cent of the increment in blood CO_2 is transported by hemoglobin as carbamino-CO_2.

The largest fraction, by far, of the added CO_2 which enters the erythrocytes undergoes the reaction,

$$CO_2 + H_2O \rightarrow H_2CO_3 \rightarrow H^+ + HCO_3^-,$$

which proceeds rapidly because the end products, H^+ and HCO_3^- ions, are removed promptly. The added H^+ ions are very effectively "neutralized" by the enhanced buffering capacity of hemoglobin incident to the transformation of HbO_2 to Hb, reduced hemoglobin being a weaker acid than oxyhemoglobin (p. 315). The added HCO_3^- ions, being produced within the erythrocytes more rapidly than in the plasma, diffuse from the erythrocytes into the plasma, an equal number of Cl^- ions passing in the opposite direction (p. 318). Within the erythrocytes, the increase in negatively charged ions (HCO_3^- and Cl^-) is balanced by the K^+ ions "released" by the transformation of HbO_2 to Hb. In the plasma, the HCO_3^- ions entering from the erythrocytes are balanced by the Na^+ ions freed by the diffusion of Cl^- ions into the erythrocytes (Fig. 66, p. 317).

About 70 per cent of the added CO_2 is carried in the blood as bicarbonate (HCO_3^-), about 60 per cent in the plasma, the remainder in the erythrocytes. However, about 90 per cent of the increment in plasma HCO_3^- originates within the erythrocytes, as indicated above, largely as a direct consequence of the enhanced buffering capacity of the hemoglobin. Directly and indirectly, Hb is responsible for the transport of over 80 per cent of the CO_2 added to the blood in the tissues.

BIBLIOGRAPHY

Annual Review of Biochemistry.
Annual Review of Physiology.
Barcroft, J.: The Respiratory Function of the Blood, London, Cambridge University Press, 1928.
Davenport, H. W.: The ABC of Acid-Base Chemistry, ed. 3, Chicago, University of Chicago Press, 1950.
Gamble, J. L.: Chemical Anatomy, Physiology and Pathology of Extracellular Fluid, Cambridge, Harvard University Press, 1950.
Gray, J. S.: Pulmonary Ventilation and Its Physiological Regulation, Springfield, Ill., Charles C Thomas, Publisher, 1949.
Haldane, J. S. and Priestley, J. G.: Respiration, New Haven, Yale University Press, 1935.
Peters, J. P. and Van Slyke, D. D.: Quantitative Clinical Chemistry, Volume I: Interpretations, Baltimore, Williams & Wilkins Company, 1931.

11

WATER BALANCE

In the normal adult organism, not undergoing changes in weight, the quantity of water supplied daily is balanced by that eliminated, a state of equilibrium being maintained.

WATER INTAKE

Water is supplied to the body from the following sources: (1) dietary liquids; (2) solid food; (3) oxidation of organic foodstuffs.

Water comprises 70–90 per cent of the weight of the average diet of adults, even apparently very solid foods consisting largely of water. Moreover, water is one of the chief products of combustion of protein, fat, and carbohydrate in the body, the quantities produced by oxidation of 1 gram of each of these substances being as follows: protein, 0.34 ml.; fat, 1.07 ml.; carbohydrate, 0.56 ml. It may be calculated that 10–15 ml. of water are formed per 100 calories of energy produced. An ordinary 3000-calorie diet therefore contains about 450 ml. of water in the solid food and may provide an additional 300–450 ml. of water of oxidation. The remainder of the water intake is supplied by dietary liquids (Fig. 62).

WATER OUTPUT

Water leaves the body in the (1) urine, (2) feces, (3) perspiration, and (4) so-called insensible perspiration (evaporation from skin and lungs) (Fig. 62).

FECES. Under normal conditions, the 3000–8300 ml. of digestive fluids (p. 328) entering the alimentary tract are almost completely reabsorbed in the intestine. On an ordinary mixed diet, about 80–150 ml. of water are excreted daily in the feces of normal adults (p. 276). This may be increased considerably on a high vegetable diet and particularly in the presence of diarrhea.

INSENSIBLE PERSPIRATION. In the absence of active perspiration, the body is continually losing water vapor from the skin surface and lungs in inverse proportion to the relative humidity of the atmosphere. Inasmuch as 0.58 calories are absorbed in the vaporization of 1 ml. of water, the heat lost by this process, termed "insensible perspiration," at ordinary room temperatures amounts to about 25 per cent of the total heat loss. The latter is proportional to the quantity of heat produced, which is a function of metabolism. The quantity of water lost by insensible perspiration is therefore an obligatory loss, determined by metabolic activity and, in a normal adult, may be calculated as 500 ml. per square meter of body surface area per day. This amounts to about 850 ml. for a 70-kg. man (1.73 sq. meters).

PERSPIRATION. When either heat production or the environmental temperature rises to the point where heat loss by the ordinary means is inadequate, the sweat glands become active. Obviously, the quantity of water lost by this route varies enormously. Moreover, in contrast to insensible perspiration, which consists solely of water, sweat contains 30 to 90 mEq./liter of Na and of Cl (Fig. 68, p. 328). It is a hypotonic solution, plasma containing about 140 mEq./liter of Na. Sweating therefore removes from the body relatively more water than electrolytes.

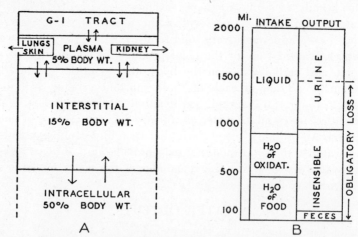

Fig. 62. A: Body water compartments. B: Sources of water to the organism, and water excretion in a 70-kg. man on an average adequate diet. (After Gamble.)

URINE. The urine is the important medium of elimination of water provided to the body in excess of its fixed requirements. The kidneys have a remarkable capacity for regulating urinary excretion of water regardless, within wide limits, of the simultaneous requirement for excretion of solids (p. 767). However, their ability to concentrate is not unlimited, a certain minimal quantity of water being required for excretion of a given amount of solute. On an average adequate diet (adults), providing about 50 grams of solids for daily urinary excretion, a minimum of approximately 500 ml. of water (300 ml./sq. meter body surface) is required for their solution. Failure to meet this obligatory urine volume requirement will result in retention of certain urinary constituents, mainly urea, in the body fluids.

EQUILIBRIUM REQUIREMENTS. As indicated above, in addition to the small amount excreted in the feces (80–150 ml.), the minimal daily water requirement is fixed by certain metabolic requirements: (1) loss of heat by insensible perspiration (normally about 850 ml.); (2) renal excretion of excess solid material, mainly urea, and therefore determined largely by the protein intake (normally about 500 ml. of water). Consequently on an average normal diet, approximately 1500 ml. of water must be available for elimination by these routes if the body temperature and blood urea N are to be maintained within normal limits. The "solid" portion of such a diet contributes about 800 ml. of water, approximately one-half of which is pre-formed, the remainder being produced in the course of oxidation of the organic foodstuffs in the body. The balance of the water requirement must be supplied by intake of liquids if the body fluids are to be maintained at a normal level.

BODY FLUID COMPARTMENTS

Water comprises approximately 70 per cent of the adult body weight and may be regarded as existing in two main compartments, (1) extracellular (20 per cent body weight) and (2) intracellular (50 per cent). Extracellular water is further subdivided into (a) blood plasma water (5 per cent body weight) and (b) interstitial fluid (lymph) (15 per cent).

These fluid compartments are illustrated in Figure 62. Water entering the organism, i.e., from the gastrointestinal tract, passes into the blood stream, an equivalent amount leaving the latter by way of the urine, lungs, skin, and feces. The water of the plasma is in equilibrium with that of the interstitial fluid, and the latter with the intracellular water, across the boundaries between these compartments, i.e., the capillary walls and the cell membranes, respectively. The interstitial fluid, serving as a sort of middle-man for the other two fluids, acts also as a buffer which prevents rather sudden changes in composition of the plasma, owing to absorption from the intestine, from being reflected directly in the intracellular fluid. Moreover, being a rather elastic compartment, it can expand or contract considerably, in conditions of excessive retention (edema) or loss (dehydration) of fluid, in the absence of comparable or even significant alterations in the volume of plasma or intracellular fluid, which must be maintained rather rigidly in the interests of normal circulation and cell function.

VOLUME OF BODY FLUID COMPARTMENTS

The volume of (1) the circulating blood, (2) the plasma, (3) total extracellular fluid, and (4) total body water could be measured by introduction of a substance into the body if that substance would fulfill the following requirements: (a) be retained exclusively in the fluid compartment in question; (b) not leave that compartment during the test period; (c) distribute itself uniformly throughout that compartment; (d) be capable of precise quantitative determination in the blood or plasma. A number of methods have been proposed, none of which is entirely satisfactory; certain of them, however, have proved useful.

BLOOD AND PLASMA VOLUME. (a) CARBON MONOXIDE METHOD. Carbon monoxide displaces oxygen from hemoglobin, volume for volume, and can be measured accurately in blood, either as CO or as HbCO. The subject breathes a known amount of CO and the concentration of HbCO in the blood is determined after allowing sufficient time for mixing. If the total hemoglobin concentration is known, one can calculate how much CO would be required to saturate the Hb to its full capacity and can arrive at the total blood volume. By determining the hematocrit value (relative volumes of packed cells and of plasma), the plasma volume can be derived.

(b) RADIOACTIVE IRON METHOD. Fe^{59} is administered to a normal or anemic subject; it becomes incorporated in the Hb of the circulating erythrocytes. A predetermined amount of the labeled red cells is injected intravenously in the test subject (compatible blood). Measurement of radioactivity in blood samples withdrawn after allowing time for mixing indicates the extent of dilution of the injected cells and permits calculation of the volumes of blood and plasma (from hematocrit value).

(c) DYE METHODS. The dye employed most commonly is Evans blue (T-1824). A known amount is injected intravenously and, after allowing time for distribution throughout the blood plasma, a sample of oxalated blood is withdrawn, centrifuged, and the concentration of dye in the plasma determined colorimetrically. The extent of dilution of the quantity injected can be calculated (plasma volume) and, knowing the hematocrit value, the total blood volume can be determined.

The CO method requires cooperation of the subject, which cannot always be secured under clinical conditions. Moreover, other technical difficulties introduce the possibility of serious errors. Furthermore, the accuracy of this procedure, as well as the Fe^{59} method, depends upon uniformity of distribution of all of the "labeled" erythrocytes in the circulation. This cannot always be assured, especially in disease states (e.g., shock), in which variable and undeterminable numbers of cells may be "segregated" in such organs as the spleen or in the splanchnic bed. Inaccuracies in the dye method arise chiefly out of the fact that a variable and undeterminable portion of the dye may leave the blood stream, particularly into the hepatic lymphatic system, which may itself vary in disease states. Correction must be made for excretion in the urine. It gives values for plasma volume about 15 per cent higher than those obtained with the CO method. In addition, calculations of total blood volume on the basis of factors measured in either cells or plasma are subject to inaccuracies arising out of variations in the ratio of cells to plasma in different portions of the circulation.

Generally acceptable average values for blood and plasma volume in normal subjects are as follows: whole blood, 2500–3200 ml./sq. meter body surface, or 63–80 ml./kg.; plasma, 1300–1800 ml./sq. meter, or 35–45 ml./kg. Values for whole blood are about 7 per cent higher for men than for women, but the plasma values are approximately the same.

TOTAL EXTRACELLULAR FLUID VOLUME. A number of substances, when injected intravenously, cross the capillary walls but not the cell walls generally, being distributed uniformly throughout both plasma and interstitial fluids (extracellular fluid compartment). These include sucrose, sulfocyanate, mannitol, sulfate, bromide, and sodium (radioactive). They should lend themselves, therefore, to calculation of the extracellular fluid volume by much the same procedure as that employed in the dye method for plasma volume, allowing more time for complete mixing and correcting for excretion in the urine. Sucrose, mannitol, sulfate, and radioactive sodium appear to be the most satisfactory for practical purposes, the others entering erythrocytes and digestive secretions (sulfocyanate) to a certain extent. Employing these methods, values have been obtained for total extracellular fluid volume approximating about 20 per cent of the body weight. Of this, about one-fourth is blood plasma and three-fourths is interstitial fluid (5 and 15 per cent, respectively, of body weight).

Table 29. Average Water Content of Tissues

TISSUE	WATER (per cent)
Muscle	75–80
Connective tissue	60
Adipose tissue	20
Bone	25
Nervous tissue	
White matter	70
Gray matter	85
Erythrocytes	60

TOTAL BODY WATER. There is no accurate method for determining total body water, inasmuch as no measurable substance has yet been found which, on injection, is distributed uniformly throughout the entire body water and undergoes no metabolic change during the test period. Heavy water, antipyrine, thiourea, and sulfonamides have been suggested. Although the procedures are not entirely free from error, heavy water and antipyrine may be satisfactory for clinical purposes.

The water content of several tissues has been determined by direct measurement (animals and human biopsy or autopsy material) (Table 29). Water comprises approximately 70 per cent of the body weight of adults (75 per cent in children), varying considerably in different tissues. Intracellular water comprises about 50 per cent of the body weight.

COMPOSITION OF BODY FLUID COMPARTMENTS

Inasmuch as water serves chiefly as a relatively inert medium in which are conducted the chemical reactions constituting living processes, its significance must be considered in relation to the other components of the body fluids which, in fact, largely determine its volume and distribution in the organism. The marked differences in composition of the intracellular and interstitial fluids and the less striking differences between the latter and the blood plasma are due to differences in permeability of the membranes separating these compartments to the solutes which these fluids contain.

MILLIEQUIVALENTS (MEQ.). Elements which combine chemically with one another do so in fixed ratios, which are functions of their atomic weights and valences. Thus, 1.008 grams of hydrogen (at. wt. 1.008) combine with 8 grams of oxygen (at. wt. 16) to form water, and with 35.457 grams of Cl (at. wt. 35.457) to form HCl. Similarly, 35.457 grams of Cl combine with 22.997 grams of Na, 39.096 grams of K, and 20.04 grams of Ca (at. wt. 40.08). These numerical values are designated "equivalent weights," because they are equivalent in their combining power. An "equivalent weight" may be defined as the weight of a molecule, or of an atom or radical (group of atoms reacting chemically as a unit), divided by its valence. A "milliequivalent" is 1/1000 of the gram equivalent weight, or the latter expressed in milligrams.

The concentrations of the solid constituents of the body fluids may be expressed in terms of weight per unit volume (e.g., milligrams per 100 ml.) or in terms of chemical combining power (e.g., milliequivalents per liter) (mEq./liter). The former may be converted to the latter according to the following formula:

$$\text{mEq./liter} = \frac{\text{mg./liter } (= \text{mg./100 ml. x 10}) \text{ x valence}}{\text{atomic or radicular weight}}$$

OSMOLAR CONCENTRATION. All body fluids, extracellular and intracellular, possess one physiochemical property in common, i.e., an equal osmotic pressure. Osmotic pressure is a function of the concentration of active chemical components in a solution, i.e., the number of ions and mols (undissociated compounds). The designation "osmol" is applied to one chemically active mol or ion. Consequently, solutions of the same osmotic pressure have an equal total osmolar concentration of solutes.

Table 30. Radicular and Equivalent Weights of Important Body Fluid Electrolytes

ELEMENT OR ION	VALENCE	ATOMIC OR RADICULAR WEIGHT	EQUIVALENT WEIGHT
H	1	1.008	1.008
Na	1	22.997	22.997
K	1	39.096	39.096
Cl	1	35.457	35.457
Ca	2	40.08	20.04
Mg	2	24.32	12.16
HCO_3	1	61.018	61.018
HPO_4	2	95.988	47.994
H_2PO_4	1	96.996	96.996
SO_4	2	96.066	48.033

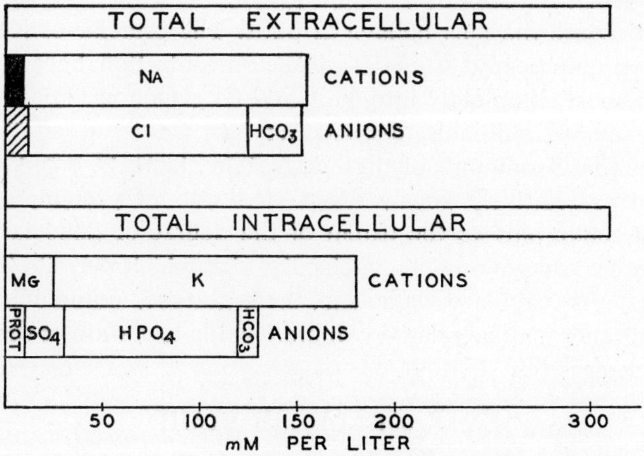

Fig. 63. Osmolar equality of the extracellular and intracellular fluids (after Gamble)

A solution containing 1 osmol (expressed in grams) per liter of water depresses the freezing point of the water by 1.86° C. The freezing point of blood plasma is −0.56° C. It must, therefore, contain osmotically active solutes in a total concentration of 0.56/1.86 or 0.30 osmols (320 milliosmols per liter of water). The other body fluids with equal osmotic pressures also have the same osmolar concentration of solutes

(320 milliosmols/liter of water), of which non-electrolytes contribute about 10 milliosmols.

In this connection, the components of the body fluids may be classified conveniently as follows:

1. Compounds of very large molecular size, e.g., proteins, lipids, glycogen, to which all but a few capillary and cell membranes are almost completely impervious. Inasmuch as osmotic pressure is proportional to the number of active chemical components per unit of water, these compounds, because of their large molecular size, exert relatively little effect on osmotic pressure in proportion to their concentration on a weight basis. For example, the concentration of plasma proteins, about 7 grams per 100 ml. of plasma, with molecular weights of about 70,000 to over 1,000,000, represents only about 2 milliosmols per liter. Moreover, since these large compounds displace a large volume of water and the osmolar concentration is expressed in terms of units per liter of water, correction must be made for this displacement. In the case of plasma, this correction factor is 0.93, the total osmolar concentration being 301 milliosmols per liter of plasma (320 milliosmols per liter of plasma water), 10 contributed by non-electrolytes.

2. Electrolytes, which cross capillary walls freely, but to certain of which various cell membranes exhibit a variable degree of impermeability under different conditions. Electrolytes dissociate into ions and therefore exert an osmotic pressure greater than their molar concentrations because the ions behave as units. The osmolar concentration of NaCl is practically twice its molar concentration because it dissociates almost completely into Na^+ and Cl^-. One millimol of $CaCl_2$ represents three millimols, dissociating into $Ca^{++} + 2Cl^-$. In the presence of large amounts of protein, certain elements, e.g., Ca and K, may exist as relatively poorly dissociated salts of protein, being osmotically active only to the extent of the degree of dissociation.

3. Organic compounds of a molecular size which permits their free diffusion across capillary walls, e.g., urea, glucose, amino acids. Some cell membranes may be relatively impermeable to certain of these, as to certain electrolytes.

EXTRACELLULAR FLUID

All body cells exist in an environment of fluids collectively designated "extracellular fluid." These include the blood plasma, interstitial fluid, lymph, and peritoneal, pericardial, pleural, joint and cerebrospinal fluids. These fluids have an essentially uniform qualitative composition and what quantitative differences exist are due chiefly to differences in the concentrations of protein, which range from about 7 per cent in plasma and but slightly less in hepatic lymph, to less than 0.1 per cent in cerebrospinal fluid. They are solutions chiefly of NaCl and NaHCO$_3$ with small amounts of Ca, Mg, K, H, phosphate, sulfate and organic acid ions, variable amounts of protein, some non-electrolytes (glucose, urea, lipids, etc.), and with pH values ranging from 7.35–7.45 under normal conditions.

The total concentration of the ionic constituents is about 310 mEq. per liter of plasma (about 335 mEq. per liter of plasma water). In accordance with the laws of electrical neutrality, cations and anions each comprise half of the total concentration, expressed in terms of chemical equivalence. Proteins, being amphoteric (p. 60 ff.), act as anions in these slightly alkaline fluids, the chemical structures of which are indicated in Figure 64. Attention should be drawn to the distinction between this anionic function of these proteins and their buffering capacity. The former is a reflection of the net over-all charge on the entire molecule at the existing pH of the solution, whereas the latter is a function almost exclusively of the imidazole groups of their histidine component (p. 115 ff.).

The milliequivalent value for protein is obtained by multiplying grams of protein per 100 ml. by 2.43 (Van Slyke factor). Each millimol (mM.) of protein represents about 8 milliequivalents (mEq.), which accounts chiefly for the discrepancy between the ionic osmolar and equivalent values for plasma. At the pH of extracellular fluid, 80 per cent of the phosphate radical carries two equivalents (B$_2$HPO$_4$) and 20 per cent one equivalent of cation (BH$_2$PO$_4$). The valence of phosphate is therefore calculated as 1.8. The commonly used designations of carbonic acid and bicarbonate values in terms of "volumes per cent CO$_2$" may be converted to milliequivalents per liter by dividing by 2.22.

The relative importance of the several components of the extracellular fluids in preserving osmotic and anion-cation (acid-base) balance is indicated by their osmolar and equivalent concentrations, respectively (Fig. 64; Fig. 63). However, those components, particularly cations, which are present in comparatively very low concentrations, viz., K$^+$, Ca^{++}, Mg^{++}, and H$^+$, exert profound influences upon a variety of physiological processes. Therefore, relatively slight deviations from their normal concentrations produce significant biological effects.

As illustrated in Figure 64, the chief structural difference between the two compartments of extracellular fluid, i.e., blood plasma and interstitial fluid, is the relatively large amount of protein in the former. The presence of this non-diffusible component results in certain readjustments of the diffusible ions in order to maintain anion-cation equivalence (Donnan equilibrium, p. 306). Consequently, the interstitial fluid contains a somewhat higher total concentration of diffusible anion and a lower concentration of cation than does the plasma.

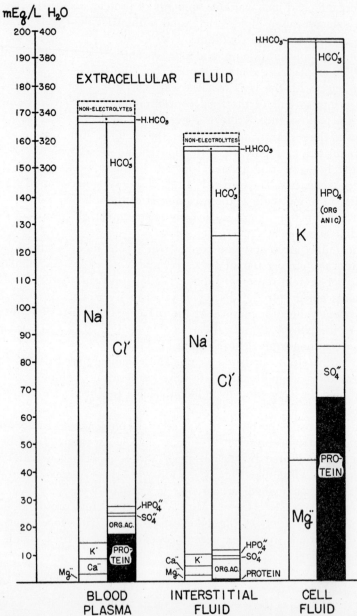

Fig. 64. *Composition of intracellular and extracellular fluids (from Gamble: Chemical Anatomy, Physiology, and Pathology of Extracellular Fluid, Harvard University Press, 1950)*

INTRACELLULAR FLUID

In contrast to the rather complete and precise information available regarding the composition of extracellular fluids, data regarding the chemical structure of intracellular fluids are fragmentary and incomplete. It seems obvious that differences in structure and function of cells of various tissues might be reflected in differences in their chemical constitution, in contradistinction to the uniformity of composition of extracellular fluids. Sufficient information is available, however, particularly on erythrocytes and muscle cells, to indicate a rather general and more or less consistent pattern of differences between the two major fluid compartments (Figs. 63, 64).

Whereas Na is the major cation in the extracellular fluid (142 mEq./liter), much smaller amounts are present in the intracellular fluids (0–40 mEq./liter), which contain also little or no Ca. The chief cations of the latter fluids are K, about 140 mEq./liter in muscle and Mg, about 40 mEq./liter in muscle (5 and 3 mEq./liter respectively in plasma). As regards anions, the intracellular fluids contain much more phosphate and sulfate ions and protein than do the extracellular fluids. Cl, the major anion of the latter, is practically absent from the former, except in the case of erythrocytes (Fig. 64), and cells of the kidney tubules, stomach and intestines. Cells of the latter organs contain Na and Cl, since they are engaged in reabsorption or secretion of these elements. However, in these situations, Na and Cl are apparently not in diffusion equilibrium with the extracellular fluid. $HCO_3{}^-$ is the only ion which exists in both fluids in concentrations of even approximately comparable magnitude. The marked differences in concentration of Na and K in the extra- and intracellular fluids indicate a certain degree of impermeability of the cell membranes to these ions. This impermeability is, however, not absolute nor fixed, both ions being able to cross the membrane more freely under certain physiological and pathological conditions (p. 602). It would appear that as K leaves the cell in increased amounts, Na enters, the total cationic concentration being thereby maintained approximately.

The bulk of the phosphate is in organic combination and the extent of dissociation of these compounds is not known. Similarly, much of the Mg and perhaps of the K is undoubtedly present as undissociated salts of protein and organic phosphate and, therefore, is not in ionic form. Furthermore, the concentration of protein ions has not been established accurately and the estimated $HCO_3{}^-$ concentration is subject to correction for carbamino CO_2 (p. 293). These factual deficiencies contribute to the present uncertainty regarding the constitution of the intracellular fluids on an osmolar and equivalent basis.

EXCHANGES BETWEEN FLUID COMPARTMENTS

The continual entrance into the body of substances from without (oxygen, water, organic and inorganic foodstuffs, etc.) and production by the cells of a great variety of metabolites, many of which must be distributed to other tissues or be excreted, imply a continual movement of various components of the body fluid compartments across the boundary membranes (capillaries and cell walls). The most important of these exchange systems may be outlined as follows:

1. *Alveolar air : blood plasma* (p. 287). This system provides for entrance of oxygen into and loss of CO_2 and water from the body.

2. *Plasma : erythrocyte* (p. 317). This system provides for ready exchange of oxygen, CO_2, water, and certain anions (particularly Cl^- and $HCO_3{}^-$) in both directions. Cations are exchanged very slowly.

3. *Plasma : interstitial fluid.* These two media are separated by the capillary walls, which are perfectly permeable to water, inorganic ions, and small organic molecules (e.g., glucose, amino acids, urea, etc.) but not to large organic molecules, such as proteins.

4. *Interstitial fluid : intracellular fluid.* These two compartments are separated by the cell membranes, across which gases, water, and small, uncharged molecules can diffuse readily, but, at least under normal conditions, cations or anions cannot, at least not freely. These membranes are also impermeable to large molecules, such as proteins, except in special situations, viz., the liver.

The first two of these systems are discussed in the section on respiration (pp. 288–294), since they are intimately concerned with the transport and exchanges of oxygen and CO_2.

GIBBS-DONNAN EQUILIBRIUM. If two solutions are separated by a membrane which is freely permeable to the solvent and solutes, the concentrations of the latter will be identical when equilibrium is established. Thus, both the chemical composition and the osmotic pressures of the two solutions will be the same.

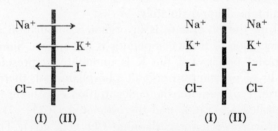

If, on the other hand, one of the solutions contains an electrolyte, e.g., NaCl, to which the membrane is permeable, and the other contains one, e.g., Na proteinate (NaR) in which R is a monovalent anion too large to pass through the membrane, the distribution of Na^+ and

Cl⁻ at equilibrium will be unequal on opposite sides of the membrane. If both electrolytes are completely dissociated, the situation at equilibrium may be represented as follows:

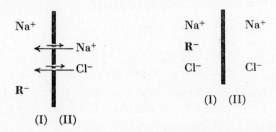

(I) (II)

Na⁺ and Cl⁻ ions diffuse in pairs, preserving electrical neutrality, from solution (II), into solution (I), and subsequently in the reverse direction, until equilibrium is established, the net result being loss of Na⁺ and Cl⁻ from solution (II) and their addition to solution (I). Let x represent the number of Na⁺ and Cl⁻ ions lost from (II) and added to (I), a the original number of Na⁺ and R⁻ ions in (I), and b the original number of Na⁺ and Cl⁻ ions in (II). The ionic distribution at equilibrium may be represented quantitatively as follows:

$$(a + x)\ Na^+ \quad\big|\quad Na^+\ (b - x)$$
$$(a)\ \mathbf{R}^-$$
$$(x)\ Cl^- \quad\big|\quad Cl^-\ (b - x)$$
$$(I) \qquad\qquad (II)$$

Inasmuch as the total number of positive and negative charges must be equal on a given side of the membrane, a Na⁺ ion cannot move in either direction without a Cl⁻ ion. The probability of these two ions reaching and passing through the membrane at the same instant is proportional to the product of their concentrations on that side of the membrane. At equilibrium, therefore, when equal amounts of diffusible electrolyte pass in opposite directions, these concentration products must be equal.

$$Na^+_{(I)} \cdot Cl^-_{(I)} = Na^+_{(II)} \cdot Cl^-_{(II)}$$

or $\quad (a + x)x = (b - x)(b - x)$ or $(b - x)^2$

This is the fundamental Donnan equation, expressing the quantitative aspects of this situation, referred to as the Gibbs-Donnan equilibrium. This equation may also be written:

$$ax + x^2 = b^2 - 2bx + x^2$$

or $\qquad ax = b^2 - 2bx$

or $\qquad ax + 2bx = b^2$

or $\qquad (a + 2b)x = b^2$

or $\qquad x = \dfrac{b^2}{a + 2b}$

Since, in solution (I) the cation Na^+ must balance two anions, R^- and Cl^-, the concentration of Na^+ will exceed that of Cl^-, whereas they will be equal in solution (II). Therefore, the product of the concentrations of Na^+ and Cl^- in solution (II) represents a square, but not in solution (I). It follows, too, that whereas Na^+ in solution (I) exceeds Na^+ in solution (II), Cl^- in solution (II) exceeds Cl^- in solution (I), the sum of the factors in a square being less than the sum of the factors in the same product which is not a square.

The quantitative ionic relations for the Gibbs-Donnan equilibrium may be stated as follows: The concentration of a diffusible positive ion (cation) is higher and that of a diffusible negative ion (anion) lower on the side of the membrane containing a nondiffusible negative ion (e.g., protein), i.e.,

$$Na^+_{(I)} > Na^+_{(II)} \text{ and } Cl^-_{(I)} < Cl^-_{(II)}$$

It must be understood that these considerations apply only when the volumes of the solutions on the two sides of the membranes remain constant and only ion transfer occurs.

It can also be shown that, in the presence of several different diffusible ions, their distribution ratios will be as follows:

$$\frac{Na^+_{(I)}}{Na^+_{(II)}} = \frac{K^+_{(I)}}{K^+_{(II)}} = \frac{\sqrt{Ca^{++}_{(I)}}}{\sqrt{Ca^{++}_{(II)}}} = \frac{Cl^-_{(II)}}{Cl^-_{(I)}} = \frac{HCO_3^-_{(II)}}{HCO_3^-_{(I)}} = \frac{\sqrt{SO_4^=_{(II)}}}{\sqrt{SO_4^=_{(I)}}}$$

GIBBS-DONNAN EFFECT AND OSMOTIC PRESSURE.   Certain additional facts arise out of the mathematical considerations outlined above, incident to the presence of a non-diffusible ion on one side of the membrane.

1. At equilibrium, if the volume of the solvent is kept constant, the sum of the concentrations of diffusible ions in solution (I) (containing the non-diffusible ion) exceeds the sum of the concentrations of the same ions in solution II. If the value for *a* and for *b* is represented as 1 mol, the value for *x*, according to the Donnan equation $(x = \dfrac{b^2}{a + 2b})$, will be 0.33 mol, and the quantitative distribution of Na^+, Cl^- and protein (R^-) will be as follows:

$$Na^+ (a + x) = 1.33 \qquad Na^+ (b - x) = 0.66$$

$$Cl^- (x) \quad = 0.33 \qquad Cl^- (b - x) = 0.66$$

$$\mathbf{R}^- (a) \quad = 1.0$$

(I) (II)

2. The total ionic concentration in solution (I) exceeds that in solution (II). Consequently, the former will have a higher osmotic pressure than the latter, determined not only by the concentration of the non-diffusible ion, but also by the higher concentration of diffusible ions.

The Gibbs-Donnan effect is of great physiological significance in biological systems involving ion exchanges across permeable membranes, especially when the fluid on one side of the membrane contains a non-diffusible component, e.g., protein, in high concentration. It finds particular application in exchanges of Cl^- and HCO_3^- between the blood plasma and erythrocyte and in water and ion exchanges between the blood plasma and interstitial fluid (i.e., across the capillary wall).

PLASMA: INTERSTIAL FLUID EXCHANGE. Exchanges between the blood plasma and interstitial fluid occur across the endothelial lining of the capillaries, which act as semipermeable membranes, allowing free passage of water and crystalloid solutes, inorganic and organic, but not of colloids of large molecular size, viz., proteins. This impermeability to proteins is not absolute nor uniform, the concentration of protein in interstitial fluids varying from 0.05–0.5 per cent in subcutaneous tissues and serous cavities to 4–6 per cent in liver. The concentrations of diffusible electrolytes on the two sides of the capillary will vary, their distribution depending upon the difference in protein concentration in the two fluids (Gibbs-Donnan effect, p. 306). The osmotic pressure will be greater in the plasma than in the interstitial fluid, owing both to the higher protein concentration (colloid osmotic pressure; C.O.P.) and to the consequent higher concentration of diffusible ions (p. 308). Such freely diffusible organic solutes as urea, glucose, creatinine, etc., being non-ionized, are not subject to the Donnan effect and are distributed equally throughout the body water. Their diffusion across semipermeable membranes is therefore determined solely by their concentration gradients.

In the absence of opposing forces, water and crystalloid solutes will tend to pass from the interstitial fluid to the plasma, which contains protein in higher concentration, thereby producing an osmotic pressure gradient. This tendency may be counterbalanced by the opposing force of the capillary blood pressure and may also be modified by the concentration gradients of the individual solutes.

The colloid osmotic pressure (C.O.P.) of the proteins of normal plasma is about 22 mm. Hg (30 cm. H_2O). The capillary blood pressure varies considerably in different tissues, but is higher than the C.O.P. at the arterial end of the capillary and lower than the C.O.P. at the venous end. Consequently, filtration from the plasma occurs at the arterial end and reabsorption into it at the venous end of the capillary. Moreover, the increasing concentration of non-diffusible colloids (viz., proteins) which results from loss of plasma water, creates a relatively small but actual gradient of C.O.P., which further favors reabsorption as the blood pressure falls in the distal end of the capillary. This mechanism (Starling hypothesis) provides for a continual circulation of fluid between the capillaries and the tissue spaces, a balance being maintained between the quantity of water filtered and that reabsorbed. Exchanges of diffusible solutes between these two fluids depend upon these circumstances and also, independently of them, upon their individual concentration gradients.

Filtration from the capillaries is opposed by the tissue tension, which varies considerably in different situations, being relatively low in loose areolar tissues (e.g., eyelids, external genitalia) and high in dense tissues (e.g., muscle, liver, etc.). Fluid leaves the tissue spaces not only by direct reabsorption into the blood plasma but also by filtration across the lymph capillaries, ultimately reaching the venous blood by way of the lymphatic circulation.

INTERSTITIAL FLUID: INTRACELLULAR FLUID EXCHANGE. Exchanges between these two compartments occur across cell membranes, which are generally freely permeable to gases, water, and small uncharged molecules (urea, glucose, etc.) but not to large colloidal molecules, such as proteins. The enormously higher concentration of proteins and other colloids in the intracellular than in the interstitial fluids would cause a much greater osmotic pressure within the cells (Gibbs-Donnan effect, p. 306) were it not for the fact that the cell membranes are generally not freely permeable to inorganic ions, especially cations. Consequently, the electrolyte composition of cells is quite as distinctive as their organic constitution (Fig. 64, p. 304). Because of this relative impermeability to inorganic ions, adjustment to deviations of osmotic pressure is usually accomplished largely by transfers of water, not by exchanges of inorganic constituents, the freely diffusible organic solutes (urea, creatinine, glucose, etc.) moving with the water. Inasmuch as the concentrations of protein in the body fluids are more stable than the concentrations of inorganic ions, the latter constitute the dominant factor in determining the total osmotic pressure and the exchanges of water between the body fluid compartments. The milliequivalent value of the extracellular fluids (310 mEq./liter) approximates their milliosmolar value (Fig. 63) because of the enormous preponderance of univalent ions. This is not true, however, of the intracellular fluids, the total milliosmolar value of which is the same as that of extracellular fluids, but the milliequivalent value of which is considerably greater (about 390), because of the relatively high concentrations of multivalent ions (Mg^{++}, $SO_4^=$, $HPO_4^=$, protein).

When Na is introduced into the blood plasma, it is distributed rapidly throughout the extracellular fluids, but penetrates the cells only very slowly. Consequently, an increase in Na concentration in the extracellular fluids will cause water to pass out of the cells, equalizing the osmotic pressure in the two fluid compartments. Withdrawal of Na from the extracellular fluids causes passage of water in the opposite direction, i.e., into the cells.

Shifts in water are also caused by changes in pH of the body fluids. The explanation frequently given is that acids remove cations from the weakly dissociated proteins, forming more completely dissociated salts and thereby increasing the number of osmotically active components. Inasmuch as the protein content of intracellular fluids is greater than that of extracellular fluids, acidification, according to this view, results in greater increase in osmotic pressure within the cells than in the extracellular fluids. Consequently, water passes into the cells under such circumstances. This explanation is not entirely satisfactory from a chemical standpoint.

The relative impermeability of cell membranes to inorganic ions is not uniform or constant. HCO_3^- ions are generally freely diffusible; Cl^- ions pass freely into and out of erythrocytes (p. 318) and the acid-secreting cells of the gastric mucosa. Although permeability to Na^+ and K^+ ions is restricted, Na^+ may enter cells in increased amounts when they lose K^+ and the passage of K^+ across cell membranes appears to be related to metabolic activities of the cells. For example, there is acceleration of the entrance of K^+ into muscle cells during muscular activity and into other cells during periods of administration of glucose or insulin (p. 603). Changes in the distribution of Na^+ and K^+ can be produced by adrenal cortical hormones (p. 678) and may occur also in dehydration (p. 604) and acidosis (p. 605).

Phosphate is present within cells in much larger amounts than in extracellular fluids. Much of this is in organic combination, e.g., as hexose and triose phosphates, ATP and ADP, nucleic acids, phosphocreatine (muscles), etc. However, the concentration of inorganic phosphate, too, is higher than in the extracellular fluids and fluctuates continually in relation to the latter at different levels of cell metabolic activity involving formation and splitting of phosphorylated metabolites. In contrast to the case of K^+, the rate of entrance of phosphate

into muscle cells is not increased significantly by muscular activity
but is increased markedly during the recovery period. It is increased
also by administration of glucose and insulin.

Considerations such as these have led to the conclusion that many
of the inorganic cations and anions do not enter and leave the cells
by simple diffusion, but that the cell membrane participates actively
in such transfers. Active transport of ions across these membranes
implies the performance of work to overcome differences in concentration or electrochemical potential. It is probable that the energy requirements for these purposes are derived from cellular metabolic
reactions to which the transferred ions are related or in which they
are involved. The concentrations of K, Na, Mg, Ca, and phosphate in
the cell can vary, within limits, in accordance with the metabolic
activity of the cell, without influencing exchanges of water, because,
presumably, considerable fractions of these substances form undissociated or poorly dissociated combinations with cell proteins and
are therefore osmotically inactive.

BIBLIOGRAPHY

Annual Review of Physiology.
Darrow, D. C.: Fluid therapy, J.A.M.A. *143*:365, 1950.
Gamble, J. L.: Chemical Anatomy, Physiology and Pathology of Extracellular Fluid, Cambridge, Harvard University Press, 1950.
Gamble, J. L.: Companionship of Water and Electrolytes in the Organization of Body Fluids, Lane Medical Lectures, California, Stanford University Press, 1951.
Gaunt, R.: Adrenal cortex and water metabolism, Physiol. Rev. *29*:281, 1949.
Kendall, E. C.: The influence of the adrenal cortex on the metabolism of water and electrolytes, Vitamins & Hormones *6*:278, 1948.
Peters, J. P.: Body Water, Springfield, Ill., Charles C Thomas, Publisher, 1935.
Peters, J. P.: Water balance in health and disease. In Diseases of Metabolism, ed. 3, edited by G. G. Duncan, Philadelphia, W. B. Saunders Company, 1952, p. 315.
Pinson, E. A.: Water exchanges and barriers as studied by the use of hydrogen iso-topes, Physiol. Rev. *32*:123, 1952.
Ravdin, I. S., Walker, J. M. and Rhoads, J. E.: Blood volume maintenance and regu-lation, Ann. Rev. Physiol. *15*:165, 1953.
Stehle, R. L.: The actions of the hormones of the posterior lobe of the pituitary gland, Vitamins & Hormones *7*:390, 1949.
Swift, H. W.: The Kidney: Structure and Function in Health and Disease, New York, Oxford University Press, 1951.

12

"ACID-BASE" (ANION-CATION) BALANCE

(NEUTRALITY REGULATION)

Normal metabolic processes involve continual production of relatively large amounts of acid substances. The most important of these include carbonic (CO_2), sulfuric, phosphoric, and organic acids, such as lactic and β-hydroxybutyric. H_2CO_3 is the chief acid formed in the course of cellular oxidations, about 10–20 or more mols being produced daily (equivalent to 1–2 liters of concentrated HCl). Sulfuric (oxidation of S of protein), phosphoric (oxidation of P of protein and lipids), and other acids are produced in quantities of about 80–120 millimols daily under ordinary conditions. Although foodstuffs provide a certain amount of alkaline substances, this is far exceeded by their potential acid content. The body is therefore faced with the necessity of continually removing large quantities of acid which is being formed within the cells. These substances must be transported to the organs of excretion in the extracellular fluids without unduly affecting their H^+ ion concentration, which is maintained at approximately pH 7.4 and is one of the most rigidly controlled features of their electrolyte pattern. The mechanisms by which these ends are accomplished comprise the mechanism of regulation of "acid-base" balance. These may be outlined as follows:

1. Dilution.
2. Buffer systems; restriction of pH change in body fluids.
3. Respiration; ultimate excretion of CO_2.
4. Renal mechanism.
   (a) Excretion of excess "acid" or "base."
   (b) Ammonia formation; "base" conservation.

Use of the terms "acid" and "base" to indicate the anions and cations, respectively, of the body fluids is not acceptable from a chemical standpoint. An acid is defined as a substance (ion, molecule, par-

313

ticle) that yields H^+ ions (protons) in solution and a base is anything that combines with H^+ ions. Accordingly, whereas H_2CO_3 is an acid, dissociating into H^+ and HCO_3^- ions, its anionic component, HCO_3^- is a base. Other examples are:

Acid   *Base*

$$HSO_4^- \rightleftharpoons H^+ + SO_4^-$$

$$CH_3COOH \rightleftharpoons H^+ + CH_3COO^-$$

$$H_2PO_4^- \rightleftharpoons H^+ + HPO_4^-$$

$NaHCO_3$ acts as a base because it yields HCO_3^- ions, which can combine with H^+ ions.

On this basis, the ionic structure of the body fluids should be regarded as consisting of anions and cations, rather than of "acids" and "bases," and the term "anion-cation" balance should be substituted for "acid-base" balance. However, the latter designation has become firmly established in clinical usage and we feel that an attempt to eliminate it entirely from a text for medical students at this time would lead to confusion. There is, in fact, some logical basis for employment of this inaccurate terminology. When an acid, e.g., acetic acid, is added to the essentially neutral (pH 7.4), buffered extracellular fluids, the H^+ ions of the acid largely disappear in the formation of a poorly dissociated molecule, viz., H_2O, and the pH of the fluid is only very slightly changed. The most obvious indication of the addition of the acid is the presence of an increased concentration of the acid anion, in this case acetate ion, which occurs at the expense of the buffer anions (HCO_3^-, $HPO_4^=$, protein). Inasmuch as the addition of the acid is reflected ultimately in the quantitative distribution of these anions, they have been referred to as the "acid" portion of the body fluid electrolytes. Conversely, the addition of alkalies, e.g., NaOH, will be reflected almost entirely in an increase in the cation Na^+, which has therefore been referred to as a "base." Although admittedly inaccurate, the designation "acid-base" balance is consequently employed synonymously with anion-cation balance.

PHYSIOLOGICAL BUFFER SYSTEMS

The capacity of the extracellular fluids for transporting acids from the site of their formation (cells) to the site of their excretion (e.g., lungs, kidneys) without undue change in pH is dependent chiefly upon the presence of efficient buffer systems in these fluids and in the erythrocytes. Each buffer system consists of a mixture of a weak acid, HA, and its salt, BA (p. 57). The most important of these are as follows:

Plasma: $\dfrac{H_2CO_3}{BHCO_3}$, $\dfrac{H \cdot protein}{B \cdot protein}$, $\dfrac{BH_2PO_4}{B_2HPO_4}$, $\dfrac{H \cdot organic\ acid}{B \cdot organic\ acid}$

Erythrocytes: $\dfrac{H_2CO_3}{BHCO_3}$, $\dfrac{HHb}{BHb}$, $\dfrac{HHbO_2}{BHbO_2}$, $\dfrac{BH_2PO_4}{B_2HPO_4}$, $\dfrac{H \cdot organic\ acid}{B \cdot organic\ acid}$

The buffer systems in the interstitial fluids and lymph are much the same as in the blood plasma, except that proteins are generally present in much smaller quantities. The buffer systems in intracellular fluids are also qualitatively much the same as in the plasma, but the cell fluids contain much higher concentrations of protein.

Although all of these buffer systems are operative to a certain extent within the physiological range of pH values, only a few of them exist in sufficiently high concentrations to be of distinct quantitative significance in the regulation of acid-base balance. In the blood plasma, the bicarbonate and plasma protein systems, and in the erythrocytes, the bicarbonate and hemoglobin systems play the most important roles in this connection.

BUFFER ACTION OF HEMOGLOBIN. The buffering capacity of Hb, as of any protein, depends upon the number of dissociated buffering groups, acidic (carboxyl) or basic (amino, guanidino, and imidazole), which varies with the pH of the medium (p. 65). Within the pH range 7.0–7.8, most of the physiological buffering action of Hb is due to the imidazole groups of histidine (Fig. 65).

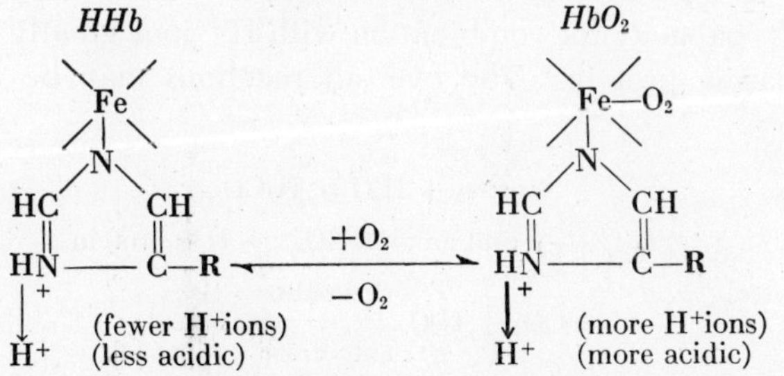

Fig. 65. *Effect of oxygenation and reduction on the buffering action of the imidazole group (histidine) of hemoglobin*

The degree of dissociation of a buffering group in a protein, which determines its buffering capacity, is influenced by adjacent groups in the molecule. In the case of the imidazole group of histidine, which is intimately associated with the iron of hemoglobin, its strength as a buffer is affected by changes in the degree of oxygenation of hemoglobin. When oxygen is removed, the imidazole group is rendered less acidic, consequently less dissociated, removing a hydrogen ion from solution and becoming electrically positive. This effect is reversed with increasing oxygenation of the hemoglobin molecule. This reaction, illustrated in Figure 65, indicates that not only is the buffering capacity of Hb related to the degree of its oxygenation, but also that its ability to accept or liberate oxygen is influenced by the acidity of the medium. A decrease in acidity facilitates oxygenation of Hb and an increase in acidity facilitates liberation of oxygen, producing characteristic changes in the oxygen dissociation curve of Hb (p. 290).

The implications arising from these considerations may be summarized as follows:

1. Oxygenation of Hb increases its acidity, causing it to give up hydrogen ions to the medium; i.e., oxyhemoglobin is a stronger acid than reduced hemoglobin.

2. Reduction of oxyhemoglobin (i.e., deoxygenated Hb) decreases its acidity, removing hydrogen ions from the medium.

3. Introduction of an acid, e.g., H_2CO_3, into a medium containing oxyhemoglobin facilitates loss of oxygen, i.e., formation of reduced hemoglobin. The latter, being less acid (i.e., more basic) than oxyhemoglobin, is better able than the latter to counteract the acidifying effect of the added acid (p. 318).

The buffer mechanisms involved in the case of H_2CO_3, the anhydride of which (CO_2) is volatile, differ from those for the stronger, non-volatile, fixed acids (sulfuric, phosphoric, lactic, etc.).

BUFFER SYSTEMS FOR H_2CO_3 (CO_2). H_2CO_3 is buffered chiefly by the imidazole groups of Hb in the erythrocytes and proteins in the plasma (p. 315; Fig. 65). Hb exerts by far the greater effect in this connection because its capacity for combination with H^+ ions greatly exceeds that of the plasma proteins. The over-all reactions may be indicated as follows:

(Plasma)
$$CO_2 + H_2O \rightleftharpoons H_2CO_3$$
$$H_2CO_3 + protein \rightleftharpoons HCO_3^- + H^+ \cdot protein$$

(Erythrocytes)
$$CO_2 + H_2O \underset{anhydrase}{\overset{carbonic}{\rightleftharpoons}} H_2CO_3$$
$$H_2CO_3 + Hb \rightleftharpoons HCO_3^- + H^+ \cdot Hb$$
$$H_2CO_3 + HbO_2 \rightleftharpoons HCO_3^- + H^+ \cdot HbO_2$$

The effect of addition of CO_2 is to increase both H_2CO_3 and $BHCO_3$, the latter owing to removal of additional H^+ ions by Hb and, to a minor extent, by the plasma proteins. The liberation of oxygen by Hb in the tissues, which occurs simultaneously with the addition of CO_2, increases the buffering capacity of the Hb, as indicated elsewhere (p. 318). The reciprocal exchanges of Cl^- and HCO_3^- ions between the plasma and erythrocytes (chloride shift) constitute an additional important phase of the extremely efficient mechanism for buffering and transport H_2CO_3 (p. 318) (Fig. 66, p. 317).

CO$_2$ ENTERS PLASMA IN TISSUES (P. 293). As indicated below, the largest portion of the added CO$_2$ diffuses into the erythrocytes. The remainder stays in solution in the plasma, reacting with water as follows:

$$CO_2 + H_2O \rightleftharpoons H_2CO_3$$

This reaction occurs slowly; the equilibrium is far to the left, the concentration of dissolved CO$_2$ being about 1000 times that of H$_2$CO$_3$. The small increase in the latter which occurs when CO$_2$ is added to the plasma in the tissues ionizes (H$_2$CO$_3 \rightleftharpoons H^+ + HCO_3^-$), the added H$^+$ ions being buffered by the relatively weak plasma buffer systems (viz., proteins). The pH falls slightly.

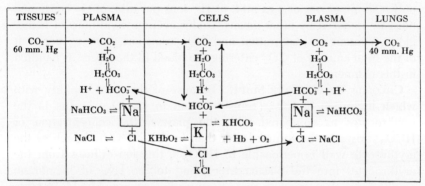

Fig. 66. *Exchange of HCO$_3^-$ and Cl$^-$ between the red blood cells and the plasma in the tissues and the lungs (chloride shift). The heavy arrows indicate the direction of the changes in these situations*

CO$_2$ ENTERS ERYTHROCYTES (P. 293). The bulk of the added CO$_2$ diffuses into the erythrocytes chiefly because the reaction, CO$_2$ + H$_2$O $\rightleftharpoons$ H$_2$CO$_3$, progresses very rapidly to the right by virtue of the catalytic action of the enzyme, carbonic anhydrase (C-A). A small amount of CO$_2$ remains as such in solution. Considerably more forms carbamino compounds with Hb (R-NH$_2$ + CO$_2$ $\rightleftharpoons$ R-NHCOO– + H$^+$). This reaction is facilitated by the simultaneous liberation of oxygen, with an increment in reduced Hb, which is a weaker acid than oxyhemoglobin. The capacity for forming carbamino compounds should not be confused with their buffering capacity. The latter is a function almost exclusively of the imidazole groups of their histidine component (p. 315), whereas the former is a reflection of the free amino groups in the entire molecule (p. 118).

Most of the H$_2$CO$_3$ newly formed in the erythrocytes undergoes ionization (H$_2$CO$_3 \rightleftharpoons H^+ + HCO_3^-$). This reaction proceeds to the right chiefly because both ions are removed rapidly, H$^+$ being buffered by Hb, and HCO$_3^-$ diffusing into the plasma.

BUFFERING OF CO_2 BY Hb. Reduced Hb, being a considerably weaker acid than oxyhemoglobin, has a higher H^+-binding capacity than the latter. At the erythrocyte pH (7.25), 1 mM. of HbO_2 yields 1.88 mEq. of H^+ ion, whereas 1 mM. of Hb yields only 1.28 mEq. Consequently, in the tissue capillaries, the liberation of each millimol of O_2 (22.4 ml.) permits binding of 0.6 mEq. more of H^+ ion, permitting the formation of 0.6 mM. of $BHCO_3$ from 0.6 mM. of CO_2 (13.4 ml.) with no change in pH. At a respiratory quotient of 0.6, i.e., $\dfrac{0.6 \text{ mM. } CO_2 \text{ produced}}{1.0 \text{ mM. } O_2 \text{ consumed}}$ (p. 333), 0.6 mH. of H^+ ions will be formed (from 0.6 mM. H_2CO_3), which will be completely buffered as a result of reduction of Hb. At the usual respiratory quotient of 0.82, therefore, only 0.82 minus 0.6, or 0.22 mM. of H^+ ions per mM. of O_2 consumed must be buffered by other means. Under average conditions of hemoglobin content and saturation and CO_2 transport, over 73 per cent of the total amount of CO_2 entering the blood in the tissues is handled in this manner.

CHLORIDE-BICARBONATE SHIFT. Because of the great rapidity with which hydration of CO_2 (transformation to H_2CO_3) occurs in the erythrocytes as compared with the plasma, the concentration of HCO_3^- rises in the former faster than in the latter. Inasmuch as the erythrocyte wall is permeable to HCO_3^-, this ion diffuses from the erythrocytes into the plasma. According to the laws of membrane equilibrium, the ratios of the concentration of individual diffusible monovalent ions in the cells and plasma must be equal, i.e.,

$$\frac{[HCO_3^-] \text{ cells}}{[HCO_3^-] \text{ plasma}} = \frac{[Cl^-] \text{ cells}}{[Cl^-] \text{ plasma}}.$$

Consequently, as HCO_3^- passes from the erythrocytes into the plasma, Cl^- passes in the opposite direction. In order to preserve electrical neutrality of the cell and plasma fluids, the numbers of negative ions (i.e., Cl^- and HCO_3^-) exchanged must be identical. The Cl^- ions passing into the erythrocytes are balanced electrically by the K^+ ions previously balanced by the HCO_3^-, while the latter ions entering the plasma are balanced by the Na^+ ions, previously balanced by the diffused Cl^-. As a result of these changes, most of the HCO_3^-, although formed originally in the erythrocytes, is actually transported in the plasma (Table 28, p. 292).

All of the above reactions are reversed in the lungs, the quantity of CO_2 entering the blood in the tissues passing into the alveoli and the quantity of oxygen lost in the tissues being restored from the alveolar air.

BUFFER SYSTEMS FOR FIXED ACIDS. Neutralization of fixed (non-volatile) acids entering the extracellular fluids is accomplished chiefly by the

$H_2CO_3/BHCO_3$ buffer system. Such acids (e.g., HCl, H_2SO_4, lactic, etc.) react with $BHCO_3$ as follows:

$$HCO_3^- \text{ (from } NaHCO_3) + H^+ \text{ (from HCl)} \rightleftharpoons H_2CO_3$$

Protein and phosphate buffer systems may also be involved, but to a relatively minor extent.

$$\text{Protein} + H^+ \rightleftharpoons H^+ \cdot \text{Protein}$$
$$HPO_4^- + H^+ \rightleftharpoons H_2PO_4^-$$

Bicarbonate is particularly efficient in this connection because (1) it is present in higher concentration than the other buffer salts, and (2) the acid product of the reaction, H_2CO_3, is effectively buffered (p. 316) and is readily disposed of by the lungs (p. 320) by virtue of the volatility of its anhydride, CO_2, rendering the reaction irreversible.

$$H_2CO_3 \rightleftharpoons H_2O + CO_2 \nearrow \quad \text{(expired air)}$$

If a fixed base (e.g., NaOH) enters the extracellular fluid, it reacts with the acid components of these buffer systems, chiefly H_2CO_3:

$$H_2CO_3 + OH^- \text{ (from NaOH)} \rightleftharpoons Na^+HCO_3^- + H_2O$$
$$H^+ \cdot \text{Protein} + OH^- \rightleftharpoons \text{Protein} + H_2O$$
$$H_2PO_4^- + OH^- \rightleftharpoons HPO_4^- + H_2O$$

NET EFFECT OF BUFFER MECHANISMS. Because of the relative abundance of bicarbonate in extracellular fluids, the chief effect of the entrance of metabolic acids, both carbonic and fixed acids, is to increase the concentration of H_2CO_3. In the case of the fixed acids, this is done at the expense of $BHCO_3$. In either case, the ratio, $H_2CO_3/BHCO_3$, which largely determines the pH of these fluids (p. 325), is increased, with a consequent increase in H^+ ion concentration. Under normal conditions this increase is but slight because (1) H_2CO_3, a weak acid (i.e., weakly dissociated), forms relatively few H^+ ions, (2) it is effectively buffered (p. 318), and (3) it is readily eliminated by the lungs as CO_2, the increase in concentration of both H_2CO_3 and H^+ being thereby minimized.

$$CO_2 + H_2O \leftarrow H_2CO_3 \rightleftharpoons H^+ + HCO_3^-$$

The carbonic acid produced in the course of oxidative metabolic processes is thus effectively disposed of, chiefly by the hemoglobin mechanism, with very little change in pH (p. 318). The fixed acids can be buffered efficiently by bicarbonate as long as adequate amounts of the latter are present in the extracellular fluids. Because of this fact, and because the other buffer systems are in equilibrium with the

$H_2CO_3/BHCO_3$ system, the blood bicarbonate, representing the extra-cellular fluid bicarbonate, is a measure of the alkali available for neutralization of fixed acids, and has been termed the "alkali reserve."

RESPIRATORY REGULATION OF ACID-BASE BALANCE. Participation of the respiratory mechanism in the regulation of acid-base balance is dependent upon (1) the sensitivity of the respiratory center (medulla) to very slight changes in pH and in pCO_2, and (2) the ready diffusibility of CO_2 from the blood, across the pulmonary alveolar membrane, into the alveolar air (p. 292).

An increase in blood pCO_2 of only 1.5 mm. Hg (0.2 per cent increase in CO_2) results in a 100 per cent increase in pulmonary ventilation (stimulation of respiratory center), which increases also with slight increases in H^+ ion concentration of the blood. The excess CO_2 is thereby promptly removed from the extracellular fluids in the expired air. Decrease in blood pCO_2 or H^+ ion concentration causes depression of activity of the respiratory center, with consequent slow, shallow respiration, hypoventilation, and retention of CO_2 in the blood until the normal pCO_2 and pH are restored. This respiratory mechanism therefore tends to maintain the normal $H_2CO_3/BHCO_3$ ratio in the extracellular fluids in the face of the continual addition of H_2CO_3 as a result of the metabolic production of both CO_2 and fixed acids. According to the Henderson-Hasselbalch equation (p. 325), at pH 7.4, the $H_2CO_3/BHCO_3$ ratio is 1:20, which conforms to the observed concentration ratios of these substances in normal plasma, viz., 1.35 mEq. $H_2CO_3/27$ mEq. $BHCO_3$ per liter (3 vol. % $H_2CO_3/60$ vol. % $BHCO_3$).

RENAL REGULATION OF ACID-BASE BALANCE. Under ordinary dietary conditions, the amount of fixed acid produced daily exceeds the intake of available base by about 50 to 100 mEq. As indicated above, these acids are effectively buffered, at the expense, however, of a decrease in $BHCO_3$, the chief component of the buffer base available for this purpose (total about 1000 mEq.). This "alkali reserve" would eventually be exhausted if the increment in fixed acids (H^+ ions), temporarily neutralized by HCO_3^- anions, were not removed from the body and the $BHCO_3$ restored. This is accomplished by the kidneys, which are, consequently, the ultimate regulators of the acid-base balance, providing the most important final defense of the pH of the body fluids.

In the course of urine formation, a protein-free filtrate of blood plasma passes through the glomerular capillaries, the final composition of the excreted urine resulting from subsequent changes in this filtrate in the tubule (p. 756). In normal subjects, under ordinary dietary conditions, the urinary pH is about 6.0. The difference in titratable acidity between the pH of the urine and that of plasma

(7.4) represents the amount of acid removed by renal action from the plasma. Under conditions of extreme requirement for removal of excess acid or alkali respectively, the H^+ ion concentration of the urine can vary from pH 4.5 to 8.2 if the kidneys are functioning normally. This ability to excrete urine of variable acidity (or alkalinity) removes from the blood the quantity of excess acid or alkali required to preserve the normal H^+ ion concentration of the body fluids.

RENAL EXCRETION OF ACID. Even at the maximal attainable urinary acidity, pH 4.5, all $SO_4^=$ and Cl^- anions must be electrically balanced by B^+ cations, chiefly Na^+ and K^+, i.e., they cannot exist as free acids (sulfuric, hydrochloric). The same is true of over 90 per cent of the lactate anions. Consequently, at any urinary pH, these anions remove from the body practically the same amount of B^+ ("base") as is required to balance them electrically during their transport in the blood plasma; no significant deviation from the pH of the plasma (7.4) could be effected inasmuch as no H^+ ions could be carried out by these strong acid anions ($SO_4^=$ and Cl^-).

Increase in urinary acidity is accomplished by excretion of increased amounts of the weakly acidic BH_2PO_4 and certain weak organic acids, e.g., β-hydroxybutyric, acetoacetic, citric. In the plasma, at pH 7.4, phosphate exists as a mixture of about 80 per cent B_2HPO_4 and 20 per cent BH_2PO_4 ($Na_2^{++}HPO_4^=/Na^+H_2PO_4^- = 4/1$). At pH 4.8, about 99 per cent is in the form of BH_2PO_4 ($Na_2^{++}HPO_4^=/Na^+H_2PO_4^- = 1/99$). According to these ratios, every five phosphate molecules circulating in the plasma and entering the glomerular filtrate carry nine negative charges, which must be balanced by nine positive charges, i.e., nine Na^+ ions. In the urine at pH 4.8, these five phosphate molecules, being virtually all in the form of $B^+H_2PO_4^-$, carry only slightly more than five negative charges and require only about five Na^+ ions for their neutralization. This degree of acidification of the urine, accomplished, as indicated below, by the addition of H^+ ions from the tubular cells, effects a saving of about four Na^+ ions for every five phosphate molecules excreted in the urine, the Na^+ being returned to the blood plasma.

A similar situation obtains with respect to weak organic acids, such as β-hydroxybutyric, acetoacetic, and citric. Anions of these acids must be transported in the plasma, at pH 7.4, completely covered by Na^+ cations, but a considerable portion can exist as the free acids in urine at pH 4.8. For example, at pH 4.8, about 45 per cent of the β-hydroxybutyrate anion in the urine exists as free acid and, consequently, excretion of each mol of this anion at this urinary pH releases and restores to the blood 0.45 mol of the Na^+ with which it had been carried in the plasma.

The process of acidification of the urine appears to be explicable most plausibly by the ionic exchange theory, although other explanations have been advanced. According to this view, CO_2 formed in the cells of the distal portion of the tubule (where acidification of the urine occurs), under the influence of carbonic anhydrase, is rapidly transformed to H_2CO_3, which undergoes ionization:

$$CO_2 \text{ (metabolic)} + H_2O \xrightleftharpoons[\text{anhydrase}]{\text{carbonic}} H_2CO_3 \rightleftharpoons H^+ + HCO_3^-$$

The H^+ ions thus formed are passed into the lumen of the tubule, an equal number of Na^+ ions passing in the opposite direction into the cells (Fig. 64). Thus, a number of Na^+ ions, previously balancing $HPO_4^=$, citrate$^-$, β-hydroxybutyrate$^-$, etc., ions in the glomerular filtrate, are exchanged for H^+ ions:

$$Na_2^{++} HPO_4^- + H^+ \rightarrow Na^+ H_2PO_4^- + Na^+$$

$$Na^+ \beta\text{-hydroxybutyrate}^- + H^+ \rightarrow \beta\text{-hydroxybutyric acid} + Na^+.$$

The Na^+ ions, entering the cell, are absorbed into the blood stream with HCO_3^- ions formed from the H_2CO_3, thereby supporting the bicarbonate structure of the extracellular fluids (Fig. 67).

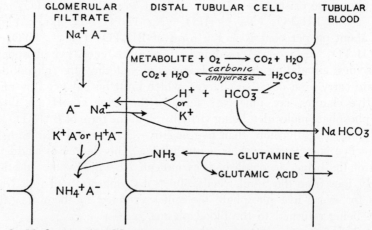

Fig. 67. *Mechanism of acidification of urine and of ammonia formation and excretion by the kidney, indicating exchange of H^+ and/or K^+ for Na^+ (after Pitts)*

A portion of the urinary potassium enters the uriniferous tubule by active excretion by the distal tubular epithelium, in addition to the larger amount which filters through the glomeruli (p. 600). In this region (distal tubule), K^+ and H^+ ions apparently compete for some component of a common excretory mechanism, either ion being exchanged for Na^+ (Fig. 67). With increased concentration of K^+ in the renal tubular cells, more K^+ and fewer H^+ ions are exchanged for

Na+, the acidity of the urine falls and that of the body fluids increases. Conversely, when the tissue cells (including kidney) are depleted of K+, more H+ and fewer K+ ions are exchanged for Na+, and the urine becomes more acid even though a state of alkalosis may exist. Inhibition of renal carbonic anhdrase results not only in inability to acidify the urine but also in striking increase in excretion of potassium, another indication of the competition between these two ions for tubular excretion.

With increasing acidification of the glomerular filtrate, progressively more HCO_3^- is converted to H_2CO_3 and, consequently, to H_2O and CO_2, the latter diffusing across the tubule into the blood, the pCO_2 of which is in equilibrium with that of the fluid in the uriniferous tubule. This decrease in bicarbonate content of the urine, which may fall to zero as the acidity increases, is accompanied by a simultaneous increase in chloride. Changes in the reverse directions occur in the concentrations of these substances in the blood.

The phenomena described above occur in response to a stimulus provided the kidney by an increase in H+ ion concentration of the plasma and glomerular filtrate (increased requirement for excretion of acid and reabsorption of bicarbonate). If the plasma pH rises (alkalosis), the renal mechanism is stimulated in the opposite direction, i.e., decreased excretion of acid, decreased reabsorption of bicarbonate. The urinary acidity falls as a result of decreased exchange of H+ and Na+ ions, increasing amounts of phosphate being excreted in the form of Na_2HPO_4 and of organic acids as sodium salts. With increasing pH, up to 8.2, there is increased urinary excretion of HCO_3^- and of Na+, the cation with which it is chiefly associated, excretion of Cl− decreasing simultaneously. Changes in the reverse direction occur in the concentrations of these substances in the blood, tending to restore the normal pH of the plasma.

EXCRETION OF AMMONIA. A normal subject, under ordinary dietary conditions, excretes 30 to 50 mEq. of ammonia daily. If the plasma H+ ion concentration rises, the urinary ammonia increases, even tenfold in severe diabetic acidosis. A decrease occurs in alkalosis. The urinary NH_3 is formed in the cells of the distal portion of the uriniferous tubule, the site of acidification of the urine. About 60 per cent is derived from the amide group of glutamine (by the enzyme glutaminase) and the remaining 40 per cent from the α-amino group of certain amino acids (p. 512). Adrenal cortical hormones may perhaps exert a stimulating influence on this deamination process and, therefore, on NH_3 formation.

The NH_3 (gas) diffuses into the lumen of the tubule, combining with the H+ ions in the acidified fluid to form NH_4^+ ions (Fig. 67). This effectively prevents undue accumulation of H+ ions in the fluid, and therefore permits continued exchange of H^+ for Na^+ ions. The amount of Na^+ ion absorbed in the distal tubule is consequently reflected in the amount of both H^+ and NH_4^+ ions in the urine.

The urinary NH_3 begins to increase shortly after H^+ ion concentration of the blood rises, but the increase continues for some time after the blood and urine pH and bicarbonate content have reached their lowest level. The stimulus to NH_3 formation by the kidney is apparently similar to that producing acidification of the urine, i.e., decrease in pH and bicarbonate of the blood and glomerular filtrate. However, the duration of application of this stimulus influences NH_3 formation but not acidification of the urine.

ABNORMALITIES OF "ACID-BASE" (ANION-CATION) BALANCE

It is obvious from the preceding discussion that a number of interrelated factors and mechanisms are involved in the maintenance of the normal electrolyte pattern and pH of the body fluids, commonly referred to as "acid-base" balance, but more properly designated "anion-cation" balance (p. 314). Several of these do not lend themselves to direct quantitative study. However, factors operating in the blood can be investigated more or less readily because of accessibility of this medium. The most important of these are:

1. *Total "base"* (B^+): the sum of the concentrations (in mEq./liter) of all cations.

2. *H_2CO_3 content:* the concentration of H_2CO_3 (in mM./liter), which is in equilibrium with the pCO_2 (CO_2 tension) [pCO_2 (in mm. Hg) $\times$ 0.3 = H_2CO_3 (in mM./liter)].

3. *CO_2 content:* the concentration (in mM./liter) of total CO_2 in solution (HCO_3 plus H_2CO_3).

4. *HCO_3^- content:* the concentration (in mEq./liter) of HCO_3^-, usually calculated as the difference between the CO_2 and H_2CO_3 contents (thus including the carbamino-CO_2).

5. *CO_2 capacity or "combining power":* the HCO_3^- (or CO_2) content of blood or plasma saturated with 5.5 per cent CO_2 at 25° C.

6. *pH:* the logarithm of the reciprocal of the H^+ ion concentration.

7. *"Buffer-base":* the "base" equivalent to the sum of the concentrations (in mEq./liter) of buffer anions (whole blood = HCO_3^- plus Hb and plasma proteins; plasma = HCO_3^- plus plasma proteins).

The important role of Hb as a buffer has been pointed out elsewhere (p. 318), as has the difference in this connection between oxyhemoglobin and reduced hemoglobin. For most precise analysis of the state of "acid-base" balance, the following factors must be determined: (1) hematocrit (relative proportions of erythrocytes and plasma); (2) pH; (3) CO_2 content; (4) buffer base; (5) H_2CO_3 content (calculated from pCO_2 of blood or alveolar air). However, for practical clinical purposes, certain of these may usually be dispensed with (viz., hematocrit, buffer base) inasmuch as significant abnormalities due to changes in hemoglobin are reflected in the pH and HCO_3^- content.

As indicated below, clinical aberrations of "acid-base" balance are classified conveniently as primary disturbances in either HCO_3^- (bicarbonate) or H_2CO_3, the relation of which to the pH is expressed by the Henderson-Hasselbalch equation: $pH = pK + \log \frac{HCO_3^-}{H_2CO_3}$. At pH 7.4, the $HCO_3^-:H_2CO_3$ ratio is 20:1 (27 mEq.: 1.35 mEq./liter of plasma water). Knowledge of any two of these three factors (pH, HCO_3^-, H_2CO_3) therefore permits derivation of the third. Determination of the total CO_2 content (HCO_3^- plus H_2CO_3) and any one of the three factors mentioned permits derivation of the other two. Consequently, the most widely employed approach to the investigation of clinical disturbances of "acid-base" balance centers about these factors, perhaps the most useful for practical purposes being the simultaneous determination of pH (plasma or serum) and CO_2 content (plasma, serum, or whole blood).

Primary change in HCO_3^- (metabolic acidosis and alkalosis, pp. 327, 329) is by far the most common cause of acidosis and alkalosis of clinically significant degree. For this reason, reliance is frequently placed on determination of this factor alone for the diagnosis of acidosis (decreased HCO_3^-) and alkalosis (increase). The term "alkali reserve" has been applied to the plasma bicarbonate because of its important buffer action when fixed (non-volatile) acids or bases are added to or removed in excess from the body fluids. Determination of the "CO_2 combining power (CO_2 capacity)" is often employed as a substitute for the HCO_3^- or CO_2 contents. It must be noted, however, that disturbances due to primary changes in H_2CO_3 (respiratory acidosis and alkalosis) are accompanied by alterations (secondary, compensatory) in HCO_3^- and CO_2 content in directions opposite to those which occur in "metabolic" acidosis and alkalosis (p. 327 ff.; Table 31). Unless the true nature of the disturbance is recognized, which is often possible (e.g., diabetes mellitus, nephritis, vomiting, diarrhea, hyperventilation, etc.), an incorrect diagnosis may be made on the basis of determination of this isolated factor.

ACIDOSIS

Increase in the H^+ ion concentration of the body fluids results from the formation or absorption of acids at a rate exceeding that of their

Table 31. Biochemical Characteristics of Uncompensated and Compensated Acidosis and Alkalosis*

PLASMA	NORMAL	ACIDOSIS				ALKALOSIS			
		HCO₃⁻ DEFICIT		H₂CO₃ EXCESS		HCO₃⁻ EXCESS		H₂CO₃ DEFICIT	
		Uncomp.	Comp.	Uncomp.	Comp.	Uncomp.	Comp.	Uncomp.	Comp.
HCO_3^-	mM./liter 23–28 (26) vol. % 51–62 (53.4)	− −	−	+	+	+ +	+	−	−
CO_2 capacity	mM./liter 24–35 (30) vol. % 53–78 (65)	− −	−	+	+	+ +	+	−	−
H_2CO_3	mM./liter 1.1–1.5 (1.3) vol. % 2.4–3.3 (2.9)	−	−	+ +	+	+	+	− −	−
pCO_2	mm. Hg 35–45 (40)	−	−	+ +	+	+	+	− −	−
CO_2 content	mM./liter 24–33 (28) vol. % 53–75 (62)	− −	−	+ +	+	+ +	+	− −	−
$\dfrac{HCO_3^-}{H_2CO_3}$	20	−	N	−	N	+	N	+	N
pH	7.35–7.45 (7.4)	−	N	−	N	+	N	+	N
Urinary acidity and ammonia	<27 ml./kg. 0.1 N acid (+NH₃) per 24 hrs.	+	+	+	+	−	−	−	−

* Values in parentheses indicate means; + = increase; − = decrease; N = normal.

"neutralization" or elimination. It may also result from loss of excessive quantities of base from the body fluids. As indicated previously, disturbances of this nature are reflected in the bicarbonate-carbonic acid buffer system of the blood and may be investigated on the basis of the Henderson-Hasselbalch equation. Inasmuch as the pH of this system is a function of the $[BHCO_3]$: $[H_2CO_3]$ ratio, it is evident that acidosis may be caused by either a disproportionate decrease in $[BHCO_3]$ or a disproportionate increase in $[H_2CO_3]$.

PRIMARY BHCO₃ (ALKALI) DEFICIT. A variety of fixed (non-volatile) acids may be produced and/or accumulate in the body in excess under abnormal conditions. These include acidic ketone bodies (diabetes mellitus); phosphoric, sulfuric, and organic acids (renal insufficiency); lactic acid (anoxia, hemorrhage, ether anesthesia, prolonged strenuous exercise, etc.). These acids are buffered principally by bicarbonate (p. 318), the added H^+ ions entering into the formation of H_2CO_3 and the anion of the acid increasing in concentration at the expense of HCO_3^-. The increased plasma H_2CO_3 and H^+ ion concentrations stimulate the respiratory center (p. 288), with consequent increased pulmonary ventilation and increased excretion of CO_2, thereby dissipating the secondary increase in $[H_2CO_3]$. Similar phenomena follow administration of excessive amounts of these fixed acids or their ammonium salts (NH_4Cl, NH_4NO_3, etc.), the ammonia of which is converted to urea in the liver.

An excessive quantity of base ($BHCO_3$) may be lost from the body in such conditions as severe, protracted diarrhea and external pancreatic or intestinal fistulas. These result in the loss of large volumes of digestive fluids, which are more alkaline than the blood plasma, i.e., they have a higher concentration of HCO_3^- ions (Fig. 68). The respiratory response is identical with that indicated above, i.e., hyperventilation and decrease in plasma H_2CO_3 concentration.

COMPENSATORY MECHANISMS. If functioning normally, the respiratory apparatus and the kidneys attempt to maintain the blood pH within normal limits. The action of the former is indicated above; as a result of increased pulmonary ventilation the plasma (i.e., extracellular fluid) H_2CO_3 concentration is reduced. In all but very mild cases, however, if the cause continues to operate, the decrease in $[HCO_3^-]$, being the primary event, is proportionately greater than that in $[H_2CO_3]$, the secondary event.

The kidneys (unless damaged) attempt to support the falling plasma HCO_3^- concentration by returning increased amounts of HCO_3^- to the blood in the distal renal tubules. This is accomplished by stimulation of the $H^+ - Na^+$ exchange mechanism and of NH_3 formation, as evidenced by increased urinary ammonia and titratable acidity (pp. 321, 323).

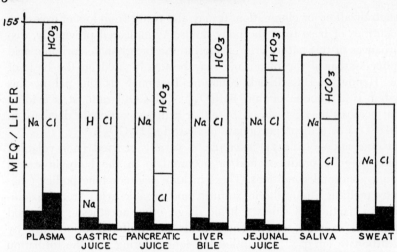

Fig. 68. *The electrolyte composition of certain important body fluids, compared with that of blood plasma (Gamble)*

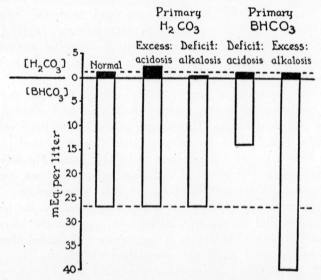

Fig. 69. *The four primary mechanisms of "acid-base" imbalance (from Fulton: Howell's Textbook of Physiology, ed. 16, W. B. Saunders Company, 1950; modified from Gamble: Chemical Anatomy, Physiology, and Pathology of Extracellular Fluid, Harvard University Press, 1950)*

BIOCHEMICAL CHARACTERISTICS (TABLE 31). Acidosis of this type is commonly designated "metabolic acidosis." If uncompensated, it is characterized biochemically (plasma or blood) as follows: (1) disproportionate decrease in $[HCO_3^-]$; (2) decrease in $[H_2CO_3]$ (pCO_2); (3) decrease in CO_2 content ($[HCO_3^-]$ plus $[H_2CO_3]$);

(4) decrease in $[HCO_3^-]$: $[H_2CO_3]$ ratio; (5) decrease in pH. If fully compensated, the CO_2 content is low, but the decrease in $[HCO_3^-]$ and $[H_2CO_3]$ is proportionate, the $[HCO_3^-]$: $[H_2CO_3]$ ratio and pH remaining within normal limits. The urinary ammonia and titratable acidity are increased (if kidneys are functioning normally).

PRIMARY H_2CO_3 (CO_2) EXCESS. The respiratory center is so sensitive to an increased H_2CO_3 or H^+ ion concentration and pulmonary alveoli so highly permeable to CO_2 that accumulation of excessive amounts of H_2CO_3 in the plasma is virtually impossible if these structures are functioning normally, unless the CO_2 content of the inspired air is excessively high. This condition can occur under the following circumstances: (1) depression of the respiratory center (morphine, barbiturates, brain lesions); (2) extensive pulmonary lesions (pneumonia, emphysema, fibrosis, congestion); (3) mechanical obstruction of air passages; (4) rebreathing or breathing air with high (5–7 per cent) CO_2 content.

COMPENSATORY MECHANISMS. Inasmuch as the fundamental cause of this type of acidosis is inability of the respiratory apparatus to remove CO_2 from the body efficiently, the brunt of the task of compensating for this defect falls on the kidneys. These organs respond as in the case of primary HCO_3^- deficit (q.v.), by increasing urinary acidity and ammonia and returning increased amounts of HCO_3^- to the blood (p. 321 ff.).

BIOCHEMICAL CHARACTERISTICS (TABLE 31). Acidosis of this type is commonly designated "respiratory acidosis," for obvious reasons. If uncompensated, it is characterized biochemically (plasma or blood) as follows: (1) disproportionate increase in $[H_2CO_3]$ (pCO_2); (2) increase in $[HCO_3^-]$; (3) increase in CO_2 content; (4) decrease in $[HCO_3^-]$: $[H_2CO_3]$ ratio; (5) decrease in pH. If fully compensated, the CO_2 content is high, but the increase in $[H_2CO_3]$ and $[HCO_3^-]$ are proportionate, the $[HCO_3^-]$: $[H_2CO_3]$ ratio and pH remaining within normal limits. The urinary ammonia and titratable acidity are increased (if kidneys are functioning normally).

ALKALOSIS

Decrease in the H^+ ion concentration of the body fluids results from excessive loss of acids from the body without comparable loss of base, or the formation or supply of base at a rate exceeding that of its "neutralization" or elimination. In terms of the bicarbonate buffer system, alkalosis may be caused by either a disproportionate increase in $[BHCO_3]$ or a disproportionate decrease in $[H_2CO_3]$.

PRIMARY BHCO$_3$ (ALKALI) EXCESS. This may be produced by administration of excessive amounts of alkali (e.g., NaHCO$_3$) and by protracted vomiting (or removal) of gastric juice with a high HCl content (duodenal or pyloric obstruction; gastric lavage or drainage). In the latter instance, HCO_3^- ions replace the Cl^- ions lost from the body fluids.

COMPENSATORY MECHANISMS. If functioning normally, the respiratory apparatus and the kidneys attempt to maintain the blood pH within normal limits. The increased pH depresses the respiratory center (p. 288), with consequent slowing of respiration, hypoventilation, and decreased excretion of CO_2. The blood (and extracellular fluid) H_2CO_3 concentration increases.

The kidneys (unless damaged) attempt to rid the body of the excess HCO_3^- by decreasing the extent of $H^+ - Na^+$ exchange and NH_3 formation in the distal tubules, thus returning less HCO_3^- to the blood stream (p. 321 ff.). The urinary acidity and ammonia are decreased; in severe cases the urine may become alkaline and contain bicarbonate.

BIOCHEMICAL CHARACTERISTICS (TABLE 31). Alkalosis of this type is commonly designated "metabolic alkalosis." If uncompensated, it is characterized biochemically (plasma or blood) as follows: (1) disproportionate increase in $[HCO_3^-]$; (2) increase in $[H_2CO_3]$ (pCO_2); (3) increase in CO_2 content; (4) increase in $[HCO_3^-]$: $[H_2CO_3]$ ratio; (5) increase in pH. If fully compensated, the CO_2 content is high, but the increase in $[HCO_3^-]$ and $[H_2CO_3]$ are proportionate, the $[HCO_3^-]$: $[H_2CO_3]$ ratio and pH remaining within normal limits. The urinary ammonia and titratable acidity are decreased (if kidneys are functioning normally).

PRIMARY H_2CO_3 (CO_2) DEFICIT. Excessive quantities of CO_2 may be removed from the blood by prolonged pulmonary hyperventilation (excessively rapid, deep respiration). This may occur in hysteria, fever, anoxia (high altitudes), high external temperature (e.g., hot baths), certain cases of encephalitis (brain lesion), and after administration of certain drugs which stimulate the respiratory center (e.g., sodium salicylate in large doses).

COMPENSATORY MECHANISMS. In view of the pathogenesis of this condition, the task of compensating for this defect falls on the kidneys. These organs (unless damaged) respond, as in the case of primary HCO_3^- deficit, by decreasing the $H^+ - Na^+$ exchange and NH_3 formation, returning less HCO_3^- to the blood stream.

BIOCHEMICAL CHARACTERISTICS (TABLE 31). Alkalosis of this type is commonly designated "respiratory alkalosis." If uncompensated, it is characterized biochemically (plasma or blood) as follows: (1) disproportionate decrease in $[H_2CO_3]$ (pCO_2); (2) decrease in $[HCO_3^-]$; (3) decrease in CO_2 content; (4) increase in $[HCO_3^-]$: $[H_2CO_3]$ ratio; (5) increase in pH. If fully compensated, the CO_2

content is low but the decrease in $[HCO_3{}^-]$ and $[H_2CO_3]$ are proportionate, the $[HCO_3{}^-]$: $[H_2CO_3]$ ratio and pH remaining within normal limits. The urinary ammonia and titratable acidity are decreased (if kidneys are functioning normally).

BIBLIOGRAPHY

Berliner, R. W.: Relationship between acidification of the urine and potassium metabolism, Am. J. Med. *11:*274, 1951.

Darrow, D. C.: Fluid therapy, J.A.M.A. *143:*365, 1950.

Davenport, H. W.: The ABC of Acid-Base Chemistry, ed. 3, Chicago, University of Chicago Press, 1950.

Gamble, J. L.: Chemical Anatomy, Physiology and Pathology of Extracellular Fluid, Cambridge, Harvard University Press, 1950.

Gamble, J. L.: Companionship of Water and Electrolytes in the Organization of Body Fluids, Lane Medical Lectures, California, Stanford University Press, 1951.

Ogston, A. G.: The definition and meaning of pH, Physiol. Rev. *27:*228, 1947.

Peters, J. P.: Body Water, Springfield, Ill., Charles C Thomas, Publisher, 1935.

Peters, J. P.: Water balance in health and disease. In Diseases of Metabolism, ed. 3, edited by G. G. Duncan, Philadelphia, W. B. Saunders Company, 1952, p. 315.

Peters, J. P. and Van Slyke, D. D.: Quantitative Clinical Chemistry, Volume 1: Interpretations. Baltimore, Williams & Wilkins Company, 1931.

Pitts, R. F.: Renal excretion of acid, Federation Proc. *7:*418, 1948.

13

ENERGY METABOLISM

Throughout the discussions of the metabolism of organic foodstuffs, attention has been focused particularly on the mechanisms and nature of their chemical transformation. Various components of the tissues are undergoing degradation (catabolism) and resynthesis (anabolism) continually. Certain of the chemical reactions involved in these metabolic processes are exergonic, i.e., they are accompanied by liberation of energy, whereas others are endergonic, i.e., they require the introduction of energy. The manner in which energy is produced, stored, transferred, and utilized is considered elsewhere (p. 371).

Obviously, even under resting conditions, the maintenance of life and normal function requires the constant performance of work by a variety of tissues. This implies the utilization of energy, which must be supplied from external sources if the body stores of energy are to be preserved at a constant level. We shall concern ourselves here with the magnitude of the energy requirement under normal conditions and the factors that may influence it.

CALORIC VALUE OF FOODS. Following the demonstration by early investigators in this field that production of heat in the body was dependent primarily on oxidative processes, attempts were made to relate the quantity of heat produced to the amounts of foodstuffs metabolized. This was feasible because the heat produced by burning (oxidizing) these substances outside the body can be determined readily in a combustion calorimeter, the average values (in Calories) obtained per gram being: glucose, 3.96; starch, 4.2; animal fats, 9.5; animal proteins, 5.6 (vegetable proteins lower). A "Calorie" (kilocalorie) is the amount of heat required to raise the temperature of 1 kg. of water 1° C. (i.e., from 15° to 16° C.). In the body, protein does not undergo complete oxidation, a portion of its amino groups being converted to and excreted as ammonia and urea; this involves a loss of about 1.3 Cal. per gram, leaving 4.3 Cal. produced per gram of protein metabolized. Taking into consideration the variations in caloric value of individual carbohydrates, fats, and proteins, their average energy value when metabolized may be represented as follows (Calories per gram): fat, 9.3; carbohydrate, 4.1; protein, 4.1. When these corrected figures are applied, it is found that the amount of energy (Calories) produced by a given quantity of these foodstuffs in the body is the same as that (heat) produced by their combustion outside the body, within the limits of experimental error. Inasmuch as ingested foods are not completely assimilated, the caloric values of the fats, carbohydrates, and proteins of the diet are usually calculated as 9, 4, and 4 Cal./gram, respectively.

HEAT PRODUCTION. In living tissues, the bulk of the energy derived from the metabolism of organic compounds is liberated, not as a single burst of heat, as occurs in their combustion outside the body, but rather in a stepwise fashion through a series of integrated enzymatic reactions (p. 373 ff.). Therefore, although in the complete oxidation of these compounds (e.g., glucose to CO_2 and H_2O) their full potential energy value is ultimately realized, relatively small fractions of the total are made available at each stage of their degradation. Presented in small parcels, energy is utilized much more efficiently than if it had been liberated explosively.

The energy thus produced is disposed of as follows: (1) A portion is primarily converted to heat for the maintenance of body temperature. (2) A portion is utilized for the performance of work, e.g., mechanical (muscle contraction), electrical (nerve impulse), secretory (glandular, intestinal, renal tubular cells, etc.), chemical (endergonic metabolic reactions). Such work is ultimately reflected largely in heat production. (3) A portion may be stored very temporarily in "energy-rich" phosphate bonds (p. 373), or for longer periods in the form of substances (e.g., fat, glycogen) that may be called upon to provide energy at some future date. The over-all body composition and weight of normal adults does not vary appreciably from day to day; i.e., there is little or no accretion or loss of tissue, new components being formed only in amounts required for replacement (metabolic turnover, "dynamic state," p. 487). On an adequate diet, the organism is therefore in a state of equilibrium with its environment; this applies to its intake of energy as well as of H_2O, N, and inorganic elements. Consequently, an amount of heat must be lost, either actual (radiation, conduction, vaporization of water) or potential (constituents of urine and feces), that is equal to the caloric value of ingested proteins, fats and carbohydrates (i.e., caloric equilibrium). This has been demonstrated to be the case by direct measurement of heat loss (direct calorimetry).

RESPIRATORY QUOTIENT. In the process of oxidation, carbohydrates, fats, and proteins react with definite amounts of oxygen and definite amounts of carbon dioxide and water are formed. The designation "respiratory quotient" or "R.Q." is applied to the ratios of the volume of CO_2 produced to that of O_2 utilized in this process (R.Q. = Vol. CO_2/Vol. O_2).

CARBOHYDRATE R.Q. Complete oxidation of glucose may be represented as follows:

$$C_6H_{12}O_6 + 6O_2 \rightarrow 6CO_2 + 6H_2O$$

$$(1 \text{ mol}) + (6 \text{ mols}) \rightarrow (6 \text{ mols}) + (6 \text{ mols})$$

$$(180 \text{ grams}) + (192 \text{ grams}) \rightarrow (264 \text{ grams}) + (108 \text{ grams})$$

The glucose R.Q. is therefore 6/6, or 1.0. Inasmuch as 1 mol of gas occupies a volume of 22.4 liters, the volume of O_2 and of CO_2 involved in this reaction is 22.4 x 6, or 134.4 liters. Consequently, 1 gram of glucose reacts with 134.4/180, or 0.75 liter of oxygen, forming 0.75 liter of CO_2. Since oxidation of 1 gram of glucose liberates 3.74 Cal., 1 liter of O_2 is the equivalent of 3.74/0.75, or 5.0 Cal. when glucose is oxidized. This (5.0 Cal.) is the caloric value of 1 liter of oxygen for glucose oxidation in the body.

Table 32. Caloric, O_2, and CO_2 Equivalents of Carbohydrate, Fat, and Protein

	CARBOHYDRATE	FAT	PROTEIN
Calories per gram	3.7–4.3	9.5	4.3
Liters CO_2 per gram	0.75–0.83	1.43	0.78
Liters O_2 per gram	0.75–0.83	2.03	0.97
Respiratory quotient	1.0	0.707	0.801
Caloric value per liter O_2	5.0 Cal.	4.7 Cal.	4.5 Cal.

FAT R.Q. Complete oxidation of tripalmitin may be represented as follows:

$$2(C_{51}H_{98}O_6) + 145O_2 \rightarrow 102CO_2 + 98H_2O$$

$$(2 \text{ mols}) + (145 \text{ mols}) \rightarrow (102 \text{ mols}) + (98 \text{ mols})$$

$$(1612 \text{ grams}) + (4640 \text{ grams}) \rightarrow (4488 \text{ grams}) + (1764 \text{ grams})$$

The R.Q. for tripalmitin is therefore 102/145, or 0.704. That for triolein is 0.712. The R.Q. for mixed fats in the body is regarded as 0.707. The volumes of O_2 and CO_2 involved in this reaction are 3246.6 liters (145 x 22.4) and 2283.9 liters (102 x 22.4), respectively. Consequently, 1 gram of tripalmitin reacts with 3246.6/1612, or 2.01 liters of O_2. Since oxidation of 1 gram of this fat liberates 9.5 Cal., 1 liter of O_2 is the equivalent of 9.5/2.01, or 4.7 Cal. when tripalmitin is oxidized. Essentially the same value applies to other animal fats and, therefore, 4.7 is the caloric value of 1 liter of oxygen for fat oxidation in the body.

PROTEIN R.Q.   Amino acids do not undergo complete oxidation in the body and, therefore, the type of equation written for carbohydrates and fats is not applicable to proteins. However, the approximate quantitative relationships between O_2 and CO_2 in the metabolic oxidation of amino acids may be calculated from data on the average composition and metabolism of meat protein. These are indicated in Table 33.

Table 33. *Average Elemental Composition and Metabolism of 100 Grams of Meat Protein (Loewy)*

	100 GRAMS MEAT PROTEIN	EXCRETED IN FECES AND URINE	INTRAMOLECULAR WATER	REMAINING FOR OXIDATION
	(grams)	(grams)	(grams)	(grams)
C	52.38	10.877		41.5
H	7.27	2.87	0.96	3.4
O	22.68	14.99	7.69	
N	16.65	16.65 (16.28 urine)		
S	1.02	1.02		

In its oxidation to CO_2, 12 grams of C combine with 32 grams of O_2; in forming H_2O, 2 grams of H combine with 16 grams of O_2. Consequently, 41.5 grams of C require 110.66 grams of O_2 and will produce 152.17 grams (3.46 mols) of CO_2, while 3.4 grams of H require 27.52 grams of O_2 [total O_2 utilized is 138.18 grams (4.32 mols)]. The R.Q. for protein oxidation is therefore 3.46/4.32, or 0.801. The volumes of O_2 and CO_2 involved were 96.7 liters (4.32 x 22.4) and 77.46 liters (3.46 x 22.4) respectively (per 100 grams protein). Since oxidation of 1 gram of protein liberates 4.3 Cal., 1 liter of O_2 is the equivalent of 4.3/0.967, or 4.5 Cal., which represents, therefore the caloric value of 1 liter of O_2 for protein oxidation in the body.

As indicated in Table 33, the metabolism of 100 grams of protein gave rise to urinary excretion of 16.28 grams of nitrogen. Each gram of urinary N therefore represented the metabolism of: 100/16.28, or 6.15 grams of meat protein; 96.7/16.28, or 5.94 liters of O_2; 77.46/16.28, or 4.76 liters of CO_2. On the basis of analytical data for the average protein, it is generally estimated that 1 gram of urinary N represents: (1) the metabolism of 6.25 grams of protein; (2) utilization of 5.91 liters of O_2; (3) production of 4.76 liters of CO_2; (4) liberation of 26.51 Cal.

EXAMPLE. The following data were obtained under basal conditions (overnight fast): (1) urinary N, 0.18 gram/hour; (2) O_2 consumption, 12.2 liters/hour; (3) CO_2 production; (9.2 liters/hour. Information desired: (1) heat (Calories) production; (2) quantities of protein, carbohydrate, and fat metabolized; (3) percentages of total heat produced by oxidation of protein, carbohydrate, and fat, respectively.

0.18 gram of urinary N represents:

$0.18 \times 6.25 = 1.125$ grams of protein metabolized
$0.18 \times 5.91 = 1.06$ liters of oxygen
$0.18 \times 4.76 = 0.85$ liter of carbon dioxide
$0.18 \times 26.51 = 4.77$ Calories

Total O_2 (12.2 liters) minus protein O_2 (1.06 liters) = non-protein O_2 (11.14 liters)

Total CO_2 (9.2 liters) minus protein CO_2 (0.85 liter) = non-protein CO_2 (8.35 liters)

Non-protein R.Q. $= 8.35/11.14 = 0.75$

As indicated in Table 34, a non-protein R.Q. of 0.75 represents the liberation of 4.739 Cal. per liter O_2, 15.6 per cent of which comes from carbohydrate and 84.4 per cent from fat oxidation.

11.14 liters $O_2 \times 4.739 = 52.79$ Cal. (non-protein)
15.6 per cent of 52.79 = 8.24 Cal. from carbohydrate (2.01 grams)
84.4 per cent of 52.79 = 44.55 Cal. from fat (4.79 grams)
52.79 + 4.77 (protein Cal.) = 57.56 total Cal./hour, of which
1.125 grams protein provided 4.77/57.56, or 8.3 per cent,
2.01 grams carbohydrate provided 8.53/57.56, or 14.3 per cent,
4.79 grams fat provided 44.55/57.56, or 77.4 per cent.

SIGNIFICANCE OF R.Q. The chief practical value of the calculations discussed above lies in the fact that they permit estimation of the amounts of protein, fat, and carbohydrate metabolized during a given period, from knowledge of (1) the urinary N excretion, (2) the O_2 consumption, and (3) the CO_2 production.

If the organism (or isolated tissue, *in vitro*) were utilizing carbohydrate exclusively the R.Q. would be 1.0, if utilizing fats exclusively it would be 0.7, and if utilizing proteins exclusively it would be 0.8. Conversion of carbohydrate to fat results in R.Q. values greater than 1.0, because some of the oxygen of the carbohydrate, which contains relatively more of this element in proportion to carbon than do fats, becomes available for oxidative processes, decreasing the quantity of O_2 required from the inspired air. On the same basis, theoretically, conversion of fat to carbohydrate would produce R.Q. values below 0.7. Such values have been observed (e.g., in diabetes mellitus), but fatty acids have not been shown to produce a net increase in carbohydrate. The R.Q. for conversion of protein to glucose has been estimated as 0.632–0.706.

It has been found that in the average normal adult, studied under "basal" conditions, i.e., at complete mental and physical rest, fourteen to eighteen hours after taking food, the R.Q. is approximately 0.82. At this level, the caloric value of oxygen is 4.825 Cal./liter (Table 34). Progressive decrease in the proportion of carbohydrate being oxidized in the "metabolic mixture" (i.e., carbohydrate deprivation, diabetes mellitus) is reflected in progressive lowering of the R.Q., approaching 0.7 and occasionally falling below this value (excessive gluconeogenesis from protein).

Table 34. Respiratory Quotient and Caloric Equivalent of Oxygen for Different Mixtures of Fat and Carbohydrate

R.Q.	PERCENTAGE OF TOTAL O_2 CONSUMED BY		PERCENTAGE OF HEAT PRODUCED BY		CALORIES PER LITER O_2
	Carbohydrate	Fat	Carbohydrate	Fat	
0.707	0	100	0	100	4.686
0.75	14.7	85.3	15.6	84.4	4.739
0.80	31.7	68.3	33.4	66.6	4.801
0.82	38.6	61.4	40.3	59.7	4.825
0.85	48.8	51.2	50.7	49.3	4.862
0.90	65.9	34.2	67.5	32.5	4.924
0.95	82.9	17.1	84.0	16.0	4.985
1.00	100	0	100	0	5.047

CALORIMETRY. On the basis of what has been stated concerning heat production, it is evident that measurement of the amount of heat lost over any given period of time affords an approach to the estimation of the energy production (oxidative metabolism) of the body during that period. This may be accomplished either directly (direct calorimetry) or indirectly (indirect calorimetry).

DIRECT CALORIMETRY. The subject is placed in an insulated chamber (calorimeter) so constructed as to permit direct and precise measurement of heat loss from the body. Water is circulated through tubes within the chamber; the rate of flow is recorded automatically, as is the temperature of the water entering and leaving the chamber. Air is circulated through the calorimeter and measurements are made of the rate of flow, and of changes in temperature and water vapor. On the basis of these data, one may calculate the actual heat loss very accurately. Determinations may be made simultaneously of the consumption of oxygen and excretion of carbon dioxide by analyses of the air entering and leaving the chamber, permitting calculation of the respiratory quotient.

This procedure requires elaborate and expensive apparatus and is now chiefly of historical interest. It was early found that calculation of heat production from data on O_2 consumption and CO_2 production gave results which approximated very closely those obtained by direct calorimetry. This observation formed the basis for the application of the widely employed procedure of indirect calorimetry.

INDIRECT CALORIMETRY. As illustrated by the example cited on page 336, the amount of heat lost during an experimental period can be calculated accurately from the following data: (1) urinary N excretion during that period; (2) O_2 consumption; (3) CO_2 excretion. The validity of this calculation rests upon the following facts: (1) 1 gram of urinary N represents the metabolism of 6.25 grams of protein, the consumption of 5.91 liters of O_2, the production of 4.76 liters of CO_2, and the liberation of 26.51 Cal.; (2) oxygen has a known fixed caloric value per liter at any given R.Q. level.

For usual clinical purposes, determination of urinary N may be dispensed with, inasmuch as 90–95 per cent of the heat produced is derived from oxidation of carbohydrate and fat. Two general types of apparatus may be employed: (1) the open-circuit system; (2) the closed-circuit system. The former is the more accurate; the latter is much more convenient, is sufficiently accurate for clinical purposes, and is used most widely.

Open-Circuit System. The subject breathes atmospheric air of determined composition, the expired air being collected in a rubber bag or a spirometer. Determination of the volume, and O_2 and CO_2 contents of the expired air permits calculation of the volumes of O_2 absorbed and CO_2 produced and also, therefore, the R.Q. From the R.Q., one can ascertain the caloric value of 1 liter of oxygen, and, therefore, the heat production during the test period.

Closed-Circuit System. Several different types of apparatus are available, all of which are based on essentially the same principle. The subject breathes from and into a system filled with pure oxygen, the expired CO_2 and H_2O being trapped by soda lime. Decrease in the total volume of gas in the closed system is therefore due to and is a direct measure of oxygen consumption. The test period usually occupies six or eight minutes.

Inasmuch as CO_2 production is not measured, the R.Q. cannot be determined. However, the assumption that the R.Q. is approximately 0.82 (p. 337) under basal conditions is quite satisfactory for most clinical purposes. The caloric value per liter of O_2 is known to be 4.825 at this R.Q. Consequently, determination of the amount of O_2 consumed permits calculation of the approximate heat production during the test period.

BASAL METABOLISM. The terms "basal metabolism" or "basal metabolic rate" (BMR) are applied to the heat produced per unit time under "basal" conditions, i.e., at complete physical and mental rest, and in the postabsorptive state fourteen to eighteen hours after taking food). It was indicated previously that energy is derived by the organism from the metabolism (mainly oxidation) of exogenous (dietary) and endogenous proteins, carbohydrates, and lipids. This energy is dissipated in the form of heat and work, or is stored in the body. Under the specified "basal" conditions, the exogenous source of energy is removed and loss of energy in the form of work by voluntary muscles is virtually abolished. Under these conditions energy is expended in the maintenance of respiration, circulation, muscle tonus, gastrointestinal contractions, and body temperature, and the functional activities of various organs (e.g., kidneys, liver, endocrine glands, etc.). Although the respiratory, heart, and other involuntary muscles continue to function, their activity does not result in permanent increase in the potential or kinetic energy of the materials on which they act, viz., the blood, respiratory air, lungs, etc. Consequently, the organism, under these conditions, is deriving its energy solely from stored sources and is dissipating it almost exclusively in the form of heat. Inasmuch as the amount of energy lost must be equal to that produced, measurement of the heat loss over a given period of time is an index of the rate of energy production, i.e., metabolism. As indicated previously, this is usually done clinically by the indirect procedure, using a closed system.

Table 35. Calories per Square Meter per Hour (DuBois Standards)
(Modified by Boothby and Sandiford)

AGE	MALES	FEMALES	AGE	MALES	FEMALES
5	(53.0)	(51.6)	20–24	41.0	36.9
6	52.7	50.7	25–29	40.3	36.6
7	52.0	49.3	30–34	39.8	36.2
8	51.2	48.1	35–39	39.2	35.8
9	50.4	46.9	40–44	38.3	35.3
10	49.5	45.8	45–49	37.8	35.0
11	48.6	44.6	50–54	37.2	34.5
12	47.8	43.4	55–59	36.6	34.1
13	47.1	42.0			
14	46.2	41.0	60–64	36.0	33.8
15	45.3	39.6	65–69	35.3	33.4
16	44.7	38.5			
17	43.7	37.4	70–74	34.8	32.8
18	42.9	37.3			
19	42.1	37.2	75–79	34.2	32.3

Physiological Variations in BMR. Basal metabolism varies with body size, age, and sex (Table 35). As would be anticipated, the magnitude of energy exchange increases with body size, but more directly in relation to surface area than to either height or weight. Tables are available for derivation of surface area from the latter two factors. The BMR is therefore commonly expressed in one of three ways: (1)

kilocalories/sq. meter body surface/hour; (2) liters of oxygen consumed/sq. meter/hour; (3) percentage above or below the mean normal for the subject in question. The last mode of expression is the one used most widely clinically, but it may occasionally obscure certain important facts, e.g., in obesity.

The average normal BMR for young adult men (20–30 years old) is about 40 Cal./sq. meter/hour (8.3 liters O_2/sq. meter/hour), increasing progressively below this age level (to 5 years) and diminishing progressively with increasing age. Normal values for females are about 6–10 per cent lower than for males (Table 35). For average individuals (e.g., 70-kg. man, 1.73 sq. meters), this would amount to about 1300 to 1600 Cal. daily. As indicated above, deviations from the average normal may be expressed for clinical purposes in terms of percentage increase or decrease. Inasmuch as the BMR falls between ± 10 per cent of the mean in almost 90 per cent of normal subjects, plus 10 to minus 10 are usually regarded as acceptable normal limits, although certain normal subjects yield values beyond this range (to ± 15 per cent).

Table 36. Recommended Daily Caloric Requirements

| | CALORIES PER DAY | |
	MALE	FEMALE
Adults*		
Sedentary	2400	2000
Moderate activity	3000	2400
Strenuous activity	4500	3000
Pregnancy (latter half)		2400
Lactation		3000
Children		
16–20 years	3800	2400
13–15 years	3200	2600
10–12 years	2500	2500
7–9 years	2000	2000
4–6 years	1600	1600
1–3 years	1200	1200
Under 1 year	110/kg.	110/kg.

* Men 70 kg., women 56 kg.

During sleep the BMR falls by about 10 per cent. It is below normal in undernourished individuals (caloric restriction) and tends to be lower in hot than in cold climates. Acclimatization to a cold environment apparently involves an increase in thyroid activity, which is responsible for this change in oxygen consumption. Reported race variations may be dependent largely on differences in nutrition and climate. The BMR increases about 13 per cent for each 1° C. rise in body temperature (7.2 per cent per 1° F.), except in the presence of severe undernutrition, e.g., in tuberculosis.

Approximately 40 per cent of the basal oxygen consumption (heat production; oxidative metabolism) is due to the action of the thyroid hormone (p. 685), the BMR falling to minus 35–40 in athyroid subjects. In such individuals, administration of 1 mg. of thyroxine results in an increase in BMR of about 2.8 per cent. Abnormal increase in thyroid function (hyperthyroidism) is accompanied by an increase in BMR, roughly in proportion to the degree of hyperactivity. Consequently, determination of the BMR is of great value in the diagnosis of hypo- and hyperthyroidism, this being its chief clinical application.

Increased values are obtained during pregnancy and lactation, and in certain disease states (e.g., hyperfunction of adrenals or anterior pituitary). A decrease occurs in pathological conditions other than hypothyroidism (e.g., adrenal and anterior pituitary hypofunction, malnutrition, shock).

OTHER FACTORS. In interpreting BMR values, other factors must be considered that produce a state which is not exactly "basal." Anxiety, apprehension, fear, and pain or other discomfort cause an increase in metabolism. A number of drugs also produce an increase, including epinephrine, dinitrophenol, benzedrine, caffeine, and nicotine (smoking). The usual sedatives lower the metabolic rate of normal subjects only slightly, even in hypnotic doses.

SPECIFIC DYNAMIC ACTION (SDA) OF FOODS. Ingestion of food by subjects in an otherwise "basal" state results in an increase in heat production. This phenomenon is referred to as the specific dynamic action (SDA), or calorigenic action of foods. The extent of this increase above the basal level depends on the nature and quantity of the food. It is greatest for protein, less for carbohydrate, and least for fat. It is usually stated that ingestion of protein (25 grams) equivalent to 100 Cal. gives rise to 130 Cal., and that ingestion of equicaloric amounts of carbohydrate and of fat gives rise to 106 and 104 Cal., respectively. The increments must be derived from body tissue sources and is "waste heat," not available for work.

The SDA of foodstuffs, therefore, is an expression of the "cost" of their metabolism, and adequate provision must be made to meet this expenditure if energy equilibrium is to be maintained. The values indicated above are of academic rather than practical importance, inasmuch as these foodstuffs administered together do not exert their SDA in an additive manner, the observed values being invariably lower than the calculated values. In calculating the dietary caloric requirement (mixed diet), it is recommended that the SDA be provided for as follows: 5–6 per cent of the total food calories should be added for a maintenance diet and 6–8 per cent for a liberal diet. More should be added (about 15 per cent) if the diet is very high in protein. On this basis, a subject with a BMR of 1600 Cal./day must be given an average mixed diet providing at least 1680–1696 Cal. in order to preserve caloric equilibrium.

The nature of the specific dynamic action of foods is not clear. It is not a reflection of the energy expended in digestive and absorptive processes, since it manifests itself after intravenous injection of amino acids. Amino acids vary in the magnitude of their SDA, which is apparently related to the metabolism of the non-nitrogenous moiety. For example, oxidative deamination, with transformation to urea, is accompanied by a larger heat increment than transamination. Phenylalanine, glycine, and alanine exert a particularly marked effect in this connection. There is evidence also that the increment is greater during the process of lipogenesis from glucose than during its oxidation to CO_2 and H_2O.

TOTAL METABOLISM (CALORIC REQUIREMENT). If a normal subject is to remain in energy (caloric) equilibrium, the daily diet must provide at least as much energy as is expended each day. The daily expenditure may be classified in the following categories: (1) basal metabolism (BMR), which is quite constant for any given individual, and is influenced, as indicated elsewhere (p. 339), by age (growth), sex, body size, environmental temperature (and barometric pressure), and such physiological states as pregnancy and lactation; (2) specific dynamic action of food; (3) muscular activity, the most important variable under normal conditions.

Table 37. Approximate Increments in Hourly Caloric Requirement (above Basal) for Different Occupations

OCCUPATION OR ACTIVITY	INCREASED REQUIREMENT CAL./HOUR
Sitting quietly	35
Reading aloud	40
Standing quietly	40
Tailor	70
Typing	75
Housework	110
Painter	145
Carpenter	150
Walking (moderate)	235
Sawing wood	380
Walking (fast)	550
Walking up stairs	1000

Extremely strenuous exercise may increase the energy expenditure more than ten-fold above the "basal" level (Table 37), or, for very brief periods (swimming race), as much as one hundred-fold. In the case of a painter (1.7 sq. meters body surface) the daily caloric requirement might be calculated as follows:

8 hours sleep, at 65 Cal./hour	=	520 Cal.
8 hours work, at 210 Cal./hour	=	1680 Cal.
2 hours light exercise, at 170 Cal./hour	=	340 Cal.
6 hours sitting quietly, at 100 Cal./hour	=	600 Cal.
		3140 Cal.
Specific dynamic action (6 per cent)	=	188 Cal.
Daily caloric requirement	=	3328 Cal.

In Table 37 are indicated the recommendations of the Food and Nutrition Board of the National Research Council with regard to the average caloric requirements at various levels of activity.

BIBLIOGRAPHY

Annual Review of Physiology.

DuBois, E. F.: Basal Metabolism in Health and Disease, ed. 3, Philadelphia, Lea & Febiger, 1936.

Keys, A.: Energy requirements of adults. In Handbook of Nutrition, American Medical Association, Philadelphia, Blakiston Company, 1951, p. 259.

Keys, A.: Undernutrition. In Diseases of Metabolism, ed. 3, edited by G. G. Duncan, Philadelphia, W. B. Saunders Company, 1952, p. 573.

Lusk, G.: Science of Nutrition, ed. 4, Philadelphia, W. B. Saunders Company, 1928.

14

METHODS OF INVESTIGATING
INTERMEDIARY METABOLISM

Intermediary metabolism, in a broad sense, refers to the chemical events which take place between the ingestion of a foodstuff and the excretion of its metabolic end-products. In certain cases the processes of digestion and absorption are excluded from the definition of intermediary metabolism, presumably on the grounds that the gastrointestinal tract is continuous with the outer surface of the body, so that foodstuffs are not within the body until they have entered the blood stream or the lymphatics.

The problems for investigation in intermediary metabolism are pre-

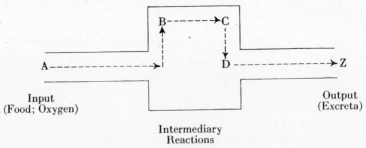

Fig. 70. Intermediary metabolism

sented in Figure 70. A foodstuff, "A," is shown entering the body, and a waste product, "Z," is excreted. One problem which immediately presents itself concerns the identity of intermediary metabolites, since the breakdown of any organic foodstuff to waste products is a stepwise process. Assuming the existence of these intermediates, a second problem is the mechanism of conversion of one compound into the next in the metabolic sequence. Also, from the quantitative stand-

344

point, the kinetics of the over-all conversion of the foodstuff to the waste product, as well as of the intervening steps, is of interest. A final problem concerns the influence of regulatory factors (e.g., hormones) on the particular series of reactions under investigation.

GENERAL METHODS

IN VIVO. The two major subdivisions of methods for investigating intermediary metabolism are known as "in vivo" and "in vitro," meaning in the living organism and in the glass vessel, respectively. One of the oldest of the in vivo methods makes use of the normal animal and "normal" foodstuffs, and depends upon the fact that the feeding or injection of a chemical compound is frequently followed by a demonstrable increase in one or more metabolites of that compound in the excreta or tissues. Suspected intermediates in the metabolic sequence can then be tested to ascertain whether they produce the same results. Often rather massive doses of the precursors are administered, in the hope that accumulation of an intermediate may occur as a result of a slow step in the series of reactions.

Although methods of this sort produced many of the data accumulated in the early years of biochemistry, it soon became evident that these procedures were of limited use and that the data were not always susceptible to unambiguous interpretation. Many foodstuffs, for example, are very smoothly metabolized to such undistinguished end-products as CO_2 and H_2O, and the difficulty in inducing accumulation of intermediates is matched by the absence of an identifiable excretory product. Furthermore, the mere fact that administration of compound A results in increased amounts of compound Z in the tissues or excreta does not prove that a direct conversion has occurred; the "precursor" may be stimulating a reaction in which some other compound produces Z. Objections of this type made it evident that "labeled" compounds were required. These substances would result in identifiable end-products or intermediates, and simultaneously would prove the direct conversion of one compound into another. In the days before the advent of isotopes the labeling was purely chemical; fatty acids, for example, were "tagged" with terminal benzene rings or were halogenated at double bonds. Such compounds differed considerably from "normal" metabolites in their physical and chemical properties, so that, despite the fact that interesting data were obtained by their use, the question always remained whether they were being metabolized by normal pathways. In the case of the isotopic labels which are being used currently (p. 349), this question can generally be answered in the affirmative.

The problem of inducing an accumulation of a metabolic intermediate is neatly solved in a few cases by the occurrence of spontaneous abnormalities in human beings or experimental animals. Diabetes mellitus, with its accumulation of glucose and ketone bodies, falls into this category, as does a series of genetic abnormalities known as "inborn errors of metabolism" (p. 255). In all of these abnormalities one or more intermediary metabolites accumulate in the organism to such an extent that they may be easily demonstrated in the tissues or urine. Such accumulations are due to the inhibition, overloading, or actual deficiency of one or more enzymes.

Since many aspects of metabolism are not covered by abnormalities occurring as such in nature, the biochemist creates desired pathological states in experimental animals. The administration of certain enzyme inhibitors, for example, can cause the accumulation of compounds normally metabolized by the enzymes being inhibited. Surgical removal of an organ such as the liver is sometimes resorted to in order to demonstrate the participation of that organ in the metabolism of a given compound. Excision of an endocrine gland often yields information regarding the hormonal control of metabolic processes, as does the converse procedure of overdosage with the hormone itself.

Although restricted at present to certain lower forms of life, the technic of inducing genetic variants by irradiation, chemicals, and other means places at the disposal of the investigator mutant strains of organisms, many of which suffer from metabolic blockages similar to those which occur naturally in the "inborn errors of metabolism."

Many otherwise hidden metabolic relationships are exposed by the imposition of dietary deficiencies. For example, the omission of a certain substance from the diet may result in the retardation of a particular metabolic reaction, indicating that the missing factor plays some essential role therein. A more sophisticated approach at the present time involves the inclusion, in a complete diet, of a metabolic antagonist (p. 635) of the compound in question.

IN VITRO. It is difficult, and in certain cases impossible, to probe into the finer details of intermediary metabolism in so complex and highly integrated a system as the complete animal. The biochemist has consequently fragmented the organism, working his way down into systems of decreasing complexity, from a single organ to a single enzyme. Each step in the process of simplification, although it facilitates the investigation of basic mechanisms, nevertheless removes the system one step farther from the intact organism. It is always possible in these cases, therefore, that the investigator may find himself pursuing an artifact. By and large, however, the results of in vitro investigations have fitted in quite well with the known metabolic behavior of the intact organism.

The oldest of the in vitro technics is the perfusion of organs. The organ in question has pumped through it blood, or, more commonly, an artificial salt mixture, to which has been added the compound under investigation. After an appropriate length of time the perfusion fluid is examined for products of the metabolism of the original compound. In this way the metabolism of amino acids, for example, can be examined in the isolated liver, without interference by the kidneys or other tissues.

Tissue culture is an *in vitro* method of quite recent vintage. In this technic, explants of animal tissues are grown under aseptic conditions in nutrient media. Although it is not as yet possible to obtain growth of these tissues in completely synthetic media, it is probably only a matter of time until this goal will be realized. It will then be possible to study the individual nutritional requirements of isolated tissues, which, after all, are the component parts of the over-all nutritional requirements of the organism.

Perhaps the greatest technical advance in the field of *in vitro* biochemistry was the adaptation by Otto Warburg of certain types of existing manometric apparatus to the measurement of the gas exchanges of tissue slices. Slices of tissue, cut thin enough to allow adequate diffusion of oxygen (from the gas phase) into the interior of the slice, are shaken in a medium containing the required buffers and substrates. Alkali in a center well of the flask absorbs any metabolic CO_2 that is produced, so that the only gas exchange remaining is the utilization of O_2 by the tissue. This is measured by the fall in pressure observed in a manometer attached to the flask. At the end of the experiment changes in the concentrations of substances in the medium or the slices can be determined and correlated with the uptake of oxygen.

With the aid of the Warburg technic it is possible to investigate the metabolism of many foodstuffs and intermediates in tissues which, although removed from their native environments in the body, nevertheless seem to maintain their normal metabolic patterns for periods of an hour or more. Much pioneer work on the finer details of intermediary metabolism has been and is being conducted with tissue slices. However, the very fact that cellular integrity is maintained in the slices has necessitated the adoption of even simpler systems. For example, the accumulation of intermediates is frequently difficult to observe in the intact slice. Moreover, the cell walls impose barriers to the entrance into the cell of many substrates, particularly of the ionized type. Finally, unless the animal has previously been depleted in some way, the slices will have a full complement of natural substrates and cofactors, rendering difficult the observation of the effect of the addition of such supplements to the Warburg vessels.

The first type of simpler system to be used was the mince or "brei," made by grinding the tissue with sand or in a relatively crude mechanical grinder. The resulting preparation was heterogeneous, being composed of many intact cells, cellular debris (membranes, walls, etc.), nuclei and other intracellular particles, as well as the soluble part of the cytoplasm. Minces of this type were used in place of slices in the standard Warburg technic.

In order to attain a more definite state of organization (or disorganization!), cell-free homogenates are used at the present time. These preparations can be made with a mechanical "blendor," or more satisfactorily in a motor-driven mortar and pestle device in which the tissue (in suitable buffer) is subjected to considerable shearing force while passing between the stationary and rotating components. Such homogenates consist of nuclei, mitochondria, microsomes, and the soluble phase of the cytoplasm, together with certain unavoidable amounts of debris. The virtual absence of intact cells solves, on one level at least, the problem of permeability. Dilution of the tissue, either during or after homogenization, makes feasible the demonstration of the effects of added substrates and cofactors, since endogenous materials are then present in low concentrations.

A further refinement makes use of differential centrifugation to separate the individual particulate fractions of the homogenate (p. 254). By the judicious use of these fractions, singly, combined, and with added cofactors, it has been possible to theorize, at least, concerning the probable intracellular localization of certain metabolic processes.

Enzymes occurring in the soluble phase of the cytoplasm can be fractionated by the standard procedures of protein chemistry (pp. 59–72) to yield, in many cases, preparations containing a single enzyme. In favorable instances the enzyme can be obtained in a crystalline state. The availability of purified enzymes makes possible the detailed physicochemical investigation of the mechanism, kinetics, and equilibrium of a unit metabolic process.

The enzymes which reside in the particulate matter of the cell offer considerable resistance to extraction and purification, owing partly to the organized nature of the particles and partly to the lability of many of the enzyme systems involved. Nevertheless, some success has been reported recently in the liberation of certain enzymes from the mitochondria.

Enzymes of a rather stalwart nature can withstand the action of organic solvents, particularly at low temperatures (p. 70). Simultaneous dehydration and delipidation of tissues with acetone in the cold results in so-called "acetone powders." Many of these preparations are stable on storage, and can be extracted with buffers to yield active enzyme mixtures which can be fractionated. Owing to the destruction of particulate organization by the acetone, it is probable that extracts of acetone powders contain enzymes in addition to those originally found in the soluble phase of the cytoplasm.

MICROORGANISMS. Owing to the essential unity of life, many metabolic processes are widely distributed among living organisms. Microorganisms have many advantages as experimental material, and not a few of the metabolic pathways known to occur in mammalian tissues were originally discovered in bacteria, fungi, and yeasts. Glycolysis in muscle and alcoholic fermentation in yeast, for example, correspond closely up to the terminal stages, a fact which was of considerable assistance in the development of certain aspects of mammalian biochemistry (p. 388).

ISOTOPE METHODS

INTRODUCTION. The widespread use of isotopes in modern investigations of intermediary metabolism justifies separate treatment of this subject. For the sake of brevity, no mention will be made of the use of isotopes in strictly physiological investigations, or of their medical applications in diagnosis and treatment.

Isotopes may be defined as atoms having the same atomic number but different atomic weights. In other words, isotopes are varieties or sub-species of the same chemical element, and occupy the same position in the periodic table, but have somewhat different physical properties. The atomic constitution of three isotopes of hydrogen is illustrated below. Superscripts are used to indicate atomic weights.

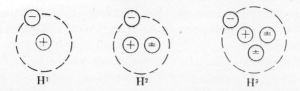

H^1, or ordinary hydrogen, consists of a nucleus containing a proton (charge: $+1$, mass: 1), around which revolves an electron (charge: -1, mass: 1/1850). H^2, "heavy hydrogen," also known as deuterium, contains an additional nuclear particle, a neutron (charge: 0, mass: 1). Tritium, or H^3, contains two neutrons. Since the atomic number (which determines the chemical character of the element) is given by the net nuclear charge, these three atoms are evidently varieties of the same element. Deuterium has twice the weight of ordinary hydrogen, whereas tritium has three times the weight, and is radioactive in addition.

There are two general classes of isotopes. The so-called "stable" isotopes, which have no distinguishing characteristics other than their mass, are concentrated for use from natural sources by means of fractionation procedures. Radioactive isotopes not only differ in mass from their stable brothers, but are also characterized by the possession of unstable nuclei. This causes them to decompose spontaneously, emitting radiation which may be particulate or in the form of waves (e.g., electrons and gamma radiation). Radioactive isotopes occur in traces in nature, but are prepared for experimental use by bombardment in the cyclotron or the atomic pile.

The abundance of stable isotopes in nature is expressed in "atoms %," meaning the number of atoms of the particular isotope present per hundred atoms of all isotopes of the element in question. In experimental materials the concentration of a stable isotope is frequently given in terms of "atoms % excess," i.e., the excess of the concentration of the isotope in question, in units of atoms %, over its concentration in nature or in a standard sample.

Concentrations of radioactive isotopes are conveniently expressed in terms of intensities of radiation emitted (p. 353). The applicability of a given radioisotope to biological problems depends in part on the rate at which it decomposes, since this determines whether a measurable amount of isotope will be present at the end of the experiment. The instability of these isotopes is commonly expressed as their "half-life," which is the time required for the concentration of isotope in any given sample to decrease to half its initial value.

Table 38 lists certain of the more commonly used isotopes and indicates their major fields of application in biochemistry. The abundance in nature is given for the stable isotopes; half-lives are indicated in the case of the radioactive elements. More detailed examples of the employment of the various isotopes will be found in the chapters on intermediary metabolism.

The use of isotopically labeled compounds has several advantages in certain types of investigations. For one thing, such labeling enables one to distinguish newly administered molecules or atoms from those already in the body. By this means it is possible to follow the uptake of an element or compound in various tissues or tissue fractions, and, once labeled, the course of loss of the label can also be traced. The conversion of one compound into another can be proved by isotopic labeling, even in those cases in which no net increase occurs in the concentration of the product (it may even decrease!). The molecular mechanism of such conversions can also be investigated, which is difficult or impossible with the older technics. Finally, certain special isotopic procedures permit the demonstration of the existence of metabolic intermediates which are so labile that they cannot be isolated by the usual technics.

TECHNICS. (*a*) PREPARATION OF LABELED MATERIAL. In the case of investigations in inorganic metabolism, no complicated procedures are required. Labeled salts are used as purchased or after simple exchange reactions. Many labeled organic compounds are available commercially, but for special purposes a complicated synthesis may be required. A simple example of a procedure for labeling a fatty acid in the carboxyl group involves the Grignard reaction and labeled CO_2:

$$R—CH_2—Mg—Br \xrightarrow[\text{then acidify.}]{C^{14}O_2,} R—CH_2—C^{14}OOH.$$

Table 38. Biochemically Useful Isotopes

ISOTOPE	ABUNDANCE IN NATURE (ATOMS %)	HALF-LIFE	MAJOR FIELDS OF APPLICATION
H^2	0.02		Body water, auxiliary label to trace C chains
H^3		12.1 yrs.	Body water, auxiliary label to trace C chains
C^{13}	1.1		Metabolism of all classes of organic compounds
C^{14}		5568 yrs.	Metabolism of all classes of organic compounds
N^{15}	0.38		Metabolism of protein, nucleic acids, phospholipids
O^{18}	0.20		Mechanisms of hydrolysis, photosynthesis, biol. oxidation
P^{32}		14.3 days	Transphosphorylation, phospholipids, nucleic acids, carbohydrates, inorganic P metab., calcification
S^{35}		87.1 days	Protein metabolism, sulfate conjugations
Fe^{55}		2.91 yrs.	Iron metab. in general, hemoglobin metab.
Fe^{59}		46.3 days	Iron metab. in general, hemoglobin metab.
I^{131}		8 days	Thyroid hormone synthesis, function, and metab.
Ca^{45}		180 days	Calcification
Na^{24}		14.8 hrs.	Permeability, water partition, electrolyte balance
K^{42}		12.4 hrs.	ditto
Cl^{36}		4.4×10^5 yrs.	ditto
Cl^{38}		37 min.	ditto

(b) INTRODUCTION INTO BIOLOGICAL SYSTEM. The biological system used may range from the intact animal to a purified enzyme, employing essentially the various technics covered earlier under "General Methods." The basic assumption underlying the isotopic method is that the organism (or its enzymes) cannot differentiate a labeled compound from the normal molecule which it usually encounters, so that the metabolic fate of the former is truly representative of that of the latter. There have been few instances in which the validity of this basic assumption has been questioned.

(c) ISOLATION AND DEGRADATION OF METABOLITES. In order to assay the isotope content of a metabolic product, it is advisable (and frequently essential) to isolate it in a pure state. When the metabolite is present in amounts too small to be handled conveniently, it is isolated by the "carrier" technic. In this procedure an appropriate amount of unlabeled metabolite is added to the mixture; the molecules of labeled and unlabeled metabolite mix and are isolated together. Of course, sufficient isotope must be present in the labeled metabolite to permit the degree of dilution caused by the carrier, otherwise there would not be enough left to assay in the compound as isolated.

The purification of isolated metabolites is sometimes difficult, for mere chemical purity is not synonymous with isotopic purity. Removal of isotopic contaminants is frequently effected by passing the isolated compound through one or more chemical derivatives, in addition to physical procedures such as chromatography. If the identity of the possible contaminants is known (and one such is always the starting material used in the experiment), a "washing out" technic is used. This consists of adding to the isolated metabolite an excess of an unlabeled specimen of the suspected contaminant, then removing it and re-isolating the metabolite by standard procedures. Any isotope in the isolated metabolite due to the suspected contaminant will then be diluted to a negligible concentration.

In certain cases the isolated metabolite can be used as such in the isotopic assay. More frequently it is necessary to convert the isotope to some convenient form for purposes of assay, viz., CO_2 or $BaCO_3$ for carbon, N_2 for nitrogen, $BaSO_4$ for sulfur, H_2O for hydrogen, etc.

When questions of the molecular mechanism of metabolic reactions arise, it is necessary to determine the isotope concentration in individual parts of the metabolite molecule. This calls for special procedures of degradation, specific enough so that it is certain, for example, that the CO_2 evolved in a given degradation reaction comes from a carboxyl group and no other part of the molecule in question.

(d) METHODS OF ASSAY. The assay of stable isotopes is based upon the difference in atomic weight between the normal element and the isotope used. In the case of deuterium (H^2), the density of D_2O is so much greater than that of H_2O that a method of assay has been developed which measures this density in a "falling drop" apparatus. This involves determination of the rate of descent of a drop of the sample "water" through a column of organic solvents of the appropriate density.

Most assays of stable isotopes are performed in the mass spectrometer. The sample, in a gaseous state (CO_2, N_2, low molecular weight hydrocarbons), is ionized by an electron beam into electrons and heavy positive ions. Regulation of the electrical or magnetic field permits the collection of ions of any desired mass at a collecting plate. The ion current resulting from this process is a measure of the quantity of ion being collected.

Radioactive isotopes are generally determined by means of the Geiger-Müller counter. Particles or rays from the decay of the isotope enter an ionization chamber, interacting with the gas contained therein to form ions which cause a discharge of current between a highly positive central wire and a grounded cathode plate. The current from this discharge is amplified and registered automatically in a counting device, which registers the total number of counts for any desired period of time. Isotope concentrations can then be expressed as counts per unit time per unit weight of sample.

For certain purposes it is desirable to locate a radioactive isotope (in a qualitative way, at least) within a tissue or cell. In this case two adjacent sections of the tissue are used. One is stained and mounted by the usual histological methods, whereas the other is left in contact with a photographic plate or film for an appropriate length of time, after which the image is developed. Comparison of the "radioautograph" with the stained section then permits the determination of areas of high isotope concentration.

BIBLIOGRAPHY

General Metabolic Methods

Baldwin, E.: Dynamic Aspects of Biochemistry, London, Cambridge University Press, 1952, Chapter 8.
Dixon, M.: Manometric Methods, London, Cambridge University Press, 1951.
Holmes, E.: The Metabolism of Living Tissues, London, Cambridge University Press, 1937, Chapter 3.
Umbreit, W. W., Burris, R. H. and Stauffer, J. F.: Manometric Techniques and Tissue Metabolism, Minneapolis, Burgess Publishing Company, 1949.
White, A.: Protein metabolism. In Diseases of Metabolism, ed. 3, edited by G. G. Duncan, Philadelphia, W. B. Saunders Company, 1952, pp. 107–113.

Isotope Methods

Textbook:
Kamen, M. D.: Radioactive Tracers in Biology, New York, Academic Press, Inc., 1951.

Advanced Reference Books:
Calvin, M., Heidelberger, C., Reid, J. C., Tolbert, B. M. and Yankwich, P. F.: Isotopic Carbon, John Wiley & Sons, Inc., 1949.
Hevesy, G.: Radioactive Indicators, New York, Interscience Publishers, Inc., 1948.
Siri, W. E.: Isotopic Tracers and Nuclear Radiations, New York, McGraw-Hill Book Company, Inc., 1949.

Symposia and Reviews:
A Symposium on the Use of Isotopes in Biology and Medicine, Madison, University of Wisconsin Press, 1948.
Amino Acids and Proteins, Cold Spring Harbor Symp. Quant. Biol., 13, (1949).
Isotopes in Biochemistry (Ciba Symposium), New York, Blakiston Company, 1951.
Lawrence, J. H. and Hamilton, J. G., (eds.): Advances in Biological and Medical Physics, 1: 1948 and 2: 1951.

15

BIOLOGICAL OXIDATIONS

INTRODUCTION

DEFINITION AND NOMENCLATURE. The term "oxidation" has meant a number of things during the history of chemistry, such as the incorporation of oxygen into a compound, the positive increase of valence of an atom or ion, and the removal of hydrogen from an organic compound. What all of these processes have in common is the removal of electrons from the substances being oxidized, although this basic phenomenon is obscured by other factors in some cases.

$$Fe^{++} \rightarrow Fe^{+++} + e^-$$

$$
\begin{array}{l}
COOH \\
| \\
CH_2 \\
| \\
CH_2 \\
| \\
COOH
\end{array}
\longrightarrow
\begin{array}{l}
COOH \\
| \\
CH \\
\| \\
CH \\
| \\
COOH
\end{array}
+ 2H \ (H = H^+ + e^-)
$$

$$Cu + O \rightarrow [Cu^{++}O^=]$$

$$2H\cdot + \overset{\circ\circ}{\underset{\circ\circ}{O}}{\overset{\circ\circ}{_\circ}} \rightarrow H \overset{\circ\circ}{\underset{\circ\circ}{\overset{\circ}{O}}} H$$

Referring to the above reactions, the oxidation of ferrous to ferric ion is a clear-cut example of the removal of electrons, achieved by any one of various means which will be discussed later. In the dehydrogenation of succinic to fumaric acid, the hydrogen atom may be taken as equivalent to a hydrogen ion plus an electron, both being removed from the succinic acid simultaneously. The combination of copper with oxygen to form cupric oxide would seem to involve no removal of electrons. However, such a compound, although usually written CuO, is actually an ionic crystal resulting from a transfer of electrons from the copper to the oxygen. Combinations with oxygen to form covalent compounds are somewhat more difficult to fit into the general scheme. In the case of the formation of water from hydrogen and oxygen, the electron which originally was possessed solely by the hydrogen is shared between the hydrogen and the oxygen in the water molecule. This removal of a partial share of an electron from the hydrogen may be considered an oxidation. From the standpoint of the oxygen, the acquisition of extra electrons brought in by the hydrogen atoms is certainly a reduction. For our purposes, oxidation will be defined as the removal of, and reduction the addition of electrons.

Inasmuch as electrons are not stable in the free state, their removal from one substance implies their acceptance by another. In other words, every oxidation is accompanied by a reduction. The proper name for all such reactions is then "oxidation-reduction," frequently abbreviated to "redox." The electron donor is called the "reductant," the acceptor the "oxidant."

Although some biological redox reactions proceed by the transfer of single electrons, e.g., valence changes undergone by copper or iron, in most cases pairs of electrons or hydrogen atoms are involved. There is evidence that the latter reactions occur stepwise, with the formation of radicals as intermediates. For purposes of simplification, all two-electron transfers will be considered unitary reactions in the following discussions.

SIGNIFICANCE OF BIOLOGICAL OXIDATIONS. The importance of redox reactions in biochemistry resides in the fact that they comprise practically all of the known energy-yielding reactions which living organisms have at their disposal. As compared to all other reactions which can occur in a physiological environment (hydrolysis, simple decarboxylation, aldol condensation, etc.), redox reactions by and large furnish the most energy per mol of compound. Perhaps this is why organisms at all levels of complexity, from the lowly bacterium oxidizing elementary sulfur to the gourmet with his varied intake of combustible foodstuffs, have retained redox reactions as sources of energy during the long evolutionary struggle.

FUNDAMENTAL REACTION OF BIOLOGICAL OXIDATIONS. As indicated elsewhere (p. 372), the over-all reaction of photosynthesis in green plants involves the splitting of water into hydrogen and oxygen, utilization of the hydrogen to reduce carbon dioxide to the level of carbohydrate, and liberation of the oxygen. Biological oxidation, essentially, reverses this process. Its main task is the achievement of a union between hydrogen atoms (found in substrates such as carbohydrates) and gaseous oxygen to form water, carbon dioxide being liberated in the process.

$$6CO_2 + 6H_2O \xrightarrow[\text{Biological oxidation}]{\text{Photosynthesis}} C_6H_{12}O_6 + 6O_2$$

Earlier views of biological oxidation assumed that the respiratory CO_2 was formed by a direct combination of respiratory oxygen with the carbon of the substrate, while the water resulting from oxidations was abstracted from the hydrogen and oxygen atoms contained in the substrate (taking carbohydrate as the example). Actually, as shown by experiments with isotopic oxygen and by other means, the situation is quite the opposite. The inspired oxygen is used primarily to form water with the hydrogen atoms of the substrates, and the oxygen contained in the CO_2 is largely derived from the substrate itself, or from the body water (by an indirect route).

An example of the types of reactions which form the major sources of water and CO_2 in the Krebs cycle (fig. 73, p. 398) is given below.

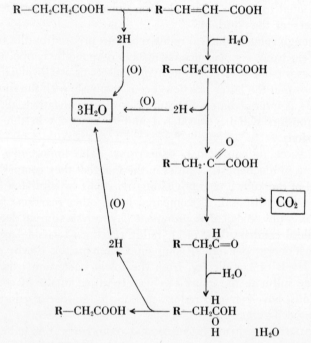

Net reaction: $RCH_2CH_2COOH + 3(O) \rightarrow RCH_2COOH + [3H_2O - 2H_2O] + CO_2$

A pair of hydrogen atoms is removed from an organic acid, forming an α, β-unsaturated acid. This compound is then hydrated to an α-hydroxy acid, from which two hydrogen atoms are taken, producing an α-keto acid. An oxidative decarboxylation then takes place, which may or may not proceed in discrete steps, as shown. At any rate, all pairs of hydrogen atoms are combined with oxygen to form water, and it will be noticed how incidental to this major process is the liberation of CO_2. The remainder of this chapter, then, will concern itself with the mechanisms by which hydrogen atoms (to be regarded as combinations of hydrogen ions and electrons) of substrates unite with oxygen to form water.

REDOX POTENTIAL

ELECTRON AFFINITY. In order to present a coherent picture of biological oxidations, it is necessary to digress briefly and discuss, in a qualitative way only, the general physical concepts involved in electron-transfer systems.

It is a matter of common experience that substances or systems differ in their affinity for electrons. The ordinary dry cell, for instance, sends a current of electricity (a stream of electrons) through an external circuit because the system on one side of the cell ($+$) has a much greater affinity for electrons than the system on the other side ($-$). By setting up standard conditions, it is possible to construct a table of all redox systems in order of electron affinity. The electron affinity can even be given a definite numerical value, called the "redox potential." Although a quantitative treatment of these matters is outside the scope of this book, it will be useful to consider the relative positions of various systems on the redox potential scale.

REDOX POTENTIAL AND ELECTRON TRANSFER. Biochemically speaking, oxygen has the highest redox potential (i.e., electron affinity) of all systems in the living cell, while the lowest values are assigned to the hydrogen atoms attached to the various substrates. Any other substances discussed in this chapter have potentials intermediate between these two extremes.

As might be expected, electrons are transferred from systems of lower redox potential to systems of high potential. A "coupled" redox reaction can thus occur between two systems:

$$\text{Red}_1 \diagup \text{Ox}_2$$
$$\diagdown$$
$$\text{Ox}_1 \diagup \diagdown \text{Red}_2$$

System 2 has a greater redox potential than System 1, hence can accept electrons from it. The reductant of System 1 provides these electrons by changing to its oxidant form, while the oxidant of System 2 accepts the electrons, and in so doing changes to its reductant form.

The movement of electrons up the redox potential scale is an energy-yielding process, the details of which are discussed elsewhere (p. 379). The amount of energy liberated in transferring electrons from one system to another is determined by the difference in redox potential between the two systems.

From the foregoing one might expect that electrons could be transferred directly from substrates to oxygen, for that is certainly the direction of transfer. However, the redox potential gap or span between the two systems seems to be too great. Possibly, if such a large burst of energy were to be liberated all at once, most of it would be wasted, for the reaction in essence would be the direct combination of hydrogen and oxygen, a rather explosive phenomenon. Whatever the reason, the cell transfers its electrons (or hydrogen pairs) stepwise to oxygen, and the energy is liberated in correspondingly small packets (p. 378). In order to effect this stepwise process the cell makes use of electron "carrier" systems, intermediate in redox potential between substrates and oxygen. Electrons (or hydrogen pairs) are passed along a veritable "bucket brigade" of increasing potential. The links in this chain are discussed in the next section.

REDOX CHAINS IN NATURE

TYPES OF OXIDATIVE ENZYME SYSTEMS. In the simplest type of oxidative system only one electron carrier is interposed between the substrate and oxygen. Two subdivisions of this sort of system exists, the oxidases and the aerobic dehydrogenases. These differ essentially in that, in oxidases the electron carrier couples to oxygen and no other substance, whereas the aerobic dehydrogenases can pass electrons to certain reducible dyestuffs (e.g., methylene blue) as well as to oxygen. Aerobic dehydrogenases form hydrogen peroxide as their end-product, whereas almost all oxidases form water. The third main group of oxidative enzymes comprises the anaerobic dehydrogenases, which transfer electrons over a system of several carriers to oxygen, forming water. This group can also use dyestuffs as the final electron acceptors instead of oxygen. The peroxidases and catalase form a fourth division of oxidative enzymes with such special properties that they will be discussed separately.

The relationships between the first three groups of enzymes may be illustrated as shown on page 359.

The oxidase enzyme is shown catalyzing the transfer of a pair of hydrogen atoms (hydrogen ions plus electrons) from a substrate to a carrier, which in turn passes them on to oxygen. The oxidized form of the carrier is thus regenerated, enabling it to operate in a cyclical manner. As found in nature, the carrier is a coenzyme or a prosthetic group which may be attached to the oxidase protein.

The aerobic dehydrogenase system is constructed similarly, and again the carrier is a coenzyme or a prosthetic group of the dehydrogenase protein. In this case, however, the transfer of hydrogen to oxygen usually (but not always) results in the formation of hydrogen peroxide. Furthermore, the electron carrier can be artificially coupled to a reducible dyestuff, which is not possible in the case of the true oxidases.

The anaerobic dehydrogenase system is characterized by the possession of multiple carriers, and by the formation of water as the final product of the reaction with oxygen. Again, a reducible dyestuff can be made to act as a final electron acceptor. In the case of certain anaerobic dehydrogenases the first carrier shown is a coenzyme or prosthetic group belonging to the dehydrogenase protein, but in other cases it may be an independent protein bearing its own reducible prosthetic group. All secondary or tertiary carriers beyond this are of the latter type.

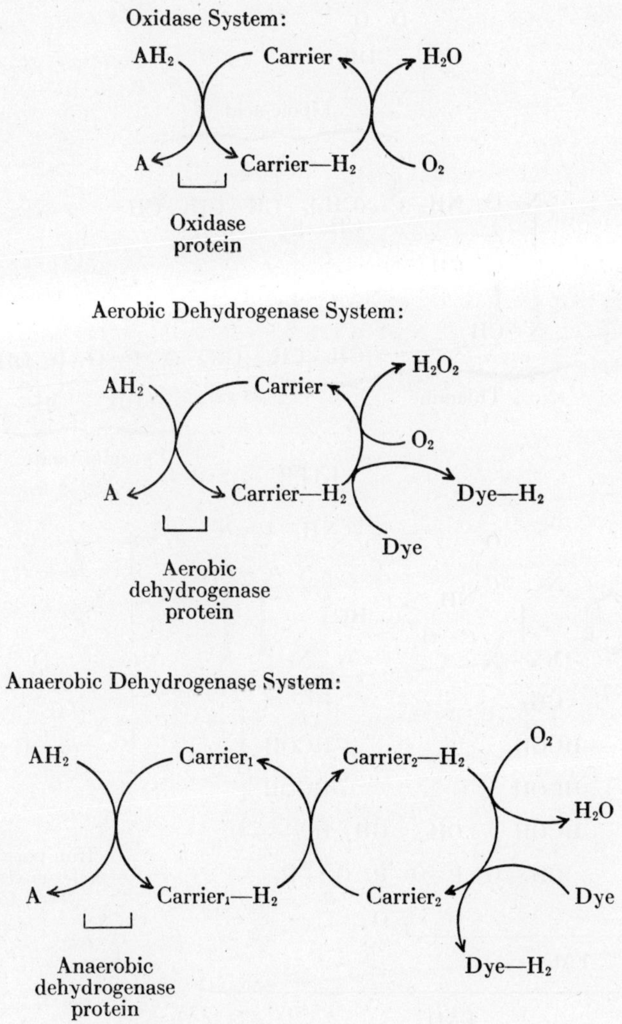

Oxidase System:

AH_2 — Carrier — H_2O

A — Carrier—H_2 — O_2

Oxidase
protein

Aerobic Dehydrogenase System:

AH_2 — Carrier — H_2O_2

— O_2

A — Carrier—H_2 — Dye—H_2

Dye

Aerobic
dehydrogenase
protein

Anaerobic Dehydrogenase System:

AH_2 — Carrier$_1$ — Carrier$_2$—H_2 — O_2

— H_2O

A — Carrier$_1$—H_2 — Carrier$_2$ — Dye

Dye—H_2

Anaerobic
dehydrogenase
protein

Three groups of oxidative enzymes

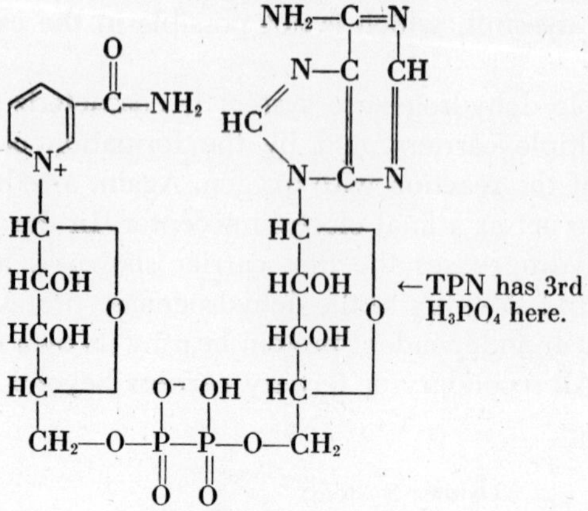

←TPN has 3rd
H_3PO_4 here.

DPN

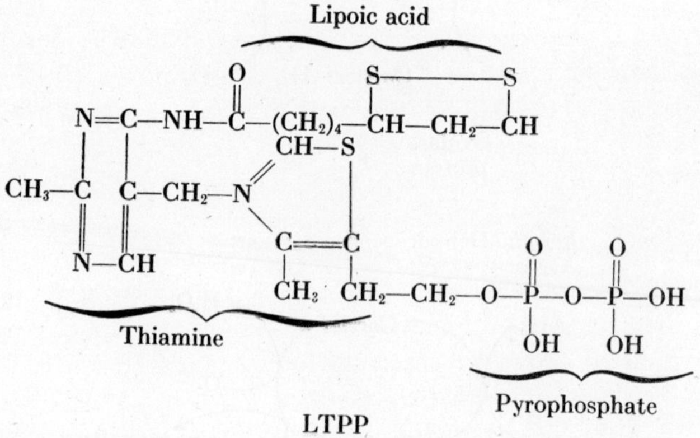

Lipoic acid

Thiamine

Pyrophosphate

LTPP

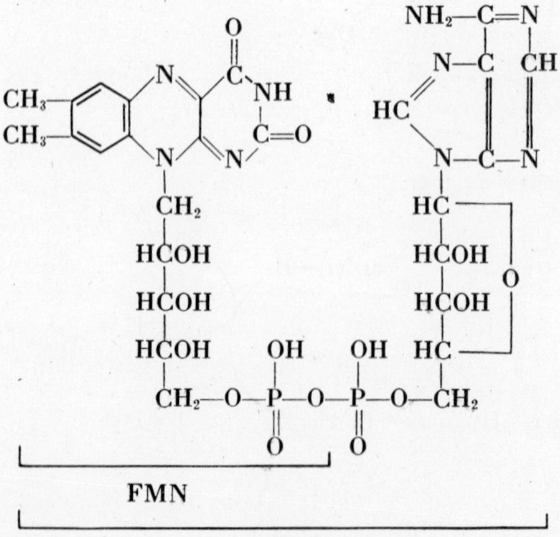

FMN

FAD

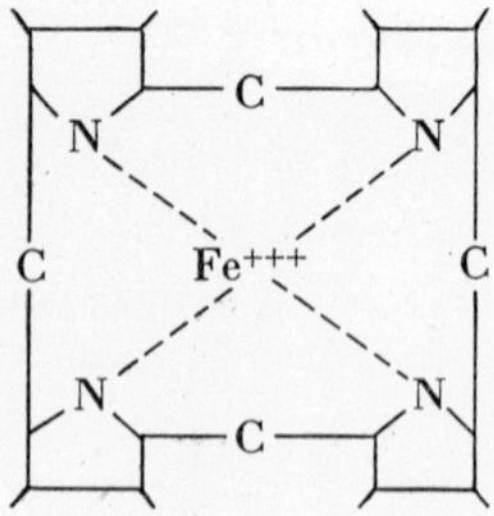

Iron porphyrin
skeleton structure
(ferric form)

COENZMES AND PROSTHETIC GROUPS OF REDOX SYSTEMS. In order to understand how the transfer of electrons or hydrogen atoms from substrate to oxygen is effected, it is necessary to examine the structures of the coenzymes and prosthetic groups involved, since they are the actual carriers. On page 360 are the structural formulas of the most important substances of this group.

The dinucleotide of nicotinamide and adenine, called "diphosphopyridine nucleotide" (DPN), "cozymase," or "coenzyme 1," and the related "triphosphopyridine nucleotide" (TPN) or "coenzyme 2," are both commonly occurring coenzymes for many anaerobic dehydrogenases. Nicotinamide, it should be noted, is one of the B vitamins (p. 182). Riboflavin, another B vitamin (p. 177), forms part of flavin mononucleotide (FMN) and flavin-adenine dinucleotide (FAD) (alloxazine-adenine dinucleotide), which act as coenzymes or prosthetic groups for some of the aerobic dehydrogenases, and also for some of the intermediate carriers which operate in conjunction with the anaerobic dehydrogenases. Although non-oxidative decarboxylations of α-keto acids require thiamine pyrophosphate (TPP) as coenzyme (p. 243), oxidative decarboxylations of certain of these compounds involve a more complex derivative of thiamine, lipothiamide pyrophosphate (LTPP). The lipoic acid moiety (thioctic acid, protogen, pyruvate oxidation factor) of this coenzyme contains a disulfide group capable of participating in redox reactions. The iron-porphyrin skeleton structure will be recognized as occurring in heme (p. 110), the prosthetic group of hemoglobin. Similar prosthetic groups are found in catalase and peroxidase (to be discussed later), in the cytochromes, which are intermediate electron carriers, and in cytochrome oxidase, the most important terminal link in biological oxidations.

The mechanisms of action of the compounds and groups just mentioned are indicated at the top of page 362.

The nicotinamide, lipoic, and flavin compounds reversibly add on pairs of hydrogen atoms in the positions shown. On the other hand, the iron-porphyrin systems act strictly as electron carriers, the mechanism being a reversible change in the valence of the iron. A number of oxidases of the plant world, and a few found in animal tissues, contain copper. It is not known whether the copper is present simply attached to the protein, or fixed in some more complex prosthetic group, although there is no evidence for the latter possibility. In terms of mechanism, it is probable that copper undergoes a valence change as does iron during the transfer of electrons.

OXIDASES. As seen in Table 39, there are few true oxidases in the strict sense of the definition. Plants contain a number of phenol oxidases, all of which are copper-proteins. The only enzyme of this type which is of any great importance in animal metabolism is tyrosinase

$$\text{(nicotinamide structure)} + 2H \longrightarrow \text{(reduced nicotinamide structure, RH)}$$

$$\text{(flavin structure, R)} + 2H \longrightarrow \text{(reduced flavin structure, R)}$$

$$\text{LTPP} \overset{S}{\underset{S}{\diagdown}} + 2H \rightleftharpoons \text{LTPP} \overset{SH}{\underset{SH}{\diagdown}}$$

$$Fe^{+++} + e^- \rightleftharpoons Fe^{++}$$

$$Cu^{++} + e^- \rightleftharpoons Cu^+$$

Table 39. Oxidases and Aerobic Dehydrogenases

ENZYME	COENZYME OR PROSTHETIC GROUP	REACTION
Oxidases		
Tyrosinase	Cu	Tyrosine → dopa → melanin
Uricase	?	Uric acid → allantoin + CO_2 + H_2O_2
Cytochrome oxidase	Fe-porphyrin	Ferrocytochromes → ferricyto-chromes
Aerobic dehydrogenases		
D-Amino acid dehydrogenase	FAD	D-Amino acid → keto acid + NH_3
L-Amino acid dehydrogenase	FMN	L-Amino acid → keto acid + NH_3
Glycine dehydrogenase	FAD	Glycine → glyoxylic acid + NH_3
Xanthine dehydrogenase	FAD + ?	Hypoxanthine → xanthine Xanthine → uric acid Aldehydes → acids
Aldehyde dehydrogenase	FAD + ?	Aldehydes → acids
Acyl-CoA dehydrogenase*	FAD + Cu	Acyl-CoA ⟶ α, β-unsat. acyl-CoA
Monoamine dehydrogenase	?	Amines → aldehydes + NH_3
Diamine dehydrogenase	(FAD ?)	Amines → aldehydes + NH_3

*Recent data indicate that this enzyme is probably not a true aerobic dehydrogenase.

(identical with "dopa oxidase"). Its role in the formation of adrenaline and melanin is discussed elsewhere (p. 554).

Uricase, or uric acid oxidase, is found in those mammals excreting allantoin as the end-product of purine metabolism; it is not present in the tissues of man and the higher apes (p. 569). The electron-carrying group in uricase has not been identified. This enzyme is unusual among oxidases in that it produces hydrogen peroxide instead of water. Some systems of classification place uricase among the aerobic dehydrogenases, where it is considered an unusual dehydrogenase, since it will not reduce dyestuffs.

Cytochrome oxidase contains an iron-porphyrin prosthetic group. The importance of this enzyme in biological oxidations is indicated by the fact that cyanide, which inhibits this oxidase, produces an almost total block in cellular respiration. A group of proteins, the cytochromes, which themselves contain iron-porphyrin prosthetic groups, constitute the substrates for cytochrome oxidase. This relationship is discussed more fully under the anaerobic dehydrogenases.

In conformity with the mechanism for oxidases which was shown above, the carriers of this group of enzymes all react directly with oxygen, uricase by some as yet unknown mechanism, the metalloenzymes by means of valence changes in the metals. Since the metals can act only as carriers of electrons, the hydrogen atoms of the substrates dissociate into hydrogen ions and electrons, the former going into solution, the latter being transferred by the metal to oxygen. The negatively charged oxygen ion (possibly $O^=$, which may have a transient existence while attached to the oxidase prosthetic group) then picks up hydrogen ions from the solution to form H_2O. In order to simplify the situation, this additional complication was omitted previously. It will be considered again in the case of the anaerobic dehydrogenases, since they are all indirectly coupled with a metalloprotein terminal link in the redox chain (cytochrome oxidase).

AEROBIC DEHYDROGENASES. As indicated in the lower part of Table 39, all of the prosthetic groups which have been identified in the aerobic dehydrogenases are flavin nucleotides. Enzymes with such prosthetic groups are called "flavoproteins" or "yellow enzymes" (from the color which the flavin group imparts to the protein). There is some evidence that the xanthine and aldehyde enzymes contain other prosthetic groups in addition to FAD.

Like the oxidases, the enzymes in this group catalyze the direct transfer of substrate electrons (as hydrogen atoms, in this case) via the flavin carriers to oxygen, forming peroxide instead of water, however. Evidently the reduced form of the flavin is spontaneously autoxidizable in air. As dehydrogenases, these enzymes will also reduce dyes in place of oxygen.

The metabolic significance of the D-amino acid dehydrogenase is unknown, since D-amino acids do not occur in animal tissues, in which the enzyme is found in considerable quantities. On the other hand, the L-amino acid dehydrogenase, which might be expected to play a more important metabolic role, is not widely distributed and, moreover, has very low activity. This problem is discussed in more detail elsewhere (p. 509). It is thought at present that glycine dehydrogenase participates in one phase of glycine metabolism.

Xanthine dehydrogenase is quite unusual in that it has two series of substrates. The available evidence indicates that this enzyme oxidizes aldehydes, in addition to its specific action on xanthine and hypoxanthine. Aldehydes are also oxidized by a specific aldehyde dehydrogenase of the aerobic type, and another of the anaerobic type. The acyl-CoA dehydrogenase is important in the metabolism of fatty acids (p. 450).

There are dehydrogenases which can oxidize monoamines, such as adrenaline, and diamines, such as histamine. These reactions may be of importance in "detoxication" (p. 279).

CYTOCHROME-LINKED ANAEROBIC DEHYDROGENASES. Two groups of anaerobic dehydrogenases are indicated in Table 40. The first and smaller group has a shorter redox chain, and is sometimes said to couple "directly" with the cytochromes. Actually, there is evidence for the existence of carriers interposed before the cytochromes in certain cases, but the nature of these substances is not known. An example of a "cytochrome-linked" anaerobic dehydrogenase system is shown below, constructed on the assumption that the first carrier is of the "transhydrogenase" rather than of the "transelectronase" type, meaning that it transfers whole atoms of hydrogen instead of only electrons from the substrate.

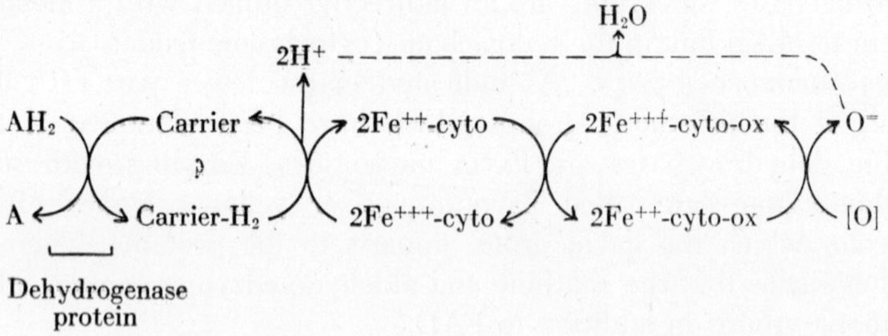

$$H_2O$$

$$2H^+ \;\text{-----------------}\; \uparrow \;\text{---------}$$

$$AH_2 \searrow \nearrow \text{Carrier} \leftarrow \nwarrow \nearrow 2Fe^{++}\text{-cyto} \searrow \nearrow 2Fe^{+++}\text{-cyto-ox} \nwarrow \nearrow O^=$$
$$\qquad\qquad\qquad ?$$
$$A \leftarrow \nearrow \searrow \text{Carrier-}H_2 \nwarrow \searrow 2Fe^{+++}\text{-cyto} \leftarrow \nwarrow \searrow 2Fe^{++}\text{-cyto-ox} \searrow [O]$$

Dehydrogenase
protein

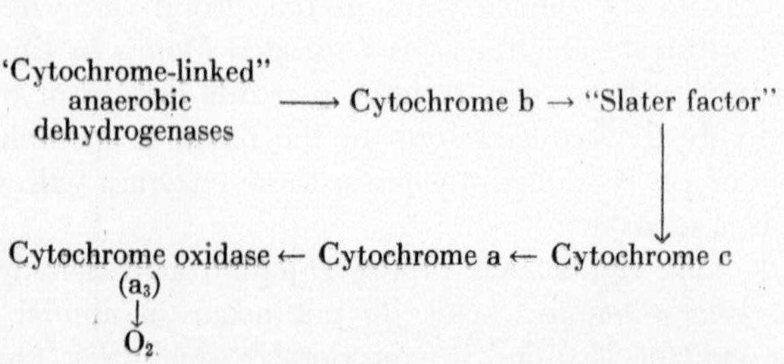

"Cytochrome-linked"
    anaerobic $\longrightarrow$ Cytochrome b $\rightarrow$ "Slater factor"
dehydrogenases

$$\downarrow$$

Cytochrome oxidase ← Cytochrome a ← Cytochrome c
   (a_3)
   $\downarrow$
   O_2

The next group of carriers in this chain, the cytochromes, act as transelectronases, hence any preceding carrier sends its hydrogen ions into solution and its electrons to the cytochromes. As pointed out earlier, the cytochromes are iron-porphyrin proteins. Several different

Table 40. Anaerobic Dehydrogenases

ENZYME	COENZYME, PROSTHETIC GROUP	SECONDARY AND TERTIARY CARRIERS	REACTION
Succinic dehydrogenase	?	Cytochromes, cytochrome oxidase	Succinate ⇌ fumarate
L-α-Glycerophosphate dehydrogenase	?	" " "	Glycerophosphate ⇌ phosphoglyceraldehyde
Choline dehydrogenase	?	" " "	Choline → betaine aldehyde
D-α-Glycerophosphate dehydrogenase	DPN	Flavoproteins, cyto, cyto-ox	Glycerophosphate ⇌ dihydroxyacetone phosphate
Lactic dehydrogenase	DPN (TPN)	"	Lactate ⇌ pyruvate
Malic dehydrogenase	DPN (TPN)	"	Malate ⇌ oxalacetate
β-Hydroxybutyric dehydrogenase	DPN	"	Hydroxybutyrate ⇌ acetoacetate
Alcohol dehydrogenase	DPN	"	Alcohols ⇌ aldehydes
Glucose dehydrogenase	DPN (TPN)	"	Glucose → gluconic acid
L-Glutamic dehydrogenase	DPN, TPN	"	Glutamate ⇌ ketoglutarate + NH_3
Triosephosphate dehydrogenase	DPN + Glutathione	"	Phosphoglyceraldehyde ⇌ diphosphoglyceric acid
Aldehyde dehydrogenase	DPN	"	Aldehydes → acids
β-Hydroxyacyl-CoA dehydrogenase	DPN	"	β-Hydroxyacyl-CoA ⇌ β-ketoacyl-CoA
Glucose-6-phosphate dehydrogenase	TPN	"	Glucose-6-phosphate → gluconic acid-6-phosphate
Isocitric dehydrogenase	TPN	"	Isocitrate ⇌ oxalosuccinate
"Malic enzyme"	TPN	"	Malate ⇌ pyruvate + CO_2
Pyruvic carboxylase ("oxidase")	LTPP + CoA + DPN	"	Pyruvate → "acetate" + CO_2
Ketoglutaric carboxylase ("oxidase")	LTPP + CoA + DPN	"	Ketoglutarate → succinate + CO_2

proteins of this type are found in the cell, most of them rather firmly attached to the mitochondria. Of the three main types (a, b, and c) only cytochrome c has been obtained in true solution, the others having been studied by means of their characteristic spectra. The cytochromes accept pairs of electrons (two mols of cytochromes required) from the primary carrier, converting the cytochromes into their ferrous forms. Regeneration of the ferric forms is accomplished by electron transfer to cytochrome oxidase.

In the case of these shorter redox chains (e.g., succinic dehydrogenase), it is believed that electrons are passed from the substrate (or a primary carrier) to cytochrome b, which transfers them to the "Slater factor" (probably also a hemoprotein, p. 124), thence to cytochrome c and cytochrome a, successively. Cytochrome oxidase (now regarded as identical with a cytochrome formerly designated a_3) is the acceptor of electrons from cytochrome a.

Like the cytochromes themselves, cytochrome oxidase is an iron-porphyrin protein, firmly attached to the mitochondria. It accepts electrons from the cytochromes and passes them on to oxygen, which in its negatively charged state then combines to form water with the hydrogen ions released at an earlier stage. Cytochrome oxidase is inhibited by cyanide, azide, and carbon monoxide, this last-named inhibition being reversed by exposure to light.

Of this group of dehydrogenases, the enzyme attacking succinic acid is probably of greatest importance, because this reaction is one of the steps in the tricarboxylic acid cycle (p. 398), a mechanism whereby compounds derived from all classes of foodstuffs are degraded to CO_2 and H_2O.

COENZYME-LINKED ANAEROBIC DEHYDROGENASES. The larger group of anaerobic dehydrogenases is sometimes designated "coenzyme-linked," for reasons which are obvious from the data in Table 40. Most of these enzymes utilize DPN as coenzyme, a few can substitute TPN but at an inferior reaction rate (indicated by parentheses), while some require TPN specifically. The glutamic enzyme can use either coenzyme quite well. The general course of hydrogen and electron transfer in these systems is illustrated at the top of page 367.

Under the influence of the dehydrogenase enzyme, hydrogen atoms from the substrate are transferred to the pyridine nucleotide coenzyme as the first step in the series.

The secondary hydrogen carriers in these redox chains are shown in the figure as flavoproteins ("yellow enzymes"). Although the prosthetic groups of these proteins are similar to those of the aerobic dehydrogenases, the substances as a whole differ from the latter, since they specifically catalyze the transfer of electrons to the cytochromes and are not directly oxidizable by oxygen. Individual flavoproteins

$$AH_2 \quad DPN \leftarrow \quad Flavo\text{-}H_2 \quad 2Fe^{+++}\text{-cyto} \leftarrow \quad 2Fe^{++}\text{-cyto-ox} \quad [O]$$

$$A \quad DPN\text{-}H_2 \quad Flavo \quad 2Fe^{++}\text{-cyto} \quad 2Fe^{+++}\text{-cyto-ox} \quad O^=$$

$$2H^+ ------------- H_2O$$

Dehydrogenase
protein

$$H_2O$$

"Coenzyme-linked"
anaerobic $\rightarrow$ DPN, TPN $\rightarrow$ Flavoproteins
dehydrogenase
$\downarrow$
"Slater factor"
$\downarrow$
Cytochrome oxidase $\leftarrow$ Cytochrome a $\leftarrow$ Cytochrome c
(a$_3$)
$\downarrow$
O$_2$

seem to be linked to the different coenzymes, and therefore may be regarded as "coenzyme dehydrogenases." Since they reduce the cytochromes, they have also been called "cytochrome reductases." Earlier flavoprotein preparations which were found to link the coenzymes to dyestuffs (as methylene blue) were given such names as "diaphorase" and "coenzyme factor." Until the situation is clarified further, it may be best to treat all of the flavoproteins in this group as transhydrogenases, operating between the coenzymes and the cytochromes. In any event, the reduced forms of the flavoproteins transfer electrons to the "Slater factor" (p. 366) and send hydrogen ions out into the solution. From this point on, the redox chain resembles that which was described for the first group of anaerobic dehydrogenases (p. 364).

This group of dehydrogenases includes enzymes which participate in many phases of intermediary metabolism. Lactic dehydrogenase is involved in the anaerobic metabolism of carbohydrate, as is the triosephosphate dehydrogenase. The latter enzyme is unusual, in that a molecule of phosphoric acid apparently is added to the aldehyde group of the substrate before it is oxidized, thus accounting for the two phosphate groups attached to the glyceric acid which results. The actual mechanism of this reaction is somewhat more complex; it is discussed in detail elsewhere (p. 379). Glutamic dehydrogenase is of considerable importance in amino acid metabolism (p. 509). The β-hydroxyacyl-CoA dehydrogenase is involved in the metabolism of lipids (p. 450). Oxidation of glucose-6-phosphate is the initial step in the synthesis of pentoses (p. 403). Malic and isocitric dehydrogenases are parts of the tricarboxylic acid cycle, as is the oxidative decarboxylase of ketoglutaric acid (p. 398). The so-called "malic enzyme" is most unusual, since it seems to catalyze a one-step, simultaneous dehydrogenation and decarboxylation of malic acid without going through the stage of oxalacetic acid. The last two enzyme systems in the table are much more complex than the others. They require lipothiamide pyrophosphate (p. 360) as well as DPN. Coenzyme A is also a part of these systems as they occur naturally, and it is probable that the initial products of oxidation are acetyl-CoA and succinyl-CoA. These matters are discussed more fully elsewhere (p. 397)

MISCELLANEOUS REDOX SYSTEMS

HYDROPEROXIDASES. In addition to the well-organized group of oxidizing enzymes already discussed, living tissues contain several other systems that do not readily lend themselves to easy classification with the former groups. One such class of enzymes is designated the "hydroperoxidases," and includes the catalases and peroxidases.

Formerly it was customary to emphasize the differences, or more properly the supposed differences, between the catalases and the peroxidases. With the advent of newer technics of investigation, it has been possible to demonstrate a common reaction pattern for both types of enzymes.

All catalases and peroxidases are iron-porphyrin proteins, the iron apparently remaining in the ferric state and not undergoing changes of valence during the reaction. The hydroperoxidases are inhibited by cyanide, azide, sulfide, and hydroxylamine. Although there are exceptions to the generalization, peroxidases are more prevalent in plant tissues and catalases in animals.

The reactions catalyzed by the hydroperoxidases are presented below:

General Reaction:

$$H_2O_2 \;+\; H_2R \xrightarrow{\text{hydroperoxidase}} 2H_2O + R$$

    Substrate   Donor

Special *Catalatic* Reaction ($R = -O-O-$):

$$H_2O_2 \;+\; H_2O_2 \xrightarrow{\text{catalase}} 2H_2O + O_2$$

    Substrate   Donor

Hydrogen peroxide or the closely related alkyl hydrogen peroxides are considered the substrates. The general reaction involves reduction of the substrate by means of hydrogen atoms contributed by a donor molecule, the end-products being the reduced substrate and an oxidized donor. The special reaction whereby catalase differs from peroxidase (the "catalatic" reaction) simply utilizes one molecule of hydrogen peroxide as substrate and a second as donor; the resulting evolution of oxygen gas gave rise in the past to the idea that there was some essential difference in the mechanism of reaction of the two groups of enzymes.

Table 41 lists some typical substrates and donors for the hydro-peroxidases. Both catalases and peroxidases can utilize alkyl hydrogen peroxides as substrates, but the substituted peroxides are less effective for the catalases than for the peroxidases. Unsubstituted hydrogen peroxide is the best substrate for all of these enzymes. Among the donors, there are significant differences in specificity between the two groups of enzymes. Catalases can use hydrogen peroxide itself, formaldehyde, certain alcohols, and nitrous and formic acids, whereas aromatic organic compounds of the types listed in the table are the best donors for the peroxidases. Ascorbic acid is one of the enediols which is oxidized.

Table 41. Typical Substrates and Donors for Hydroperoxidases

	SUBSTRATES	DONORS
Catalases:	HOOH	HOOH
	CH_3OOH	$H_2C(OH)_2$ (hydrated formaldehyde)
	C_2H_5OOH	CH_3OH
		C_2H_5OH
		HNO_2
		HCOOH
Peroxidases:	HOOH	Aminophenols
	CH_3OOH	Diamines
	C_2H_5OOH	Diphenols
		Leuco dyes
		Enediols
		Uric acid
		$DPN-H_2$

Little can be said of the physiological importance of the hydro-peroxidases. It has been thought for many years that catalase serves a protective function in the cell, by disposing of the hydrogen peroxide resulting from the action of enzymes such as the aerobic dehydrogenases. At present, however, it is believed by some that the peroxidatic rather than the catalatic reaction predominates, and few metabolic reactions are known in which a peroxidase plays an important role in animal tissues. (True peroxidases are said to occur in the thyroid gland and in the leukocytes.)

Non-enzymatic "pseudoperoxidatic" reactions are catalyzed by high concentrations of heme compounds. The common medicolegal tests for blood (guaiac, etc.) depend upon such reactions, which can be differentiated from enzymatic reactions by their stability toward heat.

GLUTATHIONE AND ASCORBIC ACID. The reduced and oxidized forms of glutathione and ascorbic acid form reversible redox systems.

$$2GSH \xrightarrow[+2H]{-2H} G-S-S-G$$

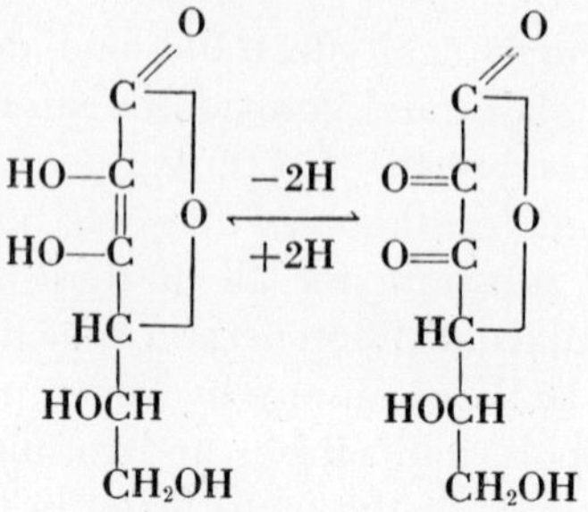

It has been assumed for many years that these compounds must be involved in biological oxidations, but attempts to correlate their redox properties with their over-all physiological functions or distribution in tissues met with little success until recently. Glutathione is now recognized as a prosthetic group of glyceraldehyde-phosphate dehydrogenase (p. 392). It is also a coenzyme of glyoxalase, an enzyme of questionable physiological significance (p. 242). Some investigators have concluded that glutathione also functions as a "sulfhydryl-preserver," i.e., that it helps to maintain certain proteins (as the sulfhydryl-containing enzymes) in the reduced state which is essential for their activity.

Ascorbic acid is a vitamin, and has been implicated in the metabolism of tyrosine (p. 552). The somatic symptoms resulting from a lack of this compound, however, seem to have little relation to the metabolism of the aromatic amino acids (p. 145).

BIBLIOGRAPHY

Introductory Textbooks

Baldwin, E.: Dynamic Aspects of Biochemistry, London, Cambridge University Press, 1952, especially Chapters 6 and 7.

Sumner, J. B. and Somers, G. F.: Chemistry and Methods of Enzymes, New York, Academic Press, Inc., 1953, Chapters 9–14.

Advanced Treatises

Green, D. E.: Mechanisms of Biological Oxidations, London, Cambridge University Press, 1940.

Lardy, H. A. (ed): Respiratory Enzymes, Minneapolis, Burgess Publishing Company, 1949.

Meyerhof, O., et al.: A Symposium on Respiratory Enzymes, Madison, University of Wisconsin Press, 1942.

Sumner, J. B. and Myrbäck, K. (eds.): The Enzymes, New York, Academic Press, Inc., 1950–1952, Chapters 44, 52, 53, 55, 56, 57, 58 in Volume 2.

16

BIOENERGETICS AND HIGH-ENERGY PHOSPHATE

INTRODUCTION

FUNDAMENTAL CONCEPTS. Life represents an unstable state. An organism in stable equilibrium with its environment is dead. In order to remain alive, the organism must expend energy to overcome the ever-present forces of destruction. The raw materials used by the organism as sources of energy and as building-blocks for its tissues were described in the first few chapters, while the catalytic machinery for the breakdown of these substances (and, in some cases, for their resynthesis into more useful forms) was discussed in the chapters on enzymes and biological oxidations. We must consider now the manner in which the organism secures the energy liberated during the catabolism of foodstuffs and utilizes it for the maintenance of life.

Energy is defined as the capacity to do work. The types of work which are of special biological significance include mechanical, chemical, osmotic, and electrical work, all of which will be discussed in greater detail in a later section. For living organisms, which remain at a relatively constant temperature (in thermodynamics, "isothermal systems"), two types of energy come under consideration: (1) heat energy, which can serve to maintain the body temperature, but is of no use for any other purpose; (2) free energy, which is available for work. Energy of both types may be expressed numerically in small calories, one such calorie being defined as the amount of heat required to raise the temperature of one gram of water by one degree centigrade. We will be concerned largely with the number of calories of free energy taken up or liberated in a chemical reaction, usually on the basis of one mol of the compound in question.

ULTIMATE ORIGIN OF ENERGY. Although nitrogenous and sulfur-containing compounds may be degraded by the animal body to products

371

such as urea and sulfate, the greatest fraction of catabolic reactions concerns the breakdown of combined forms of carbon and hydrogen to CO_2 and H_2O. This discussion, therefore, will be restricted mainly to compounds of this type.

Animals obtain their food by consuming other animals or plants. The animals which serve as food for larger animals are themselves dependent on still smaller animals or plants for nutriment, and if the food chain is traced back far enough, it becomes evident that the green plants are the major source of food for the remainder of organisms inhabiting this planet. The question then revolves around the source of the rather complex organic compounds (such as carbohydrates) produced by the plants. In a word, the answer to the question is photosynthesis, the production of complex compounds from simpler compounds by the use of radiant energy from the sun, mediated in some as yet unknown fashion by chlorophyll (a magnesium-porphyrin).

The over-all reaction of the photosynthesis of carbohydrate-like compounds is indicated by the equation:

$$6CO_2 + 6H_2O + 686,000 \text{ cal.} \rightarrow C_6H_{12}O_6 + 6O_2$$

| Low energy level | Free energy from sun | High energy level |

Compounds of low potential energy (CO_2 and H_2O) are built up into compounds of high potential energy (hexose), the 686,000 cal. of free energy required per mol of hexose being supplied in the form of solar radiation. The hexose then has built into it, so to speak, 686,000 cal. of free energy available to any system which can reverse the photosynthetic reaction. The animal organism, for instance, is potentially capable of securing this amount of free energy in oxidizing glucose to CO_2 and H_2O. In reality, no machine is 100 per cent efficient, so that we find that some 67 per cent of the total energy is actually obtained by the cells as free energy, the remainder being lost in side reactions as heat. It should be mentioned at this point that, although some organisms do emit light (photonic work), the free energy obtained in "reversing" the photosynthetic reaction is unrestricted, since, as will be seen, it is converted into a common currency which is utilizable for work of all types.

BIOENERGETIC SYSTEMS

BASIC REQUIREMENTS. The first requirement of a bioenergetic system is for a source of energy, i.e., a compound capable of being degraded to products of lower potential energy. Since most energy-yielding reactions are oxidative, the requirement more specifically calls for oxidizable foodstuffs.

Secondly, a mechanism is needed which will degrade the foodstuffs. As indicated in previous chapters, this mechanism is enzymatic. Also, it is stepwise (e.g., the oxidative chains), allowing the fractional packet of energy liberated at each step to be handled easily.

Mechanisms must be available for the collection and storage of the liberated free energy, which otherwise would go to waste. It will be seen shortly that these mechanisms involve unusual types of phosphorylated compounds.

A final, obvious requirement is for mechanisms of utilization of the stored energy. These mechanisms, most of which are discussed separately in various sections, convert free energy into such types of work as muscle contraction (mechanical); secretion, absorption, and kidney function (osmotic); synthetic, anabolic reactions (chemical); and nervous impulses (electrical).

OVER-ALL SCHEME OF BIOENERGETICS. A picture of the workings of the systems which have been under discussion is presented in diagrammatic fashion below.

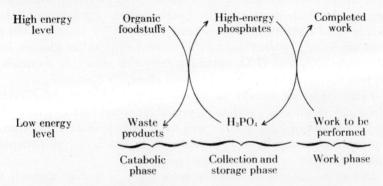

High energy level	Organic foodstuffs	High-energy phosphates	Completed work
Low energy level	Waste products	H_3PO_4	Work to be performed
	Catabolic phase	Collection and storage phase	Work phase

This holds not only for the general scheme of bioenergetics in the total metabolism of the organism, but also for the individual reaction sequences which make up this totality.

The degradation of foodstuffs of high potential energy to products of low energy (an energy-yielding process) is shown coupled to a mechanism for collection and storage of energy. This mechanism, in brief, consists of the conversion of inorganic phosphate into "high-energy phosphate" compounds (defined in the next section), a process which requires energy and obtains it from the coupled degradation reaction already mentioned. These high-energy phosphate compounds can in turn be degraded back to inorganic phosphate, a reaction which yields energy. Another coupling mechanism insures that this energy is turned into useful work. The rest of this chapter will be devoted to a consideration of the individual phases of this over-all scheme.

ENERGY LEVELS OF FOODSTUFFS. The relationship between the energy levels of the various foodstuffs and their degradation products is shown at the top of page 374.

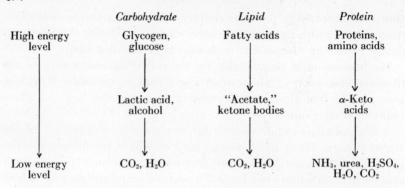

	Carbohydrate	Lipid	Protein
High energy level	Glycogen, glucose	Fatty acids	Proteins, amino acids
	↓	↓	↓
	Lactic acid, alcohol	"Acetate," ketone bodies	α-Keto acids
	↓	↓	↓
Low energy level	CO_2, H_2O	CO_2, H_2O	NH_3, urea, H_2SO_4, H_2O, CO_2

Glycogen or glucose may be catabolized only partially under anaerobic conditions, producing lactic acid or alcohol, depending on the organism involved. Lactic acid formation (glycolysis) makes available about 36,000 cal., and alcohol formation (fermentation) about 50,000 cal., so that only a small fraction of the 686,000 cal. in glucose is available in organisms which must halt their carbohydrate catabolism at these points (and further corrections must be made for less than 100 per cent efficiency). Higher animals in general can oxidize glucose completely to CO_2 and H_2O, obtaining from this substance as much of its free energy as their efficiencies will allow.

Fatty acids are usually degraded completely, but under certain abnormal conditions "acetate" (probably acetyl-CoA), which is a major product of fatty acid as well as of carbohydrate catabolism, is not oxidized as rapidly as it is produced, in which case this transient intermediate forms ketone bodies (p. 450).

During its catabolism, protein, proceeding as it does through the many and varied amino acids, is not usually thought of as passing through a common intermediate stage similar to that passed through by the fats and carbohydrates. However, since the deamination of amino acids to α-keto acids is almost universal, and furnishes some but not all of the energy available from the former compounds, it seems reasonable to consider this stage as intermediate in protein breakdown. The nitrogen of the amino groups eventually forms ammonia and urea, the sulfur of cysteine and methionine produces sulfuric acid, and the rest of the amino acid skeleton is degraded to CO_2 and H_2O.

ENERGY LEVELS OF HYDROLYZABLE LINKAGES. The concept of energy levels of compounds can scarcely be discussed without reference to the energy evolved from or required for the scission of certain types of chemical bonds. Oxidative reactions, such as those involved in the complete catabolism of the foodstuffs mentioned in the preceding section, are concerned with the cleavage of C—H and O—H linkages, with the eventual formation of CO_2 and H_2O. Such reactions are too complex for quantitative treatment on an introductory level. Suffice it to say that the free energy liberated or consumed in any reaction, oxidative or not, is the resultant of the free energy liberated or consumed in the dissolution of the relevant bonds in the reactants, balanced by the free energy changes occurring in the formation of the required bonds in the products of the reaction.

Many compounds of biochemical interest consist of two or more components united by "anhydrosynthesis," i.e., by abstraction of the elements of water from between the two participants in a linkage. Such compounds are at a higher free energy level than are their products of hydrolysis. For certain purposes it is helpful to know the free energy liberated during the hydrolysis of one mol of such compounds, rather than the free energy change attendant upon their complete catabolism to metabolic end-products. Table 42 lists certain hydrolyzable linkages, examples of biochemically important compounds containing them, and approximate values for the free energy of hydrolysis, expressed in negative kilocalories (k cal.) per mol (the negative indicating that the energy is evolved rather than consumed).

Among the non-phosphorylated compounds listed, "low-energy" hydrolyzable linkages (several k cal.) occur in simple esters, glycosides, and peptides. "High-energy" bonds (*ca.* 16 k cal.) are found in thioesters of coenzyme A (p. 249) and related compounds, as well as in β-keto acids. The significance of these facts will become apparent in the discussions of intermediary metabolism.

It was indicated in the previous discussions that there exist phosphorylated compounds of different energy levels. The energy level assigned to a given compound is determined by the free energy liberated in the hydrolysis of that compound to inorganic phosphate and the organic residue to which the phosphate group was attached. On this basis there are three general levels of phosphorylated compounds: (1) inorganic phosphate itself, the zero level; (2) low-energy phosphates, mainly esters of phosphoric acid with alcohol groups; (3) high-energy phosphates, which include compounds of phosphoric acid with itself, and with guanidine, enolic, and carboxyl groups. The low-cnergy phosphates have a free energy of hydrolysis of 2000–4000 cal. per mol, whereas the high-energy compounds liberate 10,000–16,000 cal. It is customary to ascribe the high energy of a compound to the linkage between the phosphorus and the rest of the molecule, and this high energy bond is written as $\sim$ instead of the ordinary dash.

Some of the above compounds have been encountered previously. ADP and ATP, it will be recalled, were mentioned in connection with the enzymes catalyzing transphosphorylations (p. 247). Adenylic acid (AMP), the parent compound, contains only a low-energy phosphate bond (ester type). The di- and triphosphates, on the other hand, contain respectively one and two high-energy bonds of the pyrophosphate type. ADP and ATP are important in the collection and utilization of free energy. ATP, in fact, is the "common currency" of energy which was mentioned earlier. So far as is known, ATP is formed in all energy-yielding (exergonic) reactions, and utilized in all energy-requiring

Table 42. Free Energies of Hydrolysis of Linkages

LINKAGE	FORMULA	OCCURRENCE	FREE ENERGY OF HYDROLYSIS, IN NEGATIVE K CAL./MOL
Carboxyl ester	$R-C(=O)\vdots O-R'$	Glycerides	3.0
Phosphoric ester	$R-O\vdots PO_3H_2$	Hexose phosphates	2.0–4 0
Glycoside	(H, OR on C)	Polysaccharides	4.8
Peptide	$R-C(=O)\vdots NH-R'$	Proteins	3.0
β-Keto acid	$R-C(=O) \sim CH_2COOH$	Acetoacetic acid	16.0
Thioester	$R-C(=O) \sim SR'$	Acetyl-CoA	16.0
Thiophosphate	$R-S \sim PO_3H_2$	Phosphoryl- or pyrophosphoryl-CoA	*ca.* 16.0
Pyrophosphate	$R-P(=O)(OH)-O \sim P(=O)(OH)-R'$	ATP	12.0
Guanidine phosphate	$R-NH-C(=NH)-NH \sim PO_3H_2$	Phosphocreatine	14.0
Enol phosphate	$R=C(H)-O \sim PO_3H_2$	Phosphoenol-pyruvic acid	16.0
Carboxyl Phosphate	$R-C(=O)-O \sim PO_3H_2$	#1 phosphate in diphosphoglyceric acid	16.0

(endergonic) reactions, directly or indirectly. It is rather unstable and is found in tissues in only small quantities, so that it is not quite so important for the storage of energy. Phosphocreatine is the major storage form of high-energy phosphate, especially in muscle and liver (in invertebrates its place is taken by phosphoarginine). Any surplus high-energy phosphate is transferred from ATP to creatine (transphosphorylation) for storage as phosphocreatine. When the need arises, this high-energy phosphate is transferred to ADP, re-forming ATP.

Phosphoenolpyruvic acid and diphosphoglyceric acid are compounds which arise during the anaerobic catabolism of glucose (p. 390). They contain high-energy phosphate groups which can be transferred to the adenylic system. Acetyl phosphate is also a high-energy compound, but is of importance only in bacteria.

As can be seen from the formulas, the low-energy phosphate compounds are all esters. They include the hexose phosphates, pentose phosphates, triose phosphates, and those glyceric acid phosphates which do not involve the carboxyl group.

TRANSPHOSPHORYLATIONS.   In order to understand the nature of the coupling mechanisms involved in the collection of energy and its utilization, a short digression on transphosphorylation is necessary. This reaction is defined as the transfer of phosphate groups from one compound to another without going through the stage of inorganic phosphate.

Table 21 in the chapter on enzymes (p. 247) listed the various transphosphorylases. It was indicated that some of the reactions were reversible, while others were not. The explanation for this can now be given. Reversible transphosphorylation can occur if the two compounds involved belong to the same energy level of phosphate. Thus, transfers on either the high level or the low level proceed with very little liberation or absorption of energy, hence they can easily be reversed in direction. This group of transphosphorylations includes the phosphomutases and the reversible phosphokinases.

The transfer of a phosphate group from a high energy level to a low level, or from a low level to zero level (inorganic phosphate), liberates so much energy that, for all practical purposes, these reactions must be considered irreversible. Any apparent reversals which occur in living systems actually proceed by indirect pathways and with the aid of outside sources of energy. This group of reactions includes the irreversible phosphokinases and any simple hydrolytic breakdown of phosphorylated compounds, such as those catalyzed by the various phosphatases.

The hydrolytic splitting of phosphate compounds and the various mutase reactions do not require the participation of the adenylic system. All other transphosphorylations use ADP and ATP as transmitters. The diagram below indicates how various compounds of the high-energy phosphate type act as donors to the adenylic system, which in turn transfers phosphate groups to other compounds to form both high- and low-level phosphates.

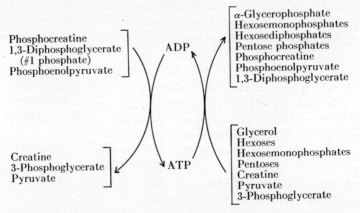

Phosphocreatine
1,3-Diphosphoglycerate
  (#1 phosphate)
Phosphoenolpyruvate

ADP

α-Glycerophosphate
Hexosemonophosphates
Hexosediphosphates
Pentose phosphates
Phosphocreatine
Phosphoenolpyruvate
1,3-Diphosphoglycerate

Creatine
3-Phosphoglycerate
Pyruvate

ATP

Glycerol
Hexoses
Hexosemonophosphates
Pentoses
Creatine
Pyruvate
3-Phosphoglycerate

COUPLING MECHANISMS: SUBSTRATE PHOSPHORYLATION. One of the important recent discoveries concerning phosphorylation has been that the coupling of high-energy phosphate formation with energy-yielding (exergonic) reactions can occur at two levels of metabolism, one at the point where a substrate is oxidized and passes its hydrogen atoms over to a primary carrier, and the second along the oxidative chain, where the hydrogen atoms or electrons are transferred over various carriers to oxygen. The exact manner of operation of these two types of phosphorylation is not known, but, of the two, somewhat more information is available concerning the first type, often called "substrate phosphorylation."

An example of definite substrate phosphorylation occurs in the anaerobic breakdown of glucose (glycolysis), in which phosphoglyceraldehyde (containing a low-energy ester phosphate) is oxidized to diphosphoglyceric acid (p. 392), one of the phosphates of which is attached to the carboxyl group, making it a high-energy type. The ordinary oxidation of an aldehyde to an acid, such as occurs in many enzymatic reactions, may be depicted as follows:

$$\underset{\text{OH}}{R-\overset{H}{C}=O} + H_2O \rightleftharpoons R-\overset{H}{\underset{|}{C}}-OH$$

$$R-\overset{H}{\underset{|}{C}}-OH + DPN \xrightarrow{\text{Dehydrogenase}} R-\overset{O}{C}-OH + DPN-H_2$$

An initial hydration of the aldehyde group is followed by a dehydrogenation, the pair of hydrogen atoms being passed to DPN under the influence of the dehydrogenase enzyme. Without inquiring further into the fate of the reduced DPN at this time, it will be noted that no energy has been conserved in this reaction. Since an aldehyde group is at a higher energy level than a carboxyl group, the transformation of the former to the latter liberates energy, but in the example shown this energy is simply lost.

In the glyceraldehyde-phosphate dehydrogenation, the initial reaction involves the formation of an addition product of the carbonyl group of the substrate and the sulfhydryl group of glutathione, which is the firmly bound prosthetic group of the enzyme. Oxidation of this product to a thioester (by hydrogen transfer to DPN) is followed by phosphorolysis, or transacylation to phosphate. Transfer of the carboxyl phosphate from the diphosphoglyceric acid to ADP to form ATP is catalyzed by a phosphokinase (p. 247).

$$\begin{array}{c} H \\ R-C\!\!=\!\!O + GSH \longrightarrow \end{array} \quad \begin{array}{c} H \\ R-\underset{\underset{S-G}{|}}{C}-OH \end{array}$$

$$\begin{array}{c} (H) \\ R-\underset{\underset{S-G}{|}}{C}-O(H) + DPN \longrightarrow \end{array} \quad R-\overset{O}{\overset{\|}{C}} \sim SG + DPN-H_2$$

$$R-\overset{O}{\overset{\|}{C}} \sim SG + H_3PO_4 \longrightarrow R-\overset{O}{\overset{\|}{C}}-O \sim PO_3H_2 + GSH$$

Formation of a carboxyl phosphate preserves much of the energy liberated by the oxidation. These reactions bear a striking resemblance to those involving coenzyme A.

The substrate phosphorylations which occur in the oxidation of pyruvate and ketoglutarate to acetate and succinate, respectively, seem to require coenzyme A, in addition to DPN as hydrogen carrier and LTPP as cofactor for the decarboxylations. It is quite probable that in these cases the sulfhydryl and disulfide groups of coenzyme A and LTPP participate in a series of reactions much like those just described (pp. 397, 399).

COUPLING MECHANISMS: OXIDATIVE CHAIN PHOSPHORYLATION. Most biological oxidations begin with a transfer of pairs of hydrogen atoms to the pyridine nucleotides (p. 361). At this point in the oxidative chain, the hydrogen atoms or electrons are at an energy level not very different from that of the substrate. However, in traversing the pathway over the flavoproteins, the cytochromes, and cytochrome oxidase, the energy levels become progressively lower until, with the formation of water, all of the potential energy (from a biochemical standpoint) is drained from the hydrogen atoms. At each stage in electron transfer, therefore, a certain amount of free energy is liberated. By means of mechanisms which are unknown at the present time, this energy is captured and transformed into high-energy phosphate bonds.

Whereas only one high-energy bond can be generated per mol of substrate *at the substrate level* (see preceding section), it has been found that approximately three mols of high-energy phosphate are formed during the passage of each mol of hydrogen from the pyridine nucleotides to oxygen. In those few cases which are known to involve substrate phosphorylation (phosphoglyceraldehyde, pyruvate, and ketoglutarate), a total of four high-energy bonds can therefore be produced per mol of substrate oxidized. (In the case of pyruvate, one of these bonds is used to "drive" the synthesis of citrate [p. 398].) Most other oxidations form only three such bonds. The succinic dehydrogenase system, because it bypasses some of the oxidative chain and couples rather directly to the cytochromes, yields only two high-energy bonds per mol of succinate converted to fumarate.

SUMMARY OF GENERATION OF HIGH-ENERGY PHOSPHATE. Referring back to the diagram on page 373, which, as was mentioned before, applies to individual bioenergetic reactions as well as to the complete scheme, the generation of high-energy phosphate may be summarized as follows. An organic compound (or a pair of hydrogen atoms) is degraded from its initial energy level to a lower level. In the course of this degradation, inorganic phosphate is raised to the high-energy phosphate level, thus conserving the energy liberated in the degradation reaction. With the aid of a phosphokinase, this new high-energy phosphate group is transferred to ADP to form ATP. If it is to be stored, the phosphate group is again transferred, this time from ATP to creatine, forming phosphocreatine. When required, the phosphocreatine returns the group to regenerate ATP. In any case, ATP is the agent directly concerned in the generation and utilization of high-energy phosphate.

UTILIZATION OF HIGH-ENERGY PHOSPHATE. Since ATP represents the "common currency" of bioenergetics, the number of examples of its utilization is as great as the number of types of physiological work carried on by the cell. Considerable sections of this book will be devoted to these examples. It may suffice at this point to cite one instance only.

Even though it is impossible physicochemically without an outside source of energy, many living membranes are able to transfer glucose from a region of low to a region of high concentration, an example of osmotic work. The cell does not violate the laws of physical chemistry in doing this; it simply has available a source of energy which can help to overcome the concentration gradient.

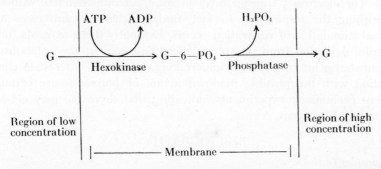

In the above diagram, glucose is phosphorylated in a hexokinase type of reaction at one side of the membrane, at the expense of one high-energy phosphate bond of ATP. Since the product, glucose-6-phosphate, is different from glucose itself, it allows a continuous diffusion of glucose to occur into the membrane from the left, because no "back-gradient" develops. At the right side of the membrane the ester is hydrolyzed by a phosphatase, regenerating glucose and liberating inorganic phosphate. Again, diffusion effects are minimized, since the two molecular species are also different on this side of the membrane. The over-all picture, then, is the transfer of glucose against a concentration gradient. This requires the input of energy, which is provided by ATP. It will be noted that the over-all change in the phosphate part of the system is a degradation of one of the high-energy bonds of ATP down to the zero level of inorganic phosphate, in agreement with the general scheme presented previously.

Other examples of ATP utilization follow the same general pattern; a direct reaction occurs between ATP and some member of the system, work is performed, and inorganic phosphate is produced from the original high-energy bond.

UNCOUPLING OF PHOSPHORYLATIONS. Some years ago, compounds such as 2,4-dinitrophenol were used in the treatment of obesity, since they had the faculty of increasing oxidative reactions in the body (increased caloric output) without stimulating anabolic processes (which might cause increases in weight). Although the medical use of these compounds has been abandoned because of their toxicity, there has been a recent surge of interest in their *in vitro* effects.

As was indicated previously, most high-energy phosphate bonds are generated by unknown mechanisms which operate to couple the oxidative chain to the phosphorylative process. This coupling is very labile, in the sense that many conditions and agents disturb the phosphorylative side of the couple much more than the purely oxidative. Dinitro-

BIOCHEMISTRY

phenol and certain other reagents, in appropriate concentrations, are able to suppress the generation of high-energy phosphate at the hydrogen- (or electron-) transfer level in respiring mitochondria without disturbing the respiration. In fact, under certain circumstances an actual stimulation of respiration occurs. Evidently these reagents "uncouple" oxidation from phosphorylation, and convert the catabolism of substrates into a profitless undertaking. Of special interest in connection with the possible mode of action of hormones are certain recent preliminary experiments indicating that thyroxine may act as an uncoupling agent.

BIBLIOGRAPHY

Elementary Textbook

Baldwin, E.: Dynamic Aspects of Biochemistry, London, Cambridge University Press, 1952, Chapter 3.

Advanced Reviews and Monographs

Fruton, J. S. et al.: Energy relationships in enzyme reactions, Ann. New York Acad. Sc. 45:357, 1944.

Johnson, M. J.: Energy relations in metabolic reactions. In Respiratory Enzymes, edited by H. A. Lardy, Minneapolis, Burgess Publishing Company, 1949, p. 255.

Kaplan, N. O.: Thermodynamics and mechanism of the phosphate bond. In The Enzymes, Volume 2, edited by J. B. Sumner and K. Myrbäck, New York, Academic Press, Inc., 1951, p. 55.

Lipmann, F.: Metabolic generation and utilization of phosphate bond energy, Advances in Enzymology, 1:99, 1941.

McElroy, W. D. and Glass, B. (eds.): A Symposium on Phosphorus Metabolism, Baltimore, Johns Hopkins Press, 1951, Volume 1, sections V and IX; 1952, Volume 2, sections II, III, and VII.

17

CARBOHYDRATE METABOLISM

INTRODUCTION

Whether from the standpoint of synthesis within the organism, or of absorption from the diet, glucose is quantitatively the most important carbohydrate available to the body for various purposes. To a considerable extent, therefore, the discussion of the metabolism of carbohydrates resolves itself into a consideration of the metabolism of glucose and its closely related derivatives. The metabolism of other carbohydrates will be considered insofar as warranted by their biological importance.

The sections immediately following will be devoted to the general metabolism of glucose, considering first the sources of glucose to the organism, and then the several routes available for its utilization. Later parts of this chapter will present in greater detail the reactions underlying these general metabolic pathways.

SOURCES OF GLUCOSE TO THE ORGANISM

EXOGENOUS. Although certain non-carbohydrate constituents of the diet (e.g., protein) are potential sources of carbohydrate in the body, the conversion of these substances to carbohydrate is identical with that undergone by endogenous compounds of the same type, hence consideration of this topic will be deferred (p. 407). The direct exogenous source of carbohydrate is obviously the carbohydrate of the diet, and a consideration of the mechanisms whereby it becomes available to the organism involves a description of the processes of digestion and absorption.

DIGESTION AND ABSORPTION. The indigestible carbohydrates of foodstuffs (celluloses, pentosans) are not utilizable by man and pass out of the bowel in the feces. The digestible polysaccharides and disaccharides are hydrolyzed by digestive enzymes in the intestine (pp. 257 ff.) to their monosaccharide components: viz., starch, glycogen,

383

and maltose to glucose; lactose to glucose and galactose; sucrose to glucose and fructose. In addition to these sugars, foodstuffs contain small amounts of pentose and mannose.

All monosaccharides are practically completely absorbed, almost entirely in the small intestine. The rate of absorption diminishes from the duodenum downward, at least in the case of glucose, which is the major absorbable carbohydrate. The amount and concentration entering the intestine have comparatively little effect on the rate of absorption, which, in experimental animals, is relatively constant for each sugar and for each segment of the bowel. Hyper- and hypotonic solutions are brought to approximate isotonicity prior to absorption of the solutes. In the dog, glucose is absorbed at an average rate of approximately 1 gram/kg. body weight/hour. Although a portion enters the thoracic lymph, by far the major portion passes into the portal blood, by which it is carried directly to the liver.

The comparative rates of absorption of the monosaccharides may be indicated as follows: galactose (110) > glucose (100) > fructose (43) > mannose (19) > pentoses (15–9). These striking differences, in conjunction with the fact that they are all absorbed from the peritoneal space at the same low rate, i.e., that of pentoses, suggest that at least galactose, glucose, and fructose are transferred across the intestinal mucosa by some active process, and not entirely by diffusion. Moreover, the rate of absorption of a hexose is modified by simultaneous administration of another sugar; e.g., that of galactose is diminished when it is given with glucose. Two mechanisms are apparently involved: (1) simple diffusion, dependent on the sugar concentration gradients between the intestinal lumen, mucosal cells, and blood plasma; (2) an active process, probably involving phosphorylation in the intestinal epithelial cells. According to this concept, glucose, diffusing into these cells from the intestinal lumen, is transformed rapidly to glucose-6-phosphate (glucokinase + ATP), thus facilitating the entrance of additional glucose by diffusion, inasmuch as the concentration gradient of free sugar between the lumen and the interior of the cell is thereby increased. Glucose-6-phosphate is promptly hydrolyzed (non-specific phosphatase) and the sugar passes into the interstitial fluid and portal capillaries (and thoracic lymph) in its original form. This active process involves expenditure of energy (from ATP). Fructose probably undergoes similar phosphorylation (fructokinase + ATP) to fructose-6-phosphate, which, through the action of isomerase (p. 392), is converted to glucose-6-phosphate, with which it is in equilibrium. By this reaction, a portion of the fructose may be transformed to glucose in the intestinal wall. However, this transformation occurs much more actively in the liver.

$$
\begin{array}{ccc}
 & \text{Fructose} + \text{ATP} & \text{Glucose} + \text{ATP} \\
\text{(to blood)} & \downarrow & \downarrow & \text{(to blood)} \\
\text{Fructose} + \text{Phosphate} \leftarrow \text{F—6—P} & \rightleftharpoons & \text{G—6—P} \rightarrow \text{Glucose} + \text{Phosphate}
\end{array}
$$

Phosphorylation of galactose also is assumed to occur (galactokinase + ATP). In this case, the 1-phosphate ester may be formed, inasmuch as galactose-6-phosphate has not been demonstrated in biological systems. Whether other monosaccharides undergo a similar transformation in the intestinal wall is not clear; pentoses are apparently absorbed solely by diffusion.

In common with other substances, the rate of absorption of sugars from the bowel is influenced by such general factors as the state and area of the absorptive surface (i.e., condition of intestinal mucosa) and the intestinal motility (i.e., duration of contact with areas of optimal absorption). Thyroxine accelerates absorption of hexoses (e.g., increased in hyperthyroidism, decreased in hypothyroidism).

Certain B vitamins, i.e., thiamine, pyridoxine, and pantothenic acid, are required for optimal absorption of these sugars, which is consequently decreased in the presence of deficiency in these factors. Diminished absorption in adrenal cortical insufficiency is dependent upon the decreased concentration of Na and Cl in the body fluids, not upon a specific influence of the adrenal hormones on the absorptive process.

FATE OF ABSORBED CARBOHYDRATE. After absorption into the portal blood, carbohydrates must pass through the liver before entering the systemic circulation, a fact of considerable physiological significance. Certain hepatic mechanisms contribute to the withdrawal of carbohydrates from the blood: (1) uptake of hexoses such as fructose and galactose for conversion to glucose by the liver cells; (2) conversion of glucose to glycogen for storage in the liver (glycogenesis); (3) utilization of glucose, by oxidation, for energy production; (4) utilization of glucose for the synthesis of other compounds, such as fatty acids and certain amino acids. Opposed to these mechanisms are others which lead to the release of glucose by the liver to the blood: (1) formation of blood sugar from hexoses other than glucose by the liver; (2) conversion of liver glycogen to blood glucose (glycogenolysis*); (3) synthesis of blood glucose by the liver from non-carbohydrate sources, such as certain amino acids (gluconeogenesis). The amount of glucose reaching the systemic circulation at any instant is consequently the resultant of the operations of these two groups of opposing processes.

Once it is in the systemic circulation, blood glucose becomes available for utilization by the extrahepatic tissues. From what has been said about portal absorption, it is evident that these tissues are presented with carbohydrate which has already been "picked over" by the liver in a selective manner. It is to be expected, therefore, that the

---

* The term "glycogenolysis" is used by some authors to mean any breakdown of glycogen, whether it leads to blood glucose (one of the two available pathways in liver), or down the glycolytic sequence of reactions to pyruvic and lactic acids (the second of the two pathways in liver, and the probable sole pathway in muscle).

physiological state of the liver will have a profound influence on the carbohydrate metabolism of the entire organism, an expectation abundantly fulfilled in practice.

ENDOGENOUS.   Among the minor carbohydrate sources of body glucose may be listed the small quantities of endogenous galactose, mannose, and, possibly, pentoses which may be converted to glucose under certain circumstances. The major endogenous carbohydrate source is liver glycogen. The glycogen of muscle is not directly convertible to blood glucose; however, the lactic acid formed during glycolysis of muscle glycogen can be converted to glucose and glycogen in the liver.

Certain non-carbohydrate sources are available to the organism for production of glucose. Although it is generally believed that the fatty acids cannot undergo net conversion to carbohydrate, the glycerol moiety of lipids can serve as a source of glucose (from which it can also be derived). However, the amino acids are the major raw material for the synthesis of carbohydrate from non-carbohydrate sources (gluconeogenesis). It has been estimated that over half of the average animal protein is potentially capable of conversion to carbohydrate (p. 516). Those amino acids which are carbohydrate-formers are called "glucogenic." It is of interest that the major site of gluconeogenesis is the liver.

UTILIZATION OF GLUCOSE

STORAGE.   When a molecule of glucose is introduced into the body or synthesized *de novo* therein, several metabolic pathways are open to it. In the absence of urgent physiological demands for oxidative energy or conversion to special products, excess glucose may be deposited as glycogen in the liver and other tissues (glycogenesis). Inasmuch as the amount of glycogen which can be stored in the body is limited, quantities of glucose in excess of this upper limit are converted to fatty acids and stored as triglycerides in the fat depots. There seems to be no fixed limit to this process, as may be seen from everyday observations on human beings.

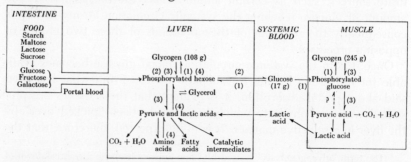

(1) Glycogenesis; (2) Glycogenolysis; (3) Glycolysis; (4) Gluconeogenesis

Fig. 71. Sources and routes of utilization of carbohydrate. (Numerical data for 70 kg. man)

OXIDATION. In response to physiological demands for energy, glucose may be completely oxidized to CO_2 and H_2O, a process which occurs in all tissues. At certain times, special circumstances in muscle may result in only partial degradation of glucose (glycolysis). The product, lactic acid, is then largely disposed of by other tissues, notably liver.

CONVERSION TO FAT. As indicated above, a net conversion of glucose to fatty acids occurs when accommodations for storage as glycogen are exceeded. However, since one of the major metabolites of glucose is in rapid equilibrium with fatty acids (p. 447), a constant interconversion occurs between certain molecules common to the carbohydrate and fatty acid pathways. This interconversion is very rapid, and investigations with isotopes have led to the conclusion that a large proportion of glucose that is oxidized actually forms fatty acids before final degradation to CO_2 and H_2O. It must be noted that the over-all conversion of glucose to fatty acids is irreversible, for reasons which will be pointed out subsequently (p. 482). In contrast, the transformation of glucose to the glycerol moiety of the lipids is readily reversible.

CONVERSION TO OTHER CARBOHYDRATES. Small amounts of glucose are used, directly or indirectly, in the synthesis of certain other carbohydrates which play important roles in the economy of the organism. These include (1) ribose and desoxyribose, required for the synthesis of the nucleic acids (p. 94), (2) mannose, glucosamine, and galactosamine, which form parts of the mucopolysaccharides and glycoproteins (p. 18), (3) glucuronic acid, also involved in the mucopolysaccharides and in "detoxication" reactions (p. 281), and (4) galactose, which is a component of the glycolipids (p. 34) as well as of the disaccharide, lactose, secreted in milk (p. 729).

CONVERSION TO AMINO ACIDS. Certain amino acids are not required in the diet, although they occur in the tissue proteins. It may be concluded, therefore, that they are synthesized by the body. Evidence at hand indicates that this group of amino acids, commonly designated "dispensable" or "non-essential" (p. 516), derives its carbon skeletons from glucose or its metabolites. Although all amino acids which are formed from glucose are also "glucogenic," the converse generalization does not hold.

MISCELLANEOUS PATHWAYS. As will be indicated in detail elsewhere, a large proportion of the catabolic sequences of reactions is of a cyclic nature, and, as such, requires the presence of adequate amounts of certain compounds which perform a catalytic function. These compounds are derived, more or less directly, from glucose. Disturbances in the metabolism of glucose, consequently, result in more than proportionate derangement of the total metabolism of the organism.

The ingestion of sufficient glucose, or compounds rapidly converted to glucose, to cause significant hyperglycemia may result in the excretion of glucose in the urine (p. 428). This is not, however, a normal pathway of disposal.

THE INTERMEDIARY METABOLISM OF CARBOHYDRATE: INTRODUCTION

The sequence of catabolic reactions whereby glucose is degraded to CO_2 and H_2O may be divided, for didactic convenience, into anaerobic and aerobic phases. It is currently believed that these phases do not involve separate pathways, but that an initial, anaerobic series of reactions takes place, continuing directly in an aerobic series in the presence of oxygen. The anaerobic phase of glucose metabolism (pp. 389–396) occurs whether oxygen is present or not, its anaerobic character deriving from the fact that participation of oxygen is not required in any of its reactions. "Glycolysis" is the term commonly applied to the production of lactic acid from glucose or glycogen, a phenomenon which is rare under physiological conditions, being largely restricted to circumstances of muscle contraction (p. 409) in which the rate of metabolism of carbohydrate outstrips the oxygen supply to the tissue (relative anaerobiosis).

Under the usual aerobic conditions, lactic acid is either not produced at all, or, if formed, is immediately reoxidized, *in situ*, to pyruvic acid (p. 396). In any event, the aerobic phase of glucose metabolism begins with the end-products of the anaerobic phase, lactic or pyruvic acids, which, by means of an ingenious cyclic mechanism (p. 397), are degraded stepwise to CO_2 and H_2O. The efficiencies of the anaerobic and aerobic phases are remarkably similar, insofar as recovery of liberated free energy (p. 371) is concerned. However, if calculated in terms of energy obtained per molecule of glucose degraded, the aerobic is superior to the anaerobic by a factor of about 15–20. It is interesting to speculate that the energy requirements of the lowly anaerobic organisms, as rather primitive bits of protoplasm, can be satisfied by a process which necessitates the turnover of a large amount of fuel for a small amount of energy, whereas the higher organisms, which have to "get up and go," have had their "burners" converted to more efficient forms.

Although much less is known of pentose than of hexose metabolism, the important role of pentoses in the formation of nucleic acids and other biologically active compounds warrants consideration of our current knowledge in this field (pp. 403–405). It appears at present that pentoses are derived from hexoses or products of hexose metabolism.

The major portion of the discussion of carbohydrate metabolism in this chapter is devoted to those general features of the processes which are known to occur in practically all tissues. However, certain peculiarities or deviations from the general pattern are exhibited in particular tissues or organs. The individuality in carbohydrate metabolism shown by liver (p. 406) and muscle (p. 408), for example, has a sufficiently significant influence on the metabolism of the entire organism to justify separate consideration.

The metabolic pathways of the several major foodstuffs are so intimately related that a true picture of the metabolism of carbohydrate cannot be drawn by assuming that it occurs in biochemical isolation. It is necessary, therefore, to introduce a discussion of the metabolic interrelations between carbohydrates, fats, and proteins (p. 434) even before the latter two groups are considered formally in detail.

ANAEROBIC METABOLISM OF GLUCOSE (GLYCOLYSIS)

The anaerobic metabolism of glucose can be subdivided into the phases of initial phosphorylation, glycogen synthesis, conversion to trioses, the oxidative step, and the formation of lactate (or ethanol). Figure 72 presents the complete picture of the anaerobic metabolism of glucose.

INITIAL PHOSPHORYLATION (REACTION 1, FIG. 72). It seems probable that glucose must be phosphorylated for transfer across cell walls or membranes, such as occurs during its absorption from the intestine and in the passage of blood glucose into the tissues. At any rate, glucose (and other sugars) undergoes an obligatory phosphorylation as its initial step in metabolism. This phosphorylation is catalyzed by one of a group of enzymes, the "irreversible phosphokinases" (p. 247). In the case of glucose, the enzyme has been called "hexokinase" or "glucokinase."

The product of the reaction of ATP and glucose, in the presence of the appropriate phosphokinase and Mg^{++}, is glucose-6-phosphate. Formation of an ester phosphate at the expense of a high-energy phosphate bond explains the practical irreversibility of this reaction (p. 377). Other sugars are brought into the glucose pathway at the points shown in Figure 72. It will be noted that all of these compounds are capable of conversion to glucose-6-phosphate, which means, as will be shown later, that they are potential sources of blood glucose and liver glycogen (p. 394).

It has been reported that the hexokinase reaction is inhibited by hormones of the anterior pituitary and adrenal cortex, this effect being counteracted by insulin (p. 423).

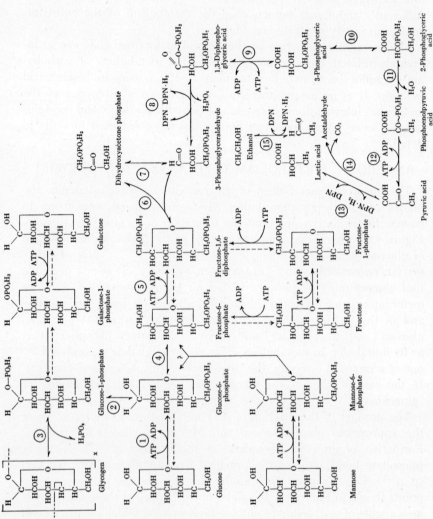

Fig. 72. Anaerobic metabolism of glucose and related hexoses

SYNTHESIS OF GLYCOGEN (REACTIONS 2–3, FIG. 72). Glucose-6-phosphate, in the presence of Mg^{++} and an enzyme called "phosphoglucomutase," is reversibly transformed to glucose-1-phosphate. The mechanism of this reaction, involving glucose-1,6-diphosphate as coenzyme, is presented elsewhere (p. 248).

Phosphorylase, acting as a transglycosidase (p. 244), transfers the glucose moieties of glucose-1-phosphate to the free carbon 4 positions at the non-reducing termini of pre-existing polysaccharidic chains, liberating inorganic phosphate in the process. A "primer" of branched polysaccharide, the main linkages of which are α-1,4, is essential for the action of animal phosphorylase. In the absence of other enzymes, phosphorylase synthesizes linear, α-1,4-linked polysaccharides similar to the amylose fraction of starch (p. 14). "Branching enzymes" (p. 245) are required for the formation of the highly ramified glycogen molecule, which contains 1,6-linkages at the branching points. The fine structure of glycogen seems to be somewhat variable, depending in part on the type of carbohydrate given and the route of administration. Glycogen from both liver and muscle contains fractions of different solubility and correspondingly different biological lability.

The phosphorylase reaction is easily reversible. As might be anticipated from a consideration of the reactants involved, the direction of the reaction is strongly influenced by the concentration of inorganic phosphate. This may be of physiological importance (p. 402). It is of interest that the concentration of glycogen has no significant effect on the equilibrium. This has been explained on the plausible basis that the reaction involves not the entire polysaccharide molecule, but only the end groups, the number of which remains constant throughout the course of the reaction.

In the breakdown of glycogen to glucose-1-phosphate, phosphorylase acts only on the 1,4-linkages. Splitting of the 1,6-linkages (branching points) is due to amylo-1,6-glucosidase (p. 234), a purely hydrolytic enzyme. This reaction is obviously not a simple reversal of the synthesis of 1,6-linkages by the "branching enzymes," which appear to be transglycosidases.

In liver and muscle, an equilibrium exists between active and inactive forms of phosphorylase. This equilibrium is shifted to favor the active form in liver under the influence of the "hyperglycemic factor" of the pancreas (p. 693), and in both liver and muscle under the influence of adrenaline (epinephrine) from the adrenal medulla (p. 672). Although there is some indication that adenylic acid may be a prosthetic group of muscle phosphorylase, the evidence is not as yet conclusive.

CONVERSION TO TRIOSES (REACTIONS 4–7, FIG. 72). As may be seen in Figure 72, glucose-6-phosphate is at the crossroads of carbohydrate metabolism. It is formed from glucose, glycogen, and (as will be discussed elsewhere, p. 394) substances in the process of forming glucose or glycogen. Conversely, glucose-6-phosphate is convertible to glucose (by means of a specific phosphatase of limited distribution, p. 231), glycogen, and compounds on the pathway to lactic acid.

The formation of lactic acid, the end-product of anaerobic glucose metabolism (glycolysis) in animals, is preceded by cleavage of the hexose skeleton into trioses. The first reaction undergone by glucose-6-phosphate on this metabolic route is its conversion to fructose-6-phosphate, catalyzed by phosphohexoisomerase (p. 244). Little is known concerning the mechanism of this reaction.

Fructose-6-phosphate is phosphorylated by ATP in the presence of Mg^{++} and phosphofructokinase (p. 248), forming fructose-1,6-diphosphate. In this reaction, as in the hexokinase reaction discussed previously, an ester phosphate is formed at the expense of a high-energy phosphate bond. Consequently, the reaction is practically irreversible, its apparent biological reversibility being due to the action of a phosphatase which liberates inorganic phosphate, and does not regenerate the pyrophosphate linkage in ATP. An analogous situation obtains with regard to the formation of glucose from glucose-6-phosphate (p. 389).

Fructose-1,6-diphosphate is split into two molecules of triose phosphate by aldolase (p. 244), an enzyme catalyzing a reversible reaction somewhat resembling the aldol condensation of organic chemistry. No coenzymes or activators are required by animal aldolase. The product of the reaction is an equimolecular mixture of D-glyceraldehyde-3-phosphate and dihydroxyacetone-phosphate.

Triose phosphate isomerase (p. 244) catalyzes the interconversion of the two triose phosphates. It is of interest that the equilibrium constant of the isomerization favors the ketotriose, although glyceraldehyde-3-phosphate is the compound which undergoes the subsequent reactions of the glycolytic pathway. At any rate, the presence of the isomerase insures the eventual complete utilization of both triose moieties formed from the hexose diphosphate.

OXIDATIVE STEP (REACTION 8, FIG. 72). The conversion of D-glyceraldehyde-3-phosphate to D-1,3-diphosphoglyceric acid is the first of two reactions in glycolysis in which high-energy phosphate bonds are generated. Since the oxidative chain is not available under anaerobic conditions, all of the high-energy phosphate produced in glycolysis is due to "substrate phosphorylation" (p. 378).

Glyceraldehyde-3-phosphate dehydrogenase (p. 367) is a "double-headed" enzyme, in the sense that its action involves both a prosthetic group (glutathione) and a coenzyme (DPN). Owing to its sulfhydryl groups, the enzyme is inhibited by sulfhydryl reagents (p. 251) and oxidants in general. The mechanism of action of this dehydrogenase has been elucidated only recently. It consists of the following steps:

$$R{-}\overset{\text{H}}{C}{=}O + HS{-}Enz \rightleftharpoons R{-}\overset{\text{H}}{\underset{\text{OH}}{C}}{-}S{-}Enz$$

$$R{-}\overset{\text{H}}{\underset{\text{OH}}{C}}{-}S{-}Enz + DPN \rightleftharpoons R{-}\overset{O}{C}{\sim}S{-}Enz + DPN{\cdot}H_2$$

$$R{-}\overset{O}{C}{\sim}S{-}Enz + H_3PO_4 \rightleftharpoons R{-}\overset{O}{C}{-}O \sim PO_3H_2 + HS{-}Enz$$

The aldehyde group of glyceraldehyde-3-phosphate first condenses with the sulfhydryl group of the enzyme-bound glutathione. The condensation product is then dehydrogenated to an acyl mercaptide or thioester type of compound, the pair of hydrogen atoms being accepted by DPN (the fate of the reduced DPN is discussed below). Although it contains no phosphate, the thioester linkage is energetically equivalent to a high-energy phosphate bond. Consequently, in the subsequent exchange reaction with inorganic phosphate (a phosphorolysis, or transacylation to phosphate), a high-energy carboxyl phosphate is produced. Much of the energy liberated in the oxidation of the aldehyde group to a carboxyl group is therefore conserved. Another physiologically important consequence is that the reaction becomes reversible.

The high-energy phosphate bond produced in the oxidative step is converted into ATP, the "common currency" of bioenergetics, by means of phosphoglycerate kinase, one of the reversible phosphokinases (p. 247). In the presence of Mg^{++}, the kinase transfers the carboxyl phosphate of the diphosphoglyceric acid to ADP, forming ATP and 3-phosphoglyceric acid. Since each mol of hexose metabolized results in the formation of two mols of triose, two high-energy phosphates are produced in this and a subsequent exergonic reaction in glycolysis.

FORMATION OF LACTATE (OR ETHANOL) (REACTIONS 10–13, 10–15, FIG. 72). 3-Phosphoglyceric acid is reversibly converted to 2-phosphoglyceric acid by phosphoglyceromutase (p. 248), utilizing 2,3-diphosphoglyceric acid as a coenzyme.

2-Phosphoglyceric acid undergoes a reversible dehydration to phosphoenolpyruvic acid under the influence of enolase (p. 241). Mg^{++}

is required for the action of this enzyme; inhibition by fluoride in the presence of phosphate is explained by the formation of a magnesium fluorophosphate. The phosphate linkage in phosphoenolpyruvic acid is of the high-energy type (p. 375), and is reversibly transferred to ADP by pyruvate kinase (p. 247) in the presence of Mg^{++} and K^+. Two mols of high-energy phosphate are produced per mol of hexose metabolized.

The enolpyruvic acid formed in the preceding step spontaneously reverts to the more stable keto tautomer. At the stage of pyruvic acid, there is a bifurcation in the metabolic pathway, the route taken depending on the organism involved.

The reactions described up to this point take place in yeast as well as animals. There is an anaerobic pyruvic decarboxylase ("carboxylase," p. 243) in the yeast cell which converts pyruvic acid to CO_2 and acetaldehyde. Thiamine pyrophosphate ("cocarboxylase," p. 172) and Mg^{++} are required. Acetaldehyde is reduced to ethanol, the endproduct of alcoholic fermentation, by means of alcohol dehydrogenase (p. 365) working "in reverse." The $DPN \cdot H_2$ required for this reduction comes from the oxidative step discussed previously. The regenerated DPN can again act as coenzyme for the triose oxidation; thus, it shuttles back and forth between the two reactions in a cycle of its own.

In animal tissues, the decarboxylation of pyruvic acid is oxidative (p. 397). Under anaerobic conditions, pyruvic acid is reduced to L-lactic acid by lactic dehydrogenase (p. 365) and $DPN \cdot H_2$, the reduced coenzyme coming from a catalytic cycle analogous to that described above.

REVERSIBILITY. All of the reactions from glycogen to lactic acid are reversible, at least with respect to the organic molecules involved. Any phosphorylations of the "irreversible phosphokinase" type are reversed only in the sense that the phosphate ester may be hydrolyzed by a phosphatase. For example, fructose-1,6-diphosphate can be converted to fructose-6-phosphate, but by hydrolysis, not by transfer of the phosphate to ADP, which would be impossible energetically. Similarly, glucose can be formed from glucose-6-phosphate in the liver (not in muscle) by a specific phosphatase, not by reversal of the hexokinase reaction. The reversal of glycolysis therefore entails a loss of energy, but the reversal of any exergonic process must necessarily be endergonic.

OTHER HEXOSES. As indicated previously, a number of hexoses are known to form and be synthesized from glucose (and glycogen). Since these interconversions proceed largely by way of the glycolytic path, it is appropriate to consider them at this point.

The hexokinase of brain (p. 247) forms the 6-phosphate esters from glucose, fructose, and mannose. In muscle, separate glucokinases and fructokinases exist, producing glucose-6-phosphate and fructose-1-phosphate, respectively. A similar situation obtains in liver, in which tissue there is also a phosphokinase which phosphorylates galactose in the 1 position (p. 247). In all cases, ATP is the source of the phosphate group.

Fructose-6-phosphate is on the main glycolytic pathway. Fructose-1-phosphate is taken into this pathway by conversion to fructose-1,6-diphosphate, by means of ATP and a phosphofructokinase different from that which acts on fructose-6-phosphate. The fact that fructose can bypass glucose formation for catabolic purposes is indicated by the utilization of the former under conditions in which glucose phosphorylation is inhibited.

Mannose-6--phosphate is reversibly converted to glucose-6-phosphate by an isomerase (p. 242) in muscle. It is not certain whether this conversion is direct or proceeds via fructose-6-phosphate.

Galactose-1-phosphate is transformed to glucose-1-phosphate by phosphogalactoisomerase, also called "galactowaldenase", in the presence of the coenzyme, uridine-diphosphate-glucose (p. 244). It has been suggested that the galactowaldenase reaction takes place in two steps:

$$\text{Gal—1—PO}_4 \quad \text{UDP—Glu}$$
$$\text{Glu—1—PO}_4 \quad \text{UDP—Gal}$$

$$(1) \qquad\qquad (2)$$

The first reaction involves an exchange of hexose moieties between substrate and coenzyme, followed by the actual Walden inversion of C_4 of the hexose within the molecule of the coenzyme. It is not known whether the synthesis of galactose from glucose in the animal takes place by a simple reversal of these reactions.

Galactose is the probable precursor of the galactosamine found in certain mucopolysaccharides (p. 18), occurs as such in the glycolipids (p. 34), and, with glucose, forms the disaccharide, lactose, secreted in milk (p. 12).

ENERGETICS OF FERMENTATION AND GLYCOLYSIS. The fermenting yeast cell degrades glucose, a compound of relatively high potential energy, to CO_2 and ethanol, compounds of low potential energy (p. 374). The free energy (p. 371) liberated in this process amounts to 50,000 cal. Examination of Figure 72 reveals that two high-energy phosphate bonds of ATP are expended in the course of transforming glucose to these catabolic products, one at the hexokinase step, and one in the formation of hexose diphosphate. On the other hand, four new high-energy phosphate bonds are generated, two in the oxidative step, and two as a result of the enolase reaction (in each case, *two* mols of triose must be considered per mol of hexose metabolized). Consequently, a net synthesis of two high-energy phosphate bonds occurs. Taking the free energy of formation of an ATP pyrophosphate bond to be 12,000 cal., then 24,000 cal., or 48 per cent of the free energy liberated in fermentation is captured and available to the organism for various purposes.

The free energy liberated in glycolysis from glucose is about 36,000 cal. Since the phosphorylation reactions are essentially the same as in fermentation, it follows that 67 per cent of the liberated free energy is recovered. Superficially, it would appear that a greater yield of high-energy phosphate could be obtained if the glycolytic process began with glycogen instead of glucose, since the loss of one high-energy bond in the hexokinase reaction would be avoided. As a matter of fact, the energy level of glycogen is sufficiently above that of glucose so as to practically nullify the apparent gain. Furthermore, in order to derive net energy from glycogen, it must be synthesized from glucose or other hexoses via the phosphokinase reactions. Glycogen is formed from non-carbohydrate sources only by means of a reversal of the entire glycolytic sequence, a process which consumes more energy than the glycogen can again produce.

INTRACELLULAR LOCALIZATION. The enzymes and cofactors necessary for glycolysis are found in the particle-free supernatant fraction of the cytoplasm, as prepared by differential centrifugation (p. 254). This fact may be of importance in the regulation of the balance between the anaerobic and aerobic metabolism of carbohydrate (p. 402).

AEROBIC METABOLISM OF CARBOHYDRATE

Although various attempts have been made to show that the aerobic metabolism of carbohydrate proceeds by a pathway entirely separate and distinct from the anaerobic, most of the available evidence indicates that the major route of aerobic metabolism in animals is identical with the anaerobic through the stage of pyruvic acid. Aerobically, pyruvic acid is oxidized to CO_2 and H_2O, instead of being reduced to lactic acid. Part of the explanation for this change lies in the oxidation of DPN·H_2 (from the oxidative step of glycolysis) via the respiratory chain of catalysts (p. 366) under aerobic conditions; it is therefore not available for the reduction of pyruvic to lactic acid by lactic dehydrogenase. If a period of anaerobiosis is followed by one of aerobiosis, accumulated lactic acid is oxidized to pyruvic acid by lactic dehydrogenase, DPN being the hydrogen acceptor. Therefore, in any case, pyruvic acid is the initial compound to be considered in the strictly aerobic metabolism of carbohydrate.

INITIAL OXIDATION OF PYRUVIC ACID. The oxidative decarboxylase which attacks pyruvic acid (p. 365) is a rather complex system, the details of which are still in the process of being elucidated. For didactic purposes, the reaction may be regarded as occuring in three steps:

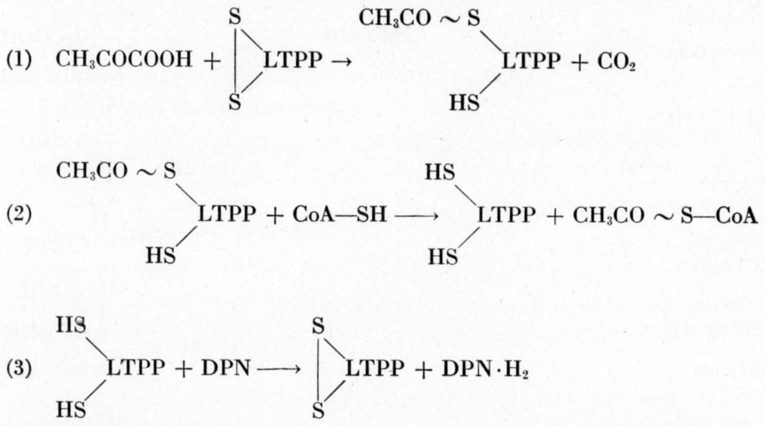

$$(1) \quad CH_3COCOOH + \underset{S}{\overset{S}{\diagdown}}\diagup LTPP \rightarrow \underset{HS}{\overset{CH_3CO \sim S}{\diagdown}}\diagup LTPP + CO_2$$

$$(2) \quad \underset{HS}{\overset{CH_3CO \sim S}{\diagdown}}\diagup LTPP + CoA{-}SH \longrightarrow \underset{HS}{\overset{HS}{\diagdown}}\diagup LTPP + CH_3CO \sim S{-}CoA$$

$$(3) \quad \underset{HS}{\overset{HS}{\diagdown}}\diagup LTPP + DPN \longrightarrow \underset{S}{\overset{S}{\diagdown}}\diagup LTPP + DPN{\cdot}H_2$$

In the first step, pyruvic acid condenses with the disulfide form of lipothiamide pyrophosphate* ("LTPP," p. 360, shown above with its reactive group written out separately), losing a molecule of CO_2 in the process. The energy yielded by the concomitant dehydrogenation is retained in the reaction product, since the thioester linkage is energetically equivalent to a high-energy phosphate bond (p. 376). Reaction of the acetylated LTPP with the sulfhydryl group of CoA (p. 104) in a "thioacyl exchange" produces acetyl-CoA and the disulfhydryl form of LTPP, which is reconverted to the disulfide form by transfer of hydrogen atoms to DPN. Reoxidation of $DPN{\cdot}H_2$ proceeds via the usual aerobic oxidative chain of catalysts.

Acetyl-CoA is a very versatile intermediary metabolite. In addition to its participation in carbohydrate oxidation, it is formed in the course of the catabolism of fatty acids (p. 450) and certain amino acids (p. 517). Although the concern at this point is with the oxidation of this substance, it has many anabolic uses in the body (p. 454).

TRICARBOXYLIC ACID CYCLE. The complete oxidation of the acetyl moiety of acetyl-CoA is effected by means of a cyclic metabolic mechanism known variously as the "citric acid," "tricarboxylic acid," or "Krebs" cycle (this last referring to the man largely responsible for its formulation). Figure 73 illustrates the reactions involved.

---

* At present it is uncertain whether lipoic acid participates in these reactions in the free state or in the conjugate form shown. This uncertainty does not materially affect the mechanism indicated above.

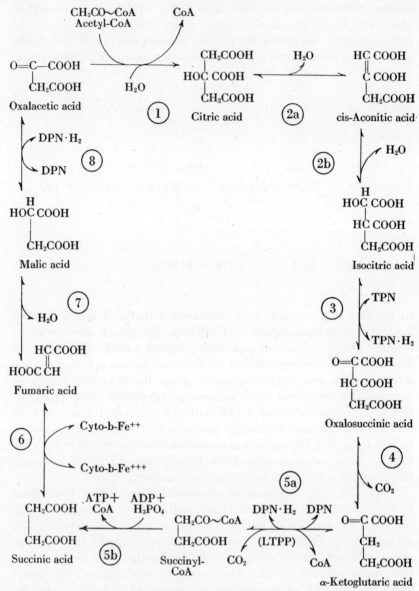

Fig. 73. *Tricarboxylic acid cycle*

The initial reaction in this cycle (Reaction 1, Fig. 73) is a condensation between oxalacetic acid and acetyl-CoA, forming citric acid and regenerating CoA. For practical purposes this reaction can be considered irreversible, since it proceeds with the liberation of some 7720 cal. of free energy. It should be noted that the oxidation of pyruvic acid to the acetyl level permits one potential "substrate phosphorylation" (p. 378), if the $\sim$ S bond in acetyl-CoA is so used. If the acetyl moiety is to be oxidized by way of the tricarboxylic acid cycle, however, this potential $\sim PO_4$ is sacrificed to "drive" the citrate condensation. The condensing enzyme, which has been obtained in crystalline form, apparently requires no coenzyme or prosthetic group for its action.

Aconitase (p. 243) catalyzes the second reaction of the cycle (Reaction 2 a, b, Fig. 73), which involves an equilibration between citric, cis-aconitic, and isocitric acids. The over-all isomerization takes place stepwise, a molecule of water being first removed to create a double bond, then replaced in such a way as to locate the hydroxyl group in a new position. Although the equilibrium of the isolated system favors citric acid, it is easily reversed if the isocitric acid is removed by a subsequent reaction. It has been reported that Fe^{++} is a cofactor of aconitase. The enzyme is inhibited by *trans*-aconitic acid (competing with cis-aconitic) and fluoroacetic acid. The latter compound is converted to fluorocitric acid, the actual inhibitor, by some evidently uncritical enzymes which normally act on acetic acid.

Isocitric acid is reversibly oxidized (Reaction 3, Fig. 73) to oxalosuccinic acid by isocitric dehydrogenase (p. 365), an enzyme requiring TPN. The two hydrogen atoms acquired by the coenzyme are oxidized to water via the respiratory chain of catalysts (p. 366). As yet it has not been possible to separate isocitric dehydrogenase activity from the oxalosuccinic decarboxylase activity discussed below. The two reactions may be catalyzed by the same enzyme, as in the case of the "malic enzyme" (p. 367).

Oxalosuccinic acid, like many β-keto acids, is rather unstable and decarboxylates spontaneously. In animal tissues, this reaction (Reaction 4, Fig. 73) is catalyzed by an enzyme (perhaps the apoenzyme concerned with isocitric acid dehydrogenation) requiring Mn^{++} (p. 242). The decarboxylation is non-oxidative, producing α-ketoglutaric acid. Although the equilibrium is unfavorable, uptake of CO_2 can be made to occur under certain conditions (p. 407), suggesting a possible physiological reversal of the reaction.

The oxidative decarboxylation of α-ketoglutaric acid (Reaction 5 a, b, Fig. 73) is quite similar to that of pyruvic acid (p. 397). Although the details are not entirely settled, the mechanism of the reaction may be outlined tentatively as shown at the top of page 400.

Simultaneous dehydrogenation and decarboxylation of α-ketoglutaric acid produces a succinyl derivative of LTPP (p. 360), which exchanges its high-energy thioester linkage (p. 367) with CoA (p. 104). The disulfide form of LTPP is regenerated by reaction with DPN; $DPN \cdot H_2$ is reoxidized via the aerobic oxidative chain. A high-energy phosphate bond is formed by reaction of succinyl-CoA with inor-

$$
\text{(1)} \quad HOOCCH_2CH_2COCOOH + \underset{S}{\overset{S}{\big|}}LTPP \rightarrow \overset{HOOCCH_2CH_2CO\frown S}{\underset{HS}{\Big\rangle}}LTPP + CO_2
$$

$$
\text{(2)} \quad \overset{HOOCCH_2CH_2CO\frown S}{\underset{HS}{\Big\rangle}}LTPP + CoA\!-\!SH \rightarrow \overset{HS}{\underset{HS}{\Big\rangle}}LTPP + HOOCCH_2CH_2CO \sim S\!-\!CoA
$$

$$
\text{(3)} \quad \overset{HS}{\underset{HS}{\Big\rangle}}LTPP + DPN \rightarrow \overset{S}{\underset{S}{\big|}}LTPP + DPN\!\cdot\!H_2
$$

(4) $HOOCCH_2CH_2CO\frown S\!-\!CoA + H_3PO_4 + ADP \rightarrow HOOCCH_2CH_2COOH + CoA\!-\!SH + ATP$

The oxidative decarboxylation of α-ketoglutaric acid.

ganic phosphate and ADP ("substrate phosphorylation," p. 378). A phosphorylated derivative of CoA may be an intermediate. In alternative reactions, succinyl-CoA may be used in the acylation of sulfonamides (p. 404) and in the synthesis of the porphyrin ring (p. 587). There is evidence that, in animal tissues, succinic acid cannot directly form α-ketoglutaric acid, although the reaction is reversible from the stage of succinyl-CoA.

Succinic acid is reversibly oxidized to fumaric acid (Reaction 6, Fig. 73) by succinic dehydrogenase (p. 366), a system which is coupled rather directly to the cytochromes. If, as seems possible, no flavoprotein carrier is involved, the hydrogen atoms released during the reaction would donate their electrons to the cytochromes and enter the medium as hydrogen ions. The inhibition of succinic dehydrogenase by malonic acid is the classic example of competitive inhibition (p. 636). Sulfhydryl groups are involved in the combination of the enzyme with its substrate as well as with inhibitors such as malonic acid.

Fumaric acid is reversibly hydrated to malic acid (Reaction 7, Fig. 73) by fumarase (p. 242), an "adding and removing" enzyme. No coenzyme is required, but phosphate is said to have an activating effect.

Although a special reaction is open to it in liver (p. 407), in the tissues generally malic acid is reversibly dehydrogenated (Reaction 8, Fig. 73) to oxalacetic acid by malic dehydrogenase (p. 365) and DPN. TPN can also act as the coenzyme, but at a slower rate. The reduced coenzyme is oxidized by the aerobic oxidative chain (p. 366). The cycle is thus completed with the formation of oxalacetic acid, which can now react with another molecule of acetyl-CoA.

Theoretically, one molecule of oxalacetic acid (being regenerated in the cycle as described) can catalyze the oxidation of an infinite number of acetyl groups. Practically speaking, quantities of oxalacetic acid above the minimum are probably necessary in order that the cycle proceed at a rapid enough rate for physiological requirements. Nevertheless, relatively small amounts of oxalacetic acid may suffice in many tissues. In certain tissues, however, e.g., liver, a continuous loss of oxalacetic acid occurs via decarboxylation and other side reactions. In such cases the supply of oxalacetic acid may be maintained by synthesis from pyruvic acid by CO_2 assimilation (p. 407).

The over-all oxidation of pyruvic acid is represented by:

$$CH_3COCOOH + 5 (O) \rightarrow 2H_2O + 3CO_2.$$

As can be seen in Figure 73, the three carbon atoms of pyruvic acid are accounted for as three molecules of CO_2, one produced initially in the formation of acetyl-CoA, the others in the cycle proper. Five pairs of hydrogen atoms are combined with five atoms of oxygen to form water by way of the oxidative chain. Three molecules of water are taken up in hydration reactions, so that the final result corresponds to the above equation.

ENERGETICS OF AEROBIC OXIDATION OF CARBOHYDRATE. Of the 686,000 cal. of free energy liberated in the complete oxidation of glucose to CO_2 and H_2O (p. 372), less than 10 per cent is produced in the anaerobic phase of the process (p. 395). The tricarboxylic acid cycle is the major source of the free energy of higher organisms. An estimate of the actual amount of free energy recovered by the organism under aerobic conditions can be made as shown in Table 43. As calculated

Table 43. High-energy Phosphate Balance in Aerobic Degradation of a Mol of Glucose

REACTION	HIGH-ENERGY PHOSPHATE EXPENDED	SUBSTRATE PHOSPHORYLATION	OXIDATIVE CHAIN PHOSPHORYLATION	NET
Hexokinase	−1			−1
Phosphohexokinase	−1			−1
Oxidative step (×2)		+2	+6	+8
Enolase step (×2)		+2		+2
Pyruvate → citrate (×2)	−2 (see text)	+2 (see text)	+6	+6
Isocitrate → Oxalosuccinate (×2)			+6	+6
Ketoglutarate → succinate (×2)		+2	+6	+8
Succinate → fumarate (×2)			+4	+4
Malate → oxalacetate (×2)			+6	+6
			Total	+38

previously for glycolysis (p. 395), two high-energy phosphate bonds are expended in phosphorylations of hexose and phosphohexose, whereas four such bonds are generated by substrate phosphorylations (oxidative step and enolase reaction). Under aerobic conditions, the DPN·H$_2$ produced in the oxidative reaction of glycolysis is oxidized by the respiratory chain of catalysts, the two pairs of hydrogen atoms furnishing six high-energy bonds in the process (p. 380).

The oxidation of two molecules of pyruvic acid to acetyl-CoA produces the expected six high-energy bonds due to reoxidation of DPN·H$_2$. Two potential substrate phosphorylations are sacrificed in the citrate condensation. In the cycle proper, the oxidation of TPN·H$_2$ and DPN·H$_2$ accounts for six high-energy bonds in the oxidation of each two molecules of isocitric, α-ketoglutaric, and malic acids. In addition, substrate phosphorylation occurs in the case of ketoglutarate. Oxidation of succinic to fumaric acid, since it bypasses a part of the oxidative chain, yields only four high-energy bonds per two molecules.

As can be seen in Table 43, a total of 38 high-energy phosphate bonds is produced per molecule of hexose completely oxidized. Taking the average free energy of such a bond as 12,000 cal., a total of 456,000 cal. is recovered by the organism from the 686,000 cal. made available in the course of the reactions, an efficiency of 67 per cent.

Under normal physiological conditions, the regulatory mechanisms of the cell maintain a certain balance between the rates of generation and utilization of high-energy phosphate. There are indications (from *in vitro* experiments) that overproduction of high-energy bonds is prevented, in the absence of sufficient utilization in the performance of work, by the action of ATP-ase (p. 232). The balance between phosphorylation and dephosphorylation may be concerned in the Pasteur effect, discussed below.

INTRACELLULAR LOCALIZATION. The systems necessary for the initial oxidation of pyruvic acid, the reactions of the tricarboxylic acid cycle, and oxidative chain phosphorylation are largely concentrated in the mitochondria (p. 254). The spatial separation of these systems from those of glycolysis (p. 396) may have some physiological significance.

PASTEUR EFFECT. When tissue slices are incubated in the presence of glucose under anaerobic conditions, the glucose is converted to lactic acid (glycolysis) at a rate which is characteristic of the individual tissue. In the presence of oxygen, the utilization of glucose is decreased and the accumulation of lactic acid is largely suppressed (exceptions are noted below). This phenomenon is known as the "Pasteur effect," after its discoverer. Many conflicting explanations of this effect have been proposed, no one of which is universally accepted at this time. Whatever the explanation, the Pasteur effect can be regarded as a regulatory mechanism which operates to increase the consumption of fuel under conditions in which the energy-yield per unit of fuel is decreased. Since only two high-energy phosphate bonds are produced per molecule of hexose during glycolysis, whereas thirty-eight are formed in complete oxidation, it is obvious that an augmented consumption of glucose under anaerobiosis would tend to counteract the lower yield of energy per molecule. The adjustment falls short of the ideal; the average tissue can increase its consumption of glucose anaerobically to the point of yielding one-third to one-half the energy normally obtained by the aerobic catabolism of a lesser quantity of glucose.

Retina, kidney medulla, intestinal mucosa, and certain tumors continue to form appreciable quantities of lactic acid even in the presence of oxygen (aerobic glycolysis). Intestinal mucosa, as a matter of fact, exhibits no Pasteur effect.

PENTOSE METABOLISM

A tentative scheme of pentose metabolism, based on current investigations, is presented in Figure 74. The best established sequence of reactions is that concerned with the synthesis of ribose. It will be noted that the sequence begins with glucose-6-phosphate, and that it opens to this compound an aerobic alternative to the glycolytic pathway. In the presence of glucose-6-phosphate dehydrogenase ("Zwischenferment") and TPN, glucose-6-phosphate is first oxidized to gluconic acid-6-phosphate. A second enzyme, also requiring TPN, then oxidizes the acid at the third carbon atom. It is not certain whether the decarboxylation of the carboxyl group is catalyzed by the dehydrogenase, or occurs as a subsequent reaction. In any case, the first product to be identified is the phosphoketose, ribulose-5-phosphate. This is in equilibrium with ribose-5-phosphate, presumably through an enediol, catalyzed by phosphoriboisomerase. A phosphoribomutase converts the 5-phosphate to the 1-phosphate, which can be used in the synthesis of nucleosides (p. 566).

There is little information on the catabolism of ribose. It is possible that a reversal of the steps from hexose phosphate may occur, enabling ribose to be metabolized via the glycolytic route. Another pathway is indicated by the existence of a pentose aldolase, catalyzing the cleavage of ribose-5-phosphate to glyceraldehyde-phosphate and a "diose," which may be glycolaldehyde. (Thiamine pyrophosphate is said to be the coenzyme.) The triose could join the glycolytic pathway, whereas the diose may be oxidized to oxalic acid and excreted (p. 773), or may be converted to glyoxylic acid and enter into the metabolism of glycine and "formate" (p. 520). A 7-carbon keto sugar (sedoheptulose) has been suggested recently as an intermediate in ribose metabolism.

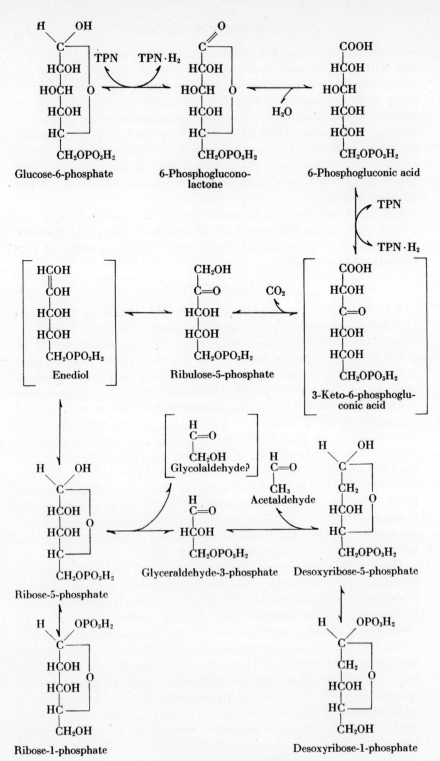

Fig. 74. Pentose metabolism

There is no evidence that desoxyribose is formed directly from a hexose. It can be synthesized reversibly by an aldolase type of reaction between glyceraldehyde phosphate and acetaldehyde. The latter may be derived physiologically from a non-oxidative decarboxylation of pyruvic acid. Desoxyribose-5-phosphate, the product of the condensation, is converted to the 1-phosphate by a mutase, after which transformation it can enter into nucleoside metabolism (p. 566).

The catabolism of desoxyribose may involve the reversal of its synthesis. Triose phosphate can be disposed of as indicated previously; acetaldehyde may be oxidized to the acetyl level and combusted by way of the tricarboxylic acid cycle.

The rare pentose, L-ketoxylose, excreted in the inborn error of metabolism known as pentosuria (p. 778), may be derived from D-glucuronic acid (p. 17).

METABOLISM OF SUBSTITUTED AND DERIVED CARBOHYDRATES

ALCOHOLS AND CYCLITOLS. Although a number of sugar alcohols are capable of being metabolized, there is no evidence that any of these substances other than glycerol are natural intermediates in metabolism. Glycerol is an important constituent of several types of lipids (p. 28). It is related to the compounds of the glycolytic series by the following reactions:

$$\text{Glycerol} \underset{\text{phosphatases}}{\overset{\text{ATP} + \text{a phosphokinase}}{\rightleftharpoons}} \text{L--}\alpha\text{--glycero-phosphate} \underset{}{\overset{\alpha\text{--glycerophosphate dehydrogenase} + \text{DPN}}{\rightleftharpoons}} \text{dihydroxy-acetone-phosphate}$$

In this way, depending on physiological needs, glycerol can be synthesized from glucose, or conversely can form the latter.

Inositol (p. 21) is converted to glucose in small amounts. It is not certain that this is a major pathway of inositol metabolism.

AMINO SUGARS AND ACIDIC CARBOHYDRATES. Little is known of the metabolism of the amino sugars (p. 17). Glucosamine and galactosamine are acetylated on the nitrogen by acetyl-CoA in the presence of a transacetylase in liver, the N-acetyl derivatives thus formed probably being used in the synthesis of the mucopolysaccharides (p. 18). Glucosamine is phosphorylated by ATP and hexokinase (forming the 6-phosphate), but the physiological significance of this reaction is not known.

Glucuronic acid (p. 17) is used by the organism for coupling or conjugation with many substances of natural and artificial origin in what have been called "detoxication reactions" (p. 281). Although there is evidence that the synthesis of glucuronic acid may take place by means of a condensation of two triose fragments, recent data have shown a direct conversion of C^{14}-labeled glucose to glucuronic acid, with little cleavage of the 6-carbon chain. In addition to its excretion in urine, glucuronic acid is also oxidized to CO_2 by unknown pathways. Its possible role as a precursor of L-ketoxylose was mentioned previously.

In the rat, a direct conversion has been demonstrated of carbon 1 of glucose (labeled with C^{14}) to carbon 6 of ascorbic acid (p. 141), indicating that the non-acidic end of the vitamin is derived from the aldehyde end of the sugar. The catabolism of ascorbic acid results in the formation of CO_2 and oxalic acid.

The sulfatation reactions which form certain of the acidic sugar units of the mucopolysaccharides (p. 18) are largely unknown, although it has been demonstrated that radioactive sulfate (with S^{35}) is incorporated into the chondroitinsulfuric acid (p. 20) of cartilage.

ROLE OF LIVER IN CARBOHYDRATE METABOLISM

GLYCOGENESIS AND GLYCOGENOLYSIS. In addition to the general reactions of carbohydrate metabolism shown in Figure 72, the liver is able to perform certain transformations peculiar to itself. One of these is the glucose-6-phosphatase reaction. As a result of the presence of this specific phosphatase in liver, the following equilibria obtain:

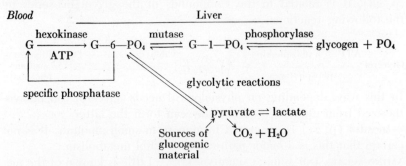

Glycogenesis (p. 385) in liver can occur from blood glucose or from any substance capable of giving rise to pyruvate. In the latter category are glycerol (p. 405), blood lactate (from muscle, p. 409), and the glucogenic amino acids (p. 516).

Owing to the glucose-6-phosphatase, liver glycogen can contribute directly to blood sugar (glycogenolysis, p. 385) by way of glucose-1-phosphate and glucose-6-phosphate. (In certain tissues, non-specific phosphatases may substitute for glucose-6-phosphatase.) It should be pointed out that, according to the above scheme, glucogenic substances in liver can form blood sugar without necessarily passing through the stage of liver glycogen.

The concentration of glycogen in the liver at any time is the resultant of glycogenolysis and the various routes of glycogenesis, the influx of dietary carbohydrate being one of the most important of the latter. Human liver contains, on the average, some 5–6 per cent glycogen. In dogs, the concentration may rise to 10–15 per cent after heavy carbohydrate feeding, and falls to less than 1 per cent on fasting. In certain cases of glycogen storage disease in human beings (von Gierke's disease), a deficiency of glucose-6-phosphatase has been found in the liver. Inability to carry out glycogenolysis, in the face of undiminished glycogenesis from blood sugar, probably accounts for the abnormal accumulation of liver glycogen in these subjects. The level of the blood sugar itself is a major factor in determining the relative rates of glycogenesis and glycogenolysis (p. 420). Endocrine influence on the several reactions involved is discussed elsewhere (p. 422).

GLUCONEOGENESIS. The major conversions of other types of foodstuffs into carbohydrate occur in the liver. The pathway whereby glycerol may be converted to glucose was indicated previously. This, however, is a relatively minor source of carbohydrate; the chief gluconeogenetic substances are the amino acids. The nitrogen-free carbon skeletons of certain amino acids, as will be shown elsewhere (p. 516), are capable of conversion to pyruvic acid, from which point glucose or glycogen can be formed by reversal of the glycolytic reactions. This process is accelerated under conditions of carbohydrate deprivation. Gluconeogenesis from amino acids is under the control of adrenal cortical hormones (p. 680).

ASSIMILATION OF CO_2. Although carbon dioxide is usually considered a waste product of metabolism, ample evidence has been accumulated in recent years to support the view that this substance is an important building-block in anabolic reactions. The utilization of CO_2 in the synthesis of purines and pyrimidines is discussed elsewhere (pp. 567, 571).

Most examples of CO_2 assimilation in animal tissues have been found to involve reversal of the decarboxylation of β-keto acids. The case of oxalosuccinic acid has been mentioned already (p. 399). Assimilation by means of this reaction is probably not a significant factor under physiological conditions. The reactions which appear to account for much of the CO_2 assimilatory activity of the animal body occur largely in liver, and may be regarded as adjuncts to the reactions of the tricarboxylic acid cycle. One such reaction in liver is the reversible β-decarboxylation of oxalacetic to pyruvic acid, which, however, is known to be much more complex than appears on the surface. A second reaction is due to the "malic enzyme," which catalyzes a simultaneous oxidation and decarboxylation of malic to pyruvic acid, completely bypassing the stage of oxalacetic acid. A tentative scheme of these reactions and their relationship to the tricarboxylic acid proper is shown below:

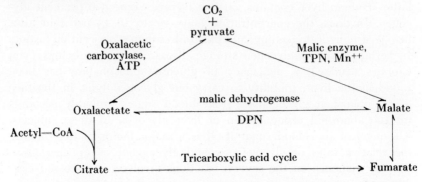

The physiological significance of the above reactions would seem to be that the liver, in contrast to other tissues in which such reactions are not so well developed, can readily synthesize its own supply of catalytic acids for the cycle (e.g., oxalacetic), as long as a source of pyruvate is available. (CO_2, of course, is always in plentiful supply in any living tissue.) During the metabolism of carbohydrate, pyruvic acid is formed as a normal intermediate, hence the aerobic catabolism of carbohydrate is never retarded as a consequence of lack of oxalacetate. In the case of fatty acid catabolism, on the other hand, the provision of adequate oxalacetate from carbohydrate metabolism may be an important factor in determining whether the fatty acids will be completely oxidized to CO_2, or shunted into ketone bodies as a side reaction (p. 450).

MUSCLE IN CARBOHYDRATE METABOLISM

The following discussions of carbohydrate metabolism will be concerned chiefly with skeletal muscle. Certain peculiarities of other muscle masses should be noted, however. Cardiac muscle, for example, differs from skeletal in its ability to utilize blood lactate, and in the increase in its glycogen content during starvation. Diaphragm, in contrast to skeletal muscle, is able to reverse the glycolytic sequence of reactions and synthesize glycogen from pyruvate or lactate.
GLYCOGENESIS. The formation of muscle glycogen from blood glucose follows the same path as in liver (Reactions 1–3, Fig. 72 [p. 390]). The absence of glucose-6-phosphatase from muscle, however, makes it impossible for muscle glycogen to contribute directly to blood sugar; consequently glycogenolysis, as ordinarily defined, does not occur in muscle. It should be noted that non-specific phosphatases, which might be expected to catalyze the same reaction, are also virtually absent from muscle.

The level of muscle glycogen varies with the dietary intake of carbohydrate and its precursors, but does not fluctuate as widely as liver glycogen. The average concentration in human muscle is 0.4–0.6 per cent. In general, muscle glycogen is subject to the same hormonal controls as liver glycogen (p. 422), except in the case of the hyperglycemic factor of the pancreas (p. 424). As discussed below, muscle glycogen is probably not formed to any extent by gluconeogenesis; its sole source would thus seem to be blood glucose.

GLYCOLYSIS. The glycolytic reactions in muscle follow the general course outlined previously. In muscle, however, the process seems to be irreversible, since experiments have shown that isotopically labeled lactic acid is not converted to labeled glycogen in the perfused muscle, although it is readily oxidized to CO_2. The reason for the irreversibility has not been definitely established, although the reported deficiency in skeletal muscle of fructose-1,6-diphosphatase, a necessary enzyme on the return path, may be relevant. Another consideration is the great permeability of muscle to lactic acid; any that is formed (under anaerobic conditions) is readily lost to the blood. This lactic acid is taken up by the liver, and may be converted to glycogen or blood glucose, the complete route of: blood glucose $\rightarrow$ muscle glycogen $\rightarrow$ lactate $\rightarrow$ liver glucose-6-phosphate $\rightarrow$ blood glucose, being known as the Cori cycle (p. 386).

The problem of the relative importance of the anaerobic and aerobic catabolism of carbohydrate in muscle is discussed below in connection with muscle contraction. It may be noted at this point, however, that the lactic acid content of the blood in the resting or moderately active organism is probably largely derived from extramuscular tissues, such as the erythrocytes (p. 738) and those tissues characterized by a significant rate of aerobic glycolysis (p. 403).

MUSCLE CONTRACTION. (*a*) INTRODUCTION. As a form of work (mechanical), it is to be expected that muscle contraction would use as its source of energy that common currency of bioenergetics, ATP (p. 380). It might also be surmised that the nature of the phenomenon would be more or less as follows:

1. Interaction of ATP and the contractile substance of muscle, probably producing ADP and a phosphorylated (or in some other way "activated") form of the contractile substance.

2. Contraction of the substance, thus performing work, and liberation of inorganic phosphate in the process.

3. Spontaneous reversion of the "deactivated" substance to a state of lower potential energy, the resting or relaxed state of muscle.

It must be confessed at this point that, whereas current data are not in disagreement with the hypothetical sequence of events outlined above, there is, on the other hand, no direct proof of the over-all scheme, and much disagreement as to details. The problem is being actively investigated at the present time. All that can be done in this section, therefore, is to report the "current state of the art."

(b) MODEL EXPERIMENTS. Before describing in detail the constituents of muscle and their purported roles in contraction, it may be helpful to present certain experiments which constitute at least partial proof that the data obtained from fractionated and highly simplified systems have some physiological relevance.

If a strip of skeletal muscle is stored in 50 per cent glycerol at 0° C. for a time, the more soluble activators and cofactors are extracted, leaving behind the "structural" materials. Bundles of fibers taken from this preparation will, in the presence of salts (KCl or NaCl) and small amounts of Mg^{++}, contract when ATP is added to the suspending medium. The tension developed is the same as that produced by the original muscle *in vivo*. If the glycerinated muscle is homogenized to a pulp in water and suspended in dilute KCl, a loose, flocculent precipitate is formed. The addition of ATP to this system causes what has been called "superprecipitation," formation of a compact, granular precipitate, which settles out readily. This phenomenon has been regarded as "contraction without architecture."

At the other end of the scale, there can be produced from muscle a substance called "actomyosin" (discussed in detail below), which, in the form of gels or flocs, also undergoes superprecipitation under the influence of ATP. Furthermore, it is possible to spin actomyosin, under proper conditions, into threads which contract in the presence of ATP.

From experiments such as these it has been concluded: (1) that the true contractile substance of muscle is actomyosin; (2) that the *in vitro* reactions of actomyosin are, to a considerable degree, related to the phenomena produced in the glycerinated muscle; (3) that these phenomena are basically similar to those occurring in the intact muscle; (4) that the fundamental contractile act involves some sort of interaction between actomyosin and ATP.

(c) PROTEINS OF MUSCLE. In addition to the proteins to be mentioned in this section, certain non-protein substances naturally play important roles in contraction, viz., ATP, Mg^{++}, Ca^{++}, K^+, and creatine. The proteins, however, claim our main attention, since a phenomenon such as contraction of a muscle on the macro scale must be a reflection of some type of "molecular" contraction on the micro scale, and contractions of significant magnitude can be undergone by few types of molecules other than proteins.

If minced muscle is extracted with dilute salt solutions, of a molarity corresponding to that existing in the native muscle, a mixture of albumins and globulins is obtained. Dialysis of this extract causes precipitation of a fraction known as "globulin X," a little-investigated mixture of proteins constituting 10–20 per cent of the total protein of muscle. A similar percentage of the total protein remains dissolved in the albumin fraction, called "myogen." Many of the enzymes of glycolysis are found in this fraction. Although the proteins of the dilute salt extract account for about 40 per cent of the total protein of muscle, they seem to have no direct connection with the contractile event proper. This involves, rather, two proteins, actin and myosin, which are extractable only with concentrated salt solutions.

Myosin is a fibrous protein (approximate dimensions—1500 Å x 30–35 Å) with a molecular weight of 850,000, comprising about 45 per cent of the total protein of muscle. It has marked ability to bind ions, such as Ca^{++}, K^+, and Mg^{++}. As ordinarily prepared, it exists as the Mg^{++} complex. The combination of myosin with ATP or actin, and its ATP-ase activity (discussed below), depend upon intact sulfhydryl groups in the myosin.

The most striking property of myosin is its activity as an adenosinetriphosphatase (ATP-ase, p. 232). Association of enzymatic action with a "structural" protein has been regarded as such an unusual occurrence that numerous attempts have been made to dissociate the enzyme activity from the myosin proper, but with no clear-cut success. The ATP-ase activity is dependent upon the presence of salts, activation being exhibited by salts of Li^+, Na^+, K^+, NH_4^+, Co^{++}, Mn^{++}, and Ca^{++}. The optimum pH is about 6.5; in the presence of Ca^{++}, a second and stronger optimum is found at pH 9.2. Purified myosin ATP-ase is inhibited by Mg^{++}, especially in the presence of optimal concentrations of Ca^{++}. It has been calculated that, under the conditions prevailing in muscle, myosin ATP-ase breaks down ATP at a rate only $\frac{1}{100}$ of that estimated to occur during contraction. Therefore, there is considerable doubt concerning the physiological importance of myosin ATP-ase (see below, however, under actomyosin ATP-ase).

Myosin has also been found to catalyze the hydrolytic deamination of adenylic acid to inosinic acid and ammonia (p. 240). This reaction proceeds optimally in the pH range 5.9–6.1, and is activated by both Ca^{++} and Mg^{++}. Liberation of ammonia probably is not a significant reaction under physiological conditions in muscle.

It may be mentioned parenthetically that an ATP-ase unrelated to myosin is found in the water-soluble fraction of muscle. This enzyme appears to be a lipoprotein, has an optimum pH of 6.8, is activated by Mg^{++} and inhibited by Ca^{++}. In its natural environment, it has been calculated to have an activity about ten times that of myosin.

Actin differs from myosin in that its most interesting characteristics are physical rather than enzymatic. It can be prepared, in the absence of salts, as a globular protein with a molecular weight of 57,000. This form is known as G-actin, solutions of which have relatively low viscosity. The affinity of actin for Ca^{++} is such that most of the Ca^{++}

of muscle is probably bound to actin. Actin constitutes some 12–15 per cent of the total protein of muscle. It has no known enzyme activity.

Solutions of G-actin undergo marked changes in the presence of salts, including the development of high viscosity and strong streaming birefringence (p. 73). These changes are due to the polymerization of G-actin to F-actin, a fibrous molecule with a molecular weight of about 1.5 million. The conversion requires the presence in the actin of a native group of ATP, which undergoes breakdown to ADP in the course of the reaction. It is thought that, in muscle, actin is normally present in the F-form. Both G- and F-actin combine with myosin, but only the combination involving the latter is of significance for muscle contraction (to be discussed below).

Proteins other than those mentioned, which may have some role in muscle contraction, are tropomyosin, nucleotropomyosin, and contractin. So little is known of these substances, however, that further discussion of them would be unprofitable.

Actomyosin is formed by the combination of F-actin and myosin in the presence of Mg^{++}, in the approximate ratio of one part actin to three parts myosin. This combination is accompanied by a large increase in viscosity and streaming birefringence, indicative of the formation of very long molecules. The complex may be dissociated by urea, high concentrations of salts (2 M KCl), and relatively small amounts of ATP. The character of the effect of ATP on actomyosin depends upon the physical state of the latter. Solutions of actomyosin decrease in viscosity and related properties on the addition of ATP; gels or flocs of actomyosin undergo "superprecipitation," whereas threads of actomyosin contract. As mentioned previously, these properties are very similar to those of the glycerol-extracted muscle fiber.

Actomyosin, as the Mg^{++} complex, is said to be an active ATP-ase at the pH of muscle, but only in salt concentrations below 0.12 M. When added separately, both Mg^{++} and Ca^{++} enhance the ATP-ase activity; together, they inhibit. It is thought by some that actin and myosin are present as separate entities in muscle, combining to form actomyosin only during certain phases of contraction.

(*d*) CONTRACTION. Most current theories of muscle contraction agree that the contractile event proper involves some sort of reaction between actomyosin and ATP, resulting in the over-all formation of contracted actomyosin, ADP, and inorganic phosphate. It is not certain whether the G- to F-actin transformation is a part of the mechanism, and whether combinations and dissociations of myosin and F-actin occur. Also obscure are the mechanisms whereby the energy of ATP is transformed from chemical potential to mechanical work, the nature of the initial stimulus setting off the chain of events, and the possible role of the various ATP-ases.

Although it cannot be pretended that the details of muscle contraction are understood at the present time, a reasonable if oversimplified picture of the chemical events of contraction and recovery can be drawn as follows:

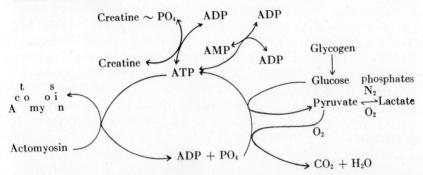

The initial event in contraction is a reaction between actomyosin and ATP, such that a high-energy bond of the latter is split, and, by some as yet unknown mechanism, the energy thus liberated is utilized to actuate the contraction of actomyosin. It will be noted that this phenomenon is completely non-specific as regards the source of ATP. Although it is probable that carbohydrate is the major fuel of muscle, any and all exergonic reactions which can occur in this tissue (such as the oxidation of fatty acids and ketone bodies) may be involved in the supply of energy for contraction.

Concomitantly with the utilization of ATP in the contractile act, there occurs the first of a series of recovery processes. Phosphocreatine, the most important storage form of high-energy phosphate in muscle, reacts with ADP to regenerate ATP, a reaction (the "Lohmann reaction") catalyzed by creatine kinase (p. 247). Under certain circumstances, as when the regeneration of high-energy phosphate from other sources is inadequate and the supply of phosphocreatine is low, additional ATP may be provided by the myokinase reaction (p. 247). This is a rather wasteful process, however, since it requires two mols of ADP to produce one ATP, and since the adenylic acid (AMP) which is formed is rapidly deaminated.

More usually, the Lohmann reaction is accompanied or shortly followed by the glycolytic sequence of reactions. It will be noted that the contractile event proper and the recovery processes mentioned thus far are essentially anaerobic, since oxygen is not involved. If the muscle fiber is in a state of relative anaerobiosis (see below), the glycolytic reactions form lactic acid as an end-product; this largely diffuses out into the blood for utilization elsewhere (p. 409). Although regeneration of ATP occurs as a result of glycolysis (p. 395), its rate is insufficient to cope with continuous muscular exertion for sustained periods.

Aerobic recovery processes, actually practically synonymous with the operation of the tricarboxylic acid cycle, have a sufficiently high rate of generation of ATP (p. 401) to meet the requirements of sustained exertion. The question remains, to what extent muscle contraction is aerobic. A partial answer is furnished by the levels of blood lactate in various conditions, since this compound is very rapidly lost from the muscle if it is formed. At rest, the blood lactate level is probably a reflection of aerobic glycolysis in certain extramuscular tissues (p. 403). In moderate exercise the blood lactate rises, but drops back to a steady level only slightly higher than that obtaining in rest. Only in violent muscular exercise does the blood lactate attain a high concentration. From these observations it may be concluded that muscular contraction, including the recovery phases, usually occurs under aerobic conditions, but that a state of relative anaerobiosis may prevail when the rate of physical activity outstrips the oxygen supply. The situation probably varies from one type of muscle to another. Some are constructed in such a way that vigorous contraction shuts off the blood supply, whereas certain physiological mechanisms actually tend to increase the circulation in others. The presence of oxygenated myoglobin (p. 123) probably aids in the preservation of aerobiosis for a time. Myoglobin, intermediate in oxygen-affinity between hemoglobin and cytochrome oxidase, is well suited to play the role of "oxygen buffer." To illustrate, myoglobin is 94 per cent saturated at the oxygen tension prevailing in venous blood, and 50 per cent saturated at the tension in which the cytochrome system is operative.

To sum up the changes occurring during contraction and recovery under various conditions, one may begin with the observation that the concentration of ATP in the muscle will show no net change, owing to the rapidity of the processes of replenishment. Immediately after the energy-yielding reaction in which ATP is converted to ADP and inorganic phosphate, phosphocreatine, in the first of the recovery step, reacts with the ADP to re-form ATP. In a somewhat slower sequence of reactions, glycogen is degraded to lactate (if conditions are anaerobic), resulting in a further regeneration of ATP. Anaerobically, then, the initial reaction of contraction and the very rapid recovery-reaction involving phosphocreatine result in the liberation of inorganic phosphate, disappearance of phosphocreatine, and appearance of creatine. The slower reactions of glycolysis then bring about a disappearance of glycogen and inorganic phosphate, formation of lactate, and resynthesis of phosphocreatine from creatine. Aerobic contraction differs only in that lactate may never be formed, the pyruvic acid being oxidized immediately via the tricarboxylic acid cycle (p. 396). Aerobic phosphorylations are so efficient that the concentration of phosphocreatine may remain relatively constant, the only measurable change being a loss of glycogen, and, possibly, other substrates.

When muscle is at rest, the usual oxidative catabolism of carbohydrate (and probably other substrates) produces a surplus of ATP. This excess of high-energy phosphate is stored as phosphocreatine via the Lohmann reaction, thus providing a ready reservoir of potential ATP for future contractions.

(*e*) FATIGUE AND RIGOR. No generally acceptable chemical interpretation of the sensation of fatigue is available at the present time. Among factors which have been implicated in this phenomenon from time to time are depletion of metabolites, accumulation of end-products (lactic acid), development of acidity, loss of ability to regenerate high-energy phosphate at optimum rate, etc., all of which are probably related rather than independent phenomena. The stiffness of muscle in rigor mortis has been clearly shown to be due to depletion of ATP. Accumulation of lactic acid, which is insufficient in itself to explain the findings in rigor mortis, nevertheless contributes to the depletion of ATP, since the water-soluble ATP-ase (mentioned previously) is activated by the low pH thus produced.

CARBOHYDRATE METABOLISM IN OTHER TISSUES

As the major fuel of the body, carbohydrate is utilized by all tissues for the generation of ATP, which in turn is the immediate source of energy for all biological functions. The metabolism of carbohydrate in brain is discussed elsewhere (p. 721). The provision of ATP for certain specific functions, such as the transmission of the nerve impulse (p. 704) and the functions of the kidney (p. 429), will be discussed in connection with those respective functions. The metabolism of carbohydrate in cardiac muscle exhibits a number of peculiarities. In starvation and after experimental pancreatectomy, the glycogen content of heart increases. There is also evidence that, in contrast to skeletal muscle, the heart is able to take up and utilize lactic acid from the blood.

POSTABSORPTIVE BLOOD SUGAR CONCENTRATION

In the resting, postabsorptive state (overnight fast), glucose is present in systemic venous blood in the following concentrations: whole blood, 60–100 mg./100 ml.; plasma, 70–110 mg./100 ml. There is no clinically significant sex or age difference, although average values are somewhat higher in elderly subjects. Certain analytical procedures in common use yield higher values, i.e., 80–120 mg./100 ml. whole blood, because they include also non-sugar reducing substances, e.g., thioneine and glutathione, present chiefly in the erythrocytes. In the fasting state, the concentration of glucose in arterial (or capillary) blood is slightly higher (2–10 mg./100 ml.) than in venous blood, owing to its continual passage into and utilization by tissue cells. This "arterial-venous blood sugar difference" is increased under conditions of decreased blood flow or increased glucose utilization, e.g., following administration of carbohydrate (with rise in blood sugar) or of insulin (p. 423). In man, glucose is distributed equally in the water of the plasma and erythrocytes. The lower concentration in the cells as compared to plasma, per unit volume, is due to their lower water content (because of large amount of hemoglobin). This uniform distribution of glucose between erythrocytes and plasma does not occur in other mammalian species (except anthropoids).

Owing to the operation of an efficient regulatory mechanism (p. 420), the postabsorptive blood sugar concentration is maintained within the limits indicated in normal subjects except under unusual circumstances. What deviations do occur are usually relatively slight and transitory. Pain and emotional excitement (especially apprehension, anxiety, fear, anger) produce a brief rise (10–20 mg./100 ml.), due to acceleration of hepatic glycogenolysis resulting from increased epinephrine secretion. As the blood sugar rises, insulin secretion is stimulated, which, together with the accelerated blood flow induced by the epinephrine, results in increased utilization (i.e., removal) of glucose by the tissue cells and, consequently, prompt fall in blood sugar. The same may occur with brief, strenuous exercise (increased hepatic glycogenolysis), but may here, too, be dependent largely on the accompanying emotional excitement. Protracted strenuous exercise (e.g., marathon race) may at times result in a fall in blood sugar as a result of depletion of hepatic glycogen. During a prolonged fast in subjects whose activity is maintained, the blood sugar falls somewhat after about two days, usually reaching a minimum at four to six days (average drop 15–30 mg./100 ml.), occasionally falling as low as 40–50 mg./100 ml. The fall is of greater degree and occurs more promptly in infants than in adults (greater utilization of glucose and faster depletion of hepatic glycogen). With continued fasting, the blood sugar rises gradually during the second week to approximately the original level. The initial drop is due to depletion of preformed hepatic glycogen, which is necessarily maintained subsequently solely by gluconeogenesis from tissue protein (small amount from lactic acid). The gradual return to normal is effected by the homeostatic mechanism; important adjustments include decreased secretion of insulin (due to hypoglycemia) and thyroxine (due to starvation), with consequent decrease in utilization of glucose, and increased adrenocortical activity (due to stress of starvation), and consequent increased gluconeogenesis.

GLUCOSE IN BODY FLUIDS OTHER THAN BLOOD. Glucose diffuses readily across blood and lymph capillary walls and, therefore, in the postabsorptive state, is equally distributed in the water of the blood plasma and interstitial fluid (also synovial fluid). Its concentration in cerebrospinal fluid removed from the ventricles is about 10–20 mg./ 100 ml. lower, and that in the lumbar fluid about 20–30 mg./100 ml. lower than in the blood plasma obtained simultaneously (postabsorptive state). The glucose content of the aqueous humor of the eye is also somewhat lower than that of blood plasma, per unit of water. These facts support the view that the cerebrospinal fluid and aqueous humor are not simple dialysates of blood plasma. Increase in the blood sugar concentration, e.g., after ingestion of glucose, is reflected in the other extracellular fluids, the increase in the latter lagging somewhat behind that in the former.

The digestive secretions, with the exception of bile, contain virtually no glucose, even at high blood sugar concentrations. The same is true of milk and of secretions of the prostate and seminal vesicles. Unless the blood sugar is raised to unphysiological levels, viz., by intravenous injection, glucose does not appear in the urine of normal subjects except in negligible quantities. There are occasional exceptions to this statement, e.g., in pregnancy (p. 778). Although glucose diffuses perfectly through the glomerular capillaries, it undergoes practically complete reabsorption in the renal tubules under normal circumstances (p. 755), phosphorylation being probably involved in this process, as in its absorption from the intestine.

The concentration of glucose in intracellular water varies considerably in different tissues, but is uniformly considerably lower than in the plasma, except, occasionally, in the liver. The hepatic cells differ from other cells in this connection in that they form glucose (from glycogen) in addition to receiving it from the extracellular fluid. This sugar cannot be stored, as such, to any significant extent in the cells and, consequently, is utilized at least as rapidly as it enters. Indeed, there is evidence that free glucose does not pass readily across the tissue cell membranes by passive diffusion, but is phosphorylated at the surface. Variations in the concentration of glucose in the blood, e.g., after administration of glucose, epinephrine, or insulin, are reflected in that in the tissue cells, more closely in liver and kidney, less so in muscle and brain, in which the concentration of free glucose is relatively low.

SUGARS OTHER THAN GLUCOSE IN BODY FLUIDS. Sugars other than glucose are not present in the blood or interstitial fluid in detectable amounts under normal conditions in the postabsorptive state. In a considerable proportion of normal lactating women, a small portion of the lactose which is formed from glucose in the breast and is excreted in the milk (p. 729) passes into the blood stream, and, not being utilizable by the tissues, is excreted in the urine (p. 778). However, its concentration in the blood is rarely sufficiently high to permit its detection by ordinary methods. Fructose, galactose, and pentoses are readily absorbed in the intestine from dietary sources. However, under ordinary conditions of intake their removal from the circulation and their utilization (p. 394) proceed so rapidly that they are not detectable in the blood of normal subjects. The same is true in subjects with essential fructosuria and essential pentosuria (p. 778), in which conditions the excretion of these sugars in the urine presupposes their presence in the blood. Fructose phosphates are continually formed in all cells during the process of glycolysis (p. 392), but apparently do not leave the cells. Pentoses and galactose also are formed in the organism, from glucose, the former being incorporated in nucleotides and nucleic acids, the latter in galactolipids (and lactose, in lactating breast). However, they, too, are either utilized completely *in situ* or enter the blood stream in amounts too small to permit their detection.

After fructose or galactose has been ingested in supertolerance quantities (e.g., 40 grams) by normal subjects, a sufficient quantity may escape prompt conversion to glycogen in the liver to cause its transitory appearance in the systemic circulation (thirty to seventy-five minutes) in demonstrable amounts. It is also excreted in the urine under such circumstances, inasmuch as, in contrast to glucose, it does not undergo reabsorption from the glomerular filtrate in the uriniferous tubules. This may occur, too, in subjects with liver damage (i.e., impaired glycogenesis) after ingestion of small amounts of fructose or galactose. An alimentary form of pentosuria is also encountered occasionally, usually without appreciable amounts in the blood.

The absence of glucose from gastrointestinal and other secretions has been referred to (p. 417), even in the presence of high concentrations in the blood. Lactose is present in milk, being synthesized in abundance by lactating mammary tissues from glucose and galactose, both of which originate in the blood glucose, the galactose, too, being formed *in situ*. Insulin is apparently not involved in this process. Fructose is present in high concentration (300–700 mg./100 ml.) in seminal fluid. It is apparently formed by the seminal vesicular epithelium, this function, in common with others of that structure, being stimulated by androgens (e.g., testosterone) and decreased by castration or hypophysectomy.

REGULATION OF BLOOD GLUCOSE CONCENTRATION

The concentration of glucose in the blood is the resultant of two general factors: (1) the rate of its entrance into and (2) the rate of its removal from the blood stream. In the normal postabsorptive state (no glucose in the intestine), it is probably contributed to the blood solely by the liver (p. 406), entering the hepatic vein at the rate of approximately 115 mg. ($\pm$ 10%)/sqM./min. Inasmuch as its concentration in the blood remains fairly constant under these conditions (resting, fasting), it must leave the blood, in the capillaries, at approximately the same rate. These two general processes are influenced by a number of factors under physiological conditions.

RATE OF SUPPLY OF GLUCOSE TO BLOOD. Except for a possible minor contribution by the kidney, which probably does not occur under physiological conditions, the blood glucose may be derived directly from the following sources: (1) hepatic glycogen; (2) amino acids (gluconeogenesis, in liver; (3) other glucose precursors, e.g., lactic acid, fructose, galactose; (4) glucose absorbed from the intestine, which may be incompletely removed from the portal blood by the liver.

HEPATIC GLYCOGENESIS AND GLYCOGENOLYSIS. In the postabsorptive state in a well-nourished person, the most important of these, quantitatively, is the liver glycogen. Under physiological conditions the following factors influence the rate of hepatic glycogenesis and glycogenolysis:

(a) *Blood Glucose Concentration.* A rise in blood sugar increases, and a fall in blood sugar decreases the rate of hepatic glycogenesis. This results in part perhaps from a "mass action" effect (glucose $\rightleftharpoons$ glycogen), and also from the incident changes in secretion of insulin by the pancreatic islet cells. A fall in blood sugar to hypoglycemic levels stimulates secretion of epinephrine, with consequent increased hepatic glycogenolysis.

(b) *Insulin.* Increase in the amount of insulin reaching the liver increases the rate of hepatic glycogenesis. It is particularly interesting in this connection that the blood glucose concentration is the most important if not the only factor governing secretion of insulin, which increases as the blood sugar rises and decreases as it falls.

(c) *Epinephrine.* Increase in the amount of epinephrine reaching the liver increases the rate of hepatic glycogenolysis. Secretion of epinephrine is stimulated by hypoglycemia, however induced, and by a variety of emotional and other factors, including fear, anxiety, apprehension, anger, pain, unusual exertion, etc.

(d) *Thyroxine.* Increase in the amount of thyroxine reaching the liver increases the rate of hepatic glycogenolysis. This may occur during exposure to cold.

(e) *Muscular Activity.* Vigorous exercise is accompanied by an increase in the rate of hepatic glycogenolysis (epinephrine ?).

GLUCONEOGENESIS. If provided in adequate amount, dietary carbohydrate is the main source of liver glycogen. In carbohydrate restriction, increasing amounts, and in starvation virtually all of the liver glycogen is derived from amino acids. This process of gluconeogenesis (p. 516) is accelerated by the 11-oxygenated adrenal hormones and is retarded by insulin. If adequate amounts of glycogen are present in the liver, glucose may be formed directly by gluconeogenesis and pass into the blood stream.

ABSORPTION FROM INTESTINE. A variable portion of the glucose absorbed from the intestine is removed from the portal blood by the liver (glycogenesis, lipogenesis, oxidation). The remainder passes directly into the systemic circulation. The relative proportions taking these routes depends largely upon (1) the capacity of the liver, at the moment, for further storage of glycogen, and (2) the rate of absorption of glucose from the bowel. The latter is increased by thyroid hormone and is decreased in the presence of increased intestinal motility, the glucose being hurried through the upper intestine, the region of maximal absorption.

RATE OF REMOVAL OF GLUCOSE FROM BLOOD. Glucose leaves the blood in all tissues, being utilized by all cells for the production of energy (oxidation), and by certain cells for more specialized purposes, e.g., glycogenesis, lipogenesis, etc. (p. 447). Inasmuch as free glucose cannot be stored as such in cells in significant amounts, the rate of utilization of glucose in the tissues will determine the rate at which it is removed from the blood. Under physiological conditions, this is influenced by the following factors:

(a) BLOOD GLUCOSE CONCENTRATION. A rise in blood sugar increases and a fall in blood sugar decreases the rate of glucose utilization. As in the case of hepatic glycogenesis, this may be due in part to a "mass action" effect (glucose → end products), and also to the incident changes in insulin secretion.

(b) INSULIN. Increase in the amount of insulin reaching the tissues increases the rate of utilization of glucose for all purposes (oxidation, glycogenesis, lipogenesis). Again, attention is directed to the fact that secretion of insulin increases as the blood sugar rises and decreases as it falls.

(c) ADRENOCORTICAL AND PITUITARY HORMONES. Oxidation of glucose is depressed by a factor (growth hormone?) or factors secreted by the anterior pituitary, and by the 11-oxygenated adrenocortical hormones. Increase in the latter occurs, under physiological conditions, in response to a great variety of "alarming" stimuli (alarm reaction), which include practically all unpleasant emotions (anger, fear, anxiety, etc.) and pain, as well as other types of stress (exposure to cold, physical and mental tension, etc.).

FUNDAMENTAL REGULATORY MECHANISM. The processes of hepatic glycogenesis and tissue utilization of glucose are sensitive to relatively slight deviations from the normal blood sugar concentration. As the latter rises, glycogenesis is accelerated and utilization increased, with consequent fall in blood sugar. The reverse occurs as the blood sugar concentration falls. The normal balance between production and utilization of blood sugar at a mean level of circulating (plasma) glucose of approximately 80 mg./100 ml. (70–110 mg.) is therefore dependent upon the sensitivity of these processes to variations above and below this concentration. This level of sensitivity is determined to a considerable extent by the balance between insulin, on the one hand, and hormones of the adrenal cortex and anterior pituitary on the other.

The over-all effect of insulin is to lower the blood sugar, that of the adrenocortical and pituitary factors to raise it. Inasmuch as these two sets of factors are mutually antagonistic in this respect and, indeed, in several aspects of their metabolic actions, it is the ratio between them rather than their absolute amounts that is of primary importance in this connection. With minor differences, decrease in insulin produces much the same effects on carbohydrate metabolism as does increase in adrenocortical hormones or in the appropriate anterior pituitary principles. Similarly, the effects of increase in insulin resemble closely those of decrease in either of the other factors. The fundamental importance of this balance is demonstrated strikingly by the fact that diabetes induced by removal of the pancreas is ameliorated considerably by subsequent hypophysectomy (Houssay preparation) or adrenalectomy (p. 433).

The processes of hepatic glycogenesis and glycogenolysis and glucose utilization, and also the blood sugar concentration, are continually exposed to disturbing influences under physiological conditions. These include absorption of glucose from the intestine, physical and mental activity, emotional states, etc. The primary effect of the

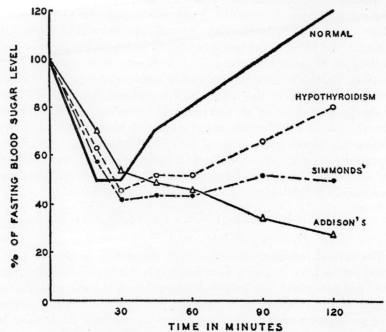

Fig. 75. *Insulin tolerance test (from Cantarow and Trumper: Clinical Biochemistry, ed. 4, W. B. Saunders Company, 1949)*

majority of these is a rise in blood sugar. As indicated previously, this automatically results in a net decrease in the delivery of glucose by the liver and acceleration of its utilization by the tissues. There is a simultaneous increase in secretion of insulin, stimulated by the elevated blood sugar concentration, with consequent increase in the ratio of insulin to adrenocortical and anterior pituitary hormones. This change in hormonal balance results in increased hepatic glycogenesis, decreased gluconeogenesis, and increased utilization of glucose. The blood sugar falls accordingly. A drop in blood sugar below the normal resting level is accompanied by decreased secretion of insulin, decrease in the ratio of insulin to the antagonistic adrenocortical and pituitary hormones, increased production of blood sugar, and decreased glucose utilization. Accordingly, the blood sugar rises. If the blood sugar falls to hypoglycemic levels, an additional emergency mechanism comes into operation; i.e., stimulation of epinephrine secretion (by hypoglycemia), resulting in acceleration of hepatic glycogenolysis and rise in blood sugar. The increase in epinephrine may also stimulate production of ACTH and, therefore, adrenocortical hormones, causing increased gluconeogenesis.

In the ultimate analysis, the blood sugar concentration regulates itself. Efficient operation of this autoregulation at physiological levels, however, requires a normal balance between insulin and the carbohydrate-active adrenocortical and anterior pituitary hormones, and also normal responsiveness of the pancreatic islet cells to variation in blood sugar. This constitutes the central regulatory mechanism. If it is intact, the blood sugar tends to remain within rather narrow limits in the face of periodic disturbances which may cause temporary fluctuations. On this basis it can be readily understood why conditions of abnormal function of the islands of Langerhans, the adrenal cortex, or the anterior pituitary are accompanied by serious and fundamental disturbances in carbohydrate metabolism and blood sugar regulation. Changes in blood sugar induced by other factors, e.g., epinephrine, thyroxine, exercise, glucose absorption from bowel, etc., are promptly and effectively counteracted by this control mechanism and are therefore usually limited in extent and of rather brief duration.

ENDOCRINE INFLUENCES IN CARBOHYDRATE METABOLISM

The several processes concerned with the supply of glucose to the blood by the liver and with its utilization in the tissues must be regulated and integrated, not only with one another, but also with certain phases of the metabolism of proteins and lipids. Endocrine organs play an important role in this homeostatic mechanism. These may be placed in two categories in this connection: (1) those which exert a fundamental regulatory influence, their normal function being essential for normal carbohydrate metabolism (viz., pancreatic islet cells, adrenal cortex, anterior pituitary); (2) those which influence carbohydrate metabolism, but are not essential for its regulation (viz., adrenal medulla, thyroid). The metabolic effects of secretion of these organs are considered in detail elsewhere (p. 654 ff.). It will suffice here merely to summarize their most important effects on carbohydrate metabolism.

INSULIN (P. 690). Administration of insulin is followed by a fall in blood sugar, to hypoglycemic levels if adequate amounts are given. This results from (1) net decrease in the rate of delivery of glucose to the systemic blood by the liver, and (2) increase in the rate of utilization of glucose by tissue cells.

The diminished supply of glucose to the blood is due primarily to increased hepatic glycogenesis. Gluconeogenesis (from protein) is decreased. The liver glycogen tends to increase, although this may be obscured by the hypoglycemia, which itself tends to accelerate hepatic glycogenolysis (p. 420).

Glucose is removed from the blood more rapidly and is utilized more actively for (1) energy production (oxidation), (2) lipogenesis, and (3) glycogenesis. The exact manner in which insulin produces these effects has not been established unequivocally. Data have been obtained which support two views, which are not necessarily mutually exclusive: (1) that its facilitates the entrance of glucose into the cells; (2) that, in the presence of adrenocortical and anterior pituitary hormones, it accelerates the hexokinase reaction, the first step in the utilization of glucose (i.e., formation of glucose-6-phosphate). In the latter case, and perhaps also in the former, it acts antagonistically to the adrenal 11-oxysteroids (p. 679) and an anterior pituitary factor (growth hormone?, p. 700). Insulin is not essential for the utilization of glucose, but, at least in the presence of these adrenal and pituitary factors, it is essential for adequate utilization at normal blood sugar levels.

ADRENAL CORTICAL HORMONES (P. 673). Administration of the 11-oxygenated adrenocortical hormones is followed by a rise in blood sugar and an increase in liver glycogen and total body carbohydrate. These phenomena are due to (1) acceleration of gluconeogenesis (from protein) and (2) diminished utilization of glucose (p. 420). In producing the latter effect, there is some indication that these hormones may act by enhancing an inhibitory influence of an anterior pituitary factor on the hexokinase reaction (initial phosphorylation of glucose). Insulin antagonizes both of these effects of the adrenocortical hormones.

ANTERIOR PITUITARY FACTORS. The adrenocorticotrophic (ACTH) and thyrotrophic (TSH) hormones, by stimulating secretion by their respective target organs (adrenal cortex; thyroid), produce effects on carbohydrate metabolism identical with those produced by adrenocortical hormones and thyroxine. In addition, unfractionated anterior pituitary extracts cause a rise in blood sugar and a decrease in R.Q. in adrenalectomized and thyroidectomized animals, which, therefore, cannot be due to ACTH or TSH (p. 701). There is also an increase in muscle glycogen ("glycostatic" action).

The "diabetogenic" action of such extracts (hyperglycemia, decreased R.Q.) has been attributed to the growth hormone (p. 700), but may be due, in part at least, to an unidentified factor separable from this principle. These effects are apparently dependent upon inhibition of utilization of glucose. Although the underlying mechanisms have not been established definitely, there is evidence that the following may be involved: (1) inhibition of the hexokinase reaction (enhanced by adrenocortical hormones and counteracted by insulin); (2) interference in the glycolytic pathway at some point between glucose-6-phosphate and pyruvic acid, i.e., beyond the hexokinase reaction; (3) inhibition of uptake of glucose by tissue cells (counteracted by insulin).

EPINEPHRINE (P. 670). Epinephrine produces an increase in blood sugar and blood lactic acid. These are due to acceleration of glycogenolysis in the liver and muscles, respectively, and are accompanied by a decrease in the glycogen content of these structures. The mechanism involved is apparently stimulation of phosphorylase activity (reactivation of inactivated phosphorylase). There is some evidence, too, that epinephrine may diminish the uptake of glucose by tissue cells, thus interfering with its utilization.

THYROID HORMONE (P. 681). Thyroxine accelerates hepatic glycogenolysis, with consequent rise in blood sugar. This effect is partially offset by simultaneously increased utilization of glucose incident to the acceleration of metabolism and blood flow (p. 416). Thyroxine also increases the rate of absorption of hexoses from the intestine.

HYPERGLYCEMIC FACTOR OF PANCREAS (P. 693). The physiological significance of this factor is not known. Apparently formed in the alpha cells of the islands of Langerhans (and in gastric mucosa, in the dog), it causes an increase in blood sugar, when injected intravenously, by accelerating hepatic glycogenolysis. This effect is produced apparently by reactivating (resynthesizing) liver phosphorylase from an inactive form.

BLOOD SUGAR AFTER GLUCOSE ADMINISTRATION

Ingestion of glucose, starch, and, to a lesser degree, other carbohydrates (fructose, galactose) or protein (but not fat) is followed, in normal subjects, by a rise in blood sugar. The degree of elevation depends somewhat upon the amount of glucose contained in or produced from the ingested material, but this relationship is by no means quantitative. This "alimentary reaction" forms the basis for the carbohydrate tolerance tests commonly employed for the detection of disturbances of carbohydrate metabolism. The characteristics of a normal response may be illustrated by describing the changes which follow ingestion of 100 grams of glucose (oral glucose tolerance test). Samples of blood are obtained before, and at intervals (Fig. 76) after, administration of the glucose.

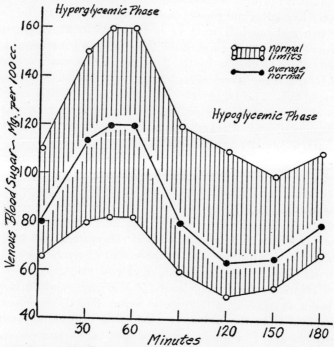

Fig. 76. Venous blood sugar curve after ingestion of 100 grams glucose (from Cantarow and Trumper: Clinical Biochemistry, ed. 4, W. B. Saunders Company, 1949)

The characteristic changes in venous blood are as follows:

1. A sharp rise to a peak, averaging about 50 per cent above the fasting level, within thirty to sixty minutes. The extent of the rise varies considerably, but the maximum should not exceed 170 mg./100 ml. in normal subjects, regardless of the initial level. This rise is due directly to the glucose absorbed from the intestine, which temporarily exceeds the capacity of the liver and tissues for removing it. As the blood sugar concentration increases, however, the regulatory mechanism (p. 420) comes into play: hepatic glycogenesis is accelerated

and glucose utilization increases; insulin secretion is stimulated, accentuating these phenomena. The peak of the curve is reached when utilization is accelerated to the point where the glucose is removed from the blood stream as rapidly as it enters. This point is usually reached while glucose is still being absorbed from the intestine.

2. A sharp fall to approximately the fasting level at the end of one and one-half to two hours. Glucose is now leaving the blood faster than it is entering. This is due to continuing stimulation of the mechanisms indicated above (increased utilization and hepatic glycogenesis) and to slowing or completion of glucose absorption from the bowel.

3. Continued fall to a slightly sub-fasting (10–15 mg. lower) concentration (hypoglycemic phase) and subsequent rise to the fasting level at two and one-half to three hours. This hypoglycemic phase of the curve is due to the inertia of the regulatory mechanism. The decreased output of glucose by the liver and the increased utilization, induced by the rising blood sugar, are not reversed as rapidly as the blood sugar falls. The higher the initial rise, e.g., after intravenous injection of glucose, the more pronounced the hypoglycemic phase.

The changes in arterial (capillary) blood differ from those in venous blood characteristically as follows:

1. The rise begins somewhat earlier. When the blood sugar has increased about 20 mg./100 ml., the rise in venous blood begins to lag behind that in arterial blood.

2. At the peak, usually reached at thirty to forty-five minutes, the level in arterial blood (150–220 mg./100 ml.) may be 20–70 mg. (average 30) higher than in venous blood. This arterial-venous blood sugar difference is an expression of the extent of removal of glucose from arterial blood by the tissues, i.e., of glucose utilization.

3. The return to the fasting level (at one and one-half to three hours) is not as rapid as in the case of venous blood, indicating that active removal from the blood, i.e., increased utilization, continues beyond the period of hyperglycemia. The two curves converge at the resting level or slightly below in two and one-half to three hours.

FACTORS INFLUENCING ABSORPTIVE BLOOD SUGAR RESPONSE. In normal subjects, the height to which the blood sugar rises increases with increasing doses of glucose up to about 50 grams, which produces a curve approximating that described above. The blood sugar rises no higher (in normal subjects) following ingestion of increased amounts of glucose (to 200 grams or more), but the fall may be somewhat delayed. This is due to the fact that absorption of glucose from the intestine proceeds at a relatively constant rate regardless, within wide limits, of the quantity present. As soon as the increasing rate of utilization matches the increased rate of entrance of glucose into the blood stream, no further increment occurs in blood sugar concentration regardless of continuing absorption from the bowel. This is not the case in the presence of defects in the blood sugar regulating mechanism, e.g., in diabetes mellitus, in which the degree of elevation of blood sugar increases with increasing doses of glucose (p. 430).

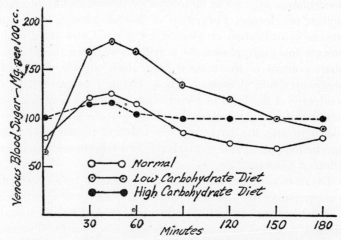

Fig. 77. *Effect of previously high and low carbohydrate diets on oral glucose tolerance curves (from Cantarow and Trumper: Clinical Biochemistry, ed. 4, W. B. Saunders Company, 1949)*

The antecedent diet has an important effect on the alimentary glucose response. If the subject is in a state of relative carbohydrate starvation, the rise in blood sugar following ingestion of glucose is more pronounced and its fall more delayed than under normal conditions of nutrition. A diet low in carbohydrate for a few days prior to performance of the test, especially if it is also high in fat, may result in a curve typical of carbohydrate starvation. This phenomenon is related to the amount of glycogen in the liver and to the "readiness" of the blood sugar regulating mechanism to cope with a sudden influx of exogenous glucose.

When glucose is administered repeatedly at intervals of one to two hours, each successive dose produces a smaller rise in blood sugar than the one preceding. This phenomenon, which forms the basis for a type of glucose tolerance test, the one-hour, two-dose test, is attributable to the development of a state of increased responsiveness and efficiency of the blood sugar regulating mechanism.

The rise in blood sugar is higher and more prolonged in old age; the curve may resemble that seen in mild diabetes. Prolonged strenuous exercise before ingestion of glucose may cause an excessive rise (as in carbohydrate starvation), whereas strenuous exercise after its ingestion may produce an abnormally marked and prolonged hypoglycemic phase (stimulation of utilization and depletion of liver glycogen).

PHENOMENA ASSOCIATED WITH ABSORPTIVE RESPONSE. The increased utilization of glucose which follows its absorption from the intestine in normal subjects is accompanied by other biochemical changes.

(*a*) DECREASED SERUM PHOSPHATE. The inorganic phosphate of the blood plasma appears to be intimately related to the intermediary metabolism of glucose. Formation of hexose phosphates occurs in the process of utilization of glucose (p. 389). Consequently, during this process inorganic phosphate is withdrawn from the plasma; the phosphate content of the tissues, particularly muscle, increases and phosphate excretion decreases. These changes in phosphate occur independently of the level of blood sugar; e.g., they continue beyond the period of hyperglycemia induced by glucose administration and occur also during the hypoglycemia induced by administration of insulin. The hypophosphatemia is therefore a reflection of the increased utilization of glucose.

(*b*) DECREASED SERUM POTASSIUM. Stimulation of glucose utilization is accompanied by a shift of potassium from extra- to intracellular fluids. This occurs most strikingly when glucose and insulin are administered after a period of carbohydrate restriction or to subjects with uncontrolled diabetes mellitus. This shift may be sufficiently pronounced to produce a fall in the serum potassium concentration. The basis for this phenomenon is not clear, but it may be related to the passage of phosphate ion in the same direction, i.e., to the increased utilization of glucose.

(*c*) INCREASED RESPIRATORY QUOTIENT. An increase in R.Q. above the normal resting level (0.82) is usually regarded as an indication of increased carbohydrate utilization (oxidation, lipogenesis) (p. 334). About one to one and one-half hours after oral administration of glucose (100 grams) the R.Q. rises from 0.82 to 0.88–0.90, reaching 0.95 or 0.96 in about two hours and then gradually falling to the resting level in about four hours. The period of this increase coincides approximately with that of hypophosphatemia, discussed above.

EXCRETION OF SUGAR IN URINE (MELITURIA)

Under ordinary dietary conditions, in normal subjects, glucose is the only sugar present in the free state in the blood plasma in demonstrable amounts. Although normal urine contains virtually no sugar, under certain circumstances glucose or other sugars may be excreted in the urine. This condition is called "melituria," the terms "glycosuria," "fructosuria," "galactosuria," "lactosuria," and "pentosuria" being applied specifically to the urinary excretion of glucose, fructose, galactose, lactose, and pentose, respectively. Some employ the term "glycosuria" to indicate the presence of any sugar in the urine, and the term "glucosuria" to indicate the urinary excretion of glucose.

MECHANISM OF GLYCOSURIA (GLUCOSURIA). Glucose is present in the glomerular filtrate in the same concentration as in the water of the blood plasma (arterial). Under normal conditions it undergoes practically complete reabsorption by the renal tubular epithelial cells and is returned to the blood stream. In normal subjects a very small amount (< 0.5 gram daily) may escape reabsorption and be excreted in the urine (p. 778). Under controlled conditions, normal kidneys are capable of reabsorbing 250–350 mg., and perhaps as much as 450 mg. of glucose per minute. If one assumes an average glomerular filtrate volume of 125 mg., and a maximum arterial blood sugar concentration of about 200 mg./100 ml. (after glucose ingestion), the quantity of glucose delivered to the tubules seldom exceeds 250 mg./min. in normal subjects.

Excretion of abnormal amounts of glucose in the urine may be due to two types of abnormality: (1) increase in the amount entering the tubules per minute; (2) decrease in the glucose-reabsorptive capacity of the tubular epithelium.

1. The quantity of glucose entering the tubules is the product of (a) the minute volume of glomerular filtrate and (b) the concentration of glucose in the filtrate, i.e., in the arterial blood plasma. Inasmuch as glomerular filtration is rarely increased markedly, glycosuria of this type is due almost invariably to an increase in the blood sugar concentration above the so-called "threshold" level, i.e., 160–170 mg./100 ml. (venous blood). This may be designated "hyperglycemic glycosuria." It should be pointed out that the amount of glucose presented to the tubules may remain within normal limits in the face of considerably higher blood sugar concentrations if the volume of glomerular filtrate is reduced simultaneously (e.g., glomerular damage complicating diabetes).

2. Reabsorption of glucose by the renal tubular epithelium is accomplished mainly by an active process, presumably enzymatic, and probably involving phosphorylation. The capacity for reabsorption may be diminished by induced (phlorizin), hereditary ("renal" glycosuria), or acquired (certain types of kidney disease) defects in this specific enzyme mechanism, with consequent glycosuria in the presence of normal or subnormal blood glucose concentrations. These are forms of so-called "renal glycosuria" ("lowered renal threshold" for glucose).

OTHER SUGARS IN URINE. The renal tubular epithelial cells are apparently unable to reabsorb significant amounts of sugars other than glucose. Consequently, when these appear in the blood (and, therefore, in the glomerular filtrate) in demonstrable concentrations, they are eliminated in the urine, as indicated elsewhere (p. 778).

EXPERIMENTAL DIABETES MELLITUS

Metabolic counterparts of clinical diabetes mellitus can be produced experimentally by disturbing the balance between insulin, on the one hand, and adrenocortical and anterior pituitary hormones on the other (p. 423). This induced imbalance is in the direction of a decrease in the amount of insulin in relation to that of the other two types of hormones. The importance of the balance between these fundamental regulatory factors is reflected in the following facts: (1) the typical diabetic state, with minor differences, results from either (a) absolute deficiency in insulin or (b) absolute excess of anterior pituitary or adrenocortical hormones (i.e., relative deficiency in insulin); (2) the severe diabetes produced by total pancreatectomy is alleviated strikingly by subsequent removal of either the anterior pituitary or the adrenals.

TOTAL PANCREATECTOMY. Surgical removal of all pancreatic tissue is followed by characteristic manifestations of diabetes mellitus, the severity of which vary considerably in different species (e.g., severe in dog and cat; moderately severe in man; mild in monkey, goat, pig; none in duck). Removal of the source of insulin (islet β-cells) (in susceptible species) results in the following metabolic phenomena (p. 691):

1. Decreased utilization of glucose, indicated by: (a) decreased glucose tolerance (blood sugar curve) (p. 431); decreased R.Q. (p. 333); fasting hyperglycemia (p. 415); glycosuria (p. 429).

2. Increased gluconeogenesis (from protein), indicated by negative nitrogen balance and increasing urinary G:N ratio. This is due to relative preponderance of adrenocortical hormones (p. 680).

3. Increased mobilization of body lipids, due to relative preponderance of pituitary and adrenocortical hormones (p. 481). This is reflected in loss of body fat and increase in blood plasma lipids.

4. Increased oxidation (in liver) of the fatty acids, mobilized in excess, to active 2-carbon fragments (p. 449). These cannot be utilized adequately for lipogenesis in the absence of insulin, and are present in amounts greater than can be oxidized in the liver (tricarboxylic acid cycle). They are therefore diverted in increased amounts to the formation of acetoacetate and cholesterol. This results in ketosis, ketonuria, and hypercholesterolemia.

5. Excessive production of acetoacetic and β-hydroxybutyric acids results in acidosis, owing to reduction in bicarbonate (p. 327).

6. Dehydration, initiated by the polyuria incident to the glycosuria. Excessive amounts of Na, and K are lost from the organism, in addition to water. In advanced stages, e.g., in diabetic coma, the plasma volume decreases, and shock and renal failure develop.

In man and the dog, the diabetes produced by removal of 90–95 per cent of the pancreas is more severe than that which follows total pancreatectomy. This has been attributed to the aggravating influence, in the former case, of the hyperglycemic factor, presumably secreted by the α-cells of the pancreatic islets. Residual β-cells undergo degeneration as a result of prolonged hyperglycemia, as indicated below.

SUBTOTAL PANCREATECTOMY.   In certain species, if an amount of pancreatic tissue inadequate to produce diabetes is removed and the blood sugar is maintained subsequently at a high level by various means, diabetes ensues. At first this is mild and reversible; later it is severe and irreversible. The hyperglycemia may be induced by intraperitoneal administration of glucose, administration of a high caloric diet, Bernard puncture, or anterior pituitary extracts (p. 700).

The elevated blood sugar constitutes a stimulus to the remaining β-cells, which, if the hyperglycemia continues, presumably pass through phases of hyperfunction, functional exhaustion, vacuolization, and other degenerative changes eventuating in hyalinization or fibrosis, i.e., permanent destruction. The importance of hyperglycemia in inducing morphological damage of the β-cells is indicated by the fact that these lesions do not develop if the elevation of blood sugar is prevented by simultaneous administration of insulin or phlorizin.

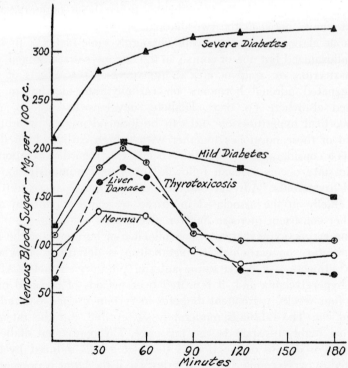

Fig. 78. *Blood sugar curves characteristic of decreased tolerance* (100 grams glucose) (*from Cantarow and Trumper: Clinical Biochemistry, ed. 4, W. B. Saunders Company, 1949*)

ALLOXAN ADMINISTRATION. Injection of alloxan, a substance related to the pyrimidine bases (p. 571), causes permanent diabetes, after brief transitory phases of hyper- and hypoglycemia. The diabetes is due to degeneration and resorption of the β-cells of the pancreatic islets, the α-cells and acinar tissue being unaffected. The alloxan acts directly, promptly, and specifically on the β-cells, and its effect can be prevented by administration of cysteine, glutathione, BAL (dimercaptopropanol), or thioglycolic acid immediately before or within a few minutes after injection of the alloxan. This protective action is due apparently to the —SH content of these compounds, the alloxan being perhaps reduced to an inactive substance. A similar diabetogenic effect is produced by dehydroascorbic and dehydroisoascorbic acids (p. 141), which resemble alloxan structurally.

There are interesting differences between the diabetes that follows pancreatectomy and that produced by alloxan. In alloxan diabetes, hyperglycemia and glycosuria are more severe and the insulin requirement is higher, but the animals survive longer without insulin than do depancreatized animals, show little ketonuria, and do not go into coma. If alloxan diabetic dogs are subsequently depancreatized, glycosuria and the insulin requirement diminish but ketosis and coma supervene rapidly if insulin is withheld. It has been suggested that the differences between the two diabetic states are dependent upon a hormone elaborated by the α-cells (hyperglycemic factor?), present in the alloxanized but not, of course, in the depancreatized animal.

ADMINISTRATION OF ADRENOCORTICAL HORMONES. The effects of the 11-oxygenated adrenal hormones on carbohydrate metabolism are discussed elsewhere (p. 679). Diabetes develops in subjects with adrenocortical hyperfunction and can be induced in rats by administration of these hormones together with a high carbohydrate diet. There is a considerable species difference in this regard. A temporary diabetic state occurs in man following prolonged administration of adrenal oxysteroids. "Adrenal diabetes" differs from "pancreatic diabetes" chiefly in the associated increased resistance to insulin and the rather consistent increase in liver glycogen.

ANTERIOR PITUITARY EXTRACTS. The influence of hormones of the anterior pituitary on carbohydrate metabolism is described elsewhere (p. 700). Injection of crude saline anterior pituitary extracts (APE) causes hyperglycemia and, if repeated over periods of one and one-half to four weeks, permanent diabetes in certain species, e.g., adult dog and cat. The rabbit is moderately susceptible, but the rat and mouse are highly resistant to this influence. The permanent diabetes so induced is due to destruction of the islet β-cells induced by the prolonged hyperglycemia. It does not develop if the latter is prevented by simultaneous (with APE) administration of insulin.

This "diabetogenic" action of anterior pituitary extracts is not due entirely to ACTH, for it occurs in adrenalectomized animals. It has been attributed to the pituitary growth hormone or to some principle intimately associated with it (p. 700).

THYROID ADMINISTRATION. Diabetes ("metathyroid diabetes") can be produced in partially pancreatectomized dogs in which hyperglycemia is maintained by administration of thyroid hormone. The islet β-cells undergo degeneration, as described above with hyperglycemia induced by other means (p. 431).

CARBOHYDRATE METABOLISM IN HYPOPHYSECTOMIZED-DEPANCREATIZED ANIMALS. Houssay demonstrated that manifestations of diabetes in depancreatized animals are prevented or alleviated by hypophysectomy. Such animals ("Houssay animals") differ from those merely depancreatized as follows:

1. Glycosuria and polyuria are diminished and at times absent.

2. They survive for longer periods, with less weight loss, are less susceptible to infection, and wounds tend to heal more rapidly.

3. The blood sugar is maintained at lower levels and is occasionally subnormal.

4. The Houssay animal is extremely sensitive to insulin, as is the simply hypophysectomized animal.

5. There is less ketosis, and the plasma bicarbonate remains within normal limits.

6. Hepatic and muscle glycogen may be normal and the R.Q. may exhibit an almost normal increase following ingestion of glucose.

7. The glucose tolerance curve in some cases is less distinctly abnormal, although it usually remains of the "diabetic" type.

8. The nitrogen balance becomes less markedly negative.

These animals are, however, far from normal. They are rather precariously balanced between hypoglycemia and hyperglycemia. The blood sugar exhibits wide fluctuations, responding unduly to abstinence from (hypoglycemia) and administration of (hyperglycemia) carbohydrate. The ameliorating influence of hypophysectomy on pancreatic diabetes is apparently due to diminished gluconeogenesis and ketogenesis, and improved utilization of glucose at a more normal blood sugar concentration. Similar improvement occurs in depancreatized animals if the adrenals are removed, and not the pituitary. These observations emphasize the physiological importance in this connection of the balance between insulin, on the one hand, and hormones of the anterior pituitary (p. 700) and adrenal cortex (p. 679) on the other.

NON-DIABETIC GLYCOSURIA

As indicated elsewhere (p. 429), glycosuria may occur whenever the quantity of glucose entering the uriniferous tubules exceeds their glucose reabsorptive capacity. This is usually due to either (1) hyperglycemia or (2) a functional defect in the tubular epithelium ("renal" glycosuria).

HYPERGLYCEMIC GLYCOSURIA.   Apart from the conditions discussed in connection with the production of diabetes mellitus, anything which causes sufficient elevation of the blood sugar for a sufficiently long period can cause glycosuria. The following may be cited as examples: pain, emotion (anger, fear, anxiety, etc.), asphyxia and anesthesia (opiates, barbiturates, ether, chloroform), Bernard ("diabetic") puncture.

RENAL GLYCOSURIA.   The classical experimental prototype of this condition is the glycosuria which follows administration of phlorizin. This substance causes selective inhibition of renal tubular reabsorption of glucose, apparently by inhibiting its phosphorylation in or at the surface of the tubular epithelial cells. Glucose is excreted in the urine in concentrations of 5–15 per cent or higher. The tissue glycogen stores are depleted and the blood sugar is normal or subnormal. The blood glucose tolerance curve is normal. Gluconeogenesis, fat mobilization, and ketogenesis are accelerated, and acetone and acetoacetic and β-hydroxybutyric acids may appear in the urine. The urinary G:N ratio (p. 517) rises to about 3.6–3.65 (fasting, phlorizinized dog), indicating that all of the urinary sugar is derived from protein. The metabolic picture therefore simulates that of severe diabetes mellitus, with the very important exceptions of the normal (or subnormal) blood sugar concentration and normal glucose tolerance.

A mild glycosuria of this type occurs spontaneously, possibly as a hereditary, familial trait, persisting throughout life and due to a defect in the renal tubular enzyme mechanism responsible for reabsorption of glucose. It is referred to clinically as "renal glycosuria." As in the case of phlorizin glycosuria, there is no other abnormality of carbohydrate metabolism. Under ordinary dietary conditions, the body stores of carbohydrate are never depleted to the point where fat and protein catabolism are significantly increased, as they are in the phlorizinized animal. However, deprivation of carbohydrate may cause hypoglycemia, increased sensitivity to insulin, and ketosis more readily than in normal subjects.

INTERRELATION OF CARBOHYDRATE, PROTEIN, AND FATTY ACID METABOLISM

As has been mentioned previously in several connections, the metabolism of the three major foodstuffs exhibits many points of interaction. Metabolites of carbohydrate can form fatty acids and the carbon skeletons of certain amino acids, and many amino acids can be converted in turn to carbohydrate. Fragments from all classes of foodstuffs are eventually channeled into a common pathway of aerobic catabolism, the tricarboxylic acid cycle. Although the detailed treatment of the metabolism of amino acids and fatty acids will be left to the appropriate chapters, it may prove useful to summarize the metabolic relations between the foodstuffs at this point. The diagram below, for reasons which have been mentioned previously, applies particularly to the metabolism of liver:

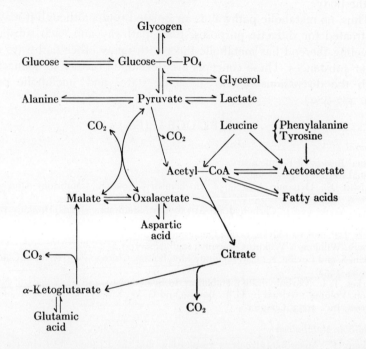

Certain amino acids, such as alanine, aspartic, and glutamic acids, are directly interconvertible with α-keto acids, which are products and precursors of carbohydrate. Many other amino acids follow the same pathways after preliminary transformations. A few are "ketogenic," forming acetate or acetoacetate. Metabolic fragments from both groups join in a final common route of oxidation through the tricarboxylic acid cycle. Only the first group of amino acids ("glucogenic") can produce new molecules of pyruvate, and consequently can effect a net synthesis of carbohydrate.

Although fatty acids are eventually metabolized via the same acetyl fragments as carbohydrate, they cannot achieve a net synthesis of the latter, since the decarboxylation of pyruvate is irreversible in animal tissues. The glycerol moiety of lipids, on the other hand, is directly convertible to trioses and thence to hexoses. The importance of a supply of oxalacetate in the oxidation of acetyl fragments from fatty acids is evident from the diagram. It is obvious that normal carbohydrate metabolism is a prerequisite to the complete oxidation of fatty acids. It is also probable that carbohydrate deprivation, in addition to causing an acceleration of the catabolism of fatty acids and amino acids for energy production, leads to a further breakdown of amino acids to form members of the tricarboxylic acid cycle, upon the proper functioning of which depends a major part of the metabolism of the body.

Thus, no metabolic pathway is an isolated route, although it may be so treated for didactic purposes. Each pathway and each substance traveling thereon has metabolic links with many other pathways and other substances. These concepts are developed further in connection with the discussions of the "dynamic state" and "metabolic pool" (pp. 487–489).

BIBLIOGRAPHY

General

Annual Review of Biochemistry.

Annual Review of Physiology.

Baldwin, E.: Dynamic Aspects of Biochemistry, London, Cambridge University Press, 1952, Chapters 15–17.

Najjar, V. A. (ed.): Carbohydrate Metabolism, Baltimore, Johns Hopkins Press, 1952.

Peters, J. P. and Van Slyke, D. D.: Quantitative Clinical Chemistry, Volume 1, Baltimore, Williams & Wilkins Company, 1946, Chapters 2–4.

Soskin, S. and Levine, R.: Carbohydrate Metabolism, Chicago, University of Chicago Press, 1952.

Sourkes, T. L.: Carbohydrate metabolism. In Biochemistry and Physiology of Nutrition, Volume 1, edited by G. F. Bourne and G. W. Kidder, New York, Academic Press, Inc., 1953, Chapter 4.

Anaerobic Metabolism

Dickens, F.: Anaerobic glycolysis, respiration, and the Pasteur effect. In The Enzymes, Volume 2, edited by J. B. Sumner and K. Myrbäck, New York, Academic Press, Inc., 1951, Chapter 63.

Tricarboxylic Acid Cycle

Krebs, H. A.: The intermediary stages in the biological oxidation of carbohydrate, Advances in Enzymology 3:191, 1943.

Martius, C. and Lynen, F.: Probleme des Citronensäurecyklus, Advances in Enzymology 10:167, 1950.

Metabolism of Polysaccharides, Hexoses, Pentoses, Trioses, Pyruvate, and Acetate

McElroy, W. D. and Glass, B. (eds.): Phosphorus Metabolism, Volume 1, Baltimore, Johns Hopkins Press, 1951, parts I–IV.

Muscle Contraction

Mommaerts, W. F. H. M.: Muscular Contraction, New York, Interscience Publishers, Inc., 1950.

Szent-Györgyi, A.: Chemistry of Muscular Contraction, New York, Academic Press, Inc., 1951.

Szent-Györgyi, A.: Chemical Physiology of Contraction in Body and Heart Muscle, New York, Academic Press, Inc., 1953.

Hormonal Influences

Bouckaert, J. P.: The action of insulin, Physiol. Rev. 27:39, 1947.

deBodo, R. C. and Sincoff, M. W.: Anterior pituitary and adrenal hormones in the regulation of carbohydrate metabolism, Recent Progress in Hormone Research 8:511, 1953.

Mirsky, I. A.: The etiology of diabetes mellitus in man, Recent Progress in Hormone Research 7:437, 1952.

Mote, J. R. (ed.): Clinical ACTH Conferences, Philadelphia, Blakiston Company, 1950, 1951.

Sprague, R. G.: Effects of cortisone and ACTH, Vitamins & Hormones 9:265, 1951.

Sprague, R. G., Mason, H. L. and Power, M. H.: Physiologic effects of cortisone and ACTH in man, Recent Progress in Hormone Research 6:315, 1951.

Sutherland, E. W.: The effect of the hyperglycemic factor of the pancreas and of epinephrine on glycolysis, Recent Progress in Hormone Research 5:441, 1950.

Thorn, G. W. and Forsham, P. H.: Metabolic changes in man following adrenal and pituitary hormone administration, Recent Progress in Hormone Research 4:229, 1949.

18

THE METABOLISM OF LIPIDS

Although certain structural functions are ascribed to specialized types of lipids, the body uses these compounds mainly as fuel. On a weight basis, the calorific value of fat is more than twice that of carbohydrate or protein (p. 333), it can be stored in practically anhydrous condition and in almost unlimited quantities, and it is metabolically sufficiently labile to be readily mobilized when needed. Nevertheless, carbohydrate, and not fat, is the preferred fuel of the body, and any attempt to oxidize appreciable quantities of fat without concomitant degradation of adequate amounts of carbohydrate can lead to serious consequences (p. 430).

Although the total number of compounds that must be considered in discussing the metabolism of lipids does not equal, for example, the number of proteins and amino acids, the chemical types represented are much more heterogeneous. First are the fatty acid esters of glycerol (triglycerides, neutral fats) and of other alcohols (waxes). Then there are the "glycerophosphatides," some of which contain fatty acids (as esters), phosphoric acid, and a base (ethanolamine, choline, serine), and a few of which contain fatty aldehydes. The sphingomyelin type of phospholipid and the glycolipids contain the unusual basic alcohol, sphingosine, to which fatty acids are attached in amide linkage. The carbohydrate components of the glycolipids and the presence of inositol in certain phospholipids add to their diversity. Finally, substances must be mentioned that are related to the lipids, partly by metabolic connections, largely by common solubilities, e.g., the sterols and bile acids, other steroids, and the fat-soluble vitamins and provitamins.

In considering the metabolism of the individual constituents of the lipids, it is obvious that most of them are only remotely connected with the lipids. The carbohydrates of the glycolipids and the glycerol moiety of the fats and phospholipids are synthesized and degraded via pathways common to the general metabolism of carbohydrates. Serine, ethanolamine, and choline are more directly related to amino acids than to lipids in their anabolism and catabolism. In fact, the only constituents of lipids that have a completely "lipoid" metabolism are the fatty acids, most of the other components entering into this area of metabolism only at such points as they are incorporated into the lipid molecule in the process of its formation. Consequently, although the incorporation of all constituents into the lipids must be considered, discussion of anabolism and catabolism of the lipids consists largely in a treatment of the synthesis and degradation of the fatty acids themselves.

As a consequence of the diversity of compounds encompassed by the class of lipids, the treatment of the metabolism of these substances necessarily differs from that applicable to the carbohydrates and proteins. The individual carbohydrates are connected, more or less directly, with the glycolytic sequence of reactions, and a common thread of metabolism runs through the reactions of the proteins and even of the individual amino acids, with few exceptions. On the other hand, the metabolism of the individual types of lipids and their constituents must be considered independently, for practically no metabolic interrelations are known among these substances of a type characteristic of the other major foodstuffs.

Another unusual feature of lipid metabolism is the importance of certain phenomena of transport and deposition. Although mobilization of carbohydrate and protein from one site in the body to another certainly occurs, as does deposition of stores of surplus (at least in the case of carbohydrate), these phenomena do not occupy the prominent position or display such aberrations under abnormal conditions as in the case of lipids.

DIGESTION AND ABSORPTION

Digestion of fats and other lipids is discussed elsewhere (pp. 263, 270). There is considerable difference of opinion as to both the completeness of hydrolysis of fats in the bowel under physiological conditions and the mechanism of absorption of the digestion products. Absorption occurs most actively in the upper small intestine.

The two main current viewpoints on this subject are embodied in the so-called (1) "lipolytic" and (2) "partition" hypotheses. According to the lipolytic hypothesis, fat in the intestine undergoes emulsification (by bile acids, etc., p. 268) and more or less complete hydrolysis (by lipase) to fatty acids and glycerol, which are then absorbed. The fatty acids tend to form soluble complexes with bile acids (hydrotropic action), facilitating their entrance into the epithelial cells of the intestinal mucosa. Within these cells, the fatty acids are separated from the bile acids and are reincorporated into triglyceride (neutral fat) and perhaps also phospholipid molecules, which are passed largely, by way of the lacteals, via the intestinal lymphatics to the thoracic duct and thence into the systemic circulation. The bile acids return to the liver mainly by way of the portal circulation (enterohepatic circulation of bile acids). Glycerol may be absorbed into the portal blood, as may also perhaps a small percentage of the fatty acids (particularly short-chain).

According to the partition hypothesis, fat in the intestine undergoes emulsification and only partial hydrolysis to glycerol, fatty acids, mono- and diglycerides. The fats are thus "partitioned" into fatty acid and glyceride (mono-, di-, and tri-) fractions. The fatty acids are absorbed as such (with the aid of bile acids) and pass mainly to the liver by way of the portal vein; glycerides of short-chain fatty acids also may take this route. The glycerides, with particle diameters below $0.5\ \mu$ as a result of emulsification, are absorbed as such by the intestinal epithelial cells and pass into the lymph stream (intestinal lymphatics and thoracic duct) and thence into the systemic circulation.

Experimental findings contradict certain features of both of these hypotheses. Inasmuch as no entirely acceptable mechanism can be presented on the basis of available evidence, it seems advisable merely to indicate certain facts that are apparently fairly well established.

The conditions existing normally in the small intestine are not optimal for pancreatic lipase activity (p. 263). The products of fat digestion presented for absorption (small intestine) probably include unchanged fats (triglycerides), di- and monoglycerides, fatty acids, and glycerol.

After ingestion of large amounts of either neutral fats or free fatty acids (particulary long-chain), the lipid content of the intestinal and thoracic duct lymph increases enormously. This increase is largely in neutral fat in both cases. There is little if any free fatty acid in either blood or lymph. Phospholipid increases also (lymph), but to a relatively slight extent. Ingestion of either neutral fats or fatty acids results in an equal degree of lipemia (increased plasma lipid content, mainly neutral fat). These observations suggest that triglycerides and phospholipids are synthesized from fatty acids during the process of absorption (intestinal epithelial cells).

Simultaneous administration of choline accelerates absorption of fats. The mechanism of production of this effect is not known. Choline increases the turnover of phospholipids in the intestine. However, the formerly prevailing view that phosphatides are important intermediates in the transport of fat across the intestinal mucosa has been refuted. It has been found that there is no increase in the amount or turnover rate of phosphatides in the intestinal wall during fat absorption.

When labeled free, long-chain fatty acids are fed, 70 to 90 per cent are recovered in the thoracic duct lymph. This is evidence against the partition hypothesis, according to which free fatty acids are absorbed mainly into the portal circulation and glycerides mainly by the lymphatics. However, short-chain fatty acids (e.g., butyric) may be preferentially absorbed by the portal route.

Despite certain contradictory evidence, absorption of fatty acids is apparently facilitated by bile acids (hydrotropic action). Fatty acids may also combine with cholesterol in the intestinal mucosa, and enter the lymph as cholesterol esters.

Phosphatides, entering the intestine in the food or in digestive secretions (e.g., bile, intestinal juice), may be absorbed as such, perhaps more readily than triglycerides because of their hydrophilic nature. Lecithins and cephalins may also be hydrolyzed in the intestine by lecithinases (p. 230); lecithinase A apparently removes the unsaturated and lecithinase B the saturated fatty acid. The end-products of complete digestion by these enzymes are free fatty acids, and glycerylphosphorylcholine in the case of lecithins and glycerylphosphorylethanolamine or -serine in the case of cephalins. The glycerylphosphate linkage may be hydrolyzed, probably in the intestinal mucosa, by phosphomonoesterases.

Cholesterol enters the small intestine in the food (mainly cholesterol esters) and in the intestinal secretions and bile (mainly free cholesterol). Pancreatic juice, bile, and intestinal epithelial cells contain (1) cholesterol esterase, which hydrolyzes cholesterol esters to free cholesterol and fatty acids, and (2) other enzymes which esterify cholesterol. Esterification apparently occurs actively during the process of absorption; after feeding free cholesterol, most of the increased cholesterol in the thoracic duct lymph is in the ester form. The passage of cholesterol from the intestinal lumen into the mucosal epithelium may be facilitated by the formation of complexes with bile acids (hydrotropic action).

QUALITATIVE DISTRIBUTION OF LIPIDS

NORMAL TISSUE DISTRIBUTION. The occurrence of the various types of lipids was indicated in connection with the discussion of their chemistry (pp. 27–41). The salient points will be summarized here in a qualitative way. Approximate quantitative data for the major lipid deposits are indicated in Figure 79 (p. 443). Quantitative aspects of blood lipids are discussed elsewhere (p. 471).

Outside of the liver, neutral fat (triglyceride) is confined normally largely to the fat depots (adipose tissue), e.g., the subcutaneous, intermuscular, perinephric, omental, and mesenteric fat. Relatively large quantities of unsaturated fatty acids are found in the liver, as compared with other tissues.

Phospholipid constitutes the dominant type of lipid in tissues other than adipose. Lecithin and the several types of cephalin are found in practically all tissues in significant concentrations. The concentration of sphingomyelin is generally low except in lung and brain. Acetal phospholipids are especially abundant in muscle and brain, whereas inositol-containing phospholipids have been isolated from liver and brain, but not much is known of their general distribution.

Glycolipids are found in many tissues, but in appreciable quantities only in nervous tissue, in which cerebrosides occur largely in the white matter and gangliosides in the gray.

Cholesterol is found in small amounts in many tissues, usually in the free state. Free cholesterol occurs in high concentration in the brain. Both free and esterified cholesterol are found in plasma and liver. The adrenal cortex is rich in cholesterol esters.

INTRACELLULAR DISTRIBUTION. The liver contains representatives from every class of lipids, as befits an organ occupying such a central position in lipid metabolism. Since the liver has been the favorite subject of most of the research on cell fractionation (p. 348), much more is known concerning the intracellular distribution of the various types of lipids in this tissue than in others. Stated generally, the soluble phase of the cytoplasm contains neutral fat, whereas phospholipids are confined mainly to the nucleus, mitochondria, and microsomes. Nuclear lipids are found in the nucleolus and nuclear membrane, but are present only in traces, if at all, in the chromosomes. Practically all of the phospholipid of the cell occurs as lipoprotein complexes (p. 38).

ABNORMAL DEPOSITS OF LIPIDS. Abnormal accumulations of specific lipids characterize certain disease states. Among the most striking of these are: deposits of cholesterol and its esters in the skin, mucous membranes, spleen, liver, dura, and subcutaneous tissues in Hand-Schüller-Christian disease; deposits of sphingomyelin (and to a lesser extent, lecithin and cephalin) in the spleen, liver, lymph nodes, bone marrow, and central nervous system, together with an increase in brain gangliosides, in Niemann-Pick's disease; increased concentrations of gangliosides in brain and spleen (and decreased sphingomyelin) in Tay-Sach's disease; deposits of cerebrosides (especially cerasin) in the spleen, liver, lymph nodes, and bones in Gaucher's disease.

GENERAL SURVEY OF LIPID METABOLISM

The major subdivisions of lipid metabolism to be considered are: (1) synthesis and degradation of the fatty acids; (2) synthesis and degradation of the simple and compound lipids and related substances; (3) phenomena of lipid transport and deposition. Related matters include the interrelations between the metabolism of lipids and that of other substrates, the special lipid metabolism of certain tissues, and the general biological role of the individual types of lipids. This section constitutes a brief summary of these topics, which are discussed in detail subsequently.

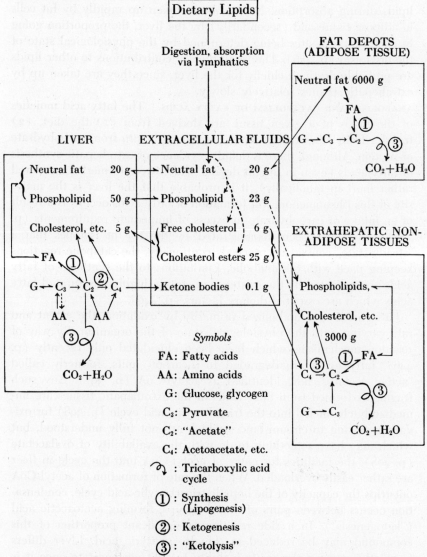

Fig. 79. Over-all metabolism and distribution of lipid in 70 kg. man

A scheme of the general metabolism of lipids is presented in Figure 79. The numerical values which indicate the quantitative distribution of lipids are to be taken as rough approximations, since there is little reliable information on these items for the human being, and, in any case, there are wide variations between individuals.

FATE OF DIETARY LIPID. The appearance of newly absorbed lipid in the plasma, as indicated elsewhere (p. 439), occurs by way of the lymphatics. Dietary lipid manifests itself largely in the neutral fat fraction of the plasma lipids, although increases occur also in other lipids during absorption. Neutral fat is taken up rapidly by fat cells in adipose tissue and (secondarily) by the liver, the proportion going to each of these sites being determined by the physiological state of the organism (p. 476). The small dietary contributions to other lipids are probably destined chiefly for the liver, since they are taken up by extrahepatic tissues relatively slowly.

ANABOLISM AND CATABOLISM OF FATTY ACIDS. The fatty acid moieties of the lipids of a given tissue are derived from (1) the diet, (2) transfer from other tissues, or (3) synthesis *in situ* from carbohydrate or protein. Although there is definite evidence of extrahepatic synthesis of fatty acids (even in the fat depots, which were formerly considered rather inert metabolically), it is probable that the liver is the major site of this phenomenon. *Net* formation of fatty acids occurs as a result of an intake of carbohydrate in excess of immediate requirements (p. 387), but it has been demonstrated by the use of isotopes that a "steady-state" conversion proceeds continually, the catabolic reactions keeping pace with the anabolic. Limitations to the synthesis of fatty acids are indicated by the existence of certain highly unsaturated fatty acids which are essential dietary factors (p. 449).

Fatty acids are catabolized primarily by oxidation, the extent and rate varying with the physiological state of the organism. By way of reaction mechanisms which have been elucidated only recently (p. 446), fatty acids are degraded to 2-carbon units, formerly called "active acetate," now identified as acetyl-CoA (p. 397). Any such fragments formed from fatty acids in the extrahepatic tissues are immediately channeled into the tricarboxylic acid cycle (p. 398) for oxidation. Owing to circumstances which are not fully understood, but which may have something to do with the availability of oxalacetate (p. 408), the facilities for entry of acetyl-CoA into the cycle in *liver* are rather easily overloaded. When the rate of formation of acetyl-CoA outstrips the capacity of the hepatic tricarboxylic acid cycle, condensation occurs between pairs of acetyl groups, forming acetoacetic acid ("ketogenesis"). In a side reaction, a significant proportion of this compound may be reduced to β-hydroxybutyric acid. Liver differs from other tissues also in its inability to split acetoacetate once it is formed. Acetoacetic acid, acetone (formed by the spontaneous decarboxylation of acetoacetic acid), and β-hydroxybutyric acid (collectively called "ketone bodies") therefore are sent into the blood stream under normal circumstances ("ketonemia"). Excessive ketonemia is designated "ketosis." The extrahepatic tissues have a great capacity for cleavage and oxidation of ketone bodies ("ketolysis"), which, however, may be exceeded, resulting in ketosis and excretion of detectable amounts of ketone bodies in the urine ("ketonuria").

ANABOLISM AND CATABOLISM OF LIPIDS. Within each tissue, fatty acids and other constituents of lipids are involved in a constant interchange between free and bound molecules. The rate of "turnover" of each type of lipid, as well as the general direction of net movement (synthesis or degradation), is determined by the chemical character of the lipid, its location in the body in general and in the tissue in particular, as well as by the physiological exigencies of the moment.

LIPID TRANSPORT AND DEPOSITION. Lipids synthesized or stored in one tissue may, in response to physiological demands, be transferred to another site. The mechanism of transport in the blood plasma appears to involve lipoproteins (p. 470), a group of substances currently under intensive investigation due to a suspected relation to abnormal lipid deposits in the blood vessels (atherosclerosis). The level of lipid in the blood is a resultant, on the one hand, of the rate of influx from the diet, synthesis in such tissues as the liver, and mobilization from the fat stores of the depots, and on the other, the rate of oxidation in the various tissues and deposition in the depots. Excessive levels of blood lipid ("hyperlipemia") may result from an imbalance between these sets of factors.

In periods of nutritional plenty, dietary lipids as well as those synthesized from carbohydrate in the liver are sent to the depots for storage. In "lean" times, these stored materials are mobilized from the depots to the liver (and possibly other tissues) for oxidation. The concentration of lipid in the liver, then, is a resultant of the rates and directions of mobilization of lipid between liver and depots, as well as of the rates of synthesis and utilization within the liver. Imbalances may result in the development of "fatty liver" (p. 476). Agents which promote the clearance of lipid from the liver are said to be "lipotropic."

METABOLISM OF FATTY ACIDS

As a result of recent research in this field, a comprehensive theory of the anabolism and catabolism of fatty acids has become available. A metabolic scheme incorporating these recent advances is shown in Figure 80. Parts of the scheme are designated as hypothetical; other possible objections or modifications will be mentioned in the subsequent discussion. Although the broad outlines of the picture are firmly established, current and future investigations will unquestionably necessitate revision of the finer details.

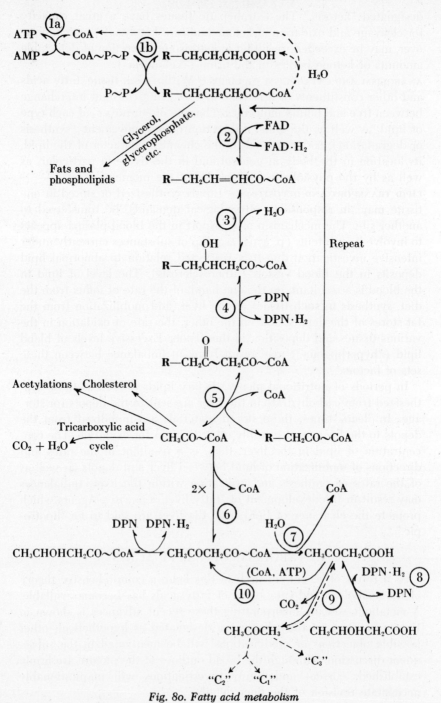

Fig. 80. Fatty acid metabolism

It has been known for some years, largely on the basis of experiments with isotopes, that fatty acids can be degraded oxidatively to 2-carbon units, "active acetate," which, depending on circumstances, either may condense to form acetoacetate or may be oxidized completely via the tricarboxylic acid cycle. Other experiments have indicated that fatty acids are synthesized by means of reductive condensations of these same acetate units. The most important concept resulting from the current revolution in our notions of fatty acid metabolism is that it is not the fatty acids themselves which undergo the various dehydrogenations, hydrations, etc., but rather their thioester derivatives with coenzyme A. Establishment of this concept has permitted correlation of a great many previously unrelated observations.

SYNTHESIS AND INTERCONVERSION. Carbohydrate is the major raw material for the synthesis of fatty acids. Pyruvic acid, by means of oxidative decarboxylation, forms "active acetate," now known to be acetyl-CoA (p. 397):

$$CH_3COCOOH \xrightarrow{\text{LTPP, DPN, CoA}} CH_3CO \sim CoA$$
$$\searrow$$
$$CO_2$$

Metabolic pathways are also available for the synthesis of fatty acids from amino acids. The glucogenic amino acids (p. 516) are convertible to pyruvic acid; the ketogenic amino acids (p. 517) form acetate or acetoacetate, both of which are lipogenic. In any case, acetyl-CoA is the immediate starting material for the formation of fatty acids.

According to current theories (Fig. 80), the pathway from acetyl-CoA to the fatty acids is a direct reversal of the pathway from the fatty acids to acetyl-CoA. Since the degradative reactions will be discussed in detail below, it will suffice at this point to summarize the purported anabolic path as follows: (1) condensation of acetyl-CoA on the "carboxyl end" of another acyl-CoA, splitting out one molecule of CoA, and forming a β-keto acyl-CoA (Reaction 5); (2) successive reduction, dehydration, and reduction, forming an acyl-CoA (Reactions 4, 3, and 2); (3) removal of the CoA moiety by hydrolysis to yield, finally, a fatty acid containing two more carbon atoms than the molecule with which the acetyl-CoA originally condensed.

Although the interconversion of fatty acids of different chain length (discussed below) certainly proceeds by the addition or removal of acetate units, it is possible that the total synthesis of a fatty acid involves certain features which differ materially from the degradative pathway. This is suggested by the finding that insulin is required for the formation of long-chain fatty acids from short-chain fatty acids (e.g., acetate), whereas no such requirement exists in the catabolic direction. However, no pathway alternative to the one shown can be suggested at this time. It is possible that the energy and sub-strates provided by normal carbohydrate metabolism (requiring insulin) are necessary for the synthesis of fatty acids, but not, of course, for their degradation.

It is also not entirely clear at present whether the conversion of acetyl-CoA to acetoacetate and its derivatives (Reaction 6 et seq.) is on the direct line of ascent to the long-chain fatty acids, or constitutes a metabolic bypath. In other words, does the first step in the synthesis of long-chain fatty acids involve the self-condensation of two mole-cules of acetyl-CoA, or *must* the condensation-partner in Reaction 5 be an acyl-CoA of much greater chain-length? The former possibility implies the participation of relatively short-chain fatty acids as inter-mediates in the synthesis. Evidence for this is available only in the case of milk fat (p. 729), which is perhaps exceptional. Other available data favor the second alternative.

The synthesis of fatty acids is an endergonic reaction (p. 377). Energy must be provided, for example, in the reductive steps. The reduced forms of the coenzymes involved in these reactions are sup-plied by other exergonic reactions, such as occur in the anaerobic and aerobic breakdown of carbohydrate.

Apart from total synthesis of fatty acids, mechanisms exist whereby interconversions can be effected between saturated fatty acids of different chain length, by addition or removal of 2-carbon units. These reactions, which undoubtedly proceed by the scheme already discussed, were originally studied with the aid of deuterium-labeled fatty acids. Some of the interconversions shown were:

$$\text{Myristic} \xrightleftharpoons[-C_2]{+C_2} \text{Palmitic} \xrightleftharpoons[-C_2]{+C_2} \text{Stearic}$$

Singly unsaturated fatty acids are easily formed in the body from the saturated fatty acids of corresponding chain length:

$$\text{Palmitic} \xrightleftharpoons[+2H]{-2H} \text{Palmitoleic} \qquad \text{Stearic} \xrightleftharpoons[+2H]{-2H} \text{Oleic}$$

The enzymes catalyzing these conversions are probably different from those forming the α,β-unsaturated intermediates in the metabolic scheme of Figure 80, since the double bonds are in quite different locations. Unsaturated acids of the oleic type are synthesized more slowly than the saturated acids. There is evidence that a different pathway may be involved.

The rate of renewal of fatty acids (synthesis and degradation), as indicated by studies employing isotopes, is highest in the liver and intestinal mucosa, intermediate in other internal organs, lowest in muscle, skin, and nervous system. (The half-life of triglyceride fatty acids in the liver, carcass, and brain of the rat, expressed in days, is 1–3, 6–9, and 10–15 respectively.) It is under the control of both hormonal and dietary factors.

ESSENTIAL FATTY ACIDS. There seem to be limits to the ability of the animal organism to desaturate fatty acids. Certain polyunsaturated fatty acids are considered dietary essentials, viz., linoleic, linolenic, and arachidonic (p. 30). At the present time, evidence that human beings require these fatty acids is regarded as suggestive, not conclusive. Definite symptoms have been produced in the mouse, chick, dog, and rat, maintained on diets deficient in these substances. They may be grouped conveniently as follows (rat):

1. Cessation of growth. Interpreted as possibly indicating a structural role for these fatty acids. Fatty liver (p. 478).

2. Skin lesions, viz., acanthosis (hypertrophy of prickle cells), parakeratosis (keratin collected into globules), hyperkeratosis (hypertrophy of stratum corneum). The visible cutaneous signs bear a superficial similarity to those characteristic of pyridoxine deficiency, but differences are quite evident histologically.

3. As a result of the skin lesions listed above, the skin becomes abnormally permeable to water. The increased loss of water increases the basal metabolic rate, and is accompanied by an increased intake of water and food.

Growth is restored in the deficient rat by the administration of the polyunsaturated fatty acids, the order of decreasing potency being: arachidonic > linoleic > linolenic and a C_{22} hexaenoic (6 double bonds) acid. The skin lesions are cured equally well by linoleic and arachidonic, but much less effectively by linolenic. There is evidence for an *in vivo* conversion of linoleic acid to arachidonic, and linolenic to a C_{22} hexaenoic. (Pyridoxine is in some way involved in these conversions.) It cannot be concluded from these data that arachidonic is the only absolutely "essential" fatty acid, since linolenic, which has a certain degree of potency, is not converted into arachidonic in the rat.

DEGRADATION OF FATTY ACIDS TO ACETATE. (*a*) REACTION 1 (A AND B) (FIG. 80). The initial step in the catabolism of a fatty acid involves a reaction with ATP and CoA. This reaction, which has been termed a "sparking" or "priming" phenomenon, may occur in two phases, the first being a reaction between ATP and CoA, the purpose of which is to activate the thiol group of the latter at the expense of the former. Once the thiol group of CoA is raised to the energy level of a thioester (p. 376), it is capable of condensation with the carboxyl group of the fatty acid in a reversible ester-exchange reaction, as a result of which free CoA is regenerated. It may be mentioned that this activation step (or steps) is endergonic, thus being somewhat analogous to the priming step in carbohydrate metabolism (hexokinase reaction), in which energy is expended initially in order to initiate a chain of events leading to the subsequent production of still more energy. One is reminded of the mercantile maxim, "You have to spend money to make money."

(b) REACTION 2 (FIG. 80). The fatty acid thioester is next dehydrogenated in the α,β-position by a dehydrogenase (p. 362) bearing an FAD prosthetic group and Cu (p. 361). Whether such an oxidation is capable of generating high-energy phosphate (p. 379) has not been determined.

(c) REACTION 3 (FIG. 80). A molecule of water is added to the unsaturated linkage so as to form a β-hydroxy compound. This reaction is catalyzed by a hydrase (p. 242).

(d) REACTION 4 (FIG. 80). The second dehydrogenation occurs in Reaction 4. A β-keto compound is formed under the influence of an anaerobic dehydrogenase (p. 365), DPN (p. 361) being the coenzyme. Since the subsequent reactions of the aerobic oxidative chain (DPN, flavoproteins, cytochromes, etc.) are known to produce high-energy phosphate (p. 379), this step must account for a portion of the energy evolved in the breakdown of fatty acids.

(e) REACTION 5 (FIG. 80). The β-keto linkage,

$$R-\overset{\overset{\displaystyle O}{\|}}{\underset{|}{C}}-CH_2-\overset{\overset{\displaystyle O}{\|}}{\underset{|}{C}}-R',$$

is energetically equivalent to the thioester (and high-energy phosphate) bond (p. 376). Therefore, a reaction similar to hydrolysis, but involving CoA instead of water, can take place (thiolysis), splitting off a molecule of acetyl-CoA and leaving a fatty acid thioester containing two less carbon atoms than the original. This thioester can repeat the sequence of reactions just described, beginning with Reaction 2 (since it is already "activated"). Thus, fatty acids can be degraded stepwise, each over-all sequence of reactions producing a molecule of acetyl-CoA.

KETOGENESIS. In most extrahepatic tissues, and to a large extent in liver, the units of acetyl-CoA produced in the degradations described above are either taken up immediately by the tricarboxylic acid cycle for oxidation in order to produce energy, or are utilized for certain syntheses by means of transacetylation reactions (discussed below). As a result of factors which are not understood at present, the rate of entry of acetyl-CoA into the tricarboxylic acid cycle is severely limited in liver. Owing evidently to accumulation of small amounts of acetyl-CoA even under normal circumstances, a side reaction occurs (Reaction 6, Fig. 80) in which two molecules of acetyl-CoA condense with the loss of one molecule of CoA (similar to Reaction 5 in the anabolic direction), forming acetoacetyl-CoA. Hydrolysis catalyzed by a deacylase produces free acetoacetic acid and CoA (Reaction 7, Fig. 80). A major fraction of the acetoacetic acid thus formed is reduced in the liver by β-hydroxybutyric dehydrogenase and DPN·H$_2$ (p. 365) to β-hydroxybutyric acid (Reaction 8, Fig. 80). A minor fraction undergoes spontaneous decarboxylation to acetone (Reaction 8, Fig. 80). Acetoacetic acid, β-hydroxybutyric acid, and acetone are collectively designated "ketone bodies" or "acetone bodies," and the process of their formation as "ketogenesis."

Although ketogenesis occurs to some extent in extrahepatic tissues (e.g., kidney), the further metabolism of the ketone bodies in these tissues is so rapid that their formation is actually difficult to demonstrate. In liver, on the other hand, acetoacetic acid, once formed, is not reconverted to acetyl-CoA to any significant extent. This fact, coupled with the rather sluggish rate of oxidation of acetyl-CoA in liver, as mentioned previously, leads to the formation in liver, and to the entry into the blood stream, of detectable quantities of ketone bodies under conditions of normal lipid metabolism. Although it is quite true that even under these circumstances the majority of acetyl-CoA molecules are oxidized via the tricarboxylic acid cycle in liver, only a slight acceleration in the rate of lipid metabolism suffices to overload the disposal system of the liver. These increased quantities of ketone bodies pass into the systemic circulation and are carried to the extrahepatic tissues, where they are oxidized to completion under normal circumstances.

Ketogenesis from amino acids is discussed elsewhere (p. 517).

KETOLYSIS. The oxidation of ketone bodies to completion is known as ketolysis. Acetoacetic and β-hydroxybutyric acids, to the extent that they are formed in the liver, are carried by the blood stream to the extrahepatic tissues, mainly the kidneys and muscles, where they are oxidized by way of the tricarboxylic acid cycle. The hydroxy acid undergoes preliminary oxidation to the keto acid; the latter then participates in a β-keto acid activation reaction (Reaction 10, Fig. 80), analogous to that given in Reactions 1a and 1b. The resulting acetoacetyl-CoA then reacts with a second molecule of CoA (reversal of Reaction 6, Fig. 80), forming two molecules of acetyl-CoA, which then are oxidized in the usual manner.

The oxidation of acetyl-CoA formed from fatty acids, whether occurring directly in liver and extrahepatic tissues, or only after ketogenesis in the liver and ketolysis elsewhere, is the source of the major fraction of the energy available to the organism from the catabolism of fatty acids. It may be assumed that the number of high-energy phosphate bonds generated during the oxidation of each unit of acetyl-CoA derived from a fatty acid is the same as that produced in pyruvate oxidation (p. 401), if the energy of the oxidative decarboxylation of pyruvate is omitted. On this basis, twelve high-energy bonds are produced in the tricarboxylic acid cycle per mol of acetyl-CoA. Oxidation of $DPN \cdot H_2$ produced in Reaction 4, Figure 80, accounts for three high-energy phosphate bonds, whereas the energetics of Reaction 2 remains in doubt. The total quantity of energy derivable from a long-chain fatty acid can be approximated by multiplying the expected number of acetyl units by 12, adding 3 times the number of acetyl units less one, and from this product subtracting the energy expended in the initial activation step (one or two high-energy bonds, depending on whether the bond in the pyrophosphate is recoverable or lost in a hydrolytic reaction). Palmitic acid (C_{16}), for example, will produce eight acetyl fragments, the oxidation of which will yield $(8 \times 12) + (3 \times 7) = 117$ high-energy bonds. Allowing for a loss of two bonds in the activation reaction $(117 - 2 = 115)$, and taking 12 k cal. as the average energy value of a high-energy phosphate bond (p. 376), the approximate quantity of free energy recoverable as high-energy phosphate from the combustion of a mol of palmitic acid is $115 \times 12 = 1380$ k cal. Since the complete oxidation of palmitic acid releases approximately 2340 k cal. per mol (not corrected to physiological conditions), it can be calculated that the high-energy phosphate obtained by the organism in this case represents a recovery of about 59 per cent $(1380/2340 \times 100)$, which is comparable to the figures obtained in the case of glucose (p. 401).

Acetone, which is formed in small quantities by the spontaneous decarboxylation of acetoacetic acid, has been considered to be metabolically inert until quite recently. It is now known, however, that small amounts of acetone can be metabolized by the organism. One pathway involves a C_2–C_1 cleavage (possibly via 1,2-propanediol), producing fragments of the acetate and "formate" (p. 540) types, which are then disposed of in the manner normal to each of these groups. Acetone is also converted to intermediates (again possibly 1,2-propanediol) which can in turn form lactic and pyruvic acids.

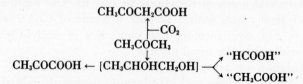

Lest it be concluded from this statement that a suitable pathway exists for the conversion of fatty acids to carbohydrate, it should be pointed out that, regardless of the findings with acetone, it has been shown that no significant quantity of acetoacetic acid traverses this route. Finally, it has been found, by the use of isotopic tracers, that small amounts of acetone (via unknown intermediates) can be carboxylated to acetoacetic acid.

Under certain conditions (e.g., carbohydrate deprivation), the metabolism of fat is greatly accelerated. As indicated elsewhere (p. 451), such a state of affairs overloads the capacity of the liver to metabolize the fragments of acetyl-CoA derived from the fatty acids, causing the formation of significant quantities of ketone bodies. These substances are liberated into the blood in greater than normal concentrations. The extrahepatic tissues have a great capacity for the utilization of ketone bodies (ketolysis); however, when the rate of ketogenesis by the liver exceeds the rate of ketolysis in the periphery, the concentration of ketone bodies in the blood increases (ketosis) and they appear in the urine (ketonuria). If severe, ketosis may eventuate in acidosis, e.g., in uncontrolled diabetes (p. 430). The role of carbohydrate in maintaining the normal balance between ketogenesis and ketolysis is discussed elsewhere (p. 483).

OMEGA OXIDATION. The general pathway of catabolism of the fatty acids outlined above involves, fundamentally, β-oxidation (beginning at the carboxyl end of the molecule) and cleavage of acetyl units. To some extent, certain fatty acids can undergo oxidation at the carbon atom farthest removed from the carboxyl group (the "omega" carbon), producing a dicarboxylic acid, which is then subjected to β-oxidation and cleavage to form successively smaller dicarboxylic acids. However, there is considerable evidence that omega oxidation is at best a minor pathway of fatty acid metabolism.

ODD CARBON AND BRANCHED CHAIN FATTY ACIDS. Although most of the fatty acids found in nature contain an even number of carbon atoms, the metabolism of the odd members of the series has been of some interest. The acids containing an odd number of carbon atoms appear to be metabolized by the same mechanisms as the even-numbered acids, losing two carbon atoms at a time. However, when the terminal 3-carbon unit is reached, a new pathway is taken. Propionic acid is glucogenic rather than ketogenic, although its route to pyruvic acid is believed to be indirect. The odd carbon fatty acids, therefore, participate in both the lipid and the carbohydrate pathways.

A few branched chain fatty acids occur in nature in association with lipids. Those which are of general interest, however, arise in the course of the metabolism of certain amino acids, and will be discussed in that connection (pp. 524, 544).

ETHANOL. Although ethanol is not considered part of the normal diet, its imbibition in greater or lesser quantities by human beings on festive and funereal occasions confers more than passing interest on its metabolism. Ethyl alcohol is oxidized to acetaldehyde by an alcohol dehydrogenase present mainly in liver, DPN being the coenzyme. The enzyme is sufficiently active to account for the rate of oxidation of alcohol *in vivo*. It is also concerned in the metabolism of rhodopsin (p. 135).

Acetaldehyde is oxidized to acetic acid either by xanthine oxidase (p. 362) or by an aldehyde dehydrogenase of liver. It is of interest that both enzymes are inhibited by "antabuse" (tetraethylthiuram disulfide), a drug used in the treatment of chronic alcoholism. (Apparently, the accumulation of acetaldehyde causes such disagreeable symptoms that drinking an alcoholic beverage becomes something less than a pleasant event.) Acetic acid, after activation by ATP and CoA, is completely oxidized in the normal manner of acetyl-CoA. It is apparent that the oxidation of alcohol can liberate considerable energy in the body (potentially, about 328 k cal. per mol or 7 k cal. per gram, heat of combustion [not free energy]).

GENERAL ASPECTS OF ACETYL METABOLISM (2-CARBON FRAGMENT)

In addition to its role in the metabolism of lipids, the acetyl group (and several other acyl groups) is involved in a great variety of reactions of other types of compounds. Although most of these reactions are discussed in their relation to specific aspects of intermediary metabolism, the universality of the "trans-acylation" reaction warrants a unified presentation at this point. Typical "donor" and "acceptor" compounds for acyl groups are indicated in Figure 81.

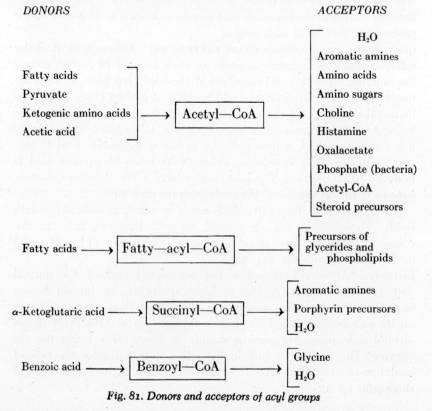

DONORS   *ACCEPTORS*

Fatty acids
Pyruvate
Ketogenic amino acids   →   Acetyl—CoA   →
Acetic acid

H₂O
Aromatic amines
Amino acids
Amino sugars
Choline
Histamine
Oxalacetate
Phosphate (bacteria)
Acetyl-CoA
Steroid precursors

Fatty acids → Fatty—acyl—CoA → Precursors of glycerides and phospholipids

α-Ketoglutaric acid → Succinyl—CoA → Aromatic amines / Porphyrin precursors / H₂O

Benzoic acid → Benzoyl—CoA → Glycine / H₂O

Fig. 81. Donors and acceptors of acyl groups

DONORS. All major classes of foodstuffs are sources of acetyl-CoA. Pyruvic acid, in the course of its oxidative decarboxylation (p. 397), forms acetyl-CoA. This provides a pathway not only for carbohydrate, but also for the glucogenic amino acids (p. 516). The ketogenic amino acids can form acetyl-CoA by means of reactions which are discussed elsewhere (p. 517). Fatty acids (and ketone bodies) are sources of this compound by the routes indicated in this chapter, the reactions being, in all probability, reversible. Free acetic acid itself can form acetyl-CoA via an activation step similar to that undergone by the long-chain fatty acids.

Succinyl-CoA is formed in the course of the oxidative decarboxylation of α-ketoglutaric acid in the tricarboxylic acid cycle (p. 399). Benzoyl-CoA appears to be synthesized by an activation reaction, involving, as usual, ATP and CoA. It is probable that many other acyl-CoA molecules are formed in a similar manner. It has also been shown recently that a second acyl-CoA can be synthesized at the expense of a preformed acyl-CoA by acyl exchange:

Succinyl-CoA + Butyric acid ⟶ Butyryl-CoA + Succinic acid.

ACCEPTORS. Water may be considered an acceptor of acyl groups from all types of acyl-CoA compounds; deacylases which attack these compounds hydrolytically are of widespread occurrence.

Aromatic amines, e.g., sulfanilamide, are acetylated and succinylated. Since the aromatic amines are foreign to the body, such acylations are classified as "detoxications" (p. 283), although the products of certain of these reactions are more harmful than the original compounds. It is probable that the body performs its normal reactions with any compound, native or foreign, without regard to toxicity.

Several types of aliphatic amino groups are also acylated. Many amino acids can be acetylated, although the significance of the reaction is not known. The acetylation of histamine may be another instance of "detoxication." Succinyl-CoA is involved in the synthesis of porphyrins (p. 587), probably by way of succinyl-glycine. Benzoyl-glycine (hippuric acid) is the form in which ingested benzoic acid is excreted from the body. Glucosamine and galactosamine are both acetylated on the amino group, the products doubtless being intermediates in the synthesis of mucopolysaccharides (p. 18).

Alcohol groups may also be acylated, viz., the formation of various types of lipid precursors by the reaction of glycerol with fatty acid esters of CoA (pp. 463, 466), and the esterification of choline by acetyl-CoA. The latter reaction, carried out by the choline acetylase system of nervous tissue (and striated muscle), is an important preparatory step in electrical conduction, a phenomenon which involves the neurohormone, acetyl-choline (p. 704).

Inorganic phosphate can serve as an acceptor of acetyl groups from acetyl-CoA in bacteria, leading to the formation of acetyl-phosphate.

This reaction, which is reversible owing to the energetic equivalence of the thioester and carboxyl-phosphate linkages, does not occur in animal tissues.

In all of the reactions enumerated thus far, the carboxyl portion of the acetyl group was involved in the condensations. At least two instances are known, however, in which the methyl group of the acetyl-CoA is the reactive site. One of these is the condensation of acetyl-CoA with another acyl-CoA, forming a β-keto acyl-CoA containing two more carbon atoms than the original. Such a reaction takes place in the synthesis of fatty acids from smaller units, and in the formation of acetoacetic acid from fatty acids. The second such reaction is the condensation of acetyl-CoA and oxalacetic acid to form citric acid, the first step in the tricarboxylic acid cycle (p. 398).

A more complex sequence of reactions, the details of which are not understood at present, utilizes acetyl units (and acetoacetyl units) to synthesize the steroid ring system (p. 457).

It is therefore apparent that trans-acetylation or, stated more generally, trans-acylation, is a reaction of widespread occurrence in the organism. It is employed in the catabolism of the major classes of foodstuffs, in the synthesis of complex compounds from simpler starting materials, and, to a certain extent, in the preservation and transfer of high-energy bonds.

METABOLISM OF STEROLS AND BILE ACIDS

SYNTHESIS OF CHOLESTEROL. The reasons for discussing the sterols and bile acids in connection with the lipids have been presented elsewhere (p. 35). Of the many sterols in nature, cholesterol is the only one which is of any great significance in animal metabolism. (The products of ultraviolet irradiation of the plant sterol, ergosterol, are absorbed through the intestine and certain of them have vitamin D activity in animals [p. 149].) It has been known for some time that the animal organism can synthesize cholesterol, although the mechanism was completely obscure until quite recently. With the aid of isotopic labeling, small fragments such as acetic acid, acetoacetic acid, and the isopropyl moiety of isovaleric acid (p. 544) have been shown to be precursors of the sterol molecule. Recent evidence suggests that "isoprene" units, derived from these fragments, may be important building blocks in both animals and plants. In the plant, these units condense to form terpenes, carotenoids, and rubber. In animals the condensation leads, by way of unknown intermediates, to squalene, an unsaturated hydrocarbon hitherto thought to be restricted to shark liver. Squalene has recently been found in various animal tissues, and has been shown to be a precursor of cholesterol. The current theory of the formation of squalene and cholesterol from small fragments can be illustrated as follows:

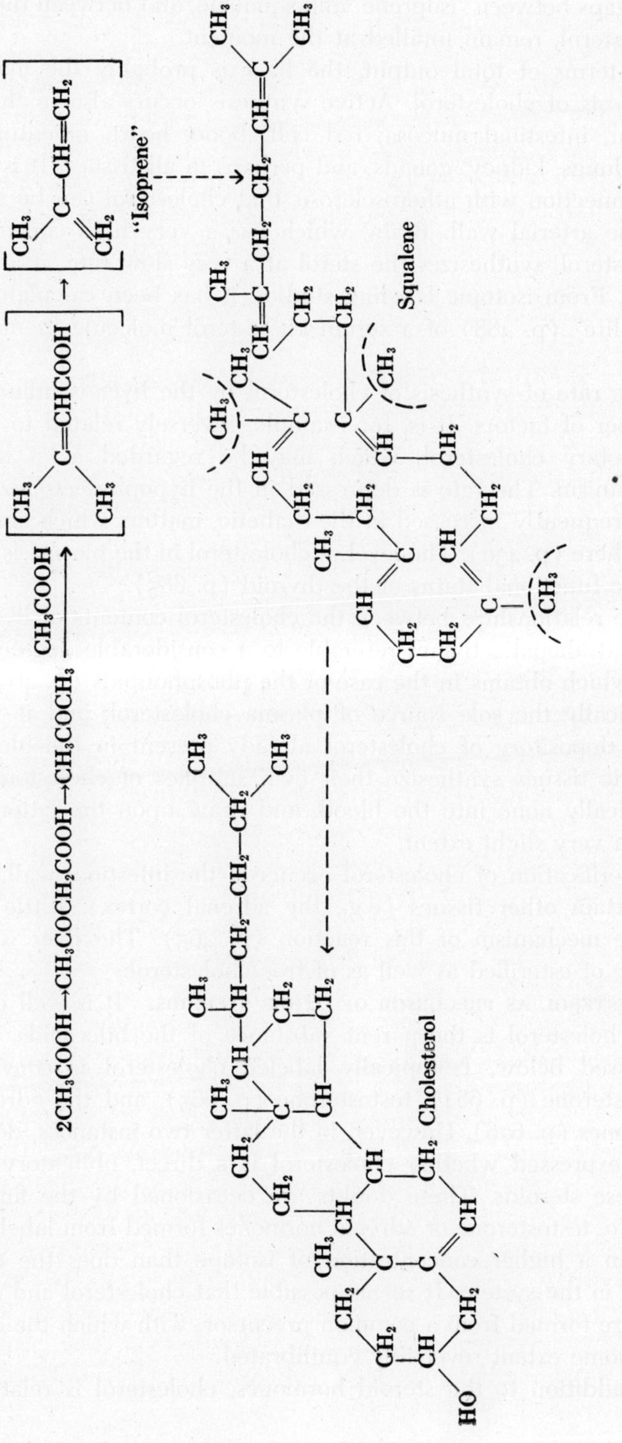
2CH₃COOH →CH₃COCH₂COOH →CH₃COCH₃
CH₃COOH
C=CHCOOH
C—CH=CH₂
"Isoprene"
Squalene
Cholesterol
HO

The gaps between "isoprene" and squalene, and between the latter and cholesterol, remain unfilled at the moment.

In terms of total output, the liver is probably the major site of synthesis of cholesterol. Active synthesis occurs also in the adrenals, spleen, intestinal mucosa, red cell, bone, heart, omentum, muscle, skin, lungs, kidney, gonads, and perhaps in all tissues. It is of interest in connection with atherosclerosis that cholesterol can be synthesized by the arterial wall. Brain, which has a very high concentration of cholesterol, synthesizes the sterol at a very slow rate, if at all, in the adult. From isotopic labeling studies, it has been calculated that the "half-life" (p. 488) of a serum cholesterol molecule in man is eight days.

The rate of synthesis of cholesterol by the liver is influenced by a number of factors. It is, for example, inversely related to the supply of dietary cholesterol, which may be regarded as a homeostatic mechanism. The rate is depressed in the hypophysectomized animal, and frequently increased in the diabetic, matters which are discussed elsewhere (p. 430). The level of cholesterol in the plasma is influenced by the functional status of the thyroid (p. 685).

The relationships between the cholesterol contents of liver, plasma, and extrahepatic tissues resemble to a considerable degree the situation which obtains in the case of the phospholipids (p. 465). Liver is practically the sole source of plasma cholesterol, and it is also the main depository of cholesterol already present in the blood. Extrahepatic tissues synthesize their own supplies of cholesterol, liberate practically none into the blood, and draw upon the latter source to only a very slight extent.

Esterification of cholesterol occurs in the intestinal wall, liver, and in certain other tissues (e.g., the adrenal cortex). Little is known of the mechanism of this reaction (p. 465). The liver is the chief source of esterified as well as of free cholesterol.

CHOLESTEROL AS PRECURSOR OF OTHER STEROIDS. It is well established that cholesterol is the parent substance of the bile acids, as will be discussed below. Isotopically labeled cholesterol is converted into progesterone (p. 664), testosterone (p. 665), and the adrenocortical hormones (p. 676). However, in the latter two instances, doubts have been expressed whether cholesterol is a direct, obligatory precursor of these steroids. These doubts are occasioned by the finding that, *in vitro*, testosterone or adrenal hormones formed from labeled *acetate* contain a higher concentration of isotope than does the cholesterol found in the system. It seems possible that cholesterol and other steroids are formed from a common precursor, with which the cholesterol is to some extent reversibly equilibrated.

In addition to the steroid hormones, cholesterol is related chemically and biologically to the D vitamins (p. 148). In the liver and intestinal wall (and possibly in the skin), cholesterol is dehydrogenated in ring B to 7-dehydrocholesterol, which is transformed to vitamin D_3 under the influence of ultraviolet light (p. 150).

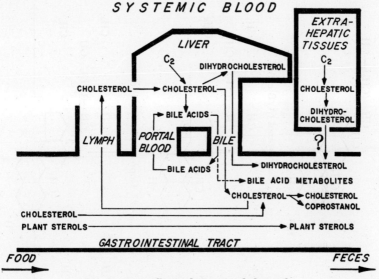

CATABOLISM AND EXCRETION OF CHOLESTEROL; CONVERSION TO BILE ACIDS. The general pathways of catabolism of cholesterol and the routes of excretion of the waste products are indicated in Figure 82. The more

Fig. 82. Over-all metabolism of cholesterol

detailed chemical relations between the various compounds are presented in Figure 83. For convenience, the catabolism of cholesterol may be divided into two compartments, the excretory route via neutral sterols, and that involving the bile acids.

(*a*) NEUTRAL STEROLS. In the liver and other tissues, cholesterol is reduced to cholestanol (dihydrocholesterol), a compound in which rings A and B are in trans relationship to each other (p. 656). There is evidence that cholestenone is an intermediate in this conversion. If, as seems probable, the reduction of cholestenone proceeds stepwise, cholestanone may also be an intermediate. A certain amount of

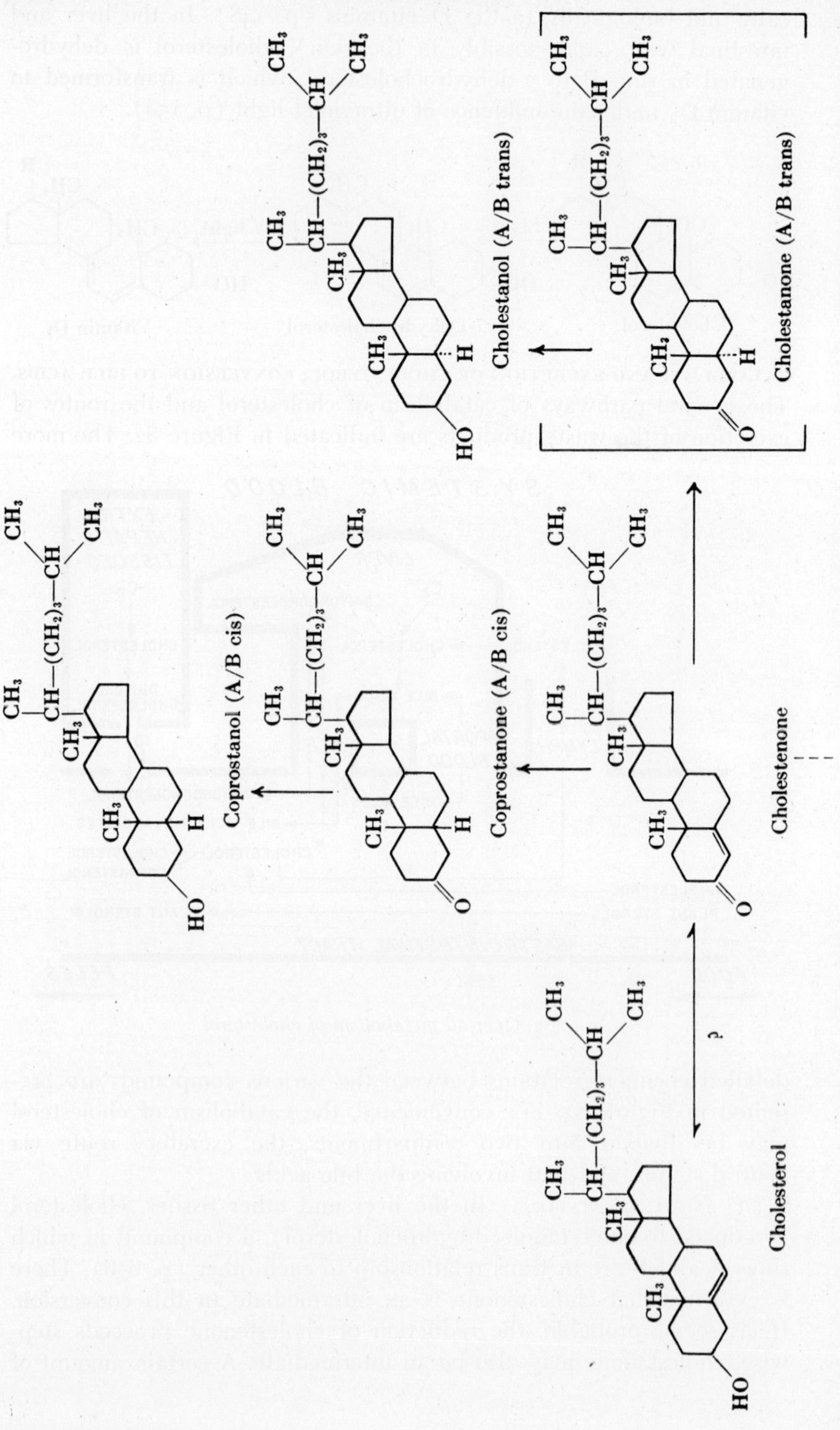
Cholestanol (A/B trans)
Cholestanone (A/B trans)
Coprostanol (A/B cis)
Coprostanone (A/B cis)
Cholestenone
Cholesterol

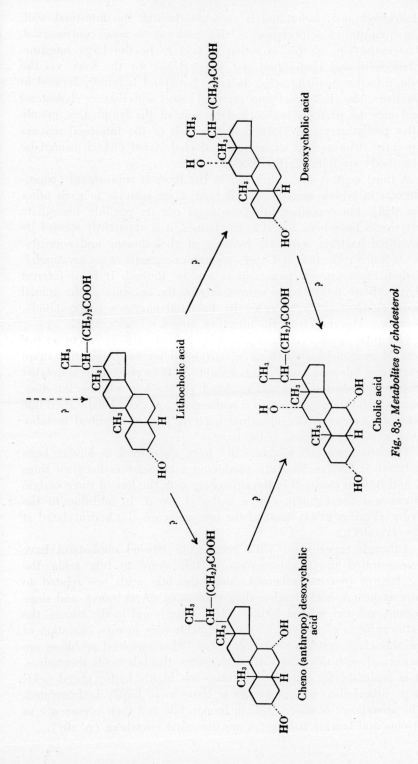

CH₃

CH—(CH₂)₂COOH

CH₃

CH₃

H O
CH₃

CH₃

H

HO

Desoxycholic acid

?

?

CH₃

CH—(CH₂)₂COOH

CH₃

CH₃

CH₃

H

HO

Lithocholic acid

?

?

CH₃

CH—(CH₂)₂COOH

CH₃

CH₃

H O
CH₃

OH

CH₃

H

HO

Cholic acid

Fig. 83. Metabolites of cholesterol

?

CH₃

CH—(CH₂)₂COOH

CH₃

CH₃

OH

CH₃

H

HO

Cheno (anthropo) desoxycholic acid

cholesterol and cholestanol is excreted through the intestinal wall; the quantitative importance of this pathway is now controversial. The major site of this excretion is said to be the large intestine. Cholesterol and cholestanol are excreted also by the liver, via the bile, into the small intestine. Biliary cholesterol is largely formed in the liver. The cholesterol thus excreted mixes with dietary cholesterol and may be partially reabsorbed by way of the lymphatics, mainly after preliminary esterification in the cells of the intestinal mucosa (p. 441). Unabsorbed cholesterol and cholestanol (which cannot be absorbed) are found in the feces.

A third neutral sterol excreted in the feces is coprostanol (coprosterol), in which rings A and B bear a cis relation to each other (p. 656). Since neither this compound nor its possible immediate precursors have been found in the tissues, it is apparently formed by intestinal bacteria, probably by way of cholestenone and coprostanone. Since reduction at C_5 of cholestenone produces an asymmetric carbon atom (p. 3), two isomers can be formed. It is of interest that both are produced in nature, one by the enzymes of the animal body (cholestanol), the other by bacterial enzymes (coprostanol). Neither is absorbed from the intestinal lumen.

(b) BILE ACIDS. As determined by isotopic tracers, 10 to 20 per cent of exogenous cholesterol is accounted for in the neutral sterol fraction of bile and feces. The remaining 80 to 90 per cent is converted to bile acids in the liver and excreted via the bile into the intestine, from which the major fraction is reabsorbed (p. 268). Unabsorbed bile acids are converted by intestinal bacteria into unidentified metabolites, which are excreted in the feces.

The bile acids differ chemically from cholesterol in having been reduced at C_5 (incidentally producing a cis relation between rings A and B) and oxidized in the side-chain with the loss of three carbon atoms and the formation of a carboxyl group. In addition to the hydroxyl group at C_3, most of the bile acids are also hydroxylated at C_7 or/and C_{12}.

Although experiments with isotopically labeled cholesterol have demonstrated the transformation of this sterol to bile acids, the mechanism remains unknown. Since the bile acids are related to coprostane (A/B:cis) rather than cholestane (A/B:trans), and since coprostanol and related compounds are not found in the tissues, the pathway from cholesterol to the bile acids may involve oxidation of the side-chain prior to reduction at C_5. Other unsolved problems are concerned with the interrelations between the bile acids themselves. It is probable, for example, that the less highly hydroxylated acids (e.g., lithocholic) are precursors of those more highly hydroxylated. The abundance of these acids in human bile and their occurrence as glycine and taurine conjugates are discussed elsewhere (p. 267).

METABOLISM OF FATS AND WAXES

FATS (P. 28). Neutral fat comprises a large portion of the dietary lipid. It is also the major storage form of lipid in the body (fat depots), available for rapid mobilization to the liver in time of need. Oxidation of its fatty acid constituents provides the major source of energy derived from the catabolism of lipids, although degradation of the glycerol of the triglycerides via carbohydrate pathways also provides energy from substances of lipid origin. Considering their ubiquity and relative chemical simplicity, surprisingly little is known of the intermediary metabolism of the neutral fats. The pathways of synthesis and degradation of the fatty acid component have been outlined previously. The glycerol moiety of the fats is derived from, and reconvertible to, carbohydrate (glycolytic intermediates) by the following reactions:

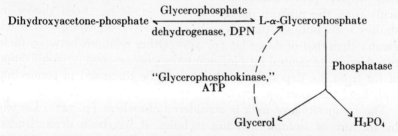

The anabolic pathway from glycerol and the fatty acids to the triglycerides is not entirely clear, but in view of recent discoveries concerning trans-acylation, the following tentative scheme is suggested:

$$\text{Fatty acid} \xrightarrow[\text{ATP, CoA}]{\text{"Activation"}} \text{Fatty-acyl-CoA} \xrightarrow{\text{Glycerol}} \text{Fatty-acyl-monoglyceride}$$

Triglycerides could be constructed by repetition of this process. Nothing is known concerning the mechanisms which determine the types of fatty acid units incorporated into a given triglyceride molecule, the chronological order of the esterifications, or the location taken by each acyl radical.

The available evidence indicates that the fats must be hydrolyzed before they are oxidized. Glycerol and the fatty acids are presumably liberated by intracellular lipases, after which they may be degraded by mechanisms already discussed.

In the animal organism, neutral fat is found normally in significant quantities only in adipose tissue (fat depots) and in liver. The types of triglycerides present in the fat depots appear to represent the resultant of two metabolic "forces." One of these is the mechanism for synthesis of fatty acids from carbohydrate, which, in the average land animal, results in a triglyceride mixture containing approximately

one third saturated fatty acids (largely palmitic) and two thirds unsaturated (oleic and related acids). This composition is approached
by the depot fat of animals on high-carbohydrate, low-fat diets. The
second factor contributing to the composition of adipose tissue is the
fat of the diet. The component fatty acids of the dietary lipids enter
into the triglycerides of the depots to a considerable degree, especially
if the quantity of fat in the diet is high. The "native" pattern of depot
fat can therefore be altered by dietary means, a fact of considerable
commercial importance, e.g., in the production of bacon and lard
with an appropriately high melting point (high-carbohydrate diet).

The triglycerides of liver tend to contain more unsaturated fatty
acids than those of the depots. This was interpreted at one time as
indicating preliminary desaturation of fatty acids in the liver, preparatory to their complete oxidation. It is currently believed, however,
that the liver preferentially selects the more highly unsaturated fatty
acids from the mixture offered by the diet. It has been shown by
studies with isotopes that the rate of turnover of liver fat is much
greater than that of depot fat (p. 448). Other relations between these
two deposits of neutral fat (including the phenomenon of mobilization
of fat from the depots to the liver) will be discussed in connection
with lipid transport (p. 470).

The composition of milk is considered elsewhere (p. 727). Largely
by the use of isotopic labeling technics, it has been demonstrated
that milk fat (including the glycerol as well as the fatty acids) is
mainly synthesized in the mammary gland, rather than derived from
the lipids of the blood as was believed formerly. In non-ruminants,
glucose is the precursor of the fatty acids; in ruminants, its place is
taken by acetate, large amounts of which are absorbed from the digestive tract, where it is formed from the cellulose of the diet by bacteria.
The glycerol moiety is synthesized from glucose in all cases (as is
lactose, cf. p. 395).

WAXES (P. 31). The biological significance of waxes is obscure. It
is possible that the waxes of the skin aid in maintaining its pliability
and rendering it waterproof, in man as in the apple. Cholesterol esters
do not appear to play a significant role in lipid transport in the blood,
as believed formerly; their occurrence at sites of active cholesterol
metabolism (intestinal mucosa, liver, adrenal cortex), however, suggests their importance in that respect, but their role remains undefined.

Information concerning the intermediary metabolism of the waxes
is even less plentiful than that concerning the fats. Practically nothing
is known about the synthesis and breakdown of the waxes derived
from aliphatic alcohols, except that the alcohols themselves (e.g.,
cetyl, C_{16}) can be synthesized in the body from the fatty acids of
corresponding chain length. The origin of the steroid alcohols, sterols,

is discussed elsewhere (p. 456). The mechanism of esterification in the waxes is presumably the same as in the case of the triglycerides and phospholipids; the synthesis of cholesterol esters by cholesterol esterase (p. 230), as suggested in occasional reports, is highly improbable on thermodynamic grounds. Cholesterol is esterified in the course of its absorption from intestine, and also by the liver. Other features of cholesterol ester metabolism will be mentioned in connection with lipid transport and storage.

METABOLISM OF PHOSPHOLIPIDS

SYNTHESIS. The class of phospholipids includes a wide variety of compounds. Those containing glycerol (frequently designated "glycerophosphatides") are perhaps simplest in structure (p. 32), being composed of fatty acids or aldehydes, phosphoric acid, and a base, in addition to glycerol. The sphingomyelins (sometimes included with the glycolipids in a group designated "sphingolipids") contain, in addition to phosphoric acid, fatty acid, and choline, the basic alcohol, sphingosine (p. 33). Least well defined of all are the phosphoinositides (p. 33), which contain, among other constituents, the cyclic alcohol, inositol. The diversity of constituents enumerated indicates the complexity which may be anticipated in the discussion of the metabolism of the phospholipids.

It seems probable that all tissues synthesize phospholipids, but at widely varying rates. In all tissues but one, these compounds are apparently synthesized, used, and degraded *in situ*. Liver is exceptional, in that a large proportion of the phospholipids synthesized in this organ is liberated into the plasma. As a matter of fact, liver is practically the sole source of plasma phospholipids, and is also the chief site of their further metabolism or degradation. Although there is every indication that the phospholipids play important roles in intermediary metabolism, the nature of these roles can scarcely be conjectured at this time. The beliefs formerly held in this respect and the reasons for their current untenability are presented in detail below (p. 467).

(a) ORIGIN OF COMPONENTS. The sources of the inorganic phosphate, glycerol, and fatty acid moieties of the phospholipids present no problem in general, although certain of the highly unsaturated acids which seem to be selectively incorporated into phospholipids (p. 469) belong to the group of "essential" fatty acids (p. 449), and must therefore be secured from the diet. Inositol, required for the synthesis of the phosphoinositides (p. 33), is commonly regarded as one of the members of the vitamin B group (p. 211). The fatty aldehydes of the acetal phospholipids (p. 33) are probably derived from the fatty acids, but no data are available on this point.

Of the constituent bases of the phospholipids, nothing is known of the origin of sphingosine (p. 33). Serine is derived from the pathways of protein metabolism, specifically from glycine (p. 519). Ethanolamine is formed by the decarboxylation of serine (p. 522). Stepwise methylation of ethanolamine yields choline. The process of transmethylation is discussed in detail elsewhere (p. 536); suffice it to say at this point that methionine is the immediate source of the methyl groups of choline.

$$
\text{Glycerol}
\begin{cases}
\text{CH}_2\text{O}-\overset{\overset{\text{O}}{\|}}{\text{C}}-(\text{CH}_2)_7-\text{CH}=\text{CH}-(\text{CH}_2)_7-\text{CH}_3 \ \} \ \text{Oleic acid} \\[2ex]
\text{CHO}-\overset{\overset{\text{O}}{\|}}{\text{C}}-(\text{CH}_2)_{16}-\text{CH}_3 \ \} \ \text{Stearic acid} \\[2ex]
\text{CH}_2\text{O}-\overset{\overset{\text{O}}{\|}}{\underset{\underset{\text{O}^-}{|}}{\text{P}}}-\text{OCH}_2\text{CH}_2\overset{+}{\text{N}}(\text{CH}_3)_3
\end{cases}
$$

$\underbrace{\qquad\qquad}_{\text{Phosphoric acid}}$ $\underbrace{\qquad\qquad}_{\text{Choline}}$

A Typical Lecithin

(*b*) MECHANISMS OF SYNTHESIS. It can be said at the outset that only fragmentary data are available on this topic, and these are restricted to the synthesis of the glycero-phosphatides. Radioactive inorganic phosphate is incorporated into the phospholipids of liver mitochondria. The reaction requires high-energy phosphate, and is accelerated by glycerol, α-glycerophosphate being a probable intermediate. Systems recently purified from liver have been found to catalyze the following series of reactions:

$$\text{Fatty acids} \xrightarrow[\text{ATP, CoA}]{\text{``Activation''}} \text{Acyl-CoA's}$$

α-Glycerophosphate + Acyl-CoA → Mono-acyl-phosphatidic acid

Mono-acyl-phosphatidic acid + Acyl-CoA → Diacyl-phosphatidic acid

The phosphatidic acids (p. 33) thus formed may be intermediates in the synthesis of phospholipids; it has been postulated that they may condense with phosphorylcholine or phosphoryl-ethanolamine (both of which can be synthesized by various tissues), splitting out one phosphate residue. Other evidence, however, points to the possibility that such compounds as glyceryl-phosphoryl-ethanolamine and glyceryl-phosphoryl-choline may be the direct precursors of the phospholipids, possibly being esterified by acyl-CoA molecules. It is possible that the organism makes use of several pathways for the synthesis.

TURNOVER. By "turnover" is meant the rate at which a given type of molecule is renewed in the organism. Turnover may be a measure of the rate of total synthesis or degradation of the molecule in question, or, as is frequently the case in isotopic-labeling experiments, it may merely indicate the rate at which one segment of the molecule "exchanges" with its free brethren in the "metabolic pool" (p. 488).

Whether measured by labeling the phosphate, fatty acids, or bases, the turnover of phospholipids exhibits the same relative rates in the various tissues; liver, intestine, and kidney comprise the most active group, such organs as pancreas, adrenals, and lungs having intermediate activity, and muscle and brain being in the slowest category.

Since several components enter into the structure of the phospholipids, it might be anticipated that each would turn over at a characteristic rate. However, choline, phosphate, and fatty acids apparently exhibit comparable rates of turnover in the phospholipid fraction of liver (or plasma, which is largely a reflection of events in the liver in the case of the phospholipids). The possibility remains that divergent rates may be exhibited under various physiological or pathological conditions.

Data obtained in experimental animals using labeled acetate indicate that, in liver and plasma, neutral fat turns over more rapidly than phospholipid, whereas the converse holds true in most other organs (including mesenteric lipid). Turnover rates are equal for fat and phospholipid in the carcass. The half-life of liver and plasma phospholipid is a matter of hours rather than days.

A few data are available on relative rates of turnover of individual types of phospholipids. In liver and intestine, lecithin turns over more rapidly than cephalin, whereas the opposite is the case in brain. Sphingomyelin is renewed less rapidly than the other phospholipids of liver, but more rapidly in muscle. All of the phospholipid fractions of kidney turn over at approximately equal rates.

As might be anticipated, the turnover of phospholipids is markedly affected by dietary or metabolic influences. Fat feeding increases the turnover in liver and intestine, decreases that of the kidney, and has no effect on other organs. Experimental diabetes results in markedly increased turnover in liver and plasma, whereas other tissues are affected slightly or not at all. Administration of choline increases the rate of turnover of the lecithin fraction of liver.

CATABOLISM. There is little information concerning the processes of breakdown of phospholipids in the tissues. The initial reactions are presumably hydrolytic, similar to those taking place in the digestive tract. Various "lecithinases" (p. 230), which are not specific for lecithin, are found in animal tissues. The liberated components are then free to pursue their individual metabolic pathways.

FUNCTIONS OF THE PHOSPHOLIPIDS. (a) STRUCTURAL. Early investigations led to the conclusion that there are two types of lipids, from the standpoint of metabolic lability: (1) a fraction undergoing relatively wide fluctuations in concentration in the tissues in response to dietary changes—the *"élément variable"*; (2) a fraction, predominantly phospholipid, characterized by constancy of concentration, even in the face of death by inanition—the *"élément constant."* Exceptions and contradictions to this point of view soon resulted from numerous investigations performed by the classical technics; modern studies with isotopes render dubious a claim of durability of any constituent of the body.

Although the phospholipids, or any fraction thereof, can scarcely be considered metabolically inert, this fact in itself does not prevent these compounds from serving a structural function (cf. the discussion of the dynamic state, p. 487). Indeed, it is probable, although the evidence is largely indirect, that phospholipids do participate in the lipoprotein complexes (p. 38) which are thought to constitute the matrix of cell walls and membranes (and probably of such structures as mitochondria and microsomes). In this role, they impart certain physical characteristics to these structures, viz., unexpectedly high permeability toward certain non-polar (hydrophobic) molecules, and lysis by surface-active agents (detergents, bile salts, etc.).

Certain enzymes appear to require tightly bound phospholipid for their action. Whether or not the phospholipid deserves the status of a prosthetic group (p. 222), the fact remains that its removal from the enzyme protein irreversibly inactivates the latter. This function may be considered to be structural in the broad sense.

(*b*) BLOOD COAGULATION. Substances having the properties of phospholipids (possibly cephalins) are believed to function as parts of both "thromboplastin" and "antithromboplastin" in the mechanism of blood coagulation (p. 734). The specific compounds involved have not been identified.

(*c*) LIPID TRANSPORT ACROSS CELL WALLS. It has been thought for some time that phospholipids act as carriers of fatty acids into and out of cells, particularly during the absorption of fatty acids from the intestine, and in the passage of lipids from the blood plasma into the tissues. Although no data are available on the latter point, the role of phospholipids in intestinal absorption has been reduced to, at best, a minor status. By the use of isotopes, the increased turnover rate of the phospholipids of the intestinal mucosa during fat absorption has been found to be inadequate to account for any major fraction of absorbed fatty acids. Furthermore, the phospholipid fraction of lymph does not transport any significant proportion of the absorbed fatty acids from the intestine to the thoracic duct.

(*d*) LIPID TRANSPORT BETWEEN TISSUES. Another purported function of phospholipids is the transport of fatty acids from one tissue or organ to another, e.g., between liver and depots. This concept has had to be abandoned. According to present information, the phospholipids of the plasma are synthesized almost exclusively in the liver, and are removed from the plasma mainly by the same organ. Other tissues synthesize their own phospholipids, liberate practically none into the plasma, and absorb very little from that source.

A possible indirect role of phospholipids in lipid transport in the blood is suggested by recent investigations of the relation between the phospholipid: cholesterol ratio of plasma and the state of aggregation of the lipoproteins. This is discussed more fully elsewhere (p. 470).

(a) OXIDATION OF FATTY ACIDS. Since the phospholipids, on the average, contain fatty acids that are more highly unsaturated than those of the neutral fats, it has been suggested in the past that the fatty acids are desaturated, and perhaps otherwise degraded, while they form a part of the phospholipid molecule. In addition to certain direct contradictory evidence, this hypothesis has been rendered superfluous by the currently established CoA mechanism (p. 446).

The ease of autoxidation of the polyunsaturated fatty acids (which are to be found mainly in the phospholipids) has led to the theory that the phospholipids act as catalysts of biological oxidations. No good evidence supports this theory. Furthermore, certain phospholipids are effective antioxidants *in vitro,* and are so used commercially.

That phospholipids nevertheless play some role in the metabolism of fatty acids, at least in the liver, seems probable from the observations cited previously, in which the turnover of phospholipids is correlated with the intensity of fat metabolism (fat feeding and diabetes). At this time, however, it must be concluded that the specific nature of the function served by the phospholipids remains a mystery.

METABOLISM OF GLYCOLIPIDS

Little can be said of the metabolism of this group of lipids, even the chemistry of which is not entirely settled (p. 34). The sphingosine moiety of the cerebrosides was discussed in connection with the phospholipids (p. 33). Galactose doubtless is derived from glucose by the usual pathways, although no data are available in the case of the glycolipids. Certain abnormalities of glycolipid deposition have been mentioned elsewhere (p. 442).

METABOLISM OF CAROTENOIDS

These compounds are mentioned here solely for the sake of completeness. The relation of the carotenes to the vitamins A and important functions of the latter, e.g., in the biochemistry of vision, are discussed elsewhere (p. 128).

TRANSPORT OF LIPIDS

The subjects of lipid transport, deposition, and storage cannot, at the present time, be discussed as satisfactorily as can comparable phases of the metabolism of carbohydrate and protein. Many facts are well established, but in many cases their significance is still in doubt. This state of uncertainty is reflected in the present status of knowledge concerning the blood lipids, despite the accumulation of information on this topic in recent years.

Phospholipids (chiefly lecithin), cholesterol, and neutral fat are the most abundant lipids in the plasma. There are small amounts of glycolipids and minute quantities of certain important hormones, and vitamins of lipid nature. Normal values for the major plasma lipids are indicated in Table 44, p. 472. Because of the heterogeneity of this group of substances and because different components have different metabolic origins, fates, and significance, it is necessary to consider them individually from these standpoints. Before doing so, however, certain general features of their state in the plasma should be reviewed. These have to do largely with recent observations concerning the intimate relationship between the plasma lipids and certain fractions of the plasma proteins.

STATE OF LIPIDS IN BLOOD: LIPOPROTEINS.   As has been indicated previously (p. 38), practically all of the lipids of plasma are present as lipoprotein complexes. These substances are described from the standpoint of protein chemistry in the discussion of the plasma proteins (p. 501). Electrophoretic studies of plasma protein fractions precipitated by ethanol at low temperatures (p. 502) have disclosed the presence of two groups of lipoproteins, one migrating with the α_1-globulins, the other with the β_1-globulins. Ultracentrifugal analysis by the flotation technic (p. 503) has led to the detection of a hierarchy of lipoproteins of varying particle weight.

The lipoproteins in flotation group $S_f 12-20$ are of particular interest, since it is claimed that the occurrence of appreciable quantities (abnormal) of these substances in human sera is correlated with the incidence of atherosclerosis. Significant reductions in the levels of these substances in the blood are said to follow dietary restriction of cholesterol, and particularly of fat.

The plasma lipoproteins contain cholesterol (free and esterified), phospholipids, neutral fat, and traces of the lipid-soluble vitamins and the steroid hormones. Transport of the latter substances in a water-soluble form may be an important function of the lipoproteins. The α_1-lipoprotein referred to above contains 12 per cent cholesterol, 21 per cent phospholipid, and 57 per cent protein, whereas the β_1-lipoprotein and the protein in flotation group $S_f = 4$ (which are probably identical) contain about 30 per cent cholesterol, 25–29 per cent phospholipid, and 23–25 per cent protein, in addition to traces of vitamins A, D, and E, and of estrogens. The chemical composition of the lipoproteins isolated by flotation appears to vary regularly with the density of the molecule: as one proceeds from $S_f = 4$ to $S_f = 40,000$, the content of cholesterol, phospholipid, and protein decreases gradually, as does the fraction of cholesterol present as ester (75 per cent of the total cholesterol in class $S_f = 4$). The content of triglyceride, which is negligible up to class $S_f = 17$, increases progressively thereafter to a value of 75–85 per cent in the molecules of the highest S_f groups, which are therefore practically fat droplets (chylomicrons). The phospholipid:cholesterol ratio in the lipoproteins varies with the species of molecule in question. There are indications that the size of the lipoprotein aggregates is controlled to some extent by the over-all phospholipid: cholesterol ratio of the plasma, turbidity resulting from ratios below certain critical values. Slowing of the blood flow through the capillaries, which occurs under these circumstances, may be of clinical significance.

Heparin and certain fractions of the plasma proteins appear to exert a "clearing" action on turbid plasma. This is accomplished also by high molecular weight dextrans. These recently observed phenomena have been tentatively outlined as follows, where the Roman numerals refer to plasma fractions obtained by the Cohn procedure (p. 502):

$$\text{Fraction IV—1} \xrightarrow{\text{Heparin + Tissue factor (heart, lung)}} \text{Clearing factor}$$
$$\text{(Fraction III—1,2,3)}$$

$$\text{Turbid lipoproteins, high } S_f \xrightarrow[\text{+ Coprotein (III—O)}]{\text{Clearing factor}} \text{Decreased turbidity, lower } S_f$$

This "clearing" action of heparin is prevented by protamine (doubtless due to salt formation between the acidic heparin and the basic protamine) (p. 96). Pathological concentrations of the S_f 12–20 lipoproteins could conceivably result from a deficiency in one or more of these factors.

POSTABSORPTIVE PLASMA LIPID CONCENTRATION. It is apparent (Table 44) that the range of normal variation in the concentration of plasma lipids is unusually wide, even in the postabsorptive state. Moreover, although the three major components, i.e., triglycerides (neutral fat), phosphatides (phospholipids), and cholesterol, frequently vary in the same direction, although not to the same degree, this is not always the case. Total fatty acids and neutral fat are particularly variable, even in the same individual. The cholesterol:phospholipid ratio is more stable and uniform, although its significance is not apparent. Little is known concerning the intrinsic mechanisms which regulate the equilibrium levels of the blood lipids. It is conceivable that the choles-terol:phospholipid ratio may be influenced, if not fixed, by the hepatic mechanism for synthesis of the lipoproteins in which these molecules are found. There is no significant sex or racial difference in the concentrations of plasma lipids. Although there is no complete agreement on this point, there is evidence that "adult" patterns of blood lipid concentrations are established at an early age (first few days of life), and change but little, if at all, in later years in normal subjects. Low values for cholesterol and phospholipids have been re-ported in the newborn.

Table 44. Main plasma lipids (postabsorptive).

SUBSTANCE	CONCENTRATION
	(mg./100 ml.)
Total lipid	385–675 (530)
Neutral fat	0–260 (140)
Phospholipids	110–250 (165)
Lecithin	80–200 (110)
Cephalin	0– 30 (10)
Sphingomyelin	10– 50 (30)
Cholesterol	140–260 (200)
Ester	90–200 (145)
Free	40– 70 (55)
Total Fatty Acids	110–485 (300)

CHOLESTEROL. Cholesterol exists in the plasma in two forms, (1) free and (2) esterified (combined with fatty acids), both of which are incorporated in lipoprotein molecules (p. 470). Free cholesterol comprises about 20–40 per cent, and ester cholesterol about 60–80 per cent of the total of 140–260 mg./100 ml. This ratio is usually preserved with remarkable constancy even in the presence of wide variations in the total owing to disease states that are not accompanied by dis-turbance of liver cell function. Although cholesterol is undoubtedly synthesized by a number of tissues, the liver is the main if not the only source of plasma cholesterol as well as the main site of its esterifica-tion (also intestinal mucosa, p. 465). This organ is therefore funda-mentally concerned in the maintenance, not only of the level of cholesterol in the plasma, but also of the ester:free cholesterol ratio. It plays an important role, too, in the removal of this substance from the blood, and in its subsequent metabolism, as indicated by the fact that the bulk of exogenous cholesterol is recoverable as bile acids in the bile (p. 462).

Apart from the low values in the newborn (about 50 mg./100 ml.) and an increase during pregnancy, reaching a maximum (about 35 per cent above non-pregnant state) at about the thirtieth week, there are no significant variations under physiological conditions (postabsorptive). There is statistical evidence, of questionable validity, of an increased concentration in advanced years. Abnormalities in certain disease states can be explained on the basis of aberrations of known physiological mechanisms, although many cannot.

In severe impairment of liver cell function (e.g., hepatocellular jaundice) the ester cholesterol decreases, resulting in hypocholesterolemia and a decrease in the ratio of ester to free cholesterol. This is presumably due to diminished production and esterification of plasma cholesterol by the damaged liver cells. In cases of obstruction of the common bile duct (obstructive jaundice) the plasma cholesterol concentration rises, if the liver cells are not seriously damaged. The explanation for this phenomenon is not clear, but recent observations suggest that the hypercholesterolemia is in some manner dependent upon the increase in bile acids in the plasma which occurs under these circumstances (regurgitation as a result of biliary obstruction). These differences in plasma cholesterol in hepatocellular and obstructive types of jaundice may aid in differential diagnosis of these conditions.

Hypercholesterolemia occurs in uncontrolled diabetes mellitus (p. 430). This may be due to diversion of abnormally large amounts of 2-C fragments ("acetate") to cholesterol synthesis (also ketogenesis) in the liver as a consequence of (1) increased catabolism of fatty acids and (2) decreased availability of oxalacetate, due to insulin deficiency (p. 408).

The mechanism underlying abnormalities of plasma cholesterol concentration in certain other diseases is not well understood: e.g., the increase in hypothyroidism and decrease in hyperthyroidism (p. 685); the increase in glomerulonephritis and nephrosis; the decrease in certain types of anemia, infections, and inanition. Estrogens have a profound influence on lipid metabolism in certain species (e.g., producing hyperlipemia in birds; lipotropic action [p. 478] in rats). There are reports that they cause a decrease in plasma cholesterol in man and alter its distribution between the plasma lipoprotein fractions, but these effects are still uncertain.

Diet has little influence on the plasma cholesterol concentration under normal conditions. A high cholesterol intake depresses cholesterol synthesis in the liver. It has been found, however, that rigid restriction of dietary lipids may lower abnormally high plasma cholesterol concentrations in certain disease states.

Attention has been directed toward the possible implication of an increase in plasma cholesterol, particularly in the S_f 12–20 lipoprotein category (p. 470), in the pathogenesis of atherosclerosis. This important subject is currently under intensive investigation.

PHOSPHOLIPIDS. The range of normal variation in plasma phospholipids is indicated in Table 44. Lecithin is the main component of this fraction, which, like other lipids, occurs in the blood plasma in association with certain globulins, as lipoprotein complexes (p. 470). It has been shown, by the use of isotope-labeling technics, that the plasma phospholipids, similarly to cholesterol, not only originate in the liver but are also removed from the blood and metabolized probably exclusively by that organ. It appears, therefore, that plasma phospholipids undergo their complete metabolic cycle within the liver, with a temporary sojourn in the blood stream, the purpose of which is not readily apparent. The constancy of the cholesterol:phospholipid ratio suggests that this factor (ratio) is of physiological significance. Present evidence renders untenable the formerly prevailing view that the plasma phospholipids serve as an important medium of transport of fatty acids between the liver and extrahepatic tissues.

In common with other lipids, the concentration of phospholipids in the plasma is low in the newborn and increases during pregnancy. It varies in a number of disease states in the same direction, although not necessarily to the same extent as the cholesterol concentration, viz., hyper- and hypothyroidism, diabetes mellitus, nephritis and nephrosis, hepatocellular and obstructive jaundice.

TRIGLYCERIDES (NEUTRAL FATS). The variable concentration of neutral fat in the plasma in the postabsorptive state is indicated in Table 44. The components of this fraction, too, exist as lipoprotein complexes (p. 470), but, during the period of absorption of fats from the intestine, they occur temporarily also in free form in plasma (chylomicrons, p. 744). In the postabsorptive state they represent mainly triglycerides mobilized from the fat depots, en route to the liver, where they undergo their primary metabolic changes (p. 475). They may also include triglycerides from the liver, en route to the fat depots.

The role of growth hormone (p. 701), adrenocortical hormones (p. 680), and carbohydrate unavailability (p. 483) in stimulating mobilization of fat deposits is discussed elsewhere. It is apparent that fat enters the blood from the fat depots at an accelerated rate under a variety of conditions in which carbohydrate is either not provided in adequate amounts in the diet or cannot be utilized adequately because of hormonal or other abnormalities. Increase in blood fat (hyperlipemia) occurs therefore in starvation (early, before deposits are depleted), dietary carbohydrate restriction, and diabetes mellitus (insulin deficiency). It may be present also in severe anemias (deficient oxidation?) and in glomerulonephritis (starvation effect?).

INFLUENCE OF FOOD AND NUTRITION. After a high-fat meal, the plasma lipids begin to rise within two hours, reach a peak in four to six hours, and then tend to drop rather rapidly toward the resting level. Most of the increment is due to neutral fat; cholesterol and phospholipids make minor contributions (p. 440). This temporary absorptive hyper-lipemia is due to the fact that the major portion of the dietary lipid is absorbed by the intestinal lympatics and enters the blood stream directly, via the thoracic duct (p. 440). If large amounts of fat are ingested the plasma may become opalescent, owing to the presence of small aggregates of neutral fat (chylomicrons) in suspension. So-called "normal" meals often produce no significant rise in plasma lipids.

There is no general correlation between the blood lipid levels and the amount of body fat, but chronic malnutrition and wasting diseases are often accompanied by subnormal levels of phospholipids and cholesterol. In the initial stages of starvation, or of carbohydrate deprivation, after depletion of the preformed glycogen stores (about thirty-six hours), hyperlipemia occurs as a result of increased mobilization of depot fat. This may be accompanied by "fatty liver" (p. 476). Ketogenesis is increased, owing to the accelerated degradation of fatty acids in the liver, in conjunction with the shortage of oxalacetic acid (normally derived mainly from carbohydrate). Overloading of ketolytic mechanisms of the extrahepatic tissues soon results, followed by a significant degree of ketonemia and ketonuria. If the fasting period is prolonged to the point of depletion of available fat stores, the concentrations of blood lipids and ketone bodies may fall.

DEPOSITION AND STORAGE OF LIPIDS

ROLE OF LIVER IN LIPID METABOLISM. Although incidental mention has been made of the role of the liver in various aspects of lipid metabolism, it seems desirable to summarize here the pertinent information on this point, since the phenomena to be discussed in this section involve the liver primarily.

1. The liver is the chief site of synthesis of fatty acids from carbohydrate, and of cholesterol from acetate fragments.

2. The liver is probably the sole source of bile acids.

3. The phospholipids and cholesterol (free and esterified) of the plasma, and the lipoproteins in which they are incorporated, are synthesized by the liver.

4. In the other direction, the liver is the organ chiefly concerned in removal of phospholipids, cholesterol, and probably also the lipoproteins from the plasma.

5. The liver is the major site of degradation of fatty acids of dietary or depot origin, when the physiological state of the body calls on fat for the major provision of energy.

6. The liver is the only physiologically significant site of formation of ketone bodies.

7. The liver is one of poles of the "liver-depot axis," along which

fat is transported in one direction or the other in response to physiological needs. In this connection, the level of fat in the liver at a given
time reflects the current status and net direction of the mobilization
mechanisms.

FATTY LIVER AND LIPOTROPISM.   The amount of lipid in the liver at any
given time is the resultant of several influences, some acting in conjunction with, some in opposition to others. (Normal total lipid about
4 per cent, three-fourths of which is phospholipid, one-fourth neutral
fat.) This situation is illustrated below with respect to the fatty acids,
neglecting for the sake of simplification the form of lipid in which the
acids may occur.

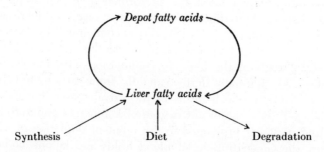

(Adapted from D. Stetten and J. Salcedo, J. Biol. Chem. *156*:27, 1944.)

Factors that tend to increase the fatty acid content of the liver are:
(1) the synthesis of fatty acids in that organ from carbohydrate and
protein, (2) influx of dietary lipid, and (3) mobilization of fat to the
liver. Decrease in liver fatty acids results from: (1) mobilization of
fat to the depots from the liver, (2) passage of cholesterol esters and
phospholipids into the blood, (3) degradation of the fatty acids
within the liver itself. Normal levels of lipid in the liver are the result
of maintenance of a proper balance between these factors. A *relative*
increase or decrease in the rate of one or other of these processes can
result in the accumulation of abnormal quantities of lipid in the liver,
so-called "fatty liver." On this basis, five types of fatty liver can be distinguished, in theory at least, due to the following causes: (1) over-
feeding of fat; (2) oversynthesis of fat from carbohydrate; (3)
overmobilization from depots to liver; (4) undermobilization from
liver to depots; (5) underutilization in the liver. Although it is doubtful whether all of these types have been observed in uncomplicated
form, a summary of the probable general features characteristic of
each is presented in Table 45.

TYPE 1.   Although fatty livers of pure Type 1 can be produced in
experimental animals, they are frequently deliberately aggravated by
the imposition of conditions conducive to the development of Types

2 or 4. The lipids deposited in Type 1 reflect the composition of the dietary lipid, as would be expected. The "cholesterol fatty liver" may belong to this category, although it is usually considered in another context (v. infra, Type 4).

Table 45. Classification of fatty liver

TYPE	EFFECT ON BLOOD LIPIDS	EFFECT ON LIVER LIPIDS	EFFECT ON DEPOT LIPIDS	IMMEDIATE CAUSE	CURATIVE AGENTS* (LIPOTROPIC FACTORS)
1. Overfeeding	None	Increase	Increase	Excessive fat in diet	Choline and precursors or substitutes
2. Over-synthesis	None	Increase	Increase	Excessive carbohydrate, cystine, B vitamins in diet	Choline and precursors or substitutes
3. Overmobilization to liver	Increase, normal pattern	Increase, normal pattern	Decrease	Carbohydrate deprivation (dietary, hormonal)	
4. Undermobilization from liver	Decrease, especially in phospholipid and cholesterol	Increase in fat and cholesterol; decrease in lecithin	Decrease	Deficiency of: Essential fatty acids	
				Pyridoxine	Inositol
				Pantothenic acid	Choline and precursors or substitutes
				Choline (direct or indirect)	Choline and precursors or substitutes, lipocaic
				Excess of: Diet cholesterol	Choline and precursors or substitutes, plus inositol or lipocaic
				Biotin	Inositol; lipocaic
5. Underutilization	Increase in phospholipid and cholesterol Decrease later, if severe	Increase	Increase; decrease ?	Deficiency of pantothenic acid; hepatotoxic agents	Choline and precursors or subsititutes

* Other than direct removal of cause.

TYPE 2. Oversynthesis from carbohydrate can result from forced feeding; it is more generally produced experimentally by the administration of excessive amounts of certain B vitamins (thiamine, biotin, riboflavin) or cystine, which seem to stimulate the appetite. Increased consumption of fat as well as carbohydrate lends to this type of fatty liver certain of the characteristics of Type 1. The situation is even more complex, however. The increase in general metabolic activity occasioned by the inclusion of large quantities of B vitamins or cystine in the diet results in a greater demand for certain factors, such as inositol and choline (v. infra, Type 4). The consequent *relative* deficit in these factors actually produces fatty livers of Type 4.

TYPE 3. Fatty liver of this type is referred to by some as "physio-logical" fatty liver, because it represents merely an exaggeration of a normal process, the mobilization of fat from the depots to the liver. The normal proportions among the various types of lipids in blood and liver are maintained: all are equally elevated in concentration. Fatty livers of this type develop in conditions involving greatly increased utilization of fat as fuel, which is the physiological equivalent of saying all conditions in which there is interference with the oxidation of carbohydrate. Such conditions exist in: (1) diabetes, human or experimental, of the hypoinsulin, hyperpituitary, or hyperadreno-cortical types; (2) "pseudodiabetes" induced by phlorizin; (3) starvation; (4) carbohydrate deprivation. The fat which accumulates in the liver is derived from the depots, the fat content of which decreases accordingly. In addition to fatty livers, this condition is characterized also by ketosis and, in advanced cases, acidosis (p. 430).

TYPE 4. Fatty liver of this type has been differentiated from the preceding type by being designated "pathological." It is accompanied by a decrease in plasma lipids (hypolipemia) which affects mainly the phospholipids and cholesterol esters. The pattern of liver lipids is also abnormal; fat and cholesterol esters are especially increased, whereas lecithin is present in less than the usual proportion. Fatty livers of this type may eventuate in cirrhosis of the liver and there may be associated hemorrhagic lesions in the kidneys. They appear to be caused by agents or conditions which produce either an absolute or a relative deficiency in certain of the ingredients used by the liver for synthesis of phospholipids, viz., choline, inositol, and the poly-unsaturated fatty acids. The resulting condition appears to reflect some sort of blockage of metabolism of fat in, or its movement through the liver. According to certain investigators, the degradation of fatty acids is impaired; the majority opinion holds that the integrity of phospho-lipid metabolism in the liver is necessary for the mobilization of fat from that organ.

Agents (e.g., choline, methionine, betaine, and inositol) which have the apparent effect of facilitating the removal of fat from the liver are said to be "lipotropic," the phenomenon itself being called "lipot-ropism." Antagonistic agents and the converse condition are "anti-lipotropic" and "antilipotropism," respectively.

Fatty livers of Type 4 may be roughly classified according to the causative agent or phenomenon:

(a) Deficiency of Essential Fatty Acids. The fatty livers due to deficiency of the essential fatty acids are cured only by the reintroduction of these substances into the diet. Since the phospholipids of the liver are characterized by a relatively high content of polyunsaturated fatty acids, it is surmised that a shortage of the latter substances results in impairment of synthesis or turnover of the former.

(b) *Imbalance of B Vitamins.* Deficiencies of pyridoxine (p. 189 and pantothenic acid (p. 193), and excessive amounts of biotin (p. 197) in the diet give rise to fatty livers, the etiologic factor of which is in dispute. It is possible that the fatty liver of pantothenic acid deficiency properly belongs to Type 5 rather than 4, since a shortage of CoA (of which pantothenic acid is a part) might be expected to result in impairment of the degradative mechanisms for fatty acids. Lack of pyridoxine and a surplus of biotin are said to elicit a greater demand upon the supply of inositol, thus supposedly interfering with the synthesis of inositol-containing phosphatides. Although the fatty livers in these conditions respond well to inositol, this explanation leaves much to be desired.

(c) *"Cholesterol" Fatty Livers.* Fatty livers resulting from administration of excessive amounts of cholesterol are sometimes regarded as belonging to Type 4, although they may perhaps as readily fit the requirements of Type 1. One explanation advanced for the former classification is that cholesterol may compete with phospholipids for the polyunsaturated fatty acids, for the acids found in cholesterol esters are, on the average, even more highly unsaturated than those of phospholipids.

(c) *Choline Deficiency.* The remaining fatty livers of Type 4 are due, more or less directly, to a deficiency of choline. Since choline is synthesized by the successive methylation of ethanolamine, it is true that induced deficiencies of the methyl group produce fatty livers, solely, however, because of the resulting shortage of choline. The use of the phenomenon of lipotropism to demonstrate the reaction of transmethylation (p. 536) has to some extent obscured the essential point that choline, and not the methyl group or transmethylation *per se*, is the lipotropic agent. This is indicated by the observation that certain compounds, completely incapable of transmethylation, are nevertheless lipotropic, and, in some cases, are actually incorporated into the phospholipids as substitutes for choline. Such compounds are arsenocholine (arsenic in place of the choline N), sulfocholine (sulfur in place of N), and the triethyl analog of choline.

Animals maintained on diets deficient in the usual sources of preformed methyl groups (choline, methionine, betaine), and also in the vitamins necessary for synthesis of methyl groups from appropriate precursors (folic-folinic acid group, B_{12}), develop fatty livers of Type 4. These fatty livers are cured by the methyl donors mentioned above, by choline itself or its proper analogs, and, as shown recently, by folic acid.

A deficiency of choline can be induced also by inclusion in the diet of compounds which will compete with ethanolamine for available methyl groups. Nicotinic acid or amide and guanidoacetic acid, for example, are methylated in the body to N^1-methylnicotinamide and creatine, respectively (pp. 186, 521). Administration of greatly excessive quantities of these compounds depletes the supply of methyl groups available for the synthesis of choline, and fatty liver results.

Pancreatectomized animals maintained adequately with insulin develop fatty livers, not of the overmobilization type characteristic of diabetes, but of Type 4. The condition is alleviated by the administration of raw pancreas. According to one school of thought, "lipocaic," a purported *internal* secretion of the pancreas, is the lipotropic agent responsible. The majority believe that an *external* secretion of the pancreas is involved, probably a proteolytic enzyme which specifically facilitates the liberation of methionine from the proteins of the food.

Other substances exert a lipotropic action the mechanism of which has not been explained, e.g., estrogens and threonine.

TYPE 5. As suggested previously, it is possible that the fatty livers of pantothenic acid deficiency are of this type, i.e., underutilization. Those due to hepatotoxic agents (chloroform, carbon tetrachloride, phosphorus) may also belong to this group, although they present in addition certain of the features of Type 4. The initial elevation of the serum lipids (during which time the depots may have an increased content of fat) may be due to impairment of the mechanisms for the degradation of fatty acids, but not of the mobilization of fat from the liver to the depots. The second, or hypolipemic phase (during which time the depots are probably somewhat depleted), may reflect interference with the mobilizing mechanisms of the liver. In support of the probably composite nature of the pathogenesis of this type of fatty liver, it may be mentioned that it is possible to counteract or mitigate with choline or methionine the fatty infiltration due to the hepatotoxic agents, if the therapeutic agent is given promptly after administration of the toxic agent, or better, prophylactically.

ABNORMAL DEPOSITS OF LIPIDS. The general features of the abnormal deposition of certain types of lipids in specific tissues have been mentioned previously (p. 442). The biochemical mechanisms of these "lipidoses" remain obscure.

ENDOCRINE INFLUENCES IN LIPID METABOLISM

Hormones play an important role in the coordination of various phases of lipid metabolism and in their integration with carbohydrate metabolism (p. 481). The most important hormones in this connection are insulin, the 11-oxygenated adrenal cortical hormones, and anterior pituitary factors (growth hormone, or some principle intimately associated with it; adrenocorticotrophic hormone, acting via the adrenal cortex). The metabolic effects of these factors are considered in detail elsewhere (p. 654 ff.). It will suffice here merely to summarize their important effects on lipid metabolism.

INSULIN (P. 690). Administration of insulin is followed by increased synthesis of fatty acids from 2-C fragments (lipogenesis), representing one phase of the increased utilization of glucose induced by this agent. Ketogenesis is depressed, another consequence of the stimulation of glucose utilization in the liver, which increases the supply of oxalacetate for incorporation of 2-C fragments from fatty acid into the Krebs cycle (p. 398).

As in the case of carbohydrate metabolism, there is some degree of functional antagonism between insulin and the lipid-active adrenocortical and anterior pituitary hormones at certain points. In the absence of adequate amounts of insulin, e.g., in pancreatic diabetes (p. 430), decreased lipogenesis and increased ketogenesis, referable to the insulin actions indicated above, are accompanied by acceleration of mobilization of fat from the fat depots, with consequent increase in blood and liver lipids (p. 478). These phenomena are attributable to increased amounts or activity of the adrenal and pituitary hormones (q. v.), or to increased sensitivity of the depot fat to their action, unbalanced by normal amounts of insulin. Insulin deficiency is accompanied also by increased synthesis of cholesterol (liver) from 2-C fragments from the increased amounts of fatty acid mobilized from the fat stores; the plasma cholesterol rises.

ADRENOCORTICAL HORMONES (P. 673). Administration of adrenal oxysteroids (p. 680) is followed by diminished lipogenesis from carbohydrate and increased ketogenesis, these hormones antagonizing the actions of insulin in these respects. Acting in conjunction with a fat-mobilizing principle of the anterior pituitary, apparently growth hormone or some factor intimately associated with it (p. 701), these hormones stimulate mobilization of fat from the fat depots, with consequent increase in plasma and liver lipids (p. 474).

ANTERIOR PITUITARY HORMONES (P. 695). Administration of anterior pituitary extracts is followed by increased mobilization of fat from the fat depots, with loss of body fat and increase in plasma and liver lipids and in ketogenesis. The fat-mobilizing effect is attributable primarily to the growth hormone ("trigger action") or some factor intimately associated with it (p. 701), but requires also an increase in adrenal oxycorticoids. Neither factor alone can produce this effect.

THYROID HORMONE (P. 681). Administration of thyroxine is followed by a decrease in plasma cholesterol and phospholipids, which increase following removal of the thyroid gland. The mechanism of action of thyroxine in this connection is not known.

METABOLIC INTERRELATIONS OF LIPIDS, CARBOHYDRATES, AND PROTEINS

The diagram on page 482 illustrates the metabolic interrelations between the major types of lipids and other foodstuffs.

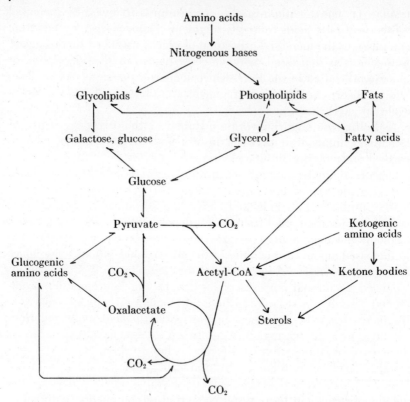

The lipids do not contribute significant quantities of material to the synthesis of amino acids. Glycerol is the only major raw material which may be provided for the synthesis of carbohydrate from lipid sources, although it is probable that the usual net flow of this substance is in the reverse direction. The characteristic relation of lipids to other foodstuffs involves either synthesis of the former from the latter, or some type of coupling between the rates of synthesis and degradation of the two families of compounds.

Carbohydrate is converted to lipid in various ways. Small amounts of galactose (and in some cases glucose) are undoubtedly provided for the synthesis of cerebrosides and gangliosides. The glycerol moiety of the triglycerides and glycerophosphatides is formed readily from the intermediates of glycolysis. However, the major conversion in this direction, and the one usually meant by the phrase, "synthesis of fat from carbohydrate," is the formation of fatty acids from acetyl units, which are in turn derived from the oxidative decarboxylation of pyruvic acid. The irreversibility of this decarboxylation, incidentally, forms the basis of the current view that fatty acids cannot be converted into carbohydrate.

The concluding statement of the previous paragraph seems to be belied by many experiments with isotopes, in which labeled carbon atoms from fatty acids have been shown to be incorporated into glucose or glycogen. The contradiction is more apparent than real, however. Inspection of the reactions of the tricarboxylic acid cycle (p. 398) subsequent to the condensation of acetyl-CoA and oxalacetic acid reveals that the two carbon atoms lost as CO_2 from the cycle are not the same atoms which entered the cycle as acetate. The carbon atoms of the acetate finally appear in the regenerated oxalacetic acid, which can form pyruvic acid by decarboxylation. Hence a labeled atom from acetate or a fatty acid can be incorporated into glucose or glycogen. Nevertheless, the "material balance" shows that two carbon atoms have reacted with a molecule of oxalacetic acid to form two molecules of CO_2 and regenerate the oxalacetic acid. Since no additional molecules of oxalacetic acid are formed, no net synthesis of pyruvic acid or carbohydrate from fatty acids has occurred, despite the transfer of carbon atoms from one to the other.

Amino acids contribute to the synthesis of lipids. Ethanolamine, choline, and serine, for example, components of the phospholipids, are derived from the pathways of protein metabolism. The ketogenic amino acids (pp. 544, 551) form acetic or acetoacetic acids, from which fatty acids can be derived. The glucogenic acids (p. 516), directly or indirectly, form pyruvic acid, which can be used for the synthesis of either carbohydrate or fatty acids.

An intimate quantitative relationship exists between the metabolism of fatty acids and of carbohydrate. When the rate of oxidation of carbohydrate, the preferred fuel of the body, falters, fat is mobilized from the depots to the liver, probably by a mechanism involving the pituitary and adrenals (p. 481). The rate of degradation of fatty acids in the liver is then increased. The mechanism of the "coupling" involved is not known, but it seems reasonable to postulate that, when carbohydrate is oxidized at a rapid rate, the production of acetyl-CoA molecules from pyruvic acid results in virtual coverage of the condensation enzyme of the tricarboxylic acid cycle, thus forcing the equilibrium of fatty acid ⟶ acetyl-CoA toward synthesis. Adequate energy for the anabolic pathway toward fatty acids is also provided by the oxidation of pyruvic acid. There are several reasons, therefore, why a diminution in the number of pyruvic acid molecules being oxidized per unit time will automatically cause an augmented breakdown of fatty acids. This metabolic stratagem, however, carries with it dangers of its own. A decreased rate of oxidation of carbohydrate results, in the liver at least, in a shortage of oxalacetic acid, due to various wasteful side reactions. The resulting increase in ketogenesis and its consequences have been described previously (p. 430). It

would appear, then, from the foregoing remarks that, whereas carbohydrate may be considered a competing substrate to fatty acids in
one sense, it is a necessary partner in their oxidation in another.

Although this discussion of the metabolism of fatty acids and carbohydrates has stressed the net flow of metabolites in one direction or
another, it may be well to conclude with the reminder that, regardless
of net synthesis or catabolism or steady states, all groups of molecules
connected metabolically interchange material continually, as indicated
by isotopic labeling. Whether the physiological situation of the moment calls for oxidation predominantly of carbohydrate or of fat, a
certain amount of conversion of carbohydrate to fat always takes
place. These and other aspects of the "dynamic state of the body constituents" are considered in greater detail in connection with the
metabolism of protein (p. 487).

BIBLIOGRAPHY

General

Annual Review of Biochemistry.
Annual Review of Physiology.
Baldwin, E.: Dynamic Aspects of Biochemistry, London, Cambridge University
Press, 1952, Chapter 18.
Bloor, W. R.: Biochemistry of the Fatty Acids, New York, Reinhold Publishing
Corporation, 1943, Chapters 2–6.
Frazer, A. C.: Lipid metabolism. In Biochemistry and Physiology of Nutrition, Vol-
ume 1, edited by G. F. Bourne and G. W. Kidder, New York, Academic Press,
Inc., 1953, Chapter 7.
Lipmann, F. et al.: Symposium on chemistry and functions of coenzyme A, Fed.
Proc. 12:673, 1953.
Peters, J. P. and Van Slyke, D. D.: Quantitative Clinical Chemistry, Volume 1, Balti-
more, Williams & Wilkins Company, 1946, Chapters 5–7.
Williams, R. T. (ed.): Lipid Metabolism, Biochemical Society Symposia No. 9, Lon-
don, Cambridge University Press, 1952.

Phospholipids, Glycolipids, Cholesterol, Lipoproteins

Gould, R. G.: Lipid metabolism and atherosclerosis, Am. J. Med. 11:209, 1951.
McElroy, W. D. and Glass, B. (eds.): Phosphorus Metabolism, Volume 2, Baltimore,
Johns Hopkins Press, 1952, Part III.
Thannhauser, S. J. and Schmidt, G.: Lipins and lipidoses, Physiol. Rev. 26:275, 1946.
Tullis, J. L. (ed.): Blood Cells and Plasma Proteins, New York, Academic Press, Inc.,
1953, Section VII: The Lipoproteins of Blood and Other Tissues.
Wittcoff, H.: The Phosphatides, New York, Reinhold Publishing Corporation, 1951,
Chapters 20–25.

Hormonal Influences

Levin, L. and Farber, R. K.: Hormonal factors which regulate the mobilization of
depot fat to the liver, Recent Progress in Hormone Research 7:399, 1952.
Mote, J. R. (ed.): Clinical ACTH Conferences, Phliadelphia, Blakiston Company,
1950, 1951.
Sprague, R. .: Effects of cortisone and ACTH, Vitamins & Hormones 9:265, 1951.

19

PROTEIN METABOLISM

As indicated elsewhere in various connections, proteins are of primary importance in intermediary metabolism. Not only are the amino acid constituents of proteins metabolically interrelated with fat, carbohydrate, and other substances, but the proteins themselves form the structural framework of the body and its working machinery as well. In addition to such apparently static components of the body as walls and membranes, the body's catalysts, the enzymes, are proteins. So also are many of the regulators of metabolism, the hormones. Obviously, the importance of the proteins cannot be exaggerated. Because of the numerous facets of this subject which must be considered, it may be useful, for purposes of orientation, to indicate the various segments into which the discussion will be divided.

Mention has been made elsewhere concerning the concepts of the "dynamic state of body constituents" and the "metabolic pool." Although the application of these concepts is by no means restricted to the proteins, the ideas developed originally largely with reference to protein metabolism and many of the best illustrations of the concepts are to be found in that field. For these reasons the discussion of protein metabolism (after a brief review of digestion) is initiated with a consideration of the general concept of dynamics and pools.

Since much information can be obtained concerning protein metabolism from a study of the metabolism of nitrogen, the intake, excretion, and various states of nitrogen balance are discussed. Included in this connection are the essential amino acids, nutritional aspects of the proteins, and certain interrelations with other foodstuffs.

The over-all metabolism of protein, as of all foodstuffs, consists of both anabolic and catabolic phases. Of particular importance is the topic of protein synthesis, including rates, mechanisms, and illustrations of the synthesis of particular proteins.

Plasma proteins are of such central importance in protein metabolism and of such diagnostic value clinically that a separate section is devoted to them. Particular attention is paid to the fractions made available by newer physicochemical technics.

A consideration of hormonal influences concludes the section on general protein metabolism.

Although the amino acids are prime examples of metabolic "rugged individualism," they undergo certain chemical reactions in common. The general methods are described for the separation of the nitrogenous moieties of the amino acids from their carbon skeletons, followed by a consideration of the pathways available for the disposal of each of the fragments.

The discussion of the metabolism of the individual amino acids, always a most vexing topic to treat on an introductory level, is preceded by an outline of the interrelations existing between them, thus providing at least certain threads of connection between topics otherwise virtually isolated and independent.

The chapter is concluded with a discussion of the metabolic interrelations between the proteins and other major foodstuffs.

DIGESTION AND ABSORPTION

The course of protein digestion and the factors involved are discussed in detail elsewhere (pp. 257–270); it is necessary here merely to review briefly the most important features of this process.

Mainly through the hydrolytic action of the proteinases, pepsin (stomach), trypsin (pancreas), and chymotrypsin (pancreas), the large protein molecules are broken down to polypeptides and free amino acids. Completion of digestion, i.e., complete hydrolysis of the peptides, is accomplished by the action of carboxypeptidase (pancreas), and amino-, tri-, and dipeptidases of the intestinal secretions. The process consists essentially in the production of progressively smaller peptides by cleavage of internal peptide linkages (endopeptidases) and liberation of amino acids by cleavage of terminal peptide linkages (endo- and exopeptidases).

If an intact "foreign" protein, i.e., other than human, is introduced into the organism, it acts as an antigen, i.e., it stimulates the formation of specific antibodies, "sensitizing" the organism to this protein (allergic state). Subsequent exposure to the latter results in a serious, and sometimes fatal reaction (anaphylaxis). Obviously, if this phenomenon is to be avoided, food proteins must be so altered before absorption that they have lost their species specificity and thereby their capacity for inducing this state of sensitization. This is accomplished effectively by digestion to the stage of amino acids, which, of course, exhibit no such specificity. It is possible, too, that small peptide molecules escape complete hydrolysis and are absorbed without harmful effect. There is immunological evidence, however, that intact native protein molecules may occasionally be absorbed from the intestine in an unaltered state, constituting the basis for allergic reactions in certain cases.

Food proteins are generally readily digested (90–97 per cent) under normal conditions, very little escaping in the feces. The only important exception is the insoluble fibrous protein, keratin, which is not hydrolyzed by enzymes of the human digestive tract. Most proteins are profoundly altered by many procedures commonly used in the preparation of foods. Heating to coagulation temperatures causes polymerization; superheated steam, excluding air (pressure cookers), causes hydrolysis; dry heat may cause oxidation. In the majority of instances, the digestibility and biological value (p. 495) of these proteins are not affected by such procedures. However, proper cooking may facilitate digestion and utilization, e.g., cooked egg albumin is digested more readily than raw; heating soybeans increases their biological value by inactivating a component with antitryptic activity (p. 263). The nutritional value of cereal proteins is lowered by overheating or toasting (e.g., certain breakfast cereals).

With the few exceptions indicated above (i.e., small peptides, occasionally native protein), food proteins enter the organism in the form of their constituent amino acids. Certain aspects of protein digestion that have an important bearing on their nutritional value, e.g., variation in the rates of liberation of amino acids, are discussed elsewhere (p. 631). The amino acids are readily soluble in water and are promptly absorbed from the small intestine, mainly into the portal circulation (to the liver), and to a much smaller extent, via the lacteals, into the thoracic duct and thence directly into the systemic circulation. Only small amounts of free amino acid are found in the intestinal contents during the process of digestion, indicating the rapidity of their absorption. This is reflected also in the rather prompt postprandial increase in blood amino acid concentration (p. 746).

METABOLIC DYNAMICS AND POOLS

DYNAMIC STATE. It was realized even for some time prior to the use of isotopes, but particularly clearly since the introduction of labeling technics, that the constituents of the body are in a constant state of flux. All molecules, even of the "structural" variety, are constantly being broken down and rebuilt. The apparent stability of the adult organism is the result of a balance between the rates of synthesis and degradation of its constituents. In a growing organism, the rates of synthesis of many of its constituents must exceed the rates of breakdown, in order that new tissue may be constructed. Wasting diseases, starvation, and related states are characterized by rates of catabolism which are greater than the rates of anabolism.

In a given physiological (or pathological) state, the rate of synthesis or degradation of a specific compound will be characteristic of (1) the chemical nature of the compound in question, (2) its location in a particular tissue or organ, and (3) its intracellular location.

Several methods of expression are currently used to describe the rate of synthesis or breakdown of a body constituent. Most of these have been developed in connection with isotopic-labeling technics. The "half-life" is the time required for replacement of one-half of the molecules of the compound in question, the definition being analogous to that used in describing the unstable isotopes (p. 350). The "average life" of a given compound is the time required to replace the molecule of "average stability." Sometimes the rate of a synthetic or degradative process is expressed directly in terms of mass of compound transformed per unit time per unit weight of tissue or animal, e.g., "mols of urea synthesized per day per kilo body weight." On other occasions the rate of turnover of a compound is stated as the percentage of the amount present which is metabolized per unit time.

METABOLIC POOL.   Since the "endogenous" molecules are in a state of flux, they and their metabolites must be constantly mixing with those derived from the diet ("exogenous"). This mixture of originally endogenous and exogenous materials, which is drawn upon for both anabolic and catabolic reactions, constitutes a reservoir or "metabolic pool" of the compounds in question. For example, the alanine derived from the continuous breakdown of body protein and that obtained from dietary protein mix to form an "alanine pool." The amino group of the alanine, together with the amino groups of all other amino acids which are able to participate in nitrogen exchange reactions (e.g., transamination, p. 510), form a pool of metabolically labile nitrogen.

Members of one pool are metabolically equilibrated with other pools. Alanine, for example, is reversibly converted by deamination to pyruvic acid, hence the carbon skeleton of this amino acid is involved in the pyruvic acid pool, which is directly connected to the carbohydrate pool.

The size of a pool is the quantity of constituent instantaneously present and available for all of the reactions leading into and from that particular pool. Although the quantitative determination of "pool size" with the aid of isotopes has been begun only recently, a few data are already available. The pool of metabolically labile amino groups in the human being, for example, has been estimated at 2 grams of nitrogen (70-kilogram man), i.e., of the same order of magnitude as the free amino acids of the tissues.

The concepts of dynamic state and metabolic pool have been invaluable in the interpretation of data resulting from experiments with isotopic labeling. For example, consider the case of an adult experimental animal in nitrogen balance (p. 492) being fed a dose of glycine labeled with N^{15} (p. 351). According to the classical theories of biochemistry, the metabolic paths of endogenous and exogenous compounds are compartmentalized, hence exogenous glycine, since it is not required for tissue construction (adult animal, nitrogen equilibrium), should be degraded directly and the nitrogen excreted as urea within approximately twenty-four hours. What is found experimentally is that a quantity of extra urea is excreted, equivalent to the glycine administered. However, only a small fraction of the N^{15} is excreted in this urea; several days are required for the recovery of an appreciable fraction. Hence, the nitrogen output is equivalent to the intake, but the atoms excreted are mainly not those ingested. To begin with, the ingested glycine enters the glycine pool, so that the concentration of N^{15} in the average glycine molecule is lowered by dilution with all of the N^{14}-glycine molecules. Secondly, the amino group of glycine is readily equilibrated with that of most other amino acids (transamination), resulting in further dilution or spread of N^{15} throughout most of the amino acids of the body. The nitrogen pool which is drawn upon for the synthesis of urea, therefore, contains a much lower concentration of molecules labeled with N^{15} than did the sample of glycine administered. A simplified illustration of such situations follows:

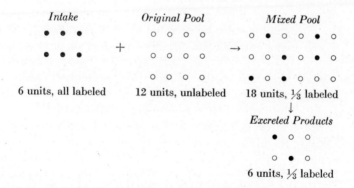

It is obvious that the classical concept of independent exogenous and endogenous metabolism is directly contradicted by such observations, and can no longer be maintained.

GENERAL PATHWAYS OF PROTEIN METABOLISM

The most important of the metabolic pathways of proteins and amino acids may be illustrated as shown at the top of page 490.

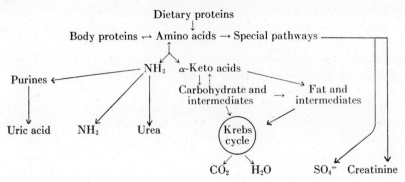

In accord with what was said in the preceding discussion, the proteins of the body are continually undergoing breakdown to (and resynthesis from) their constituent free amino acids. The proteins of the diet, upon digestion and absorption, contribute their amino acids to the general pool. This amino acid pool is drawn upon, on the one hand, for anabolic purposes, such as the synthesis of protein, and on the other, for catabolic purposes.

Most of the catabolic (and a few of the anabolic) reactions are preceded by a cleavage of the amino acid into its nitrogenous (amino group, ammonia) and non-nitrogenous (carbon skeleton, α-keto acid) moieties. These fragments then follow separate pathways. The nitrogen may be used in certain synthetic reactions, such as the synthesis of purines; the final excretory product of this pathway is uric acid. The nitrogen may also be excreted as ammonia itself, or as urea, which is the major nitrogenous excretory product of protein metabolism.

The carbon skeletons of the amino acids, present as α-keto acids, join the pathways of either carbohydrate or fat (specifically, ketone bodies), in either case being eventually oxidized to CO_2 via the tricarboxylic acid cycle. Certain amino acids follow special metabolic routes; among them are some leading to the final excretion of sulfate and creatinine.

OVER-ALL METABOLISM OF PROTEIN

NITROGEN METABOLISM.   (*a*) IMPORTANCE OF NITROGEN.   Much of the information on the metabolism of protein can be expressed (and is frequently measured) in terms of nitrogen, the reasons for which are readily apparent. The carbon and hydrogen atoms of the proteins form CO_2 and H_2O as end-products of metabolism, indistinguishable from the end-products of the metabolism of carbohydrates or fatty acids. Although certain proteins contain phosphoric acid, this constituent is more characteristic of the nucleic acids, phospholipids, and certain intermediates in carbohydrate metabolism. Sulfur is an almost invariable constituent of proteins, but its metabolism reflects only the reactions of cystine and methionine. In contrast to these elements, nitrogen is uniquely characteristic of proteins, from the standpoints of both its high concentration in the protein molecule (average, 16 per cent) and its specialized excretory products (ammonia, urea, etc.).

(*b*) NITROGEN OF THE FOOD. Protein nitrogen outweighs all other forms of nitrogen in the diet. Traces of inorganic nitrogen are ingested in the form of nitrates and nitrites. Small amounts of organic non-protein nitrogen (NPN) are also present in the food, including nucleic acids and their derivatives, and amino acids and peptides.

(*c*) NITROGEN OF THE BODY. Many nitrogenous compounds are found in the tissues and fluids of the body. Protein itself averages about 20 per cent of the wet weight of most tissues. In the blood, in addition to protein, several types of NPN are found. Urea, the major waste product of protein catabolism, formed in the liver, passes into the blood stream to the kidneys for excretion. Blood creatine may be en route to muscle for the synthesis of phosphocreatine, or may have leaked out of muscle. Creatinine is a waste product, formed from phosphocreatine and creatine. Uric acid is the end-product of purine catabolism. Free amino acids are also found in the blood; they are in transit from one organ to another, for purposes of synthesis or breakdown. Other components of the blood NPN include polypeptides, glutathione, purines and pyrimidines, ATP, and ergothionine.

(*d*) EXCRETION OF NITROGEN. Fecal nitrogen appears not to be related to the nitrogen of the ingested protein. Its quantity varies with the bulk of the diet, and does not normally represent unabsorbed dietary protein. In the adult human, it amounts to 1–2 grams N/day. Perspiration, unless sweating is excessive, accounts for a loss of only 0.3 gram N/day or less.

The urine is the major route of excretion of nitrogen (p. 769). In the average, normal, human adult, the total nitrogen of the urine is about 13 grams/day, and this is normally all NPN (no significant quantities of protein are found in the urine normally). Urea (ca. 85 per cent of the total) and ammonia (ca. 3 per cent) vary directly with the level of protein in the diet. Creatinine (5 per cent of the total) excretion is related to the muscle mass and is quite constant for an individual. Creatine is not normally excreted by adult males or by most females. Only traces of amino acids are found in the urine. Uric acid (1 per cent of total) output fluctuates with the level of dietary purines. About 5 per cent of the total is composed of compounds not ordinarily determined. The factors which influence the urinary excretion of the various nitrogenous substances are discussed elsewhere (p. 769).

(*e*) Nitrogen balance. Since most of the nitrogen of the diet represents protein, and most of the nitrogenous excretory products are derived from protein catabolism, it is apparent that the balance between the two will reveal significant features of protein metabolism. Nitrogen balance is defined as the quantitative difference between the nitrogen intake and the nitrogen output, both expressed in the same units (such as grams N/day). By intake is meant the nitrogen of the food. Included in output are such routes of excretion as urine, feces, milk, sweat, expectoration, vomitus, desquamation of skin, menstrual fluid, and loss of hair; in practice, however, only the first two are taken into account except under unusual circumstances.

Positive nitrogen balance exists when intake exceeds output. This condition obtains whenever new tissue is being synthesized, such as during growth of the young, in pregnancy, and in convalescence from states of negative nitrogen balance (see below).

In negative nitrogen balance, the output exceeds the intake. This condition, which obviously cannot continue indefinitely, occurs on inadequate intake of protein (fasting, diseases of the gastrointestinal tract), in states of accelerated catabolism of tissue protein (fevers, infections, wasting diseases), and when the loss of protein from the body is accelerated in some way (lactation on inadequate diets, albuminuria). Experimentally, negative nitrogen balance occurs also in the absence from the diet of an "essential" amino acid (see below).

From the preceding discussion, it is evident that nitrogen equilibrium (intake = output) can be achieved only in the adult organism, and only in the absence of the abnormal conditions enumerated above. An "adequate diet" must also be specified, which means that all requirements for minerals and vitamins are fulfilled, that the protein of the diet is of high "biological value" (p. 495) and is administered at a sufficiently high level, and that the caloric needs of the body (p. 332) are met satisfactorily by the carbohydrate and fat of the diet. In these circumstances, the nitrogen output equals the intake, and an increase or decrease in the intake is followed, within a day or two, by a corresponding adjustment in the output, so that nitrogen equilibrium is established at a new level. There appears to be no marked tendency toward storage of surplus nitrogen, as there is in the case of the fats and carbohydrates.

CALORIGENIC VALUE OF PROTEIN. The fuel value of protein (p. 332) is approximately the same as that of carbohydrate, 4 k cal./gram. The "specific dynamic action" (p. 341) of protein is the highest of all the foodstuffs. A detailed discussion of these matters will be found in the pages cited.

ESSENTIAL AMINO ACIDS. It is possible to replace the protein of the diet completely with pure amino acids. The so-called "dietary requirement" for protein is, therefore, really a requirement for amino acids, and is expressed in terms of protein only because the amino acids of the available foodstuffs are found in that form.

By the elimination of single amino acids from an otherwise complete diet, it has been found that the organism can successfully dispense with certain of these compounds, but not with others. Evidently all amino acids are not synthesized with equal facility by the body. An "essential," or "indispensable," amino acid is defined as one which cannot be synthesized by the organism, from substances ordinarily present in the diet, at a rate commensurate with certain physiological requirements. The definition includes the phrase, "cannot be synthesized by the organism, from substances ordinarily present in the diet . . . ," because certain of these amino acids may be replaced by the corresponding α-keto or α-hydroxy acids, or by their D isomers. Since such substances do not occur in diets unless placed there experimentally, the topic is of interest only to investigators of the metabolism of amino acids and will not be discussed further. The requirements specified in the most extensive series of investigations are: (1) optimal growth of the young, and (2) maintenance of nitrogen equilibrium in the adult.

Although the amino acid requirement for growth has been investigated in several species, the most thorough experiments have been performed in the white rat. The ten amino acids required by this animal for optimal growth (and, in the absence of data to the contrary, the same list is assumed to apply to other mammals, including man) are indicated in the accompanying figure. In the case of arginine, the requirement is not absolute; the animals grow, but sub-optimally, in its absence, indicating a slow and (for this physiological requirement) inadequate rate of synthesis of this amino acid.

Fig. 84. *Essential amino acids*

The requirement for nitrogen equilibrium in the adult appears to be less stringent. In the human being (more specifically, in graduate students at the University of Illinois) only eight amino acids are required for maintenance of nitrogen equilibrium, the list differing from the preceding in the absence of histidine and arginine. It has been possible to quantitate the requirements. These are shown in Table 46.

Table 46. Quantitative Requirements of Amino Acids for Nitrogen Equilibrium

AMINO ACID	MINIMUM FOUND (GRAMS/DAY)	MINIMUM RECOMMENDED (GRAMS/DAY)
Isoleucine................	0.7	1.4
Leucine.................	0.5–1.1	2.2
Lysine..................	0.4–0.8	1.6
Methionine.............	1.1	2.2
Phenylalanine............	0.8–1.1	2.2
Threonine..............	0.5	1.0
Tryptophan..............	0.15–0.25	0.5
Valine..................	0.8	1.6

A curious fact concerning the essential amino acids is that the complete group must be administered to the organism at the same time. If a single essential amino acid is omitted from the group and fed separately several hours later, the nutritional effectiveness of the entire group is impaired. From this fact, and from the effects on growth and nitrogen balance of the omission of a single essential amino acid from the diet, it seems probable that the organism will synthesize either *complete* proteins or none at all, and that the entire fabric of the protein is formed, if not simultaneously, within a relatively short period of time.

The lists of essential amino acids must be taken provisionally, particularly in their application to human nutrition. In the case of the ten amino acids required for growth, there is a certain risk in transferring nutritional requirements from one species to another (glycine, for example, is essential for the chick!). Although the nitrogen equilibrium experiments in human adults seem satisfactory, they were run for periods of time which represent only small fractions of the lifetime of the individual. It is possible that additional requirements, quantitative and qualitative, exist if longer periods of time are considered, or if the individual is subjected to stress.

It has been claimed that proteins contribute something to nutrition in addition to amino acids, and that experimental animals grow more rapidly on diets of protein than on mixtures of amino acids simulating the composition of the protein. The difference is attributed to small peptides resulting from incomplete digestion of the protein. One such peptide (of unknown structure) has been called "strepogenin," since it appears to stimulate the growth of certain streptococci. This subject is controversial at present, and it is by no means certain that the effects attributed to peptides derived from partially hydrolyzed proteins are not due to the association of certain B vitamins with the proteins in natural foods (p. 205).

BIOLOGICAL VALUE OF PROTEINS (P. 629). In order that a food protein may have value to the organism, it must be digested and absorbed. Keratins (p. 46), for example, are practically immune to the action of digestive enzymes, and consequently are of no value in the diet. Even if digestible, a protein may be nutritionally inadequate owing to the absence (or presence in inadequate amount) of an essential amino acid. Gelatin (no tryptophan) and zein (no lysine, low tryptophan) are in this category (cf. Table 6, p. 80). In general, animal proteins are nutritionally superior to plant proteins (p. 631). The latter may be satisfactory if the food contains a sufficiently wide variety, but many individual plant proteins are seriously deficient in one or more of the essential amino acids.

DIETARY PROTEIN REQUIREMENTS. (a) GENERAL NUTRITION. If it is assumed that the protein of the diet is biologically adequate, the nutritional requirements can be discussed in terms of quantities of protein, rather than of amino acids. As a further assumption, sufficient fat and carbohydrate must be included in the diet to cover the caloric requirements of the individual. Under these conditions, quantitative recommendations can be made for the infant, the growing child, and the adult (p. 624). Increased requirements occur in certain situations, viz., pregnancy, lactation, and convalescence.

In connection with protein nutrition, the subject of "storage protein" is of interest. From the relatively rapid adjustment of nitrogen excretion to variations in intake in adult organisms, it appears that no significant quantity of protein is stored. It is nevertheless true that, in states of protein deprivation, certain tissues are able to contribute significant quantities of their protein for the preservation of certain vital functions. Although there is no chemically or morphologically distinct storage form of protein, corresponding to glycogen or depot fat, the more metabolically labile proteins of the tissues are available in case of need. These include the plasma proteins (however, other tissue proteins are usually sacrificed to provide plasma protein), and the proteins of the liver, gastrointestinal tract, and kidney. Only a small percentage of muscle protein appears to be labile, but the size of the muscle mass is such that it provides the greatest absolute amount of protein in conditions of deprivation.

(b) SYNTHESIS OF SPECIAL PROTEINS. Owing to practical considerations, studies of nutrition of necessity have been confined largely to the entire animal, although it is obvious that the nutritional requirements of the organism are a composite of the requirements of the individual tissues, complicated somewhat by tissue-tissue interactions. It is to be hoped that, at some future date, the technic of tissue culture (p. 347) will provide more exact information on the needs of the individual tissues.

If some of the blood is removed from an animal, centrifuged, and the cells suspended in saline and reinjected into the same animal, it is possible to lower the plasma protein level considerably ("plasmapheresis" technic). Initial bleedings of this type in dogs result in rapid regeneration of the plasma protein (from the labile protein of the tissues). Repeated plasmapheresis of dogs kept on appropriate diets eventually depresses the plasma proteins to a low, constant level. The effect can then be tested of various proteins or amino acids in the diet on the synthesis of plasma proteins. In order of decreasing potency in influencing regeneration of plasma protein are the proteins of serum, liver, egg-white, and milk. Among the amino acids, cystine and tyrosine are particularly important.

Similar experiments in which the red cells are removed and the plasma replaced lead to an anemia-type of depletion. Iron, of course, is very important in the regeneration of hemoglobin. Plasma proteins, if fed, are quite effective in hemoglobin synthesis, as are liver, egg-white, and kidney (order of decreasing potency). It is of interest that, in animals suffering from a double deficiency (plasma proteins and hemoglobin), the process of regeneration favors hemoglobin over the plasma proteins. Recent experiments have shown that certain proteins preferentially promote the regeneration of one fraction of the plasma proteins, e.g. lactalbumin appears to stimulate the synthesis of plasma albumin, but has little effect on globulins.

As might be expected, dietary proteins effective in the repletion of the protein of one depleted tissue often are ineffective in the "nutrition" of another. Restoration of the protein content of the livers of animals which have been deprived of proteins for various periods of time is accomplished effectively by certain dietary proteins which are considerably less efficient in the regeneration of plasma proteins.

In an *in vitro* study of the synthesis of amylase (p. 233) by slices of pancreas, it has been found that ten of the sixteen amino acids involved in the structure of amylase are required in the medium for a maximum rate of synthesis. The list includes all of the essential amino acids present in the enzyme and one "non-essential," which is evidently essential for the tissue in question.

(c) PROTEIN-SPARING EFFECTS. It has been observed that the dietary requirement for protein is influenced markedly by the level in the diet of fat and carbohydrate, these latter foodstuffs appearing to have a "protein-sparing" effect. This phenomenon is best understood by consideration of the physiological functions of the major foodstuffs. Fat, although it has certain structural uses, functions primarily as a fuel. Carbohydrate also serves as a fuel, but in addition is required for the synthesis of certain catalytic compounds of metabolic cycles (e.g., oxalacetic acid in the tricarboxylic acid cycle), and provides the carbon skeletons for the synthesis of the non-essential amino acids. Protein has an obvious structural role, but even more important from the dynamic point of view is its catalytic function, the enzyme proteins forming a major part of the actual working machinery of the body.

In the absence of fat and carbohydrate from the diet, protein must be degraded to provide fuel and catalytic compounds of metabolic cycles. Essential amino acids may be broken down to supply the raw materials for the synthesis of the non-essential amino acids. To provide for these increased burdens, the protein intake consequently must be increased. Conversely, addition of fat to the diet will take care of the caloric needs, a relatively small amount of carbohydrate will furnish the catalytic compounds of the cycles and carbon skeletons of the non-essential amino acids, and the protein requirement will be decreased as a result. These effects are discussed again in connection with metabolic interrelations (p. 557).

(d) PROTEIN DEPRIVATION. As stated previously, protein forms the structural framework of the body and the active machinery as well. Liver, intestinal mucosa, and kidney are sites of very active protein metabolism. The turnover rate of protein is very high in these tissues, and they also happen to discharge functions in protein digestion or metabolism which are important to the body as a whole. Protein deprivation, therefore, is particularly harmful to the activity of these tissues. Impairment of their metabolic efficiency results in further disturbances in protein digestion and metabolism, thus aggravating the state of deprivation. A "cycle of degeneration" sets in, reversal of which becomes increasingly difficult. It is obvious, therefore, why so much emphasis has been placed by the medical profession in recent years on the state of protein nutrition of the patient.

ANABOLISM AND CATABOLISM OF PROTEINS

PROTEIN TURNOVER. As discussed elsewhere (p. 487), all proteins in the body are constantly breaking down to their constituent amino acids and being resynthesized (dynamic state), the rate of this turnover varying for different proteins in different tissues. The amino acids from the body proteins and those derived from the food form a metabolic pool, the members of which are drawn upon for reactions in either the anabolic or catabolic direction.

The metabolic lability of the proteins in the various tissues can be investigated by noting the rapidity with which each tissue loses protein when the organism is depleted (i.e., on a protein-free diet) and regains protein on repletion. A more recent technic measures the rate of uptake into the proteins of each tissue of an isotopically labeled amino acid, or, in certain cases, the rate of loss of an isotope already incorporated. Whatever the method, high rates of turnover have been shown in plasma proteins, intestinal mucosa, pancreas, liver, and kidney, and low rates in muscle, skin, and brain. Certain numerical data are available (Table 47).

Table 47. Rates of Turnover of Protein

ANIMAL	TISSUE OR PROTEIN	HALF-LIFE IN DAYS
Man............	Whole body	80
Man............	Serum protein and liver	10
Man............	Muscle	180
Rat.............	Whole body	17
Rat.............	Liver, plasma, internal organs	6
Rat.............	Muscle	24–30

PROTEIN SYNTHESIS. (*a*) FUNDAMENTAL REACTION. The formation of the peptide linkage (p. 50) is the basic reaction of protein synthesis:

$$
\underset{R_1}{NH_2} \atop R_1-CH-COOH \; + \; R_2-CH-COOH \; \rightarrow \; R_1-CH-C-NH-CH-COOH \; + \; H_2O
$$

As in the case of most reactions involving the splitting out of water in an aqueous medium, the equilibrium is far toward the side of hydrolysis (p. 376). Since the reaction in the anabolic (reverse) direction is endergonic, an outside source of energy is needed. Although much of the evidence is indirect, it appears probable that ATP provides the required energy.

(*b*) PSEUDOPEPTIDE SYNTHESIS. A number of compounds are synthesized in the body which contain linkages closely related to peptide bonds. Many of these were mentioned earlier under the heading "Pseudopeptides" (p. 51). It is believed that a study of the mechanism of synthesis of these model compounds may shed light on the synthesis of proteins. The *in vitro* formation of acetyl-sulfanilamide and various hippurates requires the presence of ATP and CoA. Although the participation of CoA has not been demonstrated in other pseudopeptide syntheses the possibility is suggested that the formation of a peptide bond may be merely another special type of transacylation (p. 454). ATP has been implicated also in the synthesis of ornithuric acid, glutamine, and the true peptide, glutathione.

(*c*) Incorporation of labeled amino acids. The mechanism of synthesis of peptide bonds is also being investigated intensively by following the *in vitro* incorporation of isotopically labeled amino acids into proteins. Although it is controversial at present whether such incorporation represents "true synthesis" or some type of exchange reaction differing qualitatively from the actual anabolic mechanism, the results, nevertheless, should furnish information on at least one method whereby free amino acids are transformed into protein-bound molecules. In experiments with intact cells (e.g., slices), every amino acid presented to the cells is incorporated, independently of any other amino acid. The optimum concentration approximates that found in the blood. The rate of incorporation is about the same as that observed *in vivo*, i.e., 0.1–10 μ equiv./gram protein/hour. In homogenates (p. 348), the rate of incorporation is proportional to the logarithm of the concentration of most amino acids, but is directly proportional in the case of lysine. It is of interest that the presence of nuclei is not required for the incorporation of amino acids into the other fractions of the homogenate. The rates of incorporation in homogenates are generally less than in intact cells. Generally, the incorporation is inhibited by anaerobiosis, respiratory poisons, and agents which "uncouple" phosphorylation (p. 381). The behavior of lysine toward anaerobiosis is exceptional in certain systems.

(*d*) Transpeptidation. Although its relevance to protein synthesis remains to be proved, the phenomenon of transpeptidation may provide a mechanism for the redistribution of linkages already formed. It has been suggested that only a few peptide linkages may be primary, i.e., formed with the aid of ATP, and that the rest are synthesized by exchange reactions. Examples of transpeptidation are tabulated elsewhere (p. 246).

(*e*) Problems concerning the detailed nature of the synthesis. Little is known concerning the sequence of events taking place in the synthesis of a protein. There is the possibility, for example, that amino acids are joined together by the addition of one unit at a time to gradually build up the peptide chain of the protein. On the other hand, relatively small peptides may form initially, and these may be coupled to produce the macromolecule. A final possibility to be considered is the cataclysmic condensation of all of the amino acids at once. The necessity for the simultaneous feeding of all the essential amino acids in order to obtain efficient utilization of any (p. 494) speaks, perhaps, for the last possibility. This is apparently contradicted, however, by the independent "exchange" of labeled amino acids with proteins *in vitro*. The "peptide-precursor" hypothesis seems to be supported by recent findings, i.e., that the incorporation of a labeled amino acid into a protein results in different degrees of labeling in different positions of the protein molecule, suggesting that the various parts of the protein are synthesized separately, from amino acid pools of different degrees of dilution of isotope.

Proteins are known to contain amino acids linked in specific sequences (p. 77). The mechanism of production of such sequences is unknown. It has been suggested that the amino acids are linked together on the surface of a template, which may be a protein, or, according to certain speculations, a nucleic acid. A template could conceivably also influence the size of the protein being synthesized, since each protein must, in some way, be given a specific molecular weight.

Proteins are also characterized by the possession of specific shapes (p. 72) in the native state. The exact nature of the three-dimensional folding of the peptide chain could presumably be controlled by another template. Light could be shed on this problem if we knew more about the mechanism whereby an antigen influences the synthesis of globulins so as to produce configurations characteristic of their specific antibodies.

Related unsolved problems are the mechanism of influence of the gene on protein synthesis, and the formation of "adaptive enzymes," elicited by the presence of substrates (p. 255).

There is a certain amount of evidence which suggests a relationship of nucleic acids (in particular, RNA) to protein synthesis. This is discussed in connection with the physiological functions of the nucleic acids (p. 581).

SYNTHESIS OF INTRACELLULAR AND EXTRACELLULAR PROTEINS. Each tissue synthesizes its characteristic proteins. In most cases these remain within the cell. Liver is unusual in that only approximately half of the protein which it synthesizes is liver protein proper, the other half being plasma protein. Other proteins which are synthesized intracellularly and then secreted into the body fluids include the extracellular enzymes and the protein hormones, viz., insulin from the β-cells of the pancreatic islets, the enzymes of the pancreas, the enzymes of the intestinal mucosa, and the hormones of the pituitary.

BREAKDOWN OF PROTEIN IN THE TISSUES. The reactions of proteins in the catabolic direction, such as must occur continually to account for the dynamic state, are generally assumed to be catalyzed by the intracellular proteolytic enzymes, the "cathepsins" (p. 235). These enzymes are responsible for the autolysis of tissue after death. In life, their activities are balanced, in the adult, or overbalanced, in the growing organism, by the processes of protein synthesis. In contrast to the anabolic reactions, the catabolic may be expected to be exergonic. However, the release of certain amino acids from proteins has been shown recently to require a source of energy. How general this phenomenon may be, and what relation it may have to the purely hydrolytic breakdown of the proteins remain to be seen.

THE PLASMA PROTEINS

Segregation of the discussion of the plasma proteins is justified by two considerations. First, owing to their intimate relation to protein metabolism in the liver, as well as to their interaction with other tissues throughout the body, the plasma proteins occupy a central position in the metabolism of protein. The second consideration is entirely practical: the plasma proteins happen to be the most conveniently obtainable sample of protein available in the body. Because of the interrelations between the proteins of plasma and the tissues, a great deal can be learned concerning the general status of protein metabolism in the individual from the examination of the plasma proteins, and the student will find much clinical information expressed in such terms.

IDENTITY AND PROPERTIES. The heterogeneity of the plasma proteins is readily demonstrated in the ultracentrifuge (p. 69). In addition to fibrinogen, albumin, and a group of globulins sedimenting at a rate between these two, the ultracentrifugal analysis of plasma reveals a group of very rapidly sedimenting globulins and a lipoprotein, the sedimentation of which varies markedly with the density of the medium.

The degree of resolution of the plasma proteins in the ultracentrifuge is greatly inferior to that obtainable with electrophoresis (p. 65). An electrophoretic diagram of normal plasma is shown in Figure 85. It will be noted that, in addition to albumin and fibrinogen, this technic resolves the globulins into four groups (α_1, α_2, β, and γ).

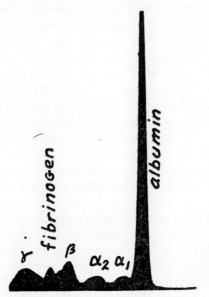

Fig. 85. *Electrophoretic pattern of normal plasma*

Most of the clinical data on the plasma proteins have been obtained by the method of salting out (p. 70). Precipitates or supernatant solutions produced by the addition to the plasma of certain concentrations of salts are analyzed for protein content by the Kjeldahl (p. 88) or biuret (p. 88) method. Sodium sulfate has generally been the salt of choice. Before the advent of the electrophoretic technic, clinical analyses of plasma by salting out were performed according to the method of Howe. The Howe fractions have since been shown to disagree markedly with the results of electrophoresis. A comparison is shown in Table 48 of the Howe method and a modern adaptation which yields fractions more closely related to those obtained electrophoretically. Quantitative data on the normal levels of the plasma proteins, and information on the mechanism of the various types of abnormalities, are presented elsewhere (p. 740).

Table 48. Plasma Protein Fractions Obtained by Salting Out

METHOD	% NA$_2$SO$_4$	NAME OF FRACTION	G %	ELECTROPHORETIC CONSTITUENTS
Howe	13.5	Euglobulin	0.2	Ca. 1/3 of γ-globulin
	21.5	Pseudoglobulin	1.8	Chiefly β-globulin, with rest of γ-globulin and some α
	Supernatant	Albumin	5.2	Albumin + α_1 + α_2 globulins
Milne	19.6	Euglobulin	1.9	β- and γ-globulins
	26.8	Pseudoglobulin	1.3	α_1- and α_2-globulins
	Supernatant	Albumin	4.0	Albumin

The fractions of the plasma proteins obtained by ultracentrifugation, electrophoresis, or salting out are chemically heterogeneous. For scientific and other purposes, methods have been elaborated which permit fractionation of the plasma proteins to the point of isolation of relatively homogeneous chemical constituents. These methods, which have been developed mainly at Harvard University under the direction of E. J. Cohn, are of interest not only in that they permit, for the first time, a closer study of the physicochemical and physiological properties of the individual proteins of the plasma, but also because they have made possible the large-scale production of plasma protein products for therapeutic use, viz., fibrin film and foam (surgery), purified albumin (shock), and γ-globulin (measles, hepatitis, poliomyelitis).

The procedure developed for use during World War II, Harvard "Method 6," is based upon the fractional precipitation of the plasma proteins with ethanol at low temperatures and low salt concentration (p. 70). Proper adjustment of the concentrations of protein, salts, and ethanol, temperature, and pH, permits the isolation of six fractions, each of which can be subfractionated by appropriate procedures into relatively pure components. The relative amounts of the plasma fractions so obtained, their natural functions, and their clinical uses, are indicated in Figure 86.

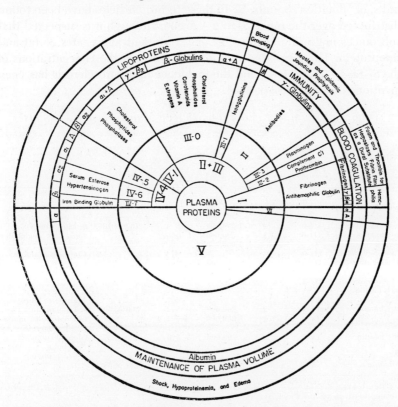

Fig. 86. Natural functions, clinical uses, and fractionation of the plasma proteins (from Edsall: Advances in Protein Chemistry, Vol. 3, Academic Press, 1947)

Methods developed more recently in the Harvard laboratories make use of protein–protein interactions to precipitate groups of proteins bearing electrical charges of opposite sign at a particular pH (p. 64), and protein–metal interactions for the precipitation of certain groups of proteins by the formation of insoluble complexes with zinc, barium, lead, and mercury. The properties of the proteins isolated by the Harvard procedures are summarized in Table 49.

Two lipoproteins, an α_1- and a β_1-globulin, have been isolated by the methods described above. However, there is evidence that a larger number of such proteins may be present in plasma. By the addition of salt to plasma, its density may be elevated to the point where the lipoproteins (having a lower density than ordinary proteins due to their lipid content) will migrate toward the axis instead of toward the periphery in the ultracentrifuge (p. 69). Whereas the rates of sedimentation of particles in conventional ultracentrifugation are expressed in Svedberg units ($S = 1 \times 10^{-13}$ sec.), those of the lipoproteins observed in the flotation method are expressed in "negative" S units, or "flotation" S units, S_f. In these terms, particles have been found distributed over the range $S_f = 2 - 40,000$, although it is suspected that substances migrating at $S_f > 17$ may represent aggregates of fat and lipoprotein. The purported relationship between the concentrations of the S_f 12–20 lipoproteins and the incidence of atherosclerosis has been mentioned elsewhere (p. 470).

*Table 49. Identities and Properties of Major Plasma Proteins**

PROTEIN OR GROUP	LOCATION IN HARVARD FRACTION	GRAMS/ LITER OF PLASMA	MW	pI	DIMENSIONS Å	SPECIAL PROPERTIES
Fibrinogen	I-2	2	400,000	< 5.3	700 × 38	
γ-Globulin	II-1,2	5	156,000	6.3	235 × 44	Antibodies
γ-Globulin	II-3	1	300,000	7.3		Antibodies
β₁-Globulin	III-0	2	1,300,000	5.4	185 × 185	β₁-Lipoprotein
β₁-Globulin	III-0	1	500,000–1,000,000	5.5		Lipid-poor euglobulins
Caeruloplasmin	III-0			4.4		Copper-containing
β₁-Globulin	III-0,2	2	150,000			
β₂-Globulin	III-1	2	150,000	6.3		Isoagglutinins
Prothrombin	III-2					
α₁-Bilirubin globulin	IV			4.7		Transports bilirubin
α₁-Globulin	IV-1	2	200,000	5.2	300 × 50	α₁-Lipoprotein
α₂-Globulin	IV-6	1	300,000	4.5–4.9		Glycoproteins, mucoteins, esterase
β₁-Globulin	IV-7	2	90,000	5.8	190 × 37	Metal-combining globulin (siderophilin)
Albumin	V	32	69,000	4.9	150 × 38	

* Data obtained from various publications of the University Laboratory of Physical Chemistry Related to Medicine and Public Health, Harvard University.

METABOLISM. From isotopic and other evidence, it has been concluded that the liver is the chief, if not the sole, site of formation of albumin, fibrinogen, prothrombin, and the α- and β-globulins. It is currently believed that the γ-globulins are synthesized in the plasma cells. They may be stored for a time in the reticuloendothelial (also lymphoid?) cells, which also may act to split aggregated antigens into immunochemically active forms. The possible role of lymphocytes in the elaboration of γ-globulins is not clear at this time.

As indicated elsewhere (p. 495), the nutritional status of the individual with respect to protein has a profound effect on the synthesis of plasma proteins, both directly, in terms of provision of raw materials of synthesis, and indirectly, due to the deleterious effect of protein deprivation on the liver. It is of interest that protein deprivation has its most marked effect on the levels of plasma albumin and γ-globulins, a decrease in the former of sufficient severity leading to edema (p.

741), a decrease in the latter fraction resulting in impaired resistance to infections.

It has been estimated from studies with isotopes, that a 70-kg. man synthesizes and degrades approximately 15–20 grams of plasma protein per day. Not all of the fractions turn over at the same rate, however. Albumin and γ-globulins are synthesized at slower rates than the α- and β-globulins.

The plasma proteins, among their other functions (discussed below), serve as a source of protein nutrition for the tissues. Indeed, a dynamic equilibrium exists between the proteins of the tissues and those of the plasma (p. 495), each group sustaining the other when the need arises. In conditions of protein deprivation, however, the normal level of the plasma proteins is apparently guarded more zealously than that of the tissue proteins, since the latter are degraded to provide for the former. As a result, considerable loss of tissue protein may occur with minimal decrease in the concentrations of plasma proteins. It has been calculated that a decrease in total circulating plasma protein of 1 gram, in hypoproteinemia due solely to protein deprivation, represents a concomitant loss of 30 grams of tissue protein.

FUNCTION. The nutritive functions of the plasma proteins, discussed above, are probably attributable largely to the albumin fraction, owing to its quantitative dominance. Intravenously administered albumin has been shown in fact to be efficiently, although slowly, utilized in human beings.

The osmotic function of the plasma proteins, of great importance in the maintenance of the normal distribution of water in the various compartments of the body (p. 309), is also due largely to the albumin. In addition to its high concentration in plasma, albumin exerts a greater osmotic pressure per gram than do the other plasma proteins because of its lower molecular weight (Table 49).

From a quantitative standpoint, the buffering ability of the plasma proteins is not very great. In whole blood, however, the combined buffering action of the hemoglobin and plasma proteins is as important as that due to the bicarbonate and other inorganic buffer systems of the blood (p. 314). Over the physiological pH range, the buffering action of the blood proteins is due largely to the imidazole groups contributed by histidine (p. 61).

The lipid-transporting functions of the plasma proteins have been discussed in detail previously (p. 470). In addition to the lipids, the lipoproteins transport certain lipid-soluble compounds, such as the steroid hormones, e.g., estriol, and the fat-soluble vitamins (e.g., A, D, and E). Bilirubin is associated with a fraction of the α_1-globulins (and is also bound by albumin). A β_1-metal combining globulin (siderophilin) is responsible for the transport of iron in the plasma. This protein can also combine with copper; however, a specific protein (caeruloplasmin) also appears to be elaborated for this purpose. Approximately half of the calcium of plasma is bound to protein in a linkage which is relatively weak in comparison to the metalloproteins just mentioned. Thyroxine (p. 684) also appears to be transported in loose association with the plasma proteins. In addition to the more or less specific transport functions already mentioned, due in most cases to the various globulins, plasma albumin has been found to exhibit considerable affinity for anions and cations having a wide variety of structures. It is probable that many drugs and dyes are transported in the plasma in combination with albumin.

In addition to fibrinogen and prothrombin (Table 49), plasma contains a number of other components which participate in the process of blood coagulation, viz., Ac-globulin, serum prothrombin conversion accelerator, antihemophilic globulin, antithrombin, heparin cofactor, antithromboplastic lipoprotein, plasminogen, and plasmin inhibitor. The more important of these factors are discussed in detail elsewhere (p. 734).

Reference has been made to the immunological functions of the plasma proteins. The γ-globulins contain a large number of antibodies, among which may be mentioned those against influenza, mumps, poliomyelitis, measles, infectious hepatitis, typhoid, whooping cough, and diphtheria. The β_2-globulin fraction contains the antibodies to the isoagglutinins, the antigens responsible for the various blood groups in man (p. 733). Two of the components of complement, a cofactor necessary in certain types of immunological reactions, are proteins of the globulin type.

The protein constituents of the plasma include a number of enzymes, the physiological functions of which are obscure in most cases. Certain of the proteins involved in blood coagulation are undoubtedly enzymic in nature (p. 734). In addition to the enzymes specifically concerned in coagulation, there are others having a wider range of activity. Among the proteolytic enzymes are plasminogen (which, although concerned in coagulation, is a proteinase of broad specificity), dehydropeptidase (p. 236), prolidase (p. 235), and several leucine peptidases (p. 236). The glycosidases include amylase (p. 233) and β-glucuronidase (p. 232). Two carboxylesterases are present in plasma, choline esterase (p. 228), and an aliphatic esterase (p. 228). Monophosphoric esters are hydrolyzed by acid and alkaline phosphatases (p. 230) in plasma. Other enzymes reported in plasma are desoxyribonuclease (p. 231), aldolase (p. 244), phenol sulfatase (p. 230), histaminase (p. 364), and folic acid conjugase (p. 236). It is possible that many of the enzymes of plasma, which occur in rather low concentrations, are the result of leakage from the tissues or arise from the fragmentation of cells.

ENDOCRINE INFLUENCES IN PROTEIN METABOLISM

Anabolism (synthesis) and catabolism (degradation) of proteins are influenced, if not indeed regulated, by certain hormones, which also influence the interrelationships between the metabolism of protein and of carbohydrate. The most important of these are the growth hormone (anterior pituitary), the adrenal 11-oxysteroids, thyroxine, androgens, and insulin. The actions of these hormones in this connection have been discussed elsewhere in detail (p. 654 ff.). It will suffice here merely to review them briefly.

GROWTH HORMONE (P. 700). This exerts a protein anabolic effect. Its administration is followed by diminished urinary excretion of nitrogen (positive N balance), with a decrease in plasma urea and amino acids and increased deposition of protein in the tissues. Insulin is necessary for the production of this effect. Somatic growth is induced in prepubertal children.

ANDROGEN (P. 665). Testosterone, too, exerts a protein anabolic effect, as do androstenediol and androstenedione, but androsterone and dehydroisoandrosterone exhibit little such action. Administration of testosterone is followed by decreased urinary excretion of nitrogen, positive N balance, stimulation of somatic growth in prepubertal children (adolescent growth spurt), and increased weight (i.e., protein deposition) not only of specific target tissues (e.g., prostate, seminal vesicles), but also of other organs, particularly the kidneys (renotropic action). Castration is followed by increased urinary excretion of creatine; this is reversed by testosterone. Methyltestosterone, a synthetic androgen which also exerts a protein anabolic effect, increases urinary excretion of creatine. It is believed to stimulate synthesis as well as storage of creatine, whereas testosterone stimulates only its storage.

ADRENAL 11-OXYSTEROIDS (P. 673). Under usual experimental and clinical conditions, the 11-oxygenated adrenocortical hormones apparently exert a protein catabolic effect, i.e., they cause increased urinary excretion of nitrogen and a negative N balance. This effect is intimately related to their action in increasing gluconeogenesis (p. 407), which probably involves increased deamination of amino acids and increased conversion of the non-nitrogenous residues to glucose (or glycogen). This stimulation of gluconeogenesis is antagonized by insulin (p. 690). It is interesting that exogenous protein is apparently not affected in this manner. Studies with labeled amino acids suggest that these hormones decrease synthesis of protein, indicating that their action in this connection may be "antianabolic" rather than, or in addition to, catabolic. They also cause increased urinary excretion of uric acid, apparently a reflection of increased catabolism of purines (i.e., nucleic acids). These hormones depress growth of embryonic tissue (chick) and tumors. They inhibit healing of wounds, interfering with the formation of granulation tissue and ground substance (p. 714).

There is evidence, however, that when administered in relatively small amounts, presumably approximating physiological quantities, these hormones may exert a protein anabolic effect, with reduced urinary nitrogen excretion and positive N balance.

INSULIN (P. 690). As has been indicated elsewhere, insulin is necessary for the protein anabolic effect of growth hormone, and antagonizes the gluconeogenic action of adrenocortical hormones. There is some indication that insulin may stimulate growth (protein anabolism) in the absence of growth hormone.

THYROXINE. (P. 681). In physiological doses, thyroxine exerts a protein anabolic effect, as indicated by a positive N balance, especially in the growing organism. This action would be inferred from the fact that removal of the thyroid in early life results in retardation of growth, which can be corrected by administration of thyroid hormone. Thyroidectomy (and hypothyroidism) is followed by accumulation in the extracellular fluids of a mucoprotein, rich in hyaluronic acid (p. 19) and similar to fetal mucin in composition (myxedema).

In unphysiological (large) doses, thyroxine exerts a protein catabolic effect, with increased urinary nitrogen excretion and negative N balance. It causes also increased urinary excretion of creatine (creatinuria, p. 771), resulting from excessive catabolism of muscle tissue and also, perhaps, from a decreased capacity for prompt resynthesis of phosphocreatine during the recovery stage of muscle contraction (p. 413).

GENERAL METABOLIC REACTIONS OF AMINO ACIDS

Although many amino acids pursue individual metabolic pathways, there are a few general reactions common to almost all of them (p. 490). With few exceptions, the catabolic pathway of amino acids begins with the separation of the amino group from the carbon skeleton of the molecule (which becomes an α-keto acid). The ammonia, whether free or combined, joins the ammonia pool, and participates in the anabolic and catabolic reactions characteristic of that area of metabolism. Being a more specialized structure, the carbon skeleton cannot be assigned to a single pool of keto acids. The majority of the α-keto acids produced from amino acids join the carbohydrate pool more or less directly; a minority are more closely related to the ketone bodies and fatty acids. Many amino acids, although they have special functions of their own, also participate in group activities such as those just enumerated. A few, however, are completely individualistic, and enter into none of the common metabolic pools. They will be discussed in the section devoted to the special metabolism of the individual amino acids (p. 517).

REMOVAL OF NITROGEN FROM THE CARBON SKELETON. (*a*) OXIDATIVE DEAMINATION. The removal of nitrogen is accomplished in mammalian tissues by two known methods; the older of these is oxidative deamination, the more recently studied is transamination. Setting aside, for the time being, certain specialized enzyme systems, there are three enzymes concerned with oxidative deamination which have potential general functions in the metabolism of the amino acids. One of these, the D-amino acid dehydrogenase (p. 363), is a flavoprotein, quite active, widespread in animal tissues, and of completely unknown significance, since its substrates, the D-amino acids, do not occur in mammalian tissues. Its counterpart, L-amino acid dehydrogenase, which attacks most of the L-amino acids, is also a flavoprotein (p. 363), but has remarkably low activity and a rather restricted distribution. It may, nevertheless, play a small role in oxidative deamination. It catalyzes reactions of the following type:

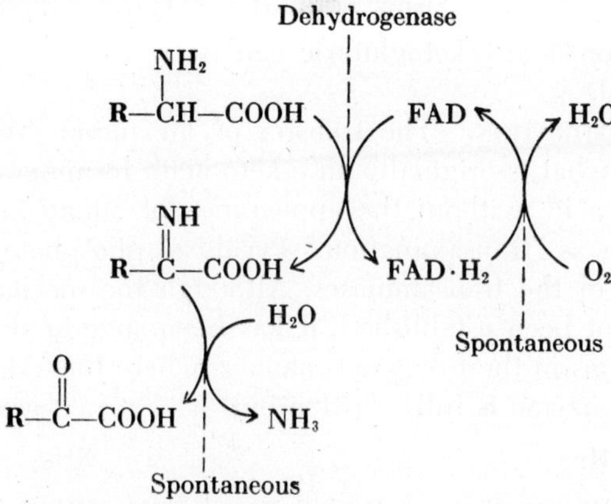

The imino acid which is first formed is unstable and spontaneously undergoes hydrolysis to ammonia and the α-keto acid. Since this enzyme is an aerobic dehydrogenase (p. 363), its prosthetic group, FAD, after reduction, is reoxidized spontaneously by oxygen. The hydrogen peroxide is decomposed by the catalase present in all cells (p. 368). There is no evidence of reversibility of the over-all reaction catalyzed by the L-amino acid dehydrogenase.

The third of the enzymes catalyzing oxidative deaminations is L-glutamic dehydrogenase (p. 365). This anaerobic dehydrogenase, although it specifically attacks one L-amino acid, probably has certain general functions which are discussed below. It is widely distributed in nature, very active, and catalyzes a reversible reaction:

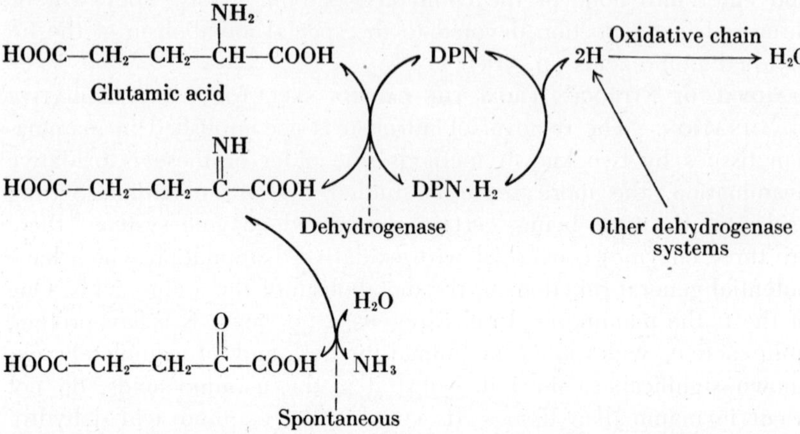

The first part of the reaction is similar to that discussed above. However, the reduced coenzyme in this case is oxidized by the flavoproteins, cytochromes, etc., of the oxidative chain (p. 366). In the presence of ammonia and a source of reduced coenzyme (easily formed by the dehydrogenation of another substrate in a system using the same coenzyme), α-ketoglutaric can be reductively aminated to L-glutamic acid.

(b) TRANSAMINATION. The transfer of an amino group from an amino acid to what is originally an α-keto acid, forming a new amino acid and keto acid, without the appearance of ammonia in the free state, is known as "transamination." Pyridoxal phosphate (p. 246) is the coenzyme of the transaminases. Although the mechanism of the reaction has not been established, it has been suggested that the coenzyme functions in the following manner, where the aldehyde group only of the coenzyme is fully written out:

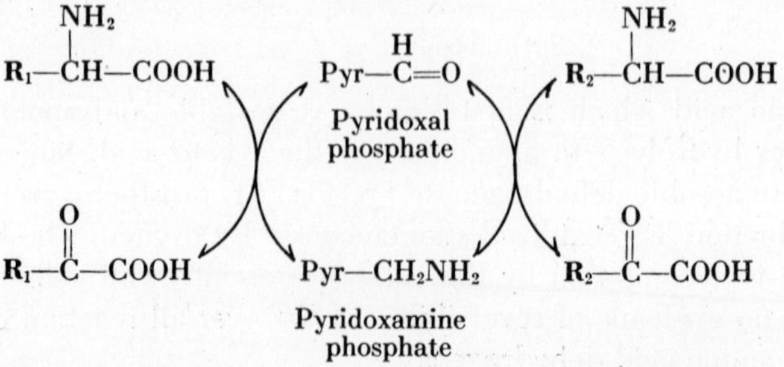

As indicated, the reaction is freely reversible. Two of the most active transaminases of animal tissues are those catalyzing the interconversions:

(1) L-glutamic acid + oxalacetic acid $\longleftrightarrow$ α-ketoglutaric acid + L-aspartic acid and (2) L-glutamic acid + pyruvic acid $\longleftrightarrow$ α-ketoglutaric acid + L-alanine.

However, many other transaminases also exist. Although most of the transaminations which have been described appear to involve a dicarboxylic amino or keto acid, in particular glutamic (ketoglutaric), certain recent data indicate that transaminations also occur between pairs of monocarboxylic acids.

Unusual transaminations have been described which involve the transfer of the amino group of glutamine or asparagine to α-keto acids and the simultaneous loss of the amide group as ammonia. The biochemical significance of this type of transamination is not known.

(*c*) TRANSDEAMINATION. Experiments *in vivo* with isotopes have shown that the transfer of amino groups from one amino acid to another is a rapid, reversible, widely occurring, and continuous reaction, in which few amino acids fail to participate. Deamination, in the general sense, is found to have similar characteristics. From what is known of the properties of the L-amino acid dehydrogenase, it seems unlikely that the physiological phenomenon of rapid and reversible deamination could involve this enzyme to any great extent. In order to reconcile the requirements of the physiological system with the properties of known enzymes *in vitro,* a combination of transamination and oxidative deamination called "transdeamination" has been suggested as a possible mechanism:

$$
\begin{array}{c}
\underset{|}{\mathrm{NH_2}} \\
\mathrm{R-CH-COOH} \qquad \text{α-Ketoglutarate} \qquad \mathrm{NH_3 + 2H} \\
\\
\underset{}{\overset{\mathrm{O}}{\underset{\|}{}}} \\
\mathrm{R-C-COOH} \qquad\qquad \mathrm{L\text{-}Glutamate} \\
\text{Transaminase} \qquad\qquad \begin{array}{c}\text{Glutamic}\\ \text{dehydrogenase}\end{array}
\end{array}
$$

The amino group is first removed from a given amino acid by transamination with α-ketoglutaric acid. The resulting glutamic acid is then deaminated by the specific L-glutamic dehydrogenase. There is every reason to expect that such a system would be widely distributed in animal tissues, very active metabolically, and readily reversible. It provides a pathway for the removal of ammonia from amino acids for catabolic purposes, and also a convenient sequence of reactions by means of which amino acids may be readily synthesized from ammonia and α-keto acids.

DISPOSAL OF THE NITROGEN. (*a*) SYNTHETIC PATHWAYS. Although deamination is ordinarily thought of as essentially catabolic, the liberated ammonia which enters the general ammonia pool of the body may be drawn upon for either anabolic or catabolic purposes. It may be used, for example, in the reductive amination of α-keto acids (derived from carbohydrate) to form new amino acids, by reversal of the transdeamination reactions. The synthesis of purines and pyrimidines (pp. 566, 571) also requires the participation of ammonia. Certain other anabolic pathways of nitrogen, such as the synthesis of porphyrins, do not make use directly of free ammonia, and will be discussed in connection with the metabolism of the "carrier" molecule concerned (in this case, glycine) (p. 520).

(*b*) GLUTAMINE PATHWAY. Ammonia is a toxic substance, and large concentrations are not permitted to accumulate in cells. One of the possible mechanisms of "detoxication" of ammonia is the synthesis of glutamine. This reaction, which occurs in extrarenal tissues, resembles somewhat the synthesis of a peptide linkage, and similarly requires a source of energy. Although the exact mechanism is not known, ATP has been shown to participate:

$$\underset{\text{HOOC—CH}_2\text{—CH}_2\text{—}\overset{\displaystyle\overset{\text{NH}_2}{|}}{\text{CH}}\text{—COOH}}{} + NH_3 + ATP \rightarrow$$

$$\underset{NH_2\text{—}\overset{\displaystyle\overset{O}{\|}}{C}\text{—CH}_2\text{—CH}_2\text{—}\overset{\displaystyle\overset{\text{NH}_2}{|}}{\text{CH}}\text{—COOH}}{} + ADP + H_3PO_4$$

The glutamine then travels from the various tissues through the blood to the kidneys, where it is hydrolyzed by glutaminase (p. 239):

$$NH_2\text{—}\overset{\displaystyle\overset{O}{\|}}{C}\text{—CH}_2\text{—CH}_2\text{—}\overset{\displaystyle\overset{\text{NH}_2}{|}}{\text{CH}}\text{—COOH} \xrightarrow{H_2O} HOOC\text{—CH}_2\text{—CH}_2\text{—}\overset{\displaystyle\overset{\text{NH}_2}{|}}{\text{CH}}\text{—COOH} + NH_3$$

The ammonia which is thus liberated accounts for about 60 per cent of that found in the urine.

(*c*) DIRECT EXCRETION. It has been assumed in the foregoing discussion either that the deamination occurs in extrarenal tissues, or that the ammonia is immediately channeled into certain metabolic pathways which bind it. If, however, the deamination occurs in the kidney, in the absence of immediate physiological requirements for synthetic purposes in that organ, the liberated ammonia may be excreted directly into the urine. This source of urinary ammonia amounts to some 40 per cent of the total. The importance to acid-base balance of the production of ammonia from glutamine and amino acids is discussed elsewhere (p. 323). It should be noted that ammonia does not normally appear in the blood as such; it is transported from other tissues to the kidneys in the form of glutamine or amino acids.

(*d*) FORMATION OF UREA. If the deamination occurs in the liver (and most of it does), the ammonia may enter the "ornithine cycle" to form urea. The development of the current view of the mechanism of urea synthesis provides an appropriate example of the application of a wide range of technics, from the classical to the most modern, over a considerable period of time, culminating in a metabolic scheme which correlates very well the known physiological facts in the whole animal with the properties of enzyme systems *in vitro*.

In the normal animal, an increase in dietary protein is followed by an increase in the concentration of amino acids in the blood (which are taken up largely by the liver), and by an increase in urinary urea. When liver function is severely impaired, e.g., in acute hepatic necrosis, there is a rise in the blood amino acids and a fall in the urea concentration of blood and urine. Similarly, removal of the liver in an experimental animal is followed by a rise in the concentration of amino acids and ammonia in the blood, and a fall in blood and urinary urea. If the kidneys are removed and the liver left intact, the blood urea rises. Removal of both liver and kidneys results in a constant level of blood urea. From all of these data, it may be concluded that the liver is the chief, if not the sole site of urea synthesis, the precursors of which are amino acids and ammonia. These conclusions are confirmed by perfusion experiments (p. 346), in which it is found that the liver, and no other organ, converts ammonia and amino acids to urea. The bulk of the amino acids (NH_2 groups) not utilized in the organism is thus transformed to urea, which is excreted in the urine as a terminal (waste) metabolite.

The actual mechanism of formation of urea began to be investigated when suitable *in vitro* methods became available. Using liver slices and the Warburg technic (p. 347), conditions were found in which urea was produced from various amino acids or ammonium salts. It was known that arginine could be hydrolyzed by the enzyme arginase of liver to ornithine and urea (p. 239). When arginine, ornithine, or citrulline (a compound structurally intermediate between ornithine and arginine) were incubated with liver slices, in contrast to the results with other amino acids, the yield of urea was greater than stoichiometric, indicating a catalytic role for these three compounds. Since ornithine, citrulline, and arginine differ structurally only by the simple addition (on paper) of CO_2 and NH_3, the following catalytic cycle was proposed for the synthesis of urea:

Although the accumulation of additional information has expanded the ornithine cycle and considerably increased its complexity, the basic formulation still stands. Experiments with isotopes have completely confirmed the *in vivo* and *in vitro* work of the past and present.

From the standpoint of energetics it is obvious that the ornithine cycle is incomplete. The synthesis of urea entails the formation of two amide linkages, an endergonic process (p. 376), and yet the cycle makes no provision for the input of energy. This defect has been remedied by recent studies with cell-free homogenates (p. 348) and partially purified enzyme systems. It has been found that CO_2 and NH_3 enter the cycle in "carrier" molecules, and that the condensations involve ATP.

In the conversion of citrulline to arginine, aspartic acid is the donor of the ammonia. A postulated mechanism for the reaction follows, hypothetical intermediates being enclosed in brackets:

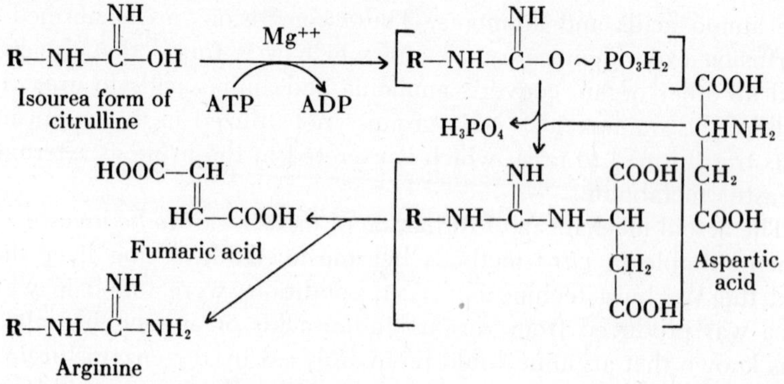

The formation of citrulline from ornithine has proved to be an especially complex reaction, the details of which are not yet completely established. The CO_2 and NH_3 which enter into this reaction are carried by carbamyl-glutamic acid, but the structure of the actual intermediate is not known. It has been shown with isotopes that the carbamyl group of carbamyl-glutamic acid is not the source of the CO_2 and NH_3. ATP is required for the synthesis of carbamyl-glutamic acid:

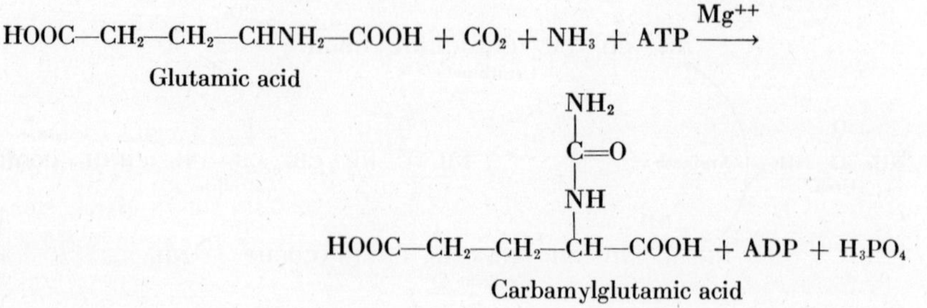

This reaction probably takes place stepwise. The carbamyl-glutamic acid then acts catalytically as follows:

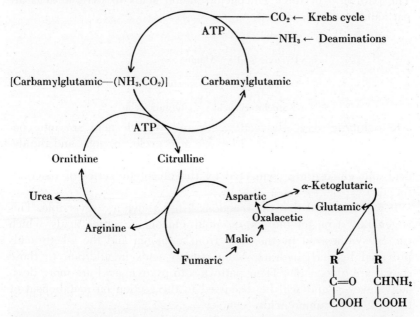

The current status of the ornithine cycle can then be formulated, with certain steps abbreviated, as follows:

The CO_2 and NH_3 which react with the carbamyl-glutamic acid presumably do so in the free state. Their probable origins are shown. The source of the aspartic acid for the synthesis of arginine is shown as glutamic acid, which transfers its nitrogen to oxalacetic acid by transamination. Since glutamic acid can in turn be synthesized from α-keto-glutaric acid and almost any other amino acid, it is apparent that a number of readily accessible pathways are open for the conversion of amino acid nitrogen to urea.

(*e*) CREATINE AND CREATININE. Creatinine, derived from creatine, is a significant excretory form of amino acid nitrogen. However, since its formation involves the special metabolism of only three, rather than the entire group of amino acids, it is logically discussed elsewhere (p. 521).

DISPOSAL OF THE CARBON SKELETON. (*a*) Synthetic pathways. The α-keto acids resulting from deamination may be reductively aminated by reversal of the transdeamination mechanism, re-forming the original amino acids. This process is continuous, as is the deamination, the net change being determined by physiological requirements. Certain fragments of the carbon skeletons are used for special syntheses, which are discussed in connection with the metabolism of the individual amino acids.

(*b*) Glucogenic pathway. Most of the amino acids are convertible to carbohydrate ("gluconeogenesis from protein"). The routes vary with the compound concerned, but all converge at pyruvic acid. The pathways of three glucogenic amino acids to pyruvic acid are particularly direct:

Glucose
↑
Pyruvic acid ←→ Alanine
↑
Oxalacetic acid ←→ Aspartic acid
↑
α-Ketoglutaric acid ←→ Glutamic acid

α-Ketoglutaric acid, oxalacetic acid, and pyruvic acid are interconvertible by means of the tricarboxylic acid cycle (p. 398) and the decarboxylating side reaction to it which occurs in liver (p. 408). Pyruvic acid and glucose are connected by the glycolytic series of reactions (p. 390).

It will be noted that the reactions listed above are reversible. This is generally true for the non-essential, glucogenic amino acids, which can be synthesized by the body from ammonia and the α-keto acids provided by carbohydrate. Many amino acids in addition to those shown are glucogenic. Their pathways to pyruvic acid are more devious, however, and will be discussed in the section on metabolism of the individual amino acids.

It has been estimated that over half of the amino acid constituents of the average animal protein are glucogenic. If a state of total diabetes or phlorizin-diabetes is induced in an experimental animal, it becomes virtually unable to utilize glucose. Preformed carbohydrate or any which may be synthesized from protein is lost practically quantitatively in the urine. If such an animal is fasted, its preformed glycogen is consumed in short order, followed by depletion of its fat stores, at which time the body attempts to support itself by the degradation of tissue protein (p. 497). All of the protein which is degraded gives rise to urinary nitrogen (urea, NH_3, creatinine, uric acid), which can be determined by a Kjeldahl analysis (p. 88). Since the animal is in a diabetic state, the glucose derived from the glucogenic amino acids of the degraded protein is excreted, unused, in the urine also.

This can be determined by any of the standard methods for reducing sugars (p. 23). The ratio of glucose to nitrogen in the urine is known as the "G/N ratio" (sometimes D/N, where D = dextrose). This varies with the severity of the diabetes, reaching a maximum value of about 3.65 in the phlorizinized animal. This means that each gram of nitrogen resulting from the degradation of tissue protein has been accompanied by the formation of 3.65 grams of glucose. Since nitrogen constitutes 16 per cent of the average animal protein (protein = N x 1/0.16), each gram of *protein* has produced 3.65 x 0.16 = 0.58 grams of glucose. Hence, 58 per cent by weight of the protein is glucogenic. Actually, there are a number of objections to this simple interpretation of the G/N ratio, and it is no longer regarded as an accurate index of the severity of the diabetes or the degree of gluconeogenesis from amino acids or proteins. However, other technics have confirmed the general findings that a large proportion of the amino acids in the average protein is glucogenic.

(*c*) KETOGENIC PATHWAY. The α-keto acids derived from a few amino acids are more closely allied to the fats than to the carbohydrates. In contrast to the glucogenic amino acids, the ketogenic group in various test systems produce ketone bodies instead of glucose. The pathways are rather specialized and complex, and will be discussed in connection with the metabolism of the individual amino acids concerned. In comparison to the glucogenic group, the ketogenic amino acids are a minority, comprising only phenylalanine, tyrosine, leucine, and isoleucine. Furthermore, certain of these amino acids are metabolized along pathways which are glucogenic as well as ketogenic.

(*d*) MISCELLANEOUS PATHWAYS. Certain amino acids traverse metabolic pathways which do not correspond to any that have been described thus far. These routes are highly individual, and are discussed in the appropriate sections of this chapter. It may be pointed out, however, that in many cases the entire amino acid undergoes the specified transformations, which are not preceded by a deamination. One such case is the conversion of tryptophan to nicotinic acid (p. 546).

METABOLISM OF THE INDIVIDUAL AMINO ACIDS

METABOLIC INTERRELATIONS. In contrast to the carbohydrates and lipids, there is no one chain or cycle of metabolic reactions followed by all of the individual amino acids. Certain common pathways have been described for the nitrogenous portions of these molecules (p. 509); brief mention has also been made of the various alternative metabolic routes available to the carbon skeletons of the deaminated amino acids. It is possible to organize these latter reactions, as well as certain direct interconversions between amino acids, into a meta-

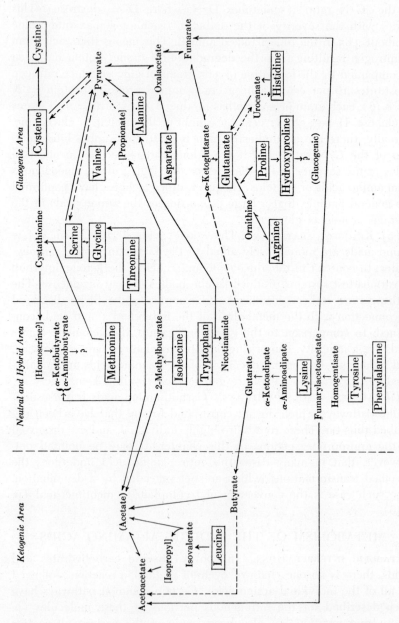

Fig. 87. Metabolic interrelations of the amino acids

bolic scheme which illustrates the major areas or metabolic pools which are shared by two or more acids. Such a scheme is shown in Figure 87, from which several conclusions may be drawn. First of all, it is obvious that most of the amino acids are more closely related to carbohydrate than to lipid (or ketone bodies). As a matter of fact, leucine is the only amino acid which is solely ketogenic. Phenylalanine, tyrosine, and isoleucine are both ketogenic and glucogenic, depending upon the particular test system employed. No satisfactory evidence has been obtained of the *net* conversion of lysine, methionine, or tryptophan to glucose or ketone bodies, although isotopic data indicate that such products can be formed from carbon atoms derived from these amino acids.

It will be noted in Figure 87 that most of the glucogenic amino acids can be arranged in two groups, one clustered about pyruvic acid, the other in close relation to α-ketoglutaric acid. These groups are interconnected by means of several members of the tricarboxylic acid cycle, with aspartic acid occupying a position between the two groups.
ALANINE. Although not the simplest amino acid in the structural sense, the metabolism of alanine is lacking in many of the complexities which are characteristic of the other amino acids. In fact, the only structural change which alanine is known to undergo metabolically is its reversible conversion to pyruvic acid (p. 516). This may take place by means of oxidative deamination, but transamination is a more likely possibility (p. 510). At any rate, this non-essential amino acid is readily formed from carbohydrate, and, conversely, can be catabolized by the same pathway.
GLYCINE. The major pathways of glycine metabolism are indicated in Figure 88. Glycine is glucogenic, non-essential, and can be synthesized from threonine (p. 523), and from serine by the following reaction:

$$\text{HOCH}_2\text{—CHNH}_2\text{—COOH} \longleftarrow \begin{array}{c} \nearrow \text{NH}_2\text{CH}_2\text{COOH} \\ \searrow \text{``Formate''} \end{array}$$

Serine is reversibly cleaved between the α and β carbon atoms to yield glycine and a 1-carbon fragment ("formate", C_1) which will be discussed elsewhere (p. 540). The interconversion appears to involve folic (folinic) acid and vitamin B_{12} (pp. 542, 200, 205).

The degradation of glycine may take either of two pathways. One is merely the reverse of the synthetic pathway indicated above, followed by the usual catabolic reactions of serine. The other involves oxidative deamination of glycine by glycine dehydrogenase (p. 362), the glyoxylic acid thus produced being split into CO_2 and a "formate" fragment, the further metabolism of which is discussed elsewhere (p. 540).

Glycine participates in the synthesis of certain heterocyclic ring systems. In combination with NH_3, "formate," and CO_2, the purine ring is formed (p. 567). Glycine and succinic acid produce pyrroles, which are then linked by 1-carbon units to form porphyrins (p. 587).

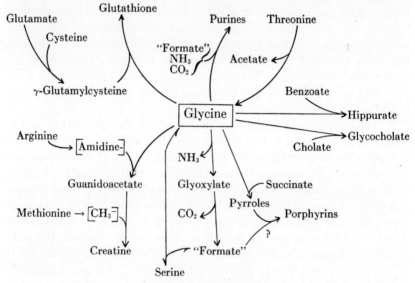

Fig. 88. *Glycine metabolism*

As mentioned previously (pp. 51, 498), glycine forms "pseudo-peptides" with the bile acids and the benzoic acids (e.g., *p*-aminobenzoic). These reactions occur in the liver. The synthesis of hippurates from the latter acids is currently believed to proceed as follows:

ATP — CoA
AMP — CoA ~ P ~ P — Benzoate
P ~ P — Benzoyl ~ CoA — Glycine
CoA — Benzoylglycine

This scheme is obviously an example of the general process of acylation (p. 454). The formation of hippurates is an example of "detoxication" (p. 283), and probably has no great physiological significance. The importance of the conjugated bile acids is discussed elsewhere (p. 268).

Glutathione is a true peptide, in the formation of which **glycine** participates. The first step in the synthesis is the combination of glutamic acid and cysteine to form the "γ" peptide, γ-glutamylcysteine, which is then condensed with glycine, yielding glutathione. Both steps (which occur in the liver) require ATP:

$$HSCH_2CHNH_2COOH \atop HOOCCH_2CH_2CHNH_2COOH \xrightarrow{ATP} HOOCCHNH_2CH_2CH_2-\overset{O}{\underset{\|}{C}}-NH-\overset{CH_2SH}{\underset{|}{CH}}-COOH$$

$$HOOCCHNH_2CH_2CH_2-\overset{O}{\underset{\|}{C}}-NH-\overset{CH_2SH}{\underset{|}{CH}}-\overset{O}{\underset{\|}{C}}-NHCH_2COOH \xleftarrow{ATP} NH_2CH_2COOH$$

It is probable that each step is a composite of several, presumably including an activation reaction preceding each condensation. Glutathione is hydrolyzed via intermediates which differ from those involved in its synthesis. The first step in the hydrolysis produces glutamic acid and cysteinylglycine; the latter is then hydrolyzed by a second enzyme system. The major metabolic role of glutathione is that of the prosthetic group of phosphoglyceraldehyde dehydrogenase (p. 379). It also participates in transpeptidations (p. 245).

Glycine is one of the building blocks in the synthesis of creatine, which takes place in two steps, the first occurring in the kidney, the second in the liver. In the first reaction, the amidine group of arginine is transferred to glycine, forming guanidoacetic acid (glycocyamine). This compound is then methylated by methionine, producing creatine. The mechanism of the first reaction is not known; it has been sug-

$$CH_2CH_2CH_2CHNH_2COOH \quad NH_2CH_2COOH \quad HN-CH_2COOH$$

(reaction scheme: Kidney → , Liver)

gested that arginase (p. 239) may act as a transferring as well as hydrolyzing enzyme. The second reaction is an example of transmethylation, the probable mechanism of which is discussed elsewhere (p. 536). Phosphocreatine (p. 413) is an important storage form of high-energy phosphate, especially in muscle. Phosphocreatine, under physiological conditions of pH, temperature, etc., spontaneously loses the elements of phosphoric acid in a ring-closure reaction, yielding creatinine. Creatine itself loses water to form the same product, but at a slower rate. These two reactions result in the steady production of an amount of creatinine which is proportional to the total amount of creatine + phosphocreatine in the body, and also to the muscle mass of the organism. Consequently, creatinine (which cannot be reutilized for any purpose) is excreted in the urine in quantities which are independent of the diet (p. 771), a circumstance giving rise at one time to the theory that there is an endogenous phase of nitrogen metabolism, uninfluenced by nitrogen from exogenous sources.

$$
\begin{array}{ccc}
\underset{\substack{|\\ \overset{|}{C}=NH \\ | \\ HN\!-\!\{PO_3H_2\}}}{CH_3-N-CH_2-C\!-\!\{OH\}}
& \xrightarrow{-H_3PO_4}
\underset{\substack{|\\ \overset{|}{C}=NH \\ | \\ HN}}{CH_3-N-CH_2-C}
& \xleftarrow{-H_2O}
\underset{\substack{|\\ \overset{|}{C}=NH \\ | \\ HN\{H\}}}{CH_3-N-CH_2-C\!-\!\{OH\}}
\end{array}
$$

SERINE. The relation of this glucogenic, non-essential amino acid to glycine has been indicated elsewhere (p. 519). An outline of its major metabolic paths is shown in Figure 89.

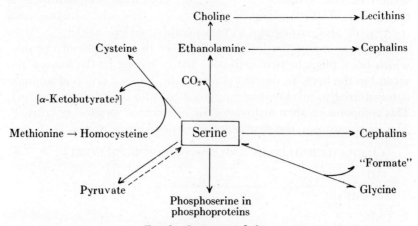

Fig. 89. Serine metabolism

Serine is deaminated by means of an unusual reaction catalyzed by a dehydrase (p. 241), the coenzyme of which may be pyridoxal phosphate:

$$
HOCH_2CHNH_2COOH \xrightarrow{-H_2O} \left[\underset{CH_2=C-COOH}{\overset{NH_2}{|}} \rightleftharpoons \underset{CH_3-C-COOH}{\overset{NH}{\|}} \right]
$$

$$
\downarrow H_2O
$$

$$
CH_3COCOOH \longleftarrow\!\bigwedge\!\longrightarrow NH_3
$$

Pyruvic acid

The glucogenicity of serine is thus easily explained. However, its non-essentiality poses a problem, since the conversion to pyruvic acid is probably not readily reversible. Glycine is the only known source of serine, which suggests the possibility that threonine, an essential amino acid known to form glycine (see below), may be the ultimate source of both glycine and serine in the absence of a dietary supply of these two amino acids.

The phosphoric acid groups of phosphoproteins (p. 46) have been shown to be attached to the hydroxyl groups of serine residues. Serine is also of importance in the structure of phospholipids. It is used as such in phosphatidyl serine, one of the types of cephalin (p. 32); it is decarboxylated to form ethanolamine, a constituent of another type of cephalin (p. 32); and it is the parent substance of choline (a constituent of lecithin [p. 31]), which is formed by the stepwise methylation (p. 538) of ethanolamine.

In a rather unusual sequence of reactions, serine provides the carbon skeleton of cysteine (p. 531) in a synthesis in which the sulfur is furnished by methionine.

Serine is an important source of 1-carbon fragments (p. 541), since, in addition to yielding one such unit in the formation of glycine (p. 519), another is produced from the α-carbon atom of glycine itself (p. 519).

THREONINE. Comparatively little is known of the metabolism of this amino acid, which is essential for growth in the young and maintenance of nitrogen equilibrium in the adult (p. 493).

In vitro, threonine is deaminated by means of a reaction similar to that undergone by serine. The α-ketobutyric acid which is first formed is rapidly aminated (by transamination) to yield α-aminobutyric acid. Both of these compounds are formed also in the metabolism of methionine (p. 531).

Threonine is glucogenic *in vivo.* It is probable, however, that the butyric acid derivatives mentioned above are not intermediates on the glucogenic pathway. Another possible route to glucose lies in the formation of glycine, although acetate (ketogenic) is formed simultaneously. The mechanism of this cleavage has not been elucidated, but it may resemble that of serine to glycine and "formate." It is not established that acetic acid itself is an actual cleavage product; the substance formed may be acetyl-CoA or another compound readily converted to acetic acid.

Threonine shares with a few other amino acids the characteristic of segregation from the nitrogen pool. Although it can be deaminated, as indicated previously, threonine appears not to be reaminated to any significant extent.

VALINE. Valine is essential for growth and nitrogen equilibrium. It is glucogenic. Recent data obtained with the aid of isotopes suggest the following pathway to carbohydrate:

$$\underset{CH_3}{\overset{CH_3}{\diagdown}} CHCHNH_2COOH \xrightarrow{NH_3} \underset{CH_3}{\overset{CH_3}{\diagdown}} CH-\overset{O}{\overset{\|}{C}}-COOH \xrightarrow[(O)]{CO_2} \underset{CH_3}{\overset{CH_3}{\diagdown}} CH-COOH$$

$$CH_3CH_2COOH \leftarrow [CH_3CH_2C{=}O] \xleftarrow{CO_2} \left[\underset{CH_3}{\overset{H}{\diagup}} C{\diagup}^O \ CH-(COO)H \right]$$
$$\downarrow$$
$$\text{Carbohydrate}$$

It is probable that the pathway from propionic acid does not proceed directly through pyruvic acid (p. 453).

ASPARTIC ACID. This non-essential amino acid is readily interconvertible with carbohydrate via its corresponding keto acid, oxalacetic acid (p. 516), with which it is rapidly equilibrated by transamination (p. 510).

The amide of aspartic acid, asparagine, is synthesized and degraded in the animal organism, but little is known of these reactions or of its metabolic role.

Aspartic acid is decarboxylated to yield β-alanine:

$$H(OOC)CHNH_2CH_2COOH \xrightarrow{CO_2} NH_2CH_2CH_2COOH$$

This unusual β-amino acid is coupled with histidine and methylhistidine to form carnosine and anserine, respectively (p. 526). (It is also a constituent of pantothenic acid [p. 193]).

A major metabolic role of aspartic acid is its participation in the conversion of citrulline to arginine, a step in the ornithine cycle (p. 514).

GLUTAMIC ACID. An outline of the metabolism of this amino acid is presented in Figure 90. Glutamic acid is non-essential, being readily synthesized from (and converted to) carbohydrate by way of α-ketoglutaric acid. The interconversion of the amino acid and keto acid may occur by either deamination (glutamic dehydrogenase [p. 509]) or transamination (p. 510). The importance of these reactions in the general deamination-reamination reactions of the amino acids was indicated previously (p. 488). Aspartic and glutamic acids are the most active amino acids in transamination.

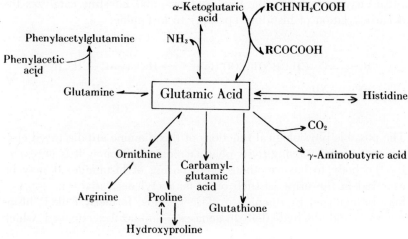

Fig. 90. *Glutamic acid metabolism*

Glutamic acid is involved in the synthesis of certain special products, viz., glutathione (p. 521), carbamylglutamic acid in the ornithine cycle (p. 514), and glutamine (p. 512). In addition to its function in the storage and transport of ammonia, glutamine participates in the "detoxication" of phenylacetic acid in man and the higher apes (p. 284), forming phenylacetylglutamine.

Glutamic acid is one of the few compounds in addition to glucose which is used as a substrate by brain tissue. Although little is known of its metabolism in brain, a decarboxylase has been found which converts glutamic acid to γ-aminobutyric acid, the further metabolism of which is uncertain:

$$H(OOC)CHNH_2CH_2CH_2\,COOH \xrightarrow{\quad CO_2 \quad} NH_2CH_2CH_2CH_2COOH$$

Pyridoxal-phosphate is the coenzyme of this decarboxylase.

Glutamic acid is a constituent of the vitamin, folic acid (pteroylglutamic acid, p. 200).

The relationship between glutamic acid and certain other amino acids was indicated in Figure 87 (p. 518). This is discussed further in connection with the metabolism of arginine (p. 528), histidine (p. 527), and the prolines (p. 529).

HISTIDINE. As was stated previously, histidine is essential for growth of the young, but apparently can be synthesized at an adequate rate in the adult human being. Whether the route of synthesis is the exact reversal of the route of catabolism via glutamic acid is not certain.

An enzyme found in the liver, kidneys, and intestine catalyzes the decarboxylation of histidine (p. 242) to histamine:

$$HC{=\!\!=\!\!=}C{-}CH_2CHNH_2(COO)H \xrightarrow{\quad CO_2\quad} HC{=\!\!=\!\!=}C{-}CH_2CH_2NH_2$$
$$\underset{\diagdown_{CH}\diagup}{N\qquad NH} \qquad\qquad \underset{\diagdown_{CH}\diagup}{N\qquad NH}$$

The possible physiological functions of this diamine are discussed elsewhere (p. 260). Owing to its pharmacological potency, it is necessary for the body to have methods of disposing of histamine. It may be excreted in the urine as such or as its acetyl derivative (p. 455), or may be oxidized by diamine oxidase (p. 362, formerly called "histaminase") and aldehyde dehydrogenases to imidazoleacetic acid, which is excreted in the urine:

$$HC{=\!\!=\!\!=}C{-}CH_2CH_2NH_2 \qquad HC{=\!\!=\!\!=}C{-}CH_2\overset{H}{C}{=}O \qquad HC{=\!\!=\!\!=}C{-}CH_2COOH$$
$$\underset{\underset{NH_3}{\diagdown_{CH}\diagup}}{N\qquad NH}\xrightarrow{\qquad} \underset{\diagdown_{CH}\diagup}{N\qquad NH}\xrightarrow{\qquad} \underset{\diagdown_{CH}\diagup}{N\qquad NH}$$

Histidine and β-alanine (from aspartic acid, p. 524) combine to form the pseudopeptide, carnosine. This compound and its methylated derivative, anserine, are found in the muscle of vertebrates, but not invertebrates. The methyl group of anserine is derived from methionine (p. 536), but it has not been established whether this transmethylation occurs before or after the histidine has condensed with the β-alanine. The physiological functions of carnosine and anserine are not known.

$$\overset{O}{NH_2CH_2CH_2{-}C{-}NH{-}CH{-}COOH} \qquad\qquad \overset{O}{NH_2CH_2CH_2{-}C{-}NH{-}CH{-}COOH}$$
$$HC{=\!\!=\!\!=}C{-}CH_2 \qquad\qquad HC{=\!\!=\!\!=}C{-}CH_2$$
$$\underset{\diagdown_{CH}\diagup}{N\qquad NH}\ \text{Carnosine} \qquad \text{Anserine}\ \underset{\diagdown_{CH}\diagup}{N\qquad N{-}CH_3}$$

The betaine of thiolhistidine, ergothionine, occurs in the blood, where, as a reducing substance, it interferes with certain methods for the determination of glucose and uric acid. It is not known whether this compound originates in the body or is strictly exogenous.

$$HC{=\!\!=\!\!=}C-CH_2-\overset{\overset{+}{N}(CH_3)_3}{\underset{|}{CH}}-COO^-$$
$$\underset{N \qquad NH}{}$$
$$\underset{C}{}$$
$$\underset{SH}{}$$

The major catabolic pathway of histidine results in the formation of glutamic acid, and accounts for the reported glucogenicity of the former amino acid. Under the influence of a series of enzymes in liver (histidase, urocanase, etc.), histidine is converted to open-chain compounds, liberating a "formate" fragment (p. 541) in the process:

$$HC{=\!\!=\!\!=}C-CH_2CHNH_2COOH \quad NH_3 \quad HC{=\!\!=\!\!=}C-CH{=}CH-COOH$$
$$\underset{N \qquad NH}{\xrightarrow{\text{Histidase}}} \qquad \underset{N \qquad NH}{} \quad \text{Urocanic acid}$$
$$\underset{CH}{} \qquad \qquad \underset{CH}{}$$

Urocanase, etc.

$$\left[O{=}C{-\!\!-}CHCH_2CH_2COOH \qquad \longleftarrow \qquad HO-C{=\!\!=\!\!=}C-CH_2CH_2COOH \right.$$
$$\underset{N \qquad NH}{} \qquad \qquad \underset{N \qquad NH}{}$$
$$\left. \underset{CH}{} \qquad \qquad \underset{CH}{} \right]$$

$$HOOC-CH-CH_2CH_2COOH \qquad HCOOH$$
$$\underset{NH}{}$$
$$---|--- \qquad \longrightarrow \qquad HOOCCHNH_2CH_2CH_2COOH$$
$$\underset{CH}{} \qquad \qquad \qquad \text{Glutamic acid}$$
$$---||---$$
$$NH \qquad \qquad NH_3$$

α-Formamidino-glutamic acid

It is not known whether this process is followed in reverse in the adult organism for the purpose of synthesizing histidine.

ARGININE. This amino acid is not required for maintenance of nitrogen equilibrium in the adult human being, but is necessary in the diet of the young animal for optimal growth, although a slow rate of growth is possible in its absence. It is obvious, therefore, that arginine can be synthesized, but at a slow rate. The anabolic pathway is probably identical with the catabolic route to glutamic acid, discussed below.

Arginine plays a catalytic role in the synthesis of urea via the ornithine cycle (p. 513), in the course of which it is hydrolyzed by arginase to ornithine and urea:

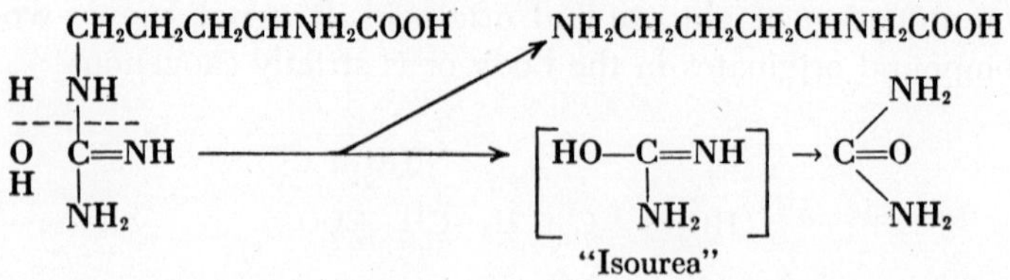

$$CH_2CH_2CH_2CHNH_2COOH \qquad NH_2CH_2CH_2CH_2CHNH_2COOH$$

$$
\begin{array}{ll}
H \quad NH & \qquad\qquad\qquad\qquad\qquad\qquad NH_2 \\
\text{---}|\text{---} & \\
O \quad C{=}NH \longrightarrow \qquad\left[HO{-}C{=}NH\right] \rightarrow C{=}O \\
H \quad | & \qquad\qquad\quad | \qquad\qquad\quad \\
\quad NH_2 & \qquad\qquad\quad NH_2 \qquad\qquad NH_2
\end{array}
$$

"Isourea"

The same amidine group which reacts with water to form urea in this reaction may also be coupled to glycine to form guanidoacetic acid in the initial step of creatine synthesis (p. 521). The mechanism of this "transamidination" is unknown.

The ornithine residue left after the above reactions undergoes a number of significant metabolic transformations. It acts as a detoxifying agent for benzoic acid in birds, forming α,γ-dibenzoylornithine, a "pseudopeptide" synthesis requiring ATP. Ornithine is converted to citrulline in the course of the synthesis of urea (p. 513). From the standpoint of the metabolism of arginine itself, however, the importance of ornithine lies in its deamination (presumably reversible) to glutamic semialdehyde, an intermediate convertible either to the prolines (discussed below) or to glutamic acid, the latter reaction explaining the glucogenic properties of arginine (and also its synthesis in the organism):

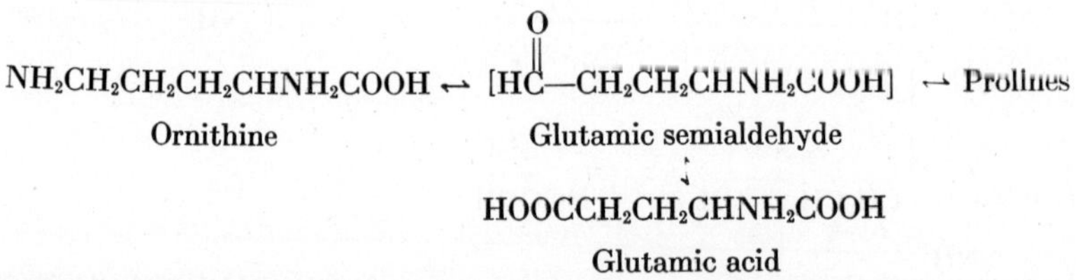

$$
\begin{array}{c}
\qquad\qquad\qquad\qquad O \\
\qquad\qquad\qquad\qquad \| \\
NH_2CH_2CH_2CH_2CHNH_2COOH \rightleftharpoons [HC{-}CH_2CH_2CHNH_2COOH] \rightarrow \text{Prolines}
\end{array}
$$

Ornithine   Glutamic semialdehyde

$$\downarrow$$

HOOCCH_2CH_2CHNH_2COOH

Glutamic acid

The α-amino group of arginine is only slowly equilibrated with the ammonia pool (p. 488); the amidine group, however, has a great avidity for metabolic ammonia, as might be anticipated from the reactions of the ornithine cycle (p. 513).

In invertebrates, phosphoarginine plays the role that phosphocreatine (p. 413) does in vertebrates.

PROLINE AND HYDROXYPROLINE. These non-essential, glucogenic amino acids are synthesized in the organism from glutamic acid or from arginine via the common intermediate, glutamic semialdehyde, as shown at the top of page 529.

Evidence obtained with the aid of isotopes suggests that most of the hydroxyproline of the tissue proteins is derived from proline, rather than from dietary hydroxyproline. The conversion does not appear to be readily reversed, which raises the problem of the pathway from hydroxyproline to carbohydrate. Hydroxyproline is converted *in vitro* into a product having the properties of γ-hydroxyglutamic semialdehyde. This in turn may be transformed into γ-hydroxyglutamic acid, which is said to be glucogenic.

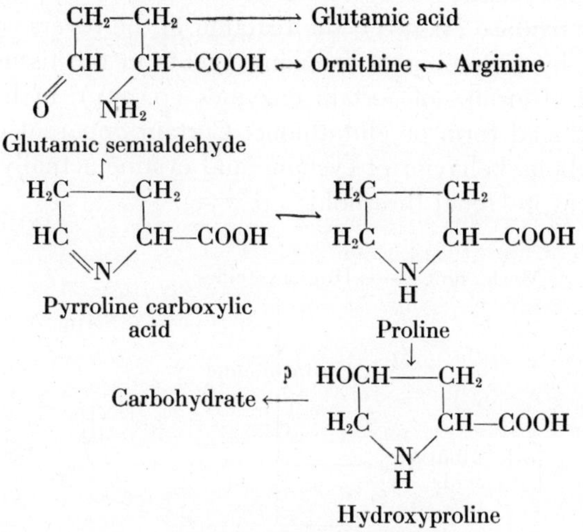

$$CH_2—CH_2 \longrightarrow \text{Glutamic acid}$$
$$CH \quad CH—COOH \leftrightarrow \text{Ornithine} \leftrightarrow \text{Arginine}$$
$$O \quad NH_2$$

Glutamic semialdehyde

$$H_2C—CH_2 \qquad H_2C—CH_2$$
$$HC \quad CH—COOH \longrightarrow H_2C \quad CH—COOH$$
$$N \qquad\qquad N$$
$$\qquad\qquad\qquad H$$

Pyrroline carboxylic acid   Proline

$$? \quad HOCH—CH_2$$
$$\text{Carbohydrate} \longleftarrow H_2C \quad CH—COOH$$
$$N$$
$$H$$

Hydroxyproline

Proline and Hydroxyproline

The oxidation of proline by kidney slices or homogenates is retarded by adrenalectomy, and is restored by the *in vivo* administration of cortisone. The general significance of this phenomenon is not known; it appears to be restricted to the kidney.

CYSTEINE AND CYSTINE. These two non-essential amino acids are the last of the "glucogenic area" of Figure 87 (p. 518) to be discussed. The separation of the discussion of methionine from that of cysteine and cystine may appear somewhat artificial from the standpoint of general sulfur metabolism. However, there are sufficient areas of metabolism in which no appreciable overlapping occurs between the two groups to justify the arbitrary division. The metabolic pathways of cysteine and cystine are outlined in Figure 91, in which methionine is included solely as a source of sulfur in the synthesis of cysteine.

Before entering into a detailed discussion of the metabolism of cysteine and cystine, it may be helpful first to consider their inter-convertibility:

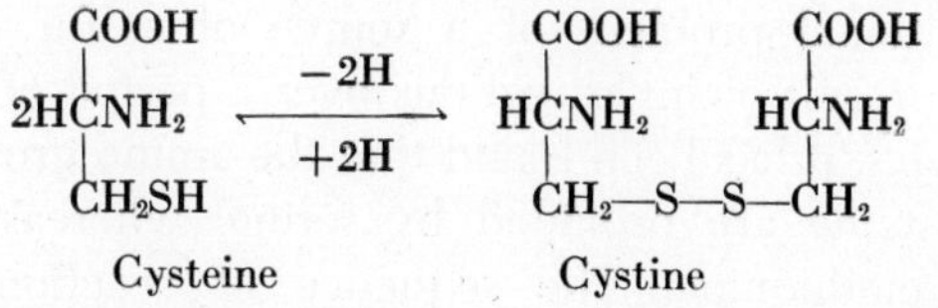

$$COOH \qquad\qquad COOH \qquad COOH$$
$$2HCNH_2 \xrightarrow[+2H]{-2H} HCNH_2 \qquad HCNH_2$$
$$CH_2SH \qquad\qquad CH_2—S—S—CH_2$$

Cysteine   Cystine

From the formulas, it would appear that these two amino acids constitute a typical redox system (p. 354), each half of the system differing from the other by two hydrogen atoms (equivalent to 2 hydrogen ions + 2 electrons). There is considerable evidence that cysteine and cystine are in fact easily interconvertible in the intact organism. The oxidation of cysteine to cystine is catalyzed by cytochrome c and cytochrome oxidase (p. 364); the reaction in the reverse direction can be effected by a number of reducing agents in the tissues, including the sulfhydryl groups of certain enzymes (p. 251), hydrogen sulfide, and the reduced form of glutathione. Certain apparent discrepancies in the metabolic behavior of cysteine and cystine actually may be due to differences in "renal threshold" (p. 755).

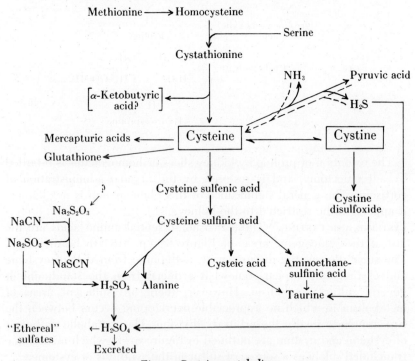

Fig. 91. Cysteine metabolism

In the case of most of the non-essential amino acids, sources must be found for the nitrogenous moiety and for the carbon skeleton. Cysteine poses the additional problem of a source of sulfur of the proper valence. As the result of investigations over a period of years, involving many technics, it has been found that the amino group and carbon skeleton of cysteine are provided by serine, whereas the sulfur is derived from methionine. The sequence of reactions involved is presented at the top of page 531.

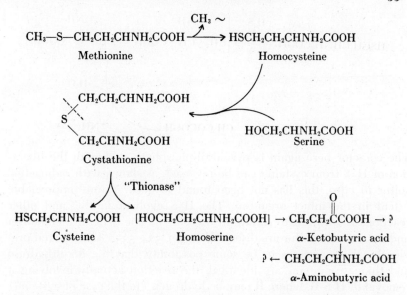

It was originally assumed that methionine simply gives up its methyl group in a transmethylation to some appropriate acceptor, leaving homocysteine. From what is known now concerning transmethylations from methionine (p. 539), it appears that the provision of homocysteine is not so simple. Nevertheless, whatever its immediate source, homocysteine condenses with serine to form the thioether, cystathionine. In animal tissues, the thioether is split specifically on the side of the sulfur which yields cysteine, and, probably, α-ketobutyric acid. (Whether any such compound as homoserine is the precursor of α-ketobutyric acid has not been established.) Pyridoxal-phosphate is the coenzyme of the "thionase" system, certain of the peculiarities of which are discussed below in connection with cysteine desulfhydrase, with which it may be identical. The α-aminobutyric acid which is excreted in the urine in certain circumstances is probably derived from α-ketobutyric acid, which in turn may originate from methionine or threonine (p. 523). The synthesis of cysteine from methionine is irreversible.

Although there is no unanimity concerning cystine, most investigations have shown cysteine to be glucogenic. Since these amino acids are interconvertible, it is probable that both should be considered glucogenic. The conversion of cysteine to pyruvic acid bears a striking resemblance to the serine dehydrase reaction (p. 522), being, however, a "desulfhydration" rather than a dehydration:

$$\text{HSCH}_2\text{CHNH}_2\text{COOH} \xrightarrow{\text{H}_2\text{S}} \left[\overset{\text{NH}_2}{\underset{|}{\text{CH}_2}}{=}\text{CH}{-}\text{COOH} \rightharpoonup \text{CH}_3{-}\overset{\text{NH}}{\underset{\|}{\text{C}}}{-}\text{COOH} \right]$$

$$\text{CH}_3\text{COCOOH} \longleftarrow \overset{\text{NH}_3}{\diagup} \quad \diagdown\, \text{H}_2\text{O}$$

The cofactor here again is pyridoxal-phosphate. Although the liberation of H_2S from cysteine *can* be reversed, as shown with radioactive sulfur *in vitro*, this has not been found to occur to any appreciable extent in the intact organism. The H_2S evolved in this and other reactions is oxidized to sulfate in the body. (The general metabolism and excretion of sulfur are discussed on pp. 534–535.) As indicated previously, there appears to be some possibility that the desulfhydrase and thionase systems are identical, the reaction actually involving a removal of H-S-R, where **R** may be hydrogen (in the case of cysteine) or a more complicated residue such as the cysteine carbon chain itself (in the case of cystathionine).

The utilization of cysteine in the synthesis of glutathione has been discussed previously (p. 521). Cysteine also participates in a novel form of "detoxication," the formation of mercapturic acids. Aromatic hydrocarbons and many of their monohalogenated derivatives are conjugated with cysteine in the body, the cysteine moiety then acetylated, and the resulting mercapturic acid excreted in the urine (p. 283). A typical foreign substance treated in this manner is bromobenzene:

HSCH$_2$CHNH$_2$COOH   S—CH$_2$CHNH$_2$COOH   S—CH$_2$CHNHCOOH

(Prob.) Acetyl-CoA

p-Bromophenyl-
mercapturic acid

The sulfur of cysteine may undergo oxidation while still attached to the organic molecule. Taurine is one of the products of this metabolic route:

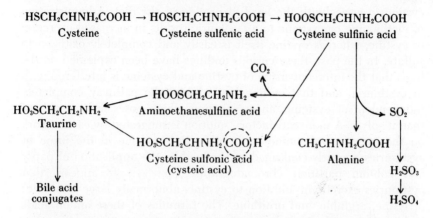

Cysteine is oxidized stepwise to a sulfinic acid. This compound may be "desulfinated" to produce sulfite (which is eventually oxidized to sulfate) and alanine, or may be further oxidized to the sulfonic acid, cysteic acid. A decarboxylase found in various tissues then converts this to taurine, with which a portion of the bile acids are conjugated (p. 268). Recent data suggest that the major pathway to taurine may involve aminoethanesulfinic acid rather than cysteic acid as intermediate. Cystine is also believed to form taurine, but by another pathway (Fig. 91, p. 530).

Thiosulfate, which is of uncertain origin in the body, is used in the detoxication of cyanide (Fig. 91, p. 530). The formation of thiocyanate from cyanide is catalyzed by rhodanese, an enzyme named at a time when it was believed that the names of synthesizing enzymes should end in "-ese" instead of "-ase."

The sulfur-containing amino acids are involved in an "inborn error of metabolism" (p. 255) known as cystinuria. In this condition, as in other inborn errors which will be discussed later, a genetically transmitted deficiency (inherited as a Mendelian recessive) in one or more enzymes causes the accumulation of an ordinarily metabolized compound, which is consequently excreted in sufficient quantities to be detected. These metabolic anomalies in themselves are not ordinarily harmful to the individual, although serious consequences sometimes result from quite accidental features of the condition. In the case of cystinuria, for example, an individual may go through life unaware of his daily excretion of cystine in the urine. On the other hand, the insolubility of cystine can lead to the crystallization of this substance in the urine, which sometimes results in the formation of cystine calculi requiring surgical intervention.

The explanation of the mechanism of cystinuria is a controversial matter. It has been shown that the quantity of cystine excreted by a cystinuric varies with the level of protein in the diet. Administration of methionine or cysteine to a cystinuric results in increased excretion of cystine, whereas cystine itself is easily and completely oxidized to sulfate. In the past, these curious findings have been explained on the basis that the interconversion of cystine and cysteine is interfered with in cystinuria, and that cystine has a metabolic pathway completely independent of cysteine, an explanation which poses more problems than it solves. A more satisfactory solution is suggested by earlier work on the excretion of amino acids other than cystine in the urine of cystinurics, recently confirmed and refined by the application of paper and column partition chromatography (p. 89). It appears that cystinurics excrete, in addition to cystine, abnormally large quantities of lysine, arginine, and ornithine. The formulas of these amino acids and cystine are shown below:

$$NH_2CH_2CH_2CH_2CH_2CHNH_2COOH \qquad \text{Lysine}$$

$$NHCH_2CH_2CH_2CHNH_2COOH$$
$$\underset{|}{\overset{|}{C}}=NH \qquad\qquad\qquad \text{Arginine}$$
$$\underset{}{NH_2}$$

$$NH_2CH_2CH_2CH_2CHNH_2COOH \qquad \text{Ornithine}$$

$$NH_2CHCH_2\!-\!S\!-\!S\!-\!CH_2CHNH_2COOH$$
$$\underset{|}{}\qquad\qquad\qquad\quad \text{Cystine}$$
$$COOH$$

It is suggested that the cystinuric inherits a defect in an enzyme system of the kidney involved in the tubular reabsorption (p. 755) of compounds possessing diamine structures of the type indicated above. Cystine itself, when fed, is absorbed only slowly from the intestine and cannot result in high levels of cystine in the blood. It is metabolized or otherwise utilized as rapidly as it enters the body and does not appear in the urine. Methionine and cysteine, on the other hand, are rapidly absorbed and rapidly converted to cystine, presumably at a rate sufficient to elevate the level of blood cystine, beyond the point of complete tubular reabsorption in the kidney, resulting in cystinuria.

Several types of compounds undergo esterification with sulfate in the body. The liver utilizes sulfate for the "detoxication" of phenol and indoxyl (p. 282), for example. (In the sulfatation of phenol, ATP is required for an initial reaction which appears to be an "activation" of the sulfate.) Other compounds forming sulfate esters in the body are the estrogens (p. 660), androgens (p. 667), and the amino sugars (p. 20). Organic sulfate esters which are excreted in the urine are called "ethereal sulfates" (p. 775).

It may be of interest to outline the over-all fate of sulfur-bearing compounds in the mammalian organism. Inorganic sulfate is ingested only in small amounts, and, although it can be utilized for esterification, is not ordinarily a significant source of this form of sulfur; it is also not appreciably reduced to lower states of oxidation. Small quantities of mercaptans derived from intestinal putrefaction (p. 275) may be absorbed into the blood and excreted in the urine. The major sources of urinary sulfur, however, are the cystine, cysteine, and methionine moieties of the dietary proteins. Normally, a certain (relatively small) proportion of these amino acids is metabolized via pathways leading to the excretion of taurine, thiosulfate, or thiocyanate. Traces of the amino acids themselves are also excreted. All compounds in the urine containing sulfur in a lower state of oxidation than sulfate are classified as "neutral sulfur." The major metabolic pathway of the sulfur-bearing amino acids results in complete oxidation to sulfate. A minor fraction of the total sulfate in the urine is ester or "ethereal" sulfate, the major fraction being free, inorganic sulfate. Quantitative aspects of sulfur partition in the urine are discussed elsewhere (p. 775).

METHIONINE. The essentiality of methionine for growth and nitrogen equilibrium was formerly believed to be due to its methyl group, since its demethylated derivative, homocysteine, could not replace it when administered to animals on certain restricted diets (supposedly "methyl-free" but otherwise complete [p. 539]) unless a source of methyl groups (e.g., choline) was provided also. Since it has been discovered that methyl groups can be synthesized in the organism (p. 540), since homocysteine can replace methionine in a methyl-free diet provided with the proper vitamins (p. 542), and since the keto acid of methionine can take its place in the diet, it appears that the structure in methionine which cannot be synthesized by the animal is the sulfur-carbon skeleton, $-S-CH_2-CH_2-\overset{|}{\underset{|}{C}}-COOH$.

Despite its close relation to cysteine, methionine does not behave as a glucogenic amino acid. This can be explained by the necessity of providing a serine molecule for every cysteine molecule synthesized from methionine (p. 531). Since serine is glucogenic in its own right, the supply of glucose precursors is not increased by the transformation. The fate of the 4-carbon skeleton of methionine (or homocysteine) is not definitely established, but its metabolism does not appear to involve pathways to carbohydrate.

Although methionine can be deaminated, there is no evidence that any significant part of its metabolism proceeds via the keto acid. In fact, there appear to be only two important metabolic routes open to methionine or its constituent chemical fragments: (1) transfer of sulfur to the carbon chain of serine to form cysteine and, probably, α-ketobutyric acid, the ultimate fate of which is in doubt; (2) utilization of the methyl group in transmethylations and the related reactions of the "formate" group. The former pathway is discussed in detail in connection with the metabolism of cysteine (p. 531); the latter will be considered here.

A general scheme of methyl donors and acceptors is shown in Figure 92, which is not to be interpreted to mean that there is a general "pool" of methyl groups in the sense that there is a pool of ammonia or acetyl, since transmethylations have been found to be not only very specific for donor and acceptor, but also largely irreversible. The methyl donors listed do not correspond exactly to the compounds commonly regarded in the older literature as possessing "labile" methyl groups. These labile groups were commonly detected by testing a given compound for its ability to replace methionine for the growth of rats on a methyl-free, homocysteine-supplemented diet. (As shown by later experiments, the diets used chanced to be deficient in folic acid and vitamin B_{12}, precluding synthesis of methyl groups from "formate" [p. 540].) The possession of labile methyl groups by this criterion did not prove that the compound in question was itself a methylating agent, e.g., the case of choline (discussed below), but did indicate that it could act as a source of methyls, even if only by way of intermediary reactions. The same type of information has been obtained in tracing the course of methyl groups in the body by labeling them with isotopic carbon or hydrogen. As indicated elsewhere (p. 479), there is no direct correlation between the lipotropic activity of a compound and its transmethylating ability. Detailed information on certain direct methyl donors has become available recently from experiments *in vitro* with more or less purified systems.

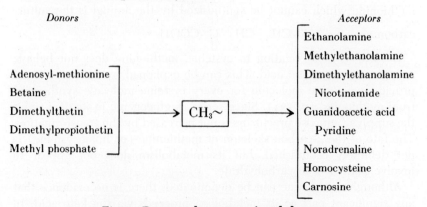

Fig. 92. Donors and acceptors of methyl groups

The structures of the known, direct methyl donors are given at the top of page 537.

$$\begin{array}{l} \text{N}=\text{C}-\text{NH}_2 \\ \text{HC} \quad \text{C}-\text{N} \end{array}$$

S-Adenosylmethionine

$$\begin{array}{c} \qquad\qquad \text{CH} \qquad\qquad\qquad\qquad \text{CH}_3 \\ \qquad\qquad\qquad \text{O} \qquad\qquad\qquad\qquad | \\ \text{N}-\text{C}-\text{N}-\text{CHCHOHCHOHCHCH}_2-\overset{+}{\text{S}}-\text{CH}_2\text{CH}_2\text{CHNH}_2\text{COOH} \end{array}$$

$$(\text{CH}_3)_3\overset{+}{\equiv}\text{N}-\text{CH}_2\text{COO}^-$$ Betaine

$$(\text{CH}_3)_2\overset{+}{=}\text{S}-\text{CH}_2\text{COO}^-$$ Dimethylthetin

$$(\text{CH}_3)_2\overset{+}{=}\text{S}-\text{CH}_2\text{CH}_2\text{COO}^-$$ Dimethylpropiothetin

$$\text{CH}_3-\text{O}-\text{PO}_3\text{Na}_2$$ Methyl phosphate

The first two compounds are the only physiological methylating agents known to occur in the animal organism, dimethylpropiothetin is found in algae, whereas dimethylthetin and methyl phosphate, so far as is known, are. purely synthetic products of the laboratory. It will be observed that all of these compounds bear a marked resemblance to the alkylating agents of the organic chemist, containing methyl groups linked either to an "-onium" atom (quaternary nitrogen or tertiary sulfur) or esterified with an inorganic acid (methyl phosphate being analogous to dimethyl sulfate). It seems reasonable to assume that all biological methyl donors have structures similar to those indicated.

The apparent ability of dietary choline to serve as a source of methyl groups obviously must be explained by its prior oxidation to betaine:

$$(\text{CH}_3)_3\overset{+}{\equiv}\text{NCH}_2\text{CH}_2\text{OH} \rightarrow (\text{CH}_3)_3\overset{+}{\equiv}\text{NCH}_2\overset{\text{II}}{\text{C}}{=}\text{O} \rightarrow (\text{CH}_3)_3\overset{+}{\equiv}\text{NCH}_2\text{COO}^-$$

Choline   Betaine aldehyde   Betaine

Indeed, it has been observed that the *in vitro* efficacy of choline as a methylating agent is contingent upon aerobiosis and the possession, by the tissue in question, of choline and betaine aldehyde dehydrogenases (p. 365), whereas transmethylations from betaine are independent of these factors. A specific transmethylase catalyzes the transfer of methyl groups from betaine to homocysteine:

$$(\text{CH}_3)_3\overset{+}{\equiv}\text{N}-\text{CH}_2\text{COO}^-\qquad\qquad \text{HSCH}_2\text{CH}_2\text{CHNH}_2\text{COOH}$$

Betaine   Homocysteine

$$(\text{CH}_3)_2\overset{+}{=}\text{N}-\text{CH}_2\text{COO}^-\qquad\qquad \text{CH}_3-\text{SCH}_2\text{CH}_2\text{CHNH}_2\text{COOH}$$

Dimethyl glycine   Methionine

The demethylated remainder of betaine is dimethylglycine, which is not a direct methyl donor. It can, however, reform betaine in the cyclic series of reactions shown in Figure 93. The second methyl group of betaine (one of the two methyl groups of dimethyl glycine) is oxidized to a "formate" fragment (p. 540), as is the third methyl group (the single methyl group of sarcosine, monomethylglycine). Complete removal of methyl groups leaves glycine, which is interconvertible with serine (p. 519) by addition or removal of a "formate" unit. By decarboxylation, serine produces ethanolamine (p. 522), which is methylated in three successive steps (discussed below) to form choline, from which betaine is finally produced by oxidation. It should be pointed out that certain of these interconversions are of importance in connection with the phospholipids (p. 466) and the phenomenon of lipotropism (p. 476). The interconversion of methyl groups and "formate" shown in Figure 93 will be discussed below.

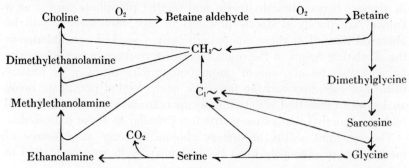

Fig. 93. Interrelations of glycine and choline derivatives in transmethylation

Much less information is available concerning transmethylations from methionine. It has been known for some time that such methylations probably involve some sort of "activation," since ATP is required. Recently the direct methyl donor, a reaction product of ATP and methionine, was isolated, and proved to be S-adenosylmethionine (p. 539). Evidently, in the activation reaction, ATP donates its entire adenosine moiety to methionine and loses three mols of phosphate (the fate of which is not settled as yet). The structure of the condensation product is of considerable historical interest, since loss of a homoserine fragment by hydrolysis would leave adenine thiomethylpentoside, a compound that was isolated from yeast as long ago as 1912. Although S-adenosylmethionine has been shown to be the active form of methionine thus far only in the methylation of nicotinamide, it is probably active generally in transmethylations from methionine to various acceptors, viz., guanidoacetic acid, ethanolamine, dimethyl-, and probably monomethyl-ethanolamine:

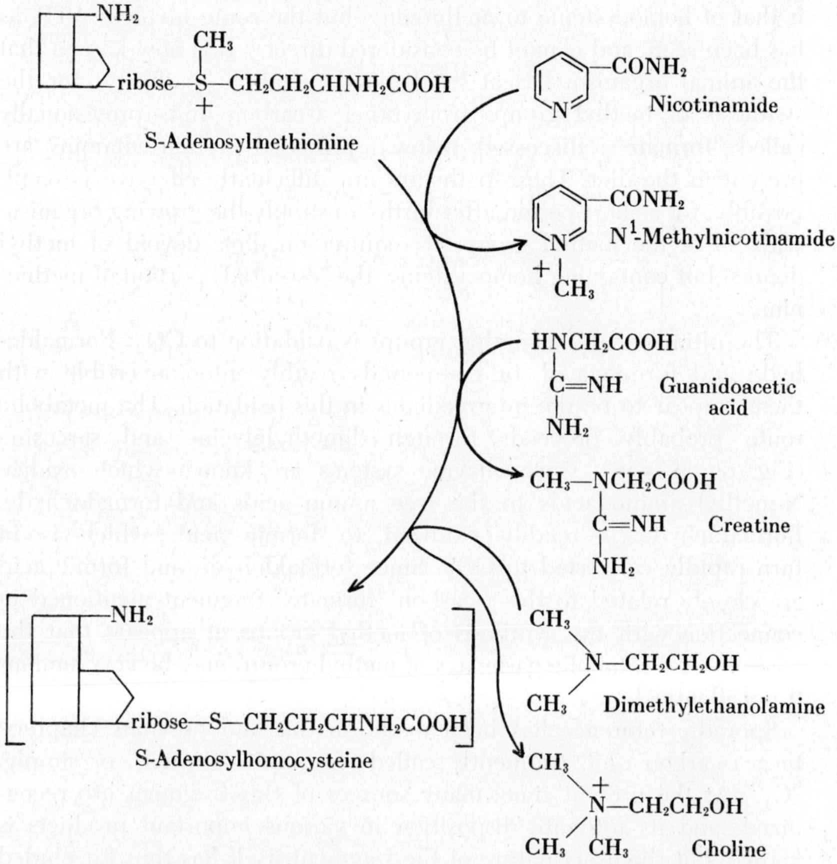

As indicated, the structure of the demethylated adenosylmethionine is not established; it is suggested as adenosylhomocysteine in the figure. Hydrolysis or phosphorolysis of adenosylhomocysteine would provide the homocysteine required for the synthesis of cysteine (p. 531).

More compounds are known to be methylated in the body than are discussed above in connection with betaine and adenosylmethionine. In the case of the examples given, however, the immediate methyl donor has been identified by *in vitro* investigations. In other biological methylations, e.g., noradrenaline (Fig. 101, p. 553) this information is either unavailable or uncertain.

The sources and ultimate disposal of methyl groups are topics which have stimulated much investigation. Preformed methyl groups are available to the organism from the methionine and choline (and betaine) of the diet. The methyl groups of such substances as creatine, N[1]-methylnicotinamide, and adrenaline are not "labile," which is another way of stating that their initial methylations are irreversible. (The only methylation which could be considered reversible, in fact, is that of homocysteine to methionine, but the route involves ATP, as has been seen, and cannot be considered direct.) It is now known that the animal organism has at its disposal metabolic pathways for the synthesis of methyl groups from other 1-carbon units provisionally called "formate" (discussed below), provided certain vitamins are present in the diet. These pathways are sufficiently effective (except, possibly, for a short period after birth) to supply the growing organism with all of the methyl groups it requires on diets devoid of methyl donors, but containing homocysteine, the "essential" portion of methionine.

The ultimate fate of methyl groups is oxidation to CO_2. Formaldehyde and formic acid, or compounds readily interconvertible with them, appear to be the intermediates in this oxidation. The metabolic route probably proceeds through dimethylglycine and sarcosine (Fig. 93, p. 538), since enzyme systems are known which oxidize N-methyl amino acids to the free amino acids and formaldehyde. Formaldehyde is readily oxidized to formic acid, which is in turn rapidly converted to CO_2. Since formaldehyde and formic acid are closely related to the 1-carbon "formate" fragment mentioned in connection with the synthesis of methyl groups, it appears that the anabolic and catabolic pathways of methyl groups may be very similar, if not identical.

Sporadic reference has been made, in this and previous chapters, to a 1-carbon unit, frequently called "formate," "formyl," or simply, "C_1." At the present time, many sources of this fragment are recognized, and its ultimate disposition in various important products is known, but the exact nature of the fragment itself has thus far eluded investigation. The situation is reminiscent of that obtaining in the case of "active acetate" some years ago, before it was discovered that the actual "2-carbon fragment" was not free acetic acid, but acetyl-CoA (p. 454), which was, under certain conditions, interconvertible with free acetate. It is probable that the 1-carbon fragment is similarly attached to a coenzyme, although it may be equilibrated with free formate or formaldehyde in certain instances.

An outline of the donors and acceptors of C_1 fragments is presented in Figure 94. As indicated, C_1 is interconvertible with "labile" methyl groups, the reaction in the direction of C_1 probably being an oxidation of the methyl groups of compounds such as sarcosine (into which all CH_3 groups may be channeled). The reverse reaction must be reductive, but its mechanism and initial products are not known. Apparently, the catabolic pathway of C_1 to CO_2 is completely irreversible, since the carbon of isotopically labeled CO_2 does not find its way into the C_1 "pool."

As indicated in Figure 94, both formaldehyde and formic acid can be converted to C_1. Indeed, it is possible that one or the other of these two compounds *is* C_1, but probably attached to a coenzyme. What the actual state of oxidation of the 1-carbon unit may be is problematical at the moment. Although the fragment is frequently called "formate," several *in vitro* systems have been described in which formaldehyde is utilized in a manner suggesting effective conversion to C_1, whereas formic acid is inert. Of course, it is not beyond the realm of possibility that there are two C_1 fragments, one of the form*yl* and one of the form*al* type.

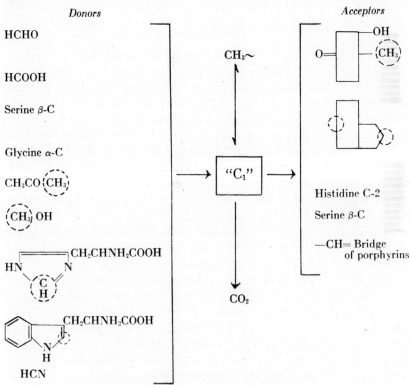

Fig. 94. Donors and acceptors of "C_1" groups

Other sources of C_1 fragments (Fig. 94) are the β-carbon atom of serine (p. 523), the α-carbon atom of glycine (p. 519), one of the methyl groups of acetone (p. 452), and carbon 2 of the imidazole ring of histidine (p. 527). Methanol can also form C_1 fragments, probably via oxidation to formic acid. The production of a formyl group in the course of the catabolism of tryptophan is discussed elsewhere (p. 546). Brief mention of the metabolism of cyanide is made below, in connection with vitamin B_{12}.

As indicated in Figure 94, C_1 fragments are involved in the synthesis of several important products. It is probable that, in the adult human being, the imidazole ring of histidine is synthesized by a mechanism similar (but in reverse) to that involved in its degradation (p. 527), consequently requiring the incorporation of a formyl group. The attachment of such a group to glycine in the conversion of that amino acid to serine has been discussed previously (p. 519). The α-carbon atom of glycine is known to be the source of the methyne bridges $(-CH=)$ of the porphyrin ring (p. 587), although it has not as yet been demonstrated that the C_1 fragment is the intermediate. In the synthesis of pyrimidines and purines, "formate" has been shown to produce the methyl carbon of thymine (p. 571) and carbons 2 and 8 of the purines (p. 567).

Two vitamins have been implicated in the metabolism of C_1 fragments, folic acid (and its derivatives) (p. 200), and vitamin B_{12} (p. 205). It is currently accepted as a working hypothesis in many laboratories that a derivative of folic acid, similar in structure to the folinic acids (p. 201), functions as a coenzyme carrier of formyl groups. Indeed, this as yet imperfectly defined compound has been named "cotransformylase" or "coenzyme F." Much of the evidence supporting this hypothesis is circumstantial, however. It is based partly on the biological activity of natural and synthetic formylated and reduced derivatives of folic acid (folinic acids, p. 201; rhizopterin, p. 203), partly on the very strong evidence that a derivative of folic acid participates in the introduction of the C2 formyl group into the purine skeleton (p. 567), and partly on the dependence of a large number of metabolic processes involving 1-carbon units on a dietary supply of the folic acid group of vitamins. Among these reactions adversely affected by a deficiency of folic acid (frequently produced at this time by the administration of biological antagonists [p. 643]) are: (1) the incorporation of isotopically labeled formic acid into serine, heme, respiratory CO_2, nucleic acid purines, and the methyl group of methionine; (2) conversion of the β-carbon atom of serine and the carbon of methanol to the methyl groups of choline; (3) the synthesis of thymine; (4) the catalysis of the peculiar exchange reaction between formic acid and carbon 2 of the purine skeleton (p. 568). In conjunction with vitamin B_{12}, folic acid is required for the *de novo* synthesis of methyl groups in the animal organism, presumably from C_1 units.

Most of the foregoing evidence supports the role of a folinic-like molecule as a cotransformylase. In one case, however, that of the conversion of the β-carbon atom of serine to the methyl groups of choline, it has been shown conclusively that an intermediate oxidation to the level of formate is not involved. It has been suggested, in explanation of this and certain other problematic cases, that an hydroxymethyl fragment, on the oxidation level of formaldehyde, may also be transferred by "Co-F".

The role of vitamin B_{12} (p. 205) is even less clearly defined. It is required for the *de novo* synthesis of methyl groups, even in the presence of adequate dietary folic acid. Apparently, it is rather specifically involved in the conversion of glycine to serine (p. 519), but not in the further steps from the β-carbon atom of serine to the methyl groups of choline (which appear to require folic acid). Unfortunately, no really consistent and clear picture of the interrelations of vitamin B_{12} and folic acid can be drawn at this time.

Although cyanide can scarcely be recommended for inclusion in the diet, it seems probable that this noxious substance is actually an intermediary metabolite. One of the unusual facts discovered concerning the structure of vitamin B_{12} ("cyanocobalamin") is its constituent cyanide group (p. 206), which appears to be in equilibrium with a small metabolic pool of cyanide. The administration of small amounts of radioactive cyanide to experimental animals results in the appearance of cyanide in the urine and in vitamin B_{12}, and HCN in the expired air. The carbon of the cyanide makes its way into thiocyanate (p. 284), respiratory CO_2, the methyl groups of choline and methionine, and the ureide carbon atom of allantoin (p. 570), which is derived from C2 and C8 of the purines. Obviously, metabolic pathways are available for the conversion of cyanide to "formate" and labile methyl groups. The possible relationship between the cyanide group of vitamin B_{12} and the C_1 fragment discussed previously can be no more than suggested at this time.

LYSINE. In the case of lysine, as with methionine, there is no evidence for net glucogenicity or ketogenicity (Fig. 87, p. 518). Lysine is an essential amino acid for growth and maintenance of nitrogen equilibrium, and is one of the few amino acids which does not participate in the ammonia pool, that is, it can lose its nitrogen to the pool, but cannot be reaminated from it. Lysine is known to undergo only one series of metabolic transformations in the animal organism, terminal oxidation to α-aminoadipic acid, followed by deamination of this product to α-ketoadipic acid, and decarboxylation to glutaric acid:

$$NH_2CH_2CH_2CH_2CH_2CHNH_2COOH \rightarrow HOOCCH_2CH_2CH_2CHNH_2COOH$$

$$HOOCCH_2CH_2CH_2COOH \leftarrow HOOCCH_2CH_2CH_2-\overset{O}{\overset{\|}{C}}-COOH$$

The fate of glutaric acid is not entirely settled. A minor pathway may involve oxidation to α-ketoglutaric acid. However, it is believed that the major catabolic route consists in oxidation to butyric acid, with final disposal of this product by cleavage to acetyl units and merger with the acetyl pool. A minor alternative path is suggested from butyric directly to acetoacetic acid.

Hydroxylysine (p. 49) occurs in a few proteins, e.g., gelatin and wool, but nothing is known of its metabolism.

ISOLEUCINE. This essential amino acid truly can be placed in the "neutral and hybrid" area of Figure 87 (p. 518), for it is both ketogenic and glucogenic in the organism. This unusual behavior is explained by the following sequence of reactions, elucidated largely by isotopic labeling technics:

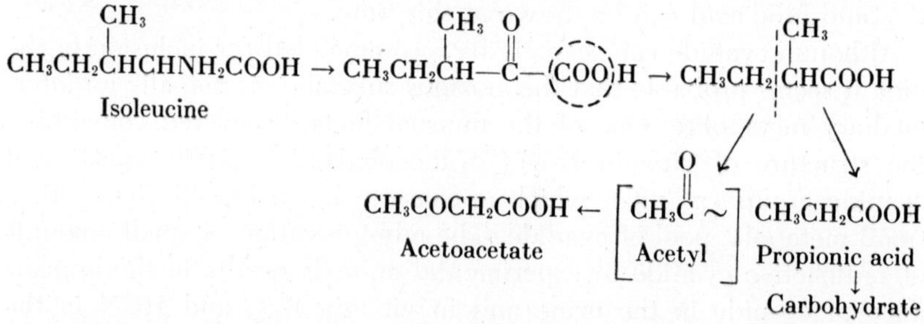

$$CH_3CH_2\overset{\overset{\displaystyle CH_3}{|}}{C}HCHNH_2COOH \rightarrow CH_3CH_2\overset{\overset{\displaystyle CH_3}{|}}{C}H-\overset{\overset{\displaystyle O}{\|}}{C}-(COO)H \rightarrow CH_3CH_2\overset{\overset{\displaystyle CH_3}{|}}{C}HCOOH$$

Isoleucine

$$CH_3COCH_2COOH \leftarrow \left[\overset{\overset{\displaystyle O}{\|}}{CH_3C} \sim \right] \quad CH_3CH_2COOH$$

Acetoacetate   Acetyl   Propionic acid
                                      ↓
                                      Carbohydrate

As indicated elsewhere (p. 453), the nature of the pathway from propionic acid to carbohydrate is somewhat uncertain, as it does not appear to proceed directly through pyruvic acid.

LEUCINE. The metabolism of this essential amino acid is similar to that of isoleucine, in that it involves deamination, decarboxylation, and cleavage, but owing to the nature of the resulting fragments, leucine is completely ketogenic. One unusual feature is the apparent assimilation of a molecule of CO_2 by an isopropyl fragment to produce acetoacetate.

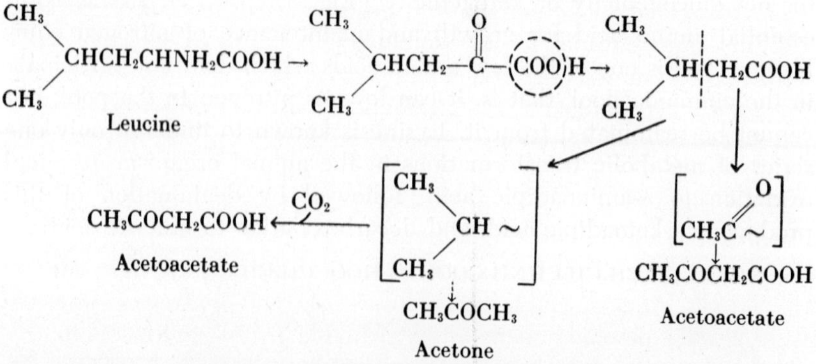

$$\begin{array}{c} CH_3 \\ \diagdown \\ CH_3 \diagup \end{array} CHCH_2CHNH_2COOH \rightarrow \begin{array}{c} CH_3 \\ \diagdown \\ CH_3 \diagup \end{array} CHCH_2-\overset{\overset{\displaystyle O}{\|}}{C}-(COO)H \rightarrow \begin{array}{c} CH_3 \\ \diagdown \\ CH_3 \diagup \end{array} CHCH_2COOH$$

Leucine

$$CH_3COCH_2COOH \overset{CO_2}{\longleftarrow} \left[\begin{array}{c} CH_3 \\ \diagdown \\ CH \sim \\ \diagup \\ CH_3 \end{array} \right] \qquad \left[CH_3\overset{\overset{\displaystyle O}{\diagup}}{C} \sim \right]$$

Acetoacetate CH_3COCH_2COOH
                    CH_3COCH_3 Acetoacetate
                    Acetone

The isopropyl fragment may form acetone directly to some extent.

TRYPTOPHAN. (Fig. 95) This essential amino acid is neither glucogenic nor ketogenic in the intact organism (Fig. 87, p. 518), although it appears to produce alanine in an *in vitro* reaction (shown below

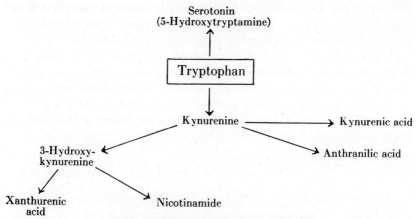

Fig. 95. *Pathways of tryptophan metabolism*

in Fig. 97). Since only small quantities of tryptophan are metabolized daily (p. 494), it is possible that the rate of formation of alanine is insufficient to influence the usual tests for glucogenicity.

Tryptophan is the probable precursor of "serotonin," a vasoconstrictor found in serum. Serotonin recently has been shown to be identical with "enteramine," isolated from chromaffin tissue of vertebrates and invertebrates, and to have the structure, 5-hydroxytryptamine:

$$HO-\text{⬡⬠}-CH_2CH_2NH_2$$

A number of compounds excreted in the urine are also derived from tryptophan (p. 282).

The major metabolic pathway of tryptophan is shown in Figure 96. It is not only unusual in its complexity, but also in its chief end-product, the vitamin nicotinamide (p. 182). For convenience in the discussion, this ramified series of reactions will be subdivided.

1. *Formation of kynurenine (Reactions 1–3, Fig. 96).* Tryptophan is initially acted upon by a peroxidase system (p. 368) to form an oxidized derivative of unknown structure. (There is evidence against 2-hydroxytryptophan as this intermediate.) The intermediate compound is then oxidized by an aerobic dehydrogenase, which splits the heterocyclic ring to yield formylkynurenine and hydrogen peroxide (p. 358), the peroxide then being available for participation in the previous reaction. The tryptophan peroxidase system is adaptive in mammals (p. 255), responding with an increase in activity within a few hours of the administration of substrate. Apparently the activity is also enhanced as a result of the "alarm reaction" (p. 671). Formylkynurenine is hydrolyzed by "formylase" to kynurenine and formic

acid (p. 540). Kynurenine is excreted in the urine of animals follow-ing administration of test doses of tryptophan and, with other trypto-phan metabolites, in pyridoxine deficiency (see below).

2. *Formation of 3-hydroxykynurenine (Reaction 8, Fig. 96).* One of the major metabolic reactions in the tryptophan series is the oxida-tion of kynurenine to 3-hydroxykynurenine. Although the mechanism of the reaction has not been studied in detail, riboflavin (p. 177) is known to be involved, probably as part of a coenzyme of the FMN or FAD type (p. 360).

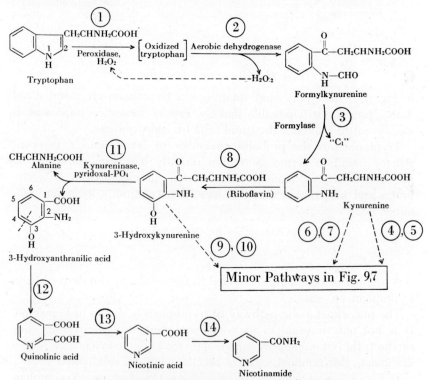

Fig. 96. *Conversion of tryptophan to nicotinamide*

3. *Formation of nicotinic acid and derivatives (Reactions 11–14, Fig. 96).* The major role of the enzyme, kynureninase, is the catalysis of the cleavage of 3-hydroxykynurenine into alanine and 3-hydroxy-anthranilic acid, pyridoxal phosphate being the cofactor. This reaction is analogous to the minor reaction, No. 6 (Fig. 97). 3-Hydroxy-anthranilic acid is oxidized and rearranged, via unknown intermedi-ates, to quinolinic acid. The reactions appear to involve scission of the benzene ring between carbons 3 and 4 (3,4-dihydroxyanthranilic acid is not the intermediate), rotation in space of the amino group and carbon 3, with carbon 2 acting as a "swivel," and subsequent incorporation of the former amino nitrogen atom into the ring by

condensation with carbon 4. The former carbon 3 of the ring consequently forms one of the carboxyl groups of quinolinic acid, enzymatic decarboxylation of which produces nicotinic acid, which is easily converted into its functional form, nicotinamide. The further metabolism of nicotinic acid and amide is discussed in connection with the vitamins (p. 182).

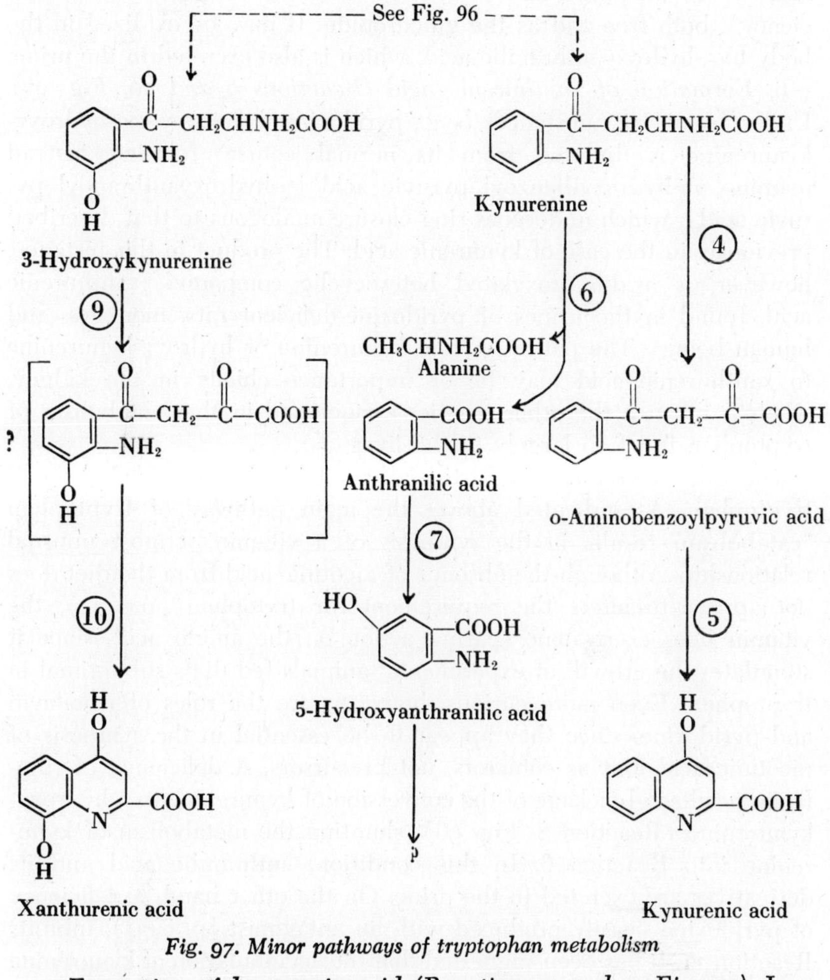

Fig. 97. *Minor pathways of tryptophan metabolism*

4. *Formation of kynurenic acid (Reactions 4 and 5, Fig. 97).* In a reaction which normally is of minor importance, kynurenine is deaminated (by means of transamination) to o-aminobenzoylpyruvic acid (anthranoylpyruvic acid), which then undergoes cyclization between the α-keto group on the side-chain and the amino group on the ring, forming kynurenic acid. Kynurenic acid is found in the urine of several species of mammals (it may not be produced in all species) as the result of incomplete metabolism of tryptophan; it is not metabolized further.

5. *Formation of anthranilic acid (Reactions 6 and 7, Fig. 97).* In a second minor reaction, kynurenine is hydrolyzed at a point between the aroyl group and the alanine moiety of the side-chain, yielding alanine and anthranilic acid. This hydrolysis is catalyzed by kynureninase, the major role of which has been discussed. Pyridoxal phosphate (p. 190) is the coenzyme of this reaction. Anthranilic acid is excreted in the urine under certain conditions (e.g., riboflavin deficiency), both free and as the glucuronide. It may be oxidized in the body to 5-hydroxyanthranilic acid, which is also excreted in the urine.

6. *Formation of xanthurenic acid (Reactions 9 and 10, Fig. 97).* Under certain circumstances (e.g., pyridoxine deficiency), 3-hydroxy-kynurenine is diverted from its normal course, forming instead o-amino, m-hydroxy-benzoyl pyruvic acid (3-hydroxyanthranoyl pyruvic acid), which undergoes ring closure analogous to that described previously in the case of kynurenic acid. The product in this instance, however, is a dihydroxylated heterocyclic compound, xanthurenic acid, found in the urines of pyridoxine-deficient rats, monkeys, and human beings. The pathway from kynurenine or hydroxy-kynurenine to xanthurenic acid may be of importance chiefly in the kidney, whereas most of the other reactions concerned in the metabolism of tryptophan function largely in the liver.

The role of vitamins is particularly notable in the metabolism of tryptophan. As indicated above, the main pathway of tryptophan "catabolism" results in the synthesis of a vitamin, a most unusual relationship. Although the absence of nicotinic acid from the diet does not appear to affect the requirement for trytophan (p. 494), the vitamin does exert some sparing action on the amino acid, since it stimulates the growth of experimental animals fed diets suboptimal in tryptophan. Even more curious, however, are the roles of riboflavin and pyridoxine, since they appear to be essential in the synthesis of nicotinic acid, but as cofactors, not precursors. A deficiency of riboflavin results in blockage of the conversion of kynurenine to 3-hydroxy-kynurenine (Reaction 8, Fig. 96), shunting the metabolism of kynurenine into Reaction 6. In this condition, anthranilic acid and its derivatives are excreted in the urine. On the other hand, a deficiency of pyridoxine (easily produced with an antagonist [p. 643]), inhibits Reaction 11. It has been suggested that the accumulation of kynurenine and 3-hydroxykynurenine (produced largely in the liver) in pyridoxine deficiency may result in the transport of sufficient quantities of the compounds through the blood to the kidney, where appreciable amounts of xanthurenic acid may be formed.

In addition to the reactions which have been described, others, as yet unknown, result in the removal of the nitrogen of the tryptophan ring (probably in the kidney) and its eventual incorporation into urinary ammonia, the ammonia pool, and urea.

Although no extended discussion of comparative biochemistry will be attempted, a few data of general interest may be mentioned at this point. 3-Hydroxykynurenine is the precursor of an eye pigment of Drosophila, the fruit-fly; much work in biochemical genetics has been done in connection with this pigmentation. In certain bacteria, an enzyme system (tryptophanase) catalyzes the cleavage of tryptophan into indole, pyruvic acid, and ammonia. Pyridoxal phosphate is the coenzyme. Tryptophan can be synthesized in microorganisms from indole and serine, pyridoxal phosphate again being the coenzyme. These reactions of indole with 3-carbon units are probably analogous to the kynureninase reaction (Reactions 6 and 11, Fig. 96 and 97), in which the same coenzyme is involved.

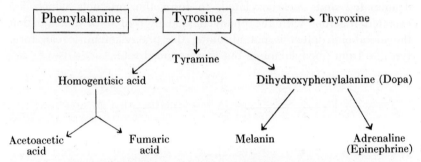

Fig. 98. Metabolic pathways of phenylalanine and tyrosine

AROMATIC AMINO ACIDS (FIG. 98). The metabolism of phenylanine and tyrosine is even more complicated than that of tryptophan. Phenylalanine itself undergoes few reactions unrelated to tyrosine metabolism (Reactions 1–3, Fig. 99). It may be deaminated (probably by transamination) to phenylpyruvic acid, which may be reduced to phenyllactic acid. Although traces of phenylpyruvic acid may be decarboxylated to phenylacetic acid (conjugated to glutamine and excreted in the urine of human beings and apes, p. 284), both phenyllactic and phenylpyruvic acids are largely reconverted to phenylalanine for further catabolism.

The relationship between phenylalanine and tyrosine is of considerable interest. Phenylalanine is an essential amino acid, whereas tyrosine is not. The conversion of phenylalanine to tyrosine (Reaction 4) is irreversible, so that tyrosine cannot wholly replace phenylalanine in the diet. However, since most of the functions of phenylalanine in the body (except that of incorporation into proteins as phenylalanine) are performed subsequent to its conversion to tyrosine, it is not surprising that tyrosine is capable of sparing approximately one-half the daily requirement of phenylalanine for growth.

The conversion of phenylalanine to tyrosine (Reaction 4, Fig. 99) is catalyzed by an anaerobic dehydrogenase found in the liver. DPN is probably the coenzyme, although TPN is somewhat active also. The enzyme exhibits decreased activity in an inborn error of metabolism known variously as phenylpyruvic oligophrenia, imbecillitas phenylpyruvica, or simply phenylketonuria. The metabolic defect is coupled, in some unknown fashion, with mental deficiency. It is characterized by the excretion in the urine of phenylalanine and phenylpyruvic, phenyllactic, and phenylacetic (as its glutamine conjugate) acids. (Phenylpyruvic acid usually predominates.) The diminished ability of the liver to hydroxylate phenylalanine results in the appearance of significant quantities of this amino acid in the blood. In the kidney, the excess phenylalanine is deaminated, deaminated and reduced, or deaminated and decarboxylated, to form the products which are excreted together with the phenylalanine. Recent data indicate that the metabolic defect is not absolute; the phenylketonuric can form tyrosine from phenylalanine, but at a reduced rate.

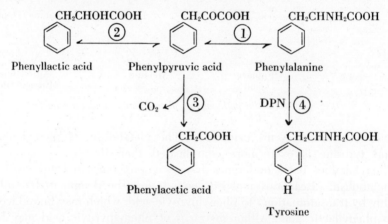

Fig. 99. Phenylalanine metabolism

The remainder of the metabolic pathways of the aromatic amino acids may be considered solely as various aspects of the metabolism of tyrosine. The material subdivides naturally into the separate metabolic routes discussed in the following sections.

(a) PATHWAY TO ACETOACETIC AND FUMARIC ACIDS (REACTIONS 5–11, FIG. 100). The route from tyrosine to acetoacetate and fumarate is normally the most important from a quantitative point of view, accounting for most of the several grams of phenylalanine and tyrosine catabolized per day. It also accounts for the classification of these amino acids as both ketogenic and glucogenic.

Tyrosine is converted reversibly into *p*-hydroxyphenylpyruvic acid by transamination with α-ketoglutaric acid (p. 510). To a minor extent,

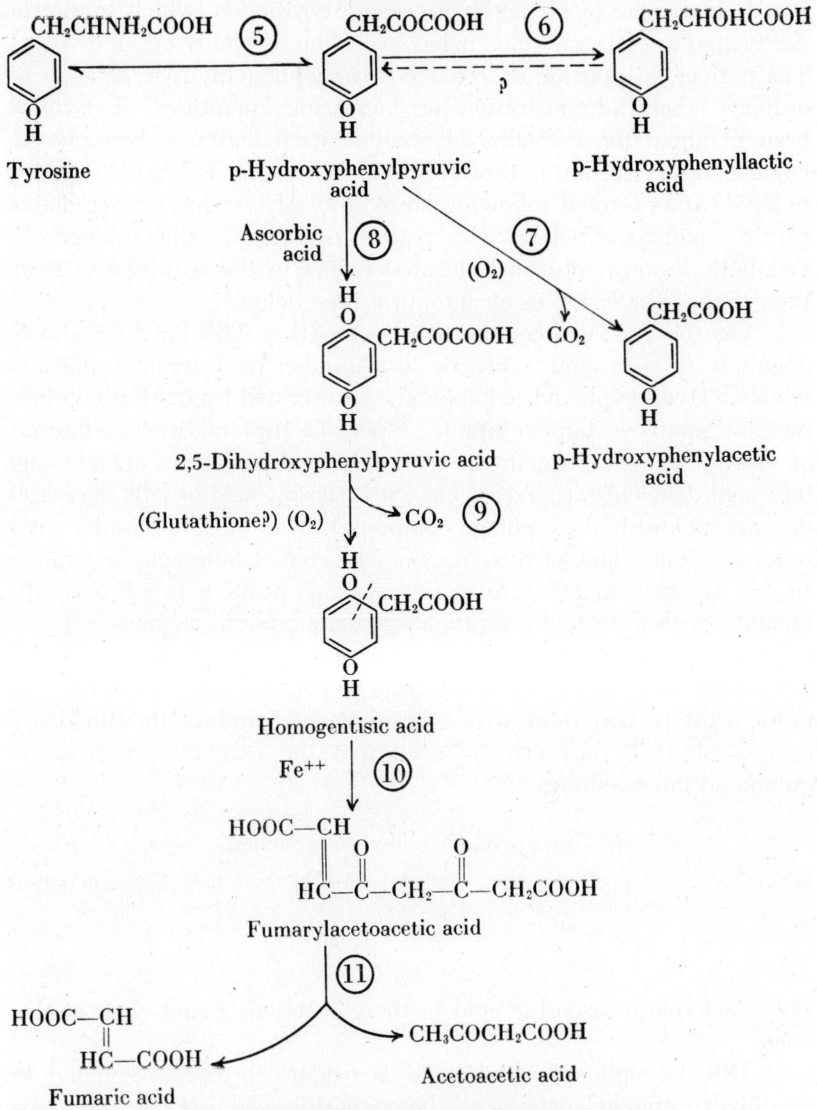

Fig 100. *Major pathways of catabolism of tyrosine*

p-hydroxyphenylpyruvic acid may be reduced to p-hydroxyphenyllactic acid or decarboxylated to p-hydroxyphenylacetic acid, neither of which is believed to be metabolized further.

The major pathway of catabolism of p-hydroxyphenylpyruvic acid involves, first, its transformation to 2,5-dihydroxyphenylpyruvic acid (Reaction 8, Fig. 100). This conversion is of considerable interest from several standpoints:

1. It is the site of a "metabolic error," tyrosinosis, which cannot be designated as "inborn" since it has been found in only one individual. The patient in question excreted *p*-hydroxyphenylpyruvic acid on an ordinary diet; administration of increasing quantities of tyrosine brought about the excretion of tyrosine itself and *p*-hydroxyphenyl-lactic acid, in addition to the keto acid. (Dopa [see below] is reported to have been excreted following large doses of tyrosine.) Since homo-gentisic acid (see below) was readily oxidized in this subject, the metabolic lesion is obviously located earlier in the sequence of reactions than is the lesion in alcaptonuria (see below).

2. Ascorbic acid is a cofactor for the reaction. This has been shown definitely *in vitro,* and indirectly in a number of different conditions *in vivo.* "Hydroxyphenyl" compounds are excreted by scorbutic guinea pigs and monkeys, human infants (especially if premature) and adults on scorbutogenic diets, patients with untreated pernicious anemia, and folic acid-deficient rats. Treatment with ascorbic acid usually decreases the excretion of hydroxyphenyl compounds in those subjects obviously suffering from a lack of this vitamin. The role of folic acid or vitamin B_{12} in tyrosine metabolism is less certain; positive *in vitro* results obtained with folic acid are probably attributable to artifacts.

3. The mechanism of the reaction is quite unusual, apparently involving the shift of the side-chain from its original position on the ring to the ortho carbon atom, with an oxidation to produce the dihydroxy compound. It is currently believed that the reaction proceeds via quinonoid intermediates:

The exact role of ascorbic acid in these reactions is not clear at this time.

2,5-Dihydroxyphenylpyruvic acid is oxidatively decarboxylated to 2,5-dihydroxyphenylacetic acid (homogentisic acid). It has been suggested recently that glutathione plays a role in this reaction, possibly analogous to that played by CoA or lipoic acid in the oxidative decarboxylation of pyruvic acid (p. 397).

The further degradation of homogentisic acid is blocked in the inborn error of metabolism, "alcaptonuria." Frequently this anomaly is discovered in infancy, since the homogentisic acid which is excreted is readily oxidized to black products in the air, especially if the urine undergoes ammoniacal fermentation on standing and becomes alkaline. Although several grams of homogentisic acid may be excreted per day, no harmful effects result directly from this condition. In later life, an accumulation of dark pigment in the cartilage (ochronosis) has been reported to accompany arthritic changes in the joints.

Homogentisic acid also has been reported to be excreted in the urine of scorbutic guinea pigs, but this finding has not been consistent. A most interesting phenomenon is the excretion of homogentisic acid by guinea pigs deprived of ferrous iron through the administration of α,α-dipyridyl (which forms a stable, red complex with Fe^{++}). Ferrous iron is indeed one of the cofactors in the reactions whereby homogentisic acid is converted to open-chain compounds. Ascorbic acid also has been implicated in these reactions, although its role may be merely that of a reducing agent, preserving the ferrous form of the iron. Whatever the cofactors or intermediates may be, homogentisic acid is known to be oxidized to fumarylacetoacetic acid, which is in turn hydrolyzed to fumaric and acetoacetic acids (Reactions 10 and 11, Fig. 100).

Under most test conditions, tyrosine and phenylalanine appear to be ketogenic (acetoacetate in Reaction 11); under certain circumstances, however, they are glucogenic (fumaric acid in Reaction 11). The underlying factors favoring one or the other of these results are unknown.

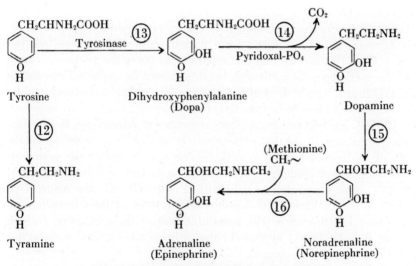

Fig. 101. *Synthesis of adrenaline and tyramine*

(*b*) DECARBOXYLATION (REACTION 12, FIG. 101, ABOVE). To a very minor extent, tyrosine may be decarboxylated to tyramine in the kidney. This reaction was considered formerly to be a step in the synthesis of adrenaline (epinephrine). It is now regarded as too slow to be of any importance.

(*c*) PATHWAY TO ADRENALINE (REACTIONS 13–16, FIG. 101, ABOVE).

In the initial step of this series, tyrosine is oxidized by tyrosinase (p. 362) to 3,4-dihydroxyphenylalanine ("dopa"), an intermediate common to the synthesis of both adrenaline and melanin. The mechanism of the tyrosinase reaction is quite complex. Tyrosinase of both plants and animals contains copper, which is believed by some to undergo changes in valence during the reaction. Tyrosinase does not act on pure tyrosine; curiously enough, traces of the reaction product, dopa, are required to initiate the oxidation. It has been postulated that dopa and its oxidation product, dopa quinone (discussed below in connection with melanin), act catalytically along with the tyrosinase to oxidize tyrosine to dopa. In animals, tyrosinase occurs in the skin and liver, and in melanomas.

The exact nature of the steps from dopa to adrenaline is not agreed upon. The reactions presented in this section are those which seem most probable at this time, and are to be regarded as tentative. An active decarboxylating enzyme for dopa (Reaction 14) is found in several tissues, but is particularly active in the kidney. Pyridoxal phosphate is the coenzyme. Hydroxytyramine, or "dopamine," is the product of the reaction.

The next probable step is the oxidation of the proximal carbon atom in the side-chain of dopamine to yield noradrenaline (norepinephrine). No information is available concerning this reaction. Noradrenaline, however, is a normal constituent of the adrenal medulla (p. 670).

Adrenaline is synthesized from noradrenaline by transmethylation (p. 536) in the adrenal medulla, methionine being the probable source of the methyl group (although betaine cannot be excluded absolutely at this time). The biological functions of adrenaline and noradrenaline are discussed elsewhere (pp. 671, 672).

Little is known concerning the catabolism of adrenaline. Recent isotopic studies indicate that approximately half of the adrenaline catabolized undergoes loss of a methylamine moiety under the action of the "monoamine oxidase" (p. 362). The methylamine is partly oxidized to CO_2, partly excreted as unidentified metabolites in the urine. Two or three metabolites of the demethylated residue of the adrenaline are also found in the urine. The remaining half of the adrenaline (which is not demethylated) appears in the urine as unidentified metabolites still bearing methyl groups.

(d) PATHWAY TO MELANIN (REACTION 13, FIG. 101, P. 553, AND 17–22, FIG. 102, P. 555). Melanin may be defined as a brown to black pigment, resulting from the polymerization of oxidation products of dopa. Its formation is apparently the result of the action of a single enzyme, tyrosinase, functioning in a specialized cell, the melanocyte (formerly, melanoblast), located in the skin and eyes of mammals. Melanin functions in mammals as a protection against ultraviolet rays.

In albinism, an inborn error of metabolism, melanin pigmentation is absent, owing to an hereditary lack of tyrosinase in the melanocytes.

It is not certain exactly how many of the steps in the synthesis of melanin are catalyzed by tyrosinase and how many are spontaneous. Most of the quinonoid intermediates are capable of reacting non-enzymatically with the polyphenolic intermediates, resulting in reduction of the former and oxidation of the latter. Consequently, the entire sequence of reactions appears to be capable of autocatalysis of a most complex type.

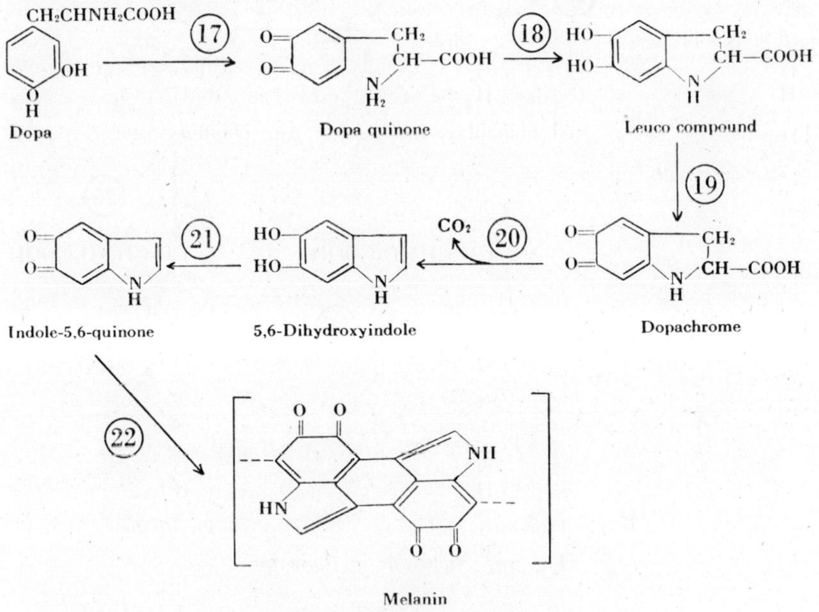

Fig. 102. Synthesis of melanin

The role of copper and of the dopa-dopa quinone system in the oxidation of tyrosine by tyrosinase (Reaction 13) has been discussed previously (p. 554). Ignoring for the sake of simplicity the autocatalytic features of the reaction, tyrosinase may be regarded as oxidizing tyrosine to dopa (Reaction 13) and dopa to dopa quinone (Reaction 17). Dopa quinone undergoes cyclization to a reduced indole derivative ("leuco compound"), which is then oxidized to the red pigment, "dopachrome" (formerly called "hallachrome," because it was erroneously believed to have the same structure as a red pigment from the annelid, *Halla*). Dopachrome is spontaneously decarboxylated to 5,6-dihydroxyindole, which is oxidized to its corresponding quinone. Polymerization of indole-5,6-quinone produces melanin, a tentative structure for which is shown in Figure 102. Owing to its quinone groups, melanin can exist in both oxidized (black) and reduced (brown) forms. As found in nature, melanin is combined with proteins (probably by interaction between the quinone groups of the melanin and sulfhydryl groups of the proteins), forming "melanoproteins."

The activity of melanocytes in the lower vertebrates is under the control of "intermedin," a hormone from the intermediate lobe of the pituitary (p. 703). It has been suggested, but not proved, that a similar control obtains in human beings.

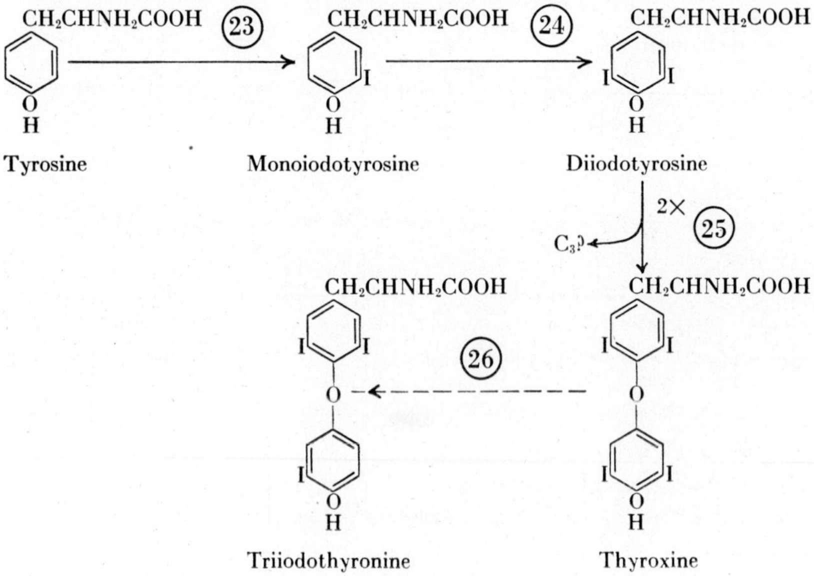

Fig. 103. Synthesis of thyroxine

(*e*) PATHWAY TO THYROXINE (REACTIONS 23–26, FIG. 103, ABOVE). Inasmuch as the synthesis of thyroxine is discussed in considerable detail elsewhere (p. 681), with particular attention being given to the reactions of iodine and to regulatory and inhibitory factors, this discussion will be confined to a brief outline of the changes undergone in the organic molecule.

Tyrosine is iodinated in the thyroid gland, probably by hypoiodite (HIO), successively to monoiodo- and diiodotyrosine. Two molecules of diiodotyrosine are then coupled, with the loss of one alanine side-chain, to form a molecule of thyroxine (tetraiodothyronine). The mechanism of Reaction 25 is not known; it has been suggested that quinonoid intermediates are involved in a reaction analogous to that occurring in the shift of the side-chain of *p*-hydroxyphenylpyruvic acid to form 2,5-dihydroxyphenylpyruvic acid (p. 552):

CH₂CHNH₂COOH   (H)   CH₂CHNH₂COOH   CH₂CHNH₂COOH

$$\text{CH}_2\text{CHNH}_2\text{COOH} \quad \xrightarrow{\quad} \quad -2H \quad (\text{H})$$

CH₂CHNH₂COOH

CH₂CHNH₂COOH   [CH₃CHNH₂COOH]   (CH₂CHNH₂COOH)

The nature of the 3-carbon fragment which is ejected is not known.

Some evidence has been presented recently that thyroxine may be deiodinated in the target tissues (Reaction 26) to form triiodothyronine, purported to be the "active" form of the hormone. The problem is not completely settled at this time.

Little is known of the catabolism of thyroxine. It is apparently converted by the liver into a conjugate which is acted upon further by intestinal bacteria after biliary excretion. Thyroxine itself constitutes only a minor fraction of the total thyroxine-related metabolites excreted in feces and urine, the feces being the major avenue of excretion.

INTERRELATIONS OF THE METABOLISM OF PROTEINS AND OTHER FOODSTUFFS

The major interrelations between proteins, fats, and carbohydrates are outlined in Figure 104. The importance of proteins in the metabolism of all types of compounds, inasmuch as enzymes and many hormones are proteins (or amino acid derivatives) in nature, is too obvious to require elaboration. Synthesis of specialized products, such as purines, pyrimidines, and porphyrins, is likewise an important function of proteins and amino acids, as has been discussed previously. The subject of interest in this section is the relationship between the metabolism of proteins and that of the two other major foodstuffs, as exemplified by direct interconversion and by caloric substitution.

The ketogenic amino acids and certain fragments derived from the metabolism of non-ketogenic amino acids form acetate or acetoacetate, thus contributing directly to the synthesis of fatty acids. The glucogenic amino acids can function similarly, but subsequent to initial conversions to pyruvate or ketoacids yielding pyruvate. Certain specialized lipid moieties are also derived from amino acids, viz., serine, ethanolamine, and choline. The pathway from the carbon skeletons of the ketogenic or glucogenic amino acids to the fatty acids is irreversible.

The majority of amino acids can form carbohydrate. In certain cases, viz., alanine, aspartate, and glutamate, the conversion to precursors of carbohydrate is direct; in others the pathway may be quite devious. The conversion is reversible for most of the non-essential, glucogenic amino acids. It must be emphasized in connection with glucogenicity that the α-keto acids produced from the amino acids (pyruvate, oxalacetate, α-ketoglutarate) function not only as raw materials for the synthesis of glucose, but also as catalysts in the channeling of acetyl units from all classes of foodstuffs through the tricarboxylic acid cycle (α-ketoglutarate and pyruvate being easily converted to oxalacetate, the actual catalytic compound of the cycle) for the provision of energy.

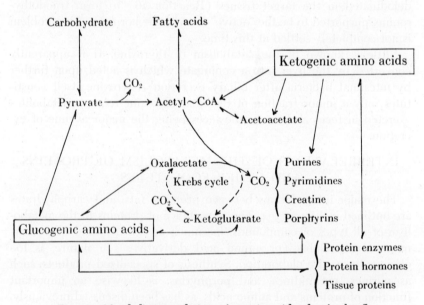

Fig. 104. *Metabolic interrelations of proteins with other foodstuffs*

The energy content of the diet influences protein metabolism, as reflected in the nitrogen balance. Nitrogen excretion is increased when the caloric intake is lowered to sub-maintenance levels. Conversely, increasing the caloric intake causes a decrease in urinary N excretion. At any given adequate level of dietary protein, the nitrogen balance is determined, in part at least, by the caloric intake. This relationship can be demonstrated in another manner. When the caloric intake is adequate, increasing the dietary protein from sub-maintenance levels leads to improvement in N balance. However, if the energy intake is below about 25 per cent of that required, this response to an increased protein intake is not obtained. Under these restricted conditions, the caloric intake is apparently a limiting factor in the utilization of dietary proteins.

On diets grossly inadequate in caloric value, nitrogen equilibrium may still be maintained, especially in obese subjects and if adequate amounts of protein and a small amount of carbohydrate are provided. During the initial days of such a regimen (or of a fast), the N excretion is lower than on subsequent days, owing to utilization of glycogen stores. Later, body fat is utilized for energy, exerting the beneficial effect on N balance indicated above for dietary fat.

These effects of the energy content of the diet are apparently largely independent of the nature of the energy-providing materials, being essentially identical, except temporarily (see below), with equicaloric amounts of carbohydrate, fat, or alcohol. They are not influenced by the time of feeding of the latter in relation to that of the protein. The mechanism of production of these effects is not known.

Dietary carbohydrate exerts an influence on protein metabolism not shared by other substances. This is independent of its caloric effect, which is shared equally by fat and alcohol; it is referred to as the specific "protein-sparing" action of carbohydrate. It manifests itself in several ways:

1. Isocaloric substitution of fat for carbohydrate in the diet is followed by an increase in nitrogen excretion. This is of relatively brief duration, however, the original level of N balance being restored after several days. This effect is observed whether or not the energy and protein contents of the diet are adequate.

2. If the protein and carbohydrate components of an adequate diet are ingested separately, at wide time intervals, there is a transitory increase in N excretion. No such effect is exhibited by fat.

3. On an exclusively fat diet, the nitrogen output is the same as during starvation, whereas administration of carbohydrate reduces the nitrogen output.

The mechanism underlying this phenomenon is not known for certain. It is apparently not mediated by hormonal influences (pituitary, thyroid, insulin) nor by improved synthesis of amino acids or of protein. It is probably a reflection of the fact that carbohydrate, in addition to its function as a fuel, also provides the major source of oxalacetate for the tricarboxylic acid cycle and the carbon skeletons of non-essential amino acids. In the absence of carbohydrate, protein is called upon specifically to assume these functions, since fat cannot. The increased degradation of protein and loss of nitrogen are necessarily greater than would occur if fat were omitted from the diet instead of carbohydrate.

BIBLIOGRAPHY

General

Annual Review of Biochemistry.
Annual Review of Physiology.
Bach, S. J.: The Metabolism of Protein Constituents in the Mammalian Body, London, Oxford University Press, 1952.
Baldwin, E.: Dynamic Aspects of Biochemistry, London, Cambridge University Press, 1952, Chapters 10–12.
Meister, A.: Amino acids. In Biochemistry and Physiology of Nutrition, Volume 1, edited by G. F. Bourne and G. W. Kidder, New York, Academic Press, Inc., 1953, Chapter 5.
Peters, J. P. and Van Slyke, D. D.: Quantitative Clinical Chemistry, Volume 1, Baltimore, Williams & Wilkins Company, 1946, Chapters 8–12.
Pollack, H. and Halpern, S. L.: The relation of protein metabolism to disease, Advances in Protein Chemistry 6:383, 1951.
Sahyun, M. (ed.): Outline of the Amino Acids and Proteins, New York, Reinhold Publishing Corporation, 1944, Chapters 7–12.
Sahyun, M. (ed.): Proteins and Amino Acids in Nutrition, New York, Reinhold Publishing Corporation, 1948.
Schoenheimer, R.: The Dynamic State of Body Constituents, Cambridge, Harvard University Press, 1946.
Tarver, H.: The metabolism of amino acids and proteins. In Amino Acids and Proteins, edited by D. M. Greenberg, Springfield, Ill., Charles C Thomas, Publisher, 1951, Chapter 13.

General Reactions of Amino Acids and Proteins

Borsook, H. and Deasy, C. L.: The biosynthesis of proteins. In Biochemistry and Physiology of Nutrition, Volume 1, edited by G. F. Bourne and G. W. Kidder, New York, Academic Press, Inc., 1953, Chapter 6.
Cohen, P. P.: Transaminases. In The Enzymes, Volume 1, edited by J. B. Sumner and K. Myrbäck, New York, Academic Press, Inc., 1951, Chapter 32.
Cohen, P. P.: Peptide bond synthesis. In The Enzymes, Volume 2, edited by J. B. Sumner and K. Myrbäck, New York, Academic Press, Inc., 1952, Chapter 68.
Cohen, P. P.: Enzymatic synthesis of glutamine. In The Enzymes, Volume 2, edited by J. B. Sumner and K. Myrbäck, New York, Academic Press, Inc., 1952, Chapter 69.
Krebs, H. A.: Oxidation of amino acids. In The Enzymes, Volume 2, edited by J. B. Sumner and K. Myrbäck, New York, Academic Press, Inc., 1952, Chapter 58.
Krebs, H. A. Urea synthesis. In The Enzymes, Volume 2, edited by J. B. Sumner and K. Myrbäck, New York, Academic Press, Inc., 1952, Chapter 67.

Plasma Proteins

Edsall, J. T.: The plasma proteins and their fractionation, Advances in Protein Chemistry 3:383, 1947.
Gutman, A. B.: The plasma proteins in disease, Advances in Protein Chemistry 4:155, 1948.
Tullis, J. L. (ed.): Blood Cells and Plasma Proteins, New York, Academic Press, Inc., 1953.
Youmans, J. B. (ed.): Symposia on Nutrition, Volume II: Plasma Proteins, Springfield, Ill., Charles C Thomas, Publisher, 1950.

Special Topics

du Vigneaud, V.: A Trail of Research in Sulfur Chemistry and Metabolism, Ithaca, N. Y., Cornell University Press, 1952.

Fromageot, C.: Oxidation of organic sulfur in animals, Advances in Enzymology 7: 369, 1947.

Krehl, W. A.: "Niacin in amino acid metabolism, Vitamins & Hormones 7:111, 1949.

Lerner, A. B.: Metabolism of phenylalanine and tyrosine, Advances in Enzymology 14:73, 1953.

McElroy, W. D., and Glass, B. (eds.): Phosphorus Metabolism, Volume 2, Baltimore, Johns Hopkins Press, 1952, Part II.

Sourkes, T. L.: Transmethylases. In The Enzymes, Volume 1, edited by J. B. Sumner and K. Myrbäck, New York, Academic Press, Inc., 1951, Chapter 33.

Hormonal Influences

Engel, F. L.: A consideration of the roles of the adrenal cortex and stress in the regulation of protein metabolism, Recent Progress in Hormone Research 6:277, 1951.

Kochakian, C. D.: The protein anabolic effects of steroid hormones, Vitamins & Hormones 4:256, 1946.

Mote, J. R. (ed.): Clinical ACTH Conferences, Philadelphia, Blakiston Company, 1950, 1951.

Sprague, R. G., Mason, H. L. and Power, M. H.: Physiologic effects of cortisone and ACTH in man, Recent Progress in Hormone Research 6:315, 1951.

20

METABOLISM OF NUCLEIC ACIDS AND
RELATED SUBSTANCES

The importance of the nucleic acids and their derivatives is of quite a different sort from that ascribed to the other classes of metabolites. It is doubtful whether significant quantities of energy are derived from the catabolism of nucleic acids, neither they nor their constituents are dietary essentials, and their only "structural" role appears to be in the composition of the chromosome. Rather, the chief role of nucleic acids and related compounds appears to be that of metabolic specialists, involved (1) in the control of the general pattern of metabolism and (2) in aiding the catalysis of certain particular reactions. The former category includes the genes, bacterial "transforming factors," viruses, embryological "evocators," and probably the cytoplasmic regulators of protein synthesis; in the latter are the adenylic system and the free nucleotides which act as coenzymes.

In the strict sense, the discussion of the compounds considered in this chapter should include the nucleoproteins, since the nucleic acids are nothing more than prosthetic groups. However, although a little is known of the identity and characteristics of a few of the nucleoproteins native to the cell (p. 95 ff.), no information is available on the metabolism of these molecules. In the absence of such data, it will be assumed that the protein components of the nucleoproteins follow the general pathways of protein metabolism, and that mechanisms are available to control the coupling and uncoupling of these proteins with their prosthetic groups.

The nucleic acids, it will be recalled, are high polymers of strongly acidic character (p. 97 ff.). Their monomeric components are the mononucleotides, consisting of base, sugar, and phosphoric acid. Two series of bases are involved, purines and pyrimidines, and two pentose sugars, ribose and desoxyribose. Consequently, it will be necessary to consider the metabolism of these individual building-blocks of the nucleic acids, as well as that of the macromolecules themselves.

In addition to the usual summary of the digestion and absorption of the nucleic acids, brief mention will be made of their intracellular localization, a topic of considerable relevance from the standpoints of their intermediary metabolism and metabolic role. Then, in order to provide a background for the more specific discussions to follow, a general survey is presented of the over-all metabolism of the nucleic acids and their constituents. This is followed by detailed discussions of the intermediary metabolism of the several constituents of the nucleic acids, i.e., pentoses, purines, and pyrimidines. Consideration of the metabolism of the macromolecules themselves (ribonucleic acid, RNA; desoxyribonucleic acid, DNA) is preceded by a section devoted to a discussion of the synthesis and degradation of the "free" nucleotides (adenylic system and nucleotide coenzymes). Following a discussion of the biological significance of the nucleic acids and related compounds, the chapter concludes with a brief consideration of interrelations between the metabolism of nucleic acids and that of other classes of foodstuffs.

DIGESTION AND ABSORPTION

The course of digestion of nucleoproteins is discussed elsewhere (pp. 264–270) and requires only brief review here. Their protein components undergo the same changes as those described for other proteins, in the progress of which the constituent nucleic acids (RNA and DNA) are liberated. These are hydrolyzed by the enzymes, ribonuclease and desoxyribonuclease, respectively (nucleodepolymerases), of the pancreatic juice into purine and pyrimidine mononucleotides. Each of these "nucleases" may in reality represent several polynucleotidases of different specificity.

The extent to which further degradation occurs in the lumen of the bowel is not clear. The intestinal mucosa, and also other tissues, contains non-specific phosphatases (alkaline and acid) which hydrolyze the sugar-phosphate bond of mononucleotides ("nucleotidase" action), forming nucleosides (purine and pyrimidine) and phosphoric acid. It is not known whether these enzymes are secreted into the intestinal lumen or whether their presence there is due to exfoliated mucosal cells. In the latter case, the reactions described cannot be regarded as part of the process of digestion, but occur largely intracellularly, during the process of absorption of nucleotides. The same question arises concerning purine "nucleosidases," found in the intestinal fluids, which split purine nucleosides into their pentose and purine base components. There is evidence that this reaction involves phosphorolysis rather than hydrolysis (i.e., "nucleosidase" = nucleoside phosphorylase), which would localize it as an intracellular rather than a digestive process. It appears likely, therefore, that the end-products of nucleic acid digestion are largely if not entirely purine and pyrimidine nucleotides, some question existing as to participation of phosphatases and purine nucleosidases in the process of digestion. These substances are absorbed readily from the small intestine. As indicated above, further degradation of nucleotides may occur within the intestinal mucosal cells, i.e., to nucleosides and phosphoric acid, through the action of phosphatases. Some of the purine nucleosides may also be split here (nucleoside phosphorylase) to purine bases and pentose. Absorption occurs mainly via the portal circulation, the bulk of the products of digestion and intestinal metabolism of nucleic acids, as of proteins, reaching the liver before entering the systemic blood stream.

INTRACELLULAR LOCALIZATION OF NUCLEIC ACIDS AND POLYNUCLEOTIDASES

DNA is confined to the nucleus of the cell, whereas RNA is found in both the nucleus and the cytoplasm; in the latter location it occurs in the mitochondria, microsomes, and particle-free fraction. These matters are discussed in greater detail elsewhere (pp. 578, 711).

Ribonuclease and desoxyribonuclease (p. 231) are apparently bound to the nuclei (although this binding may be an artifact), but occur in highest concentration in the mitochondria. No immediate explanation is available for the presence of desoxyribonuclease at a site completely devoid of substrate.

SURVEY OF NUCLEIC ACID METABOLISM

For convenience, the metabolism of the nucleic acids may be subdivided into (1) the metabolism of components, (a) non-nitrogenous and (b) nitrogenous, and (2) the metabolism of the macromolecules. The over-all picture of nucleic acid metabolism is illustrated in Figure 105.

NON-NITROGENOUS CONSTITUENTS. Phosphate is readily obtained from the diet and endogenous sources. It is excreted in the urine as inorganic phosphate at the end of its metabolic career.

Ribose and desoxyribose are derived more or less directly from glucose or its metabolites. It is doubtful whether dietary pentoses contribute significantly to the synthesis of nucleic acids. The catabolic pathways of the pentoses are not firmly established, but it is probable that they eventuate in CO_2 and water.

NITROGENOUS CONSTITUENTS. Purines liberated by digestion of nucleic acids are largely catabolized directly to waste products, with the exception of a small amount of adenine that is incorporated into nucleic acids. Pyrimidine nucleotides are probably not digested completely to the stage of the free bases; significant quantities of pyrimidine nucleosides (or nucleotides) are utilized for the synthesis of nucleic acids. Small metabolic fragments (NH_3, CO_2 "formate," glycine) are drawn upon extensively for the formation of both the purine and the pyrimidine moieties of nucleic acids, preformed bases derived from the diet playing a relatively more important role in the case of the pyrimidines than of the purines.

The unused bases of the diet, as well as those arising from the catabolism of the nucleic acids, are degraded to waste products which are excreted in the urine. Purines eventuate in uric acid in man and the higher apes, in allantoin in other mammals. Pyrimidines form urea, β-aminoisobutyric acid, and β-alanine (most of which is degraded to urea).

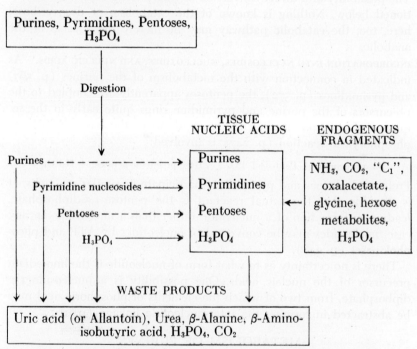

Fig. 105. *Over-all metabolism of the constituents of the nucleic acids*

NUCLEIC ACIDS. The mechanisms of synthesis of the macromolecules are not known. Degradation of the nucleic acids probably involves the polynucleotidases, phosphatases or specific mononucleotidases, nucleoside phosphorylases or nucleosidases, and various deaminases and dehydrogenases which attack the bases.

RNA appears to be synthesized or "turned over" at a rate correlated (not always closely, however) with protein synthesis and growth of the cell. Synthesis of DNA is apparently limited mainly to cell multiplication (mitosis), although turnover or exchange of certain parts of the molecule at other times is not excluded.

METABOLISM OF PENTOSES

SYNTHESIS AND DEGRADATION.   Since these topics are discussed in detail elsewhere (p. 403), it will suffice here merely to summarize the available information. Ribose appears to arise from glucose via an aerobic pathway involving, essentially, oxidative decarboxylation of the phosphorylated hexonic acid. Its catabolic pathway may be the reverse of the anabolic, or may proceed via a pentose aldolase reaction to yield smaller fragments.

Desoxyribose is not synthesized directly from a hexose, but rather in an aldolase type of reaction between a triose phosphate and a "diose." The possibility of a direct conversion of ribose to desoxyribose is mentioned below. Nothing is known of the catabolism of desoxyribose; here, too, the catabolic pathway may be merely the reverse of the anabolic.

INCORPORATION INTO NUCLEOSIDES, NUCLEOTIDES, AND NUCLEIC ACIDS.   As indicated in connection with the metabolism of the purines (p. 567) and pyrimidines (p. 572), the pentoses apparently are coupled to the precursors of the purine and pyrimidine rings quite early in the sequence of reactions leading to the synthesis of the bases. A type of phosphorylase reaction (p. 247) is involved:

$$\text{Base-precursor} + \text{Pentose-1-PO}_4 \longleftrightarrow \text{Base-precursor-pentose} + \text{H}_3\text{PO}_4$$

Preformed purines and pyrimidines participate in similar reactions. It is possible that the actual reactant is the pentose-1,5-diphosphate, leading to formation of a nucleotide rather than a nucleoside. In any case, nucleosides may be converted to nucleotides by ATP and phosphokinases (p. 248).

There is no certainty as to what form of nucleotide is the immediate precursor of the nucleic acids. One possibility is a nucleoside-3,5-diphosphate, from two of which the elements of phosphoric acid may be abstracted in forming the inter-nucleotide linkage (p. 102).

METABOLISM OF PURINES

SYNTHESIS.   Considering the relatively slight anabolic utilization of preformed purines and pyrimidines by the mammalian organism (p. 573), the synthesis of these compounds de novo must be regarded as one of the major preliminary processes in the formation of the nucleic acids. The origin of the atoms comprising the purine skeleton is illustrated in the upper part of Figure 106; the detailed reactions involved are indicated in the lower part. It will be observed that the purine skeleton is synthesized from small fragments. However, available evidence indicates that certain of these fragments probably are not used in the free state: (1) "formate" requires a folinic acid type of coenzyme as a carrier (p. 542) (homocysteine also is involved in some undefined manner); (2) ammonia is probably derived from the amide and amino groups of glutamine and glutamic acid, respectively, and possibly also from aspartic acid; (3) the "CO_2-carrier," if it exists, has not been identified.

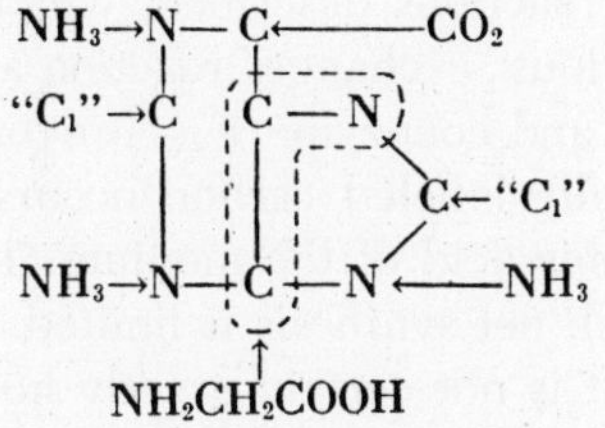

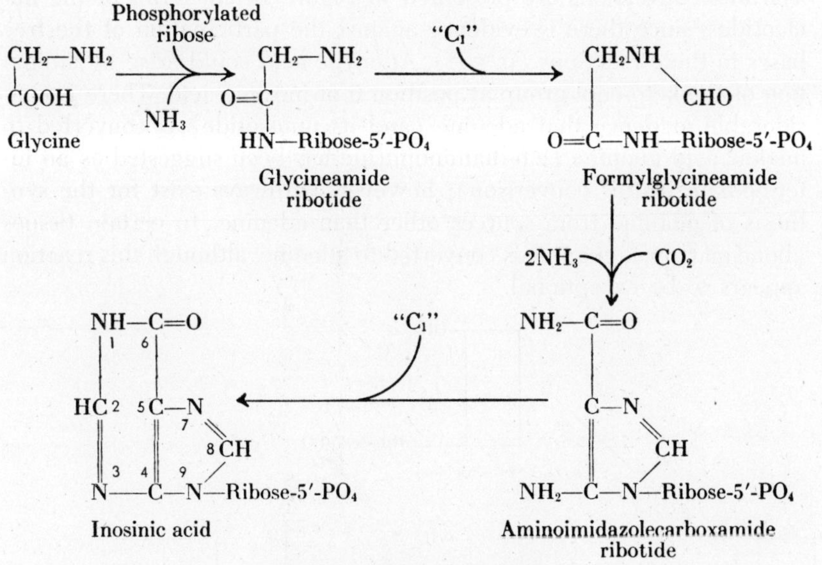

$$NH_3 \rightarrow N - C \leftarrow \!\!\!-\!\!\!-\!\!\!- CO_2$$

$$\text{``}C_1\text{''} \rightarrow C \quad C - N$$

$$C \leftarrow \text{``}C_1\text{''}$$

$$NH_3 \rightarrow N - C - N \leftarrow \!\!\!-\!\!\!- NH_3$$

$$NH_2CH_2COOH$$

Fig. 106. Synthesis of purines

The sequence of reactions presented for the synthesis of the purines is somewhat tentative, although it is currently employed as a working hypothesis. Certain of the intermediates have not been identified or isolated, and others have been found thus far only in simplified *in vitro* systems. Consequently, many of the details may be subject to future revision.

Synthesis of the purines begins with the condensation of glycine, ammonia, and a phosphorylated ribose (possibly the 1,5-diphosphate), in what is undoubtedly a stepwise process to yield glycineamide ribotide, which is then formylated. The addition of two molecules of ammonia and one of carbon dioxide (stepwise) and closure of the imidazole ring produces aminoimidazolecarboxamide ribotide, the free base of which accumulates in cultures of bacteria inhibited by sulfonamides (pp. 635, 640). Formylation of the amide to complete the purine ring results in the formation of inosinic acid (hypoxanthine ribotide), the probable parent compound of all the purines.

In addition to the reactions described, which lead to net synthesis of inosinic acid, a curious "exchange" reaction also occurs. In the presence of liver extracts and coenzyme F (citrovorum factor, p. 542), an exchange of isotopically labeled carbon occurs between carbon 2 of inosinic acid and formic acid of the medium. This reaction is favored by conditions in which net synthesis is limited.

INTERCONVERSIONS. It is not certain exactly how inosinic acid is converted to the adenylic and guanylic components of the nucleic acids. The interconversions are presented in Figure 107 in terms of the nucleotides, since there is evidence against the participation of the free bases in these reactions (p. 567). Adenylic acid could arise by amination of the keto-enol group at position 6 of inosinic acid. There is considerable evidence that adenine (and its nucleotide) is converted to nucleic acid guanine (2,6-diaminopurine has been suggested as an intermediate in this conversion); however, pathways exist for the synthesis of guanine from sources other than adenine. In certain tissues (bone marrow), guanine is converted to adenine, although this reaction appears to be exceptional.

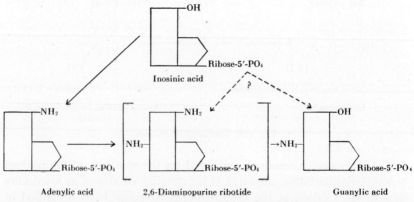

Fig. 107. Interconversions of purines

INCORPORATION INTO NUCLEIC ACIDS. Administered adenine and adenylic acid are incorporated into the adenine and guanine moieties of DNA and RNA. Neither guanine nor guanosine are utilized in this manner to any great extent (traces of guanine are assimilated by certain species of experimental animals). Guanylic acid, however, is efficiently converted to nucleic acid guanine (not to adenine). Administered purines (or derivatives) which are not utilized for the synthesis of nucleic acids are catabolized to uric acid (man and apes) or allantoin (most mammals), which are excreted in the urine. Since the purines of the diet are probably absorbed in the free state (p. 564), and since even administered adenine is diluted many-fold by endogenous adenine in the synthesis of nucleic acids, it is evident that only a fraction of the nucleic acid purines of the tissues is derived from preformed bases. Most of the nucleic acid purine component must be synthesized *de novo*.

No information is available on the mechanism of conversion of the mononucleotides to the polynucleotidic DNA and RNA, nor even on the immediate precursor compounds involved, i.e., 3′-phosphates, 5′-phosphates, or diphosphates.

CATABOLISM. The major catabolic pathway of the purines is illustrated in Figure 108. Subsequent to hydrolysis of the parent nucleic acids by polynucleotidases (p. 231), the mononucleotides are hydrolyzed to nucleosides by phosphomonoesterases (p. 231). Guanosine is attacked by a nucleoside phosphorylase (p. 245), forming free guanine. Adenosine may undergo a similar phosphorolysis, but most of the available evidence indicates that the phosphorolytic reaction is preceded by a hydrolytic deamination (p. 241) to inosine, which is then converted to the free base, hypoxanthine. Xanthine, an intermediate common to the catabolism of both adenine and guanine, is formed by the oxidation of hypoxanthine (xanthine dehydrogenase, p. 364) and by the hydrolytic deamination of guanine (guanase, p. 241). Xanthine is oxidized further by xanthine dehydrogenase, forming uric acid, the major end-product of purine metabolism in man and the higher apes. Other mammals degrade uric acid to allantoin with the aid of uricase (p. 362), an enzyme lacking in primates.

The main site of formation of uric acid in man is not known (liver; muscle; bone marrow?). It is carried in the blood stream to the kidneys, and is excreted in the urine.

The uric acid pool (p. 488) amounts to about 1 gram in normal human subjects; it may be expanded fifteen to twenty-five times in gout. The normal half-life of uric acid is somewhat less than one day. From turnover data on uric acid in man, obtained with the aid of isotopic labeling, it has been concluded by some that the uric acid excreted in the urine does not quite account for the total quantity formed. The disposition of the missing uric acid has not been determined, although it is known not to be allantoin. It has been suggested that the uric acid secreted into the gastrointestinal tract with the digestive juices may be degraded by bacterial action before reabsorption.

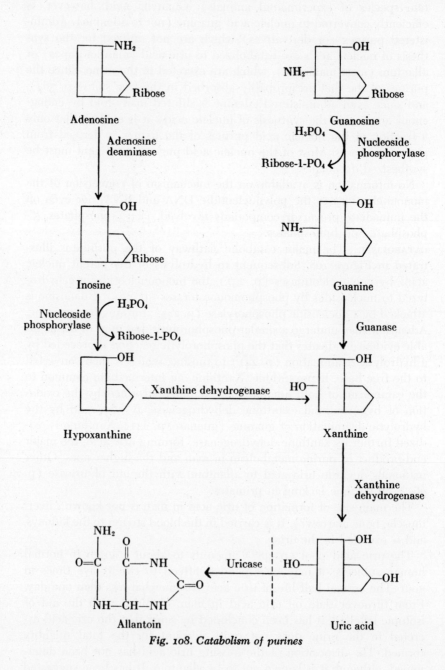

Fig. 108. *Catabolism of purines*

The rate of purine catabolism, as reflected in the daily output of urinary uric acid, is influenced by the dietary intake of purines and the rate of endogenous purine catabolism. Administration of the 11-oxygenated hormones of the adrenal cortex (p. 673), or of ACTH, increases the urinary excretion of uric acid (p. 773); it is not certain whether the effect of these hormones is primarily on the turnover of the purines or on the renal tubular reabsorption of uric acid.

It is of interest in connection with the purines and pyrimidines that alloxan, a synthetic pyrimidine, is diabetogenic (p. 432). Because of its structural similarity to uric acid and related compounds, it has been suggested that alloxan may be a naturally occurring diabetogenic agent, arising from an aberrant metabolic reaction of the purines (specifically, uric acid). However, little evidence is available on this point.

METABOLISM OF PYRIMIDINES

SYNTHESIS. Comparatively little is known of the synthesis of the pyrimidines (Fig. 109). Nitrogens 1 and 3 are derived from NH_3 (probably via a "carrier"), carbon 2 from CO_2. The chain composed of carbons 4, 5, and 6 is probably formed from three of the four carbon atoms of oxalacetic acid. "Formate" (p. 542) is the source of the methyl group of thymine (and probably that of methyl cytosine).

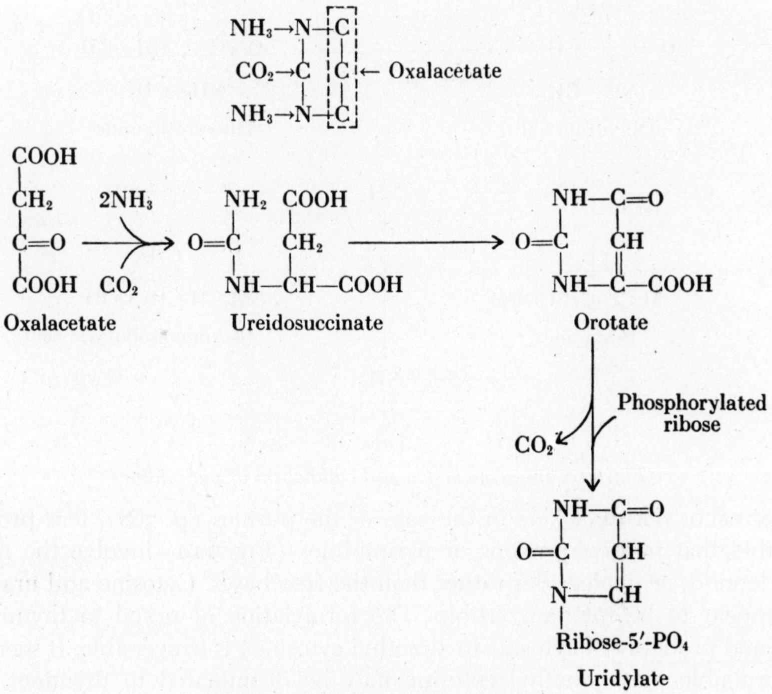

Fig. 109. *Synthesis of pyrimidines*

The sequence of reactions is assumed to begin with the condensation (probably stepwise) of two mols of NH_3 with one mol each of CO_2 and oxalacetic acid, forming ureidosuccinic acid. Ring closure produces orotic acid, which may be decarboxylated to uracil. Phosphorylated ribose is shown (provisionally) entering the sequence of reactions at orotic acid, so that uridylic acid is the actual end-product. It is possible that ribose enters at an earlier stage, as it does during purine synthesis (p. 567).

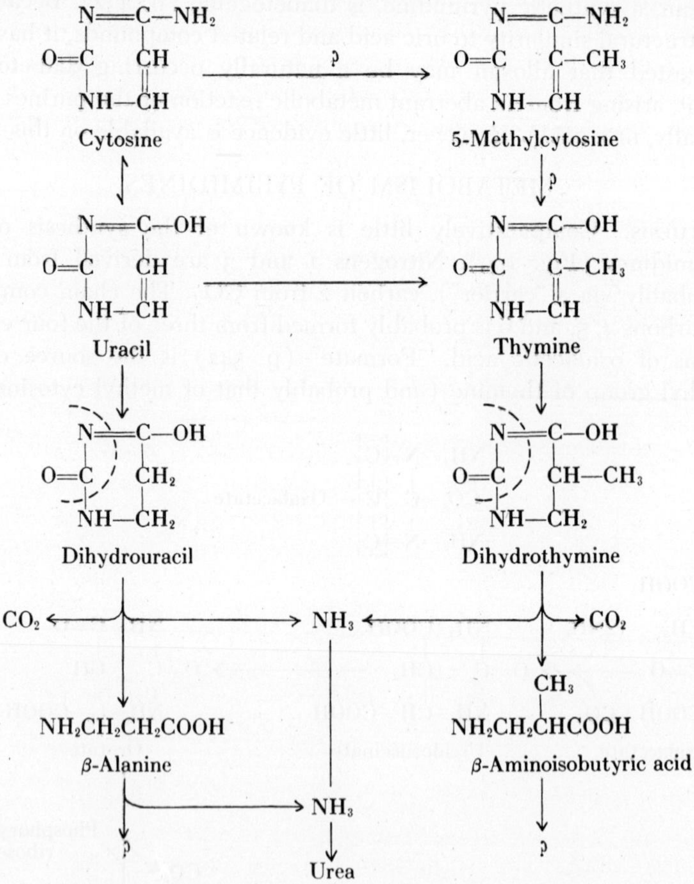

$$N{=}C{-}NH_2 \qquad\qquad N{=}C{-}NH_2$$
$$O{=}C \quad CH \xrightarrow{\ ?\ } O{=}C \quad C{-}CH_3$$
$$NH{-}CH \qquad\qquad NH{-}CH$$

Cytosine   5-Methylcytosine

$$N{=}C{-}OH \qquad\qquad N{=}C{-}OH$$
$$O{=}C \quad CH \xrightarrow{\quad\quad} O{=}C \quad C{-}CH_3$$
$$NH{-}CH \qquad\qquad NH{-}CH$$

Uracil   Thymine

$$N{=}C{-}OH \qquad\qquad N{=}C{-}OH$$
$$O{=}C \quad CH_2 \qquad\qquad O{=}C \quad CH{-}CH_3$$
$$NH{-}CH_2 \qquad\qquad NH{-}CH_2$$

Dihydrouracil   Dihydrothymine

$$CO_2 \longleftarrow \qquad \longrightarrow NH_3 \longleftarrow \qquad \longrightarrow CO_2$$

$$CH_3$$

$$NH_2CH_2CH_2COOH \qquad\qquad NH_2CH_2CHCOOH$$

β-Alanine   β-Aminoisobutyric acid

$$\longrightarrow NH_3$$

?   Urea   ?

Fig. 110. Interconversion and catabolism of pyrimidines

INTERCONVERSIONS. As in the case of the purines (p. 568), it is probable that interconversions of pyrimidines (Fig. 110) involve the nucleotides or nucleosides rather than the free bases. Cytosine and uracil appear to be interconvertible. The formylation of uracil to thymine (and probably of cytosine to 5-methyl cytosine) is irreversible. It seems probable that 5-methyl cytosine may be deaminated to thymine, as cytosine is to uracil.

INCORPORATION INTO NUCLEIC ACID. Administration of isotopically labeled uracil, uridine, uridylic acid, cytosine, or thymine to experimental animals does not result in significant labeling of the tissue nucleic acids (traces of uridine are incorporated). On the other hand, the nucleosides, cytidine, desoxycytidine, and thymidine, and the nucleotide, cytidylic acid, are incorporated into nucleic acids to a considerable extent.

It is of interest that administration of labeled cytidine results in labeling of desoxycytidine in the DNA of the tissues. Since free cytosine is not utilized, this suggests the direct conversion of a riboside to a desoxyriboside, i.e., ribose to desoxyribose, while in glycosidic linkage. The conversion appears to be irreversible.

Since digestion of pyrimidine nucleosides apparently does not proceed to completion (p. 564), it is probable that many nucleosides are absorbed as such, in which case they may be used for the synthesis of nucleic acids, as indicated by the data presented above. The relative importance of *de novo* synthesis of pyrimidines consequently may be less than in the case of the purines (p. 566).

CATABOLISM. The little that is known or conjectured concerning the catabolism of the pyrimidines is presented in Figure 110, page 572. Since it is not certain whether the various reactions are undergone by the free bases, nucleosides, or nucleotides, the participation of the nucleotidases and nucleosidases (nucleoside phosphorylases) cannot be localized. In any event, cytosine and 5-methyl cytosine undoubtedly are converted to uracil and thymine, respectively. It is probable that these two bases are reduced to the dihydro derivatives, which then lose nitrogen 1 and carbon 2 to form β-alanine (from dihydrouracil) and β-aminoisobutyric acid (from dihydrothymine). β-Alanine is readily deaminated; the ammonia thus produced, and that from the previous cleavage, form urea. Nothing is known of the further metabolism of β-aminoisobutyric acid (it has been identified in normal human urine).

METABOLISM OF THE "FREE" NUCLEOTIDES (COENZYMES)

In addition to the nucleic acids proper and their constituent nucleotides, with which they may be in equilibrium, all cells contain a small number of "free" nucleotides having the functions of cofactors in enzyme reactions. There is no reason to believe that the purine moieties of these nucleotides are synthesized by any pathway other than that involved in the synthesis of the purines of the nucleic acids. Certain of the "bases" in the coenzymes are vitamins (e.g., riboflavin, niacin) and must be supplied from sources outside the animal tissues (diet, intestinal flora). Although the "free" nucleotides may be metabolized independently of the nucleic acids, their structural similarity to the "bound" nucleotides (i.e., in the nucleic acids), their common constituents (ribose, purine, phosphate), and the probable common anabolic and catabolic pathways of these constituents justify their discussion here.

ADENYLIC SYSTEM. The metabolic role of the adenylic system in trans-phosphorylation and in the collection, storage, and utilization of energy is considered in detail elsewhere (p. 376). The synthesis of the adenine-ribose (adenosine) or adenine-ribose-5'-phosphate (adenylic acid) portion of the ADP-ATP molecule may be safely assumed to proceed as outlined for the nucleic acids. Conversion of the adenylic acid (adenosine monophosphate, AMP) to ADP is effected via the myo-kinase (adenylate kinase) reaction (p. 413):

$$AMP + ATP \longleftrightarrow 2\,ADP.$$

ATP is formed from ADP in all of the exergonic, adenylate-coupled re-actions of intermediary metabolism (p. 376).

The degradation of ATP and ADP occurs either (1) in the course of the performance of work, i.e., driving an otherwise endergonic process, or (2) wastefully, by hydrolysis catalyzed by any of several ATP-ases (p. 232). Certain special reactions are discussed below in which ATP loses pyrophosphate instead of phosphate.

It is not certain whether ADP is hydrolyzed to AMP by a specific ADP-ase, or whether it is converted (2 molecules at a time) to ATP and AMP by the myokinase reaction mentioned above. Whatever the path-way, once AMP is liberated in animal tissues, it is rapidly attacked by a deaminase (p. 569), producing inosinic acid, which joins the meta-bolic pathways of the nucleic acid purines (p. 568).

NICOTINAMIDE COENZYMES. The synthesis of nicotinamide from trypto-phan is discussed in connection with the metabolism of the amino acids (p. 546). Nicotinamide is provided also by the diet (p. 184). It is probable that the synthesis of DPN (diphosphopyridine nucleotide, cozymase, coenzyme 1, p. 361) occurs as follows:

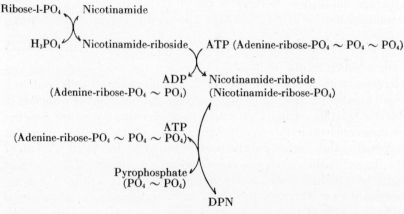

Ribose-1-PO$_4$ \ Nicotinamide

H$_3$PO$_4$ / \ Nicotinamide-riboside \ ATP (Adenine-ribose-PO$_4 \sim$ PO$_4 \sim$ PO$_4$)

ADP / \ Nicotinamide-ribotide
(Adenine-ribose-PO$_4 \sim$ PO$_4$)   (Nicotinamide-ribose-PO$_4$)

ATP
(Adenine-ribose-PO$_4 \sim$ PO$_4 \sim$ PO$_4$)

Pyrophosphate
(PO$_4 \sim$ PO$_4$)

DPN

(Nicotinamide-ribose-PO$_4 \sim$ PO$_4$-ribose-adenine)

Phosphorylation of DPN by ATP and a phosphokinase results in the formation of TPN (p. 361).

TPN is probably reconverted to DPN by a phosphatase. The degradation of DPN may take either of two pathways: (1) cleavage between nicotinamide and ribose, catalyzed by DPN nucleosidase, or (2) scission of the pyrophosphate group by a pyrophosphatase, yielding two mononucleotides (TPN is split similarly).

FLAVIN COENZYMES. Although the carbohydrate moiety of riboflavin (p. 177) is ribitol, a sugar alcohol, the vitamin is usually considered a nucleoside, and its 5′-phosphate a nucleotide (flavin mononucleotide, FMN). The nucleotide is formed under the influence of a phosphokinase, and is converted to flavin-adenine dinucleotide (FAD) by a reaction analogous to that involved in the synthesis of DPN:

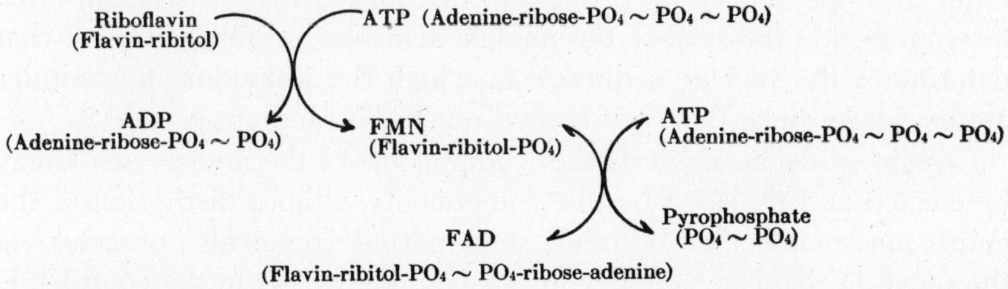

Riboflavin ⟶ ATP (Adenine-ribose-PO₄ ∼ PO₄ ∼ PO₄)
(Flavin-ribitol)

ADP
(Adenine-ribose-PO₄ ∼ PO₄) ⟶ FMN ⟶ ATP
(Flavin-ribitol-PO₄) (Adenine-ribose-PO₄ ∼ PO₄ ∼ PO₄)

FAD ⟶ Pyrophosphate
(PO₄ ∼ PO₄)
(Flavin-ribitol-PO₄ ∼ PO₄-ribose-adenine)

FAD is split at the pyrophosphate linkage by the same enzyme that attacks DPN and TPN. FMN is hydrolytically dephosphorylated by a phosphatase.

COENZYME A. This coenzyme, the functions of which have been elucidated only recently (p. 195), is synthesized in much the same manner as those discussed previously. Pantothenic acid (p. 193) condenses initially with thiolethylamine (doubtless derived from cysteine), forming pantetheine, a pseudopeptide. After reacting with ATP and a phosphokinase, the resulting phosphopantetheine acquires an adenylic acid component in a "pyrophosphorylase" reaction. CoA is finally produced by another phosphokinase reaction.

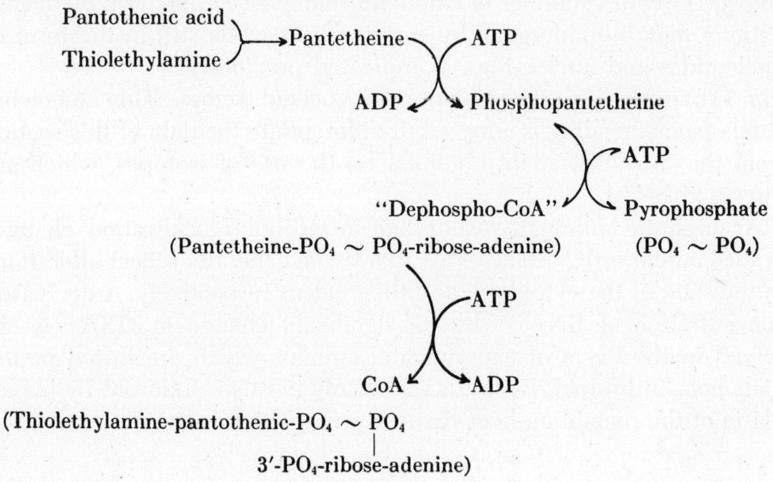

Pantothenic acid ⟶ Pantetheine ⟶ ATP
Thiolethylamine

ADP ⟶ Phosphopantetheine

ATP

"Dephospho-CoA" ⟶ Pyrophosphate
(Pantetheine-PO₄ ∼ PO₄-ribose-adenine) (PO₄ ∼ PO₄)

ATP

CoA ⟶ ADP
(Thiolethylamine-pantothenic-PO₄ ∼ PO₄
3′-PO₄-ribose-adenine)

MISCELLANEOUS.   Uridine diphospho-glucose, the coenzyme of "galac-towaldenase" (p. 395), is a true nucleotide. However, little is known of its metabolism at this time. Thiamine pyrophosphate (p. 171), lipo-thiamide pyrophosphate (p. 215), and pyridoxal phosphate (p. 189) are not nucleotides.

METABOLISM OF THE NUCLEIC ACIDS

MECHANISMS OF ANABOLISM AND CATABOLISM.   As indicated previously in various connections, no definite information is available concerning the mechanism by which nucleic acids are synthesized from their pre-cursors, or indeed the identity of the precursors. It is probable that the latter are mononucleotides, but there is no knowledge as to how the internucleotide linkages of the nucleic acids are established, nor what determines the specific sequence in which the individual nucleotides are coupled (since this now known not to be random, p. 103).

Certain evidence suggests that components of the nucleic acids may be ejected and replaced by like components without disruption of the entire macromolecule. Whether such partial "renewals" proceed via the same mechanism as net synthesis is unknown, as in the completely analogous case of protein "renewal" (p. 449).

It seems reasonable to assume, in the absence of evidence to the contrary, that the catabolism of nucleic acids is initiated by the tissue nucleodepolymerases (polynucleotidases, p. 231), which degrade the macromolecules to mononucleotides and a "core" (p. 103) which is hydrolyzed by other enzymes. The mononucleotides may be hydro-lyzed to the nucleosides, in a few instances by specific nucleotidases (p. 231), generally by phosphatases (p. 231). Certain nucleosidases have been described; however, it is probable that nucleosides are split mainly by nucleoside phosphorylases (p. 245). The free bases and sugars are then catabolized further along independent pathways (pp. 569, 571, 573). A number of catabolic changes (e.g., hydrolytic deami-nation) may be undergone by certain bases while still in the form of nucleotides and nucleosides, as indicated previously.

NET SYNTHESIS AND DEGRADATION OF NUCLEIC ACIDS.   This somewhat cumbersome heading is adopted to differentiate the data of this section from the "turnover" data obtained by the use of isotopes, which are discussed below.

As might be anticipated from their intracellular localization, changes in the content of RNA and DNA in a tissue generally reflect alterations in the state of the cytoplasm and the nucleus respectively. A decreased concentration of RNA (with no significant change in DNA) is ob-served in the livers of experimental animals which are fasted or fed diets poor in protein. Partial hepatectomy in rats is followed by hyper-plasia of the remaining liver tissue, during which large increases occur in the concentration of RNA, whereas no consistent pattern of change is observed in DNA. Intense stimulation of nerve cells results in a decrease of RNA (and protein). Increases and decreases in the concentration of RNA (particularly cytoplasmic RNA) in a given tissue generally are correlated with the rate of synthesis of cytoplasmic protein.

From what is known of the relation between DNA and the chromosomes p. 579), increases may be anticipated in the concentration of DNA in conditions involving multiplication of chromosomes, i.e., in cell division. Doubling of the DNA content of the nucleus is indeed observed during cell division. This increase is not limited to the DNA, however; according to some, it is shared also by the RNA, histones, and non-histone proteins of the nucleus.

Increases in the content of RNA, DNA, or both, in neoplastic tissue are not observed consistently, and appear to reflect the rate of growth and degree of cellularity of the tumor more than any special neoplastic peculiarity.

"TURNOVER" OF NUCLEIC ACIDS. Since the advent of the isotopic-labeling technic, many studies have been made of the rates of incorporation of various constituents (e.g., bases, phosphate) or precursors of constituents (e.g., formate, glycine) into the nucleic acids. These procedures have the advantage of applicability to situations in which no net change in quantity of nucleic acid is observed, i.e., the rate of anabolism balances the rate of catabolism. They suffer from the disadvantage that a certain ambiguity is inherent in their interpretation, since it is not known whether these technics measure the same reaction as that occurring in total synthesis or some limited exchange reaction such as that discussed in connection with formate and inosinic acid (p. 568). Nevertheless, "turnover" rates are properly regarded as reflecting an aspect of biological lability, and furnish much useful information on the comparative alterations occurring in the nucleic acids of different tissues or cell fractions under various experimental conditions.

The metabolic activity of RNA differs, depending on intracellular location. As determined by the incorporation of labeled glycine and phosphate, the turnover rate of RNA in the various fractions of liver decreases in the order: nucleus > supernatant > microsomes > mitochondria. Since the simultaneously determined turnover rate of protein is greatest in the microsomes, a question is raised concerning the purported direct relation between RNA and the synthesis of protein (p. 581).

Experiments using various types of labeled precursors have generally agreed in ascribing a more rapid rate of turnover to RNA than to DNA. The difference observed appears to vary with the precursor used, a finding indicating that the components of the nucleic acids may turn over at different rates. Certain experiments, for example, indicate a greater rate of exchange of phosphate or of glycine than of preformed adenine in RNA.

Although all of the DNA of the cell is located within the nucleus, certain data suggest metabolic heterogeneity (varying turnover rates) even within this fraction. In general, the turnover of DNA is correlated with the rate of cell division, although (as in the case of RNA) a certain amount of exchange may occur continually. The rate of turnover of DNA (incorporation of labeled formate) in various tissues is found to decrease in the order: small intestine > large intestine > spleen > testis, liver, and kidney.

BIOLOGICAL SIGNIFICANCE OF NUCLEIC ACIDS

Information accumulating in recent years has stimulated intense interest in the biochemistry of nucleic acids. The intracellular distribution of desoxyribosenucleic acids (DNA) and pentosenucleic acids (RNA) is discussed elsewhere (p. 711). It will suffice here to state merely that: (1) all of the DNA is in the chromosomes in the nucleus; (2) approximately 70 per cent of the RNA of the liver cell is in the cytoplasm (50 per cent microsomes, 20 per cent mitochondria); (3) 30 per cent of the RNA is in the nucleus (20 per cent nucleolus, 10 per cent chromosomes). The association of nucleic acids with chromosomes and viruses, and indications of their influence in protein synthesis, suggest that these substances are of great fundamental biological importance. It seems desirable here to point out certain of the directions of current studies in this field, even though there is as yet no unanimity of opinion on most of these matters.

VIRUSES. Until comparatively recently, it was generally agreed that viruses were living organisms characterized, among other things, by: (1) small size (passage through bacterial filters), (2) inability to grow and multiply on artificial culture media, (3) ability to multiply or reproduce within the living cells of the host, and (4) the development of mutation forms during multiplication. Several plant viruses have been shown to be crystallizable nucleoproteins, and many animal viruses are largely if not entirely nucleoprotein. Some contain only desoxyribosenucleoproteins, others (e.g., tobacco mosaic virus) only pentosenucleoproteins, while some contain both. It has been shown that if the crystalline tobacco mosaic virus material, non-living by usual standards, is introduced into a heathy tobacco plant, the latter develops the disease in typical form. Moreover, the virus nucleoprotein can be subsequently recovered in amounts greatly exceeding that originally introduced, i.e., it reduplicates (reproduces?) with progression of the disease.

Viruses vary widely in size and structural complexity, certain of the smaller ones exhibiting the physical and chemical behavior of molecules, whereas certain of the larger ones approach microorganisms in size and in structural and functional complexity. The observations reviewed above have led to the suggestion that viruses provide a link between molecules and "living" cells, completing the pathway from such simple structures as electrons to the highly complex structure of the mammalian organism.

Viruses possess no enzyme activity (other than virus activity); nevertheless, on entering susceptible cells, they alter and direct certain metabolic sequences within the cell into new channels. Of particular significance is the fact that metabolic precursors are derived from the host cell for construction of the nucleic acid and protein molecules of the multiplying virus. These transactions between the host and the virus are apparently irreversible. Synthesis of the host cell nucleic acids may actually cease, while the specific virus nucleic acid continues to accumulate, as in the case of bacteria infected by a bacteriophage, a bacterial virus. This phenomenon may occur without demonstrable alteration in oxygen utilization, i.e., metabolic activity, of the infected cell.

CHROMOSOMES-GENES. Present evidence indicates that chromosomes, of both spermatozoa and somatic cells, consist largely of desoxyribose-nucleoproteins. The obvious implication is that their component genes are made up largely of these substances, which, therefore, may be regarded as the "genetic material," concerned in processes of cell reproduction. It is pertinent in this connection that the amount of DNA in spermatozoa containing the haploid number of chromosomes is one-half that of the somatic nuclei of the same species. Moreover, there is a quite striking, although not absolute, uniformity and constancy in the DNA content of the nuclei. The chromosomes are the only cell elements known to contain DNA, but they contain, in addition, a pentosenucleoprotein. It is believed by some that the former is concerned in genetic functions and that the latter participates indirectly in metabolic activities of the cell by making material contributions to the cytoplasm (p. 581).

Genes resemble viruses in at least two important characteristics: (1) they are autoreproducible, their exact duplication during mitotic division endowing each daughter cell with all of the specific hereditary biochemical potentialities and mechanisms of the original cell; (2) they are capable of undergoing mutation. In determining the biochemical characteristics of the cell, dependent largely on enzymes, it appears that the DNA-proteins are responsible in some way for the synthesis of these substances and that each gene "catalyzes" the production of a single enzyme ("one gene–one enzyme" hypothesis). The manner in which this is accomplished is not known. In certain viruses (e.g., tobacco mosaic), a pure RNA-protein apparently performs this function.

"TRANSFORMING SUBSTANCE" OF BACTERIA. Certain strains (e.g., Type 3) of pneumococcus possess capsules containing specific polysaccharides (p. 18) and others (e.g., Type 2) do not. This capacity for formation of a type-specific capsule is a hereditary characteristic. If one adds to an appropriate culture of a non-encapsulated strain an extract of an encapsulated strain, the former type is transformed to the latter, developing its characteristic capsular polysaccharide, as do its progeny subsequently. The active agent (transforming factor) seems to be a desoxyribosenucleic acid. It apparently endows the bacterial cell with the capacity for synthesizing an enzyme or enzyme system that it did not previously possess, which, in turn, catalyzes the formation of the type-specific capsular polysaccharide. Inasmuch as this new function is subsequently transmissible, this may be regarded, in effect, as an example of induced mutation. Many different specific transforming factors have been found for pneumococci, one for Hemophilus and one for Escherichia coli. All appear to be desoxyribonucleates. It is perhaps of fundamental importance that these agents, as is true of genes and viruses, are reduplicated by the bacterial cell and, like viruses, can be recovered in large amounts from descendants of the cell into which they originally entered.

ROLE OF NUCLEIC ACIDS IN MUTATION AND CARCINOGENESIS. The fact that genes and viruses, largely if not entirely nucleoprotein in nature, possess in common the highly distinctive properties of autoduplication and susceptibility to mutation, raises the fundamentally important question of the relation of nucleic acids to these phenomena. The former has been referred to previously; genes and viruses are the only two sub-cellular substances known to be capable of duplicating ("reproducing") themselves. They also can undergo mutation "spontaneously," and as a result of exposure to certain mutagenic agents. The latter include: (1) ultraviolet light, (2) ionizing radiations (e.g., X and gamma rays and neutrons), and (3) certain chemicals (e.g., colchicine, nitrogen mustards, certain chemical carcinogens, e.g., methylcholanthrene).

Many if not all of these agents are capable of depolymerizing DNA, and it is possible that this is the basis of their mutagenic action. This subject may have basic relevance to the problem of carcinogenesis, which, according to some students of this subject, is one of induced mutation. This opinion is by no means unanimous. It may be significant in this connection, however, that such factors as ultraviolet light, ionizing radiations, and at least some chemicals that are mutagenic, are also carcinogenic. Moreover, certain types of malignancy are known to be due to viruses, which, as indicated elsewhere (p. 578), not only are largely if not entirely nucleoprotein in nature, but also impose upon the invaded cell their own specific nucleic acid synthesizing capacities. These observations suggest that the induction of malignancy may be related fundamentally to the development of an abnormal type of nucleic acid metabolism in the cell.

ROLE OF NUCLEIC ACIDS IN PROTEIN SYNTHESIS. Growth and maintenance of the organism require continual synthesis of protein molecules, specific for each cell. The mechanism of protein synthesis is not known (p. 498), but it unquestionably involves enzymes, which are themselves protein in nature. As indicated elsewhere (p. 579), the cytoplasmic enzyme pattern is apparently determined genetically, i.e., by the DNA-containing genes in the nucleus. However, although in this sense the nuclear nucleic acids may be regarded as the ultimate determinants of all metabolic reactions, a more intimate relation to protein synthesis has been suggested by certain observations.

RNA is present in greatest abundance in the cytoplasm of actively growing cells (e.g., embryonic, tumor, tip of plant root) and in cells engaged in the production and excretion of proteins (e.g., pancreatic acinar cells). Increased protein synthesis, e.g., stimulation of pancreatic secretion by pilocarpine, is accompanied by an increase in RNA. Conversely, when production of protein by liver cells is inhibited by starvation, their RNA content decreases simultaneously.

The nucleus apparently contains none of the important enzyme systems concerned in the metabolic activities of the cell, and nucleic acids are the only substances that have been shown to be synthesized in this situation. It would therefore appear, in view of the localization of oxidative and phosphorylating enzyme systems in the mitochondria, and of others elsewhere in the cytoplasm, that the nucleus depends on the latter for its energy supply. Opinion differs as to the relative importance of the nucleus and the cytoplasm in protein synthesis. It is generally agreed, however, although not definitely established, that nucleic acids or nucleoproteins play an important role in this phenomenon. There are indications that the nuclear RNA may be a precursor of the cytoplasmic RNA, contributing to the latter by diffusion through the nuclear membrane. It is believed by some that the RNA may act in the synthesis of proteins by inducing special molecular orientations. According to one formulation, the euchromatin (DNA) of the chromosomes is involved in synthesizing the proteins through which the genes exert their action, whereas the heterochromatin (containing both DNA and RNA) produces the pentosenucleoproteins of the nucleolus. The latter induce the synthesis of cytoplasmic pentosenucleoproteins which are immediately concerned in the synthesis of the ordinary proteins by the cell. On the basis of available data, it may be assumed that although the nucleus is not involved necessarily in the immediate metabolic activities of the cell, the latter are ultimately dependent upon contributions from both the genetic (DNA) and non-genetic (RNA) components of the nucleus. The picture evoked is that of a continuously reciprocal relationship, the nucleus deriving energy from cytoplasmic mechanisms which can be maintained only by replacement through nuclear activities.

INTERRELATIONS OF METABOLISM OF NUCLEIC ACIDS WITH OTHER FOODSTUFFS

As illustrated in Figure 111, the nucleic acids and their derivatives are related metabolically to a number of other foodstuffs. However, no obvious connections are found between the metabolism of lipids and that of nucleic acids, aside from the rather non-specific contribution of lipids to metabolic CO_2.

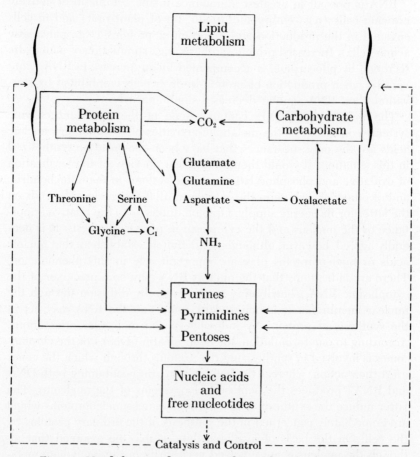

Fig. 111. Metabolic interrelations of nucleic acids with other foodstuffs

The pathways of protein metabolism provide much of the raw material for the synthesis of purines and pyrimidines, viz., glycine, formate, and "NH_3" for the former, and oxalacetate (from aspartate) and "NH_3" for the latter (in certain cases, formate also). Carbohydrate supplies oxalacetate for the synthesis of pyrimidines, and is also the ultimate source of the pentoses.

The "free" nucleotides, synthesized from the same raw materials as the "bound" nucleotides, exert a considerable influence on the metabolism of all classes of foodstuffs. As collecting, storing, and transferring agents for high-energy phosphate, and as cofactors for biological oxidation and certain other types of reactions, the free nucleotides of the tissues may control the rates of many reactions through variations in concentration.

The nucleic acids and nucleoproteins themselves, however, are probably much more important as agents controlling intermediary metabolism, although their exact roles remain speculative. They probably control the genetic pattern of potential enzymes and metabolic pathways in the cell at the nuclear level, and possibly regulate the final realization of that pattern in the cytoplasm. An abnormal variation of these functions may be seen in the mechanism of virus infections.

Thus, it is seen that a reciprocal type of relation exists between the nucleic acids (and derivatives) and other classes of metabolites; the latter provide the raw materials (and probably the energy) for the synthesis of the nucleic acids and derivatives, which in turn exert an influence over the general pattern and rate of metabolism of the other foodstuffs.

BIBLIOGRAPHY

Annual Review of Biochemistry.
Annual Review of Physiology.
Bowen, V. T. (ed.): The Chemistry and Physiology of the Nucleus, Experimental Cell Research, Supplement 2, New York, Academic Press, Inc., 1952.
Chambers, R. et al.: Symposium on Structure in Relation to Cellular Function, Ann. New York Acad. Sc. 50:815, 1950.
Christman, A. A.: Purine and pyrimidine metabolism, Physiol. Rev. 32:303, 1952.
Davidson, J. N.: The Biochemistry of the Nucleic Acids, London, Methuen & Co., Ltd., 1950.
Nucleic Acids and Nucleoproteins, Cold Spring Harbor Symp. Quant. Biol. 12 (1947).
Nucleic Acid, Symp. Soc. Exptl. Biol. 1, Cambridge, 1947.
McElroy, W. D. and Glass, B.: Phosphorus Metabolism, Volume 2, Baltimore, Johns Hopkins Press, 1952, Part IV.
Peters, J. P. and Van Slyke, D. D.: Quantitative Clinical Chemistry, Vol. 1, Baltimore, Williams & Wilkins Company, 1946, Chapter 13.
Pollister, A. W. et al.: Localization of substances in cells, Federation Proc. 10:629, 1951.
Shive, W.: The functions of B vitamins in the biosynthesis of purines and pyrimidines, Vitamins & Hormones 9:76, 1951.
Symposium on Biochemistry of Nucleic Acids (Oak Ridge), J. Cell. & Comp. Physiol. 38, Supplement 1, 1951.

21

METABOLISM OF PORPHYRINS AND
RELATED SUBSTANCES

The porphyrins are cyclic tetrapyrroles (p. 108), which, in combination with iron, form iron porphyrins or hemes. The union of a heme and a specific protein constitutes a hemoprotein. Bile pigments are open-chain tetrapyrroles (p. 112) resulting from the biological degradation of the hemoproteins.

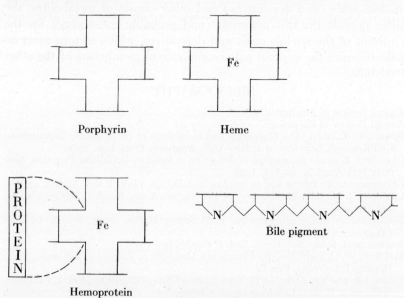

Fig. 112. Skeleton structures of porphyrin derivatives

The hemoproteins are of great importance in the economy of the animal organism. Oxygen from the atmosphere is transported in the blood stream by a hemoprotein (hemoglobin), is stored temporarily, to a limited extent, attached to another hemoprotein in the tissues (myoglobin), and is finally utilized in that combination with hydrogen atoms and electrons which marks the last phase of the biological oxidation of most substrates, a reaction catalyzed by still other hemoproteins (cytochrome oxidase, cytochromes a, b, and c). Incidental roles in biological oxidations are played also by catalases and peroxidases, both of which are hemoproteins. The metabolism of such important compounds is naturally a matter of great practical as well as theoretical interest, in both its normal and abnormal aspects.

Owing to its quantitative predominance and relative ease of investigation, much more is known of the metabolism of hemoglobin than of the other hemoproteins, a fact which is reflected in the space devoted to consideration of each of the several substances in this category. A brief survey of the over-all metabolism of porphyrins and their derivatives is followed by a discussion of their synthesis, including a consideration of certain abnormalities regarded as "inborn errors." The discussion of the degradation of the hemoproteins to bile pigments and the minor pathways of catabolism of porphyrins is followed by a consideration of their normal and abnormal excretory metabolites. The chapter concludes with a brief treatment of the metabolic interrelations of porphyrins, carbohydrates, and proteins.

OVER-ALL SURVEY OF PORPHYRIN METABOLISM

A scheme illustrating the over-all metabolism of the porphyrins is presented in Figure 113. The complex porphyrin ring is synthesized from small units, i.e., glycine, succinic acid, and a 1-carbon fragment from the α-carbon atom of glycine (probably "formate," p. 520). Two isomeric types of porphyrins are produced. Type I porphyrins form a minor metabolic path and are excreted unutilized (after minor structural modifications). Although small amounts of Type III porphyrins are also excreted, the major metabolic path of these compounds involves eventual union with iron (forming hemes) and specific proteins to yield hemoproteins.

Small amounts of open-chain tetrapyrrolic compounds, the bile pigments, are formed during the synthesis of the hemoproteins, either from precursors of the porphyrins or from unutilized heme. Traces of bile pigments may arise also from the catabolism of myoglobin, catalases, peroxidases, and cytochromes. The major source of the bile pigments, however, is the hemoglobin of the erythrocytes, liberated upon destruction of the latter at the end of their "life" span of approximately one hundred twenty-five days.

As indicated in the figure, hemoglobin is the dominant hemoprotein in the body, by sheer weight in a static sense, and by the magnitude of its metabolic turnover from the dynamic standpoint. It accounts not only for most of the porphyrin compounds synthesized daily (i.e., most of the bile pigments excreted, 300 mg.), but also for a sizeable turnover in protein (about 8 grams of globin daily) and iron (27 mg./day, which exceeds the daily dietary requirement). Although the bile pigments and traces of porphyrins which are excreted represent sheer waste, this is not a loss of great magnitude. The iron and protein moieties of the hemoproteins are reutilized.

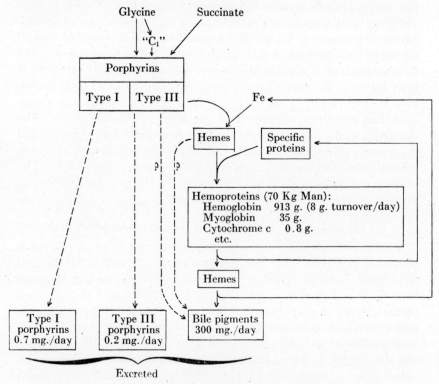

Fig. 113. Over-all metabolism of porphyrins

SYNTHESIS

It is probable that most of the hemoproteins of the body (e.g., catalases, peroxidases, cytochromes) are synthesized *in situ,* suggesting that all cells may have the ability to construct porphyrins. However, the synthesis of hemoglobin is a special case, being limited to the hemopoietic organs (mainly red bone marrow in adults). For convenience, general aspects of porphyrin synthesis will be discussed first, followed by consideration of specific hemoproteins.

GENERAL SYNTHESIS OF PORPHYRINS. (*a*) FORMATION OF PORPHYRIN RING. Unfortunately, so little information is available concerning the mechanism of formation of the porphyrin ring that any metabolic scheme, such as that presented in Figure 114, must be regarded as largely hypothetical. As indicated by experiments with isotopes, glycine and succinic acid (the latter probably reacting as succinyl-CoA, p. 455) are the precursors of the pyrrole units which constitute the porphyrins. In addition, the α-carbon atom of glycine (via "C_1"?) forms the methyne ($-CH=$) bridges between the pyrroles. Condensation of glycine with two molecules of succinic acid produces a pyrrole bearing acetic and propionic acid side-chains. At this point or shortly thereafter the carboxyl group of glycine is lost.

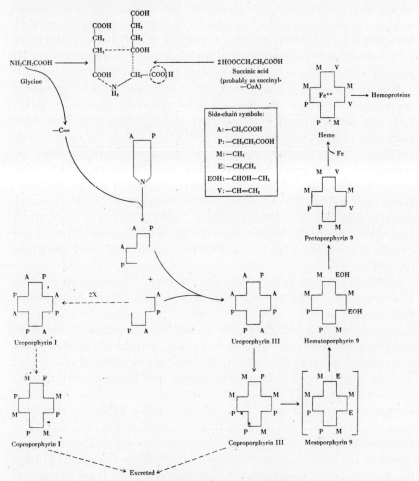

Fig. 114. Synthesis of porphyrins

Although there is as yet little evidence to suggest it, it may be helpful to assume that the synthesis of the closed tetrapyrrole ring proceeds via the formation of dipyrroles. The two monopyrrole units bearing acetic and propionic acid groups condense (bridged by a methyne group) in either of two ways: alternating (A-P-A-P) or symmetrical (P-A-A-P) with respect to side-chains.

Condensation of a symmetrical with an alternating dipyrrole (again linked by methyne groups) results in formation of uroporphyrin III (tetracetic, tetrapropionic), the probable precursor of the major porphyrins synthesized by the organism. In a minor, but normal bypath, two alternating dipyrroles unite to form uroporphyrin I. Uroporphyrins may be excreted under abnormal circumstances.

(b) FORMATION OF COPRO- AND PROTOPORPHYRINS. Decarboxylation of the four acetic acid side-chains of the uroporphyrins to methyl groups (probably stepwise) results in coproporphyrins (tetramethyl, tetrapropionic). Coproporphyrin I, formed in the minor pathway, is excreted without being utilized. Although traces of coproporphyrin III are also excreted, most of it is converted to a protoporphyrin.

Recent evidence suggests that the two propionic acid groups of coproporphin III that are destined to become vinyl groups ($-CH=CH_2$) in protoporphyrin (tetramethyl, divinyl, dipropionic) are first converted to hydroxyethyl groups ($-CHOH-CH_3$), the intermediate porphyrin being hematoporphyrin (tetramethyl, di-hydroxyethyl, dipropionic). If the propionic acid groups were decarboxylated to ethyl groups ($-CH_2CH_3$) before becoming hydroxyethyl groups, the additional intermediate thus formed would be mesoporphyrin (tetramethyl, diethyl, dipropionic). Mesoporphyrin, hematoporphyrin, and protoporphyrin, although derived from porphyrins of Type III, are frequently designated Type 9 (or IX) for reasons discussed elsewhere (p. 109).

(c) FORMATION OF HEMES AND HEMOPROTEINS. Insertion of an atom of iron into the central position of protoporphyrin 9 forms heme, which then may be coupled to various proteins to produce the conjugated hemoproteins, such as hemoglobin, myoglobin, cytochrome c, catalases, and peroxidases. Certain hemoproteins (e.g., cytochrome oxidase) contain porphyrins other than protoporphyrin, but these prosthetic groups are probably derived from protoporphyrin and hence are synthesized via the same general pathway.

SYNTHESIS OF HEMOGLOBIN. In adult man, this synthesis is restricted normally to the red bone marrow. Three components are required: (1) protoporphyrin 9, synthesized as described above; (2) globin, produced by the usual mechanisms of protein synthesis (p. 498); (3) iron, the sources, absorption, transport, and storage of which are considered elsewhere (p. 617).

In addition to the actual constituents of hemoglobin, certain cofactors are required, viz., the folic-folinic acid group (p. 207), vitamin B_{12} (p. 209) and the "intrinsic factor" necessary for its absorption (p.

209), and copper. Synthesis of hemoglobin and maturation of the erythrocyte proceed concomitantly, rendering a decision difficult as to whether a given cofactor is concerned in one process or the other. The requirement for folinic acid and B_{12} may be due to the utilization of a 1-carbon unit from glycine in the formation of the methyne bridges of the porphyrins. No satisfactory explanation of the role of copper can be offered.

As stated previously, synthesis of hemoglobin appears to proceed concurrently with the maturation of the erythrocyte. The primitive red cell contains free porphyrins rather than hemoglobin. As the cell matures, the content of porphyrin decreases and that of hemoglobin increases. These changes are correlated with alterations in staining properties of the cell. The circulating red cell contains traces of protoporphyrin, the amount being related to iron deficiency or other factors that inhibit the synthesis of hemoglobin, and coproporphyrin (mostly Type III), the quantity of which varies with the rate of erythropoiesis.

The average "life" of the erythrocyte and other features of the chemistry of this cell are discussed in connection with the formed elements of the blood (p. 737). Suffice it to mention at this point that the substances incorporated in the red cell (protoporphyrin, iron, and globin) are effectively isolated from the dynamic state and metabolic pools (p. 487) of the other constituents of the body for the "lifetime" of the cell. The iron and globin are returned to the community of metabolites upon disintegration of the cell; the porphyrin moiety is exceptional in this respect, as it is not reutilized (p. 591).

In the adult human being (70-kg. man), approximately 8 grams of hemoglobin are synthesized (and degraded) per day, corresponding to about 300 mg. of porphyrin (porphyrin ring is ca. 4 per cent by weight of hemoglobin molecule). As discussed below, only traces of porphyrins are involved in other, minor metabolic pathways. Increased synthesis of hemoglobin (compensatory polycythemia) occurs as a result of chronic exposure to low partial pressures of oxygen.

"Abnormal" hemoglobin molecules are synthesized in sickle-cell anemia (p. 115). A characteristic fetal type of hemoglobin is also recognized (p. 115).

SYNTHESIS OF OTHER HEMOPROTEINS. Practically nothing is known of the synthesis of myoglobin, the catalases, or peroxidases. The rate of turnover (p. 620) of iron in the catalase of red cells is the same as that of the iron of hemoglobin, but this is only one-eighth of that of the iron in liver catalase.

Cytochrome c turnover (incorporation of radioactive glycine) is much more rapid than that of hemoglobin in regenerating liver after partial hepatectomy. On the other hand, the turnover of cytochrome c is rather slow in skeletal muscle and heart. It is of considerable interest that the concentration of cytochrome c in all tissues is directly related to the state of thyroid function. In conditions of protein deprivation, preference is given to the synthesis of cytochrome c, as is the case with hemoglobin (p. 496).

ABNORMALITIES IN SYNTHESIS OF PORPHYRINS AND HEME. This topic is mentioned later (p. 596) in connection with the excretion of porphyrins, since it is chiefly by detection and characterization of abnormalities in the excretion of porphyrins that the underlying dysfunctions have been discovered and classified.

In general, accumulation and excretion of excessive quantities of Type I porphyrins result from a greatly accelerated rate of synthesis of heme, whereas interference with the synthesis of heme usually results in accumulation and excretion of a preponderance of Type III porphyrins. The former condition (i.e., Type I) occurs in hemolytic anemias, the latter (i.e., Type III) in lead poisoning.

"Inborn errors" of metabolism (p. 255) involving the porphyrins are designated porphyrias. Two general types are recognized:

1. *"Erythropoietic" porphyria.* This rare condition, transmitted as a Mendelian recessive characteristic, is manifested by the development, early in life, of photosensitivity, due to the accumulation of porphyrins in the skin. The bone marrow appears to be the site of the metabolic error, as a result of which large amounts of uro- and coproporphyrins of Type I appear in the urine and feces.

2. *"Hepatic" porphyria.* This relatively common metabolic anomaly, transmitted as a Mendelian dominant trait, is characterized by intermittent abdominal and nervous symptoms, rather than cutaneous. In this condition the organ responsible for the dysfunction is the liver, in which there occurs abnormal and excessive production of porphyrins (chiefly Type III), their precursors, and related compounds. Coproporphyrin (mainly of Type III) is excreted, together with uroporphyrin I, an incompletely characterized "uro-like" porphyrin of Type III (p. 596), and porphobilinogen (p. 108).

Certain classifications of the porphyrias include a "chronic," "mixed" type, having an excretory pattern similar to "hepatic" porphyria, but exhibiting photosensitivity (with or without abdominal and nervous manifestations) and occurring usually in adults. Although a familial incidence has been observed, it is uncertain whether this "porphyria" is a true "inborn error," since many cases appear to have a precipitating cause involving liver damage.

CATABOLISM OF HEMOPROTEINS AND PORPHYRINS

There is little information available on the mechanisms of degradation of hemoproteins other than hemoglobin. It has been suggested, on the basis of tenuous evidence, that myoglobin is catabolized to bile pigments; evidence of an indirect and circumstantial nature is also available with regard to catalase in this regard. Nothing is known of the pathway of catabolism of the cytochromes. The small quantities of methemoglobin (p. 118) which may be present normally in the erythrocyte are probably reduced to hemoglobin by enzyme systems in the cell; a small fraction may be degraded and excreted as porphyrin.

CATABOLISM OF HEMOGLOBIN. The degradation of hemoglobin (about 8 grams daily) is initiated with the breakdown of the erythrocytes at the end of their "life" span, and results in the formation of bile pigments (p. 112), as indicated in Figure 115. The chief normal sites of this degradation are the reticuloendothelial cells of the spleen, bone marrow, and liver, although it may occur in all tissues into which blood has extravasated, as witness the fine play of colors resulting from a "black eye."

For convenience, the conversions undergone by the bile pigments in the intestine are considered separately, after the discussion of the breakdown of hemoglobin to the stage of bilirubin.

(*a*) CONVERSION OF HEMOGLOBIN TO BILE PIGMENTS. Many of the specific details in this pathway are uncertain, several of the debated points being indicated in Figure 115. No less than three possible routes have been suggested for the conversion of erythrocyte hemoglobin to plasma bilirubin:

1. According to the least probable hypothesis, the linkage between the porphyrin ring and the globin is retained, even after the prosthetic group has been converted to an open-chain bile pigment. According to this scheme, a methyne group in the heme ring is oxidized, opening the ring and producing a compound of globin, biliverdin (green pigment), and iron. The metal is removed next, yielding biliverdin-globin, the prosthetic group of which undergoes reduction to bilirubin (yellow-orange pigment), the product (approximately 300 mg. daily) then entering and being transported in the plasma as bilirubin-globin.

2. A second suggested route is identical with the first through the stage of biliverdin-globin. The globin moiety is then believed to split off, releasing biliverdin, which undergoes reduction to bilirubin, which enters the blood stream. Bilirubin is transported in the plasma to the liver attached to a fraction of the plasma globulins, according to this theory.

3. The third possibility which has been suggested involves an initial cleavage into heme and globin, and breakdown of the heme to bilirubin by the reactions already indicated, but involving the free prosthetic group, unattached to globin. As in the second suggested route, bilirubin is assumed to be transported by the plasma globulins.

(*b*) BILIRUBIN IN PLASMA. It has been found that bilirubin mi-

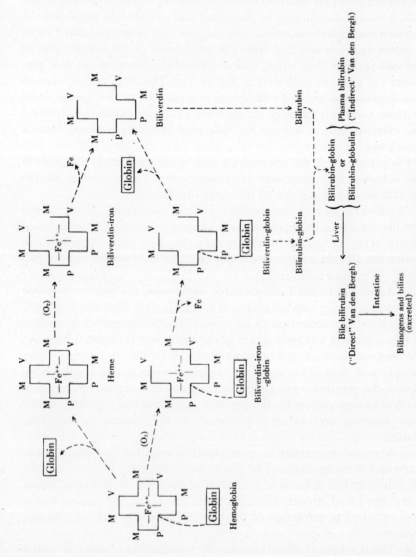

Fig. 115. Degradation of hemoglobin to bile pigments

grates in normal plasma attached to an α_1-globulin (p. 505). Whether this protein is identical with or in any way related to the original globin is not known, but this seems improbable. In this form (normally 0.1–1.0 mg./100 ml.), it is carried to the liver, where it is separated from its protein carrier by either the Kupffer or polygonal cells. The latter excrete the bilirubin into the bile canaliculi, from which it ultimately enters the duodenum in the bile (about 300 mg. daily).

There is evidence that the bilirubin normally present in plasma differs chemically from that which has been "processed" by the liver. In hemolytic disorders, the excessive breakdown of hemoglobin causes the accumulation of abnormally large amounts of the "normal" type of bilirubin in the plasma. On the other hand, in biliary obstruction, bilirubin is reabsorbed from the bile canaliculi into the plasma, where it migrates with the albumin. This "liver-processed" bilirubin, which is believed by some to be a metal complex of bilirubin and albumin, behaves chemically in a manner quite different from the bilirubin of normal plasma.

The two types of bilirubin discussed above may be differentiated by the van den Bergh reaction, the chemistry of which is discussed elsewhere (p. 114). Essentially, the test consists in treatment of the sample with a diazonium compound to produce an azo dye (blue-violet under usual conditions of the test). The test may be performed qualitatively or quantitatively, the latter procedure being more sensitive to small quantities of bilirubin.

When the diazo reagent in aqueous solution is added to normal serum or plasma (direct van den Bergh reaction), no coupling occurs within thirty to forty-five seconds (no color; negative prompt direct reaction). Coupling will occur, however, gradually, after longer periods of time (delayed direct reaction). This delay in coupling is generally attributed to binding of the normal serum bilirubin to protein (α_1-globulin). Addition of alcohol to the reaction mixture (indirect van den Bergh reaction) results in prompt coupling, probably by loosening the attachment of bilirubin to globulin, or by facilitating the transport of the diazonium salt to the methylene bridge across the protein obstacle. Alcohol is not necessary for immediate coupling of "liver-processed" bilirubin, e.g., in bile, which consequently gives a prompt direct van den Bergh reaction. This reaction is also obtained with serum in certain abnormal conditions of the liver or bile passages, when the "processed" bilirubin of the bile has re-entered the blood stream (e.g., in biliary obstruction). Both forms of bilirubin give the indirect van den Bergh reaction, which can therefore be employed in the quantitative determination of total bilirubin.

Serum (or plasma) contains 0.1–1.0 mg. of bilirubin per 100 ml. When the direct reaction (i.e., in aqueous solution) is applied quantitatively, coupling occurs within one minute to the extent of 0.00–0.24 mg. of bilirubin per 100 ml. (one-minute direct-reacting bilirubin). This amount of rapidly reacting pigment is apparently not sufficient to produce a visible color in the qualitative van den Bergh procedure. Increase in this fraction of the serum bilirubin is abnormal, even though the total is within normal limits.

(*c*) FURTHER METABOLISM OF THE BILE PIGMENTS. The reactions undergone by the bile pigments are outlined in Figure 116. Structural formulas and other chemical characteristics of these compounds are presented elsewhere (p. 112).

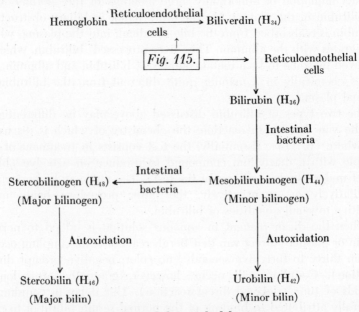

Fig. 116. *Metabolism of the bile pigments*

As indicated above (Fig. 115, p. 592), hemoglobin is converted to biliverdin by an oxidative reaction, and biliverdin (34 H atoms) is reduced to bilirubin (36 H atoms), both reactions being catalyzed by enzyme systems in the tissues. Most of the remaining reactions of the bile pigments are the result of the action of intestinal bacteria; a few are due to spontaneous autoxidation.

In the intestinal lumen, bacterial enzyme systems reduce bilirubin (ca. 300 mg.) to mesobilirubinogen (ca. 300 mg.), the quantitatively minor member of the pair of compounds in the "bilinogen" category. Since the reduction requires addition of four pairs of H atoms, there are probably four steps involved. "Mesobilirubin" (p. 113) may be an intermediate.

Most of the mesobilirubinogen is reduced further to stercobilinogen, the major component of the bilinogens. Both bilinogens are excreted to a certain extent, unchanged, in both urine and feces. A variable fraction of the bilinogens undergoes spontaneous autoxidation to the class of "bilins," stercobilinogen forming stercobilin, mesobilirubinogen forming a compound known variously as "urobilin-IX-α," "K-urobilin," or simply, "urobilin." Stercobilin and urobilin are the major and minor fractions, respectively, of the bilin group.

A variable portion of the bilinogens and bilins is excreted in the feces (40–280 mg. daily, av., 200). The remainder is reabsorbed from the intestine, passing into the portal circulation. The major part of this fraction is removed from the blood by the liver; its exact fate is unknown, but it does not appear to be re-excreted normally in the bile in significant amounts. The small amount of bilinogens and bilins that escapes the liver and enters the systemic circulation is excreted in the urine. The fraction of the total daily output of bilinogens and bilins which appears in the urine depends to some extent on conditions for reabsorption in the intestine, being increased in constipation and decreased in diarrhea. In the presence of normal liver and bowel function, the amount excreted daily in the urine does not exceed 4 mg.

For clinical purposes, the combined bilinogen fraction of the urine (called "urobilinogen") is determined by means of the Ehrlich aldehyde reagent (p. 114). Total urinary bilins plus bilinogens may be determined by the use of the same reagent, following reduction of the former to the latter. Alternatively, the bilinogens may be oxidized to bilins, and total bilins determined by the fluorescence of their zinc derivatives, or by spectrophotometry.

"EXTRA-ERYTHROCYTIC" SOURCES OF BILE PIGMENTS. Experiments using isotopically labeled glycine (p. 587) have indicated that, although the pathway delineated above is normally the major source of the bilins and bilinogens, two other pathways also are involved (accounting for about 11 per cent of the total). One of these pathways is responsible for a rather slow but continual synthesis of bile pigments, unrelated to the synthesis or breakdown of hemoglobin. It has been suggested that hemoproteins other than hemoglobin (catalase, peroxidase, cytochromes) may be the source of this fraction of bile pigments.

The other side-path in the synthesis of bile pigments appears to be related to the synthesis of hemoglobin itself. It is believed that this fraction may be derived from the breakdown of hemoglobin occurring accidentally during the maturation of the erythrocyte, from immediate precursors of the heme group or from unutilized heme itself. The fraction of the bile pigments derived from this pathway increases in conditions characterized by increased synthesis of porphyrins or of hemoglobin, as in pernicious anemia and porphyria.

EXCRETION OF PRODUCTS OF PORPHYRIN METABOLISM

Although much of this material has been mentioned in connection with each of the several aspects of porphyrin metabolism, it may be helpful to collect and coordinate the information here, together with certain other data on the excretion of porphyrin metabolites.

BILE PIGMENTS. The bilinogens and bilins, which constitute the major final catabolites of porphyrins in the body, are excreted in the total amount of about 300 mg. daily, most of which is in the feces (p. 595). Bilirubin is not a normal constituent of the urine or feces (pp. 595, 276).

PORPHYRINS. (*a*) NORMAL EXCRETORY PATTERN. Traces of porphyrins are excreted normally, mainly in the feces. The average daily output of coproporphyrin I is about 0.7 mg., that of coproporphyrin III, 0.2 mg. Urinary coproporphyrin ranges from 60 to 280 μg. (average 160) daily, of which 60 to 80 per cent is Type I, 20 to 40 per cent Type III. Fecal coproporphyrin amounts to 300 to 1100 μg. daily of which 70 to 90 per cent is Type I. Uroporphyrins are not excreted normally. The small amount of protoporphyrin found in the feces is probably derived mainly from the hemoglobin of the meat in the diet. Traces are found also in the bile, but not normally in the urine.

It should be mentioned that much of the coproporphyrin in normal urine is excreted as a "porphyrinogen," or precursor, which is converted to coproporphyrin spontaneously on standing, or by chemical treatment with mild oxidants.

(*b*) PORPHYRINURIAS. Under certain conditions, excessive amounts and "abnormal" types of porphyrins are excreted. Table 50 summarizes data on the general conditions characterized by excretion of large quantities of porphyrins in the urine (and feces).

The porphyrias have been discussed elsewhere (p. 590). It is of interest that the porphyrins excreted in the urine in "hepatic" and "mixed" porphyrias are present as Zn complexes, whereas those of "erythropoietic" porphyria are in the free state. The two former conditions are characterized also by the excretion of porphobilinogen (discussed below). Uroporphyrins are apparently excreted only in porphyric porphyrinuria; coproporphyrin is found alone in other types of porphyrinuria. The "uro-like" porphyrin referred to in the table belongs to Type III, but seems to possess 7 instead of 8 carboxyl groups.

Coproporphyrin III is excreted in excessive quantities as the result of (1) exposure to certain toxic chemicals and heavy metals (e.g., lead), (2) acute alcoholism (temporary increase in output), (3) cirrhosis of the liver in chronic alcoholics (persistent porphyrinuria), and (4) in certain miscellaneous disorders.

Abnormally large quantities of coproporphyrin I are found in the urine in (1) obstructive jaundice (deviation from biliary excretion),

(2) certain liver diseases (including cirrhosis in non-alcoholics), and
(3) certain blood dyscrasias.

Table 50. Porphyrinurias

GENERAL TYPE	SPECIFIC CONDITIONS	CHIEF URINARY PORPHYRINS	OTHER CHARACTERISTICS
Hereditary	Erythropoietic porphyria	Uroporphyrin I Coproporphyrin I	Increased porphyrins in bone marrow
	Hepatic porphyria	Coproporphyrin, mainly III. Uroporphyrin I. "Uro-like" porphyrin III	Increased porphyrins in liver. Porphobilinogen in urine.
Hereditary or acquired?	"Mixed," chronic porphyria	Coproporphyrin, mainly III. Uroporphyrins as above	Increased porphyrins in liver. Porphobilinogen in urine
Acquired	Toxic agents: Chemicals Heavy metals Acute alcoholism Cirrhosis in alcoholics	Coproporphyrin III	
	Certain liver diseases: Infectious hepatitis Cirrhosis in non-alcoholics	Coproporphyrin I	
	Certain blood dyscrasias: Hemolytic anemias Pernicious anemia Leukemia	Coproporphyrin I	
	Obstructive jaundice	Coproporphyrin I	
	Miscellaneous conditions: Poliomyelitis Aplastic anemias Hodgkin's disease	Coproporphyrin III	

OTHER RELATED METABOLITES. A compound known as "porphobilinogen" is excreted in "hepatic" and "mixed" porphyrias. It may be a precursor of the porphyrins, although it is not clear whether it belongs to a normal or abnormal metabolic pathway. Although regarded formerly as a dipyrrolic compound, recent evidence suggests that it may be a monopyrrole. Certain of its chemical characteristics are discussed elsewhere (p. 108).

RELATION OF PORPHYRIN METABOLISM TO THAT OF OTHER METABOLITES

Figure 117 illustrates the major interrelations between the porpyhrins (and their derivatives) and the carbohydrates and proteins. Carbohydrate provides the succinyl portion, protein the glycine and methyne parts of the porphyrin ring. Combination with iron produces the hemes (iron porphyrins), which are coupled with specific proteins to form the hemoproteins.

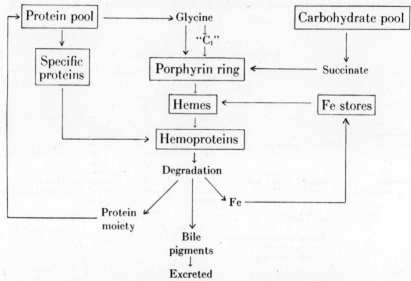

Fig. 117. Interrelations of porphyrins with other metabolites

In the degradation of the hemoproteins, the iron and protein moieties are returned to their respective pools for reutilization. The non-metallic portion of the prosthetic group (derived from glycine and succinate, originally) is discarded completely by the organism in the form of the bile pigments.

BIBLIOGRAPHY

Annual Review of Biochemistry.

Annual Review of Physiology.

Drabkin, D. L.: Metabolism of the hemin chromoproteins, Physiol. Rev. 31:345, 1951.

Gray, C. H.: The Bile Pigments, London, Methuen & Co., Ltd., 1953.

Lemberg, R. and Legge, J. W.: Hematin Compounds and Bile Pigments, New York, Interscience Publishers, Inc., 1949, Chapters 10–13.

Watson, C. J.: Porphyrin metabolism. In Diseases of Metabolism, edited by G. G. Duncan, Philadelphia, W. B. Saunders Company, 1952, Chapter 19.

22

INORGANIC METABOLISM

SODIUM, POTASSIUM, AND CHLORIDE METABOLISM

RELATED PHYSIOLOGICAL MECHANISMS. The metabolism of Na, K, and Cl is intimately related to certain fundamental physiological mechanisms which are considered elsewhere in detail and will therefore be mentioned here only briefly:

(*a*) WATER BALANCE AND OSMOTIC PRESSURE (P. 301). The maintenance of normal hydration and osmotic pressure depends primarily on the total base content of the body fluids. Since Na constitutes the largest fraction of the total base of the extracellular fluids (142/155), it plays a dominant role in this connection.

(*b*) ACID-BASE BALANCE (P. 314). At any given H_2CO_3 concentration, the H^+ ion concentration of extracellular fluids depends upon the bicarbonate concentration (p. 320). Since the latter is determined by the amount of total base in excess of ions other than HCO_3, and since Cl constitutes by far the largest fraction of the total anions of the extracellular fluids (103/155), it follows that the maintenance of the normal pH of these fluids depends largely on the presence of normal concentrations of Na^+ and Cl^- (p. 320).

(*c*) NEUROMUSCULAR IRRITABILITY. Neuromuscular irritability and excitability are influenced by the relative proportions of certain ions, which may be expressed as follows:

$$\text{Irritability} \propto \frac{Na^+ + K^+}{Ca^{++} + Mg^{++} + H^+}$$

Na is the chief cation and Cl the chief anion of extracellular fluids, whereas K is the chief cation of intracellular fluids (p. 305). Some movement of K occurs from cells to extracellular fluids (including plasma), especially under abnormal conditions of excessive loss of intracellular fluid, the mobilized K being usually excreted promptly in the urine. Some movement of Na occurs in the opposite direction, i.e.,

from extra- to intracellular fluid, especially under the conditions indicated above. Any considerable increase or decrease of K in the
extracellular fluids produces serious and at times fatal disturbances
in muscle irritability, respiration, and myocardial function. Moreover,
no other cation can replace considerable amounts of K in the intracellular fluids without interfering to some extent with the functional
activity of the cell.

ABSORPTION AND EXCRETION. An average adequate diet contains about
3–4 grams (75–100 mEq.) of K and 8–15 grams (130–250 mEq.) of NaCl
daily, the latter being contributed to by the addition of salt to the
food. Normally, Na, K, and Cl are practically completely absorbed
from the gastrointestinal tract, less than 2 per cent of ingested Na and
less than 10 per cent of the K being eliminated in the feces. In subjects with diarrhea, large amounts are lost in the feces, owing in large
measure to failure of reabsorption of constituents of digestive fluids,
the electrolyte composition of which is indicated in Figure 68 and
Table 51. Na and Cl are eliminated chiefly in the urine and, to a lesser
extent, in the perspiration. K is normally eliminated almost entirely
in the urine.

EXCRETION IN URINE. The amounts excreted in the urine are indicated elsewhere (p. 777). Suffice it to state here that under normal conditions the daily urinary excretion of these electrolytes approximates
the intake except under conditions of sudden increase of NaCl intake
following a period of restriction. Na and Cl are removed from the
circulating plasma by glomerular filtration, over 1000 grams of NaCl
entering the renal tubules daily in the glomerular filtrate. Under normal
conditions 99 per cent or more undergoes reabsorption into the blood
stream by the tubular epithelium. About 80–85 per cent of this is reabsorbed in the proximal portion of the tubule, the remainder in the
distal portion. Adrenocortical hormones probably influence chiefly the
latter fraction (enhancing reabsorption of Na and Cl) but perhaps
also the former. In the distal portion, too, about 1–2 per cent of the
Na^+ reabsorption occurs in exchange for H^+ ions (also for K^+) (p.
321) as part of the mechanism of acidification of the urine. Under
normal conditions the regulation of Na and Cl reabsorption and conservation is so efficient that equilibrium can be maintained on a NaCl
intake as low as 0.5 gram daily, Na virtually disappearing from the
urine.

K is removed from the plasma by glomerular filtration and, like Na
and Cl, undergoes extensive (over 90 per cent) reabsorption in the
tubules. However, unlike Na and Cl, it is also excreted into the tubular
lumen by the cells of the distal portion of the renal tubules. This
active process, which apparently competes with H^+ ions in the Na^+
exchange mechanism (p. 322), is perhaps the phase of K excretion

which is influenced by adrenocortical hormones (enhancing K excretion). In the presence of normal kidney function, K is very promptly and efficiently removed from the blood plasma even in the face of a considerably increased supply, preventing undue increase in its concentration in the extracellular fluids.

EXCRETION BY THE SKIN. The Na and Cl content of perspiration is usually lower than that of blood plasma (Table 51). Their concentrations in sweat are decreased by the salt-active adrenal cortical hormones (q.v.), which are secreted in increased amount during acclimatization to heat. This constitutes an adaptive mechanism for conservation of body Na and Cl, the sweat glands producing a progressively more dilute fluid. In normal subjects, the loss of Na and Cl in the perspiration is compensated by a corresponding diminution in their urinary excretion. However, considerable amounts may be lost from the body under conditions of prolonged strenuous exertion at extremely high temperatures and humidity. If, under such circumstances, large amounts of salt-poor water are taken to alleviate thirst, the concentration of NaCl in the body fluids may fall to the point of producing symptoms (muscle cramps, intense headache, exhaustion, mental dulness). These may be relieved by administration of NaCl.

EXCRETION IN DIGESTIVE FLUIDS. The approximate electrolyte composition of certain digestive fluids is indicated in Figure 68 (p. 328) and in Table 51. Under normal conditions these fluids are virtually completely reabsorbed in the bowel but, in the presence of protracted vomiting or diarrhea, it is obvious that large amounts of water and electrolytes may be lost from the body. This is of great importance in the treatment of the dehydration and dislocations of acid-base balance that occur under these circumstances.

Table 51. Approximate Concentration of Certain Electrolytes in Digestive Fluids and Perspiration (mEq./liter)

FLUIDS	NA	K	CL	HCO₃
Gastric juice	20	8	145	0
Pancreatic juice	140	5	40	110
Jejunal juice	138	5	110	30
Bile	140	8	108	38
Perspiration	82	5	85	0
Blood serum	140	4.3	100	25
Interstitial fluid	145	3.3	110	28

NA, CL, AND K IN BLOOD. The normal amounts of Na, Cl, and K in 100 ml. of blood plasma (or serum) are as follows: Na, 300–335 (average 320) mg. (132–144 mEq./liter); Cl, 340–370 mg. (96–105 mEq./liter), or 570–620 mg. expressed as NaCl; K, 14–19 (average 16) mg. (3.6–4.8

mEq./liter). In man, erythrocytes contain little or no Na, smaller amounts of Cl than does the plasma, and large amounts of K (about 370 mg./100 grams). The distribution of Cl^- between plasma and erythrocytes is similar and intimately related to that of HCO_3^-, in accordance with Donnan's law governing the distribution of diffusible monovalent ions (p. 306). The factors which influence this distribution and the changes that occur under physiological conditions are considered elsewhere (p. 318). Suffice it to recall here that shifts of Cl^- and HCO_3^- between the plasma and the erythrocytes play an important role in the maintenance of a constant pH in the blood.

The concentrations of Na, Cl, and K in the plasma vary but slightly under physiological conditions. The plasma Cl may fall somewhat during periods of active gastric secretion of HCl and may rise again in the post-digestive period (reabsorption from intestine). It is affected but slightly by marked variations in Cl intake; the same is true of the plasma Na and K concentrations. The plasma K decreases somewhat during periods of increased carbohydrate utilization (oxidation and glycogen deposition), as following administration of glucose or insulin. This is due apparently to its passage from extracellular fluids into the cells in increased amount under these circumstances.

The influence of adrenal cortical hormones (especially the desoxycorticosterones) in increasing plasma Na and Cl and decreasing K is considered elsewhere in detail (p. 678). It is the result apparently of their effect on renal tubular reabsorption of these ions and on their distribution between intra- and extracellular fluids.

DISTRIBUTION AND INTERMEDIARY METABOLISM. Reference is made elsewhere (p. 302 ff.) to differences in the composition of intra- and extracellular fluids. These are illustrated in Figure 64 (p. 304). We are concerned here mainly with the striking differences in the concentrations of Na, K, and Cl in these fluid compartments. It should be understood that the concentration of electrolytes varies in the intracellular fluid of individual tissues, but the general pattern is rather uniform. Skeletal muscle is the tissue studied most thoroughly in this connection. The rather strict localization of relatively large amounts of K in the intracellular and of Na and Cl in the extracellular fluid is attributable to a rather high degree of selective relative impermeability of most cell membranes to these ions. However, this impermeability is neither absolute nor fixed. In different functional states and under certain abnormal circumstances the composition of the intracellular fluid may be altered as a result of loss of K from and entrance of Na into the cells. These changes are often accompanied by alterations in the concentrations of Cl^- and HCO_3^- in the extracellular fluid, which may seriously affect the state of "acid-base" balance (p. 604).

Some sort of equilibrium is maintained normally between the high cellular (150 mEq./liter) and low extracellular (5 mEq./liter) concentrations of K, and the reverse situation with regard to Na, although the factors operating are not well understood. The adrenal cortical hormones and the kidneys are probably involved, as may be also the oxidative energy of the cell. Under normal conditions, Na and K entering the body are distributed rapidly throughout the extracellular fluids, an equivalent amount being excreted within a short time, almost entirely in the urine. Very little Na is transferred to the cells; studies with radioactive K indicate that its transfer through the cell membrane is slow as compared to that of water, the labeled K attaining equilibrium with the intracellular K only after fifteen hours, whereas deuterium-labeled water attains equilibrium with the total body water in two hours. As indicated elsewhere (p. 311), the addition of Na to the extracellular fluids is followed by a temporary shift of water to that compartment from the cells, osmotic equilibrium being thus preserved. The addition of K is followed promptly by increased renal excretion of K (diuresis), preventing its accumulation in excess in the extracellular fluids. Certain of the factors which influence renal excretion of K are discussed elsewhere, viz., adrenocortical hormones (pp. 678, 679), K concentration in the cells (p. 322), and the state of acid-base balance (p. 323).

Table 52. Approximate Concentration of Na, K, and Cl in Intracellular Water of Muscle and Liver (mEq./liter)

TISSUE	NA	K	CL
Skeletal muscle	7	155	3
Liver	5	145	10

Table 53. Approximate Total Amount of Na, K, Cl, and HCO_3 in Body Fluid Compartments of a 70-Kg. Man (in Milliequivalents)

FLUID	NA	K	CL	HCO_3	H_2O
Extracellular	2000	45	1500	400	14,000 ml.
Intracellular	400	5200	110	340	35,000 ml.

K moves into cells at an increased rate when protoplasm grows, and also during periods of increased glucose utilization (glycogenesis, glycolysis), e.g. after administration of glucose or insulin. The latter phenomenon is perhaps related to the increase in phosphorylative processes that occurs under these circumstances, and may be reflected in a temporary slight fall in serum K concentration.

Excessive loss of K from the body, e.g., due to vomiting, diarrhea, diuresis, or excess adrenal cortical hormones, is followed by movement of K from the cells to the extracellular fluid. This occurs also in conditions of accelerated cellular breakdown, e.g., starvation, trauma, disease. It has been calculated that about 2.7 mEq. of K are released for every gram of nitrogen lost under such circumstances. Anoxia causes a similar transfer of K from intra- to extracellular fluids.

In the presence of normal renal function, passage of K out of the cells is accompanied by a movement of Na in the opposite direction, a considerable portion of the intracellular K being thus replaced by Na. The excess K in the extracellular fluid is excreted in the urine, chiefly with Cl, with a consequent decrease in the concentration of Cl^- in the extracellular fluid and a corresponding increase in HCO_3^-, i.e., a tendency toward a metabolic type of alkalosis (p. 330). Impaired renal function interferes with this exchange of Na for K in the cell and with excretion of the excess K in the blood plasma, resulting in hyperpotassemia. Appreciation of the occurrence and significance of these electrolyte shifts in a variety of common clinical disorders has been of great practical value.

SULFUR METABOLISM

Sulfur is a nutritionally essential element, occurring in proteins in the form of the amino acids, methionine, cystine, and cysteine. It is present in enzymes and certain hormones (anterior pituitary, insulin) and also in such substances as glutathione, thiamine, taurocholic acid, and chondroitin sulfuric acid. The normal requirement is undoubtedly satisfied by an adequate protein intake.

ABSORPTION. Sulfur is ingested in (1) inorganic (Na, K, Mg sulfates) but mainly in (2) organic forms. It is provided chiefly by the S-containing amino acids, methionine and cystine (pp. 529, 535), and also by sulfolipids and glycoproteins (mucoitin and chondroitin sulfuric acids). Inorganic sulfate is absorbed as such from the intestine, as are the amino acids methionine and cystine, liberated by digestion of protein. A small amount of sulfide may be formed in the bowel by the action of bacteria (p. 274). This may be excreted in the feces; if absorbed it is rapidly oxidized to SO_4.

INTERMEDIARY METABOLISM. Sulfur reaching the liver (exogenous or endogenous) undergoes the following changes:

1. The bulk of the organic S is oxidized in the liver to inorganic sulfate (SO_4). A portion of the latter, together with a portion of the inorganic sulfate absorbed as such, enters the systemic circulation and is excreted in the urine.

2. A portion of the organic S escapes oxidation. Some of this fraction is utilized for the formation of S-containing substances, such as

insulin, anterior pituitary hormones and other proteins, taurocholic acid (p. 268), glutathione (p. 370), melanin (?) (pp. 554, 717), etc. The small remainder is excreted in the urine as neutral S.

3. A portion of the inorganic sulfate is combined in the liver with various phenolic substances produced in the bowel largely by bacterial decomposition of amino acids (p. 273) or entering the body as such (e.g., benzene in certain occupations), forming "ethereal" sulfates (e.g., indican, p. 282), which are excreted in the urine. In addition to the participation of inorganic SO_4 in these "detoxication" processes, the amino acid cysteine may form conjugation products (mercapturic acids) in the liver with certain toxic compounds, such as bromobenzene (p. 283).

TRANSPORT AND EXCRETION. Sulfur is present in the blood plasma as inorganic S, 0.5–1.1 mg., ethereal S, 0.1–1.0 mg., and neutral S, 1.7–3.5 mg./100 ml. Whole blood contains 2.2–4.5 mg. neutral S/100 ml., the higher value being due in large measure apparently to the presence of thioneine and glutathione in the erythrocytes.

Sulfur is excreted almost entirely in the urine in the three forms in which it occurs in the blood plasma. The total S output, since it is usually derived mainly from protein, varies with the protein intake and tissue protein catabolism, averaging about 1.0 gram (0.7–1.5 grams) daily under normal conditions. The urinary N:S ratio normally ranges from 13 to 16 in the fasting state or when meat comprises the bulk of the protein intake.

The normal urinary total sulfate (inorganic plus ethereal SO_4) on an average mixed diet ranges from 0.6 to 1.0 gram daily, comprising 85–95 per cent of the total S output. The proportion as well as the absolute amount excreted varies directly with the protein intake. The total SO_4 excretion may be diminished in the presence of renal functional impairment (retained in the blood plasma) and is increased in conditions accompanied by excessive tissue protein catabolism (e.g., fever, increased metabolism).

Inorganic sulfate (Na, K, Ca, Mg, NH_4 sulfates) normally comprises 85–95 per cent of the total urinary SO_4, the remainder being ethereal sulfate (0.06–0.12 gram daily). This fraction consists of Na and K salts of aromatic sulfuric acid compounds (phenyl sulfate, indican, etc.) and therefore varies with the quantity of phenolic substances produced in the intestine or otherwise entering the body (e.g., occupational or accidental exposure). Increase in urine indican (potassium indoxyl sulfate, p. 776), absolute or relative, may occur in conditions accompanied by intestinal stasis (increased bacterial action on protein). In subjects having abnormally high occupational exposure to benzene the proportion of the total urinary SO_4 in the form of ethereal SO_4 may rise to as high as 75–80 per cent.

The neutral S of the urine, normally about 5 per cent of the total S, is in the form of such substances as methionine, cystine, urochrome, taurocholic acid, thiosulfate, and thiocyanate, each in very small amounts. This fraction increases in cystinuria (p. 533), melanuria (?) (pp. 554, 776), and obstructive jaundice (increased taurocholic acid).

IODINE METABOLISM

The metabolism of iodine is of particular significance in connection with the formation of thyroid hormone, which is considered in detail elsewhere (p. 681). Normal adults require about 52 μg. daily but the recommended optimal daily intake for adults is 100–200 μg., for children 50μg., and for infants 20–40 μg. The requirement is probably increased during pregnancy. The iodine of most common foodstuffs is apparently readily available to the organism but is not superior to inorganic iodides. Because of the high iodine content of sea water, marine vegetation, sea foods, and vegetables and fruits grown on the seaboard are particularly rich in this element. Plants (and animal tissues) grown far inland, especially at high altitudes, may be deficient in iodine because of its low concentration in the water. In such regions, iodide is commonly added to the drinking water or table salt in concentrations of 1:5000 to 1:200,000 to ensure an adequate intake and to prevent the development of simple goiter (iodine-deficiency goiter).

ABSORPTION AND EXCRETION.   Iodine and iodides can be absorbed from any portion of the alimentary tract, most readily perhaps from the small intestine, free iodine and iodates probably being first converted to iodide. Organic iodine compounds, e.g., diiodotyrosine and thyroxine, are in part absorbed as such and in part broken down in the stomach and intestines with the formation of iodides. Absorption can occur from other mucous membranes, the lungs, and the skin.

Iodine is excreted by the kidneys, liver, skin, lungs, and intestine, and also in milk and saliva. It is almost entirely in the form of inorganic iodide, and may be either endogenous (including liberation from degradation of thyroxine and diiodotyrosine) or exogenous (food, water). Thyroxine is not demonstrable in excreta except after administration.

The quantity excreted normally varies with the intake. About 40–80 percent is usually excreted in the urine (20–70 μg. daily in adults; 20–35 μg. in children). The urinary fraction of the total elimination is largest when the intake is lowest. Urine iodine is increased by exercise and other factors that increase metabolism (increased rate of turnover of thyroxine), except in the event of profuse sweating, when relatively large amounts are lost by this route. Urine iodine increases during pregnancy.

Iodine in the feces (2–11 μg. daily; 3–27 per cent of intake) is almost entirely exogenous (iodine in unabsorbed food), the remainder being derived from the bile and intestinal secretions. Bile contains 4–14 μg./100 ml. in the fasting state and about 50 μg./100 ml. after eating. A portion of this is reabsorbed in the intestine (enterohepatic circulation). Biliary iodine is chiefly of alimentary origin (exogenous) but is also in part endogenous (degradation of thyroxine in liver).

Under ordinary atmospheric conditions, negligible amounts of iodine are excreted by the skin. With profuse perspiration (heat, humidity, exercise), as much as 30–60 per cent of the total may be lost by this route. The amount in expired air also varies enormously, but may be as much as 10–30 μg. daily. The quantity present in milk varies with the iodine intake and may be increased by administration of iodides. Saliva contains 0–350 μg./100 ml., also depending on the intake.

BLOOD IODINE. Practically all of the iodine in the blood is in the plasma, the concentration in the resting state being 4–10 μg./100 ml. plasma (or serum). If no iodine has been administered for several days, less than 30 per cent of the plasma iodine is in inorganic form (iodide), practically all (4–8 μg./100 ml.) being bound to protein and precipitated with the latter by protein-precipitating agents. It is believed to be largely or entirely in the form of thyroxine. Measurement of the amount of this protein-bound iodine (PBI), reflecting the concentration of circulating thyroid hormone, is therefore of value in the clinical evaluation of the state of thyroid function. High values occur in hyperthyroidism (8–30 μg.) and low values in hypothyroidism (0–3 μg.).

In the fasting state the plasma inorganic iodide is quite constant even in the face of wide variations in thyroid activity (which affect only the plasma PBI) but increases strikingly after iodine is ingested, applied to the skin, or administered for purposes of cholecystography or urography.

DISTRIBUTION AND INTERMEDIARY METABOLISM. The body normally contains about 20–30 mg. of iodine, which is distributed approximately as follows: muscles, 50 per cent; thyroid, 20 per cent; skin, 10 per cent; skeleton, 6 per cent. The concentration in the thyroid (10–40 mg./100 grams) is higher than in other tissues (e.g., 0.03 mg./100 grams muscle). The amount in all tissues diminishes when the intake is lowered, but the normal thyroid retains its capacity for trapping and storing iodine even under such circumstances. This aspect of thyroid function, its mechanism and control, are considered in detail elsewhere (p. 682). Suffice it here to recall that one of the important initial phases of the formation of thyroid hormone involves this remarkable capacity of thyroid cells for trapping and concentrating iodine, which is then rapidly utilized for synthesis of thyroxine.

The normal adult thyroid contains 2–28 mg. of iodine (0.1–0.55 per cent dry weight), varying with the iodine intake and state of thyroid function. By far the largest part is in organic combination, stored in the follicular colloid as "iodothyroglobulin," a composite protein molecule containing thyroxine and diiodotyrosine in peptide combination. On demand (p. 683), thyroxine is mobilized from this compound and is passed into the systemic circulation. It undergoes metabolic degradation apparently chiefly in the liver, its iodine component being excreted in the bile largely as inorganic iodide, but also in some organic combination (thyroxine metabolites).

The liver usually contains 0.5–2.3 mg. of iodine, exhibiting wide variations during periods of absorption and excretion. Iodine entering the portal vein from the intestine in part passes through the liver into the systemic circulation and is in part removed by the hepatic cells and excreted in the bile. Organic compounds containing iodine, exogenous or endogenous, are partly or completely degraded in the liver, the iodine being liberated as iodide.

MAGNESIUM METABOLISM

Magnesium is an essential constituent of the tissues and body fluids, but little is known regarding its metabolism or requirement. It is undoubtedly provided in adequate amounts by diets adequate in other respects because of its wide distribution in vegetable and animal tissues. It ranks next to K among the cations of intracellular fluids (p. 305).

Mg^{++} ions serve as activators of important enzymes involved in intermediary metabolism, including phosphorylase, phosphoglucomutase, and enolase; it inhibits ATP-ase. It exerts an effect on neuromuscular irritability similar to that of Ca^{++}, high levels inducing anesthesia and low levels tetany.

ABSORPTION AND EXCRETION. The absorption of Mg from the bowel resembles that of Ca in many respects. An excessively high intake of fat, phosphate, Ca, and alkalies appears to diminish its absorption from the upper intestine. A high Mg intake apparently increases urinary excretion of Ca. The influence of the factors mentioned above probably depends on their influence on the solubility of Mg salts. Little information is available regarding the effect of vitamin D on Mg absorption. The fact that the Mg content of the bones in rickets is not decreased and is usually actually increased argues against the importance of vitamin D in this connection.

Like Ca, Mg is excreted in the feces and urine. Under normal conditions about 50–80 per cent is excreted in the feces (Mg of food, bile, digestive secretions) and the remainder by the kidneys. Administration of acidifying substances (e.g., NH_4Cl) is followed by increased urinary elimination of Mg (as of Ca, p. 616). On the other hand, thyroxine, which causes an increase in urinary Ca, has practically no effect on Mg excretion. The same is true of the parathyroid hormone.

BLOOD MAGNESIUM. Magnesium, unlike calcium, is present in both erythrocytes and plasma, its concentration in the former being 5.4 to 7.8 mg./100 grams (average 6.6 mg.) and in the latter 1.8 to 3.6 mg./100 ml. (1.5–3.0 mEq./liter). About 70–85 per cent (average 80) of the serum Mg is diffusible, the remainder being bound to plasma proteins. The Mg content of cerebrospinal fluid is higher than that of blood plasma, averaging about 3.3 mg./100 ml. (2.7 mEq./liter).

Little is known regarding the factors involved in the regulation of the Mg content of the blood. It is relatively unaffected by vitamin D or parathyroid hormone. There is in certain respects a reciprocal relationship between Mg and Ca in the serum; e.g., in oxalate poisoning, a decrease in serum Ca is accompanied by an increase in Mg, whereas the hypermagnesemia induced by injection of magnesium salts is accompanied by a fall in serum Ca, at times to tetanic levels.

An increase in the non-diffusible fraction of serum Mg (25–60 per cent of total; normal, 15–30 per cent) has been reported in hyperthyroidism and low values (0–5 per cent) in myxedema. The significance of these changes is not known.

CALCIUM AND PHOSPHORUS METABOLISM

Although over 99 per cent of the body Ca and 80–85 per cent of its P is in the bones, important functions of these elements are exerted in directions other than preservation of skeletal structure. Ca^{++} ions (1) decrease capillary and cell membrane permeability, (2) decrease neuromuscular excitability, and are necessary for (3) muscle contraction, (4) normal transmission of nerve impulses, and (5) blood coagulation. Ca^{++} ions also activate certain enzymes, including lipase, succinic dehydrogenase, adenosine triphosphatase, and some proteases.

The vital functions of P in various phases of organic metabolism have been referred to repeatedly. It is necessary merely to recall here the fundamental role of high-energy phosphate bonds in the storage, liberation, and transfer of energy (e.g., ATP, phosphocreatine), the importance of hexose- and triose-phosphates in the intermediary metabolism of carbohydrate, and the metabolic significance of such P-containing substances as phospholipids, nucleic acids, and nucleotides (DPN, TPN, etc.). These subjects are discussed in detail elsewhere. We shall be concerned here mainly with the role of phosphate in inorganic metabolism.

ABSORPTION. Calcium and phosphate are absorbed in the small intestine, more readily in the upper than in the lower portions. In the course of digestion of nucleoproteins and phosphoproteins, phosphate may be split off and absorbed as such. If ester forms are present, they may undergo hydrolysis (enzymes of pancreatic and intestinal juice) prior to absorption. It has been suggested that because of this fact a considerable fraction of the dietary phosphate is absorbed later than the major portion of the Ca. This may permit better absorption of both elements, especially in regions of relatively low acidity.

FACTORS INFLUENCING DEGREE OF ABSORPTION. Several factors influence the degree of absorption of Ca:

(a) Concentration in Intestine. Other factors being equal, absorption of Ca is roughly proportional to its concentration in the intestine. The same appears to be true of phosphate.

(b) Requirement of Organism. As in the case of iron, but not to the same extent, the amount of Ca absorbed varies somewhat with the requirement of the organism for this element.

(c) Intestinal pH. Calcium salts, particularly phosphates and carbonates, are quite soluble in acid solutions and are relatively insoluble in alkaline solutions. Consequently, factors which increase intestinal acidity favor absorption of Ca, and vice versa. Under conditions of normal gastric acidity, Ca salts of weak organic acids are converted to the soluble chloride and, if retained in the stomach for a sufficient period, even the less soluble basic phosphate may go into solution. The acidity in the duodenum, normally pH 2.3–7.0, is of considerable importance, determining whether more of the Ca is in the form of the more soluble acid phosphate or less soluble basic phosphate. Calcium chloride and acid phosphate are probably absorbed from the duodenum before the gastric juice acidity is neutralized. Subsequently, absorption of Ca may be favored by the presence of organic acids (e.g., lactic, citric, amino acids, fatty acids).

(d) Other Substances in the Food Mixture. An excess of Mg apparently diminishes absorption of Ca, especially if the latter is not present in adequate amounts. Considerable interest has centered in the Ca:P ratio, the optimum ratio for absorption of both elements being about 1:1 (1:2–2:1). An excessively high ratio is accompanied by decreased absorption of phosphate (rachitogenic diet, p. 154). It is stated that a low ratio does not result in decreased Ca absorption. This effect is apparently related to the influence on solubility of the products (calcium phosphates) formed under these conditions. Such substances as iron, beryllium, aluminum and strontium, which form insoluble phosphates, likewise interfere with absorption of phosphate, and can induce rickets (p. 155).

Phytic acid (inositol hexaphosphate), which occurs in cereal grains, forms insoluble salts (phytin) with Ca and Mg (insoluble above pH 3–4), with consequent impairment of absorption of these elements. This phenomenon is regarded as the basis of the rachitogenic effect of such cereals as oatmeal. Hydroxyacids such as lactic, citric, and tartaric shift the precipitation point of Ca phytate toward a higher pH (see also action of vitamin D, below and p. 153).

(e) Vitamin D. Vitamin D promotes absorption of Ca from the distal ileum, where absorption is otherwise relatively poor, but not from the upper ileum, where Ca is absorbed more readily. Intestinal absorption of phosphate is apparently increased somewhat. This may be a result of increased Ca absorption, maintaining an optimum local Ca:P ratio.

Vitamin D apparently counteracts the effect of phytic acid in binding the Ca^{++} ions and thus diminishing Ca absorption. In adequate amounts and with a high Ca intake, it suppresses the rachitogenic and anticalcifying effect of phytic acid. The mechanism of its action in this connection is not known.

Vitamin D lowers the pH in the distal ileum, cecum, and colon. This may facilitate Ca absorption or, on the other hand, may be a result, in part at least, of increased absorption, decreasing the base of the intestinal contents.

BLOOD CALCIUM AND PHOSPHATE. The inorganic phosphate of blood plasma ranges from 3–4.5 mg./100 ml. (1.7–2.5 mEq./liter) in adults and from 4.5–6.5 mg. (2.5–3.6 mEq./liter) in children. It is somewhat higher in summer than in winter (solar ultraviolet irradiation). It decreases during periods of increased carbohydrate utilization (administration of glucose or insulin), owing presumably to increased utilization for phosphorylation of carbohydrate metabolites (hexose- and triose-phosphates). A slight increase follows ingestion of large amounts of Ca and a considerable drop follows parenteral administration of Mg.

There is no Ca in erythrocytes. The Ca content of plasma (usually determined in serum) is 8.5–11.5 mg./100 ml. (usually 9–11 mg., or 4.5–5.5 mEq./liter). During infancy and early childhood (to 12 years) the average values approach the upper limit of this range, falling with advancing years.

Calcium exists in the plasma in two physiologically distinct fractions, designated (1) diffusible or ionized and (2) non-diffusible or non-ionized. The diffusible fraction (50–60 per cent of total) is capable of passing through an artificial semipermeable membrane (cellophane, collodion) and, presumably, through the living capillary wall; the non-diffusible fraction (40–50 per cent of total) cannot pass through, owing to its combination with plasma proteins. Although the two fractions may vary independently of each other under certain abnormal circumstances (e.g., hypoproteinemia, in which the non-diffusible Ca alone may be decreased; hypoparathyroidism, in which the diffusible fraction alone may be decreased), they seem to be in a state of rather unstable equilibrium, which is probably controlled to a certain extent by the parathyroid hormone. This agent exerts its influence primarily and almost entirely on the diffusible (ionized) fraction, which probably is the only physiologically active portion of the serum calcium.

Maintenance of the plasma Ca concentration within a narrow range is of vital concern to the well-being of the organism inasmuch as this ion had a profound influence on certain fundamental processes affecting cell function (e.g., membrane permeability, neuromuscular excitability). A few of the factors concerned in the preservation of the normal level of Ca in the plasma deserve special mention.

(a) PARATHYROID HORMONE.   In the fasting state (i.e., no absorption from intestine), the plasma Ca concentration is maintained primarily by the mobilization of Ca from the bones through the action of the parathyroid hormone. The metabolic actions and regulation of secretion of this hormone are considered in detail elsewhere (pp. 694, 695). It is the most important factor in the regulation of the concentration of Ca^{++} ions in the body fluids. Its effect in lowering the serum PO_4 concentration is apparently secondary to a direct primary action on the renal tubular epithelium, decreasing reabsorption of PO_4.

(b) VITAMIN D.   As indicated elsewhere (p. 153), the action of vitamin D in maintaining the normal plasma Ca concentration depends chiefly on its effect in enhancing absorption of Ca from the intestine. In the presence of vitamin D deficiency, the plasma PO_4 usually falls sooner than the Ca concentration. This is due, in part at least, to stimulation of parathyroid activity, which tends to maintain the plasma Ca concentration and, simultaneously, to lower the plasma PO_4 (p. 694).

(c) PLASMA PROTEINS.   Calcium exists in the plasma in higher concentration than would be possible in the absence of protein. As indicated above, about half of the plasma Ca (non-diffusible fraction) is bound to plasma proteins, principally albumin, decrease in which may be accompanied by a decrease in the serum Ca concentration. The calcium-binding potentialities of the plasma proteins may not be "saturated" under normal conditions, so that frequently no significant fall in serum Ca occurs at slight or moderate levels of hypoproteinemia. Such variations, since they are confined to the non-diffusible Ca fraction, are not accompanied by manifestations of altered Ca metabolism or neuromuscular excitability (e.g., tetany), and hypocalcemia of this type (i.e., due to hypoproteinemia) does not cause stimulation of parathyroid function (p. 695).

(d) PLASMA PHOSPHATE.   There is a roughly reciprocal relationship between the concentrations of Ca^{++} and $PO_4 \equiv$ ions in solutions *in vitro*. In the body fluids this relationship is exhibited to a limited extent and practically only in one direction; i.e., rather marked increase in serum $PO_4 \equiv$ may cause a fall in serum Ca^{++} concentration. This may be demonstrated experimentally by the intravenous injection of

Na$_2$HPO$_4$, and is encountered clinically in advanced renal failure with high serum PO$_4$ concentrations. Tetany may occur under these circumstances.

DEPOSITION AND MOBILIZATION OF BONE MINERALS. There is no unanimity of opinion regarding either the essential chemical nature or the mechanism of deposition of the mineral components of bone. The most important of the ionic constituents are Ca (about 26 per cent of the dry weight), PO$_4$ (about 12 per cent), CO$_3$ (about 3.5 per cent), and smaller amounts of Mg, Na, F, and citrate. On the basis of chemical analysis and X-ray diffraction studies, it would appear that the basic bone mineral has a crystal structure similar to that of the apatite group of phosphate minerals, probably a hydroxyapatite. As the crystal grows it is exposed to other elements and molecular groupings which cannot be incorporated in the lattice, the most important of which are carbonate, citrate, Mg, Na, F, Sr. These, with additional Ca and PO$_4$, are deposited on the surface of the hydroxyapatite crystal, stopping its growth. In bone, a new surface is started by the development of an independent crystal. In the case of dental enamel, a new surface is started by covering over the previous one.

The surface deposits are not part of the chemical structure of the fundamental bone mineral and are therefore more readily removed than the latter without actual dissolution of bone substance. Studies with radioactive elements indicate that these materials may be divided into two categories: (1) elements or molecular groupings which can displace or replace normal constituents of bone both on the surface and in the interior of the crystals; metabolic turnover of these components is relatively slow; (2) elements or molecular groupings which can enter a surface reaction with bone crystals, but which cannot be incorporated in the crystal lattice; metabolic turnover of these components is relatively rapid. It is believed that not more than 12 per cent of the skeletal Ca can be mobilized without actual dissolution of bone substance, including the matrix. This readily exchangeable Ca is in the form of salts (carbonate, citrate, phosphate) on the surface of the bone crystals, not in the actual lattice.

MINERALIZATION OF BONE. Bone formation involves two distinct fundamental processes: (1) construction of an organic matrix and (2) deposition of bone salts in this matrix. In areas of developing bone, reticular cells of the invading marrow turn into osteoblasts, which appear to be responsible for laying down the intercellular organic matrix (osteoid), which is largely protein in nature (p. 715). Ascorbic acid is essential for the normal formation of this organic matrix. Its role (p. 145) and that of vitamin A (p. 137) in this connection are considered elsewhere. The osteoblasts subsequently turn into osteocytes, the mature bone cells. When bone undergoes destruction, the osteocytes and osteoblasts form osteoclasts, which are actively involved in the breakdown of bone; these can in turn be transformed to osteoblasts or reticular cells.

Proper mineralization requires provision of Ca^{++} and $PO_4^{\equiv}$ ions, at the site, in their proportions in the mineral matter of bone. Mineralization will not occur if there is a deficit in one of these ions even though the other is present in adequate amounts. These ions are provided in the concentrations present in the interstitial fluid in which they, of course, exist in solution. Understanding of the process of mineralization of bone must involve an explanation of the mechanism underlying the precipitation of calcium phosphate at this site. This is not entirely clear.

Alkaline phosphatase is present invariably in areas of active mineralization, suggesting that it is involved in this process. It is present in particularly high concentration in osteoblasts and, in skeletal disorders, its concentration in the blood plasma reflects the degree of osteoblastic activity (p. 748). It was originally believed that this enzyme hydrolyzes organic esters of phosphoric acid in the developing bone, producing a local increase in $PO_4^{\equiv}$ ion concentration with consequent precipitation of calcium phosphate (local supersaturation). However, there is no evidence that such esters are present in these situations in amounts adequate to produce this effect. It has been suggested that phosphatase favors mineralization: (1) by increasing the concentration of $PO_4^{\equiv}$ ion; (2) by increasing the concentration of Ca^{++} ion by removing a complexing agent (phosphoric esters); (3) by preventing adsorption of ester phosphate, thereby eliminating a process which inhibits growth of the mineral crystals.

Recently, attention has been directed toward the possibility that glycolysis may be involved in this process. Pre-osseous cartilage contains glycogen, phosphorylase, ATP, and lactic acid, important components of the glycolytic cycle. Cartilage cells preparatory to mineralization accumulate large amounts of glycogen, which disappears abruptly just before or during the course of deposition of bone salts. Whether glycolysis provides a source of phosphoric ester substrate for phosphatase, or whether its main purpose is the provision of energy for some phase of the mechanism of bone formation is not clear.

Vitamin D is necessary for normal skeletal mineralization. The mode of its action in this connection is not known; it may perhaps provide optimum conditions of Ca^{++} and $PO_4^{\equiv}$ concentration in the bone (p. 153). It is also essential for the normal growth of bones, exerting a specific effect at the zone of provisional calcification in long bones and at corresponding sites in membranous bones (p. 154). Defects in this mechanism result in rickets.

MOBILIZATION OF CALCIUM. In common with other tissues, bone undergoes continual metabolic turnover, its various components undergoing degradation, mobilization, and replacement. This is true also of its mineral constituents. Studies with radioactive Ca have shown, as mentioned above, that this element occurs in two types of deposit (i.e., bone salt and surface deposit) which differ in their lability. Less than 12 per cent of the skeletal Ca is readily mobilizable and replaceable, probably without dissolution of the osteoid matrix; the remainder is much more stable and probably cannot be mobilized without simultaneous breakdown of osteoid tissue. Moreover, the mineral constituents of the trabecular portions of bone are more labile than those of the cortex.

The parathyroid hormone is the most important physiological factor involved in the mobilization of Ca from the skeleton. It apparently acts directly on the bones, causing its dissolution and resorption, the liberated Ca entering the blood stream. This is the major factor in the maintenance of the concentration of Ca^{++} ions in the plasma and tissue fluids (p. 611). Under normal conditions this process is balanced by resynthesis of osteoid components and mineralization of the newly formed matrix.

EXCRETION. Normal adults on an adequate Ca intake are in a state of Ca equilibrium. Ca is excreted in the urine, bile, and digestive secretions. The bulk of that in the feces is food Ca which has escaped absorption. This represents a variable but considerable fraction of the intake, since even under optimal conditions dietary Ca (e.g., in milk) is not more than 50 per cent absorbed. A small amount of the fecal Ca may be unabsorbed Ca of the digestive fluids.

At low and moderate levels of Ca intake (0.1–0.5 gram daily), about 30–35 per cent is excreted in the urine, while at high levels of intake (1.0 gram) about 10–25 per cent is so eliminated. However, there is considerable deviation from these values, due probably to variable dietary, metabolic, and gastrointestinal factors. For example, conditions which interfere with absorption of Ca from the intestine will increase the proportion excreted in the feces at the expense of urinary excretion. These include vitamin D deficiency, high phytin intake, achlorhydria or ingestion of alkalies, diarrhea, etc. The "renal threshold" for Ca excretion lies between 6.5 and 8.0 mg. per 100 ml. plasma, little being eliminated at lower serum Ca concentrations.

Inorganic phosphate is excreted in the urine and feces, the relative proportions varying under different conditions, e.g., those which influence absorption from the intestine (q.v.). The source of urinary inorganic phosphate is chiefly that of the blood plasma, although it may be contributed to by hydrolysis of phosphoric acid esters by phosphatase activity in the kidneys. On a balanced diet, urine phosphate constitutes about 60 per cent of the total excretion. As the Ca intake is decreased, the proportion of phosphate eliminated in the urine increases (increased intestinal absorption), being about 75 per cent on a low Ca, moderately high PO_4 intake. The "renal threshold" for phosphate excretion is about 2 mg./100 ml. of plasma, excretion falling to very low levels at lower concentrations. Reabsorption of phosphate from the glomerular filtrate by the renal tubular epithelium is apparently inhibited by the parathyroid hormone. Administration of this agent (or clinical hyperparathyroidism) causes increased urinary excretion of phosphate.

MISCELLANEOUS FACTORS. Estrogens and androgens exert an influence in Ca metabolism which varies widely in different species. Marked hypercalcemia occurs in birds during and just before ovulation, and may also be induced by administration of estrogen. This increase is largely in the non-diffusible fraction. Although this phenomenon does not occur in mammals, in rats estrogens produce hyperossification of the proximal epiphyseal zone of the tibia and thickening of the trabeculae, filling the upper fifth of the diaphyseal marrow cavities. This may be prevented by administration of androgens. It is questionable whether these observations are applicable to man. However, after the menopause, a type of osteoporosis often develops, with negative Ca balance, which may be benefited by administration of estrogen and/or androgen.

Osteoporosis and negative Ca balance may occur in subjects with hyperthyroidism or hyperfunction of the adrenal cortex. This may be due to the protein catabolic action of excessive amounts of thyroid hormone and the adrenal 11-oxysteroids, affecting primarily the osteoid matrix and secondarily, therefore, skeletal mineralization.

Decreased alkalinity of the body fluids (acidosis), due to any cause, may result in increased urinary excretion of Ca. The excess is presumably removed from the bones because of the increased solubility of the labile Ca deposits in a more acid medium.

Defective skeletal growth (in children) and undermineralization of the skeleton occur in the presence of disturbances of fat absorption (steatorrhea) from the intestine (sprue, celiac disease). There may be hypocalcemia and hypophosphatemia. These abnormalities are probably due in large measure to inadequate absorption of vitamin D under these conditions. The increased amounts of fatty acid in the intestine in these disorders, by binding Ca^{++} in the form of insoluble soaps, together with the incident diarrhea, may also contribute to the decreased absorption of Ca (increased excretion in feces).

Tetany (increased neuromuscular excitability) occurs whenever the concentration of Ca^{++} ions in the plasma and tissue fluids falls to sufficiently low levels, regardless of the cause of the hypocalcemia. It also occurs as a characteristic manifestation of alkalosis (p. 329), without hypocalcemia, owing perhaps to decreased ionization of the plasma Ca at decreased H^+ ion concentrations.

CALCIUM AND PHOSPHORUS REQUIREMENT. The adult daily requirement for P is 1–1.5 grams, or about 1.5 times the Ca intake. Diets adequate in other respects provide an adequate amount of P because of its wide distribution in common foods (phosphoproteins and phospholipids, inorganic phosphate), especially milk and milk products, wheat, meats, and fish.

The minimal daily adult requirement for Ca is 0.45 gram, but the recommended allowance is 1.0 gram (10–15 mg./kg. body weight), increasing to 1.5 grams or more during pregnancy and lactation. Growing children require about 45 mg./kg. body weight. Even under optimal conditions, not more than 35–50 per cent of dietary Ca is absorbed. Milk (1.0 gram per quart) and dairy products constitute the most important dietary source of this element, cereals, meats and most vegetables being low in Ca. Even those which contain relatively large amounts (viz., certain vegetable greens, and shellfish) are usually not eaten in sufficient quantities to be of practical value in this regard. The average American diet is probably usually deficient in Ca, which may be supplied satisfactorily in the form of inorganic or organic salts (e.g., phosphate, lactate, chloride, gluconate).

IRON METABOLISM

Although the amount of Fe in the body is small (about 45 mg./kg. body weight), the fact that it is an essential constituent of hemoglobin and of cytochrome and other components of respiratory enzyme systems (cytochrome oxidase, catalase, peroxidase) makes it an element of great fundamental importance. Its chief functions lie in the transport of oxygen to the tissues (hemoglobin) and in cellular oxidation mechanisms (cytochrome system).

ABSORPTION AND EXCRETION. Iron differs from practically all other electrolytes in that the quantity in the body is controlled by regulation not of its excretion, but rather of its absorption into the organism. The body stores of Fe are conserved very efficiently, only minute amounts being excreted in the urine and feces, usually less than 1 mg. daily. Relatively large amounts are, of course, lost in the menstrual flow. That present in the body in various substances, e.g., hemoglobin, is almost completely reutilized following its liberation in the course of metabolic degradation of these substances. The bulk of the Fe of the feces is unabsorbed food Fe; a very small amount enters the intestine in the bile and escapes in the feces.

Several factors make absorption of Fe difficult, regardless of the form in which it is ingested: (1) the relatively high pH in the jejunum favors the formation of insoluble basic Fe compounds; (2) Fe salts of bile acids are relatively insoluble; (3) the presence of relatively large amounts of phosphate favors the formation of insoluble Fe phosphates; (4) absorption of Fe is interfered with, therefore, in the absence of free HCl in the stomach (achlorhydria) and by administration of alkalies.

Absorption occurs chiefly in the upper duodenum and stomach, but, to a lesser extent, throughout the small intestine. Absorption of inorganic salts of Fe compares favorably with that of the Fe of foodstuffs, which is chiefly a colloidal ferric hydroxide. In general, ferrous Fe is better absorbed than ferric.

Normal gastric acidity facilitates the ionization and solution of ingested Fe and delays the formation of insoluble, undissociable compounds which may form above pH 5. At the slightly acid reaction usually encountered in the duodenum, ionizable Fe compounds are converted chiefly to ferrous or ferric hydroxides, the former being favored at higher acidities and by the presence of reducing agents in the digestive mixture (glutathione, ascorbic acid, SH-groups of proteins and digestion products).

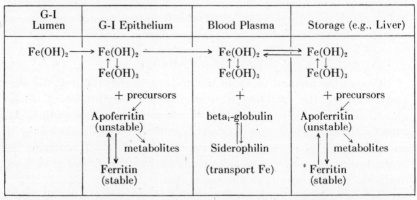

Fig. 118. Mechanism of absorption, transport, storage and mobilization of iron

The normal organism absorbs Fe only in proportion to its needs, the quantity absorbed being determined by the magnitude of the body reserves of this element. Apparently the gastrointestinal mucosa is the tissue immediately responsible for its acceptance or rejection, which is regulated by the amount of ferritin in the mucosal epithelial cells. This is an Fe-protein complex (23 per cent Fe), containing aggregates of ferric hydroxide and a protein, apoferritin (m.w. 450,-000). Apoferritin has vasodepressor (VDM, p. 765) and antidiuretic properties. Ferritin occurs also in other parenchymal cells, e.g., the liver and spleen, and in the bone marrow and reticuloendothelial cells generally. It is believed to be the chief storage form of iron.

Ferrous iron, on entering the mucosal epithelial cell, is oxidized, forming ferric hydroxide, which combines with the protein, apoferritin, synthesized in the cell, forming ferritin (Fig. 118). Apoferritin is present in very small amounts and is apparently unstable, breaking down quickly unless Fe is present to convert it to ferritin, which is more stable. The equilibrium between these intracellular forms of Fe is potentially reversible. Entrance of Fe into the cell ceases when its capacity for storing ferritin is exhausted. The amount of ferritin in the mucosal cells therefore regulates Fe absorption from the gastrointestinal tract.

TRANSPORT. In accordance with body needs, the reactions in the mucosal cell, outlined above, are reversed, the mechanism being unknown. It has been suggested that slight decrease in circulating Hb, with a fall in O_2 tension, may favor reduction of ferric to ferrous iron, causing breakdown of ferritin to apoferritin and permitting absorption of additional Fe. The ferrous iron thus mobilized passes into the blood plasma, undergoes reoxidation to the ferric state, and combines with one of the plasma β-globulins. This compound, termed "siderophilin," is present in a concentration of about 0.25 g./100 ml. plasma. The Fe content of plasma is 50–180 μg./100 ml.; this is the transport Fe (ferric).

The Fe content of whole blood is normally 40–60 mg./100 ml., averaging 45 in women and 52 in men. Practically all of this is in organic form, as hemoglobin, which contains about 0.335 per cent Fe (ferrous) (p. 110), all of which is in the red blood cells.

UTILIZATION; STORAGE. In the tissues, as needed, the plasma Fe is apparently released from siderophilin, passes out of the capillary and into the cells, where it may be utilized or stored (as ferritin). The storage mechanism is identical with that described for the formation of ferritin in the gastrointestinal mucosal cells. The liver, spleen, and intestinal mucosa are the chief storage sites, but other organs (e.g., pancreas, adrenals) and all reticuloendothelial cells contain ferritin. When Fe is deposited in abnormally large amounts, hemosiderin may be formed, a compound similar to ferritin, but containing more Fe (up to 35 per cent).

Iron is utilized chiefly in the synthesis of hemoglobin, myoglobin (muscle Hb), and certain respiratory enzymes (cytochromes, peroxidase, catalase). The latter are probably formed in all cells, myoglobin in muscle cells, and hemoglobin in the developing red blood cells (normoblasts, reticulocytes) in the erythropoietic tissues, principally the bone marrow in man. The approximate distribution of Fe in the body is as follows (Fig. 119): (1) circulating Hb, 60 per cent, (2) myoglobin, 5 per cent; (3) storage Fe, 20 per cent; (4) functional tissue Fe (respiratory enzymes), 15 per cent. Thus, about 65 per cent of the body Fe is in the form of hemoglobin, 20 per cent is in storage form, available for utilization, and 15 per cent is functional tissue Fe, not readily available for other purposes. The Fe of erythrocyte hemoglobin is readily available, but not that of myoglobin.

The quantity of Fe mobilized in the organism daily far exceeds the exogenous supply. About 0.8 per cent of the circulating erythrocytes undergo disintegration daily (life one hundred twenty-five days), liberating about 7 to 8 grams of Hb (0.34 per cent Fe). In the course of its degradation, this gives rise to about 25 mg. of Fe, the bulk of which is immediately utilized in the resynthesis of Hb (p. 588), but some may enter the blood plasma for transport to other tissues. Synthesis of Hb, and consequently utilization of Fe for this purpose, require among other things adequate amounts of pteroylglutamic acid and vitamin B_{12} (pp. 209, 210, 211).

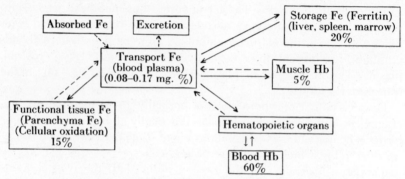

Fig. 119. *Approximate distribution of iron in the body*

Mobilization of Fe from ferritin in storage sites, e.g., liver, is accomplished by reversal of the reactions involved in its storage. As in the case of the gastrointestinal epithelium, this may involve initial reduction of ferric to ferrous Fe, the latter passing out of the cell into the blood stream; this disturbs the intracellular Fe equilibrium, ferritin breaking down to Fe and apoferritin. The latter, being unstable, continues to break down until equilibrium is restored and loss of Fe from the cell ceases. The reaction can then be reversed in the direction of ferritin formation.

REQUIREMENT. Since only minute amounts of Fe are excreted, the exogenous requirement should be correspondingly low. However, it is believed that adults require 5 to 15 mg. daily to meet ordinary and unanticipated demands; perhaps 15 to 20 mg. is more satisfactory for women (menstruation, pregnancy, lactation). Young children (4 to 8 years) require about 0.6 mg./kg. body weight and infants (to 1 year) 1 to 2 mg./kg.

BIBLIOGRAPHY

Annual Review of Biochemistry.

Annual Review of Physiology.

Albright, F. and Reifenstein, E. C., Jr.: Parathyroid Glands and Metabolic Bone Disease, Baltimore, Williams & Wilkins Company, 1948 (calcium and phosphorus).

Berliner, R. W.: Relationship between acidification of the urine and potassium metabolism, Am. J. Med. *11:274*, 1951.

Bland, J. H.: The Clinical Use of Fluid and Electrolyte, Philadelphia, W. B. Saunders Company, 1952.

Cantarow, A.: Mineral metabolism. In Diseases of Metabolism, ed. 3, edited by G. G. Duncan, Philadelphia, W. B. Saunders Company, 1952, p. 237.

Darrow, D. C.: Disturbances in electrolyte metabolism in man and their management, Bull. New York Acad. Med. *24:147*, 1948.

Darrow, D. C.: Fluid therapy, J.A.M.A. *143:365*, 1950.

Gamble, J. L.: Chemical Anatomy, Physiology and Pathology of Extracellular Fluid, Cambridge, Harvard University Press, 1950.

Gamble, J. L.: Companionship of Water and Electrolytes in the Organization of Body Fluids, Lane Medical Lectures, California, Stanford University Press, 1951.

Granick, S.: Structure and physiological functions of ferritin, Physiol. Rev. *31:489*, 1951.

Hoffman, W. S.: Clinical physiology of potassium, J.A.M.A. *144:1157*, 1950.

Keating, F. R. and Albert, A.: The metabolism of iodine in man as disclosed with the use of radioiodine, Recent Progress in Hormone Research *4:429*, 1949.

Kendall, E. C.: The influence of the adrenal cortex on the metabolism of water and electrolytes, Vitamins & Hormones *6:278*, 1946.

Macy Foundation Conferences on Metabolic Interrelations, I, II, III, IV, New York, Josiah Macy, Jr. Foundation, 1949, 1950, 1951, 1952 (calcium and phosphorus).

McClure, F. J.: Fluorine and other trace elements in nutrition, J.A.M.A. *139:711*, 1949.

Means, J. H. et al.: Thyroid function as disclosed by newer methods of study, Ann. New York Acad. Sc. *50:279*, 1949 (iodine).

Nicolaysen, R.: Physiology of calcium metabolism, Physiol. Rev. *33:424*, 1953.

Overman, R. R.: Na, K, and Cl alterations in disease, Physiol. Rev. *31:285*, 1951.

Salter, W. T.: The Endocrine Function of Iodine, Cambridge, Harvard University Press, 1940.

Shohl, A. T.: Mineral Metabolism, New York, Reinhold Publishing Corporation, 1939.

Stearns, G.: Requirement of calcium, phosphorus and magnesium, J.A.M.A. *142: 478*, 1950.

Youmans, J. B.: Mineral deficiencies, J.A.M.A. *143:1252*, 1950.

23

GENERAL BIOCHEMICAL ASPECTS OF DIET

In general terms, an adequate diet is one which permits normal growth, maintenance, and reproduction. More specifically, its minimum requirements for the adult are fulfilled (1) when the organism is in a state of equilibrium with regard to (a) calories, (b) nitrogen, and (c) inorganic elements; (2) when there is an adequate supply and utilization of vitamins and other factors (e.g., trace minerals, essential fatty acids) necessary for maintenance of special functions; (3) when reproduction is normal. In the immature organism, growth and development must proceed normally.

The functions served by the essential components of the diet and the quantities required for optimum nutrition are considered in detail elsewhere in discussing the role of each of these factors in biochemical processes, and need not be repeated here. However, certain general aspects of the subject of diet merit independent consideration.

It is necessary to appreciate the difficulties involved in arriving at satisfactory standards of diet that can be applied to large groups of peoples of different dietary habits and economic status. The bulk of present information regarding fundamental aspects of nutrition has emerged from studies in experimental animals. Despite the existence of important species differences in many respects, fortunately it has been found possible to utilize much of this information directly in practical problems of nutrition in man. Nevertheless, there are still large areas of uncertainty in important fields. For example, even in experimental animals, there is no assurance that an adequate diet, as described above, is an optimum diet. There are, in fact, indications that such is not the case. Moreover, because of the integration of various phases of intermediary metabolism and the functional interdependence of several of the factors involved, construction of a satisfactory diet must include consideration of quantitative interrelationships between certain of these principles or their precursors in the foods. For example, the protein requirement is influenced by the level of carbohydrate in the diet and also by the caloric intake; the requirement for various B vitamins is influenced by the carbohydrate, caloric, or protein intakes. These and other difficulties, some recognized and some unknown, make it necessary to provide for a rather wide margin of safety in order to insure satisfactory nutrition. The valuable recommendations of the Food and Nutrition Board of the National Research Council, indicated in Table 54, constitute an important contribution to this subject.

The food intake is influenced by geographical and economic factors as well as by personal idiosyncrasies. The diet of the Eskimo is limited by his environment largely to meat and fish. Large numbers of Orientals are forced to subsist mainly on rice, with variable supplements of other vegetables and fish. As a general principle, any type of rigid dietary restriction, voluntary or forced, carries with it the danger of deficiency in some essential factor. The greater the variety of foods, the more remote this danger becomes. Of less practical importance, perhaps, in normal subjects, is the manner of preparation of foods, i.e., seasoning, flavoring, cooking, except in that improper procedures may destroy or remove certain vitamins (q.v.) or impair the quality of the food proteins. These matters may assume importance, however, in maintaining adequate nutrition in disease, increased palatability of the food causing stimulation of appetite.

Dietary considerations of vitamins (p. 166 ff.) and inorganic elements (p. 599) are discussed elsewhere. It seems desirable to review here certain pertinent points regarding the caloric, carbohydrate, fat, and protein intakes insofar as they bear on biochemical aspects of the diet. Data on the composition of foods are available in standard works on nutrition and dietetics.

CALORIC CONTENT OF DIET. The daily caloric requirements under various physiological conditions are considered in detail elsewhere (p. 342). These are, of course, contributed by the three classes of organic foodstuffs, carbohydrate, fat, and protein. From the standpoint of adequate nutrition, of these the protein requirement is the most rigid, the accepted recommendation being not less than 1 gram per kilogram of body weight daily. This amount (e.g., 70 gram = 280 C.) would contribute about 10 per cent of the energy requirement of a moderately active 70-kg. man. It is somewhat higher in pregnant and lactating women and in children (p. 342). The relative proportions of carbohydrate and fat contributing the remainder could vary widely, but it is recommended that carbohydrate contribute at least 50 per cent and fat at least 20 per cent of the total calories. Increased energy demands incident to increased activity may be met by either of the two latter foodstuffs. However, ketone bodies may accumulate in

624

Table 54. *Food and Nutrition Board, National Research Council,*
(Designed for the Maintenance of Good Nutrition of Healthy Persons in the U.S.A.;
Temperate

	AGE Years	WEIGHT kg. (lb.)	HEIGHT cm. (in.)	CALORIES	PROTEIN gm.
Men	25	65 (143)	170 (67)	3200[2]	65
	45	65 (143)	170 (67)	2900	65
	65	65 (143)	170 (67)	2600	65
Women	25	55 (121)	157 (62)	2300[2]	55
	45	55 (121)	157 (62)	2100	55
	65	55 (121)	157 (62)	1800	55
	Pregnant (3rd trimester)			Add 400	80
	Lactating (850 ml. daily)			Add 1000	100
Infants[3]	0–1/12[4] (No specific recommendations)				
	1/12–3/12	5 (11)	58 (23)	kg. x 120	kg. x 3.5[3]
	4/12–9/12	8 (18)	67 (26)	kg. x 110	kg. x 3.5[3]
	10/12–1	10 (22)	75 (30)	kg. x 100	kg. x 3.5[3]
Children	1–3	12 (27)	87 (34)	1200	40
	4–6	18 (40)	109 (43)	1600	50
	7–9	27 (59)	129 (51)	2000	60
Boys	10–12	35 (78)	144 (57)	2500	70
	13–15	49 (108)	163 (64)	3200	85
	16–20	63 (139)	175 (69)	3800	100
Girls	10–12	36 (79)	144 (57)	2300	70
	13–15	49 (108)	160 (63)	2500	80
	16–20	54 (120)	162 (64)	2400	75

[1] In planning practical dietaries, the recommended allowances can be attained with a variety of common foods which will also provide other nutrient requirements less well known; the allowance levels are considered to cover individul variations among normal persons as they live in the United States subjected to ordinary environmental stresses. Other nutrients discussed in the text include: fat, p. 627; water, p. 297; sodium chloride, p. 600; phosphorus, p. 617; iodine, p. 606; vitamin B_6, p. 192; vitamin B_{12}, p. 207; folic acid group, p. 205; biotin, p. 200; pantothenic acid, p. 196; vitamin K, p. 166; fluorides, p. 716.

[2] These calorie recommendations apply to the degree of activity for the average active man and woman. For the urban "white-collar" worker they are probably ex-

Recommended Daily Dietary Allowances,[1] Revised 1953

Allowances are Considered to Apply to Persons Normally Vigorous and Living in Climate)

CALCIUM gm.	IRON mg.	VITAMIN A I. U.	THIAMINE mg.	RIBOFLAVIN mg.	NIACIN mg.	ASCORBIC ACID mg.	VITAMIN D I. U.
0.8	12	5000	1.6	1.6	16	75	
0.8	12	5000	1.5	1.6	15	75	
0.8	12	5000	1.3	1.6	13	75	
0.8	12	5000	1.2	1.4	12	70	
0.8	12	5000	1.1	1.4	11	70	
0.8	12	5000	1.0	1.4	10	70	
1.5	15	6000	1.5	2.0	15	100	400
2.0	15	8000	1.5	2.5	15	150	400
0.6	6	1500	0.3	0.4	3	30	400
0.8	6	1500	0.4	0.7	4	30	400
1.0	6	1500	0.5	0.9	5	30	400
1.0	7	2000	0.6	1.0	6	35	400
1.0	8	2500	0.8	1.2	8	50	400
1.0	10	3500	1.0	1.5	10	60	400
1.2	12	4500	1.3	1.8	13	75	400
1.4	15	5000	1.6	2.1	16	90	400
1.4	15	5000	1.9	2.5	19	100	400
1.2	12	4500	1.2	1.8	12	75	400
1.3	15	5000	1.3	2.0	13	80	400
1.3	15	5000	1.2	1.9	12	80	400

cessive. In any case, the calorie allowance must be adjusted to the actual needs of the individual as required to achieve and maintain his desirable weight.

[3] The recommendations for infants pertain to nutrients derived primarily from cow's milk. If the milk from which the protein is derived is human milk or has been treated to render it more digestible, the allowance may be in the range of 2–3 gm. per kg. of body weight. There should be no question that human milk is a desirable source of nutrients for infants even though it may not provide the recommended levels for certain nutrients. (See discussion in text, pp. 727–730)

[4] During the first month of life desirable allowances for many nutrients are dependent upon maturation of excretory and endocrine functions. Therefore no specific recommendations are given.

excess if carbohydrate provides much less than half of the total calories on a high-fat diet (p. 453).

If the caloric intake is insufficient to meet current demands, the body tissues will supply the deficit. If the protein intake is adequate and caloric restriction of only moderate degree, this will be derived from depot fat after the small glycogen reserves have been depleted. However, with progressive reduction in caloric intake, a deleterious influence is exerted on protein metabolism, as reflected in nitrogen balance (p. 558), this effect becoming more evident after the fat reserves have been utilized. With severe, prolonged restriction, virtually all tissues lose weight, but not equally, fat, liver, and muscle suffering considerably, whereas brain, plasma proteins, and bones are maintained for relatively long periods.

The organism adapts itself to caloric restriction to a certain extent by an associated decrease in the rate of oxidations. The BMR may decrease by about 50 per cent after prolonged semi-starvation, owing in part to the above phenomenon, but mainly to the decreased mass of metabolizing tissue.

The requirement for certain vitamins is influenced by the caloric intake. This is particularly true of the B vitamins that are concerned in oxidative mechanisms (q.v., p. 170), the requirement for which diminishes as the caloric content of the diet is reduced. In fact, frank vitamin deficiency manifestations are not often seen in total starvation, but may develop during subsequent feeding if the intake of vitamins is not increased in proportion to the caloric intake.

DIETARY CARBOHYDRATES. Inasmuch as all biologically significant carbohydrates can be synthesized in the body, their main function in the diet is to provide a readily utilizable source of energy for the maintenance of cell functions. Under usual conditions, carbohydrate should provide 50 per cent or more of the calories of the diet (p. 342), i.e., about 5–7 grams per kilogram of body weight in the average moderately active adult.

Undue restriction of dietary carbohydrate influences both fat and protein metabolism adversely, even if the caloric intake is adequate. Fat mobilization from the depots and utilization are exaggerated (p. 474), ketogenesis is increased (p. 453), and ketosis may develop. The effect on protein metabolism is apparently of a specific nature, not shared by other substances (e.g., fat, alcohol), and not related to its calorigenic action. This is referred to as the "protein-sparing action" of carbohydrate (pp. 434, 559). During a total fast, an adult may lose about 70 grams of protein daily. This may be reduced to about 35 grams by a daily intake of 100 grams of glucose, which represents approximately its maximum protein sparing effect under these circumstances. It has been estimated that a maximum effect in this connection is accomplished by 5 grams of glucose per 100 Calories produced.

Celluloses, indigestible plant polysaccharides, contribute bulk to the intestinal contents and, therefore, in normal amounts promote intestinal motility. When present in excess, they may be irritating to the intestinal mucous membrane, producing diarrhea or a spastic type of constipation. All other dietary carbohydrates are readily digested and/or absorbed. Ingestion of excessive amounts, especially in infants, may occasionally produce intestinal disturbances due to irritation induced by products of bacterial fermentation (p. 272). There is some evidence in experimental animals (rat) that continued ingestion of supertolerance amounts of galactose may result in the formation of cataract. A similar phenomenon has been suggested as possibly occurring in man, especially in children, in the presence of hepatic functional impairment, in which condition the conversion of galactose to glucose (or glycogen) may be impaired, with consequent elevation of the blood galactose concentration. It should be recalled in this connection, however, that the incidence of cataract is relatively high also in uncontrolled diabetes, a phenomenon presumably related in this case to maintenance of a persistently elevated blood glucose concentration.

DIETARY LIPID. A wide variety of lipids is provided in a balanced diet. Inasmuch as, under normal circumstances, all components of biologically significant lipids, with the exception of certain "essential" fatty acids (p. 449), can be synthesized in the body from non-lipid precursors, the main function of dietary lipids, like that of carbohydrates, is to provide energy, largely through their constituent fatty acids (p. 438). The dietary lipids serve another, indirect function in serving as a carrier of certain vitamins and provitamins (e.g., A, D, E, K, q.v.), which, because of their solubility in fats, occur in nature mainly in association with these substances. There is also some indication that they may exert a relatively minor protein-sparing effect, apart from their caloric contribution (p. 559). Neutral fats, comprising the largest fraction of food lipids, are quantitatively the most important of these substances. Under usual conditions, fat provides 20–35 per cent of the calories of the diet (p. 342), i.e., 1–2 grams per kilogram of body weight in the average moderately active adult.

The nutritional significance of the polyunsaturated "essential" fatty acids is discussed elsewhere (p. 449). Suffice it here to state that they are provided in ample amounts by a balanced diet that contains an adequate quantity of naturally occurring lipids (linoleic mainly in plants, arachidonic of animal origin).

Inasmuch as most of the common food fats contain mainly the same few fatty acids, viz., oleic, palmitic, and stearic, although in different proportions, there is little significant difference in their digestibility or biological value, whether of plant or of animal origin. When ingested in amounts that are not excessive, all of those commonly used in cooking or as foods are well digested and absorbed, most of them to the extent of about 95 per cent, but somewhat less in the case of beef and mutton fat. Of more academic than practical importance is the fact that triglycerides with unusually high proportions of longer chain saturated fatty acids, resulting in high melting points (above 38° C.), may remain solid at body temperature, and, therefore, are less readily digested and/or absorbed.

An excessively high fat intake inhibits gastric secretion and motility, producing anorexia and gastric discomfort. Intestinal irritation and diarrhea may result from excessive amounts of fatty acids in the intestine. Although of little practical importance, it is of interest that cottonseed oil contains a pigment, gossypol, which has antoxidant and antitryptic activity, diminishes appetite, and interferes with protein digestion.

DIETARY PROTEIN. The large amount of information available on nutritive aspects of food proteins has been obtained mainly from studies in the albino rat and to a limited extent in the dog (especially plasma proteins and hemoglobin). The relatively few observations that have been made on human subjects support the view that, with occasional exceptions, the results of studies in these experimental animals may be generally applied to man.

Food proteins perform a vitally important function different from that served by dietary carbohydrates and fats, the main purpose of which is to provide an adequate amount of energy. The proteins of the diet are the ultimate source of amino groups, and of the carbon skeletons of the essential amino acids required for synthesis of body proteins, which comprise the bulk of the metabolic machinery (e.g., enzymes) and of other structural and functional components of the tissues and body fluids. Taken in excess, they may also be utilized for the production of energy; they may be converted to carbohydrate or to fat. Inasmuch as all body proteins are continually undergoing degradation (p. 487) and there is an obligatory loss of nitrogen in the urine, at least this amount of nitrogen must be supplied in the diet if protein anabolism is to keep pace with its catabolism, even in the adult, non-growing state. The diet must also provide certain "essential" amino acids that cannot be synthesized in the body.

Inasmuch as growth involves formation of tissue proteins at a rate exceeding that of their degradation (i.e., positive N balance), the dietary protein is much more critically concerned in growth and tissue repair than are carbohydrates and lipids. This influence may be demonstrated readily in the growing animal, whose weight curve reflects the adequacy (quantity and quality) of the protein intake. There is evidence also that the latter determines to a significant extent the ultimate adult size of the individual, over and above genetic influences. Adult heights and weights of peoples in various geographic areas apparently vary directly with the amount and quality of protein in their diets. For example, members of certain African tribes subsisting largely on vegetables are small in stature, whereas neighboring tribes of similar origin, subsisting mainly on meat and milk, are tall. Similar correlations have been obtained in studies of genetically comparable groups of individuals in this and other countries.

Emphasis was placed originally on the quantitative protein requirements almost exclusively. With the development of more satisfactory analytical methods for amino acids, and the accumulation of information on "essential" amino acids, it became apparent that the "quality" of dietary proteins was just as important as their quantity in contributing to adequate protein nutrition.

Nitrogen equilibrium can be maintained, i.e., protein requirements can be satisfied, just as satisfactorily by intravenous as by oral administration of adequate mixtures of amino acids. The same is true of plasma proteins. Moreover, apart from the influence of certain unknown factors present in natural animal proteins (e.g., animal protein factor), intravenous injection of such mixtures can completely replace oral protein feeding, at least for periods of several days. Properly fortified protein (e.g., casein) hydrolysates and various mixtures of pure amino acids are commercially available for this purpose, and have aided considerably in maintaining satisfactory nutrition in patients in whom adequate oral feeding is impossible or undesirable, e.g., after operations on the gastrointestinal tract.

QUALITY OF FOOD PROTEINS (BIOLOGICAL VALUE). Food proteins vary considerably in the efficiency of their utilization for synthesis of body proteins (e.g., tissues, hemoglobin, plasma proteins). Any one of several procedures may be employed for evaluation of the "quality" of a protein: (1) measurement of its influence on the weight increase of weanling animals ("protein efficiency ratio" = $\frac{\text{weight increase (grams)}}{\text{grams protein consumed}}$); (2) determination of its "biological value" in terms of the percentage of absorbed nitrogen retained by the organism; (3) measurement of its influence on the rate of regain of body weight or of liver protein by previously depleted animals; (4) measurement of its influence on the rate of restoration of plasma proteins or of hemoglobin in animals previously depleted of these specific proteins (e.g., by plasmapheresis). In the case of hemoglobin, a conjugated protein, consideration must be given to other factors, including iron (p. 620) and requirements for porphyrin synthesis (p. 586) and erythropoiesis (viz., vitamin B_{12}) (p. 207).

Evaluated on the basis of these criteria, animal proteins generally are of higher "quality" than those of vegetable origin. Whole egg and milk (especially lactalbumin) proteins rank highest in this respect, meats and glandular tissues somewhat lower. Gelatin, commonly used in desserts, although a protein of animal origin (not occurring naturally as such), is a wholly inadequate protein, lacking tryptophan, valine, and tyrosine and being low in cystine. It is prepared from collagen (cartilage, bone, tendon, skin) by boiling in water.

Certain factors are known to influence the biological value of proteins: (1) the amounts and relative proportions of their constituent amino acids; (2) the nutritional availability (rates of liberation and absorption) of their constituent amino acids under conditions of digestion in the gastrointestinal tract; (3) the latter factor (2) may be influenced, adversely or beneficially, by various methods of processing (commercial) or preparation (cooking) of foodstuffs.

AMINO ACID COMPOSITION. The most important single factor, but not the only one, that influences the nutritional "quality" of a protein is its amino acid composition. The significance of the "essential" amino acids in this connection is discussed elsewhere (p. 492). These must be provided in the diet if nitrogen equilibrium is to be maintained. Inasmuch as they must all be presented to the organism virtually simultaneously for purposes of protein synthesis (p. 494), a "complete" food protein must contain all of them. However, the biological value of a protein is apparently related to the proportionality relationships among its constituent essential amino acids. The following proportional values, relative to tryptophan as unity, have been found to be optimal for growth of the rat: lysine 5, leucine 4, valine 3.5, phenylalanine 3.5, methionine 3, isoleucine 2.5, threonine 2.5, histidine 2, arginine 1, tryptophan 1. There is evidence that these ratios hold, approximately, for man. The following daily intake values (in grams) have been recommended tentatively: isoleucine 1.4, leucine 2.2, lysine 1.6, methionine 2.2, phenylalanine 2.2, threonine 1.0, tryptophan 0.5, valine 1.6. These are about double the minimal requirements and should provide an adequate excess, from which each cell may select the proper mixture for its specific protein synthesis requirements.

Despite the fact that the organism can manufacture the "nonessential" amino acids, when a mixture of the "essential" amino acids is the only source of dietary nitrogen, growth is not as satisfactory as when the same amount of nitrogen is supplied in the form of intact complete proteins or their hydrolysates, under otherwise comparable conditions (i.e., carbohydrate and fat contents). This is apparently due, in part at least, to the fact that the presence in the diet of a "nonessential" amino acid, e.g., cystine, may reduce the requirement for an "essential" amino acid, in this case methionine. It has been suggested that when the former are not provided, the necessity for their synthesis may constitute an excessive burden on the metabolic activities of the cell. This is particularly true under conditions of rapid growth (childhood, pregnancy, convalescence from wasting diseases).

AVAILABILITY OF AMINO ACIDS OF FOODS. Different proteins with similar amino acid compositions may not liberate a given amino acid at the same rate during the course of digestion, and the rates at which different amino acids are liberated may vary widely. An apparent determining factor in this connection is the nature of the amino acid linkage within the protein molecule. Digestibility of various proteins and the rates of release of amino acids may be affected by the manner of preparation of foods (e.g., heating), in some cases adversely, in others beneficially. On this basis, wide differences in the time of absorption of individual amino acids from the intestinal lumen may diminish the nutritional usefulness of a protein of satisfactory chemical constitution because of the importance of the time element in the utilization of amino acids for protein synthesis (p. 494).

SUPPLEMENTARY RELATIONSHIPS; TIME FACTOR. If a relatively low-quality protein food, such as white bread (low in lysine), is supplemented by a small amount of lysine, raising its content of this amino acid from 0.29 per cent to 0.67 per cent, its biological value is more than doubled. The utilization of an "incomplete" protein for protein synthesis is limited by the amino acid least available ("law of the minimum"). Similarly, mixtures of food proteins, each of which is "incomplete" in different respects, may provide a satisfactory amino acid balance for optimum protein nutrition.

Analysis of various types of staple protein foodstuffs reveals that their most significant deficiencies are in lysine, methionine, threonine, and tryptophan. For example, wheat, which is an important dietary protein, is deficient in lysine; this is true of cereal grains generally. Rice is, in addition, poor in threonine, and corn in tryptophan. Leguminous (peas, beans) and root vegetable proteins are generally deficient in methionine, the former also in tryptophan. The combination of wheat (low in lysine, but adequate in methionine) and potatoes or peas (adequate in lysine, but low in methionine) raises the biological value of each of these relatively low-quality proteins considerably. Similar enhancement of the utilization of relatively low-quality (vegetable) proteins is accomplished by the addition of high-quality (animal) proteins.

A protein molecule can be synthesized only if all of its constituent amino acids are available simultaneously in proper amounts. If an interval of longer than one hour is allowed to elapse between ingestion of an incomplete amino acid mixture and administration of the missing essential amino acids, these amino acid constituents are not utilized for protein synthesis. Under these circumstances, weight loss is much the same as on an equicaloric diet containing no amino acids. The same applies, of course, to mixtures of dietary proteins that supplement one another's deficiencies; they must be ingested simultaneously in order to be maximally utilized. There is evidence, too, that even high-quality dietary proteins are utilized more efficiently when distributed evenly throughout the three daily meals than if concentrated in one or two meals. The time of administration of carbohydrate in relation to protein is also of importance in this connection (p. 559).

QUANTITY OF PROTEIN. If the intake of protein is reduced gradually, urinary nitrogen excretion diminishes correspondingly and the organism may remain in nitrogen equilibrium until a critical intake level (about $\frac{1}{4}$–$\frac{1}{3}$ gram per kilogram of body weight) is reached, below which the nitrogen balance becomes negative. However, continuation of such low-protein intakes for prolonged periods may endanger health and is certainly undesirable. Animals maintained on such diets are more susceptible to subsequent protein depletion than are those receiving high-protein diets.

It has been found that protein nutrition is maintained satisfactorily in adults by a daily intake of $\frac{2}{3}$ gram per kilogram of body weight. Larger amounts are required during pregnancy (growth of fetus, placenta, uterus, breasts), lactation (production of milk proteins), childhood (body growth), and convalescence from wasting diseases (tissue repair). In order to provide for variations in nutritional quality and for fluctuations in requirement incident to contingencies of everyday existence, the Food and Nutrition Board of the National Research Council has recommended the following daily allowances (Table 54, p. 624) per kilogram of body weight: normal adults, 1 gram; during the latter half of pregnancy, 1.45 grams; during lactation, 1.8 grams; infants, 3.5 grams; early childhood, 2.2–3.3 grams; late childhood through adolescence, 1.4–2 grams.

The daily requirement is, of course, influenced by the quality of the food protein. For example, whereas nitrogen equilibrium can be maintained on 0.6 gram (per kilogram of body weight) of milk protein daily, over 1 gram (per kilogram of body weight) of white flour protein is required for this purpose. The dietary protein recommendations indicated presuppose that the diet is adequate in other respects and that high-quality proteins (whole egg, milk, meats, liver) comprise at least half of the total protein intake in the case of normal adults, half to two-thirds during pregnancy and lactation, and two-thirds to three-quarters during childhood and adolescence.

Although there is evidence that an extremely high protein intake may produce kidney damage in the rat, there is no substantial evidence that this is true in man within feasible limits of dietary protein content.

CONSEQUENCES OF PROTEIN DEFICIENCY. If the protein intake does not meet the immediate requirements, protein anabolism cannot be maintained at the required rate. In the child, growth is retarded; in the adult, weight is lost; wound healing is delayed. Hemoglobin synthesis is impaired, with consequent anemia. If the deficiency is marked, excessive amounts of fat may accumulate in the liver (p. 479), a consequence of deficiency in methionine, and degenerative changes and fibrosis (cirrhosis) may occur. Prolonged deficiency may result in inadequate synthesis of plasma proteins. If this progresses to the point of significant decrease in the plasma albumin concentration, edema may develop (p. 309), and also increased susceptibility to shock. Resistance to infections may be diminished as a result of impaired capacity for forming γ-globulins (antibodies) (p. 506). In severe protein restriction, certain hormones, protein in nature, such as those of the anterior pituitary (p. 695), may not be synthesized in adequate amounts, and endocrine abnormalities may appear, e.g., amenorrhea (gonadotrophin deficiency). Since enzymes are proteins and must be synthesized in the body, the enzyme content of certain tissues (e.g., liver) and secretions (e.g., pepsin in gastric juice) falls in advanced deficiency states. This may result in disturbances of function of the organs affected.

BENEFICIAL AND DELETERIOUS FACTORS IN FOODS. Apart from their protein content, certain animal foodstuffs (e.g., milk, liver) contain an unidentified factor (or factors) which enhances protein synthesis and growth. This has been termed "animal protein factor" (APF), and perhaps will eventually be found to belong in the category of vitamins (p. 170); vitamin B_{12}, before it was separated from this "factor," was included under this designation. This APF may contribute to the biological superiority of animal over vegetable proteins.

Certain foodstuffs, in their natural state, may contain nutritionally deleterious components. For example, soybeans contain a principle with antitryptic activity which depresses appetite and interferes with protein digestion, an effect similar to that of gossypol in cottonseed oil (p. 628). This substance, presumably protein in nature, is inactivated by heat, which explains, in part at least, the fact that the nutritional value of soybean is increased considerably by proper cooking technics.

Toxic materials may be present in certain foods, as consumed, as a result of either natural occurrence or processing. These include such factors as lead, arsenic, selenium, and copper, and a substance present in wheat flour bleached with agene (NCl_3), which causes serious nervous system manifestations (e.g., "canine hysteria"). Protection is afforded against many of these recognized hazards by appropriate legislation. A sensitizing factor in fava beans may induce a hemolytic disorder, favism. Spoiled sweet clover hay contains dicoumarin (p. 639), which, when ingested by cattle, produces a hemorrhagic condition characterized by prothrombin deficiency.

BIBLIOGRAPHY

Annual Review of Physiology.

Nutritional Reviews.

Allison, J. B. et al.: Proteins and protein hydrolysates in nutrition, Ann. New York Acad. Sc. 47:241, 1946.

Food and Nutrition Board, National Research Council: Recommended Dietary Allowances, Revised 1953, Washington, D. C.

Geiger, E.: Extracaloric function of dietary components in relation to protein utilization, Federation Proc. 10:670, 1951.

McLester, J. S.: Nutrition and Diet in Health and Disease, ed. 6, Philadelphia, W. B. Saunders Company, 1952.

Pollack, H. and Halpern, S. L.: Therapeutic Nutrition. Pub. No. 234, National Academy of Sciences, National Research Council, 1952.

Sherman, H. C.: Chemistry of Food and Nutrition, ed. 8, New York, The Macmillan Company, 1952.

Swanson, P. P.: Influence of non-protein calories on protein metabolism, Federation Proc. 10:660, 1951.

24

METABOLIC ANTAGONISM

The term "metabolic antagonism" is applied to the phenomenon of interference with the metabolism or function of a given chemical compound by a structurally related compound, the basis of the interference being their structural similarity. The metabolic antagonist also may be designated an "antimetabolite" or a "substrate analog." The topic of metabolic antagonism would scarcely merit extended treatment if it were as completely abstruse as might be suggested by this rather vague definition. As a matter of fact, the phenomenon of metabolic antagonism not only finds constant use in current biochemical investigations of a fundamental nature, but also forms the basis of many major advances in pharmacology, chemotherapy, and cancer research.

The concept of metabolic antagonism is not entirely new. Interference with the metabolism of succinic acid by structurally related compounds, e.g., malonic acid (p. 253), represents an example of this phenomenon which was recognized many years ago. However, the wide applicability of the concept was not realized until the now famous explanation of the mode of action of sulfonamides forcibly brought this subject to the attention of the scientific public.

After the efficacy of sulfonamides as antibacterial agents was demonstrated, it became of interest to inquire into the mechanism of their action. Certain natural extracts were found to be capable of "antagonizing" or reversing the antibacterial action of the sulfonamides, and it was shown that the substance responsible for this effect is p-aminobenzoic acid. It was hypothesized, without much supporting evidence at the time, that p-aminobenzoic acid is an essential nutrilite of bacteria, that it is concerned in a specific enzyme reaction, and that its combination with that enzyme is interfered with by the sulfonamides, which, by virtue of the similarity of their structures, could competitively combine with the enzyme in place of the natural substrate.

p-Aminobenzoic acid   Sulfanilamide

This theoretical "shot in the dark" proved to be well directed. p-Aminobenzoic acid was soon found to be a nutrilite of bacteria; indeed, it is a dietary requirement or "vitamin" for many species. It was eventually discovered that bacteria require p-aminobenzoic acid for synthesis of the folic acid group (p. 204), and that the sulfonamides interfere specifically with the enzyme reaction in which the p-aminobenzoic acid is incorporated into the pteroylglutamic molecule. The sulfonamides have no such effect on the animal host, since no comparable reaction occurs in animal tissues; pre-formed folic acid is required by the animal organism.

With this extraordinary elucidation of a chemotherapeutic phenomenon, arrived at by the application of the concept of metabolic antagonism, the theory has received increasing attention and application. It would be no exaggeration to state that a significant segment of current research in the basic medical sciences and in clinical medicine is influenced if not directly guided by it.

GENERAL THEORY OF ANTAGONISM

Various types of enzyme inhibition other than that by substrate analogs have been described (p. 251); they are not of concern in connection with the topic at hand.

The general hypothesis of inhibition by analogs states that, whereas the specificity of enzymes with respect to the catalysis of given chemical reactions may be high, thus requiring specific chemical groups in the substrates, the specificity of enzymes with respect to simple *combination* with various molecules is much lower. Consequently, the "combining sites" on the enzyme surface may unite with molecules other than the natural substrate, if the analogs are sufficiently similar structurally to the substrate to fit the site of combination. Since sites occupied by the analog obviously are inaccessible to substrate, and since the structure of the analog ordinarily precludes its participation in the same type of chemical reaction as the normal substrate, the velocity of an enzyme-catalyzed reaction is decreased when analogs are present in addition to substrate.

COMPETITIVE INHIBITION. The simplest type of metabolic antagonism, or inhibition by substrate analogs, is termed "competitive" and is illustrated in Figure 120. Substrate is shown combining reversibly with the enzyme to form an activated complex (p. 221), which splits to yield the products of the reaction and liberate the enzyme. An analog similarly combines reversibly with the enzyme at the same type of site, but forms an inactive complex.

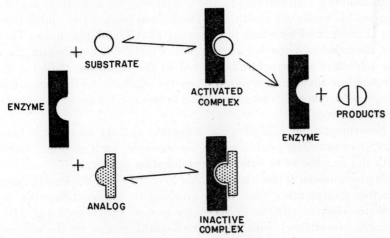

SUBSTRATE

ENZYME

ACTIVATED COMPLEX

ENZYME

+ PRODUCTS

ANALOG

INACTIVE COMPLEX

Fig. 120. Competitive inhibition

The tenacity with which substrates or analogs combine with the enzyme may be described quantitatively by standard constants of equilibrium or dissociation. Ordinarily, but not invariably, the normal substrate is held more tightly than any analog. Since the equilibrium constants are fixed for any enzyme, substrate, and analog, the degree of inhibition of the reaction varies with the ratio of concentrations of inhibitor to substrate. Sufficiently high concentrations of substrate can force the analog molecules from the enzyme sites and relieve the inhibition. The ratio of concentration of inhibitor to that of substrate required to produce a given degree of inhibition (usually set at 50 per cent of maximum) is termed the "inhibition index." True competitive inhibition is characterized by the constancy of the inhibition index over a range of inhibitor and substrate concentrations. To put the matter more concretely, let us suppose that a given enzyme reaction is inhibited 50 per cent at a substrate concentration of 0.001 M when the antimetabolite is used at a concentration of 0.1 M. Raising the concentration of substrate alone will decrease the inhibition, raising the concentration of analog will increase it, whereas raising both in the same ratio will preserve the same degree of inhibition. A substrate concentration of 0.005 M and an analog concentration of 0.5 M will result in the same 50 per cent inhibition as concentrations of 0.001 M and 0.1 M, respectively, the inhibition index being 100 in both cases. Such behavior is characteristic of competitive inhibition.

NON-COMPETITIVE INHIBITION. Unfortunately, the clear-cut relations outlined above do not obtain in all cases. Instances are known in which compounds, undoubtedly closely related to the substrate in structure, produce inhibitions not completely reversible by excess substrate at high inhibitor concentrations. At the extreme, the inhibition may be irreversible under all conditions. These "non-competitive" inhibitions are characterized by a lack of constancy of the inhibition index. They are, nevertheless, regarded as examples of metabolic antagonism, since the inhibitors are structurally related to the substrate, since the inhibitions are sometimes reversed by excess substrate, and since systems which are apparently non-competitive in one species are at times competitive in another.

Non-competitive inhibition by substrate analogs may result from various causes. The inhibitor may, for example, form so firm a union with the enzyme as to make the combination practically irreversible. This phenomenon is particularly liable to occur when the analog bears reactive groups other than those involved in combination with the ordinary enzyme site, these accessory groups then combining (frequently irreversibly) with adjacent chemical groups on the enzyme surface.

There is a special case of non-competitive inhibition which is not due to substrate analogs, but is still related quite closely to this topic. In the case of the sulfonamides (p. 635), it was stated that the inhibition of bacterial metabolism could be reversed by *p*-aminobenzoic acid. This reversal is of the competitive type. But sulfonamide inhibitions may also be relieved by folic acid, in a non-competitive manner. Folic acid, being the *product* of the reaction in which *p*-aminobenzoic acid is involved, can bypass the inhibitor when supplied pre-formed. As a general rule, the product of an inhibited reaction antagonizes the inhibitor non-competitively.

APPLICATIONS OF METABOLIC ANTAGONISM

The field of metabolic antagonism has been worked so thoroughly in recent years that the accumulated information has become unwieldy. Rather than catalog the hundreds of known antagonists to vitamins, amino acids, etc., it may be more instructive to discuss certain of the fields of application, the approaches taken by investigators in these fields, and a few actual examples of antagonism.

FUNDAMENTAL BIOCHEMISTRY. (*a*) NATURALLY OCCURRING ANTIMETABOLITES. One of the consequences of the realization of the wide applicability of the concept of biological antagonism has been the recognition of certain cases of antagonism involving naturally occurring antimetabolites. Among the oldest of these examples is ion antagonism, although in the past it was not generally regarded as belonging in this category. Illustrations of ion antagonism may be drawn from many sources. For example, certain of the transphosphorylations of glycolysis

(p. 394) require K+, which is antagonized by Na+. The antagonism between certain divalent cations has been mentioned in connection with the properties of actin and myosin (p. 411).

Inspection of the formulas of the steroid hormones reveals many similarities, suggesting the possibility that certain of these compounds may act as mutual antagonists. Evidence in support of this thesis has been obtained in the case of androgens versus estrogens, and estrogens versus progesterone.

A number of natural antagonisms have been discovered in the nutrition of microorganisms, involving purines, pyrimidines, nucleic acids, and amino acids.

The topic of antibiotics is ordinarily not regarded as related to metabolic antagonism. However, in the case of chloramphenicol (Chloromycetin), there is some evidence of antagonism with phenylalanine, although the relationship is non-competitive. Chloramphenicol, the structure of which resembles that of phenylalanine, is synthesized by certain fungi. Its inhibitory action toward Escherichia coli is reversed by phenylalanine, but only at low concentrations of the antibiotic. It must be emphasized that, in general, antibiotics are not believed to function as metabolic antagonists.

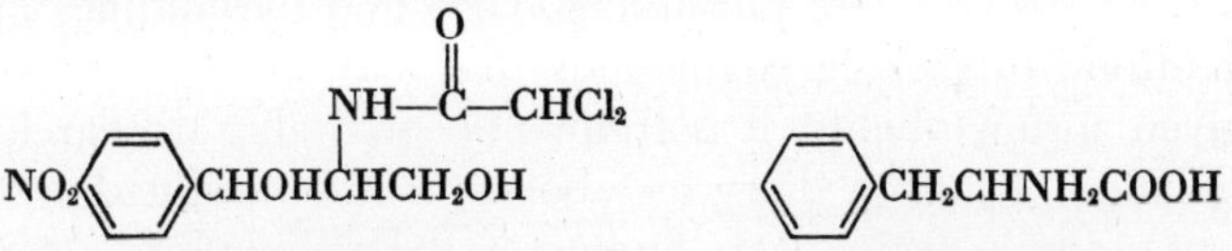

$$NO_2 \text{—} CHOHCHCH_2OH \qquad \text{NH—C(=O)—CHCl}_2$$

Chloramphenicol   Phenylalanine

Dicumarol (dicoumarin) is a particularly interesting example of a naturally occurring antimetabolite, because of its practical application in clinical medicine. Cattle suffer from a hemorrhagic condition after consuming spoiled sweet-clover hay. The causative agent is 3-3'-methylenebis-(4-hydroxycoumarin), commonly designated "Dicumarol."

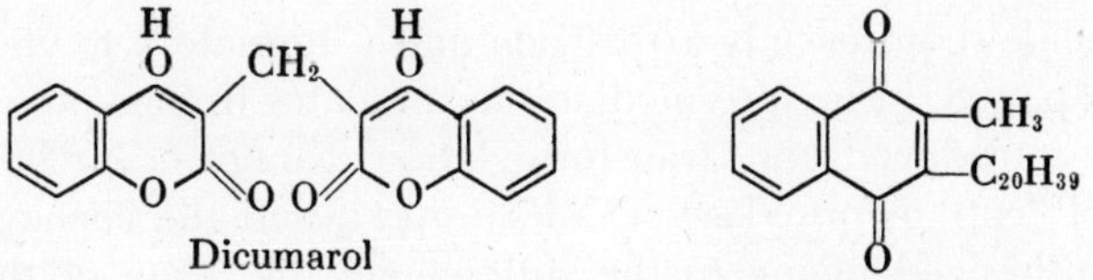

Dicumarol

Vitamin K

The mechanism of production of the hemorrhagic condition involves the induction of hypoprothrombinemia (p. 166), due to the antagonism by Dicumarol of the vitamin K required for synthesis of prothrombin. Large doses of the vitamin can counteract the effect of the antagonist, but the quantitative relation is not truly competitive. Dicumarol finds application in medicine in conditions in which excessive clotting or thrombosis must be prevented.

(*b*) DISCOVERY OF NEW METABOLITES. Elucidation of the pathways of intermediary metabolism is largely a matter of detection and identification of intermediates not ordinarily accumulated in the organism. Certain of the methods used in such investigations are discussed elsewhere (p. 344). The ability of a naturally occurring compound to counteract, in a competitive manner, the inhibitory action of a synthetic, structurally similar compound may be regarded as necessary but not conclusive evidence that the former compound is an intermediary metabolite in the system being tested. *p*-Aminobenzoic acid and the sulfonamides are a case in point (p. 635).

Counteraction of the inhibitor, non-competitively, by a compound not structurally analogous suggests that the substance may be a product of the reaction being inhibited, e.g., folic acid in the case mentioned above. In addition to folic acid, bacterial inhibition by sulfonamides has been reversed (non-competitively) by methionine, purines, and pyrimidines. These phenomena are explicable on the basis that folic (folinic) acid is involved in the metabolism of formate fragments, including interrelations with methyl groups (p. 208) and certain parts of the structures of purines (p. 567) and pyrimidines (p. 571).

In addition to seeking compounds that may reverse the inhibition of a given antimetabolite, it is frequently profitable to search for the accumulation of intermediary metabolites in the inhibited system. An excellent example of this is the finding, in the medium of bacterial cells grown under conditions of slight inhibition by sulfonamides, of a precursor of the purines, amino-imidazole-carboxamide:

$$
\begin{array}{c}
NH_2-C=O \\
| \\
C-NH \\
| \qquad\quad CH \\
NH_2-C-N
\end{array}
$$

This molecule requires only a 1-carbon unit ("formate") to yield hypoxanthine (p. 568). The intermediate accumulates because the formate cannot be introduced, the "transformylation" cannot occur because of the lack of "cotransformylase" (CoF, p. 542), and the coenzyme cannot be synthesized owing to the sulfonamide blockage of the incorporation of *p*-aminobenzoic acid into the folic acid molecule.

For experimental purposes, it is frequently desirable to inhibit the operation of the tricarboxylic acid cycle (p. 397). As mentioned previously in various connections, the succinate → fumarate step is inhibited by malonic acid, an analog of succinic acid. An example of the specificity of structure involved in substrates and antimetabolites is illustrated by trans-aconitic acid, which interferes with the metabolism of cis-aconitic acid. The inhibitory action of fluoroacetic acid is most unusual. Fluoroacetate is apparently sufficiently similar in structure to acetate to be mistaken for the latter by the enzyme systems involved in the activation of acetate and in its condensation with oxalacetate to form citrate, since a fluorocitrate of undetermined structure has been isolated. However, that is as far as the interloper can go, since the fluorocitrate acts as an antagonist of citrate in the aconitase reaction (p. 399).

COOH	COOH	COOH	COOH	HCCOOH	HOOCCH
CH₂	CH₂	CH₃	CH₂F	HOOCCH₂CCOOH	HOOCCH₂CCOO
CH₂	COOH	Ace-	Fluoro-	cis-Aconitate	trans-Aconitate
COOH	Malo-	tate	acetate		
Suc-	nate				
cinate					

(c) EXPERIMENTAL DIETARY DEFICIENCIES. Much can be learned of the metabolic role of an essential dietary constituent by selective deprivation of that factor. The design of diets complete in all but one item, however, is frequently a difficult task, and is often made more difficult by the synthesis of certain essential factors by intestinal bacteria. The advent of anti-vitamins and anti-amino acids has consequently materially lightened the labors of investigators in nutritional biochemistry. Frequently, inclusion in the diet of an antimetabolite results in deficiency in the factor being antagonized, despite adequate quantities of that factor in the diet or derived from intestinal bacteria.

A selection of antagonists for vitamins and essential amino acids in animals is presented in Figure 121. Ethionine is toxic to rats, the effect being counteracted by methionine. The analog inhibits the incorporation of methionine into proteins, possibly by being itself incorporated. It is known to "trans-ethylate," forming the triethyl analog of choline, itself a toxic antimetabolite (which, however, is lipotropic, p. 479). Thienylalanine retards the growth of rats, an effect that may be counteracted by phenylalanine.

Typical avitaminoses, cured by administration of the appropriate vitamin, are produced in test animals by pyrithiamine, β-acetylpyridine, desoxypyridoxine, and galactoflavin. The apparent avitaminosis K produced by Dicumarol (pp. 166, 639) is reversed only by very large doses of the vitamin. Many of the analogs of folic acid produce effects which cannot be counteracted by folic acid. Although scurvy-like manifestations are produced in mice and rats (animals which ordinarily do not require ascorbic acid) by glucoascorbic acid, this condition is not cured by administration of ascorbic acid. In the guinea pig, a competition between ascorbic acid and its analog can be demon-

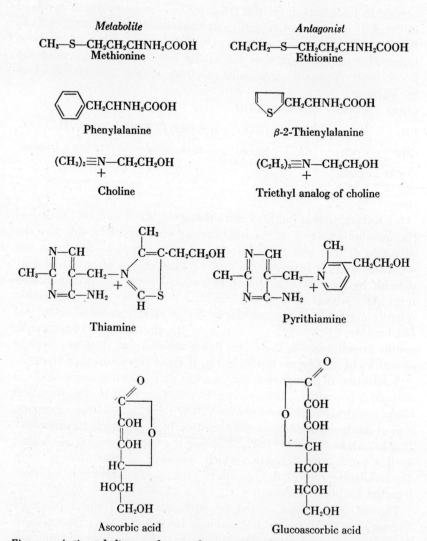

Fig. 121. *Antimetabolites used to produce nutritional deficiencies in animals (see page 643 for continuation of this figure)*

Metabolite   Antagonist

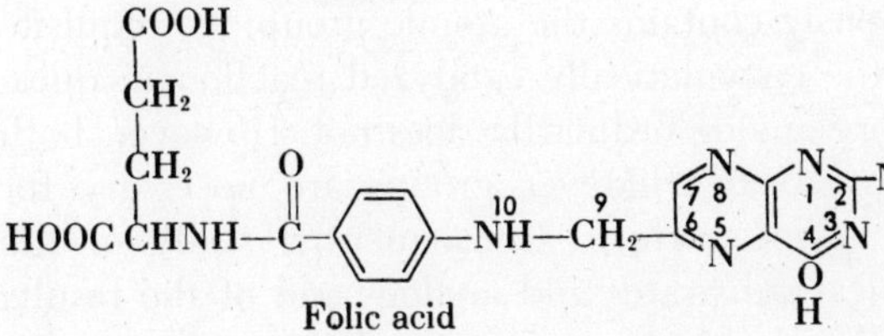

Folic acid

CH$_3$— for H— on 7 or 9.
"Methopterin"

NH$_2$— for —OH on 4.
"Aminopterin"

NH$_2$— for —OH on 4, CH$_3$— for H— on 10.
"A-Methopterin"

Aspartic for glutamic, etc.

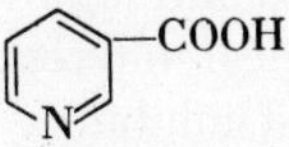

Nicotinic acid

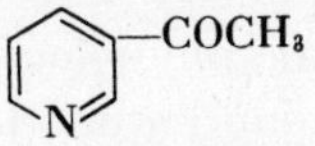

β-Acetylpyridine

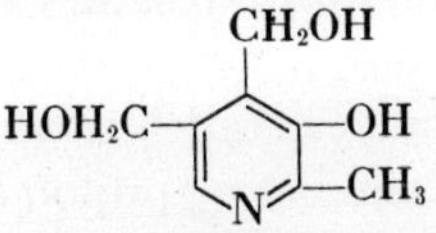

Pyridoxine

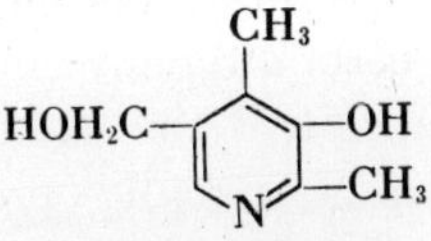

Desoxypyridoxine

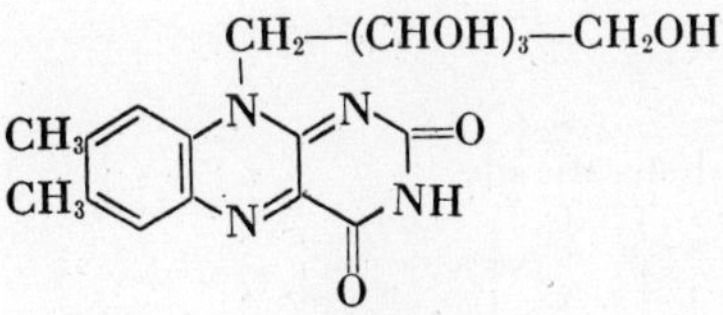

Riboflavin

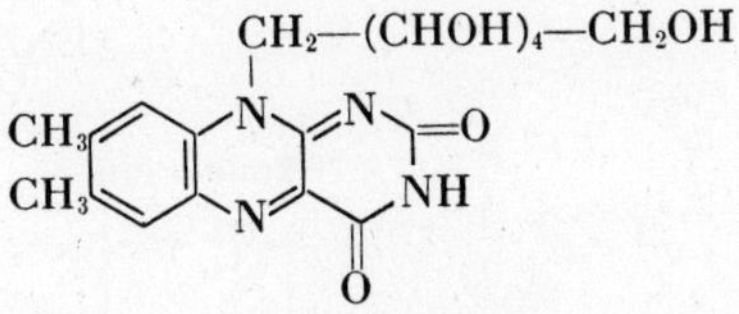

Galactoflavin

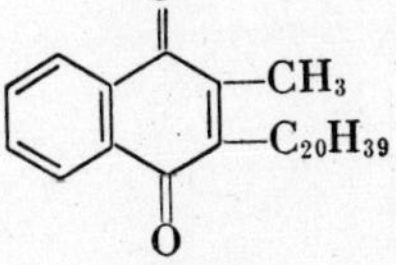

Vitamin K$_1$

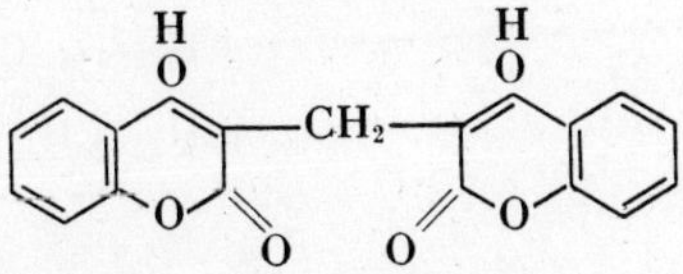

Dicumarol

Fig. 121. (Continued)

strated, but the symptoms produced by the analog in this case are not typically scorbutic. Obviously, factors in addition to simple antagonism are operating in these cases.

(d) ACTIVE CENTERS OF ENZYMES. Research on the mechanism of action of enzymes has been aided by the use of metabolic antagonists. A normal substrate obviously contains the atomic groupings requisite for the performance of the enzymatically catalyzed reaction in question, whereas an inhibitory analog ordinarily does not. However, both types of compounds must bear whatever groups are necessary for combination with the enzyme surface. Consequently, study of the functional groups of typical substrates and analogs and of the results of stepwise variation in the character or position of these groups permits certain conclusions to be drawn concerning the possible character and topical distribution of the sites on the enzyme surface.

Particularly valuable work in this direction has been performed in the case of acetylcholine esterase (p. 228), an enzyme of considerable biochemical, physiological, and pharmacological interest. From the cationic group required of substrates and most inhibitors (p. 223), it has been concluded that one of the important binding sites on the enzyme surface is anionic. Consideration of the electronic mechanism of ester hydrolysis, permissible structures of substrates, and the structures of certain types of inhibitors (fluorophosphates, p. 645) leads to the surmise that the site of hydrolysis (the "esteratic" site) contains two groups, one acidic (proton donor) and one basic (proton acceptor, electron donor). Consequently, the current view of the combination of acetylcholine and its esterase may be illustrated as in Figure 122.

ENZYME

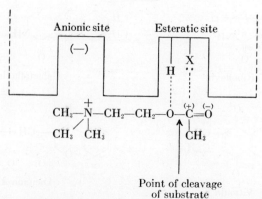

Fig. 122. Combination of acetylcholine and acetylcholine esterase

(The small positive and negative charges indicated for the acyl carbon and carbonyl oxygen atoms of the substrate, respectively, are those familiar from electronic considerations of organic structure and reactivity.) Reference is made below to the probable manner of combination of various inhibitors with this enzyme.

PHARMACOLOGICAL APPLICATIONS. Actions of drugs involve the selective stimulation or inhibition of activity of one, or at most a few organs, tissues, or receptors. Since many of these receptors are subject normally to chemical control by a specific organic compound, the concept of antagonism by analog may be expected to be applicable in this field. As indicated below, two general types of phenomena appear to occur: (1) antagonists may be found which compete with the normal "control" compound for enzymes which destroy or otherwise inactivate the latter, thus intensifying the normal effect of the control ("mimetic" type); (2) other antagonists may compete with the control compound for the effector site, thus decreasing the normal effect ("lytic" type).

Although the concept of antagonism between chemical compounds has been employed widely in pharmacology for many years, the specific hypothesis that many pharmacological agents act as analogs of normal substrates has gained acceptance only slowly. Furthermore, it is undeniably true that the actual evidence in support of this hypothesis is deficient or lacking in many cases. For these reasons, the examples of purported antagonism mentioned here are to be regarded rather as suggested than as proved. Certain of these antagonisms are illustrated in Figure 123.

(a) ANTAGONISMS INVOLVING ACETYLCHOLINE. There are two opposing groups of compounds, both of which may be regarded as antagonists of acetylcholine. The parasympathomimetic drugs (Prostigmin; DFP in Fig. 123) act largely by competition with acetylcholine for the enzyme, acetylcholinesterase. Since they block the enzyme responsible for the hydrolysis of acetylcholine, in effect they increase the concentration of the neurohormone at its effector sites, hence the designation, "parasympathomimetic." Diisopropyl fluorophosphate (DFP) is believed to react with the esteratic site of the enzyme (p. 644), whereas Prostigmin probably is attracted to both the anionic and esteratic sites. In addition to its inhibition of the esterase, Prostigmin is said to act directly on the effector cells of muscle.

The second group of acetylcholine antagonists compete with it at the effector sites, rather than at the surface of the esterase. Since they act as displacing agents, these compounds have the effect of lowering the concentration of acetylcholine in the vicinity of the effectors, and consequently are designated "spasmolytics" or "antispasmodics." There appear to be three subdivisions of this group (Fig. 123): (1) the atropine type, which displaces acetylcholine from parasympathetic effector sites (smooth muscle, glands); (2) the tetraethylammonium type, which block the action of the hormone in the ganglia; (3) the

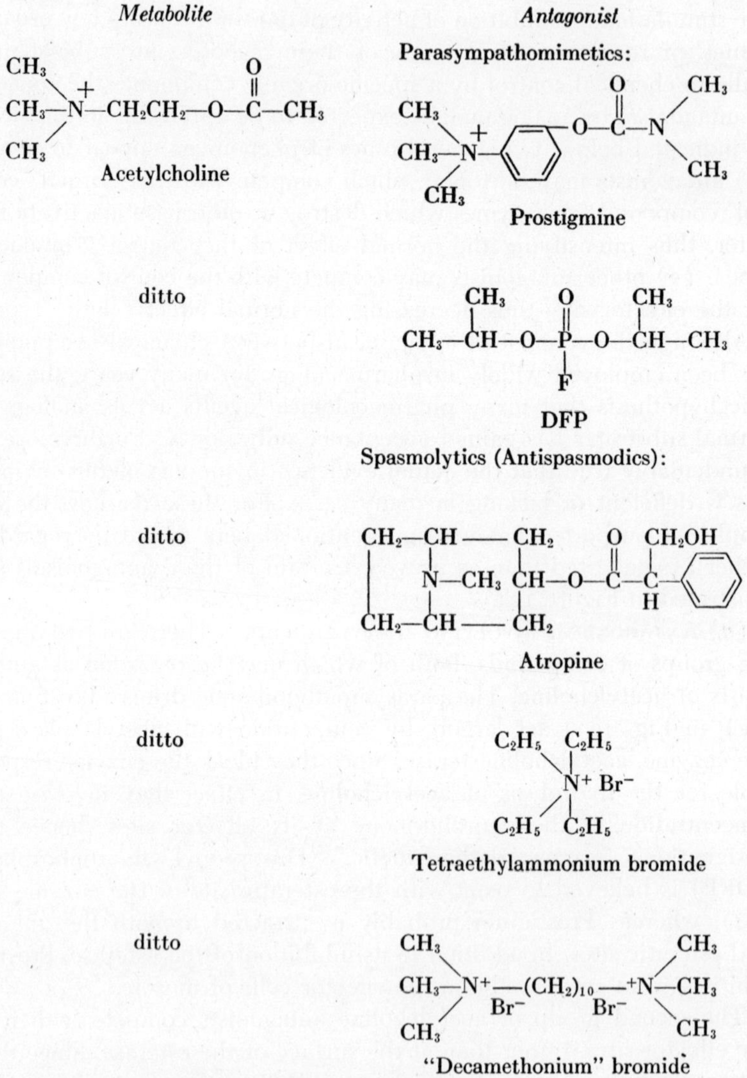

Metabolite   *Antagonist*

                                    Parasympathomimetics:

$$CH_3-\overset{\underset{|}{CH_3}}{\overset{+}{N}}-CH_2CH_2-O-\overset{\overset{O}{\|}}{C}-CH_3$$

Acetylcholine

$$CH_3-\overset{\underset{|}{CH_3}}{\overset{+}{N}}\!\!\!\diamond\!\!\!-O-\overset{\overset{O}{\|}}{C}-N\overset{CH_3}{\underset{CH_3}{}}$$

Prostigmine

ditto

$$CH_3-CH-O-\overset{\overset{CH_3}{|}}{\underset{\underset{F}{|}}{\overset{\overset{O}{\|}}{P}}}-O-\overset{CH_3}{\underset{}{CH}}-CH_3$$

DFP

Spasmolytics (Antispasmodics):

ditto

Atropine

ditto

$$\overset{C_2H_5}{\underset{C_2H_5}{\diagdown}}\overset{C_2H_5}{\underset{\diagdown}{N^+}}\overset{C_2H_5}{\diagdown}Br^-$$

Tetraethylammonium bromide

ditto

$$CH_3-\overset{\overset{CH_3}{|}}{\underset{\underset{Br^-}{|}}{N^+}}-(CH_2)_{10}-\overset{\overset{CH_3}{|}}{\underset{\underset{Br^-}{|}}{{}^+N}}-CH_3$$

"Decamethonium" bromide

Fig. 123. Purported antagonisms of pharmacological agents (see page 647 for continuation of this figure)

Metabolite	Antagonist

Sympathomimetics:

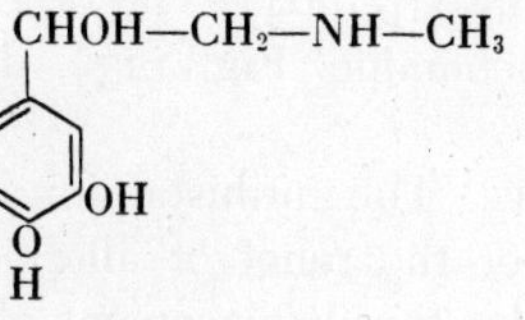

CHOH—CH$_2$—NH—CH$_3$

OH
O
H

Adrenaline

CH$_3$
CHOH—CH—NH—CH$_3$

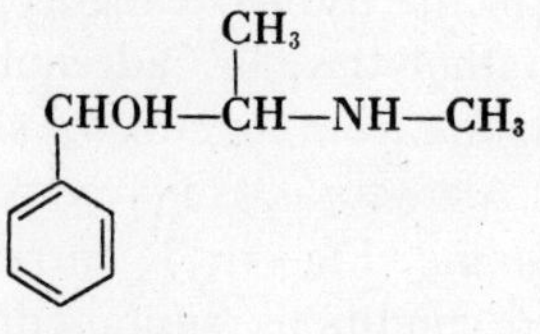

"Ephedrine"

ditto

Sympatholytics (Adrenolytics):

CH$_2$CH$_2$Cl
CH$_2$—N—CH$_2$—

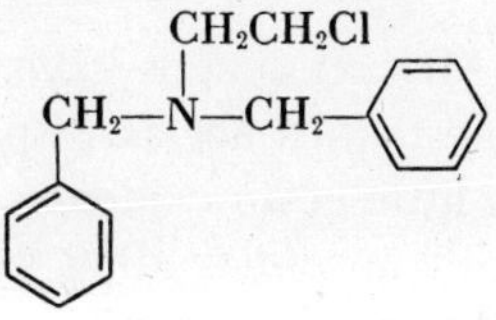

"Dibenamine"

HC══C—CH$_2$CH$_2$NH$_2$
HN   N
C
H

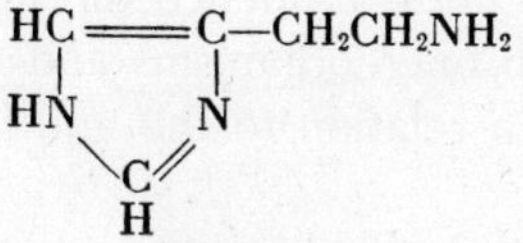

Histamine

Antihistaminics:

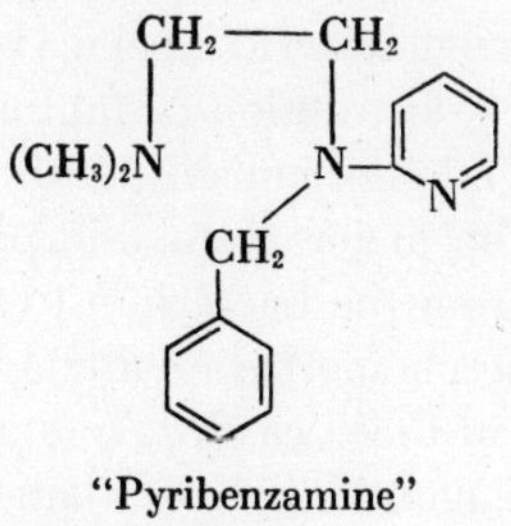

CH$_2$——CH$_2$
(CH$_3$)$_2$N   N
CH$_2$

"Pyribenzamine"

Fig. 123. (Continued)

curare and decamethonium type, antagonizing the action of acetylcholine at the neuromuscular junction.

(b) ANTAGONISMS INVOLVING ADRENALINE.   The situation here is similar to that with acetylcholine. One class of antagonists to adrenaline,
the "sympathomimetics" (ephedrine, Fig. 123), apparently function by
blocking the action of enzymes which destroy or conjugate adrenaline (in the former category, amine oxidase, p. 364). The other type,
"sympatholytics" or "adrenolytics" (Dibenamine, Fig. 123), displace
adrenaline from its effector sites.

(c) ANTAGONISMS INVOLVING HISTAMINE.   The antihistaminics (Pyribenzamine, Fig. 123), currently used for the relief of allergies and
related conditions, supposedly function by the displacement of histamine from effector sites. Since the structures of certain antihistaminics bear little superficial resemblance to histamine, the applicability
of the concept of antagonism by analog in this case is questioned by
some.

(d) MISCELLANEOUS CONSIDERATIONS.   It has been suggested that
local anesthetics act as displacing agents for acetylcholine, although
there is little or no evidence on the matter. Attempts have been made,
also, with no outstanding success, to explain the action of narcotics
on the basis of antagonism.

The structure of thiouracil, an antithyroid agent (p. 688), suggests a relation to uracil or other pyrimidines. Evidence for such an
antagonism is available from studies with microorganisms and in the
case of erythrocyte maturation, but not in relation to the antithyroid
action of this compound.

CHEMOTHERAPEUTIC APPLICATIONS.   The task of chemotherapy is the
selective destruction or inhibition of the metabolism of the cells of invading microorganisms, with minimal damage to the cells of the host.
Since the major metabolic pathways of all living cells are much the
same, from the bacterium to the bacteriologist, the design of effective
and safe chemotherapeutic agents is quite difficult. The selectivity required in these cases favors an approach such as the search for selective antagonists, rather than the older application of noxious agents
which are general tissue poisons.

In the most favorable instance, a metabolite or metabolic reaction
may be found which is essential to the life or growth of the microorganism, but is absent from or of no consequence in the cells of the
host. Such a case is the requirement for p-aminobenzoic acid by
many bacteria (p. 204). Obviously, discovery of such a differential
requirement is only half the answer to the problem; the proper antimetabolite must then be synthesized.

In many cases no such qualitative difference in metabolism can be
discovered. The investigator must then content himself with the ex-

ploitation of whatever quantitative differences may exist. The bacterium, being a rapidly growing and dividing cell, may not be able to withstand the induction of a temporary deficiency in the host, whose requirements for a given metabolite may be much more modest. This somewhat difficult approach may be aided by differences in cell permeability between microorganism and host toward the chosen antimetabolite.

The structural formulas of a number of chemotherapeutic agents and of the metabolites they are believed to antagonize are illustrated in Figure 124. It must be pointed out that many of these compounds are still in the experimental stage and may not develop into useful drugs when more information is available.

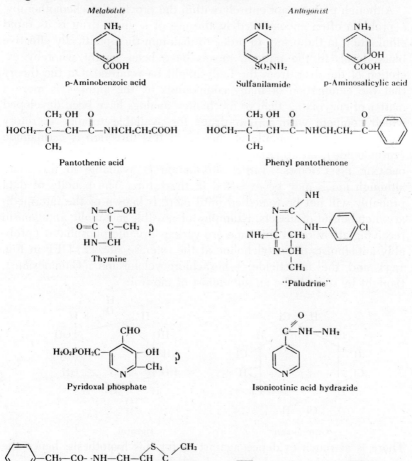

Fig. 124. *Chemotherapeutic agents as analogs*

The example of the sulfonamides and *p*-aminobenzoic acid has been discussed at length (p. 635). Another probable antagonist of *p*-aminobenzoic acid is *p*-aminosalicylic acid, which has had some clinical application in the treatment of tuberculosis. Another compound currently being tested against this disease is isonicotinic acid hydrazide ("isoniazid"), which, despite its name, is probably an antagonist of the pyridoxine group of vitamins rather than of nicotinic acid.

Phenylpantothenone has been tested experimentally as an antimalarial drug. It appears to inhibit the incorporation of pantothenic acid into CoA (p. 195). Another type of antimalarial agent is Paludrine, which is believed to be an anti-pyrimidine.

Although perhaps not entirely within the province of chemotherapy, a problem often encountered in the use of a given drug is its rapid elimination in the urine. In order to maintain therapeutically effective blood levels in the patient, means have been sought whereby excretion of the drug from the body might be retarded. On the theory that the elimination of many compounds by the kidneys is more a matter of enzymatics than of mechanics, analogs have been developed which compete with certain drugs for available tubular excretory mechanisms. One example of success in this direction is carinamide (caronamide), an apparent analog of benzyl-penicillin.

ORGANIC INSECTICIDES. Little information is available in this field, although much may be expected in the future. The paucity of data probably will not be remedied until more is known of the intermediary metabolism of insects. Examples of possible metabolic antagonism receiving attention at this time are various organic phosphates (probably antagonists of acetylcholine at the esterase site, cf., DFP in Fig. 123) and the insecticide, γ-hexachlorocyclohexane (Gammexane), thought by some to be an antagonist of inositol:

Gammexane   Inositol

There is as much evidence against as for this hypothesis; hence the question must be regarded as undecided.

APPLICATIONS TO CANCER RESEARCH. Attempts at chemical control of neoplastic growth are based essentially on the same assumptions as those underlying the chemotherapy of infections. The problem is infinitely more difficult, however, since the cells to be inhibited or destroyed are "foreign" to the body largely in behavior, not in origin. Nevertheless, it is believed that the rapid rate of growth of neoplastic tissue may result in requirements for vitamins or other cofactors which differ, possibly qualitatively, but at least quantitatively, from those of normal cells. It is possible, also, that certain "primitive" metabolic pathways may be of more importance in tumors than in normal tissue, since the former resemble embryonic tissue in certain respects.

Examples of antimetabolites which have been or are being investigated in tumor chemotherapy are presented in Figure 125.

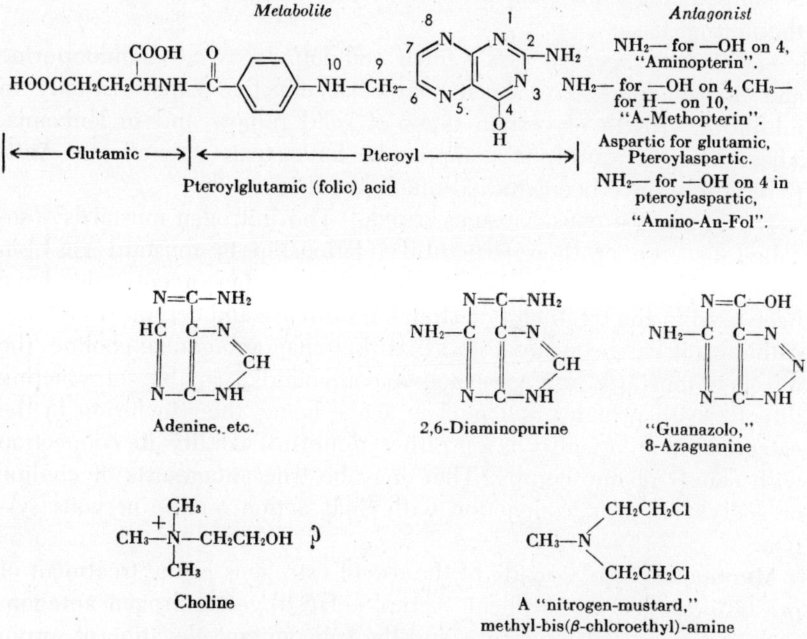

Fig. 125. Antimetabolites in cancer research

(a) FOLIC ACID ANTAGONISTS. Several factors have motivated the investigation of folic acid antagonists as tumor inhibitors. One is the rapid rate of multiplication of cancer cells, which would be expected to increase the requirements for raw materials used in the synthesis of nuclear components (nucleic acids, purines, pyrimidines), thus concomitantly increasing the need for folic acid (p. 208). Another is the leukopenia which results from a deficiency in folic acid (p. 211), suggesting application of antifolic compounds in the treatment of leukemias.

Each of the three components of the folic acid molecule, i.e., pteridyl, p-aminobenzoyl, and glutamic acid, is capable of chemical modification to yield active antagonists to the parent molecule. Replacement of the hydroxyl group at position 4 of the pteridine ring by an amino group (Aminopterin), addition of a methyl group at position 10 of the p-aminobenzoyl moiety, together with the preceding change (A-Methopterin), or replacement of the entire glutamic acid group by aspartic acid, together with placement of an amino group at position 4 (Amino-An-Fol), are examples of changes in the molecule of folic acid which yield active antagonists.

Positive results with these analogs have been reported in experimental animals and clinically in certain types of sarcoma and leukemia. The beneficial effects are only temporary, however, and are accompanied by toxic manifestations due to folic acid deficiency of the normal tissues.

(b) PURINE ANTAGONISTS. Such compounds as 2,6-diaminopurine and 8-azaguanine have been somewhat effective experimentally in inhibiting growth of certain types of solid tumors and in leukemia. They, like the anti-folic compounds, have toxic side-effects. Antipyrimidines have been studied much less extensively.

(c) MISCELLANEOUS CONSIDERATIONS. The "nitrogen mustards" (so-called because of their structural relationship to mustard gas), in addition to their potentialities as chemical warfare agents, also have been used in the treatment of Hodgkin's disease and certain leukemias. Although it has been suggested that they may antagonize choline, the nitrogen mustards are very active compounds, capable of reacting directly with proteins and nucleic acids, hence their inclusion in the category of antagonists is of rather doubtful validity in connection with cancer chemotherapy. They may be true antagonists of choline or acetylcholine in connection with their action on the nervous system.

Mention should be made of the use of estrogens in the treatment of prostatic cancer, an excellent example of estrogen-androgen antagonism. The growth of the cancer and the concomitant elevation of serum acid phosphatase (p. 231) are both directly affected by the estrogen-androgen balance.

COMMENT

Many examples of metabolic antagonism have been omitted, since the aim has been the presentation of general principles rather than the accumulation of specific details. Nevertheless, it should be obvious that the concept of metabolic antagonism is widely applicable. It would be of importance if it merely aided the understanding of facts already available; however, it does much more. It places in the hands of the biochemist new tools for the systematic investigation of metabolic pathways, the discovery of intermediary metabolites, and the mechanism of enzyme action. It provides what has been called a "rational basis" for pharmacology and chemotherapy, substituting general theory for much of the empiricism formerly characteristic of those fields. It promises for the agriculturalist new weapons against insect pests and weeds, as well as agents for improving the performance of crops. In short, the phenomenon of metabolic antagonism potentially augments immeasurably the controls which can be exercised over the cells of our own bodies and those of our biological friends and foes.

BIBLIOGRAPHY

Martin, G. J.: Biological Antagonism, New York, Blakiston Company, 1951.
Petering, H. G.: Folic acid antagonists, Physiol. Rev. 32:197, 1952.
Woods, D. D. et al.: Antimetabolites, Ann. New York Acad. Sc. 52:1197, 1950.
Woolley, D. W.: A Study of Antimetabolites, John Wiley & Sons, Inc., 1952.
Work, T. S. and Work, E.: The Basis of Chemotherapy, New York, Interscience Publishers, Inc., 1948.

25

HORMONES

A hormone is commonly defined as a chemical substance which, formed in one part of the body, is carried in the blood stream to other organs or tissues, which it influences in a specific manner. This definition is so broad that its usefulness is limited. For example, on this basis CO_2 has been referred to as a "hormone of respiration"; substances liberated by traumatized tissues as "wound hormones"; a number of factors secreted by digestive organs have been designated "gastrointestinal hormones"; acetylcholine, synthesized in nervous tissue, is frequently included in this category. It is generally agreed that the following structures should be included in the "endocrine system," i.e., tissues which produce "internal secretions" (hormones): the anterior and posterior pituitary, thyroid, parathyroid, adrenal cortex and medulla, pancreatic islets of Langerhans, ovary, testis, and placenta. Inclusion of other structures under this designation is a matter of individual preference. Of historical interest is the fact that the term "hormone" was first applied (Bayliss and Starling, 1902) to secretin, a substance produced in the duodenal mucosa, which has a stimulating effect on the secretion of pancreatic juice and bile (p. 262). It should be pointed out that although the term "hormone" implies an "exciting" influence, certain hormones are now known to exert a depressing effect on certain of their target tissues.

Information concerning the functions of hormones has been derived from (1) studies of the effects of removal or destructive disease of their tissues of origin, and (2) studies of the biological effects of excessive amounts of individual hormones resulting from either disease (hypersecretion) of various endocrine organs or experimental administration of tissue extracts or chemically pure products. The enormous advances in this field in recent years have been due largely to remarkable accomplishments in the chemical identification of several hormones, leading in important instances to their synthesis and, therefore, to their availability in amounts adequate for experimental purposes. These studies have indicated that certain hormones, in addition to biologically important actions on individual target organs (e.g., gonadotrophic and sex hormones), are intimately concerned in a variety of integrated processes, metabolic and otherwise, which serve to maintain homeostasis, i.e., a "steady state," in the organism. We are concerned here mainly with the chemistry and metabolic effects of these substances.

Certain of the hormones are protein in nature (e.g., anterior pituitary, parathyroid, insulin), some are amino acid derivatives (e.g., thyroxine, epinephrine), and others are steroids (e.g., estrogens, androgens, progesterone, adrenal cortex). The multiplicity of possibilities of stereoisomerism and of metabolic reactions inherent in the multiple-ring structure of the steroid hormones has given rise to a rather complicated system of nomenclature, the more confusing since it is subjected to periodic revision. It seems desirable to present here an outline of the currently accepted system, which applies not only to this group of hormones but to all other steroids, e.g., bile acids, cholesterol, etc. (p. 35).

NOMENCLATURE OF STEROIDS

INTRODUCTION. The term "steroid" is applied to the members of a group of compounds which have in common the cyclopentanoperhydrophenanthrene nucleus. This skeleton structure consists of a cyclopentane ring, (D), fused to a completely hydrogenated phenanthrene (A-B-C):

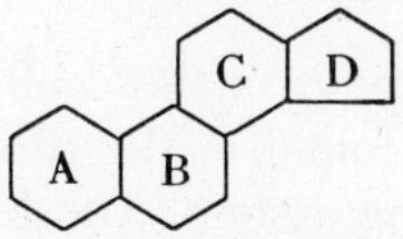

Substituents in the nucleus and on the commonly occurring sidechains are located by a standard numbering system:

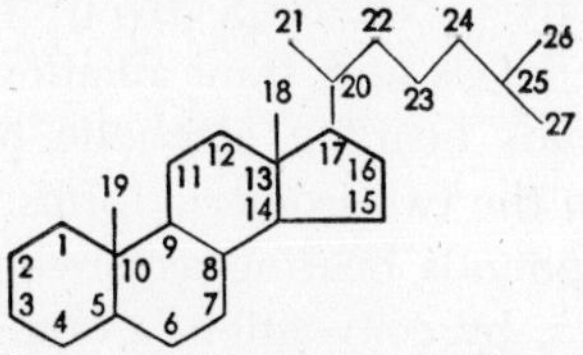

Examination of this formula and those of the substituted steroids reveals the existence of numerous asymmetric carbon atoms. Desoxycholic acid, a common bile acid, contains ten centers of asymmetry and can theoretically exist in 1024 stereoisomeric forms. Fortunately, only a few of the possible stereoisomers of the steroids actually exist in nature.

NUCLEAR STEREOISOMERISM. It is possible for each pair of adjacent rings in the nucleus to exist in two spatial configurations about the junction: cis and trans. In all naturally occurring steroids the configurations at the junctions of rings B-C and C-D are trans. At the junctions of rings A and B there is more natural variation. The estrogens, as will be seen below, do not have the possibility of isomerism at this locus, because ring A is aromatic. All other steroids can be divided into two groups: the "normal" or cis-A/B, and the "allo-," or trans-A/B.

STEREOISOMERISM OF SUBSTITUENTS. Most of the steroids which are of physiological interest carry methyl groups attached at positions 10 and 13, usually indicated merely by a short vertical line. By convention, the methyl group at C-10 is assigned a steric configuration with relation to this carbon atom such that it projects upward from the plane of the steroid nucleus, if the latter is written as above. This steric form is designated by the prefix "β-," and is indicated by a solid valence bond in structural formulas. The configurations of other substituents are assigned with reference to the methyl group at C-10. Groups projecting downward below the plane of the nucleus are designated by the prefix "α-," and are indicated in the structural formulas by valence bonds formed of broken lines.

Owing to the trans junctions involved in rings B, C, and D, the tertiary hydrogen atoms at C-9 and C-14 are α, whereas the tertiary hydrogen atom at C-8 and methyl group (No. 18) at C-13 are β. The chain attached at C-17 is β in all natural steroids. The 11-hydroxyl group which occurs in certain of the steroids of the adrenal cortex has the β configuration.

In contrast to the constancy of the configurations mentioned above, considerable variation is found in the case of substituents located at other positions on the ring system. The hydroxyl groups attached to the various bile acids have characteristic configurations (p. 461). The existence of "normal" and "allo-" series of compounds due to isomerism at junction A/B gives rise, respectively, to β and α tertiary hydrogen atoms at C-5/6 (cis and trans relations to the methyl group at C-10). Many steroids bear an alcoholic hydroxyl group at C-3, which also can exist in the two isomeric forms.

In the case of compounds bearing asymmetric centers in the side-chain attached at C-17, by convention, α-oriented groups are written as projecting to the right and β-groups to the left, if the side-chain is written vertically on the page.

PREFIXES AND SUFFIXES. In order to facilitate an understanding of the nomenclature rules presented below, the meanings of certain prefixes and suffixes are listed in Table 55. Certain of these are of common occurrence in organic chemistry; others are peculiar to the field of steroids.

Table 55. Suffixes and Prefixes for Steroids

SUFFIX OF PREFIX	MEANING
Suffix	
-ane	Saturated hydrocarbon
-ene	Unsaturated hydrocarbon
-ol	Hydroxyl group, as in an alcohol or phenol
-one	Ketone group
Prefix	
hydroxy- (oxy-)	Hydroxyl group
keto- (oxo-)	Ketone group
desoxy-	Loss of an oxygen atom
dehydro-	Loss of two hydrogen atoms
dihydro-	Gain of two hydrogen atoms
cis-	Refers to spatial arrangement of two groups on the same side of the molecule
trans-	Refers to spatial arrangement of two groups on opposite sides of the molecule
α-	Refers to group which is trans to the methyl at C-10
β-	Refers to group which is cis to methyl at C-10
epi-	Isomeric in configuration to a reference compound; specifically α at location C-3. Obsolete term
iso-	Similar to epi-, but not restricted to C-3. Obsolescent
allo-	Differing from reference compound in having 5α instead of 5β configuration; rings A and B in trans instead of cis relation to each other
etio-	Refers to final degradation product of a more complex molecule which still retains the essential chemical character of the original molecule. Obsolescent
nor-	Refers to compound similar chemically to reference substance, but having one less carbon atom in side-chain
Δ^n-	Indicates position of unsaturated linkage. Obsolescent (?)

PARENT HYDROCARBONS. All steroids may be considered derivatives of certain parent hydrocarbons. The estrogens, which are formed of monomethylated steroid nuclei, are derived from the parent compound, estrane:

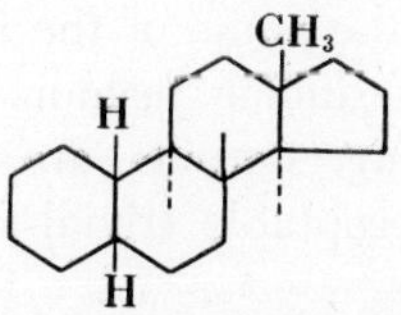

Since they are aromatic in ring A, the common estrogens are named systematically as derivatives of 1,3,5:10-estratriene.

All other steroids which are of physiological interest have in common a dimethylated nucleus, and, as indicated previously, may be grouped into two series, depending on the steric relations between rings A and B (seen as a cis or trans relation between the hydrogen atom at C-5 and the reference methyl group at C-10). Since four types of side-chains are commonly attached at C-17 in these compounds, a total of eight parent hydrocarbons exists. These are listed in Table 56.

Table 56. Parent Hydrocarbons of Steroid Hormones

5α, ALLO-, OR TRANS SERIES	R—	5β, NORMAL, OR CIS SERIES
Androstane	—H	Testane (formerly etiocholane)
Allopregnane	—C₂H₅	*Pregnane*
Allocholane	CH_3 ‹br› —CH—CH₂—CH₂—CH₃	*Cholane*
Cholestane	CH_3 ‹br› —CH—CH₂—CH₂—CH₂—CH‹CH₃›‹CH₃›	Coprostane

Compounds which, owing to structural modifications, have no asymmetry at C-5 are named from the parent compound (based on the side-chain) which is italicized in the table. The term, "allo-," is used solely to indicate the replacement of a 5 β by a 5 α configuration. Reversals at any other asymmetric centers are indicated by a prefix, consisting of the location of the group and the appropriate term, α or β, followed by the name of the reference compound. Substituents are named in a similar fashion. Illustrations of the systematic method of naming steroids are presented in Table 55, together with currently acceptable trivial names. Obsolescent trivial names are also given.

ESTROGENS

Estrogens are substances capable of producing certain biological effects, the most characteristic of which are the changes which occur in mammals at estrus. They induce growth of the female genital organs, the appearance of female secondary sex characteristics, growth of the mammary duct system, and numerous other phenomena which vary somewhat in different species.

As indicated below, the naturally occurring estrogens are steroids, but estrogenic activity is exhibited also by certain derivatives of phenanthrene and dibenzanthracene. Certain of these compounds (e.g., diethylstilbestrol; dienestrol), synthesized commercially, have been of great therapeutic value.

CHEMISTRY. The naturally occurring estrogens in the human are β-estradiol, estrone and estriol, which, for purposes of terminology, may be regarded as derivatives of the saturated hydrocarbon, "estrane" (Fig. 126).

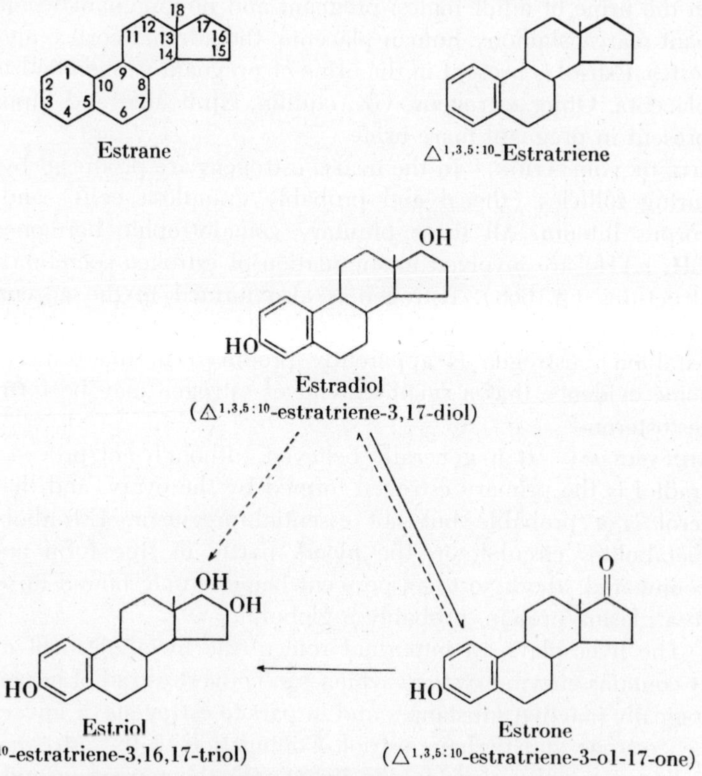

Estrane

$\triangle^{1,3,5:10}$-Estratriene

Estradiol
($\triangle^{1,3,5:10}$-estratriene-3,17-diol)

Estriol
($\triangle^{1,3,5:10}$-estratriene-3,16,17-triol)

Estrone
($\triangle^{1,3,5:10}$-estratriene-3-ol-17-one)

Fig. 126. *Interconversions and metabolism of estrogens (human)*

One of the essential features of these estrogens is the aromatic character of ring A (three double bonds), with absence of a methyl group at C-10. Because of this characteristic, the OH group at C-3 possesses the properties of a phenolic hydroxyl group (weakly acid). All contain eighteen carbon atoms.

Estrone has three double bonds, a hydroxyl (at C-3) and a ketone (at C-17) group. Its systematic name is therefore "$\triangle^{1, 3, 5:10}$-estratriene-3-ol-17-one." The superscript 5:10 indicates the position of the ends of the double bond, since the use of 5 alone would be ambiguous. Applying the same system of nomenclature, β-estradiol is "$\triangle$ 1, 3, 5:10-estratriene-3,17 (β)-diol." Estriol is "$\triangle$ 1, 3, 5:10-estratriene-3,16 (α), 17(β)-triol."

Natural estrogens are soluble in oil, ether, alcohol, acetone, and other lipid solvents. They are only very slightly soluble in water, but enter solution in alkaline aqueous media. They are also moderately soluble in solutions of certain bile acids and in serum.

OCCURRENCE. Estradiol has been found in the placenta, in the urine during pregnancy, and in the testis of the stallion. Estrone is present in the urine of adult males, pregnant and nonpregnant women, pregnant mares, stallions, human placenta, the adrenal cortex, and stallion testes. Estriol is present in the urine of pregnant women and in human placenta. Other estrogens, viz., equilin, equilenine and hippulin, are present in pregnant mare urine.

SITE OF FORMATION. In the ovary, estrogens are produced by the maturing follicles (thecal and probably granulosa cells) and by the corpus luteum. All three pituitary gonadotrophic hormones (FSH, LH, LTH) are involved in stimulation of estrogen secretion by these structures (p. 698). Estrogen is also formed in the adrenal cortex (male and female) and in the placenta. In certain species at least (stallion), estrogen is apparently produced in the testis. There is some evidence that a small amount of estrogen may be formed from testosterone.

METABOLISM. It is generally believed, although not proved, that estradiol is the primary estrogen formed by the ovary, and that cholesterol is a probable but not essential precursor. Estradiol and its metabolites circulate in the blood, partly in free form and partly conjugated, about 50 to 75 per cent being closely bound in some way to a plasma protein, probably β-globulin.

The liver plays an important role in the metabolism of estrogens. It contains enzyme systems which can convert estradiol in part to biologically inactive substances and in part to estrogens of lower activity, i.e., estrone and perhaps estriol. Conjugation of the estrogens is also believed to take place in the liver, with the formation and transfer to the blood stream of water-soluble glucuronidates and sulfates, which are ultimately excreted in the urine. Relatively large amounts of free estrogen are present in the bile of certain species, suggesting that biliary excretion may play an important part in the removal of estrogens from the circulation. Estrogens may subsequently undergo an enterohepatic circulation, being gradually degraded in the liver into compounds with no or lower estrogenic activity. There is evidence also that estrone may be converted to the more potent estradiol in this organ, a process of biological "activation." Undoubtedly, too, intermediary compounds are formed in the course of these metabolic changes which have not yet been identified.

The presumed functions of the liver in this connection may be summarized as follows: (1) it effectively removes estrogens from the systemic circulation by (a) biliary excretion and (b) metabolic degradation to less active and inactive compounds; (2) it conjugates them with glucuronic and sulfuric acids, converting them to water-soluble forms which return to the systemic circulation and are excreted in the urine; (3) it may convert estrone to the more potent estradiol.

EXCRETION. Estrogens are excreted in the urine, chiefly in conjugated form, as glucuronidates and sulfates of estriol, estrone, and estradiol. It is estimated that the urinary estrogens represent about 5 to 10 per cent of the activity of the estrogens secreted. The determination of urinary estrogens is therefore employed as an index of estrogen production, although variations in metabolic "inactivation" may conceivably interfere with accurate interpretation of such data. Normal values under different physiological conditions are presented in Tables 57, 58, and 59 (p. 664).

Table 57. Normal Urine Estrogen Values (Fluorometric)

AGE (years)	URINE ESTROGEN (ug./24 hours)
5–10............................	3.0–6.5
31–37 (Men)....................	21.6–26.2
(Women).....................	10 –50
50–65 (Women).................	0–23.4
Pregnancy (8–10 mos.)...........	365–1500

Table 58. Hormone Values in Normal Pregnancy

WEEKS	SERUM ESTROGENS (I.U./100 ml.)*	SERUM GONADOTROPHIN (m.u./100 ml.)†	URINE PREGNANEDIOL (mg./24 hours)
2	15–80		2–10
4	15–100	50–1000	5–15
8	30–125	500–33000	5–15
12	45 165	1000–33000	8–20
16	80–200	1000–33000	8–30
20	165–250	330–10000	16–32
24	165–330	200–500	20–60
28	100–400	200–500	35–80
32	250–600	200–500	40–80
36	330–750	200–500	50–100
40	330–1500	200–500	50–120

* International Units (1 I.U. equivalent to 0.1 μg. estrone).
† Mouse ovarian units.

ACTIONS. Estrogens cause growth of the epithelium and musculature of the fallopian tubes, stimulate their contraction and motility, and are responsible for cyclic changes in the tubal mucosa. They cause growth, increased tonus and rhythmic contractions of the uterine musculature, and development of the endometrial mucosa and blood vessels which plays an important role in normal menstruation. They increase the vascularity of the cervix and stimulate secretion by the cervical glands, increasing the amount of cervical mucus with a lowered viscosity, thus favoring migration, motility, and longevity of spermatozoa. Estrogens cause a characteristic proliferation of the vaginal epithelium which forms the basis for one of the methods of bioassay of estrogenic activity (Allen-Doisy). They are also responsible in large part for normal development of the external female genitalia, the duct system of the breasts, and the nipples, and the secondary sex characteristics.

Administration of estrogens is followed by an increase in glycogen and alkaline phosphatase in the endometrium. Glycogen also increases in the vaginal epithelium, which is second only to the liver in glycogen content during the reproductive years (1.5–3 per cent). The vaginal glycogen is probably the source of the lactic acid which, by increasing the acidity of the vaginal secretion (pH 4.0–5.0), favors a homogeneous flora of acid bacteria (Lactobacillus vagini).

Apart from their actions on specific target tissues, indicated above, estrogens have but little effect on metabolic processes. They (particularly estradiol) exert a slight Na, Cl, and water-retaining effect, not nearly as pronounced, however, as that of the adrenocortical hormones, testosterone, or progesterone. They apparently favor retention and skeletal deposition of calcium. In birds, estrogens cause hyperlipemia; this does not occur in mammals, being related presumably to the influence of the ovarian hormones in the formation of the egg-yolk.

PROGESTERONE

Progesterone is secreted by the corpus luteum of the ovary during the period of its functional activity. It appears suddenly on the day of ovulation or perhaps a day or two earlier, as indicated by the presence in the urine of its chief excretion product, pregnanediol. It is concerned, in the latter half of the menstrual cycle, mainly with preparing the endometrium for nidation of the fertilized ovum if conception has occurred. During early pregnancy, it is produced by the corpus luteum of pregnancy (stimulated by luteinizing and lactogenic hormones, q.v.), and perhaps by other ovarian luteinized cells, and later by the syncytial cells of the placenta. During gestation, progesterone, in association with estrogen, appears to be concerned with maintenance of a state of quiescence of the uterine muscle.

Progesterone, or a closely related compound with progestational activity, is apparently formed in the adrenal cortex (p. 675). Other adrenal steroids, such as desoxycorticosterone, may be metabolized to pregnanediol, the chief urinary metabolite of progesterone, which, however, has no progestational activity. The possibility that progesterone, or one of its precursors, may be produced in the testis, at least in certain species, is suggested by the facts (1) that the bull excretes large amounts of pregnanediol in the urine and (2) that pregnenolone, a possible precursor of progesterone, has been isolated from hog testes.

CHEMISTRY. Progesterone may be regarded as a derivative of "pregnane" (Fig. 127). It may be designated "Δ^4-pregnene-3,20,dione." It has methyl groups at C-10 and C-13 and contains twenty-one C atoms, two of which comprise an ethyl group at C-17.

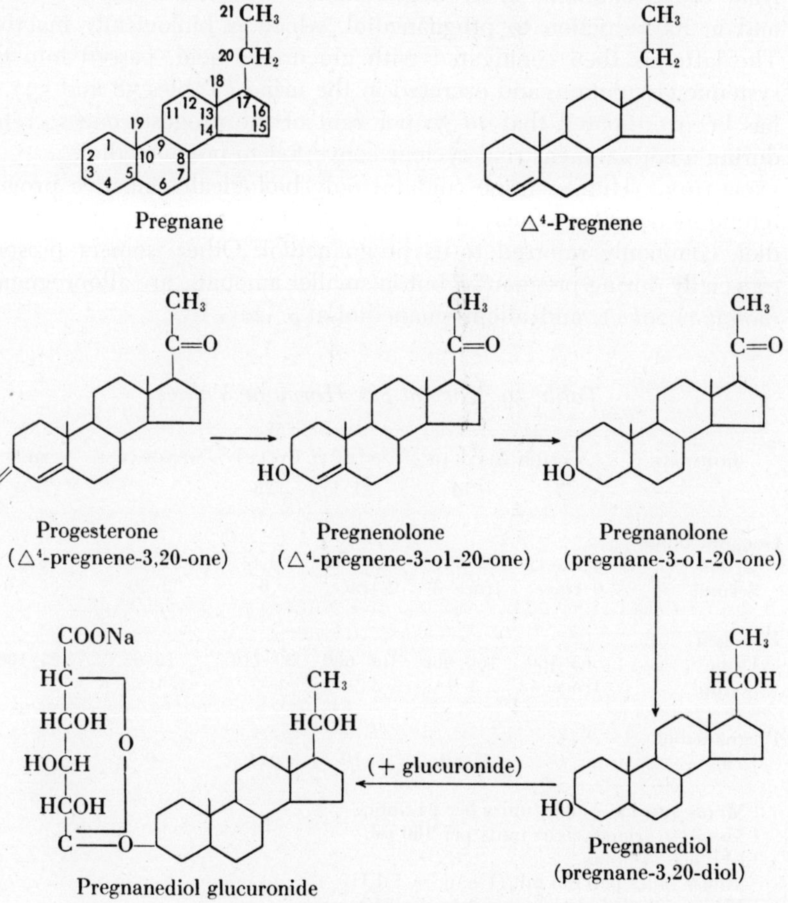

Fig. 127. *Metabolism of progesterone*

Progesterone is soluble in practically all organic solvents except petroleum ether and dilute alcohol, acetone, and pyridine. It is quite soluble in oil, moderately soluble in serum, and practically insoluble in water.

METABOLISM. There is evidence that progesterone may originate from cholesterol, although the latter is not necessarily an immediate precursor. Whether or not cholesterol is a necessary intermediate, the corpus luteum and placenta contain an enzyme system which oxidizes $\triangle$ [5]-3β-hydroxysteroids to α,β-unsaturated ketones. Acetate may be the only obligatory precursor. Comparatively little is known regarding its intermediary metabolism, although there is evidence that the liver plays an important role in this connection, as in the case of estrogens and androgens. Progesterone metabolites have been found in the bile; the liver appears to be involved in the removal of this hormone from the circulation, in its degradation to unidentified compounds, and in its reduction to pregnanediol, which is biologically inactive. The latter is then conjugated with glucuronic acid, passed into the systemic circulation, and excreted in the urine (Tables 58 and 59). It has been estimated that 10–30 per cent of the progesterone secreted during a normal menstrual cycle is converted to pregnanediol.

EXCRETION. Human urine contains only biologically inactive progesterone metabolites, chiefly the glucuronidate of pregnane-3(α),20(α)-diol, commonly referred to as pregnanediol. Other isomers present, especially during pregnancy, but in smaller amounts, are allopregnanediol-3(α),20(α), and allopregnanediol-3(β),20(α).

Table 59. Normal Sex Hormone Values

HORMONE	WOMEN (DAYS OF MENSTRUAL CYCLE)				MENOPAUSE	MEN
	7	14	21	28		
Gonadotrophin						
Urine[1]	trace–12	8–40	trace–8	0–6	32–300	4–24
Serum[2]	0–trace	trace–3	0–trace	0	3–30	0
Estrogen						
Urine[3]	65–160	160–660	160–660	30–110	10–65	25–100
Serum[4]	trace–6	3–9	3–9	0–3	0–trace	
Pregnanediol						
Urine[5]	0	3–10	3–10	0–4	0	0

[1] Mouse uterine weight units per 24 hours.
[2] Mouse ovarian weight units per 100 ml.
[3] I.U. per 24 hours.
[4] Mouse units per 100 ml. (1 m.u. = 5 I.U.).
[5] Mg. pregnanediol glucuronidate per 24 hours.

ACTIONS. In the human being, progesterone produces characteristic changes (progestational) in the estrogen-primed endometrium. It also causes an increase in glycogen, mucin, and fat in the lining epithelial cells. Alkaline phosphatase decreases. Sudden decrease in progesterone and estrogen leads to a series of changes culminating in bleeding or menstruation. Progesterone modifies the action of estrogen on the vaginal epithelium during the menstrual cycle, causing desquamation and basophilia of the superficial layer of cells and leukocytic infiltration. In conjunction with estrogen, progesterone causes development of the alveolar system of the breasts and sensitizes them for the action of lactogenic hormone. It counteracts the effect of estrogen on the fallopian tubes and uterine cervix. In large doses it exerts androgenic effects, perhaps by conversion to androgenic metabolites.

Progesterone is responsible for the rise in basal temperature which occurs during the corpus luteum phase of the normal menstrual cycle. This is believed to be related to an increase in the basal metabolic rate. It favors retention of Na and water in the tissues (premenstrual fluid retention), its effect resembling, but not being as pronounced as that of the adrenal cortical steroids.

ANDROGENS

Androgens are substances capable of producing certain characteristic masculinizing effects; i.e., they maintain the normal structure and function of the prostate and seminal vesicles and influence the development of secondary male sex characteristics, such as hair distribution and voice.

CHEMISTRY. The naturally occurring androgens in man are testosterone, androsterone, 3β-androsterone (isoandrosterone), and dehydro-3-β-androsterone (dehydroisoandrosterone). For purposes of terminology, these may be regarded as derivatives of the saturated hydrocarbon, "androstane" (Fig. 128). All have methyl groups at C-10 and C-13 and contain nineteen C atoms.

In compounds containing a ketone group at C-3 and a double bond at C-4-5, the grouping including C-3 to C-5 is termed an α, β-unsaturated ketone group. This is characteristic of the most active steroid hormones except estrogens (e.g., testosterone, progesterone, adrenal cortical hormones), and any change in this group reduces the specific activity of the hormone in question.

OCCURRENCE. Androgen (probably testosterone) is produced in the interstitial cells of Leydig of the testis. Androgenic substances have also been isolated from the adrenal cortex (p. 675) and ovaries (sow).

BIOSYNTHESIS. Testosterone can be formed by the testis (interstitial cells) from acetate, this process being accelerated by the pituitary

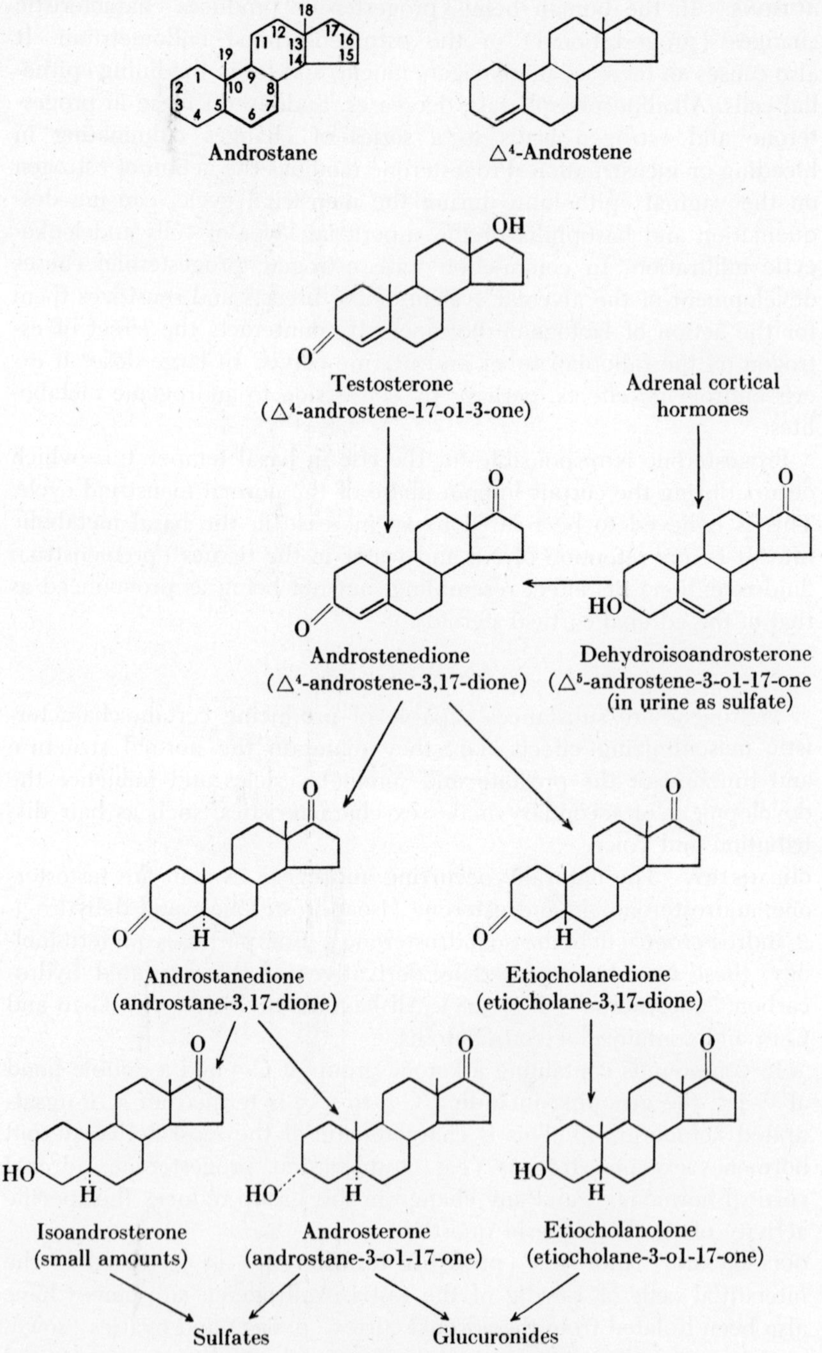

Fig. 128. Metabolism of androgens

gonadotrophic hormone, ICSH (p. 699). Cholesterol is a possible but probably not an obligatory intermediate, although the active hormone is apparently formed by oxidation of a Δ^5-3β-hydroxysteroid molecule to an α,β-unsaturated ketone.

METABOLISM. Testosterone is not found normally in the urine. The following androgen metabolites have been found in the urine of normal untreated subjects (Fig. 128): (1) androsterone, (2) 3β-androsterone (isoandrosterone), (3) dehydro-3β-androsterone (dehydroisoandrosterone), (4) 11-hydroxyandrosterone, (5) androstanediol (?), (6) androstenetriol, (7) testane-3α-ol-17-one (etiocholanolone). The last two are biologically inactive and dehydro-3β-androsterone (dehydroisoandrosterone) is apparently derived largely from adrenal androgen.

The urinary androgens occur chiefly as water-soluble sulfates and glucuronides which are biologically inactive. The liver is believed to be the chief site of this conjugation, as well as of the preceding changes in the original hormone, all of which tend to diminish its biological activity (androgenicity). The water-solubility of the final conjugated products facilitates their removal from the body in the urine.

In vitro studies indicate that mammalian liver contains two enzyme systems which act on testosterone: (1) one, requiring citrate as a cofactor, which destroys the α,β-unsaturated system in ring A without affecting the alcohol group on C-17; (2) one, requiring DPN as a cofactor, which first oxidizes the C-17 alcohol to a ketone (17-ketosteroid) and then reduces ring A to a saturated alcohol (destruction of the α,β-unsaturated system) (Fig. 128). The latter system, which produces androsterone and its isomers, appears to be the more active in man. Tissues other than liver may be involved, especially kidney, which has been shown to be capable of forming 17-ketosteroids from testosterone and of destroying the α,β-unsaturated system in ring A.

Following injection of testosterone, about 15–60 per cent (average 35) of the amount administered can be accounted for by recovery, in the urine, of the following 17-ketosteroids: (1) androsterone, (2) 3β-androsterone (isoandrosterone), and (3) testane-3α-ol-17-one (etiocholanolone). The nature of the metabolites of the remaining 40–85 per cent (average 65) is not known. *In vitro* studies indicate the possible formation also of androstanediol, etiocholanediol, androstanedione, and etiocholanedione, although about 50 per cent of the testosterone is degraded to as yet unidentified substances.

There is some evidence that androgens may be converted in part to estrogens in the organism. The site of this conversion is open to question, since it has been found to occur in the absence of the testes, ovaries, or adrenals.

URINARY NEUTRAL 17-KETOSTEROIDS. The term "17-ketosteroids" is applied to steroids which have a ketone group as position 17 (Fig. 128). This structural feature enables them to produce certain color reactions, such as the Zimmermann (*m*-dinitrobenzene) and Pincus (antimony trichloride) reactions, which are very useful in their quantitative determination. The urinary 17-ketosteroids may be further classified as either neutral or acidic. Estrone, containing a phenolic ring (Fig. 126, p. 659), is acidic; it can be therefore separated from the neutral 17-ketosteroids by washing with alkali. The neutral fraction contains metabolites of steroids produced by the testis and adrenal cortex, and determination of urinary 17-ketosteroids (the designation "neutral" is usually omitted, but implied) is used chiefly in the evaluation of the functional activity of these organs (p. 677). Since they are present in the urine as esters, they must first be freed by hydrolysis.

A number of 17-ketosteroids have been isolated from the urine. The most important of these in normal subjects are (Fig. 128): (1) androsterone (from testosterone and unidentified adrenal cortical hormone); (2) testane-3α-ol-17-one (etiocholanolone) (from testosterone and unidentified adrenal cortical hormone); (3) dehydro-3β-androsterone (dehydroisoandrosterone) (from unidentified adrenal cortical hormone); (4) small amounts of 3β-androsterone (isoandrosterone) (from testosterone and unidentified adrenal cortical hormone). In the first two of these the —OH groups at C-3 lie below the plane of the molecule, as indicated by the broken bond in Figure 128; these orientations are indicated by the designation "alpha" (α). In the last two, the —OH groups at C-3 lie above the plane of the molecule; they are, therefore, β-17-ketosteroids. The α-17-ketosteroids normally comprise 85–95 per cent of the total. Androsterone has about one-tenth and dehydro-3β-androsterone (dehydroisoandrosterone) about one-third the androgenic activity of testosterone; 3β-androsterone (isoandrosterone) is only weakly androgenic and testane-3α-ol-17-one (etiocholanolone) is inactive.

Table 60. Normal Values for Total Urinary Neutral 17-ketosteroids

	17-KETOSTEROIDS (mg./24 hours)
4–7 years.....................	0.8–2.6
7–12 years..................	1.8–5.0
12–15 years.................	5.0–12.0
15+ years	
Males.....................	8.0–20.0
Females..................	5.0–15.0
Pregnancy..................	10.0–20.0
(4–7 mos.)	

Children under 6 years of age usually excrete less than 1 mg. daily, the values increasing gradually to adult levels at 12 to 18 years of age. The daily excretion in normal adult women is 5 to 15 mg., presumably derived entirely from unknown adrenal cortical precursors. Somewhat higher values may be obtained in late pregnancy (placental origin?). In adult men, during the reproductive period, the usual average range is 7 to 20 mg., about two-thirds being derived from adrenal cortical hormones and one-third from testosterone (testis).

Abnormally high values are obtained in conditions of increased adrenocortical (hyperplasia, tumor) and interstitial-cell (certain testicular tumors) function. Low values are obtained in male hypogonadism and in hypofunction of the adrenals and pituitary (decreased gonadotrophin and adrenocorticotrophin).

METABOLIC ACTIONS. The dominant general metabolic effect of androgens is stimulation of protein anabolism. This is reflected in (1) a decrease in urinary nitrogen without an increase in blood NPN and (2) increase in body weight, due chiefly to an increase in skeletal muscle. In the growing organism, a growth spurt is induced, with increase in bone matrix and skeletal length. In addition to the specific stimulation of growth of the prostate and seminal vesicles, there is a rather selective increase in size and weight of the kidneys (renotropic action). This, together with the changes in renal enzymes and the absence of similar changes in the liver and intestine, has been interpreted as indicating that the protein anabolic effects of androgens are mediated, in part at least, by the kidney. Neither the pituitary growth hormone nor the adrenal cortex is involved in this phenomenon.

Creatine, which is virtually absent from the urine of normal men, increases after castration. This increase is abolished by testosterone, owing to increased storage of creatine in the muscles. After prolonged administration, the quantity of creatinine in the urine may increase, probably reflecting the increase in muscle mass.

Androgen reduces (and estrogen increases) the excretion of citrate in the urine. This is due apparently to increased reabsorption of citrate by the renal tubular epithelium.

The decreased urinary excretion of nitrogen (chiefly urea) that follows administration of androgens is accompanied by a lower urine volume and diminished excretion of Na, Cl, K, SO_4, and PO_4, with no increase in their concentrations in the blood plasma. The tissue retention of K, SO_4, and PO_4 is probably related to the increased storage of protein. The retention of Na, Cl, and water is apparently due to an action resembling that of the adrenocortical hormones (p. 678).

The activity of certain enzymes has been shown to be affected by testosterone: (1) increase in kidney D-amino acid oxidase, arginase, and acid phosphatase; (2) decrease in kidney alkaline phosphatase; (3) increase in prostatic acid phosphatase; (4) decreased synthesis of acetylcholine. It also increases the formation of avidin in the chick oviduct, an effect produced also by estrogens, progesterone and desoxycorticosterone. The relation of these phenomena to the general metabolic actions of testosterone is not clear.

BIOLOGICAL EFFECTS. The characteristic morphological effects of androgens are reflected in the changes induced in the male by castration. In the prepubertal castrate the prostate and seminal vesicles fail to develop; in adults, castration is followed by atrophy of these structures. The penis remains small in the former and regresses in the latter. A normal state is restored by administration of androgens. In prepubertal castrates, beard growth is absent, the body and pubic hair is scant and the voice remains high-pitched. Closure of epiphyseal lines is retarded, resulting in disproportionately long arms and legs.

Abnormally large amounts of androgen in women produce two types of effect, due to (1) "virilization" and (2) suppression of ovarian function. In the human being, the former includes: enlargement of the clitoris, growth of facial and body hair, development of a male forehead hairline, stimulation of secretion and proliferation of the skin sebaceous glands (often with acne), and deepening of the voice. The gonadal effects are due primarily to suppression of pituitary gonadotrophic function. This results in suppression of ovarian follicle maturation and ovulation (i.e., decreased estrogen and progesterone production) followed by atrophy of the uterus, vagina, and often the breasts.

ADRENAL HORMONES

The mammalian adrenal gland consists of two embryologically and functionally independent portions, the medulla and the cortex. The adrenal medulla consists of chromaffin tissue and is essentially a portion of the autonomic nervous system. Although the hormones which it secretes have pronounced pharmacological effects, extirpation of all adrenal medullary tissue is followed by no important changes. The adrenal cortex, on the other hand, an epithelial structure, secretes hormones which are essential for life. Their most important actions are metabolic in nature, whereas those of the medullary hormones are exerted predominantly on unstriated muscle, vasomotor mechanisms, and the circulation.

ADRENAL MEDULLARY HORMONES

CHEMISTRY. Two biologically active compounds have been isolated from the adrenal medulla and synthesized, viz., epinephrine (adrenaline; adrenine) and norepinephrine (noradrenaline; Arterenol) (Fig.

129). The naturally occurring forms (L-forms) are levorotatory, the synthetic are racemic (DL-forms), the former being almost twice as active as the latter. These substances are closely related to tyrosine and phenylalanine.

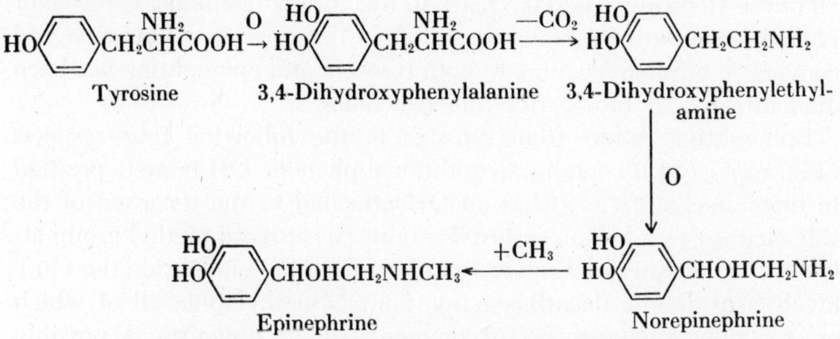

Tyrosine   3,4-Dihydroxyphenylalanine   3,4-Dihydroxyphenylethyl-amine

Epinephrine   Norepinephrine

Fig. 129. Suggested pathway of biosynthesis of epinephrine

Extracts of the adrenal glands of cattle have been found to contain L-epinephrine and L-norepinephrine in the approximate proportions of 4:1. Relatively larger amounts of the latter have been found in adrenal medullary tumors.

The term "chromaffin tissue" has been applied to tissues in which the "chromaffin reaction" can be developed, i.e., oxidation of epinephrine and certain related compounds by bichromate or iodate, with the production of a colored compound.

In man, in addition to the adrenal medulla, substances giving this "chromaffin" reaction are present in cells of the paraganglia and various parts of the sympathetic nervous system. The material in these situations, designated "sympathin," closely resembles epinephrine and norepinephrine, apparently the latter in most instances. The amounts of these substances increase after sympathetic stimulation.

Epinephrine gives a number of non-specific color reactions: (1) a green color with $FeCl_3$ in acid solution; (2) reduction of the Folin uric acid or tyrosine reagent (tungstate-molybdate), producing a blue color; (3) a red color with potassium persulfate. It also undergoes oxidation by polyphenol oxidase, producing a red pigment, adrenochrome, an indole derivative.

REGULATION OF EPINEPHRINE SECRETION. Epinephrine is secreted by the adrenal medulla in response to stimulation of nerve fibers in the thoracolumbar portion of the spinal cord (splanchnics). This stimulation may be accomplished by a variety of factors, including fear, anger, pain, and other undesirable emotional states, hypoglycemia, hemorrhage, muscular activity, and anesthetic and hypnotic drugs. There is evidence that this mechanism is involved in the initiation of the "alarm reaction" (p. 698), the discharged epinephrine stimulating secretion of ACTH by the anterior pituitary, perhaps indirectly through mediation by a hypothalamic mechanism.

BIOSYNTHESIS AND METABOLISM OF EPINEPHRINE. The mechanism of formation of epinephrine is not known. Moreover, it is not certain that all of the steps involved take place in the adrenal medulla. Tyrosine or phenylalanine are generally regarded as the primary precursors, and conversion of phenylalanine to both tyrosine and epinephrine has been demonstrated by radioactive tracer technics.

Epinephrine differs from tyrosine in the following four respects (Fig. 129): (1) it contains an additional phenolic OH in meta position to the side-chain; (2) it has an OH attached to the β-carbon of the side-chain; (3) it has no carboxyl group; (4) it has a methyl group attached to the N atom. Conversion of tyrosine to epinephrine therefore involves oxidation, decarboxylation, and N-methylation, all of which are reactions known to occur commonly in the organism. A possibly pathway of biosynthesis of these substances is indicated in Figure 129, but others have not been excluded.

Stimulation of sympathetic nerves is accompanied by liberation of a "neurohormone" with sympathomimetic properties, which has been identified in some instances as norepinephrine (Arterenol) and in others as epinephrine. It is possible, as indicated in Figure 129, that the former may be an immediate precursor of the later, the final process of N-methylation required for this conversion occurring in certain tissues (e.g., the adrenal medulla) but not in others.

Epinephrine and norepinephrine disappear rapidly following injection. Little is known about possible excreted metabolites. Oxidative deamination by a monamine oxidase, an enzyme which is widely distributed in mammalian tissues, is apparently an important mechanism of inactivation of these hormones.

METABOLIC ACTIONS. Injection of epinephrine is followed promptly by an increase in blood sugar and lactic acid concentrations, due to acceleration of glycogenolysis in the liver (glucose) and glycolysis in muscles (lactic acid), associated with stimulation of phosphorylase activity (reactivation of inactivated phosphorylase). The hyperglycemic effect of norepinephrine is about one-twentieth that of epinephrine. This mobilization of glycogen is the major metabolic effect of epinephrine. In the hepatectomized animal, this hormone causes an increase in blood lactic acid but not in glucose. The acceleration of glycogenolysis is accompanied by an accumulation of hexosephosphate, at least in muscle, and a simultaneous fall in the plasma inorganic phosphate concentration.

Utilization of carbohydrate is apparently depressed somewhat, although the respiratory quotient increases transitorily. A simultaneous increase in blood ketone acids and the increase in lactic acid produce a decrease in blood bicarbonate. The oxygen consumption (basal metabolism) increases, according to some representing a specific calorigenic effect and, according to others, merely reflecting general sympathetic stimulation and increased muscle tonus.

The effects of epinephrine on blood pressure, circulation, and unstriated muscle in various tissues are of much greater physiological significance than are its metabolic effects, but cannot be considered here.

HORMONES OF THE ADRENAL CORTEX

CHEMISTRY. The characteristic (i.e., excluding estrogen, progesterone, androgen) adrenocortical hormones that have been isolated are derivatives of "pregnane" (21 C atoms) (Fig. 127, p. 663). Inasmuch as "corticosterone" was the first "common" name applied to an adrenal cortical hormone, it has become customary to name the others according to their relation to corticosterone. The latter is designated systematically as "$\triangle^4$-pregnene-11(β),21-diol-3,20-dione," but this terminology is seldom employed. There are six compounds of importance in this category (Table 61). Three structural features are essential for all known biological actions of the adrenocortical hormones: (1) a double bond at C-4-5, (2) a ketonic group (C=O) at C-3 (i.e., an α,β-unsaturated ketone group), and (3) a ketonic group at C-20, (Fig. 130).

Certain additional structural features have a profound effect upon the biological activity of these compounds:

1. A hydroxyl (OH) group at C-21 enhances sodium retention and is necessary for activity in carbohydrate metabolism.

2. The presence of O (either as —OH or as =O, i.e., hydroxyl or ketonic groups) at C-11 is necessary for carbohydrate activity and decreases sodium retention.

3. A hydroxyl (OH) group at C-17 increases carbohydrate activity.

On the basis of these relationships between structure and biological activity, the adrenal cortical hormones may be classified in two groups: (1) Those possessing O at the C-11 position (either hydroxyl or ketonic), with activity in carbohydrate and protein metabolism and relatively little effect on electrolyte and water metabolism. These have been referred to as the "11-oxygenated corticosteroids" or "11-oxysteroids," and include corticosterone (Compound B), 11-dehydrocorticosterone (Compound A), 11-dehydro-17-hydroxycorticosterone (Compound E; cortisone), and 17-hydroxycorticosterone (Compound F; hydrocortisone). (2) Those without O at the 11-C position, with virtually no activity in carbohydrate or protein metabolism and profound effect on electrolyte and water metabolism. The most important representatives of this group are 11-desoxycorticosterone and 17-hydroxy-11-desoxycorticosterone (Compound S).

Table 61. Biologically Active Compounds Extracted from Adrenal Cortex

HORMONE	C=O	OH	DOUBLE BOND
Corticosterone (Compound B)	3,20	11,21	4,5
11-Dehydrocorticosterone (Compound A)	3,11,20	21	4,5
11-Dehydro-17-hydroxycorticosterone (Compound E)	3,11,20	17,21	4,5
17-Hydroxycorticosterone (Compound F)	3,20	11,17,21	4,5
11-Desoxycorticosterone	3,20	21	4,5
17-Hydroxy-11-desoxycorticosterone (Compound S)	3,20	17,21	4,5

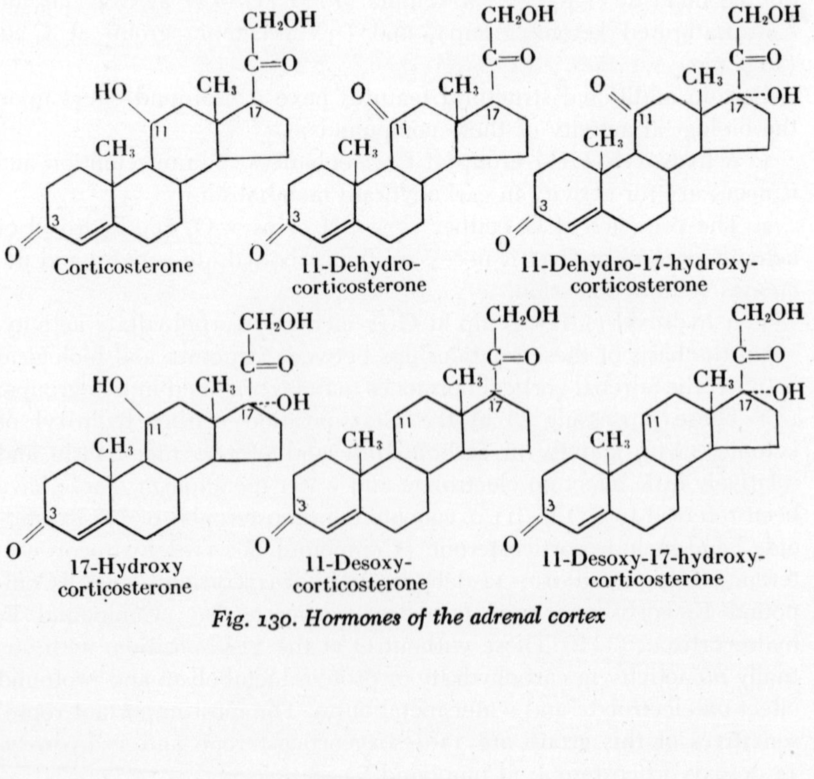

Fig. 130. Hormones of the adrenal cortex

SEX HORMONES ISOLATED FROM ADRENAL CORTEX. Estrone, progesterone, adrenosterone ($\triangle$ 4-androstene-3,11,17-trione), and $\triangle$ 4-androstene-3,17-dione have been isolated from adrenal tissue. The two latter possesses androgenic activity, but there is some question as to whether they may not be artifacts arising during the extraction and purification procedures. However, an androgenic compound which gives a reaction for 17-ketosteroids has been isolated from adrenal venous blood.

METHODS OF ASSAY. These may be divided into two categories, (a) biological and (b) chemical.

(a) BIOASSAY PROCEDURES. These are based on certain biological actions of the adrenocortical hormones in adrenalectomized animals: (1) maintenance of life; (2) improvement of work performance; (3) decrease in urinary excretion of sodium; (4) prolongation of survival during exposure to cold; (5) promotion of glycogen deposition in the liver. Of these, the last two (cold protection and liver glycogen deposition) have been used successfully for quantitative purposes. They measure only those adrenal steroids oxygenated at C-11 (11-oxysteroids), and appear to be specific for these substances. However, these procedures are time-consuming and expensive, and have been largely supplanted, for routine purposes, by less specific chemical methods.

(b) CHEMICAL PROCEDURES. All of the known biologically active adrenal steroids contain an α-ketol side chain at C-17 (Ring D) and an α,β-unsaturated 3-ketone grouping (Ring A) (Fig. 130, p. 674). These structural features constitute the basis for the following chemical assay procedures (colorimetric).

(1) *Formaldehydogenic Method.* The α-ketol or glycol side-chains of steroids react with periodic acid (glycol cleavage) with generation of formaldehyde, which may be determined quantitatively.

(2) *Phosphomolybdic Acid Reduction.* Steroids containing a primary or secondary (but not tertiary) α-ketol grouping, or an α,β-unsaturated 3-ketone grouping, can reduce phosphomolybdic acid (e.g., corticosterone, desoxycorticosterone, progesterone, etc.).

(3) *Copper Reduction.* Copper is reduced by steroids containing an α-ketol grouping. An α,β-unsaturated 3-ketone grouping does not reduce copper; consequently, compounds such as progesterone do not interfere with this procedure.

These chemical reactions are not specific for cortical hormones, being given by many other normal constituents of body fluids. However, a rather satisfactory degree of specificity is attained, particularly in urine, which is relatively free from lipid material, by the extraction procedures employed preliminary to application of the chemical assay reactions. Chemical methods yield consistently higher values (in urine) than do biological methods. On the other hand, the desoxycorticosterone type of compound will give the chemical but not the usual

biological reactions (cold protection and liver glycogen deposition).
The formaldehydogenic reaction yields values which correlate more
consistently with bioassay values than do those obtained with reduction tests.

BIOSYNTHESIS OF ADRENOCORTICAL HORMONES. Administration of adrenocorticotrophic hormone (ACTH) is promptly followed by increased hormone secretion by the adrenal cortex and increased excretion of certain steroids (adrenal hormones or metabolites) in the urine
(p. 677). Simultaneously, there is a decrease in the cholesterol and, in
most species, also in the ascorbic acid content of the adrenal cortex (p.
697). This suggests that cholesterol may be the biological precursor of
at least certain of the adrenal cortical steroids. Ascorbic acid is not an
obligatory participant in this process; possibly some other substance,
e.g., glutathione, can substitute for the vitamin in whatever function it
may serve in this connection.

Findings with adrenal perfusion experiments and studies of adrenal
vein blood suggest that 17-hydroxycorticosterone and corticosterone
are probably the most important products of corticosteroid biosynthesis. Possible pathways of synthesis of these hormones are indicated in
Figure 131.

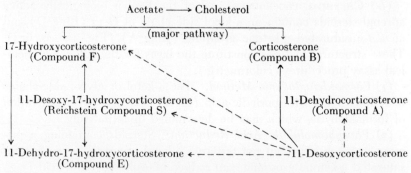

Fig. 131. Demonstrated pathways of biosynthesis and interconversions of hormones
of the adrenal cortex (corticoids)

The primary compound formed by the adrenal, *in vitro* and probably *in vivo*, from either acetate or cholesterol, is 17-hydroxycorticos-
terone. Cholesterol is probably not an obligatory direct intermediate.
Whether it is or not, the adrenal cortex contains an enzyme system
which can oxidize Δ^{5}-3β-hydroxysteroids to α,β-unsaturated ketones.
A system is present, too, which converts (*in vitro*) desoxycorticos-
terone to 11-oxygenated steroids (glycogenic adrenal steroids).

It has also been demonstrated that androsterone, androstenedione
and progesterone, brought to the adrenals from other organs of origin,
may undergo transformation upon circulation through the adrenals.
The great variety of possible intermediates, several of which are bio-

logically active, indicates the possibilities for entrance into the circulation of variable proportions of these compounds under conditions of abnormal adrenal function.

METABOLISM AND EXCRETION. The adrenocortical hormones apparently undergo rapid changes in the organism, with loss of biological activity. *In vitro* studies indicate that both the 11-oxygenated and the 11-desoxy types of hormone are inactivated by liver, and also perhaps by other tissues. Disappearance of biological activity is accompanied by loss of the α,β-unsaturated 3-ketone grouping in Ring A (disappearance of characteristic ultraviolet absorption) and loss of the α-ketol configuration on Ring D (decrease in formaldehydogenic and reducing activity). The exact nature of these changes or of the end products is not known.

Information regarding the metabolism of adrenocortical hormones has been obtained by studying changes in urinary steroids after (1) adrenalectomy (or in Addison's disease), (2) administration of ACTH and (3) of cortical hormones (or in adrenal hyperfunction). The following compounds or classes of compounds have been identified as being presumably of adrenal cortical origin:

NEUTRAL 17-KETOSTEROIDS. These substances, determined colorimetrically (Zimmermann reaction), give a measure of metabolites of adrenal and testicular hormones (p. 668) excreted as 17-ketones. In normal adult subjects, the adrenal is responsible for about two-thirds of the total urinary neutral 17-ketosteroids in men (total, 7–20 mg. daily) and for the total quantity in women (5–15 mg. daily). They can result from the catabolism of adrenal hormones of the C-21 types (corticoids) and from secretion of adrenal hormones of the C-19 type (androgens) (p. 665).

BIOLOGICALLY ACTIVE CORTICOSTEROIDS. The urine contains steroids which exert biological effects characteristic of adrenal cortical hormones (p. 678). Two have been identified in normal subjects: 17-hydroxycorticosterone (Compound F); 11-dehydro-17-hydroxycorticosterone (Compound E). These probably represent an overflow from the circulation, the quantity excreted daily being 0.15–0.4 mg. in normal adult men and 0.1–0.3 mg. in women (mg. equivalents of 11-dehydrocorticosterone, assayed by liver glycogen deposition method).

NEUTRAL FORMALDEHYDOGENIC STEROIDS (P. 675). Substances in this category are excreted normally in quantities of 0.5–0.8 mg. daily by men and 0.4–0.6 mg. by women (mg. equivalents of 11-desoxycorticosterone).

NEUTRAL REDUCING STEROIDS (P. 675). Substances in this category are excreted normally in amounts of 0.4–1.25 mg. daily by men and 0.5–1.0 mg. by women (mg. equivalents of 11-desoxycorticosterone).

IDENTIFIED METABOLITES. About eleven steroids, probably representing adrenal hormones or their metabolites, have been isolated from the urine of normal subjects. In addition to the two carbohydrate-active compounds indicated above, these include pregnanediol (0.1 mg. daily) and three 17-ketosteroids (dehydroisoandrosterone, 11-hydroxyandrosterone, and etiocholanolone). Pregnanediol is probably derived from desoxycorticosterone as well as from progesterone, which is produced by both the adrenal cortex and the corpus luteum of the ovary.

METABOLIC EFFECTS. Absence of adrenal cortical hormones (adrenalectomy; Addison's disease) or administration of excessive amounts of these hormones are accompanied by characteristic metabolic changes, which may be grouped broadly under two headings: (1) electrolyte and water metabolism; (2) carbohydrate, protein, and fat metabolism. The latter category is influenced virtually solely by the 11-oxygenated cortical hormones, whereas the former is influenced predominantly, but by no means exclusively, by the 11-desoxy type of hormone.

ELECTROLYTES AND WATER. Adrenalectomized animals and patients with Addison's disease, if untreated, exhibit the following phenomena: (1) increased urine volume, with (2) disproportionately increased excretion of Na and Cl, leading to (3) decreased concentration of Na and Cl in blood plasma, (4) decrease in body water (dehydration) and (5) decrease in plasma volume. Ultimately there is a fall in blood pressure, with circulatory collapse and impaired renal glomerular filtration, which are aggravated by, but not necessarily dependent upon the changes in electrolyte and water balance. Simultaneously with the changes in Na, the urinary excretion of K decreases and the concentration of K in the plasma increases.

The kidney is apparently the organ primarily involved in these changes in Na, and perhaps also in K metabolism. In the absence of adrenal hormones, the renal tubular epithelial cells appear to be unable to reabsorb Na (also Cl and water) adequately from the glomerular filtrate in spite of a low plasma Na concentration. They also are apparently unable to excrete K adequately (or they reabsorb it excessively) despite the increased plasma K concentration. At the same time there is a disturbance in the equilibrium between the extracellular (plasma and interstitial fluids) and intracellular fluid compartments, characterized by an increase in intracellular (muscle) water and K and a decrease in Na and Cl.

These abnormalities can be prevented or corrected by administration of desoxycorticosterone or the 11-oxygenated adrenal steroids (e.g., corticosterone, Compounds E and F), the Na-retaining potency of the latter being about 25–50 per cent that of the former. There are also qualitative differences in the actions in this connection of these two types of hormone. In the absence of the adrenals, Na is not excreted adequately when unusually large quantities are given. This difficulty is aggravated by desoxycorticosterone, which further increases retention of Na, but is corrected by adrenal cortical extracts or Compound E. Moreover, the elevation of plasma Na resulting from excessive doses of desoxycorticosterone in intact animals can be prevented by simultaneous administration of cortical extract or ACTH. It would appear that desoxycorticosterone acts unidirectionally, inducing Na retention and K excretion under all circumstances, whereas the 11-oxygenated adrenal hormones maintain homeostasis in this sphere, tending to preserve and restore the Na equilibrium regardless of the direction of deviation from the normal.

In addition to the renal effect, the 11-oxygenated hormones may influence K metabolism by favoring protein catabolism in certain tissues, releasing intracellular K to the extracellular fluids. Then, too, its action in increasing glycogen storage (especially liver) is accompanied by an increase in K in the cells involved in this process. Several aspects of the influence of the adrenocortical hormones on electrolyte and water metabolism are inexplicable at the present time.

CARBOHYDRATE METABOLISM. The fasted, untreated, adrenalectomized animal (or patient with Addison's disease) exhibits the following changes in carbohydrate metabolism: (1) striking decrease in liver glycogen; (2) less marked decrease in muscle glycogen; (3) hypoglycemia; (4) decreased intestinal absorption of glucose (corrected by administration of NaCl). These changes do not occur if a sufficient quantity of carbohydrate is given, and are prevented or corrected by administration of 11-oxygenated adrenal hormones. 17-Hydroxycorticosterone (Compound F) is three to five times as potent in this respect as corticosterone or 11-dehydrocorticosterone (Compound A), and 11-dehydro-17-hydroxycorticosterone (Compound E; cortisone) two to three times as potent. There are other indications of the influence of adrenocortical hormones on carbohydrate metabolism:

1. Adrenalectomized animals exhibit increased sensitivity to insulin.

2. Adrenalectomy results in amelioration of diabetes produced by pancreatectomy or alloxan. Administration of 11-oxygenated adrenal hormones or cortical extracts aggravates the diabetes.

3. Administration of cortical extract or 11-oxygenated adrenal hormones causes a rise in blood sugar, liver glycogen, and total body carbohydrate, glycogen formation being accelerated and its breakdown to glucose retarded.

The adrenocortical deficiency manifestations are related to two fundamental phenomena: (1) increased oxidation of glucose and (2) decreased gluconeogenesis from body protein (p. 558). Conversely, cortical hormones active in this sphere diminish oxidation of glucose and increase gluconeogenesis from body protein. One point of action of these hormones is apparently the first reaction in the course of utilization of glucose, i.e., its phosphorylation to glucose-6-phosphate, catalyzed by the enzyme, hexokinase (hexokinase reaction) (p. 389). There is evidence that adrenocortical hormones enhance the inhibitory influence of the anterior pituitary (p. 424) on this reaction, an effect which is counteracted by insulin. This inhibitory effect on glucose oxidation is reflected in a decrease in the respiratory quotient (R.Q.), which, accordingly, is increased in adrenalectomized animals.

PROTEIN METABOLISM. Administration of relatively large amounts of ACTH, adrenal extracts, or 11-oxygenated cortical hormones to fasting intact animals is followed by an increase in urinary nitrogen and a negative nitrogen balance (protein catabolic effect). As indicated above, this is accompanied by an increase in body carbohydrate, and G:N ratios indicate that about 50–70 per cent of the extra protein catabolized was converted to glucose. Exogenous protein is apparently not affected in this manner.

There is evidence that more physiological amounts of cortical hormone, on the contrary, exert a protein anabolic effect. Administration of ACTH increases the positive nitrogen balance in children, and cortical extracts, in certain dosages, reduce nitrogen excretion in the urine. It would appear that, as is true of other hormones (e.g., thyroid), the quantity secreted and the functional status of the target cells have an important bearing on the character of the metabolic response.

The mechanism of action of these cortical hormones in protein metabolism is not entirely clear. There is some evidence that they increase deamination of amino acids and that adrenalectomized fasted animals do not convert deaminized amino acid residues to glucose as readily as do normal animals. However, protein-fed adrenalectomized animals apparently behave normally in this respect. It is difficult to reconcile these observations. The suggestion has been made that the 11-oxygenated adrenal hormones may exert an "antianabolic" rather than, or in addition to, a catabolic action on protein.

LIPID METABOLISM. Adrenocortical hormones (11-oxygenated) (1) depress synthesis of fat from carbohydrate, (2) increase mobilization of depot fat to the liver, and (3) increase ketogenesis in the liver. Conversely, adrenalectomy prevents the excessive mobilization of depot fat that follows fasting, stress, or administration of anterior pituitary extracts. It also decreases the ketosis that occurs in fasting, fat-fed, or phlorizinized or depancreatized animals.

Although these adrenal hormones are necessary for the mobilization of depot fat and excessive ketogenesis under the circumstances mentioned, they are incapable of producing these effects in the absence of an anterior pituitary factor ("fat-mobilizing hormone"), which may be the growth hormone. Simultaneous action of both is required, the latter acting as a trigger mechanism in the presence of adequate amounts of cortical hormone. Both factors also apparently partially inhibit lipogenesis from carbohydrate, adrenalectomized animals tending to utilize a larger proportion of glucose over pathways of oxidation and fat synthesis. In this respect, too, the action of the adrenal hormones is antagonistic to that of insulin, which increases lipogenesis from carbohydrate.

EFFECT ON ENZYMES. The respiration (O_2 uptake) of various tissues is decreased after adrenalectomy. The concentration of cytochrome c, and cytochrome oxidase activity in heart, liver, and kidney also decrease, as does the activity of kidney alkaline phosphatase and kidney and liver arginase. The biological significance of these changes is not understood.

THYROID HORMONE

CHEMISTRY. The thyroid gland contains an iodized protein, "thyroglobulin," characteristically present in the colloid of the thyroid follicles, which apparently is the "storage form" of the thyroid hormone. It has a molecular weight of about 650,000–700,000. Hydrolysis yields two iodine-containing compounds, related to tyrosine, viz., diiodotyrosine (about 70 per cent) and thyroxine (about 30 per cent), both of which exhibit thyroid hormone activity, and possibly a third, monoiodotyrosine, which has not been studied adequately. Diiodotyrosine is believed to be the biological precursor of thyroxine, which has been synthesized *in vitro*.

A number of substances have been shown to exhibit thyroid hormone activity (relief of human myxedema), all of which contain iodine substituted in the inner aromatic ring of a compound termed "thyronine" (4-4'-hydroxyphenoxy)-phenylalanine. A low order of thyroid activity has been produced with bromine compounds.

Thyroxine contains 1.8 per cent N and 65.4 per cent I (4 iodine atoms); diiodotyrosine, with about 4 per cent of the biological activity of thyroxine, contains 3.2 per cent N and 58.7 per cent I (2 iodine atoms). The naturally occurring forms of these substances are levorotatory; synthetic thyroxine shows no optical rotation, being a mixture of D- and L- forms (racemic), the former being apparently biologically inactive. There is evidence that thyroxine may undergo partial deiodination in the tissues to the more active triiodothyronine.

BIOSYNTHESIS AND SECRETION. The function of the thyroid in the formation and secretion of thyroid hormone may be divided into six phases: (1) Entry of inorganic iodide from the circulation. (2) Concentration of inorganic iodide in the gland. (3) Synthesis of thyroglobulin in follicular cells. (4) Storage of thyroglobulin in colloid. (5)

Liberation of thyroxine from thyroglobulin. (6) Passage of thyroxine into the circulation.

ACCUMULATION OF IODINE IN THYROID. Inorganic iodide, present in the blood plasma in low concentration ($<$ 2 μg. per cent, except after administration), is actively removed by the acinar cells of the thyroid, which are able to "trap" iodine in enormously higher concentration (several hundred times) than that in the circulation. Under physiological conditions, inorganic iodide comprises only about 1 per cent of the total iodine of the thyroid gland and, in fifteen minutes after administration of tracer doses of I^{131} to rats, over 90 per cent of the radioactivity in the gland is organically bound. This suggests that the selective accumulation of this element by the thyroid is related to the ability of the acinar cells to incorporate iodine in organic compounds. However, after administration of large doses of iodide or certain antithyroid agents (p. 688), which inhibit synthesis of thyroid hormone, inorganic iodide may accumulate in the gland in high concentration, indicating the presence of a mechanism independent of that involved in the organic conversion reactions.

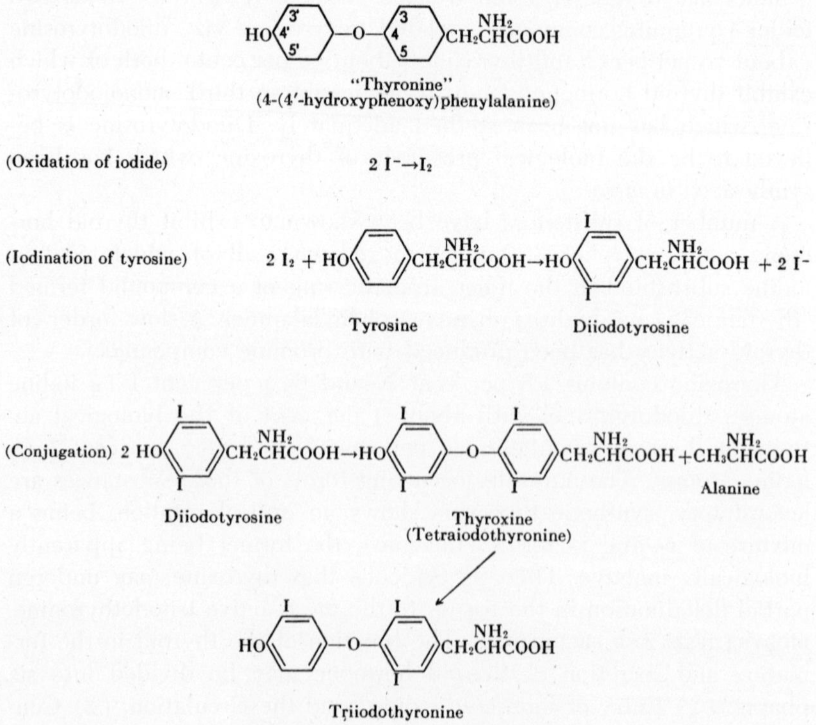

"Thyronine"
(4-(4'-hydroxyphenoxy)phenylalanine)

(Oxidation of iodide) $2 \text{ I}^- \rightarrow I_2$

(Iodination of tyrosine)

Tyrosine   Diiodotyrosine

(Conjugation)

Diiodotyrosine   Thyroxine
                              (Tetraiodothyronine)

Alanine

Triiodothyronine

Fig. 132. Biosynthesis of thyroxine

Accumulation of iodine in the thyroid is accelerated and increased by administration of thyrotrophic hormone (TSH) and is markedly reduced by thiocyanate (p. 688).

The thyroid contains inorganic iodide, monoiodotyrosine, diiodotyrosine, thyroxine, and at least two as yet unidentified iodine-containing compounds. Almost all (about 97 per cent) of the iodine in the gland is firmly bound to protein (thyroglobulin), the organic compounds mentioned above being liberated by hydrolysis. Free thyroxine (possibly loosely linked to protein), although present in small amounts (0.5 per cent of the total I), nevertheless exists in over one hundred times the concentration of protein-bound iodine in the plasma.

SYNTHESIS OF THYROID HORMONE (FIG. 132). Although all details have not been definitely established, present evidence supports the following sequence of events.

Oxidation of Iodide. Iodide ion in the follicular cell undergoes oxidation to I_2 (elemental iodine) or to IO^-. It has been suggested that a peroxidase enzyme may be involved in this process. There is also evidence that the cytochrome–cytochrome oxidase system is involved. It seems likely that the transition from iodide, through an oxidized form, to incorporation in the benzene ring of tyrosine, as indicated below, may occur almost as a single step.

Iodination of Tyrosine and Coupling. Tyrosine is iodinated, probably first to monoiodotyrosine, then to diiodotyrosine. This process may occur at the level of protein molecules since, *in vitro*, diiodotyrosine and thyroxine are formed more readily by iodination of protein than of the free amino acid, tyrosine. Two molecules of diiodotyrosine (tyrosyl radicals) then undergo oxidative coupling, with the elimination of one alanine side-chain, to form thyroxine (thyroxyl radical).

These I-binding and coupling reactions are accelerated by TSH and are inhibited by certain antithyroid agents (e.g., thiocarbamides; aminobenzenes) (p. 688). Thyroxine and its two precursors are incorporated in the protein known as thyroglobulin, which is passed into the colloid material in the lumen of the thyroid follicles, where it is stored. As indicated above, the processes of iodination and coupling of tyrosyl radicals may occur within the intact protein molecule.

Under physiological conditions there is little diurnal variation in the iodine content of the thyroid, the uptake of I and release of I-containing hormone occurring simultaneously, continuously, and at approximately constant rates.

SECRETION OF THYROID HORMONE. Present evidence favors the view that, in accordance with demand, probably under stimulation by TSH, the thyroglobulin in the gland undergoes hydrolysis by a proteolytic enzyme or enzymes, with release of its iodinated compounds, chiefly thyroxine. The latter, uncombined in peptide linkage, has been detected in thyroid tissue in about one hundred times its concentration in the plasma. It is probable that this is the form in which the hormone is secreted, passing from the colloid, through the acinar cells, into the lymphatics or blood stream. This process is accelerated by TSH. It has been estimated that about 0.33 mg. of thyroxine are secreted daily under physiological conditions.

CIRCULATING THYROID HORMONE. The plasma normally contains iodine in the form of inorganic iodide (small amounts, < 2 μg. per cent, except after administration), thyroxine (6–12 μg. per cent), and perhaps one of its unidentified metabolites (p. 683). The thyroxine, which is apparently the circulating form of the hormone, is loosely bound to plasma proteins, and its constituent iodine is referred to and determined as protein-bound iodine (PBI), ranging normally from 4 to 8 μg. per 100 ml. plasma.

It is present in highest concentration in the α- and β-globulin fractions, in lowest concentration in the γ-globulin fraction, the largest amount (about 75 per cent) being bound to albumin. It is believed that, in the tissues, the thyroxine is freed from its protein carrier, passes through the capillary wall and either penetrates the cell wall or exerts its effect upon the cell surface.

FATE OF THYROXINE. Thyroxine leaves the circulating plasma rapidly in the tissues. After injecting a large amount (dog), only 50 per cent remains in the blood stream after three minutes, and less than ten per cent after twenty-four hours. With physiological doses, a small amount (5 per cent) is excreted as such by the liver, in the bile, and by the mucosal cells of the duodenum. There is some evidence of an enterohepatic circulation. The bulk of the thyroxine is degraded, perhaps largely in the liver, with liberation of inorganic iodide. After large doses of thyroxine, a larger proportion is excreted, unchanged, in the bile and intestinal secretions, and ultimately in the feces. Only very small amounts of organically bound iodine are excreted in the urine. Its partial transformation to a more active compound, triiodothyronine, has been referred to elsewhere (p. 681).

METABOLIC EFFECTS. The action of thyroid hormone is characteristically evidenced in the relief of the manifestations of human myxedema. A great variety of effects is involved in the production of this phenomenon. Some of the important body functions influenced by thyroid activity are:

Metabolic rate (oxygen consumption)
Growth and tissue differentiation
Metabolism of carbohydrate, lipids, protein, electrolytes, and water
Vitamin requirements
Temperature sensitivity
Gastrointestinal activity
Central nervous system activity
Reproduction
Hematopoiesis
Cardiovascular function
Muscle activity
Resistance to infection
Sensitivity to acetonitrile

Consideration will be given here only to the metabolic effects of the thyroid hormone which are of immediate biochemical interest.

CALORIGENIC EFFECT. Thyroid hormone increases the rate of energy exchange and oxygen consumption of all normal tissues except the thyroid gland itself. This is reflected in an increase in the basal metabolic rate (BMR), which is the sum of the effects, of different magnitude, on various tissues.

This calorigenic effect is of smaller magnitude in young than in old subjects and is greater at low (e.g., in hypothyroidism) than at normal or high levels of metabolism. In subjects with myxedema, 1 mg. of thyroxine produces about 2.8 per cent increase in BMR. In the absence of thyroid hormone, the BMR (i.e., resting level of oxygen consumption) decreases by about 30–45 per cent (p. 341).

PROTEIN METABOLISM. In physiological doses, thyroxine favors protein anabolism, leading to increased retention of nitrogen (positive nitrogen balance). This explains the growth arrest of young thyroidectomized animals and hypothyroid children, and the resumption of growth following administration of thyroid hormone. Large, unphysiological doses stimulate protein catabolism, leading to a negative nitrogen balance.

Thyroidectomy is followed by accumulation of extracellular fluid rich in a hyaluronic acid-containing mucoprotein, apparently similar in composition to fetal mucin. This forms the basis of myxedema in human subjects.

Administration of thyroid hormone is followed by increased urinary excretion of creatine. This may be due in part to increased catabolism of muscle protein and in part to a decreased capacity for synthesizing phosphocreatine (p. 414) by the muscle cell.

CARBOHYDRATE METABOLISM. Thyroid hormone increases the rate of absorption of monosaccharides by the intestine. It enhances hepatic glycogenolysis, thus increasing the blood sugar concentration. This effect is partially offset by simultaneously increased utilization of glucose in the tissues. There is also evidence that thyroxine enhances gluconeogenesis, but in a manner different from adrenocortical hormone. For example, thyroidectomy, in contrast to adrenalectomy, does not alleviate pancreatic diabetes in the cat or dog, and administration of thyroid hormone, in contrast to adrenocortical hormone, does not increase glycosuria in the Houssay dog (hypophysectomized-depancreatized).

LIPID METABOLISM. Fatty acids participate in the increased rate of oxidative processes which follows administration of thyroid hormone. If available stores of carbohydrate are depleted, ketosis develops. However, body fat is not increased in the absence of thyroid hormone.

The state of thyroid function influences the levels of plasma cholesterol and phospholipid, which decrease in hyperthyroidism and increase in hypothyroidism. In the latter state, normal values are restored by administration of thyroid hormone.

ELECTROLYTE AND WATER METABOLISM. Administration of thyroxine to a normal subject is followed by increased urinary excretion of water, potassium, and chloride, indicating mobilization of intracellular fluid. The plasma volume is increased. Hypothyroidism is accompanied by an increase in interstitial fluid, and retention of sodium and chloride, the plasma volume being decreased.

In young, growing subjects, small doses of thyroxine enhance calcium retention. This may be secondary to increased formation of bone matrix (osteoid), resulting from stimulation of protein anabolism. Excessive amounts of thyroid hormone lead to increased mobilization of calcium from the skeleton, with increased calcium excretion in the urine and feces. There is no significant alteration in serum calcium.

In the presence of an excess of thyroid hormone, there is an increase in the proportion of "protein-bound" (nondiffusible) magnesium in the blood serum (normal 15–30 per cent of total serum Mg.).

VITAMINS. An increase in serum carotene has been observed in the absence of the thyroid. This has been attributed to interference with the synthesis of vitamin A from the provitamin, carotene, presumably in the liver, and may be accompanied by manifestations of vitamin A deficiency. Similar deficiency manifestations may occur in the presence of an excess of thyroid hormone, due presumably to excessively rapid destruction of vitamin A.

Administration of large amounts of thyroid hormone increases the requirement for certain members of the vitamin B complex (thiamine, pyridoxine, pantothenic acid) and for vitamin C. These relationships and the mechanisms involved are obscure.

GROWTH AND DEVELOPMENT. Absence of the thyroid during the growth period is accompanied by retardation of growth, which is corrected by administration of thyroid hormone. There is evidence that this growth-enhancing and perhaps the protein-anabolic effect of physiological amounts of thyroid hormone may be mediated by the growth hormone of the anterior pituitary.

Thyroid hormone also induces tissue differentiation and maturation. In man, early absence of this hormone not only arrests longitudinal growth, with consequent dwarfing, but also delays the appearance of epiphyseal centers of ossification. This defect is corrected by administration of thyroid hormone.

The effect of this agent in hastening metamorphosis of amphibians has been employed for bioassay purposes. In the absence of thyroid hormone, i.e., in the thyroidectomized tadpole, metamorphosis does not occur, e.g., the limbs do not extend and the gill and tail do not regress, although the tadpole continues to grow. Metamorphosis can be induced at any stage by administration of minute amounts of thyroid hormone. Very small tadpoles can be metamorphosed into minute frogs.

This effect in inducing tissue differentiation and development is not related directly to the calorigenic action of thyroxine, since dinitrophenol, which increases metabolism, lacks this morphogenetic effect, whereas acetylthyroxine, which exerts this effect, has no calorigenic action. Moreover, certain stages of amphibian metamorphosis, although stimulated by thyroid hormone, are not accompanied by increase in metabolic rate.

MECHANISM OF ACTION. The exact manner in which the thyroid hormone acts to produce its characteristic effects is not known. Principally because of the wide variety of these effects, the general belief is that the hormone exerts a single primary action, probably on energy metabolism, to which all other actions are secondary, depending upon specific local target-organ mechanisms and responsiveness. Some believe, however, that it has a function in tissue differentiation and development independent of its effect on energy transformations and oxygen consumption. The hormone may be concerned exclusively with energy metabolism and, at the same time, may influence the availability of energy for many specialized processes.

It would appear that control of tissue metabolism by the thyroid hormone is effected by regulation of the activity of various enzymes. This agent has been found to increase the activity of the following in liver tissue: cytochrome oxidase, cytochrome c, succinoxidase, acid phosphatase, apyrase, amino acid oxidase, and amylase. Under certain circumstances, xanthine oxidase and arginase are increased, whereas alkaline phosphatase and lactic dehydrogenase are decreased. The turnover of ATP is accelerated. Similar but not identical findings have been obtained with other tissues. It is difficult to correlate these effects with the known metabolic effects of thyroid hormone and to evaluate their functional significance. It has been found that hyperthyroidism is accompanied by a generalized increase and hypothyroidism by a decrease in cytochrome c. The concept has been advanced that the thyroid hormone regulates all metabolic functions by controlling the level of cytochrome c in the tissues (see also p. 590).

Thyroxine may influence enzyme activity in the following two ways, among others: (1) directly, by participating as a sort of coenzyme; (2) indirectly, by releasing metabolically active substances. There is evidence that it may act, in part at least, by uncoupling phosphorylation from oxidation reactions (p. 382).

AGENTS INTERFERING WITH SYNTHESIS OF THYROID HORMONE

A number of chemical agents can interfere with the formation of thyroid hormone by affecting different phases of the mechanism involved in its synthesis. These may be classified conveniently as follows: (1) thyroid hormone; (2) iodine; (3) thiocyanate; (4) antithyroid agents.

THYROID HORMONE. Administration of thyroid hormone results in regressive changes in the thyroid gland and diminished formation of hormone. This may be due in part to suppression of thyrotrophin (TSH) secretion by the pituitary; however, thyroid hormone apparently also inhibits the action of TSH upon the thyroid gland.

IODINE. Deficiency in iodine intake leads to deficient synthesis of thyroid hormone and compensatory hyperplasia of the thyroid gland (iodine-deficiency goiter). Conversely, administration of iodine to subjects with hyperthyroidism is followed by regressive changes in the gland and diminished output of hormone. High levels of circulating iodide also have a less pronounced and temporary inhibitory effect on thyroid hormone synthesis by the normal thyroid. The mechanism is not clear.

THIOCYANATE. Administration of thiocyanate results in enlargement of the thyroid (goiter), if the blood iodide concentration is low, and decreased synthesis of thyroid hormone. This effect is due to inhibition of the uptake, concentration, and accumulation of iodine by the thyroid, the gland being obliged to form hormone from the iodine which enters by passive diffusion. If the level of circulating iodine is elevated sufficiently by administration of iodine, enough may enter the gland to permit adequate function, inasmuch as thiocyanate does not influence the synthesizing mechanism *per se* (i.e., oxidation, iodination of tyrosine, and coupling). The mechanism of its action is unknown.

ANTITHYROID AGENTS (FIG. 133). This designation is applied to a large number of substances which inhibit synthesis of thyroid hormone, apparently by interfering in some way with the oxidation of inorganic iodide, necessary for iodination of tyrosine.

These compounds fall into two categories: (1) those containing a thiocarbamide grouping (e.g., thiourea, thiouracil, and related compounds); (2) those containing an aminobenzene grouping (e.g., sulfonamides).

Administration of these antithyroid compounds leads to hyperplasia of the thyroid (goitrogenic action) as a result of excessive stimulation by TSH, secretion of which by the pituitary is no longer adequately restrained by circulating thyroid hormone.

The mechanism of action of these agents is uncertain. The thiourea-like compounds react rapidly with iodine, reducing free iodine to

iodide at neutral pH, a phenomenon which could effectively interfere with iodination of tyrosyl groups. However, other substances
which react similarly with iodine, such as glutathione, cystine, and
thioglycolic acid, do not inhibit thyroid function. Moreover, the
aminobenzene derivatives, which apparently inhibit thyroid hormone
formation at this same stage, react only very slowly with iodine. Other
possible mechanisms include (1) inhibition of the oxidizing enzyme
system, (2) competition for hydrogen peroxide, or (3) competition
as a substrate.

Thiocarbamide
derivatives

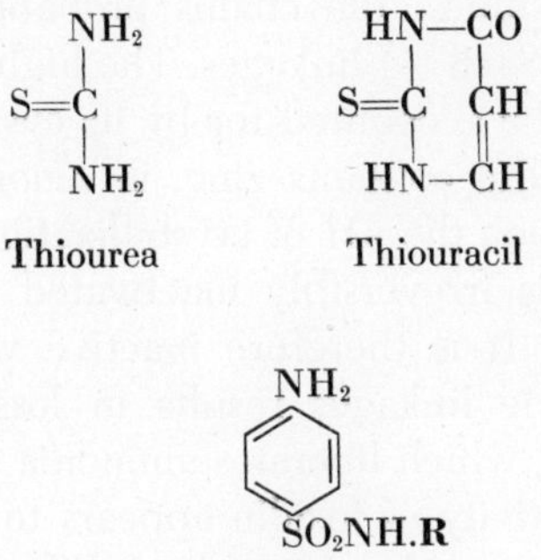

$$
\begin{array}{cc}
NH_2 & HN\!-\!CO \\
| & | \quad | \\
S\!=\!C & S\!=\!C \quad CH \\
| & | \quad \| \\
NH_2 & HN\!-\!CH \\
\text{Thiourea} & \text{Thiouracil}
\end{array}
$$

Aniline
derivatives

NH₂
(benzene ring)
SO₂NH.**R**

Sulfonamides

Thiocyanates   KSCN

Fig. 133. Examples of important classes of antithyroid agents

PANCREATIC HORMONES

The endocrine functions of the pancreas are performed by the
islands of Langerhans. These contain three main types of cells, designated α, β, and γ, respectively, the first two being granular and the
last non-granular. The β-cells are considered to be the site of production of insulin. In recent years, attention has been directed toward
the α-cells as possibly the site of production of a hyperglycemic (HG)
factor, which may or may not be of physiological significance.

Secretion of insulin is apparently regulated by the blood sugar
level. Increase in the blood glucose concentration causes an increase
in the insulin content of the pancreas, and, presumably, increased
secretion of insulin into the blood. Decrease in blood sugar causes the
reverse. This phenomenon is of fundamental importance in the regulation of the blood sugar concentration (p. 419).

Deficiency in insulin results in certain metabolic abnormalities
which characterize the condition known as diabetes mellitus (p. 430).
These are corrected by injection of adequate amounts of insulin, the
preparation of which in forms suitable for administration constituted
a most important contribution to medicine, as well as to biochemistry.

INSULIN

CHEMISTRY. Insulin has been isolated in crystalline form, and has been shown to possess the properties of a homogeneous protein. It has a molecular weight of about 46,000 and an isoelectric point of pH 5.3–5.35. The insulin molecule may undergo reversible dissociation at pH above 7.5 or below 4.0 or in dilute solutions. Studies of its amino acid content suggest that the molecule consists of sub-units with a molecular weight of 12,000, made up of four open polypeptide chains, two of which have terminal glycyl residues and two terminal phenyl-alanine residues, the chains probably being bound together by di-sulfide (—S—S—) linkages. The high sulfur content of insulin (3.3 per cent) can be accounted for by its cystine content (12 per cent). Crystalline insulin contains zinc, in amounts of 0.15 to 0.6 per cent depending upon the pH of crystallization.

Insulin is irreversibly inactivated by proteolytic enzymes or acid hydrolysis. It is therefore inactive when taken orally. Reduction of the disulfide linkages results in loss of activity, as does treatment with alkali, which liberates ammonia and hydrogen sulfide. The physiological activity of insulin appears to be a property of the entire protein molecule. Insulin from different species exhibits the same maximum activity.

ASSAY. The physiological activity of insulin is expressed in international units (I.U.), a unit being the activity contained in (1) 0.125 mg. of the international standard preparation or (2) 1/22 mg. of a standard preparation of crystalline zinc-insulin.

Two procedures are generally employed for determining the activity of insulin preparations:

1. Comparison of the incidence of convulsions in groups of mice injected intraperitoneally with unknown and standards.

2. Comparison of the hypoglycemic effect of unknown preparations and standards after subcutaneous injection in groups of rabbits (2 kg.) previously starved for eighteen to twenty-four hours.

METABOLISM OF INSULIN. Normal subjects excrete less than 1 I.U. of insulin daily in the urine; only a slight increase follows administration of insulin. Obviously, renal excretion is not an important pathway of metabolic disposal of this hormone.

An insulin-inactivating mechanism has been demonstrated, *in vitro*, in liver and, to a lesser extent, in kidney and muscle. The presence of an enzyme, designated "insulinase," has been postulated, which may be the principal means of physiological disposal of insulin. Liver extracts also contain an "anti-insulinase" factor. Preservation of a proper balance between these two principles and insulin secretion may constitute the central mechanism regulating the quantity of circulating insulin.

There is evidence that insulin and other hormones combine chemically and in some instances competitively (e.g., insulin and an anterior pituitary hormone) with muscle. It has been suggested that such competitive interaction between hormones with antagonistic metabolic effects for sites of chemical combination with the tissues of specific target organs may constitute the basis for the action of hormonal regulatory mechanisms.

Metabolic Actions of Insulin

The over-all effects of insulin on the organism are illustrated by certain observable metabolic consequences of (1) pancreatectomy and (2) administration of insulin to normal animals.

1. *Pancreatectomy* (p. 430) is followed by:
   a. Decreased glucose tolerance.
   b. Hyperglycemia and glycosuria.
   c. Depletion of glycogen in liver and muscle.
   d. Decreased rate of oxidation of glucose (decreased R.Q.).
   e. Increased gluconeogenesis; increased urinary nitrogen.
   f. Increased mobilization of depot fat; increased ketogenesis.
   g. Increase in cholesterol and other lipids in the plasma.
2. *Insulin administration* is followed by:
   a. Decrease in blood sugar.
   b. Increased oxidation of glucose (increased R.Q.).
   c. Increased muscle glycogen.

Effects on acid-base, electrolyte, and water balance are secondary to those on carbohydrate, fat, and protein metabolism and are discussed elsewhere (p. 430).

The most important known actions of insulin are as follows:

1. Acceleration of glucose oxidation.
2. Acceleration of conversion of glucose to fat.
3. Increase in liver glycogen formation (?) and/or inhibition of hepatic glycogenolysis by other hormones (?).
4. Inhibition of gluconeogenesis in liver.
5. Inhibition of excessive ketogenesis.

Increased utilization of glucose by oxidation in the tissues, for lipogenesis and for glycogen formation in muscle, accelerates its removal from the blood stream. The ability of the liver to retain more glycogen than at comparable levels of blood sugar in the absence of increased amounts of insulin decreases the rate of entrance of glucose into the blood stream. Both of these phenomena contribute to the resulting fall in blood sugar concentration. It is not known whether insulin exerts a direct influence on the formation of liver glycogen or whether it opposes hepatic glycogenolysis by other hormones. This tendency for the liver to retain glycogen is masked by the existing hypoglycemia, which itself accelerates hepatic glycogenolysis (p. 419).

There is evidence, still controversial, that insulin antagonizes the inhibitory influence of an anterior pituitary factor and adrenocortical hormones on the hexokinase reaction, thus serving to accelerate it. Inasmuch as this is the first step in the utilization of glucose, for both oxidation and glycogen synthesis, this phenomenon may represent one of the fundamental effects of insulin in this connection. Oxidation of fructose by livers of diabetic animals, contrary to that of glucose, is normal, thus localizing the metabolic block (and the action of insulin) in the conversion of glucose to fructose-6-phosphate, which includes the hexokinase reaction. It has been suggested that one of the fundamental actions of insulin may be to promote the passage of glucose from the extracellular fluid into the cell. This is, of course, a prerequisite for its metabolic utilization.

One of the major functions of insulin is to promote conversion of carbohydrate to fat (i.e., long-chain fatty acids). In the livers of diabetic animals, the conversion of glucose to fatty acids is depressed to an even greater extent than is its oxidation. Moreover, production of fatty acids from both acetate and fructose is also depressed, although their oxidation proceeds normally. These facts indicate that insulin facilitates the conversion of a 2-carbon-like metabolic intermediate to fatty acid. On the other hand, insulin is not required for the conversion of acetate to cholesterol.

In diabetes (insulin deficiency), there is an increase in liver fat, excessive ketogenesis, hyperlipemia, and hypercholesterolemia. The increase in fat in the blood and liver is due to excessive mobilization of depot fat, in consequence of the state of hormonal imbalance in the direction of relative excess of adrenocortical and anterior pituitary hormones (p. 680). In the absence of an adequate supply of insulin, the catabolism of fatty acids, which is unimpaired, results in the production of 2-carbon fragments which cannot be utilized adequately for synthesis of long-chain fatty acids, which are present in amounts exceeding the body's capacity for oxidation. They are diverted therefore in increased amounts to acetoacetate (excessive ketogenesis) and cholesterol (hypercholesterolemia).

The hormonal imbalance referred to above (adrenocortical preponderance) results also in stimulation of increased glucose production from amino acids (excessive gluconeogenesis) with associated increased protein catabolism (p. 680). This increased production of glucose, together with its decreased utilization, contributes to the hyperglycemia associated with insulin deficiency.

Stimulation of glucose utilization, by administration of either glucose or insulin, is accompanied by a decrease in the concentration of potassium and inorganic phosphate in the blood. These electrolyte changes are apparently associated with two phenomena: (1) acceleration of entrance of glucose (or other hexoses) into the tissue cells, and (2) deposition of K and PO_4 with glycogen in liver and muscles. The closely parallel changes in blood glucose, K, and PO_4 that follow administration of insulin are apparently dependent upon common cellular metabolic mechanisms, probably involving phosphorylation processes.

HYPERGLYCEMIC (GLYCOGENOLYTIC) FACTOR OF PANCREAS

A factor is present in extracts of the pancreas and of the gastric mucosa of the dog, as well as in most commercial insulin preparations, which causes an increase in blood sugar when injected intravenously. It has been designated the "hyperglycemic factor" (HG) of the pancreas. It exhibits protein characteristics, is apparently formed in the alpha cells of the islets, and is regarded as a hormone.

When purified HG preparations, free of insulin, are injected intravenously, the blood sugar begins to rise immediately, reaches a maximum in about thirty minutes, and falls to the original level in about an hour. Liver slices incubated with this factor show a decrease in glycogen and an increase in glucose-1- and glucose-6-phosphates. This action of the HG factor is due to increased phosphorylase activity. Epinephrine (p. 672) and, to a lesser extent, other sympathomimetic amines, exert the same action; however, the pancreatic HG factor does not cause the increase in blood lactic acid observed after administration of epinephrine.

It is believed that liver phosphorylase undergoes continual enzymatic inactivation and resynthesis (activation) and that the pancreatic hyperglycemic factor (and also epinephrine) accelerates its resynthesis (reactivation). The exact role, if any, of this agent in the normal regulation of carbohydrate metabolism and of blood sugar concentration is not known.

PARATHYROID HORMONE

CHEMISTRY. The parathyroid hormone has not been obtained in pure form. The most highly purified preparations are of protein nature (12.6–15.5 per cent N), containing at least two components, one of which has a relatively low molecular weight (15,000–25,000). The active fraction is soluble in water, saline solution, and aqueous alcohol and is insoluble in common lipid solvents. The hormone is inactivated by proteolytic enzymes and acid hydrolysis and is therefore inactive when taken orally. It is stable to reducing agents and unstable to oxidizing agents; amino groups appear to be essential to activity and disulfide linkages are apparently not present. Isoelectric points vary in different preparations (pH 4.5–6), indicating the presence of impurities.

ASSAY. The U.S.P. unit is defined as 0.01 of the amount of extract required to raise the serum calcium of not less than ten normal dogs (8–16 kg.) an average of 1 mg. per cent within sixteen to eighteen hours after subcutaneous injection. The Collip unit is 0.01 of the amount which will produce an average increase of 5 mg. per cent in the serum calcium of normal dogs (about 20 kg.) in fifteen hours after injection. The Hanson unit is 0.01 of the amount required to produce an increase of 1 mg. per cent in the serum calcium of a parathyroidectomized dog within six hours after injection. The most active preparations have an activity of 300 U.S.P. units per milligram of nitrogen.

METABOLIC ACTIONS. The metabolic actions of the parathyroid hormone, which are exerted primarily in the metabolism of calcium and phosphorus, are reflected in the consequences of (1) removal of the parathyroid glands and (2) injection of extracts of these glands.

EFFECTS OF PARATHYROIDECTOMY. The following phenomena occur after removal of all parathyroid tissue: (1) decreased urinary excretion of inorganic phosphorus; (2) increase in serum inorganic phosphorus concentration; (3) decreased urinary excretion of calcium; (4) decrease in serum calcium concentration, largely if not entirely in the diffusible or ionized fraction (p. 611).

As the concentration of calcium in the extracellular fluids falls, manifestations of neuromuscular hyperexcitability develop, eventuating in death with the clinical picture of tetany. Fibrillary muscle twitchings pass successively into generalized tremors, increased muscle tonus, painful clonic, and, finally, tonic spasms and violent generalized convulsions, with laryngeal spasm and asphyxia. The autonomic nerves and smooth muscles are also affected, with involvement of the heart and the gastrointestinal and urinary tracts.

EFFECTS OF PARATHYROID HORMONE INJECTION. The chief consequences of administration of this hormone are: (1) increased urinary excretion of inorganic phosphate; (2) decrease in serum inorganic phosphorus concentration; (3) increased urinary excretion of calcium; (4) increase in serum calcium concentration; (5) increased serum alkaline phosphatase activity.

The skeleton is the ultimate source of the increased urinary calcium and phosphate. Continued, repeated injection of parathyroid hormone results in the characteristic skeletal picture of diffuse osteitis fibrosa cystica, with resorption of trabecular and cortical bone, fractures and deformities, appearance of numerous giant cells and osteoclasts, and necrosis, hemorrhage and replacement fibrosis of the marrow. Healing processes, which progress simultaneously, are accompanied by the appearance of numerous osteoblasts.

The increased concentration of calcium in the body fluids is often followed by deposition of calcium phosphate in various tissues, including the myocardium, kidneys, stomach, arteries, bronchi, and pulmonary alveoli. Calculi may develop in the kidneys or lower urinary tract as a result of the high concentration of calcium and phosphate in the urine.

MECHANISM OF ACTION. Present evidence suggests that the parathyroid hormone exerts a dual effect. (1) It decreases renal tubular reabsorption of inorganic phosphate from the glomerular filtrate, with consequent excessive loss of phosphate in the urine and a fall in its concentration in the plasma. (2) It accelerates mobilization of calcium and phosphate from the skeleton, with consequent increase in the concentration of calcium in the plasma and increased urinary excretion of calcium and phosphate. The increase in serum alkaline phosphatase activity in hyperparathyroidism is a reflection of increased osteoblastic activity in areas of healing in the bones.

CONTROL OF PARATHYROID SECRETORY ACTIVITY. There is no evidence to indicate nervous or hormonal control of parathyroid function. Secretory activity is apparently regulated by the plasma calcium concentration, a decrease in which stimulates and an increase depresses parathyroid hormone secretion. Inasmuch as the effect of this hormone is to increase the level of calcium in the blood (p. 612), this is an example of a very efficient autoregulatory mechanism, as in the case of the blood sugar, in which the concentration of a constituent of the blood regulates itself.

PITUITARY HORMONES

Three anatomical divisions of the hypophysis yield extracts which, on injection, exert well-defined effects in various animal species. These divisions are (1) the neurohypophysis (posterior lobe), (2) the pars intermedia, and (3) the anterior lobe (adenohypophysis). In man and other mammals, the latter is by far the most important, inasmuch as it controls the functional activity and structural integrity of other important endocrine glands, e.g., the thyroid, adrenal cortex, and gonads, through its so-called "trophic" hormones. In addition, it produces factors which exert direct actions in certain fundamental phases of intermediary metabolism, viz., the growth hormone.

ANTERIOR PITUITARY HORMONES

Following hypophysectomy, the thyroid gland, adrenal cortex, and gonads undergo atrophy, and the animal loses weight. In addition, in young animals, longitudinal growth is arrested, closure of epiphyseal lines is delayed, and the gonads fail to mature, the animals remaining infantile. Certain metabolic defects are apparent. Oxidative processes are depressed; liver and muscle glycogen are depleted; fat oxidation is decreased; ketosis does not appear following procedures which usually induce increased ketogenesis; fat turnover is decreased, as reflected in its decreased mobilization from the fat depots. These animals are exceedingly sensitive to insulin.

All of these morphological and metabolic abnormalities can be prevented or corrected by administration of anterior pituitary extracts. In recent years, several anterior pituitary principles have been separated and purified, which exert rather characteristic effects and which are generally assumed to be different hormones. All are protein in nature. They may be placed in two categories. (1) The so-called "trophic" hormones are responsible for the structural integrity and functional activity of certain specific "target" endocrine glands. Their effects are due to stimulation of their respective target glands, and they exert no effect in the absence of these organs. They include the following: (a) thyrotrophic, (b) adrenocorticotrophic, (c) follicle-stimulating, (d) luteinizing, and (e) lactogenic hormones. (2) At least one factor, the growth hormone, exerts a direct metabolic effect on protein metabolism, perhaps also on carbohydrate and fat metabolism, not mediated by other endocrine glands.

Thyrotrophic (Thyroid-Stimulating) Hormone

CHEMISTRY. Thyrotrophic hormone (TSH) has not been isolated in pure form, but rather highly purified preparations are available. It appears to be a protein, soluble in water, with a molecular weight of about 10,000. Activity is destroyed by cysteine and by pepsin, trypsin, and chymotrypsin, but not by papain.

ASSAY. Two sensitive methods have been described: (1) determination of the number of colloid droplets in the cells of the guinea pig thyroid following injection of preparations containing TSH; (2) measurement of increase in thyroid acinar cell height and extension of the hindlimb of the stasis (starved, non-metamorphosing) tadpole following injection of preparations containing TSH.

ACTIONS. TSH is the most important factor in the regulation of thyroid function. Removal of TSH results in atrophy of the thyroid gland and cessation of thyroxine formation. Secretion of this hormone by the anterior pituitary is controlled by the level of circulating thyroxine, increase in the latter depressing and a decrease stimulating TSH production.

Injection of TSH is followed by morphological and metabolic evidences of increased thyroid function. The following phenomena have been observed: increase in thyroid acinar cell height; resorption of follicular colloid; increase of Golgi apparatus, proteolytic activity, oxidase granules, and O_2 consumption of thyroid cells; increase in the iodine content of the gland as well as in the "protein-bound" iodine of the plasma; increase in uptake of radioactive iodine by the thyroid. There is evidence that TSH is necessary for coupling of diiodotyrosine to form thyroxine (p. 683). Administration of TSH therefore produces effects on the organism (except on the thyroid) identical with those produced by thyroxine.

Adrenocorticotrophic Hormone

CHEMISTRY. Adrenocorticotrophic hormone (ACTH), as ordinarily available, is a protein with a molecular weight of about 20,000. However, there is evidence that all biological activity of this hormone resides in polypeptides with molecular weights of about 2500, which may contain as few as eight amino acids. Hydrolysates obtained after 50 per cent hydrolysis with crude pepsin are as active as the original material on the basis of total nitrogen content, the active material being ultrafilterable and only partially precipitated by trichloracetic acid.

It has been suggested that there may be two adrenocorticotrophic hormones, concerned respectively with stimulation of adrenal secretion of (1) 11-17-oxycorticosteroids and (2) precursors of 17-ketosteroids. This does not appear to be the case in man.

ASSAY. Several methods of assay of ACTH activity have been proposed:

(a) REPAIR TEST. This consists in determination of the reappearance of lipid material in the regressed adrenal cortices of hypophysectomized rats following injection of preparations containing ACTH.

(b) MAINTENANCE TEST. This consists in determination of the quantity of ACTH-containing material required to maintain the adrenal weights of rats injected immediately after hypophysectomy.

(c) *Measurement of Decrease in Adrenal Ascorbic Acid.* Measurement of the decrease in adrenal ascorbic acid of hypophysectomized rats one hour after intravenous injection of the ACTH-containing material is a highly specific and sensitive method.

ACTIONS. ACTH is the most important physiological regulator of adrenal cortical activity. The adrenals of hypophysectomized animals are reduced in size and lipid content, and are restored to a normal state by injection of ACTH. Normal secretion of adrenal corticoids is also restored. Administration of ACTH to normal subjects causes increased secretion of adrenal steroids, with decrease (temporary) in adrenal lipid and ascorbic acid (pp. 148, 676) and practically all of the phenomena observed after administration of cortical hormones, including lymphopenia, eosinopenia, hyperglycemia, negative nitrogen balance, and electrolyte and water effects (p. 678 ff.).

Release of ACTH by the anterior pituitary is apparently dependent in part upon a hormonal factor secreted by certain hypothalamic

centers which can be stimulated by nerve impulses and by epinephrine. Its release may also be influenced by the level of cortical hormone in the tissues and/or circulation, an increased level depressing
and a decreased level stimulating ACTH secretion.

Gonadotrophic Hormones

The anterior pituitary secretes three hormones which exert important effects on the gonads and are therefore termed "gonadotrophic
hormones." These include: (1) follicle-stimulating hormone (FSH);
(2) interstitial cell-stimulating hormone (ICSH) (luteinizing hormone; LH); (3) lactogenic hormone (prolactin) (luteotrophic hormone; LTH). In the female, they are responsible for the growth,
maturation, and expulsion of the ova and with the production of the
internal secretions of the ovary. In the male, they stimulate sperm-
atogenesis and production of androgen.

Hypophysectomy is followed by atrophy of the gonads, with abolition of their hormone production and, consequently, atrophy of the
target organs of these hormones, viz., uterus, vaginal mucosa, prostate,
and seminal vesicles. All of these structures and functions are restored by administration of the gonadotrophic hormones. Secretion
of these pituitary factors is controlled by the levels of androgen and
estrogen in the circulation, an increase in these steroid hormones
causing depression and a decrease stimulation of gonadotrophin production.

FOLLICLE-STIMULATING HORMONE. CHEMISTRY. Follicle-stimulating
hormone (FSH) is apparently a water-soluble glycoprotein, containing perhaps as much as 20 per cent glucose. FSH prepared from
sheep pituitaries also contains glucosamine. Activity is destroyed by
certain amylase preparations and by proteolytic enzymes.

ASSAY. Inasmuch as the activity of FSH is influenced by ICSH,
quantitative data regarding the former can be obtained only in hypophysectomized animals. The following procedures may be employed:
(1) production of increase of ovarian weight or follicular development in hypophysectomized female rats; (2) production of increase in
weight of testes without stimulation of secondary sex organs in hypophysectomized male rats.

ACTIONS. In the female, FSH stimulates the growth and maturation of ovarian follicles and prepares them for ovulation. In pure form,
this hormone does not cause secretion of estrogen by the ovary, but
does so in the presence of even minute amounts of luteinizing hormone (ICSH; LH) (p. 660). In the male, FSH stimulates spermato-
genesis.

INTERSTITIAL CELL-STIMULATING HORMONE. CHEMISTRY. Interstitial
cell-stimulating hormone (ICSH) (luteinizing hormone; LH) has

been isolated in pure form. It is apparently a homogeneous, water-soluble, carbohydrate-containing (mannose; hexosamine) protein. ICSH prepared from different species exhibits differences in immunological specificity, chemical composition, isoelectric point, and molecular weight (sheep 40,000; swine 100,000). Activity is destroyed by certain proteolytic enzymes and by reduction of disulfide linkages.

ASSAY. ICSH activity may be assayed in several ways, the following being commonly employed: (1) increase of ovarian weight and corpora lutea production in normal immature rats primed by FSH; (2) repair of ovarian interstitial cells in hypophysectomized rats; (3) increase in weight of seminal vesicles in normal immature male rats; (4) increase in weight of the ventral lobe of the prostate in hypophysectomized male rats.

ACTIONS. In the female, ICSH (LH) acts synergistically with FSH to cause ovulation of mature follicles and secretion of estrogen by the thecal and granulosa cells. It is also concerned with corpus luteum formation and, in conjunction with luteotrophic (lactogenic) hormone (LTH), it is concerned with the production of estrogen and progesterone by the corpus luteum.

In the male, ICSH (LH) stimulates the development and functional activity of Leydig (interstitial) cells, and, consequently, the production of testicular androgen (p. 665). Its administration, therefore, produces effects in the organism (except on the testis) similar to those which follow administration of testosterone (p. 669).

LACTOGENIC HORMONE. CHEMISTRY. Lactogenic hormone (prolactin) (luteotrophic hormone; LTH) has been isolated in pure form. It is apparently a homogeneous carbohydrate-containing protein, with a molecular weight of about 26,500–32,000, relatively insoluble in water. Activity is destroyed by pepsin and trypsin.

ASSAY. The method usually employed depends upon the increase in weight of the crop sac of the pigeon after injection of lactogenic hormone. An international unit (I.U.) has been defined as "the specific activity contained in 0.1 mg. of the standard preparation (international standard)."

ACTIONS. Lactogenic hormone (LTH) is responsible for lactation in the postpartum woman. It is also necessary for stimulation of functional activity (estrogen and progesterone production) of the corpus luteum. Its function in the male is unknown.

CHORIONIC GONADOTROPHIN. The placenta produces a gonadotrophic hormone which differs from the pituitary gonadotrophins but resembles ICSH (LH) in its biological actions. It reaches a maximum concentration in blood and urine usually in fifty to seventy days after the last previous normal menstrual period, this phenomenon constituting the basis for certain of the most valuable pregnancy tests (Tables 58, 59, pp. 661, 664).

The rising titer of chorionic gonadotrophin in the blood during pregnancy causes the persistence and continued function of the corpus luteum until the placental syncytiotrophoblast is capable of producing sufficient estrogen and progesterone to support the pregnancy.

Growth Hormone

CHEMISTRY. Growth hormone has been isolated in apparently pure form. It is a protein, relatively insoluble in water, with a molecular weight of about 44,250, and an isoelectric point of pH 6.85. Activity is destroyed by pepsin and trypsin. Recent reports suggest that available purified preparations may be contaminated by a separable factor or factors which (1) stimulate mobilization of depot fat and (2) depress the respiratory quotient (i.e., inhibit carbohydrate utilization).

ASSAY. The most sensitive method consists in measurement of the increase in width of the proximal epiphyseal cartilage of the hypophysectomized female rat following injection of the 'growth hormone. Other methods that have been employed involve measurement of the increase in body weight of normal, plateaued or, better, hypophysectomized female rats following injection of the hormonal preparation.

ACTIONS. Animals hypophysectomized before fully grown are dwarfed; administration of pituitary extracts results in gigantism or, if given after full growth is attained, in acromegaly. These effects on both skeletal and visceral growth are attributable to the growth hormone, but involve also participation of other factors, e.g., thyroxine and insulin, for their maximal expression. This is to be expected, inasmuch as the complicated phenomenon of growth must be dependent upon a number of interrelated metabolic processes and the state of nutrition of the organism.

Unfractionated extracts of the anterior pituitary produce effects on various metabolic processes, in part indirectly through the trophic hormones (e.g., TSH, ACTH), but also by a direct action not mediated by other glands. It is possible, but as yet not established with certainty, that most of these direct metabolic actions may be due to the growth hormone.

PROTEIN METABOLISM. Growth hormone is a protein-anabolic principle. It induces a positive nitrogen balance, accompanied by increase in tissue nitrogen, and decrease in urea nitrogen, amino nitrogen and total NPN of the blood plasma. Insulin is necessary for production of this effect.

CARBOHYDRATE METABOLISM. In vitro, crude pituitary extracts apparently inhibit the enzyme, hexokinase (p. 389), which catalyzes the phosphorylation of glucose to glucose-6-phosphate. Such extracts induce hyperglycemia and glycosuria and, if administered repeatedly, permanent diabetes in certain species (p. 432). This diabetogenic action of pituitary extracts in inhibiting carbohydrate utilization has been identified with the growth hormone. However, recent studies suggest that the respiratory quotient-lowering action previously ascribed to the growth hormone may be due to a factor which contaminates the most highly purified available preparations of growth hormone. Consequently, final decision must be reserved regarding identification of the "diabetogenic" action of anterior pituitary extracts with the growth hormone. The same applies to their action in increasing muscle glycogen, the so-called "glycostatic" action, which has been attributed to the same factor.

The R.Q.-lowering effect, referred to above, appears to be due to interference with utilization of carbohydrate at some point between the formation of glucose-6-phosphate and of pyruvic acid, i.e., beyond the hexokinase reaction. As stated previously, this effect may be due to a factor separable from the growth hormone. There is some evidence, too, that growth hormone (?) diminishes the uptake of glucose by tissues (isolated diaphragm), an effect that is counteracted by insulin.

LIPID METABOLISM. Administration of pituitary extracts stimulates mobilization of fat from the fat depots, with consequent decrease in carcass fat, increase in plasma and liver lipids (p. 481) and in ketogenesis (p. 481). Increase in adrenal cortical hormone production is necessary for this fat-mobilization (p. 680). This phenomenon has been attributed to the growth hormone, but recent evidence suggests the existence of a "fat metabolism hormone" or "ketogenic hormone" of the anterior pituitary not identifiable with any of the other factors.

POSTERIOR PITUITARY HORMONES

Injection of an extract (pituitrin) of the posterior lobe of the pituitary (neurohypophysis) produces three well-recognized effects: (1) increase in blood pressure (pressor effect); (2) contraction of the mammalian uterus (oxytocic effect); (3) decreased urine volume in mammals, with increased concentration of urinary solids (antidiuretic effect). A fourth effect, induced in lower vertebrates, i.e., melanophore expansion or melanophore dispersion, is due to a principle formed in the pars intermedia, but present as a contaminant in unfractionated extracts of the posterior lobe. In animals that have no pars intermedia (e.g., whale, chicken), this principle occurs in extracts of the anterior lobe only.

The bulk of available evidence indicates that the pressor and antidiuretic effects are produced by the same substance (pressor principle). However, opinion is divided and evidence conflicting as to the chemical basis of the pressor and oxytocic actions. According to one view, the posterior lobe produces one substance with multiple activities; according to another, it produces at least two distinct substances.

A partially purified preparation, which evokes all of the above responses, exhibits characteristics of a protein with a molecular weight of about 30,000. Two fractions have been separated from such extracts, one (pitressin) producing a maximal pressor response, with little uterine effect, the other (pitocin) evoking maximal uterine contraction (oxytocic effect), with but little rise in blood pressure. Present evidence suggests that these pressor and oxytocic substances are polypeptides, with a molecular weight of about 2000. Pitocin (oxytocin) has recently been shown to be a cyclic octapeptide and has been synthesized, an accomplishment of historical importance. The synthesis of pitressin is currently being approached in a similar manner.

ASSAY.   Pressor activity is assayed by comparing the rise in blood pressure, following intravenous injection in anesthesized dogs, spinal cats, or anesthetized rats, with that produced by known amounts of a standard preparation.

Oxytocic activity is assayed by comparing the degree of contraction of the isolated, virgin guinea pig uterus, *in vitro*, with that produced by known amounts of a standard preparation. Another method is based upon the blood pressure-lowering effect of the oxytocic principle in the anesthetized chicken.

Antidiuretic activity is assayed by comparing the reduction in urine volume following intravenous injection in hydrated unanesthetized rats or hydrated rabbits with that produced by a standard preparation.

FUNCTIONS.   Despite the pronounced pressor effect of pitressin, there is no satisfactory evidence that this factor plays a role in the physiological regulation of vascular tone or of blood pressure. Similarly, there is merely suggestive and contradictory evidence that the oxytocic principle may be implicated in the regulation of uterine contraction during parturition. On the other hand, there is unequivocal evidence that a hormone elaborated by the neurohypophysis, perhaps pitressin or a factor not yet separated from it (antidiuretic principle), is important in the regulation of water balance in mammals. This antidiuretic effect is dependent on a specific action of this factor on the epithelial cells of the distal portion of the uriniferous tubule, stimulating reabsorption of water independently of solids, and resulting in concentration of the urine (p. 756).

Secretion of this hormone is apparently regulated by nerve impulses originating in hypothalamic nuclei (e.g., supraoptic nuclei) and traversing the infundibular stalk (supraopticohypophyseal tract). It is believed that the activity of these hypothalamic nuclei is regulated by the degree of concentration of the blood plasma; i.e., a tendency toward reduction in plasma water content results in stimulation of antidiuresis with consequent renal tubular reabsorption of increased amounts of water. In the absence of this factor, the urine cannot be concentrated, and large volumes (up to 25 liters or more daily) of low specific gravity are excreted (diabetes insipidus). The presence of a functioning anterior pituitary is required for the development of this condition; i.e., total hypophysectomy does not result in diabetes insipidus.

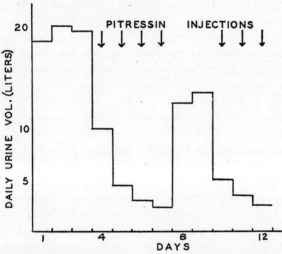

Fig. 134. The influence of administration of the antidiuretic hormone of the pituitary on the daily urine output of a patient with diabetes insipidus

Injection of commercially available posterior lobe extracts commonly results in a rise in blood sugar. This action is not consistently identified with either the separated pressor or oxytocic fractions, suggesting that it is due to some non-specific component of the extracts. In fact, highly purified preparations have no effect on the blood sugar of rabbits and it appears highly improbable that the neuro-hypophysis plays a physiological role in the regulation of carbo-hydrate metabolism. A purported anti-insulin effect of posterior lobe extracts is also now regarded as a non-specific property of these preparations.

MELANOPHORE-EXPANDING (DISPERSING) HORMONE (INTERMEDIN)

Almost all cold-blooded vertebrates (e.g., amphibians, reptiles, fishes) are able to adapt their skin coloring to their surroundings to a greater or lesser extent, a protective or deceptive device of obvious benefit to the animal. This property is due to the presence, in the skin, of certain cells, with branching processes, termed "chromatophores," which contain mobile pigment granules. In the majority of such cells the pigment is black, and the cells are called "melanophores"; xanthophores contain yellow, and erythrophores red pigment granules.

These pigment granules may be concentrated in a single mass near the center of the cell, in which case the skin becomes pale. They may, on the other hand, be dispersed throughout the cell and its processes, in which case the color of the skin is intensified. Scattering of these granules from their central position is effected by the action of the melanophore (chromatophore)-expanding (dispersing) hormone. In most species this is elaborated by the pars intermedia of the pituitary; in animals in which this structure is absent (e.g., whale, chicken), it is apparently produced in the anterior lobe. Variable amounts of this hormone are secreted, with consequent variations in skin color, in response to reflexes originating in the retina and initiated by the color of the immediate visible environment of the animal. Hypophysectomy (e.g., in the toad) results in paling of the skin; injection of the melanophore-dispersing principle restores the normal color. This forms the basis for the bioassay procedure for this hormone.

Little is known about the chemical nature of this substance. It has a molecular weight probably not much over 2000, is destroyed by tryptic but not by peptic digestion, is soluble in water, and is fairly heat stable. Its function in man is unknown. It has been suggested that it may be involved in normal and abnormal cutaneous pigmentation, but there is no satisfactory evidence that this is the case.

NEUROHORMONES

The theory of humoral (i.e., chemical) transmission of nerve impulses embodies the view that stimulation of nerves releases substances which act on the effector cells. The case is perhaps strongest for autonomic nerves, but has been invoked also for the central nervous system and somatic nerves. Stimulation of the vagus results in the production of acetylcholine (p. 455) or in its liberation from combination with an unknown precursor; stimulation of sympathetic fibers results in the formation of norepinephrine (Arterenol) (p. 672) (also acetylcholine, in certain instances). These nerve fibers are accordingly designated "cholinergic" and "adrenergic," respectively. Adrenergic fibers include most of the postganglionic sympathetic fibers. Cholinergic fibers include (1) preganglionic fibers, sympathetic and parasympathetic, (2) postganglionic parasympathetic fibers, (3) certain postganglionic sympathetic fibers, e.g., those to sweat glands, and (4) somatic motor fibers. Administration of acetylcholine produces effects that simulate those of parasympathetic stimulation (parasympathomimetic action); the response to administration of norepinephrine (or epinephrine) resembles that to sympathetic stimulation (sympathomimetic action).

There is considerable controversy over the physiological role played by these substances, particularly acetylcholine, in neuroeffector mechanisms, discussion of which is beyond the scope of a textbook of biochemistry. Classification of these agents as hormones is also questioned by some, chiefly on the basis that, under physiological conditions, the minute amounts formed or released at effector cells probably act only at the point of release, and are not carried to other effector cells. However, whereas the hormonal status of acetylcholine might be questioned on these grounds, that of epinephrine and norepinephrine is well established on the basis of their secretion by the adrenal medulla (p. 672).

The chemical nature and biosynthesis of acetylcholine (p. 455) and norepinephrine (p. 672) are considered elsewhere. Little is known regarding the metabolic degradation of the latter (p. 672). That of the former, however, has received considerable attention because rapid destruction of acetylcholine is an essential feature of certain theories of the activation of neuroeffector mechanisms. Acetylcholine is hydrolyzed to acetic acid and choline by a specific cholinesterase (p. 228), present in nerves and muscle, with a specific localization at synaptic junctions, i.e., at the sites of occurrence of bioelectrical phenomena (changes in action potential and membrane resistance and depolarization). Acetylcholine, synthesized as a result of nerve stimulation from choline by the enzyme choline acetylase in the presence of acetyl-CoA, and presumably involved in the transmission of the nerve impulse, must be inactivated rapidly in order to permit the initiation and transmission of another impulse. This specific cholinesterase acts only on acetylcholine, in contradistinction to "pseudocholinesterase" (p. 228), which has a wider natural distribution, and catalyzes the hydrolysis of many other esters.

GASTROINTESTINAL HORMONES

Secretory activities of certain digestive glands are regulated by hormones produced in localized areas of the intestinal, and perhaps also the gastric mucosa, in response to the local action of foodstuffs and non-specific agents. The actions of these humoral factors supplement those of the autonomic nervous system. Inasmuch as their only known effects are exerted on digestive functions, they will be considered here only briefly.

Of the many such substances for which hormonal status has been claimed, only two have been conclusively established as such by demonstration of release under physiological conditions, viz., secretin and cholecystokinin. The evidence is very strong but not conclusive for three others, viz., pancreozymin, enterogastrone, and gastrin.

SECRETIN. The term "hormone" was first applied to this substance by Bayliss and Starling (1904). It is produced by the upper intestinal mucosal glands, in highest concentration in the duodenum and jejunum, in response to the local action of a number of agents, the most important physiological factors being acidity, bile, and fatty acids. Other active agents include NaCl solution, alcohol, soaps, and buffer solutions. Produced in this manner, secretin enters the blood stream as a true internal secretion and exerts a characteristic effect on the flow of pancreatic juice and bile.

Secretin has been isolated in crystalline form, suitable for parenteral administration. Its chemical structure is not known, but it is believed to be a polypeptide of low molecular weight (5000). It is freely soluble in water, dialyzable, thermolabile, unstable in alkaline solution, and resistant to pepsin, trypsin, and chymotrypsin.

Administered parenterally, and by rectum, but not orally, it increases the flow of bile from the liver (cholagogue effect) and the flow of pancreatic juice. The acinar cells of the pancreas are stimulated directly (increased O_2 consumption) to produce a secretion of increased volume and bicarbonate content but relatively low enzyme concentration (as compared with vagus stimulation).

The effect of a single injection of secretin lasts about thirty minutes, the hormone disappearing rapidly from the circulation. It is inactivated by an enzyme "secretinase" present in the blood and also probably in the gastrointestinal tract. Small amounts of secretin are excreted in the urine.

CHOLECYSTOKININ. This substance is produced in the same areas as secretin (upper intestine), in response to similar stimuli, especially fat, fatty acids, dilute acids, and peptones. Its chemical structure is not known (dialyzable). It produces contraction and evacuation of the gallbladder when injected, especially intravenously, and also when administered rectally (but not orally). It is inactivated by an enzyme present in the blood.

PANCREOZYMIN. This agent, which stimulates secretion of enzymes by the pancreatic acinar cells (amylase, lipase, trypsin, chymotrypsin), is produced in the same situations as secretin (upper intestine) and in response to the same stimuli. It is soluble in water, slowly dialyzable, thermolabile, sensitive to alkali, and resistant to pepsin, but is apparently attacked by trypsin. It is inactivated by an enzyme present in the blood and tissues.

ENTEROGASTRONE. This term may include two or perhaps three separate principles, presumably elaborated in the duodenal mucosa in response to the presence of fat in the duodenum. The active agent (or agents) is soluble in water, dialyzable, thermostable (in acid solution), is sensitive to alkali, and is attacked by pepsin. When injected intravenously or subcutaneously, three types of effect are produced: (1) inhibition of gastric motility (hunger contractions and peristalsis), which is dependent on an intact vagus innervation; (2) inhibition of gastric acidity (parietal cell secretion); (3) protection against development of gastrojejunal ulcer in "Mann-Williamson" dogs.

GASTRIN. This agent is presumably elaborated by the pyloric mucosa in response to mechanical distension and the local action of secretagogues in the food. It may also be released by cholinergic impulses (vagus stimulation; acetylcholine). Secreted into the blood stream, it stimulates secretion of HCl in the fundus of the stomach (parietal cell secretion), and is believed to be important in the gastric phase of gastric secretion.

OTHER POSTULATED FACTORS. Other effects of various extracts of the mucosa of the upper intestine have been described, the physiological significance of which has not been established. The term "enterocrinin" has been applied to a purported principle, elaborated in the intestinal mucosa in response to the presence of foodstuffs, which stimulates secretion by the jejunum and ileum. The term "duocrinin" has been applied to another factor (?), produced in the same manner, which stimulates secretion by the duodenum (Brunner's glands). Other intestinal factors have been reported to stimulate motor activity of the intestine and splenic contraction. Still others have been reported to lower the blood sugar (insulin synergist). The identity of the principles responsible for these effects as hormones has not been established.

BIBLIOGRAPHY

General

Annual Review of Biochemistry.
Annual Review of Physiology.
Recent Progress in Hormone Research (annual volumes), New York, Academic Press, Inc.
Vitamins and Hormones (annual volumes), New York, Academic Press, Inc.
Dorfman, R. I. et al.: The influence of hormones on enzymes, Ann. New York Acad. Sc. 54:531, 1951.
Meyer, R. K. and McShan, W. H.: Hormone-enzyme relationships, Recent Progress in Hormone Research 5:465, 1950.
Paschkis, K. E., Rakoff, A. E. and Cantarow, A.: Clinical Endocrinology, New York, Paul B. Hoeber, Inc., 1954.
Pincus, G. and Thimann, K. V.: The Hormones, New York, Academic Press, Inc., 1948.
Thayer, S. A.: Methods of bioassay of animal hormones, Vitamins & Hormones 4:312, 1946.

Gonads

General references.

Heard, R. D. H.: The metabolism of estrogens, Recent Progress in Hormone Research 4:25, 1949.

Kochakian, C. D.: The protein anabolic effects of steroid hormones, Vitamins & Hormones 4:256, 1946.

Mason, H. L.: The 17-ketosteroids: their origin, determination and significance, Physiol. Rev. 30:321, 1950.

Samuels, L. T.: The metabolism of androgens by tissues, Recent Progress in Hormone Research 4:65, 1949.

Adrenal

General references.

deBodo, R. C. and Sincoff, M. W.: Anterior pituitary and adrenal hormones in the regulation of carbohydrate metabolism, Recent Progress in Hormone Research 8:511, 1953.

Engel, F. L.: A consideration of the roles of the adrenal cortex and stress in the regulation of protein metabolism, Recent Progress in Hormone Research 6:277, 1951.

Gaunt, R. et al.: Symposium on the adrenal cortex, Ann. New York Acad. Sc. 50:509, 1949.

Haines, W. J.: Studies on the biosynthesis of adrenal cortex hormones, Recent Progress in Hormone Research 7:255, 1952.

Kendall, E. C.: The influence of the adrenal cortex on the metabolism of water and electrolytes, Vitamins & Hormones 6:278, 1948.

Levin, L. and Farber, R. K.: Hormonal factors which regulate the mobilization of depot fat to the liver, Recent Progress in Hormone Research 7:399, 1952.

Long, C. N. H.: The relation of cholesterol and ascorbic acid to the secretion of the adrenal cortex, Recent Progress in Hormone Research 1:99, 1946.

Macy Foundation Conferences on the Adrenal Cortex, I, II, III, IV, New York, Josiah Macy Foundation, 1949, 1950, 1951, 1952.

Mason, H. L.: The 17-ketosteroids: their origin, determination and significance, Physiological Rev. 30:321, 1950.

Mirsky, I. A.: The etiology of diabetes mellitus in man, Recent Progress in Hormone Research 7:437, 1952.

Mote, J. R. (ed.): Clinical ACTH Conferences, Philadelphia, Blakiston Company, 1950, 1951.

Sayers, G.: The adrenal cortex and homeostasis, Physiol. Rev. 30:241, 1950.

Sprague, R. G.: Effects of cortisone and ACTH, Vitamins & Hormones 9:265, 1951.

Sprague, R. G., Mason, H. L. and Power, M. H.: Physiologic effects of cortisone and ACTH in man, Recent Progress in Hormone Research 6:315, 1951

Sutherland, E. W.: The effect of the hyperglycemic factor of the pancreas and of epinephrine on glycolysis, Recent Progress in Hormone Research 5:441, 1950.

Thorn, G. W. and Forsham, P. H.: Metabolic changes in man following adrenal and pituitary hormone administration, Recent Progress in Hormone Research 4:229, 1949.

Thyroid

General references.

Barker, S. B.: Mechanism of action of the thyroid hormone, Physiol. Rev. 31:205, 1951.

Charriper, H. A. and Gordon, A. S.: The biology of antithyroid agents, Vitamins & Hormones 5:274, 1947.

Keating, F. R. and Albert, A.: The metabolism of iodine in man as disclosed with the use of radioiodine, Recent Progress in Hormone Research 4:429, 1949.

Means, J. H.: The Thyroid and Its Diseases, ed. 2, Philadelphia, J. B. Lippincott Company, 1948.

Means, J. H. et al.: Thyroid function as disclosed by newer methods of study, Ann. New York Acad. Sc. 50:279, 1949.

Pitt-Rivers, R.: Mode of action of antithyroid compounds, Physiol. Rev. 30:194, 1950.

Rawson, R. W. and Money, W. L.: Physiologic reactions of the thyroid stimulating hormone, Recent Progress in Hormone Research 4:309, 1949.

Pancreas

General references.
Bouckaert, J. P.: The action of insulin, Physiol. Rev. 27:39, 1947.
Mirsky, I. A.: The etiology of diabetes mellitus in man, Recent Progress in Hormone Research 7:437, 1952.
Stadie, W. C.: The chemical combination of insulin with muscle and its hormonal regulation, Science 111:459, 1950.
Sutherland, E. W.: The effect of the hyperglycemic factor of the pancreas and of epinephrine on glycolysis, Recent Progress in Hormone Research 5:441, 1950.

Parathyroid Glands

General references.
Albright, F. and Reifenstein, E. C., Jr.: Parathyroid Glands and Metabolic Bone Disease, Baltimore, Williams & Wilkins Company, 1948.

Pituitary

General references.
deBodo, R. C. and Sincoff, M. W.: Anterior pituitary and adrenal hormones in the regulation of carbohydrate metabolism, Recent Progress in Hormone Research 8:511, 1953.
Levin, L. and Farber, R. K.: Hormonal factors which regulate the mobilization of depot fat to the liver, Recent Progress in Hormone Research 7:399, 1952.
Li, C. H.: The chemistry of gonadotropic hormones, Vitamins & Hormones 7:224, 1949.
Li, C. H. and Evans, H. M.: The properties of the growth and adrenocorticotropic hormones, Vitamins & Hormones 5:198, 1947.
Mirsky, I. A.: The etiology of diabetes mellitus in man, Recent Progress in Hormone Research 7:437, 1952.
Mote, J. R. (ed.): Clinical ACTH Conferences, Philadelphia, Blakiston Company, 1950, 1951.
Rawson, R. W. and Money, W. L.: Physiologic reactions of the thyroid stimulating hormone, Recent Progress in Hormone Research 4:309, 1949.
Sayers, G.: The adrenal cortex and homeostasis, Physiol. Rev. 30:241, 1950.
Sprague, R. G.: Effects of cortisone and ACTH, Vitamins & Hormones 9:265, 1951.
Sprague, R. G., Mason, H. L. and Power, M. H.: Physiologic effects of cortisone and ACTH in man, Recent Progress in Hormone Research 6:315, 1951.
Stehle, R. L.: The chemistry of hormones of the posterior lobe of the pituitary gland, Vitamins & Hormones 7:383, 1949.
Stehle, R. L.: The actions of the hormones of the posterior lobe of the pituitary gland, Vitamins and Hormones 7:390, 1949.
Thorn, G. W. and Forsham, P. H.: Metabolic changes in man following adrenal and pituitary hormone administration, Recent Progress in Hormone Research 4:229, 1949.
White, A.: The chemistry and physiology of adenohypophyseal luteotropin (prolactin), Vitamins & Hormones 7:254, 1949.

Gastrointestinal Hormones

General references.
Grossman, M. I.: Gastrointestinal hormones, Physiol. Rev. 30:33, 1950.

Neurohormones

General references.
Gerard, R. W.: The acetylcholine system in neural function, Recent Progress in Hormone Research 5:37, 1950.
Nachmansohn, D.: Chemical mechanisms of nerve activity. In Modern Trends in Physiology and Biochemistry, New York, Academic Press, Inc., 1952, p. 230.
Tainter, M. L. and Luduena, F. P.: Sympathetic hormonal transmission, Recent Progress in Hormone Research 5:3, 1950.

26

CHEMICAL COMPOSITION OF TISSUES

Water comprises somewhat less than 70 per cent of the body mass of the average well-nourished adult, the remainder of the body being solids. Entirely apart from the fact that these proportions can vary considerably with variations in the amount of stored fat, which occur without significant changes in water content, such figures have little biochemical significance, except perhaps to suggest the physiological importance of water. However, the amount of a substance present does not necessarily reflect its biological importance, and, therefore, isolated quantitative data on the elemental or even molecular composition of the body as a whole are of little biochemical import. On the other hand, knowledge of the substances present in a specific tissue may contribute to a better understanding of certain of its functions.

Whereas the important constituents of various organs and tissues have been known for some time, only recently has it been possible to secure detailed and precise information concerning their intracellular localization. By the use of differential centrifugation of tissue homogenates (p. 348), various particulate components of cells (nuclei, mitochondria, microsomes) may be separated from each other and from the soluble constituents of the cytoplasm. Analysis of these isolated fractions has revealed that certain substances are restricted to certain cell components, and studies of this nature have yielded valuable information on many fundamental aspects of biochemistry and physiology. Additional information in this direction has been obtained by studies on intact cells, employing special staining technics (e.g., for enzymes, nucleic acids, steroids, lipids, etc.) and ultraviolet absorption measurements (for nucleic acids). Because of the importance of current activities in this field, present knowledge regarding the general pattern of distribution of functionally significant cell constituents will be reviewed before considering the chemical composition of certain special tissues.

INTRACELLULAR DISTRIBUTION OF CHEMICAL COMPONENTS (CYTOCHEMISTRY)

Liver has been employed more extensively than other tissues in studies of isolated cell fractions because it is composed of essentially a single type of cell, which is large, readily disrupted, and provides good yields of nuclei, mitochondria, and microsomes. The quantitative data indicated here, therefore, apply specifically to liver cells, but there is every reason to believe that the general pattern exhibited by these cells applies also to others.

MITOCHONDRIA. These filamentous structures are the largest components of the cytoplasm, and represent up to 15–20 per cent of the dry weight of the liver cell. About 25 per cent of the total nitrogen (i.e., protein) of the liver is in this fraction. Mitochondria are rich in lipid (25 per cent), two-thirds of which are phospholipids. In proportion to their mass, they contain a relatively small quantity of nucleic acid, all of which is pentosenucleic acid (20 per cent of total cell PNA) (p. 578).

A large number of enzymes and coenzymes are apparently localized in these structures. These include: cytochrome oxidase, succinic dehydrogenase, oxalacetic acid oxidase, octanoic acid oxidase, glutamic dehydrogenase, DPN- and TPN-cytochrome reductases, ATP-ase, catalase, cytochrome c, riboflavin, vitamin B_{12}. Of particular significance is the fact that certain key enzymes involved in oxidative processes, i.e., cytochrome oxidase, succinic dehydrogenase, occur only in the mitochondria. It would appear, therefore, that these structures are mainly concerned with the oxidative metabolism of the cell and with the incorporation of energy released by these processes in high-energy phosphate bonds (p. 379). They may be regarded, therefore, as a sort of "powerhouse," producing energy, for use here and elsewhere in the cell, required for synthetic and other purposes.

MICROSOMES. These sub-microscopic particles in the cytoplasm contain 20–25 per cent of the total nitrogen of the cell and are rich in nucleic acid, which is exclusively PNA (50 per cent of total cell PNA). Lipid, mainly phospholipid, comprises about 40 per cent of their dry weight. Information concerning this cell fraction is as yet incomplete; in fact, there is some controversy as to its structural identity. No enzymes appear to be contained exclusively in the microsomes, although esterase activity has been identified largely with this fraction. DPN- and TPN-reductases and ATP-ase are also present.

SOLUBLE CYTOPLASMIC MATERIAL. The supernatant fluid from centrifugation of mitochondria, microsomes, and nuclei contains the soluble constituents of the cytoplasm, lipid droplets, some of the secretory granules, and possibly other very small particles. It is obviously a very complex mixture of proteins (35–40 per cent of total cell nitrogen), some PNA, and other organic and inorganic compounds of low molecular weight. This fraction contains a large portion of the acid and alkaline phosphatases of the cell (35–70 per cent of total), catalase, cytochrome c, and the enzymes concerned in anaerobic glycolysis. The latter activity apparently resides entirely in this fraction, but is enhanced considerably by the addition of microsomes.

NUCLEI. The nucleus contains about 15 per cent of the protein of the cell and about 30 per cent of the PNA (20 per cent in the nucleolus, 10 per cent in the chromosomes). All of the DNA of the cell is present in the nucleus (chromosomes). The biological significance of these nucleic acids is discussed elsewhere (p. 578). One of the most striking biochemical features of nuclei is the absence of significant amounts of important enzymes concerned in the metabolic activities of the cell (except ATP-ase and AMP-ase).

CONNECTIVE TISSUE

Connective tissue is distributed widely throughout the body in tendons, sheaths, aponeuroses, subcutaneous tissue, supporting tissues in all organs, and, in modified form, as cartilage and bone. There are three main types of connective tissue fibers: (1) collagenous fibers (tendons, aponeuroses, ligaments, cartilage and bone, etc.); (2) elastic fibers (matrix of lungs, blood-vessel walls, loose areolar tissues, ligaments, etc.); (3) reticular fibers (matrix of bone marrow, lymphoid structures and many viscera, e.g., liver, kidney, etc.). These fibers and connective tissue cells are imbedded in intercellular material (ground-substance), the quantity and consistency of which vary in different regions. Connective tissue is characterized chemically chiefly by its protein components.

PROTEINS. The most important of these are (1) the scleroproteins (albuminoids), collagen, elastin, and reticulin, and (2) a mucoprotein (mucoid). There are also small amounts of albumin and globulin.

COLLAGEN. This scleroprotein is insoluble in the usual protein solvents but, unlike keratin, it is digestible, although slightly, by pepsin and trypsin. It is further characterized by the fact that, on boiling in water or acid solution, it is transformed to gelatin, which is more soluble and readily digested by proteolytic enzymes. This transformation probably represents a denaturation process. Collagen has an unusually high content of glycine (25 per cent), and of proline and hydroxyproline (30 per cent). Collagen and elastin are the only natural animal proteins that contain significant amounts of hydroxyproline and hydroxylysine. Collagen and gelatin are lacking in tryptophan and cystine, and contain only small amounts of methionine and tyrosine.

Collagen comprises about 85 per cent of the solids of collagenous fibers (white connective tissue) and about 20 per cent of the solids of elastic fibers (yellow elastic tissue). It is also present in cartilage and in the organic matrix of bone ("ossein").

ELASTIN. This scleroprotein differs from collagen chiefly in not being converted to gelatin in boiling water, and in being more readily digested by pepsin and trypsin. It is particularly abundant in elastic fibers, in which it comprises about 75 per cent of the solids, as compared to about 4 per cent of the solids of collagenous fibers. The characteristic differences in staining reactions of these two types of fibers are due probably to these differences in protein, collagen and elastin having quite different amino acid constitutions.

RETICULIN. This scleroprotein, present in reticular fibers, is closely related to collagen in composition.

MUCOPROTEIN. All connective and supporting tissues contain mucoproteins (mucoids; glycoproteins) (p. 46) which are essentially the same as those in cartilage and bone, although different designations are commonly applied to them, i.e., tendomucoid, chondromucoid, osseomucoid. They contain as a prosthetic group the mucopolysaccharide, chondroitin sulfuric acid, which consists of multiple units of acetyl galactosamine sulfate and glucuronic acid in glycosidal linkage. These mucoproteins are quite soluble in water and relatively resistant to denaturation, presumably because of their carbohydrate component. They comprise about 3 per cent of the solids of both collagenous and elastic fibers.

Table 62. Average Composition of White and Yellow Connective Tissues

	WHITE (%)	YELLOW (%)
Water	63	58
Solids	37	42
Proteins	35	40
Collagen	30	7.5
Elastin	2.5	32
Mucoid	1.5	0.5
Coagulable	0.2	0.6
Lipids	1.0	1.1
Extractives	0.9	0.8
Inorganic	0.5	0.5

MUCOPOLYSACCHARIDE (P. 19). Mucopolysaccharides occur in certain tissues and fluids in the free state or in combination with small amounts of protein. The most important include: (1) chondroitin sulfate, which on hydrolysis yields galactosamine, and sulfuric, acetic, and glucuronic acids; (2) mucoitin sulfate, the prosthetic group of salivary and gastric mucin, which differs from the above in containing glucosamine instead of galactosamine; (3) hyaluronic acid (present in synovial fluid, umbilical cord, vitreous humor, skin, and connective tissue), which differs from mucoitin sulfate in not containing sulfuric acid groups; (4) heparin, which contains five sulfuric acid groups in each tetrasaccharide unit, instead of two; it is apparently produced in mast cells, is an anticoagulant (p. 736), and is present particularly in the liver and lungs. Chondroitin and mucoitin sulfates and hyaluronic acid are extremely hydrophilic and form viscous solutions; much of the water in connective tissues appears to be bound in this way. The mucopolysaccharides contribute viscosity and bulk to the tissues because of this property of highly polymerized hexoses.

The permeability of a tissue is determined by the amount and consistency of the ground-substance, which consists largely of mucoproteins and mucopolysaccharides, The resistance of epithelium to penetration by fluids and particulate matter (including bacteria) is high, whereas that of subcutaneous tissue, which contains relatively few cells and fibers in proportion to ground-substance, is low. Certain agents which act chemically on mucopolysaccharides alter the physical nature of the ground-substance and, therefore, its viscosity and permeability. Among these are certain mucolytic enzymes found in animal tissues (p. 234); they catalyze the breakdown of the large polysaccharide molecules (depolymerization and hydrolysis). In the tissues, this phenomenon results in decreased viscosity and increased permeability, and these enzymes are sometimes designated "spreading-factors." Hyaluronidase (p. 234) falls into this category.

The integrity of the ground-substance is influenced by certain vitamins and hormones, particularly ascorbic acid (p. 145) and gonadal hormones. Ascorbic acid is apparently required for normal formation of the mucoproteins and mucopolysaccharides, certain of the manifestations of vitamin C deficiency (scurvy) being due to defective development of the intercellular ground-substance. Metabolic turnover of hyaluronic acid (synthesis after breakdown by hyaluronidase) in the sex skin of monkeys and apes varies in different phases of the menstrual cycle and can be altered by administration of estrogens and progesterone. Deficiency in thyroid hormone (in man) results in accumulation of excessive amounts of mucopolysaccharide in the skin and subcutaneous tissues (myxedema). The influence of adrenal cortical hormones on biological reactions and disease states involving the intercellular ground-substance is being investigated intensively.

CARTILAGE

Cartilage is a modified connective tissue which chemically resembles the organic matrix of bone. It consists of cartilage cells imbedded in a dense matrix of collagenous fibers. It is about 70 to 75 per cent water, and organic substances, mainly proteins, comprise about 95 per cent of the solids. The important protein constituents are: (1) collagen; (2) chondroalbuminoid, which resembles elastin; (3) chondromucoid, which resembles the mucoproteins of connective tissue (tendons) and bone. Ossifying cartilage contains glycogen, which apparently plays a role in the mineralization of bone (p. 614). Inorganic constituents (3 to 6 per cent of solids) include Ca, Mg, Na, K, P, and Cl.

BONE

Osseous tissue is a modified connective tissue consisting of an organic matrix, resembling cartilage, in which inorganic elements (bone salt) are precipitated (mineralization) (p. 613) and a characteristic architecture is developed. It contains 20 to 25 per cent water; of the solids, about 60 per cent is inorganic and 40 per cent organic.

The nature of "bone salt" and the mechanism of mineralization are considered elsewhere (p. 613). The organic material is largely protein; there is a small amount of glycogen. The proteins include: (1) "ossein" (collagen), (2) "osseoalbuminoid," which resembles elastin; and (3) osseomucoid, a mucoprotein probably containing chondroitin sulfuric acid as a prosthetic group. Certain enzymes have been identified, including proteinases, peptidases, phosphorylase, and an alkaline phosphatase which is formed by osteoblasts and is apparently involved in the mechanism of mineralization of bone.

Vitamins A (p. 137), D (p. 145), and C (p. 153) are important for normal development of bone; the latter (ascorbic acid) is apparently involved in the production of intercellular materials of all connective and supporting tissues, i.e., collagen and mucopolysaccharides.

TEETH

In a general way the chemical composition of teeth resembles that of bone, both structures consisting of a protein-rich organic matrix in which is incorporated a complex mineral salt. There are three morphologically and chemically distinct mineralized regions in the tooth, viz., dentin, cementum, and enamel. Dentin, the largest component, forms the bulk of the internal structure into which the pulp cavity extends, containing nerves and blood vessels. It is covered by enamel on the exposed surface and by cementum on the subgingival surface.

Enamel, the hardest tissue in the body, is about 5 per cent water, about 98 per cent of the solid matter being inorganic and the bulk of the remainder protein, with a little lipid. The protein is a scleroprotein, resembling but apparently not identical with the keratin of skin. The mineral phase resembles that of bone (p. 613). It contains more calcium and phosphorus, but less magnesium and carbonate than that of dentin, as well as trace amounts of several other elements, perhaps the most important of which is fluorine.

Dentin is harder than bone; inorganic matter, apparently similar to "bone salt," comprises about 77 per cent of the solids, the organic matrix being mainly protein (22 per cent of the solids), with a small amount of lipid. The protein is largely collagen. Cementum has a consistency approximating that of bone, the mineral phase comprising about 70 per cent of the solids, the remainder being chiefly protein (collagen).

As is true of bone, vitamins A, C, and D (q.v.) influence the structure and mineralization of the teeth, and their effects are exerted particularly during the period of dental development, i.e., during fetal and early extrauterine life. However, studies with mineral isotopes indicate that at least the inorganic constituents of fully developed teeth undergo continual replacement, although they are infinitely less responsive than the bones to metabolic influences (Ca and P intake, parathyroid hormone, vitamin D, etc.). The rate of exchange of P^{32} in enamel is less than 1 per cent and in dentin less than 5 per cent of that in bone. Moreover, the largest fraction of this relatively small turnover may not represent the actual mineral lattice (hydroxyapatite), but rather deposits on the surface of the essential "bone-salt" (p. 613). Phosphate is apparently transferred from the saliva through the enamel to the dentin as well as from the blood plasma through the dentin to the enamel.

Fluorine, which occurs normally in bones and teeth in very small amounts, exerts an important influence on the structure of enamel and on its resistance to caries. Intake of abnormally large quantities of fluoride (in drinking water) during childhood results in "dental fluorosis" ("mottled enamel"), characterized by a patchy, chalky or brownish mottling of the enamel, frequently with pitting of the surface and fracture and chipping of the enamel, which is abnormally fragile. This is a reflection of imperfect formation of the enamel. Of special practical importance is the observation that ingestion of amounts of fluoride (1.0 to 1.5 parts per million in drinking water) too small to produce mottled enamel renders the teeth more resistant to caries. The increased fluoride content of the enamel makes it less soluble in acids; the F^- ion may also inhibit the activity of oral bacterial enzymes, diminishing local production of acids (from carbohydrates) which are believed by many to be important in the production of dental caries. This observation has led to widespread fluoridation of water supplies, with encouraging results.

SKIN AND APPENDAGES

The functions of the skin are, to certain extent, reflections of its chemical constitution. Certain of its characteristics of toughness, elasticity, and flexibility are undoubtedly due to the high concentration of a characteristic fibrous protein, "keratin" (p. 46).

PROTEINS. The most important and characteristic protein in the epidermis is the scleroprotein, keratin (p. 46). The deepest of the four epidermal layers, the stratum germinativum, the most active metabolically, has the highest water and glutathione content. Cells are being continually formed in this layer and pass toward the surface successively through the other layers, viz., the strata granulosum, lucidum, and corneum, their water content and metabolic activity decreasing until, in the superficial stratum corneum, the cells are dead and are lost by desquamation. The character of the proteins in these layers also differs. All are classed as scleroproteins. That in the stratum germinativum, termed "keratohyaline," occurs as irregularly scattered granules, which become more abundant in the stratum granulosum. This protein is regarded as the precursor of "eleidin," a scleroprotein present in the stratum lucidum, which undergoes further change to the characteristic "keratin" of the stratum corneum.

Keratin is not soluble in the usual protein solvents and is not digested by pepsin or trypsin. It has an unusually high cystine content, which imparts the characteristic odor to burning skin, hair and feathers, and probably contributes to the toughness of keratin by forming disulfide bridges between adjacent polypeptide chains. There are apparently two types of keratin, differing in amino acid composition and solubilities, viz., "eukeratin" and "pseudokeratin," the former containing much more cystine and predominating in the hair and nails, the latter predominating in the epidermis. Skin also contains other scleroproteins, i.e., collagen, and smaller amounts of elastin and reticulin.

LIPIDS. The small amount of extractable lipids of the skin includes neutral fat, phospholipids, cholesterol, and cholesterol esters. Steroids comprise about 20 per cent of the lipid material, one important substance in this class being 7-dehydrocholesterol (provitamin D_3), which is apparently formed from cholesterol in the intestinal mucosa and, in the skin, is transformed to vitamin D_3 by the action of ultraviolet light (p. 149).

MISCELLANEOUS. Skin contains a small amount of glycogen and most of the inorganic elements present in other tissues. Certain toxic heavy metals, e.g., arsenic, accumulate in the skin, hair and nails when abnormally large amounts have entered the body.

PIGMENT. The term "melanin" is applied to the main pigment of the skin, hair, and choroid of the eye. It is not a chemical entity, but includes a variety of yellow, red, brown, or black pigments produced by polymerization of oxidation products of tyrosine and dihydroxyphenyl compounds (dopa, epinephrine, catechol, etc.) (p. 554) to relatively insoluble substances of high molecular weight. In some cases they occur in rather firm combination with tissue proteins (melanoproteins). They contain C, H, N, O, and often S, although the latter may be in the amino acids of the bound protein rather than in the pigment itself.

Melanin is formed in a specialized cell, the melanocyte (melanophore; chromatophore), present in the deeper layers of the epidermis (also in hair and choroid). It is produced perhaps in cytoplasmic granules (mitochondria) in the form of rods (dark) or spheres (light). The depth of color depends on the degree of oxidation, the quantity of melanin and its dispersion and form of aggregation (i.e., rods or spheres). Partial or complete absence of this pigment (albinism) occurs as a recessive trait, in which melanocytes (which contain the enzyme tyrosinase) are absent from the skin, hair, and choroid.

The formation of melanin from tyrosine, catalyzed by the copper-containing enzyme, tyrosinase, is indicated elsewhere (p. 554). Normally, this enzyme is present in the skin (melanophores) in a partially inhibited state. This physiological inhibition may be due to (1) reducing substances, such as ascorbic acid or glutathione, or (2) copper-binding substances, such as organic compounds containing sulfhydryl groups (cysteine, glutathione). The increase in pigmentation which follows exposure to the sun (ultraviolet light) is apparently due to acceleration of the tyrosine-tyrosinase and "dopa"-tyrosinase reactions, the —SH groups which inhibit the enzyme being inactivated (oxidized) by the ionizing radiation. A similar mechanism (destruction of SH groups) may be involved in the pigmentation which occurs at the site of inflammatory skin lesions.

Androgens and estrogens cause pigmentation in certain specific areas, e.g., nipples, areolae, scrotum, apparently by direct action on melanocytes in these regions, the mechanism being unknown. In the frog, the "melanophore-expanding" hormone of the pituitary (p. 703) causes darkening of the skin by expanding the cutaneous melanocytes. These cells in mammals cannot undergo such changes; the function of this hormone in mammalian species is not clear. The increase in cutaneous (and mucosal) pigment (melanin) in subjects with adrenocortical insufficiency (Addison's disease) suggests that adrenal cortical hormones influence melanin production. However, their function in this connection is obscure; similar pigmentation does not occur in adrenalectomized animals.

Increased pigmentation may occur at the site of skin lesions in niacin deficiency (pellagra) (p. 187) and ascorbic acid deficiency (scurvy) (p. 145). This may result from inflammation with local destruction of SH groups and consequent increase in tyrosinase activity. Depigmentation of hair and skin has been reported in children **with multiple vitamin** deficiencies, normal pigmentation being restored by administration of liver extract and a liberal diet. Similar depigmentation occurs in certain species maintained on diets deficient in pantothenic acid (p. 196), *p*-aminobenzoic acid (p. 210), biotin (p. 200), tyrosine, and copper.

NERVOUS TISSUE

The chemical composition of nervous tissue differs in different portions of the nervous system and in different regions of the same organ. In general, the white matter has a higher solid content than the gray matter (30 per cent versus 15 per cent), owing chiefly to a larger amount of lipid material. The water content tends to decrease with age. Disregarding regional differences, the approximate average chemical composition of the adult brain is indicated in Table 63.

LIPIDS. One of the characteristic features of the chemical composition of nervous tissue is its high content of lipids, particularly phosphatides, in which it is richer than any other organ. The other lipids include galactolipids (p. 34), sulfolipids (p. 34), and cholesterol (p. 35). The fatty acid components are largely of the C-16 to C-24 series (even number) (p. 30), chiefly stearic and oleic, but also linoleic and arachidonic. Many are relatively highly unsaturated, especially in the spinal cord.

In the brain (beef), the phosphatides are partitioned approximately as follows: cephalin, 55 per cent; lecithin, 25 per cent; sphingomyelin, 20 per cent. The designation, "cephalin," includes phosphatides with different nitrogenous components; e.g., about 75 per cent of their amino nitrogen is represented by ethanolamine and about 25 per cent by serine; about 50 per cent of their non-amino nitrogen is represented by choline, the remainder being unidentified. Inositol-containing phosphatides comprise about 25 per cent of the cephalin fraction of ox brain. Sphingomyelin is a prominent constituent of myelin sheaths; it is present in nerves in higher concentration than in the brain or cord. The white matter of the central nervous system is richer than the gray matter in total lipid (65 per cent versus 35 per cent of the dry weight), phosphatide (40 per cent versus 25 per cent), and cholesterol, but contains less sphingomyelin and a smaller proportion of unsaturated fatty acids. Medullated fibers contain more galactolipid than phospholipid; the reverse is the case in non-medullated fibers.

The lipid (and protein) content of the brain and cord varies with age and the state of development. During the first several weeks of life the water content decreases and the solids increase, due chiefly to an increase in lipid and protein. The increase in phosphatide is associated with myelinization of axons (insulating lipid material). After 50 years of life, phosphatides decrease (especially unsaturated) and cholesterol increases.

PROTEINS. Relatively little detailed information is available regarding the proteins of nervous tissue. Perhaps the most characteristic is a scleroprotein, "neurokeratin," which is a component of neuroglia fibrils (supporting tissue). It contains less arginine than the keratin of the epidermis. Nerve cells contain nucleoproteins of both desoxyribose ("nucleohistone") and pentose types. The latter (in the cytoplasm) apparently decrease when nerves are stimulated and may be intimately related to nerve and cerebral function. Globulins and collagen ("neurogelatin") are also present. White matter contains somewhat more protein than gray matter (8.5 per cent versus 7.5 per cent) but protein comprises about 50 per cent of the dry weight of the latter and about 30 per cent of that of the former.

The increase in solids in brain tissue during the first several weeks of life, as indicated above, is due in part to an increase in protein. This is a reflection of the increase in enzymes and other proteins during this period of increasing metabolic activity and functional and morphological development.

Table 63. Average Chemical Composition of Adult Brain

	WHITE MATTER (%)	GRAY MATTER (%)
Water..................	70	85
Solids..................	30	15
Total lipid..............	20	2.5
Cholesterol.............	5	1.2
Phosphatide.............	5.5	0.5
Glycolipid..............	9.5	0.8
Protein.................	8.5	7.5
Extractives.............	1.0	3.0

CARBOHYDRATES. Glucose is present in somewhat lower concentration than in the blood plasma, and is by far the most important, virtually the only, foodstuff of nervous tissue. The brain contains small amounts of glycogen (about 90 mg./100 grams) and the cord somewhat more (0.2–0.3 gram/100 grams). The functions of these carbohydrates are considered below. Galactose is present, in cerebrosides, presumably serving a structural (non-metabolic) function as a component of insulating and other lipids.

ENZYMES. Nervous tissue contains all enzymes required for glycolysis and aerobic metabolism of glucose and also systems for glycogenesis and glycogenolysis (glucose $\rightleftharpoons$ glycogen). Fructokinase has not been demonstrated. Important enzymes not involved in the utilization of glucose include cholinesterase (p. 228) and carbonic anhydrase (p. 241).

MISCELLANEOUS. The so-called "extractives" of nervous tissue are similar to those of muscle and other tissues, with quantitative differences. Acetylcholine (p. 704) is of particular importance. It is apparently formed by stimulated nerve cells and is released at neuronal surfaces, playing a fundamental role in the transmission of nerve impulses. Sympathin is a substance formed in sympathetic nerve fibers on stimulation, having a biological action resembling that of epinephrine.

FOODSTUFFS OF NERVOUS TISSUE. Glucose is the chief if not indeed the only physiological source of energy available for nerve cell function. Lactate and pyruvate, which obviously are produced and utilized in the course of metabolism of glucose, are less effective than the latter when administered, owing perhaps to relative impermeability of the "blood-brain barrier" to these substances. The same is true of hexose-mono- and di-phosphates. Glutamic acid, which is metabolized by brain tissue *in vitro*, is not utilized by it when administered *in vivo*, owing also perhaps to failure to penetrate the "blood-brain barrier." Fatty acids cannot be utilized by nervous tissue as a source of energy, nor can ketone bodies (except acetoacetate, somewhat).

This virtual dependence on glucose for energy is the basis for the development of striking neurological manifestations (convulsions, coma) rather promptly after the blood glucose concentration falls to a low level. The cerebral glycogen falls during hypoglycemia, indicating that it may be drawn upon in this emergency, although it is not affected by other factors which profoundly influence liver glycogen, e.g., starvation, epinephrine, phlorizin, etc.

The brain exhibits another peculiarity in carbohydrate metabolism in that CO_2 production (i.e., glucose oxidation) is not diminished after pancreatectomy. Moreover, it does not respond to administration of anterior pituitary extracts by decreased glucose utilization, as do others tissues (p. 424). This may be due to failure of the "diabetogenic" pituitary factor to pass the "blood-brain barrier."

MUSCLE

Apart from its important structural and mechanical functions, muscle tissue plays a significant role in the total metabolism of the organism by virtue of the fact that it comprises about 40 per cent of the body mass. At rest, about 50 per cent, and during strenuous exercise about 75 per cent or more, of the total metabolism (as gaged by oxygen consumption) is due to muscle activity.

The three types of muscle, skeletal (striated), smooth, and cardiac, exhibit many points of similarity in chemical composition, but also certain rather characteristic points of difference, which may be of physiological significance. However, differences exist also in the same type of muscle in different parts of the body and in comparable muscles in different species. The significance of many aspects of these variations in chemical composition is not clearly understood, and in several particulars available quantitative data for human muscle are either lacking or unsatisfactory.

MUSCLE PROTEINS. Proteins comprise about 20 per cent of muscle tissue (weight) and about 80 per cent of its solid content. They may be classified, according to their location, as intracellular (fibrils and sarcoplasm) and extracellular (stroma). The latter are connective tissue proteins (p. 712), e.g., collagen, elastin. Interest is centered particularly in the intracellular proteins, which are intimately concerned with the functional activity of muscle. The most important of these are: (1) in the fibrils, (a) actin and (b) myosin; (2) in the sarcoplasm, (a) "myogen," (b) "globulin X," and (c) myoglobin. Actin and myosin are involved in the contractile process; "myogen" is a heterogeneous fraction which probably consists largely of enzymes; the functional significance of "globulin X" is not known; myoglobin probably acts as an oxygen-carrier similar to hemoglobin.

CONTRACTILE ELEMENT: ACTIN AND MYOSIN (P. 411). These two proteins, present in the muscle fibril, combine to form actomyosin, the contractile unit, which has globulin characteristics. Together, they comprise 40–60 per cent of the total muscle protein. Actin exists in two forms: (1) G-actin, a globular protein of relatively low viscosity, which undergoes linear polymerization to (2) F-actin, a fibrous (linear) protein of high viscosity. The latter has a strong affinity for myosin, with which it combines in a weight ratio of approximately 1 (actin): 3 (myosin) to form F-actomyosin. Contraction results from the action of ATP on F-actomyosin in the presence of proper concentrations of inorganic ions. The nature of these proteins and of the contractile process is considered in detail elsewhere (p. 409). A small amount of an ATP-ase is apparently intimately associated with myosin.

SARCOPLASMAL PROTEINS. Few of the proteins of the sarcoplasm have been as completely characterized, chemically or functionally, as have those of the myofibrils. So far as is known, none of them participates directly in the structural changes of the process of contraction. However, certain of them are known to represent biologically active and important components, e.g., enzymes, which are fundamentally concerned with the vital activity of and energy production by the muscle cells.

MYOGEN. This term is applied to a heterogeneous fraction which comprises about 20 per cent of the muscle proteins, present in the sarcoplasm, and apparently unable to enter the fibril. At least two separate components have been isolated, designated "myoalbumin" and "myogen fibrin," respectively. It is believed that this protein fraction consists largely if not entirely of enzymes, among which the following have been identified: triosephosphate isomerase, aldolase, triosephosphate dehydrogenase, phosphorylase.

Other enzymes present in the sarcoplasm include: those involved in glycolysis (in addition to the above mentioned) and aerobic carbohydrate metabolism; those of the cytochrome system; flavoproteins; pyridinoproteins; an ATP-ase which differs from that associated with myosin; myokinase, et al.

GLOBULIN. This fraction, comprising 10–20 per cent of the total muscle protein, has globulin characteristics. Its functional significance is not known.

MYOGLOBIN (MUSCLE HEMOGLOBIN). Myoglobin, like hemoglobin, is a ferrous protoporphyrin globin complex (p. 110). It is present in the sarcoplasm in relatively low concentration (about 0.1–0.2 per cent in skeletal muscle), which, however, varies in different muscles (highest in myocardium) and in different species, being related apparently to the level of activity. In contrast to hemoglobin, which has a molecular weight of 66,800, and four iron atoms (i.e., four heme groups) per molecule, myoglobin has a molecular weight of 16,700 and one iron atom (i.e., one heme group) per molecule.

Myoglobin differs slightly from hemoglobin in its absorption spectrum and rather strikingly in its oxygen dissociation curve, its affinity for oxygen at relatively low pO_2 levels being considerably greater than that of hemoglobin. For example, at 40 mm. Hg pO_2, myoglobin is 60 per cent saturated and hemoglobin 38 per cent. It may therefore provide a temporary reserve supply of oxygen under conditions of unduly prolonged restriction of circulation through a contracted muscle, or of excessive removal of oxygen from hemoglobin. It is interesting in this connection that its affinity for oxygen is intermediate between that of hemoglobin and of cytochrome oxidase. Its affinity for carbon monoxide is lower than that of hemoglobin.

CARBOHYDRATE. The glycogen content of muscle varies considerably in different muscles, and under different conditions of activity and nutrition. Ranging from 0.4–1.8 per cent (usually 0.5–1.0 per cent) in the resting state (skeletal muscle), it may approach zero during prolonged, strenuous muscular exertion. It is usually included among the "muscle extractives" (p. 725), although only a minor fraction is extractable with hot water or cold trichloracetic acid, the greater part (65 per cent) being bound in some manner to proteins, particularly myosin ("desmoglycogen"). Muscle glycogen is derived from the blood glucose. In its aerobic (to CO_2 and H_2O) and anaerobic (to lactic acid) degradation, it serves as the main source of high-energy phosphate bonds for resynthesis of adequate amounts of ATP (and phosphocreatine), depleted during the process of contraction (p. 413).

Lactic acid, the end-product of anaerobic metabolism of glycogen (and of glucose), is present in resting muscle in low concentration (0.02 per cent). At rest, or during moderate exercise, it is probable that the supply of oxygen to the muscles is adequate to provide for aerobic metabolism of carbohydrate; i.e., the bulk of the pyruvic acid formed enters the tricarboxylic acid cycle and relatively little lactic acid is produced (p. 414). However, during sudden strenuous exercise, particularly in untrained subjects, the rate of breakdown of glycogen exceeds the capacity of the muscles to oxidize pyruvic acid, owing to temporary inability of the circulation to meet the increased metabolic requirement for oxygen. Under such conditions, increased amounts of lactic acid are produced (reaching concentrations of 0.25 per cent or higher in muscle) and pass into the blood stream, with consequent rise in the blood lactic acid concentration (p. 414).

In common with other tissues, muscle contains glucose in approximately the same concentration as in the blood plasma, per unit of water content (i.e., about 50 mg./100 grams muscle). There are also small amounts of intermediates in carbohydrate metabolism, e.g., various hexose- and triosephosphates, pyruvate and Krebs cycle intermediates.

LIPIDS. The lipids of muscle include neutral fat, phospholipids (phosphatides), glycolipids, cholesterol, and cholesterol esters. The quantity varies widely in different muscles and in comparable muscles in different species; e.g., the total lipid of striated muscle of the chicken (white muscle) averages about 7 per cent (of dry weight) and of the hog about 22 per cent. These differences are due mainly, but not entirely, to differences in amount of neutral fat. This is located largely in fat cells in the interstitial tissue, and resembles the other body depot (storage) fats in its chemical constitution.

Although the non-fat or "essential" lipids vary in different muscles and species (e.g., average 5 per cent [dry weight] in chicken, 9 per cent in frog), the comparative constancy of their quantitative distribution permits certain generalizations which may have functional significance. Phospholipids comprise the bulk of this fraction, as in other tissues. In most species, they constitute from 3 to 7 per cent (dry weight) of muscle tissue, whereas the glycolipid content is usually below 2 per cent and cholesterol below 0.7 per cent. In most muscles, the phospholipids consist almost entirely of lecithins and cephalins, the former usually predominating somewhat; sphingomyelin is present in small amounts. Human myocardium, for example, gives the following average values (per cent of dry weight): total phospholipid 7, lecithin 4.5, cephalin 2.2, sphingomyelin 0.3. Heart muscle usually contains more than skeletal and smooth muscle. In general, the phospholipid content varies with the level of habitual activity of the muscle; e.g., it is higher in muscles of active animals than in corresponding muscles of sedentary animals, even of the same species. Muscle phospholipids contain a higher percentage of unsaturated fatty acids than those of other tissues, averaging 65 to 75 per cent of the total fatty acids (e.g., liver about 60 per cent).

With few exceptions, cholesterol is largely in the free state. The quantity is apparently related to the degree of automatic activity of the muscle; e.g., in man, smooth muscle (0.8 per cent dry weight) invariably contains more than skeletal muscle (0.3 per cent), with heart muscle (0.5 per cent) occupying an intermediate position. Skeletal muscle generally contains more glycolipid than cholesterol, whereas this relationship is usually reversed in smooth muscle. Because of the fact that the cholesterol content of smooth muscle is invariably higher than that of skeletal muscle, whereas their phospholipid contents are approximately the same, the phospholipid : cholesterol ratio is lower in smooth (5 : 1) than in skeletal (10–16 : 1) muscle. The significance of these relationships is not known.

MUSCLE EXTRACTIVES. The term "muscle extractives" is applied to the large and heterogeneous group of organic (nitrogenous and non-nitrogenous) and inorganic substances that go into solution when muscle is extracted with boiling water. The proteins are coagulated and lipids may be largely separated from the aqueous solution. Commercial beef extract or bouillon is a concentrate of beef muscle extractives. It will suffice here merely to enumerate the most important of these substances, their chemistry and functional significance having been discussed in detail elsewhere.

NITROGENOUS. These include: adenosine tri- and diphosphates (ATP, ADP), adenylic acid (AMP), and inosinic acid (p. 567); phosphocreatine (p. 413); creatine (p. 521), and creatinine (p. 521); acetylcholine (p. 455); histamine (p. 526); di- and triphosphopyridine nucleotides (DPN, TPN; coenzymes I and II); amino acids; two dipeptides with high buffering capacities, but otherwise of unknown function, carnosine (β-alanylhistidine), and anserine (methylcarnosine) (p. 526); thiamine (p. 171).

NON-NITROGENOUS. These include: glucose, glycogen, and intermediates in their anaerobic and aerobic degradation (p. 388 ff.); ascorbic acid (p. 141); inositol (p. 212); acetoacetic acid.

INORGANIC. These include: K, Na, Mg, Ca, and Fe, in descending order of concentration; Mn, Co, Cu, Ni, and Zn, in trace amounts; HPO_4, Cl, SO_4. The concentrations of these ions are discussed elsewhere (p. 305) in connection with the electrolyte composition of intracellular fluid. The higher concentration of Na than of Mg in muscle extract is due to the inclusion of extracellular as well as intracellular components. In addition to the important functions of these ions in regulating osmotic and "acid-base" equilibrium, a proper balance between the cations is required for the maintenance of normal muscle irritability (p. 599) and contractility (p. 599), and enzyme functions (pp. 223, 224).

BIBLIOGRAPHY

Annual Review of Biochemistry.

Bloor, W. R.: Biochemistry of the Fatty Acids, New York, Reinhold Publishing Corporation, 1943.

Chambers, R. et al.: Symposium on structure in relation to cellular function, Ann. New York Acad. Sc. 50:815–1012, 1950.

Brookhaven Symposium on The Chemistry and Physiology of the Nucleus, New York, Academic Press, Inc., 1952.

Himwich, H. E.: Brain Metabolism and Cerebral Disorders, Baltimore, Williams & Wilkins Company, 1951.

Hogeboom, G. H.: Separation and properties of cell components, Federation Proc. 10:640, 1951.

Macy Foundation Conferences on Metabolic Interrelations, I, III, and IV, New York, Josiah Macy Foundation, 1949, 1951, 1952.

Mommaerts, W. F. H. M.: Muscular Contraction, New York, Interscience Publishers, Inc., 1950.

Page, I. H.: Chemistry of the Brain, Springfield, Ill., Charles C Thomas, Publisher, 1937.

Pollister, A. W. et al.: Localization of substances in cells, Federation Proc. 10:629, 1951.

Shohl, A. T.: Mineral Metabolism, New York, Reinhold Publishing Corporation, 1939.

27

MILK

The importance of the chemical composition of milk arises out of the fact that it is the sole foodstuff of young mammals and should therefore provide for adequate nutrition during this critical period. As secreted, it is a nearly ideal food for human infants, being nutritionally inadequate only in iron and vitamin D (perhaps also copper).

Its composition varies considerably in different species, in different breeds of the same species, in different periods of lactation, and under different conditions of diet and hormonal secretion. In the breast, developed during pregnancy through the action of estrogen and progesterone, lactation is induced shortly before the onset of labor by the action of prolactin (p. 699), secreted by the anterior pituitary.

The fluid secreted during the few days before and for one to two weeks following parturition is called "colostrum." It differs from later milk in having a somewhat yellow color, more protein and mineral elements, and less fat and carbohydrate. The higher protein content is due mainly to the presence of globulins which are apparently identical with the γ-globulins of the blood plasma (main antibody fraction). In contrast to later milk, the protein of colostrum coagulates on boiling. The protein content falls and the fat and carbohydrate increase steadily to reach the true milk levels at three to five weeks postpartum.

PROTEINS. Milk contains three important proteins (casein, lactalbumin, and lactoglobulin), the amounts and relative proportions of which differ in different species. The quantity of protein (and of mineral elements) varies directly, although not strictly quantitatively, with the rate of growth of the newborn, i.e., inversely as the time required to double its birth weight. The protein content of human (average 1.5 per cent) and cow's (average 4.0 per cent) milk is indicated in Table 64, this being one of the most important practical points of difference in the milk of these species. Casein comprises about 85 per cent of the protein of cow's milk and about 65 per cent of that of human milk. The amount of lactalbumin in cow's milk is two to ten times that of lactoglobulin.

Probably none of these proteins is a homogeneous substance. A β-lactoglobulin has been isolated and its amino acid composition determined. All are quite complete proteins, nutritionally, with an unusually high content of essential amino acids.

Casein, the principal milk protein, is a phosphoprotein (0.7 per cent P), with an isoelectric point of pH 4.6. At the usual pH of fresh milk (6.6–6.9, owing to acid phosphates), it is probably present as a salt (calcium caseinate) and precipitates on acidification, as in souring (lactic acid fermentation, p. 272). The buffering capacity of milk is due largely to the presence of protein, phosphates, bicarbonate, and citrate. Casein is precipitated by mineral acids and by saturating neutral solutions with NaCl or $MgSO_4$. It does not coagulate on boiling, which, however, results in the formation of a film, consisting of a combination of casein and calcium salts. This film does not develop in acidified milk (e.g., sour milk).

Under the influence of milk-clotting (curdling) enzymes, e.g., rennin (p. 262), pepsin (p. 261), chymotrypsin (p. 263), casein is hydrolyzed to soluble paracasein, which, in the presence of Ca^{++}, is converted to insoluble casein (calcium paracaseinate), or "milk curd." The residual clear fluid is called "whey." The casein of cow's milk is more readily precipitated by acid and coagulated by rennin than that of human milk. The curd formed in human milk is more flocculent and more readily digested.

Table 64. Composition of Milk

		SOLID	PROTEIN	CARB	FAT	ASH	CA	P	MG	NA	K	CL
			(grams/100 ml.)						(mg./100 ml.)			
Human	Max.		2.5	8.0	8.0	0.3						
	Min.		1.0	4.5	1.0	0.2						
	Av.	12.5	1.5	7.0	4.0	0.25	40	30	5	130	60	40
Cow	Max.		6.0	6.0	6.5	1.2						
	Min.		2.0	2.0	1.5	0.3						
	Av.	13.0	4.0	5.0	4.0	0.7	120	90	20	50	30	110

LIPIDS. The lipids in milk are largely triglycerides (fats), with smaller amounts of cholesterol (0.01 per cent) and phospholipids (0.1 per cent). The average concentration in human and cow's milk is approximately the same, although there are wide variations (Table 64). The fat content of cow's milk (butter fat) varies considerably in different breeds and under different dietary conditions. The fats are present in a rather coarse emulsion; this is largely responsible for the white color of milk, which is contributed to also by the presence of casein in colloidal solution.

The fats of human milk differ from those of cow's milk in their fatty acid components. Oleic acid predominates in both (30–35 per cent of total), and fatty acids of the C_{12} to C_{18} series comprise 80–90 per cent of the total. However, about 10 per cent of human milk fatty acids are highly unsaturated (e.g., linoleic, linolenic), as compared to about 0.5 per cent in cow's milk. Moreover, human milk fats contain no short-chain fatty acids (i.e., below decanoic, C_{10} series), whereas these comprise 5–10 per cent of the fatty acids of cow's milk (e.g., caprylic, caproic, butyric acids). In this respect, butter fat (cow) differs strikingly from other body fats.

Available evidence (in cattle) supports the belief that milk fat is synthesized in the lactating breast, chiefly from glucose, which is supplied from the blood. It is contributed to by the blood fats or other lipids probably to only a limited extent, if at all. The fatty acids, particularly the short-chain acids (cow), are synthesized from 2-carbon precursors ("active acetate"), as in other tissues (p. 447), derived mainly from glucose. The glycerol component of the milk fats, too, probably originates largely from glucose (via dihydroxyacetone phosphate, p. 405). It may, however, together with some of the fatty acids, be derived from glycerides of the blood plasma, but to a limited extent. Insulin stimulates the synthesis of fatty acids (and of fats) by the lactating breast. The fact that the R.Q. exceeds 1.0 under these circumstances suggests conversion of carbohydrate to fat (p. 336).

CARBOHYDRATE. Lactose (milk sugar) is the characteristic carbohydrate of milk. Human milk (average 7 per cent) contains more than cow's milk (average 5 per cent) (Table 64). Its galactose component is formed by the alveolar cells of the lactating breast from blood glucose, these two sugars being then converted to lactose (p. 418).

On standing, milk undergoes souring, as a result of the production of lactic acid from lactose by fermentation (p. 272), owing to the action of bacteria (e.g., Streptococcus lactis). As indicated elsewhere (p. 728), the incident increase in acidity causes precipitation of casein.

INORGANIC CONSTITUENTS. The inorganic content of cow's milk (average 0.7 per cent) is about three times that of human milk (average 0.25 per cent) (Table 64). Both contain inadequate amounts of iron and copper for normal nutrition, the iron deficiency being particularly important in contributing to the development of anemia in infants. The high calcium content is of the greatest importance nutritionally, inasmuch as, for practical purposes, milk is the only food which can provide this element in amounts adequate for normal nutrition, even in adult life (p. 617).

VITAMINS. Under satisfactory dietary conditions, milk contains adequate amounts of vitamin A, and also carotenes (provitamins A). It is, however, rather low in B vitamins, except riboflavin and pantothenic acid, and is a poor source of vitamin D. The vitamin C content, which is relatively low in cow's milk, is further reduced by pasteurization (p. 143). The average vitamin composition of human and cow's milk is indicated in Table 65. In most instances (q.v.) these values may be influenced considerably by the vitamin intake.

Table 65. Vitamins in Milk

	A (μg.)	D (I.U.)	C (mg.)	THIAMINE (μg.)	RIBOFLAVIN (μg.)	NIACIN (μg.)	PYRIDOX-INE (μg.)	PANTO-THENIC ACID (μg.)
Human	50	5.0	4.5	15	45	180	10	200
Cow	35	2.5	2.0	45	200	80	50	350

MISCELLANEOUS. Cow's milk contains variable quantities of vegetable pigments (dietary), including riboflavin (formerly designated lactoflavin) (p. 177), carotenes (p. 131), and a small amount of xanthophylls. Vegetable pigments may also be found at times in human milk, the riboflavin content of which is usually much lower than that of cow's milk.

Certain enzymes are present, including proteases, lipase, amylase, galactase, catalase, peroxidase, phosphatase, and xanthine oxidase. The fact that the phosphatase is destroyed by pasteurization may be employed as a means of differentiating raw from pasteurized milk.

Certain foreign substances in the blood plasma may enter the milk. These include volatile oils of certain foods (e.g., onion, garlic), drugs (e.g., sulfonamides, salicylates, morphine, alcohol), and inorganic elements (e.g., As, Bi, Fe, I, Hg, Pb).

28

BLOOD AND OTHER BODY FLUIDS

BLOOD

In so highly organized an aggregation of cells as the animal body, provision must be made for maintaining a certain degree of constancy of the immediate environment of these cells, i.e., the interstitial fluid which surrounds them, in the face of continual exposure to the entrance of variable amounts of exogenous (foodstuffs) and endogenous (metabolites) materials. This phenomenon of regulation, termed "homeostasis," is accomplished through the medium of the circulating blood, which carries nutritive materials (including oxygen) to the cells and waste products (including carbon dioxide) to excretory organs, and distributes other products of cell metabolism throughout the body for utilization in or action upon cells other than those in which they originate. This must be accomplished with a minimum degree of variation in the pH of the extracellular fluids, under widely varying conditions of metabolic activity (buffer action of blood, p. 314). From a biochemical standpoint, these transport functions of blood are of paramount importance.

The plasma proteins (p. 501) play an important role in regulating the distribution of water between the intravascular and extravascular compartments of the extracellular fluid, fluid exchanges across capillary walls (p. 310), and filtration through the renal glomeruli (p. 754).

The ability of the body to maintain a rather constant temperature is due largely to the high specific heat of water. Heat produced in the course of metabolic reactions in the cells is distributed throughout the body fluids via the blood stream, the temperature in various tissues thereby tending to be equalized. Circulation of the blood at the body surface (skin, pulmonary alveoli) permits loss of excess heat by radiation and evaporation (p. 296), an essential feature of the mechanism of temperature regulation.

The blood contains factors which form the basis of certain of the

731

body's defenses against invading injurious agents. These include certain of the formed elements (granulocytes, monocytes) and antibodies (mainly γ-globulins, p. 506) against microorganisms, toxins, and foreign proteins.

The phenomenon of blood coagulation (p. 734) may be regarded as a protective mechanism against undue loss of blood following disruption of the continuity of blood vessel walls, resulting from trauma to which they are frequently subjected.

GENERAL CHARACTERISTICS. As it exists within the vascular system, blood consists of formed elements (erythrocytes, leukocytes, platelets) and a fluid portion, plasma, which contains a large number of organic and inorganic substances in solution. Apart from oxygen, which is carried virtually exclusively by hemoglobin (erythrocytes) (p. 288), and CO_2, which is carried in both plasma and erythrocytes (p. 292), the important transport functions of the blood are served by the plasma. With the exception of considerations of respiration (O_2 and CO_2), biochemical interest is focused, therefore, on the composition of this medium, which reflects the adequacy of the homeostatic mechanisms of the body in health, and, frequently, disturbances in specific directions in disease.

The in vivo fluid state of the blood can be maintained in vitro only by interfering with the mechanism of coagulation, which otherwise begins to operate as soon as the blood comes in contact with most foreign surfaces (e.g., glass, metal). This may be accomplished by defibrination, i.e., by stirring freshly shed blood with a glass rod, to which the fibrin adheres as it forms. More commonly, an anticoagulant is added. Those employed most frequently for purposes of securing whole blood or plasma for examination act by removing Ca^{++} ions from solution (p. 735), by formation of either insoluble calcium salts (oxalate, fluoride) or an undissociable calcium complex (citrate). Addition of heparin prevents coagulation of blood (p. 736); it inhibits conversion of prothrombin to thrombin (antiprothrombin action), and also inactivates thrombin (antithrombin action). The formed elements can readily be separated from the plasma by centrifugation. For analysis of blood gases (O_2, CO_2), the blood must be collected anaerobically (e.g., under mercury). The term "hematocrit value" is applied to the volume (in per cent) of packed red blood cells in a blood sample (usually 10 ml.) centrifuged under standardized conditions (Table 66).

Coagulation (p. 734) is essentially a plasma phenomenon, in which the platelets participate, however. The formed elements (erthyrocytes, leukocytes, platelets) are trapped in the meshwork of the jelly-like fibrin clot, which, under normal conditions, shrinks on standing (retraction), squeezing out a straw-colored fluid termed "serum," which may be obtained by subsequent centrifugation. Serum differs from plasma chemically chiefly in that it contains no fibrinogen, which has been transformed to fibrin in the process of coagulation. With this exception, for all practical purposes, serum and plasma may be used interchangeably for chemical studies. Plasma obtained with such anti-coagulants as sodium or potassium oxalate, fluoride, and citrate is obviously unsuitable for determinations of sodium, potassium, or calcium. Serum is usually employed routinely for such studies and, indeed, for many others, e.g., other electrolytes, pH, proteins, lipids, hormones, vitamins.

The total circulating blood and plasma volumes are indicated in Table 66. The values for women are about 7 per cent lower than for men. The methods employed for these determinations are outlined elsewhere (p. 298).

Table 66. Miscellaneous Values for Venous Blood (Fasting)

	BLOOD	PLASMA	CELLS
Volume			
ml./kg.	63–80 (72)	35–45 (40)	
liters/sqM.	2.5–3.2 (2.9)	1.3–1.8 (1.5)	
pH	7.3–7.5 (7.4)	7.3–7.5 (7.4)	
Osmolar concentration (mOsM./liter)		320	
Specific gravity	1.052–1.061 (1.056)	1.022–1.031 (1.026)	1.095–1.107 (1.098)
Colloid osmotic pressure (mm. Hg)		20–35 (24)	
Hematocrit (% cells)	40–54 (47) 37–47 (42)		
Water content (%)	81–86 (83)	93–95 (94)	(65)

BLOOD GROUPS; SPECIFIC SUBSTANCES. Human blood can be classified into four main groups and several sub-groups on the basis of the presence (or absence) of specific substances in the erythrocytes, termed "agglutinogens." These are nitrogenous, neutral, heteropoly-saccharides, containing amino acids or peptides as well as car-bohydrate groups (p. 18); they are, therefore, related to the mucopolysaccharides, containing N-acetyl-D-glucosamine, among other components. There are two major agglutinogens, designated A and B, and other minor ones, including M, N, P, and Rh. The blood group (or type) is determined by the nature of the specific agglu-tinogens (or their absence) in the red blood cells, a characteristic that is transmitted in Mendelian fashion as a genetic dominant. These substances resemble the type specific polysaccharides present in certain bacteria (e.g., pneumococci). The A and B agglutinogens react specifically with α and β isoagglutinins, respectively, globulin in nature (p. 506), present in the blood plasma. Erythrocytes containing A agglutinogen are agglutinated ("clumped") by plasma containing α isoagglutinin. Consequently, if a given agglutinogen occurs in the cells the corresponding isoagglutinin is never present in the plasma. These characteristics are of obvious importance in determining the compatibility of blood for transfusion and also in medicolegal situations involving questions of paternity. The group specific substances are present in practically all body cells and in certain body fluids (e.g., saliva, gastric juice).

CHEMISTRY OF BLOOD COAGULATION

The process of blood coagulation is a vital mechanism of defense against loss of blood in the event of disruption of the continuity of blood vessels incident to trauma to which all organisms are subjected from time to time. Defense against abnormal blood loss involves: (1) constriction and retraction of blood vessels; (2) agglutination of platelets; (3) coagulation (clotting) of plasma. We are concerned here only with the latter, which is accomplished by a series of coordinated chemical events.

The final and essential feature of the clotting process is the transformation of fibrinogen, a circulating plasma protein, to fibrin, the clot. A number of substances, most of which act as enzymes, are involved in preliminary reactions culminating in this final event. There is as yet no complete unanimity of opinion as to the identity of all of these factors nor as to their exact roles in the clotting process. In the main, however, the scheme presented here seems acceptable.

PLASMA FACTORS. The following plasma constituents participate in the clotting process: fibrinogen, prothrombin, calcium, plasma Ac-globulin (accelerator-globulin), and antihemophilia globulin.

(a) FIBRINOGEN. This is a fibrous protein (keratin-myosin group), having a molecular weight of about 460,000, with a high viscosity. It is produced in the hepatic polygonal cells and is present in the plasma in concentrations of 0.2 to 0.4 gram/100 ml. In the presence of thrombin, it undergoes irreversible polymerization to fibrin. The latter, too, is a protein of the keratin-myosin group, insoluble in plasma, which forms a clot composed of a dense meshwork of single and compound fibers. In the presence of an adequate number of normal platelets, this clot undergoes firm contraction. If the platelets are not normal, the clot is softer, jelly-like, less adhesive to surfaces, and relatively non-retractile.

$$\text{Fibrinogen} \xrightarrow{\text{Thrombin}} \text{Fibrin (clot)}$$

(*b*) PROTHROMBIN. This is apparently a glycoprotein (10–15 mg./100 ml. plasma), produced by the hepatic polygonal cells. Vitamin K is necessary for its formation (p. 165). The purest available preparations contain about 5 per cent carbohydrate and also glucosamine. Prothrombin may be regarded as a proenzyme which is activated by factors indicated below to form thrombin. The latter apparently has a chemical composition similar to that of prothrombin (molecular weight about 77,000). It acts as an enzyme in the transformation of fibrinogen to fibrin.

$$\text{Prothrombin} \xrightarrow[\substack{\text{Serum Ac-globulin} \\ \text{Platelet accelerator No. 1}}]{\substack{\text{Calcium} \\ \text{Thromboplastin}}} \text{Thrombin}$$

(*c*) PLASMA AC-GLOBULIN. This protein (accelerator-globulin) is present in plasma in minute amounts. It may be regarded as a proenzyme (inactive), which is activated by thrombin to form "serum Ac-globulin," an accelerator of coagulation, facilitating conversion of prothrombin to thrombin.

$$\underset{\text{(inactive)}}{\text{Plasma Ac-globulin}} \xrightarrow{\text{Thrombin}} \underset{\text{(active)}}{\text{Serum Ac-globulin}}$$

(*d*) CALCIUM IONS. Calcium ions act in the activation of prothrombin to form thrombin. *In vitro* coagulation of blood is most commonly prevented by addition of oxalate or fluoride, which removes calcium ions as insoluble salts, or of citrate, which removes calcium ions as undissociated calcium citrate.

(*e*) ANTIHEMOPHILIA GLOBULIN. This appears to be a plasma factor which acts with a derivative of lysed platelets to form a limited amount of thromboplastin, the most important activator of prothrombin.

TISSUE FACTOR. Tissues contain a substance or substances which accelerate blood coagulation. The active factor, originally called "thrombokinase," is now generally designated "thromboplastin." Lung and brain are the best sources. Thromboplastin acts, in conjunction with Ca^{++}, to activate prothrombin, forming thrombin. This reaction is speeded by serum Ac-globulin and platelet accelerator No. 1.

It appears to be a macromolecular lipoprotein, the lipid component being a complex mixture of cholesterol, fat, and phospholipid. It is regarded by some as a protein complex with cephalin or some other phosphatide. There is some question as to whether the lipids and proteins are in chemical or purely physical association.

PLATELET FACTORS. Platelets agglutinate and disintegrate when they come in contact with surfaces other than smooth, normal vascular endothelium (except water-repellent surfaces such as silicone). Upon lysis, apparently three substances are liberated.

1. A factor which, in conjunction with plasma antihemophilia globulin, forms a limited amount of thromboplastin.

2. Platelet accelerator No. 1, which, acting in conjunction with thromboplastin, Ca^{++}, and serum Ac-globulin, accelerates the transformation of prothrombin to thrombin.

3. Platelet accelerator No. 2, which accelerates the conversion of fibrinogen to fibrin by thrombin.

NATURAL INHIBITORS OF COAGULATION. Factors regarded as physiological inhibitors of coagulation include heparin, antithrombin, and antithromboplastin.

(a) HEPARIN. This substance was originally isolated from liver and, although it has not been identified in blood, is believed to be present in very small amounts. It belongs to the same group of substances as mucoitin-sulfuric acid (molecular weight 17,000), containing glucuronic acid, glucosamine, and about 10 per cent sulfur, present as ester sulfate. It is believed to be formed by mast cells and is rapidly destroyed in the body by the enzyme heparinase, therefore exerting a rather transient anticoagulant effect (few hours) upon single administration. It apparently acts at two points in the clotting mechanism: (1) it inhibits activation of prothrombin, a serum protein acting as an essential cofactor in this reaction; (2) it inactivates thrombin, a serum protein cofactor being required for this action also.

(b) ANTITHROMBIN. This is a substance present in plasma, associated with the albumin fraction, but not albumin. It inactivates thrombin.

(c) ANTITHROMBOPLASTIN. This is a lipid material which inactivates thromboplastin.

SUMMARY OF COAGULATION PROCESS. The following sequence of events occurs when tissue is injured and blood extravasates:

1. Injured tissues liberate thromboplastin.

2. Platelets agglutinate and disintegrate, releasing: (a) a substance reacting with plasma antihemophilia globulin to form thromboplastin; (b) accelerator factors 1 and 2.

3. Thromboplastin $+$ Ca^{++} $+$ platelet accelerator No. 1 causes slight conversion of prothrombin to thrombin.

4. This thrombin catalyzes the accelerator system, i.e., conversion of plasma Ac-globulin (inactive proenzyme) to serum Ac-globulin (active).

5. Thromboplastin $+$ Ca^{++} $+$ platelet accelerator No. 1 $+$ serum Ac-globulin causes accelerated conversion of prothrombin to thrombin.

6. Thrombin catalyzes the conversion of fibrinogen to fibrin (clot), the reaction being hastened by platelet accelerator No. 2.

The inhibitory influences of heparin, antithrombin, and antithromboplastin are overcome by adequate concentration of the clotting factors.

CHEMICAL COMPOSITION OF FORMED ELEMENTS

In contrast to the plasma, which serves as the main transport medium for nutrient materials, metabolites, vitamins, hormones, etc., the formed elements, apart from the respiratory functions of hemoglobin, have rather specific functions that are not intimately concerned in general metabolic processes. With the important exception of hemoglobin, therefore, general biochemical interest has been focused mainly upon the chemical constituents of the plasma rather than of the erythrocytes, leukocytes, and thrombocytes (platelets). Certain features of the chemical composition of the formed elements, however, have some bearing on their specialized functions, and will be reviewed briefly.

ERYTHROCYTES. The erythrocytes are not living cells in the strict sense. They contain no nucleic acids or mitochondria, cannot reproduce, and have no aerobic metabolism and no protein, fat, or carbohydrate synthetic activity. These substances and functions are lost upon conversion of normoblasts and reticulocytes to mature red blood cells. The erythrocytes' most important component, hemoglobin (p. 115), in contrast to the proteins of other cells, undergoes no degradation or resynthesis during the "life" of the cell (about one hundred and twenty days). The erythrocytes' chief function, due almost entirely to hemoglobin, lies in making possible the transport of required amounts of oxygen from the lungs to the tissues, and of carbon dioxide in the reverse direction, without undue fluctuation in the H^+ ion concentration of the blood (p. 315). The main functions of the other chemical constituents must therefore be directed toward the support of the respiratory functions of hemoglobin, the chemistry and metabolism of which are considered elsewhere (pp. 115, 588, 591).

Erythrocytes have a solid content of about 35 per cent, almost all of which is Hb (32 per cent). Most of the remaining 3 per cent is represented by proteins and lipids, which form the stromal meshwork in which the Hb is held, and which also concentrate on the cell surface as a limiting membrane (cell wall). This membrane is perfectly permeable to water and apparently to certain small organic molecules, e.g., glucose, urea, creatinine, which consequently exist in similar concentrations in the water of the plasma and erythrocytes. There is some question regarding the validity of this statement in the case of glucose. The membrane is freely permeable to certain monovalent anions (HCO_3^-, Cl^-, SCN^-, OH^-). Human erythrocytes contain virtually no calcium, and relatively little sodium, the predominant cations being potassium and magnesium. H^+ ions cross the membrane readily, Zn^{++} (influencing carbonic anhydrase activity) somewhat less freely, and K^+ still less so. The phosphate content (50 to 100 mg. per cent) is much higher than that of plasma, but only about 1 mg. per cent is inorganic phosphate, the remainder being organic. About one-half of the latter is triose-phosphate, about one-fourth each hexosephosphate and ATP, with traces of DPN and TPN. Phosphate apparently enters the cell by some active process, much more rapidly than it diffuses out, probably being utilized in phosphorylation reactions in the process of glycolysis, which apparently is the main source of energy for these cells.

The lipid content of the erythrocytes (450 to 700 mg./100 grams) is lower than that of plasma, owing chiefly to the virtual absence of neutral fat, but the glycolipid and phospholipid contents are higher. Moreover, the proportion of cephalins is greater than that of lecithins, the reverse of the situation in plasma. The cholesterol concentration (125 to 150 mg./100 grams) is lower than in plasma, all being in the free state in adults, whereas about 70 per cent of the plasma cholesterol is in the ester form.

Other organic constituents include glutathione and thioneine, which are not present in the plasma, amino acids (6 to 10 mg. amino acid N/100 grams), intermediate- and end-products of glycolysis (e.g., hexose- and triose-phosphates, lactic acid), and several enzymes. The latter include enzymes of the glycolytic system, catalase, peptidase, phosphatases, a more specific cholinesterase than that in plasma, carbonic anhydrase, which plays an important role in the mechanism of CO_2 transport (p. 317), and rhodanese, which catalyzes the transformation of cyanide to thiocyanate.

LEUKOCYTES. The chemical composition of these cells resembles that of other tissue cells. The predominating proteins are compound proteins, chiefly nucleoproteins. Lymphocytes contain relatively large amounts of γ-globulin, probably serving as a storage site for this protein (antibodies [p. 506]), which is liberated upon lysis of the cell. Granulocytes and monocytes have a high content of phosphatases and of glycolytic and proteolytic enzymes, the latter perhaps being related to the phagocytic action of these cells on bacteria and cellular debris. The cytoplasmic granules of granulocytes exhibit strong peroxidase activity, a fact which is utilized in the histochemical identification of this series of cells.

The 11-oxygenated adrenocortical hormones exert a striking influence on the production or destruction of eosinophils and lymphocytes, either depressing the former or accelerating the latter process. Administration of these hormones causes a prompt decrease in the number of these cells in the circulation and their continued administration results in virtually complete disappearance of lymphocytes from the tissues.

THROMBOCYTES (PLATELETS). These small particles of megakaryocytes contain proteins and relatively large amounts of phospholipids, much of which is cephalin. Upon lysis, they liberate three factors which participate in the mechanism of blood coagulation (p. 735).

CHEMICAL COMPOSITION OF BLOOD PLASMA

The blood plasma is the medium of transport of nutrient materials from the alimentary tract to the tissues, of metabolites from one tissue to another, of hormones from their organs of origin to target tissues, and of waste products from the sites of their production to excretory organs. Being in equilibrium with the interstitial fluid across the semipermeable capillary walls (p. 309), the chemical composition of the blood plasma may be regarded as representative of that of extracellular fluids generally, recognizing the existence of certain regional variations in the latter. As would be anticipated, studies of its chemical components have yielded valuable information on various aspects of normal and abnormal metabolism. Plasma (or whole blood) is used extensively clinically for such studies because of its accessibility and because the concentration of a given constituent reflects, although at times imperfectly, the state of metabolism of that substance, e.g., normal or abnormal formation, normal or abnormal utilization or excretion.

Development of technics that permit rapid quantitative determination of a number of substances in small volumes of blood has contributed enormously to diagnosis, prognosis, and treatment in virtually every clinical field. The availability of such procedures has also contributed in large measure to our present knowledge of the functional activities of various organs, e.g., the liver and kidneys, and the manner in which these functions may be altered in disease. A satisfactory understanding of the significance of deviations from the normal concentrations of plasma components is essential for modern clinical practice. Such abnormalities can be interpreted properly only on the basis of an understanding of the factors and mechanisms concerned in the preservation of normal levels of concentration of at least those plasma constituents that are of clinical significance.

These matters have been dealt with in detail in connection with discussions of the metabolism of proteins, nucleic acids, porphyrins, lipids, carbohydrates, inorganic elements, hormones, and vitamins, and of the regulation of "acid-base" balance and respiration. It seems desirable here to indicate again, for purposes of emphasis, the normal range of values for the substances that are of major clinical interest, with brief comments on the directions in which abnormalities may occur in certain important disease states. A comprehensive discussion of the significance of such abnormalities is beyond the scope of this book, and is available in works on clinical biochemistry. However, as indicated above, they can be readily interpreted as consequences of aberrations of normal control mechanisms. Fundamentally, abnormal increase or decrease in any constituent of the plasma must be due to an imbalance between the rate of its entrance into (production, liberation) and removal from (utilization, excretion) the blood stream. If the factors concerned in these processes are understood, the general significance of the abnormality will be apparent. The quantitative data presented in the tables, unless otherwise specified, represent normal values, at rest, in the postabsorptive state, i.e., after an overnight fast, under which conditions variations are at a minimum.

PROTEINS (TABLE 67). The nature, properties, functions, and metabolism of the plasma proteins are discussed in detail elsewhere (p. 505). It is necessary here only to review certain points of fundamental importance from the standpoint of abnormalities that may occur in disease.

The normal concentrations of the major plasma protein fractions are indicated in Table 67. It will be noted that although it is possible to obtain by a salting-out procedure (modified Milne method) values for albumin and globulins that approach those obtained by electrophoresis, this is not accomplished by other methods commonly employed (Howe). With many such procedures, about 1 gram of globulin is included in the "albumin" fraction. With the Milne procedure, pseudoglobulin corresponds rather closely to the α-globulins, and euglobulin to the β- and γ-globulins. Serum contains no fibrinogen; this is removed from the plasma during the process of coagulation, and is incorporated in the clot (fibrin).

Table 67. Plasma Protein Concentrations

PROTEIN	SALTING OUT		ELECTROPHORESIS	
	HOWE	MILNE (modified)		
	(grams %)	(grams %)	(grams %)	(% of total)
Total	6–8 (7)	6–8 (7)	6–8 (7)	100
Albumin	4.7–5.7 (5.2)	3.6–4.5 (4.0)	3.0–4.1 (3.6)	51
Globulin	1.3–2.5 (2.0)	2.1–4.2 (3.2)	2.7–3.8 (3.2)	45
Pseudo-	(1.8)	0.8–1.9 (1.3)	α (1.0)	14
Eu-	(0.2)	1.3–2.5 (1.9)	β (1.3)	19
			γ (0.9)	12
Fibrinogen	0.2–0.4 (0.3)	0.2–0.4 (0.3)	(0.3)	4

Albumin is affected more readily than globulins by nutritional factors, e.g., restricted protein intake. Because of its smaller molecular size, it is lost from the circulating plasma more readily than the other proteins by passage through capillary walls of increased permeability, e.g., inflammation (into inflammatory effusions into tissue spaces), glomerulonephritis, and nephrosis (albuminuria). Because of their different functions, metabolism, and sites of origin, plasma albumin and globulins are subject to different influences, and their concentrations may therefore vary independently of one another. Although it is possible for all fractions to be increased simultaneously, e.g., in sudden hemoconcentration, or to be decreased, e.g., in sudden hemodilution or severe malnutrition, in the majority of disease states in which the plasma proteins are altered the albumin is decreased and the globulins increased.

ALBUMIN. The plasma albumin concentration falls somewhat in the later stages of normal pregnancy, owing in part to hemodilution, and in part to decreased synthesis. The major causes for abnormal decrease in albumin (hypoalbuminemia) may be outlined as follows:

1. Excessive loss (in urine, ascitic fluid, inflammatory exudates, etc.).

2. Inadequate protein supply (dietary protein restriction, vomiting, diarrhea, etc.).

3. Impaired synthesis (liver dysfunction, chronic infection, severe anemia, cachexia, etc.).

4. Sudden plasma dilution (following sudden recovery from dehydration, as with intravenous salt solution in diabetic coma, infantile diarrhea, etc.).

If the plasma albumin concentration falls to a sufficiently low level, edema may occur. This is the most prominent clinical manifestation of hypoalbuminemia, and is due to the decrease in plasma colloid osmotic pressure, which favors retention of water in the tissue spaces (p. 310). The increase in globulins that often occurs simultaneously, e.g., in glomerulonephritis, hepatitis, chronic infections, etc., is incapable of compensating adequately for the decrease in albumin because, their molecular size being greater, the globulins are much less effective in raising the osmotic pressure (pp. 504, 505).

Study of the plasma albumin concentration is of clinical importance in relation to the investigation not only of the cause of edema, but also of the state of liver function and of protein nutrition.

GLOBULINS. The heterogeneity of the globulin fraction of the plasma proteins (p. 504) permits considerable variation in its individual components without significant alteration, at times, in the total, e.g., as determined by salting-out procedures. Further fractionation into pseudo- and euglobulin fractions may yield additional information, particularly since the latter includes the β- and γ-globulins, which are most frequently affected in disease. Reference is made elsewhere to the association of the β-globulins with plasma lipids (lipoproteins)

(p. 470), and to the fact that most of the circulating antibodies are γ-globulins (p. 506). It would be anticipated, therefore, that an increase might occur in the β-globulins in conditions in which the plasma lipids are elevated, and in the γ-globulins in infections or other conditions in which the formation of antibodies is stimulated. The α-globulins also are increased frequently in febrile disorders.

Hyperglobulinemia occurs commonly in association with hepatitis and hepatic cirrhosis, glomerulonephritis, and many acute and chronic infectious diseases (increase in euglobulin and, at times, in pseudoglobulin). In multiple myeloma there is often a striking increase, usually in the euglobulin fraction. In many of these conditions the plasma albumin is decreased, and the total protein concentration is either normal or subnormal. Occasionally (e.g., in multiple myeloma, certain cases of hepatic cirrhosis, certain chronic infections), however, the increase in globulin may be so large that the total protein concentration is elevated considerably.

For clinical purposes, the technical difficulties inherent in accurate quantitative fractionation of the plasma globulins are commonly circumvented by employing certain simple qualitative reactions which are sensitive to significant increases in either β-globulins (thymol turbidity and flocculation tests) or γ-globulin (cephalin-cholesterol flocculation; zinc turbidity). These procedures have been found particularly useful in the study of patients with liver damage and biliary tract disease.

FIBRINOGEN. Formation of fibrinogen is apparently stimulated, and the plasma fibrinogen concentration increased, in many acute infections. This, together with the increase in globulins, is the cause of the increased rate of sedimentation of erythrocytes which occurs in such conditions (sedimentation test). Although it is formed exclusively in the liver, significant decrease in plasma fibrinogen seldom occurs in liver disease, except under conditions of virtually complete abolition of hepatic function (e.g., hepatectomy in experimental animals). This determination is of little clinical value.

CARBOHYDRATES AND RELATED SUBSTANCES (TABLE 68). Glucose is the most important carbohydrate in the blood plasma from both physiological and clinical standpoints. The several factors involved in regulation of its concentration in the blood are discussed elsewhere (p. 418). There is a small amount of pentose (2–3 mg./100 ml.), apparently mainly in the form of nucleosides and nucleotides.

The designations "polysaccharides" and "glucosamine" are undoubtedly overlapping, and include, in part, substances composed of galactose, mannose, and glucosamine, some of which are also in the form of mucoprotein. Their significance is not known.

Various intermediates of the tricarboxylic acid cycle occur in low and approximately equal concentration, e.g., citric, α-ketoglutaric,

Table 68. Carbohydrates and Carbohydrate Metabolites in Blood Plasma (Fasting)

SUBSTANCE	CONCENTRATION (mg./100 ml.)
Glucose.....................	70–110 (90)
Fructose.....................	5–9 (7)
Lactose (lactation)...........	0–2
Polysaccharides..............	90–140 (110)
Glucosamine.................	50–90 (70)
Lactic acid (resting)..........	5–20 (10)
Pyruvic acid.................	0.4–2 (1.2)
Citric acid..................	1.5–3.2 (2.3)

succinic, and malic acids). They, as well as pyruvic acid, increase in diabetes mellitus. Pyruvic and lactic acids (p. 414) increase during strenuous exercise and in the presence of congestive heart failure (stagnant anoxia) and thiamine deficiency (p. 177). The lactic acid, originating mainly from muscle glycogen during the contraction process, is en route to the liver for reconversion to glycogen (or glucose); it may increase when liver function is impaired.

LIPIDS (TABLE 69). The lipid content of the plasma varies widely in normal subjects, even in the postabsorptive state. The origin and significance of the various plasma lipids are discussed elsewhere (pp. 471, 472, 474) as is the role of the plasma proteins, mainly α- and β-globulins, in their transport (lipoproteins, p. 470). Although the concentrations of the three major fractions, i.e., triglycerides (neutral fat), phosphatides (phospholipids), and cholesterol, frequently vary in the same direction, although not to the same degree, this is not always the case.

An increase occurs shortly after a high-fat meal (alimentary or postprandial hyperlipemia), returning to the fasting level in three to six hours. This is due largely to an increase in neutral fat, particles of which (chylomicrons), ranging in size from 35 mμ to 1 μ, may be seen with the microscope under darkfield illumination; if the concentration is sufficiently high the plasma may be opalescent. Dextran sulfate or heparin causes disappearance of this opalescence (p. 471), the effect of the latter being reversed by protamine. There is also some increase in phospholipid and cholesterol after meals rich in fat.

The plasma lipids rise during normal pregnancy, particularly after the twelfth week. They increase early in starvation (or carbohydrate restriction), owing to stimulation of mobilization from the fat depots, and fall later in the course of severe malnutrition (dietary inadequacy or wasting disease). The concentration of cholesterol tends to rise in individuals of advanced age. The important question of the possible relation of this increase to the incidence or development of athero-sclerosis is being investigated intensively (see lipoproteins, p. 470).

The hyperlipemia and hypercholesterolemia that occur in diabetes mellitus are reflections of important metabolic aberrations resulting from deficiency in insulin (pp. 430, 481). Since the liver is the main if not the only source of the plasma cholesterol, particularly the ester fraction, hypocholesterolemia, with a decrease in the ratio of the ester to the free fraction, occurs in the presence of severe liver cell damage (hepatocellular jaundice). Endocrine influences (e.g., thyroid, adreno-cortical, insulin) on plasma lipids are considered in the discussions of the individual hormones (q.v.).

Table 69. Lipids, Ketone Bodies, and Bile Acids in Plasma (Fasting)

SUBSTANCE	CONCENTRATION (mg./100 ml.)
Total lipid......................	385–675 (530)
Neutral fat......................	0–260 (140)
Phospholipids....................	110–250 (165)
Lecithin......................	80–200 (110)
Cephalin......................	0–30 (10)
Sphingomyelin.................	10–50 (30)
Cholesterol.....................	140–260 (200)
Ester.........................	90–200 (145)
Free..........................	40–70 (55)
Total fatty acids.................	110–485 (300)
Neutral fat × 0.95..............	
Phospholipid × 0.65............	
Cholesterol ester × 0.43........	
Ketone bodies (as acetone)........	0.2–0.9
Bile acids (as cholic).............	0.2–3.0

KETONE BODIES (TABLE 69). The concentration of ketone bodies (acetoacetic acid, β-hydroxybutyric acid, acetone), normally very low, increases during dietary restriction or inadequate utilization of carbo-hydrate (excessive ketogenesis, pp. 430, 481).

BILE ACIDS (TABLE 69). These substances, formed in the liver and ex-creted in the bile, undergo an enterohepatic circulation (p. 268), only small amounts entering the systemic circulation under normal condi-tions. High concentrations (which are rarely encountered) are actively hemolytic, because of their powerful action in lowering surface ten-sion. The quantity in the plasma increases in the presence of obstruc-tion of the common bile duct, if the liver cells continue to function adequately (obstructive jaundice). This diversion of bile acids into the blood stream is accompanied by and apparently responsible for an increase in plasma cholesterol (carried from the liver), a phenomenon of clinical importance at times in differentiating obstructive jaundice (hypercholesterolemia) from hepatocellular jaundice (hypocholesterolemia).

NON-PROTEIN NITROGENOUS SUBSTANCES (TABLE 70). This is a heterogeneous group of nitrogen-containing substances not precipitated by protein-precipitating agents (e.g., tungstic acid). They are all metabolic intermediates or end-products. Of the total NPN, about 50 per cent is represented by urea, and about 25 per cent by free amino acids. The remaining 25 per cent includes a large number of substances of varied origin and metabolic significance, such as creatine, creatinine, uric acid, bilirubin, choline, epinephrine, thyroxine, adenosine-containing compounds (e.g., nucleotides, ATP), etc. Glutathione (p. 520) and thioneine are present in the erythrocytes, but not in appreciable amounts in the plasma.

Table 70. Certain Non-protein Nitrogenous Components of Venous Blood (Fasting)

SUBSTANCE	WHOLE BLOOD (mg./100 ml.)	PLASMA (mg./100 ml.)
Total NPN...............	16–40 (30)	16–40 (30)
Urea N..................	8–23 (15)	10–23 (16)
Free amino acid N.........	5–8 (7)	3.5–6 (5)
Creatinine...............	1–2 (1.5)	0.8–1.0 (0.9)
Creatine.................	2.5–5 (4)	0.2–0.7 (0.4)
Uric acid................	2–4 (3)	2.5–6 (4)
Ammonia.................	(0.004)	
Bilirubin................		0.1–1.0 (0.4)
Glutathione..............	(40)	0

UREA NITROGEN (TABLE 70). Urea is the chief nitrogenous end-product of protein metabolism, representing the amino groups ingested (or produced in the body) in excess of the requirements (or capacity) for synthesis of body proteins or other nitrogenous substances (p. 513). It is formed in the liver, from amino acids, is passed into the blood stream, and is excreted in the urine (p. 769). It diffuses readily through capillary walls and cell membranes, and is present in intracellular and extracellular fluids in virtually identical concentration (per unit of water), and also occurs in cerebrospinal fluid, saliva, perspiration, and gastrointestinal secretions.

The blood urea nitrogen may rise temporarily to the upper limits of normal (Table 70) following a meal rich in protein. Low normal values are observed during periods of dietary protein restriction and also during pregnancy (increased nitrogen requirement for growth of fetus, placenta, uterus, breasts). The concentration falls also following administration of growth hormone and androgens (stimulation of protein anabolism).

Urea is the chief solid component of the urine under usual dietary conditions (p. 770); consequently, impairment of excretory function of the kidneys is reflected most consistently in a tendency toward urea retention in the body fluids. This is manifested first by decrease in urea "clearance" (p. 762) and later by abnormal increase in the blood urea nitrogen concentration. Low values may be obtained in the presence of very severe liver damage (diminished production).

FREE AMINO ACIDS (TABLE 70). The "dynamic equilibrium" that exists between the various body proteins (e.g., tissues, plasma, hemoglobin) (p. 487) implies the existence of an amino acid "pool," which is contributed to continually by degradation of these proteins and which is drawn upon continually for their resynthesis. Accordingly, the concentration of free amino acids in the plasma, representing the extracellular fluids, is the resultant of these catabolic and anabolic processes.

The amino acid content of the plasma rises sharply after a protein meal, returning to the resting level in a few hours. It falls during stimulation of protein anabolism, e.g., by growth hormone or androgen, and also after insulin administration. A marked increase may occur in the presence of severe liver damage (decreased deamination), with a corresponding decrease in urea.

URIC ACID (TABLE 70). Uric acid is the chief end-product of purine catabolism in man (p. 569). The site of its formation is not known (liver; muscles; marrow?). It is excreted in the urine. Its concentration in the plasma is normally affected but slightly by changes in the intake of purine-rich foods. It increases slightly during pregnancy.

Being excreted by the kidneys, it tends to be retained in excess in the body fluids in renal insufficiency, as does urea. It may increase in the plasma also when excessively large numbers of cells are undergoing metabolic degradation (e.g., chronic myeloid leukemia). However, clinical interest is centered particularly in the increase that occurs in gout, owing apparently to increased production of uric acid, the mechanism underlying which is not understood. Defective excretion (decreased uric acid clearance) occurs also in toxemia of pregnancy (eclampsia). The plasma uric acid may fall in the presence of severe acute liver damage (decreased production).

CREATINE AND CREATININE (TABLE 70). The metabolic origin and the significance of creatine and creatinine are discussed elsewhere (p. 521). The latter is a metabolic end-product of the former, is formed (in muscle) in relatively small amounts, passes into the blood stream, and is excreted in the urine (p. 771). Its concentration in the blood increases in renal functional insufficiency, usually later than the increase in blood urea.

INORGANIC ELEMENTS (TABLE 71). The significance of these plasma constituents is considered in the discussions of acid-base balance (p. 313) and of the metabolism of inorganic elements (pp. 599–620).

Table 71. *Important Inorganic Constituents (and Bicarbonate) in Blood Plasma (Fasting)*

SUBSTANCE	CONCENTRATION* (mg./100 ml.)	(mEq./liter)
Total "base"		142–158 (150)
Sodium	300–350 (325)	132–152 (142)
Potassium	14–21 (17)	3.6–5.3 (4.4)
Calcium	8.5–11.5 (10)	4.2–5.7 (5)
Magnesium	1.7–2.8 (2.2)	1.4–2.4 (1.7)
Bicarbonate	55–72 (62) (vol. %)	24–31 (27)
Chloride	340–380 (360)	97–108 (103)
Phosphate (as P)	3–4.5 (3.5)	(HPO₄) 2.2–4.2 (3.2)
Sulfate (as S)	1–2 (1.5)	(SO₄) 0.7–1.5 (1.0)
Iron	0.03–0.18 (0.1)	
Iodine (protein-bound)	0.004–0.008 (0.006)	
Copper	0.08–0.16 (0.12)	
Lead	0.008–0.06 (0.03)	

* To convert mEq./liter to mg./100 ml., multiply mEq./liter by:

$$Na = 2.3 \quad\quad Cl = 3.5$$
$$K = 3.9 \quad\quad HCO_3 = 2.3 \text{ (vol. \%)}$$
$$Ca = 2.0 \quad\quad HPO_4 = 1.8$$
$$Mg = 1.2 \quad\quad SO_4 = 1.6$$

ENZYMES. A number of enzymes have been demonstrated in the blood, e.g., adenosine polyphosphatases, aldolase, amylase, arginase, carbonic anhydrase (cells), catalase, cholinesterase, pseudocholinesterase, dehydropeptidase, β-glucuronidase, glyoxalase, histaminase, lipase, phenolsulfatase, acid and alkaline phosphatases. Only a few of these have been studied adequately from a quantitative standpoint, and still fewer have any established clinical significance. Enzymes concerned in coagulation are considered elsewhere (p. 734).

AMYLASE (TABLE 72). The relatively small amount in normal plasma originates apparently in the pancreas (p. 263) and salivary glands. A marked increase occurs during the first twenty-four to forty-eight hours of certain forms of acute pancreatitis, due to liberation of preformed amylase from the degenerating acinar cells directly into the blood stream. This is of considerable diagnostic significance. An increase may occur in patients with obstruction of the pancreatic duct, particularly after administration of secretin or parasympathicomimetic agents (viz., β-methylcholine). The serum amylase may increase also in inflammation of the parotid gland (parotitis; mumps).

LIPASE (TABLE 72). This enzyme apparently originates mainly in the pancreas (p. 263). It increases in the pancreatic disorders mentioned in connection with serum amylase and has the same diagnostic significance as the latter.

ALKALINE PHOSPHATASE (TABLE 72). The alkaline phosphatase (optimum pH about 9) of normal plasma originates largely in the bones, being formed chiefly by osteoblasts (p. 614). An increase in the plasma in skeletal disorders is regarded as a reflection of increased osteoblastic activity and is of great clinical value in differentiating between osteomalacia (high phosphatase activity) and osteoporosis (normal activity), as well as in the diagnosis of other skeletal diseases characterized by osteoblastic proliferation (e.g., Paget's disease of bone).

Table 72. Certain Clinically Important Enzymes in Blood Plasma

ENZYME	ACTIVITY PER 100 ML. PLASMA
Amylase	80–150 units (mg. glucose liberated)
Cholinesterase	132–365 mM. acetylcholine hydrolyzed per mm.
Lipase	0–2 ml. N/20 NaOH to neutralize fatty acid formed
Alkaline phosphatase	2–4.5 Bodansky units (adults)
	<14 Bodansky units (infants)
Acid phosphatase	0.5–1.5 Gutman units

The serum alkaline phosphatase is increased also in biliary obstruction (obstructive jaundice) and, usually to a lesser degree, in certain cases of hepatic disease (hepatocellular jaundice). According to some, this represents retention in the blood of the enzyme, originating in the skeleton, which is normally excreted in the bile. It seems more likely that the enzyme that accumulates in the blood in these disorders originates in the liver (parenchyma or bile duct cells) and, biliary excretion being impaired, is absorbed into the lymphatic and blood streams.

Table 73. Vitamins in Blood Plasma (Fasting) Under Average Adequate Dietary Conditions

VITAMINS	CONCENTRATION (μg./100 ml.)	
Vitamin A (carotene)	10–60	(24)
	40–400	(150)
Vitamin D	1.5–4.5	(3.0)
Vitamin E	900–1900	(1200)
Ascorbic acid	400–1700	(900)
Thiamine	5–14	(9)
Niacin	20–150	(75)
Riboflavin	2–4	(3)
Pantothenic acid	6–35	(15)
Pyridoxine (monkey)	.1–18	(8)
Biotin	(1)	
Folic acid	1.5–5	(2)
Cobalamin (whole blood)	0.05–0.15	(0.1)

VITAMINS (TABLE 73). With few exceptions, determination of the concentration of various vitamins in the blood has proved of little aid in the evaluation of nutritional adequacy in these substances. This matter is considered in the discussion of individual vitamins (pp. 126–216).

OTHER BODY FLUIDS

Interstitial fluid, i.e., fluid in the tissue spaces, is in dialysis equilibrium with the blood plasma across the semipermeable capillary walls. In general, allowing for regional differences, the chemical composition of this fluid differs from that of plasma mainly in the concentrations of: (1) proteins, which are relatively non-diffusible through most capillaries but which vary considerably in fluids in different tissues; (2) other substances, either inherently non-diffusible or rendered so by adsorption by or combination with plasma proteins, e.g., lipids, certain dyes; (3) diffusible electrolytes, the distribution of which on the two sides of the capillary wall is influenced by the difference in protein content of the two fluids (Donnan phenomenon, p. 306). The composition of interstitial fluid is discussed in detail elsewhere (p. 302).

The small amounts of fluid normally present in the peritoneal, pleural, and pericardial spaces likewise have the characteristics of protein-poor dialysates of blood plasma, and may be regarded as a portion of the interstitial fluid. Synovial fluid, too, is apparently of similar origin, but contains, in addition, protein material derived from the periarticular connective tissue. Cerebrospinal fluid, however, exhibits features that makes it necessary to regard it as other than a simple dialysate or ultrafiltrate of plasma. Chemical studies of these and other body fluids are at times of diagnostic value. Certain of their most important characteristics will be reviewed briefly.

LYMPH. Lymph is the fluid within the lymph vessels; this term is sometimes erroneously applied also to the interstitial fluid (p. 302). The latter, i.e., the fluid in the extracellular space surrounding tissue cells, is derived from two sources, (1) the cells and (2) the blood plasma. Nutrient and other materials pass into the cells from these tissue spaces, which are drained by two channels, (1) the blood capillaries and (2) the lymphatic capillaries. The latter lead into larger lymphatic vessels, the course of which is interrupted by lymph nodes, and which empty ultimately into the subclavian veins. Lymphocytes, originating in these nodes and in intestinal lymphatic tissue, enter the blood stream by this route.

Substances that can pass through blood capillary walls readily also enter the lymph without difficulty. Consequently, readily diffusible substances are present in blood plasma, interstitial fluid, and lymph in essentially identical concentrations (per unit water volume), e.g., glucose, urea, creatinine, amino acids, etc. As would be expected in view of the fact that it is in direct equilibrium with the interstitial fluid rather than the blood plasma, lymph resembles the former rather than the latter in its content of protein and certain electrolytes, i.e., generally higher chloride, lower sodium and protein (p. 303), and lower calcium (p. 611) than plasma. Inasmuch as these discrepancies in concentrations of electrolytes are due to differences in protein content, they vary with the latter in lymph (and interstitial fluid) in different regions of the body. Lymph coming from the liver has a high protein content, about 5 per cent, representing an important pathway of delivery of plasma proteins from the liver cells to the blood stream. Lymph coming from subcutaneous tissues, on the other hand, usually contains less than 1 per cent protein under normal conditions. That in the thoracic duct may contain 2–4 per cent. Lymph coagulates slowly when removed from the body, owing to the presence of small amounts of fibrinogen and other clotting factors (p. 734).

The lymphatic capillaries are more permeable than the blood capillaries. Consequently, colloidal particles, e.g., India ink and certain dyes, injected subcutaneously, enter the lymph much more readily than the blood. The same is true of fat. During absorption of fat from the intestine, its concentration in the thoracic duct lymph may reach 5 to 15 per cent; the milky appearance of such fluid (chyle) is due to the large amount of suspended fat droplets. A similar situation exists, although not to the same degree, in lymph coming from regions of fat storage (depot fat, e.g., subcutaneous, mesenteric, perirenal, pericardial, omental) during periods of excessive mobilization of fat, e.g., carbohydrate restriction, starvation.

SYNOVIAL FLUID. This is a clear, straw-colored, viscous fluid, serving to lubricate articular surfaces. It has a specific gravity of 1.008–1.015 and a solid content of 1.2–4.4 per cent (postmortem specimens). It has the electrolyte and diffusible non-electrolyte (e.g., urea, urate, glucose) composition of extracellular fluids, supporting the view that it is fundamentally a dialysate of blood plasma, to which protein is added from the connective tissue surrounding the joint. The protein content ranges from 0.1–2.2 per cent, about half of which is albumin and globulin, and half mucoprotein (mucin) containing mucoitin sulfuric acid as a prosthetic group (p. 19). It also contains hyaluronic acid (acetyl-glucosamine-glucuronide) (p. 19) and certain enzymes, including hyaluronidase ("spreading factor," p. 234), dehydrogenases, protease, lipase, amylase, and systems capable of metabolizing glucose and fructose.

CEREBROSPINAL FLUID. Cerebrospinal fluid is formed in the choroid plexuses, enters the lateral ventricles, and passes through the third and fourth ventricles into the subarachnoid space, from which it is reabsorbed into the blood chiefly by the subarachnoid villi. It is a clear,

colorless fluid, the total volume (adult) being about 100–150 ml., and
the specific gravity (spinal fluid) 1.005–1.009. When collected with
precautions to prevent escape of CO_2, the pH is essentially that of
blood plasma, i.e., 7.35–7.4, and the HCO_3 40–60 volumes per cent
(average 22.5 mEq./liter). Although in its chemical composition it
corresponds in many respects to a dialysate of the blood plasma (i.e.,
interstitial fluid, p. 000), the few instances in which it does not (e.g.,
Mg, PO_4) indicate that it is, in part at least, a product of secretory
activity of the choroid plexus.

ORGANIC CONSTITUENTS. Cerebrospinal fluid contains but little protein (15–45 mg./100 ml. in that obtained from the spinal canal, with
lower concentrations in the fluid from the cisterna and from the ventricles). Approximately 80 per cent of the protein is albumin, the remainder globulin, derived from the blood plasma.

The glucose concentration in the postabsorptive state, 45–80
mg./100 ml., varies with the plasma sugar concentration, but not quantitatively. There are small amounts of lactic acid present (10–25
mg./100 ml.), minute amounts of cholesterol (0.05–0.25 mg./100 ml.),
and non-protein nitrogenous substances in approximately the same
concentration as in blood plasma (e.g., urea nitrogen, 7–15 mg./100
ml.).

The fluid also contains certain hormones (e.g., anterior pituitary),
enzymes (amylase, lipase, oxidases), and vitamins (e.g., ascorbic acid
in same concentration as in blood plasma).

INORGANIC CONSTITUENTS. The inorganic composition (mg./100
ml.; mEq./liter) is as follows: sodium, 300–350 mg. (130–150 mEq.);
potassium, 11–16 mg. (average 4 mEq.); calcium, 4–6 mg. (average
2.5 mEq.); magnesium, 3 mg.; phosphorus, 1–1.5 mg.; chloride, 700–
750 mg. (as NaCl) (average 125 mEq.).

The relatively higher concentration of chloride than in plasma ac-
cords with predictions based on Donnan's equilibrium, and the amount
of calcium corresponds to that of the normal diffusible fraction of the
serum calcium. However, changes in the latter are not always reflected
quantitatively in the spinal fluid calcium. Moreover, the concentration
of magnesium is usually higher and of inorganic phosphate lower than
in the blood plasma. These facts indicate that this fluid is not a simple
dialysate of the plasma.

SEMEN. Seminal fluid, as normally ejaculated, is a mixture of spermatozoa and secretions of the prostate, seminal vesicles, vas deferens,
epididymis, and bulbo-urethral and urethral glands. It is quite viscid,
and clots promptly (fibrinogen), but the clot undergoes liquefaction
rapidly (minutes) owing to the presence of fibrinolysin (from prostate). Its quantitative composition varies widely depending on the
relative volume contribution from these sources at the time of collec-

tion. However, certain characteristics are of interest, although their significance may not be apparent.

The pH of semen approximates that of blood plasma, but semen contains much less protein, cholesterol, and chloride, and much more calcium, phosphate, and urea than does the latter fluid. The spermatozoa consist largely of nucleoproteins. The prostate contributes the polyamino compounds, spermine and spermidine; the latter is apparently responsible for the rather characteristic odor of seminal fluid.

Acid phosphatase (p. 231) is present in very high concentration (500–5000 units /ml.); it is derived from the prostate. The concentration varies with the functional activity of the prostatic epithelial cells, which is under androgenic control (p. 670). The functional significance of this enzyme is not clear. Hyaluronidase is another enzyme present in abundance in semen that has aroused considerable interest. Because of its action in depolymerizing hyaluronic acid, it has been suggested that it may play an important role in facilitating penetration of the perifollicular gelatinous material in the ovum by the sperm, thus aiding fertilization (p. 714). This hypothesis has not been supported by recent observations.

In contrast to other body fluids, the main carbohydrate in seminal fluid is not glucose but fructose, which originates in the seminal vesicles, and is present in high concentration (200–600 mg./100 ml.). Citrate and lactate are also present in much larger amounts than in blood plasma or other body fluids.

AMNIOTIC FLUID. The fluid in the amniotic sac probably originates as a dialysate of the maternal and fetal blood plasma, its original composition being essentially the same as that of protein-poor interstitial fluids. As the fetus develops, this fluid apparently becomes progressively more diluted with the hypotonic fetal urine. One of its characteristic differences from the maternal blood plasma during this period is its relatively high uric acid content (2–9 mg./100 ml.).

BIBLIOGRAPHY

Annual Review of Biochemistry.

Annual Review of Physiology.

Albritton, E. C. (ed.): Standard Values in Blood, Philadelphia, W. B. Saunders Company, 1952.

Biggs, R. and Macfarlane, R. G.: Human Blood Coagulation and Its Disorders, Springfield, Ill., Charles C Thomas, Publisher, 1953.

Cantarow, A. and Trumper, M.: Clinical Biochemistry, ed. 4, Philadelphia, W. B. Saunders Company, 1949.

Edsall, J. T.: The plasma proteins and their fractionation, Advances in Protein Chemistry 3:383, 1947.

Gutman, A. B.: The plasma proteins in disease, Advances in Protein Chemistry 4: 155, 1948.

Haurowitz, F.: Chemistry and Biology of Proteins, New York, Academic Press, Inc., 1950.

Lemberg, R. and Legge, J. W.: Hematin Compounds and Bile Pigments, New York, Interscience Publishers, Inc., 1949.

Merritt, H. H. and Fremont-Smith, F.: The Cerebrospinal Fluid, Philadelphia, W. B. Saunders Company, 1937.

Peters, J. P. and Van Slyke, D. D.: Quantitative Clinical Chemistry, ed. 2, Vol. I: Interpretations, Baltimore, Williams & Wilkins Company, 1931; 1946.

Sunderman, F. W. and Boerner, F.: Normal Values in Clinical Medicine, Philadelphia, W. B. Saunders Company, 1949.

Tullis, J. L. (ed.): Blood Cells and Plasma Proteins, New York, Academic Press, Inc., 1953.

Youmans, J. B. (ed.): Symposia on Nutrition, Robert Gould Research Foundation, Inc., Vol. II: Plasma Proteins, Springfield, Ill., Charles C Thomas, Publisher, 1950.

29

URINE FORMATION—RENAL FUNCTION

The chief function of the kidneys is to remove from the body waste and other undesirable substances and whatever water and solid material may have been formed in or introduced into the body in excess of the quantity required. These organs constitute an important route of elimination of certain drugs, poisons, and other toxic agents. Formation of ammonia by the renal tubular epithelium and regulation of the excretion of anions and cations play an important part in the regulation of the acid-base equilibrium (p. 320). By virtue of these functions, the kidneys also play an essential role in the regulation of water balance and the osmotic equilibrium between the blood plasma and the tissue fluids and cells. The uriniferous tubule is the functional unit, there being about 1,200,000 in each kidney. From a physiological standpoint, the activity of the glomerulus must be considered apart from that of the tubule.

GLOMERULAR FILTRATION

Studies of glomerular fluid and serum filtrate (protein-free) in amphibians have shown that the pH, vapor pressure, conductivity, and concentrations of urea, glucose, chloride, inorganic phosphorus, exogenous uric acid, exogenous creatinine, bicarbonate, and other substances in these fluids are practically identical within the error of the methods employed. These observations indicate that the glomerulus acts merely as an ultrafilter. According to this view, therefore, which rests upon sound experimental evidence, glomerular urine is formed by a process of filtration alone. The effective filtration pressure is the resultant of the blood pressure in the glomerular capillaries and the opposing forces of the colloid osmotic pressure of the blood plasma (24 mm. Hg) (p. 310) and the tension within Bowman's capsule (capsular pressure). The mean glomerular pressure may be regarded as about 50 per cent of the mean systemic arterial pressure (90 mm.

Hg), thus averaging about 45 mm. Hg. This is subject to regulation by variation in the relative degree of constriction of the afferent and efferent arterioles of the glomerulus. Under stimulation, the latter may be constricted more than the former to such a degree as to raise the pressure within the glomerular capillaries to about 63 mm. Hg in the blood entering the glomerulus; since the capsular pressure is about 15 mm. Hg, it is obvious that the initial effective filtration pressure is at least 45 minus (24 [C.O.P.] + 15), or 6 mm. Hg, and may rise to 63 minus (24 + 15) or 24 mm. Hg. As fluid (and diffusible solids, but little or no protein) leaves the plasma within the capillaries as a result of this force, the plasma protein concentration increases and may reach a point where the effective filtration pressure is so reduced as to impair glomerular filtration. Further constriction of the efferent arteriole may then still increase the glomerular blood pressure (to 63 mm. Hg), allowing filtration to continue. In addition to the influence of these pressure factors, the volume of glomerular filtrate is influenced significantly by (1) the surface area of the filter (glomerular capillary surface, normally 1.56 sq. meters) and (2) the minute volume flow of blood plasma over this surface (normally about 600 ml. plasma or 1100 ml. blood per 1.73 sq. meters body surface).

TUBULAR FUNCTION

If, as has been estimated, the rate of formation of glomerular urine under normal conditions is approximately 125 ml. per minute, while the rate at which urine passes into the bladder under the same conditions is approximately 1–2 ml. per minute, it is obvious that in its passage through the uriniferous tubules about 99 per cent of the water of the glomerular filtrate must have been reabsorbed. Furthermore, since the glomerular filtrate contains glucose in practically the same concentration as the blood plasma, whereas the bladder urine contains none, or very little, this substance, too, must have undergone practically complete reabsorption in the tubules. Quantitative studies of the excretion of other solids, such as chloride and phosphate, in glomerular and bladder urine indicate a variable degree of reabsorption during their passage through the uriniferous tubules. The important observations of Richards and Walker and their associates have thrown considerable light upon the site of reabsorption of several of these solids in the renal tubules of amphibians. It was found that reabsorption of glucose occurs entirely in the proximal convoluted tubule (the degree of reabsorption of glucose was lessened by an increase in the rate of urine flow through the tubule and by high concentrations of glucose in the blood plasma), reabsorption of chloride in the distal tubule, and acidification of the urine in the terminal portion of the distal tubule. The proximal tubule appeared to be capable of actively reabsorbing phosphate.

Insofar as excretory functions are concerned, therefore, the function of the renal glomeruli may be regarded as that of ultrafiltration (protein-free filtrate of the blood plasma) and that of the tubular epithelium as chiefly "selective" reabsorption (water, glucose, chloride, etc.). However, there is evidence that certain of the urinary constituents pass from the blood into the urine at some point in the tubules beyond the glomeruli. There appears to be a distinct species difference in this regard, but it is probable that creatinine, ammonia, Diodrast, phenol red, and Hippuran are added to the urine in the course of its passage through the tubules. Inasmuch as the average rate of glomerular filtration is 120–130 ml. per minute (about 70 ml. per sq. meter of body surface), it follows that more than 170 liters are filtered through the glomeruli from the plasma daily, the tubules subsequently reabsorbing about 168.5 liters of water, 1000 grams of NaCl, 360 grams of $NaHCO_3$, 170 grams of glucose and smaller amounts of phosphate, sulfate, amino acids, urea, urate, etc., in order to excrete about 50–60 grams of NaCl, urea, and other waste products in about 1500 ml. of urine.

The factors involved in the regulation of tubular reabsorption are not clearly understood, but there is evidence that the total quantity of any substance present in the glomerular filtrate is important in this connection. For example, under normal conditions the tubules can reabsorb up to 350 mg. of glucose per minute (p. 429); this would be the quantity entering the tubules with a glomerular filtration rate of 125 ml. per minute and a plasma glucose concentration of 280 mg. per 100 ml. The same quantity would enter the tubules per minute if the volume of glomerular filtrate was reduced to 75 ml. per minute and the plasma glucose concentration raised to 465 mg. per 100 ml. If tubular reabsorption was not impaired simultaneously, glucose would not necessarily escape in the urine regardless of the considerable elevation of blood sugar. The extent to which the various constituents of the glomerular filtrate are reabsorbed may be ascertained by determining their "clearance" simultaneously with the clearance of inulin (p. 762). By this method it has been found that 40–50 per cent of the urea and about 90 per cent of the urate (uric acid) of the glomerular filtrate is reabsorbed in the tubules under normal conditions. In the course of the reabsorption of the several solid constituents, about 87.5 per cent of the water entering the proximal convoluted tubules and loop of Henle is reabsorbed iso-osmotically, a phenomenon designated "obligatory reabsorption." A variable proportion of the remaining 12.5 per cent is reabsorbed ("facultative reabsorption"), probably as a result of the action of the "antidiuretic hormone" of the pituitary gland, which exerts its influence directly upon the renal tubular epithelium in the thin segment of the loop of Henle. The first (obligatory) phase is constant and is determined by the extent of reabsorption of solids; the second (facultative) phase is variable, being subject to alteration in physiological demands, and constitutes the mechanism of production of a urine which is hypertonic as compared to protein-free blood plasma. Hyposthenuria (decrease in maximum attainable specific gravity) results from decreased efficiency of facultative reabsorption, which, when extreme, results in isosthenuria.

Secretion of the antidiuretic hormone is under the control of nerve fibers passing through the pituitary stalk from the supra-optic nuclei in the hypothalamus. Secretion of this principle may be interfered with either by resection of or injury to the posterior pituitary or by lesions in the hypothalamus involving either the supra-optic nuclei or the nerve pathways leading to the posterior pituitary. In the absence of the antidiuretic hormone and in the presence of some hormonal influence exerted by the anterior pituitary, probably the adrenocorticotrophic hormone, the capacity of the renal tubules to reabsorb water (facultative reabsorption) is reduced and polyuria results. This constitutes the condition known as diabetes insipidus, in which, when complete, as much as 12.5 per cent of the volume of glomerular filtrate may escape reabsorption, the urine volume rising to as much as 25,000 ml. daily, with a very low specific gravity (1.001–1.003). This condition may be corrected promptly by administration of adequate doses of posterior pituitary extract or of Pitressin.

There is evidence that several substances that are excreted by the renal tubular epithelium are handled by a single mechanism; the same is true of the reabsorption of certain substances by these cells. These substances compete for these mechanisms so that the excretion or reabsorption of one is depressed by the simultaneous presence of another which is handled by the same mechanism. Thus, Diodrast, phenol red, Hippuran, and penicillin are excreted by the same tubular mechanism, for which they compete when given simultaneously.

Similar competition, in this instance for reabsorption, is exhibited between creatine, glycine, and other amino acids, and also between glucose and xylose. It has also been shown that reabsorption of ascorbic acid is depressed by Hippuran and sodium chloride, that of phosphate by glucose and that of uric acid by Diodrast.

As indicated elsewhere (p. 323), ammonia is formed from glutamine (60 per cent) and amino acids (40 per cent), through the activity of the renal tubular epithelium, in response to and in proportion to the requirement for conservation of base. The substitution of ammonia for sodium in the excretion of anions ("acid radicals") in the urine effects an economy of cations ("base") which is essential for the maintenance of the normal pH of the body fluids under conditions of excessive accumulation of acids in the body. Ammonia is formed from glutamine and amino acids by hydrolysis (glutaminase) and deamination (p. 512), respectively. The exact stimulus to its increased production is not clear. The kidneys also serve to limit loss of sodium from the organism by converting the slightly alkaline glomerular filtrate to an acid urine (p. 321). These functions of the kidney play an important part in the regulation of the "acid-base" balance of the organism.

Although not strictly accurate from a physiological standpoint, from a practical standpoint the chief functions of the kidney which have a significant clinical bearing may be enumerated as follows:

1. The elimination of water in accordance with the requirements of the organism.

2. The elimination of salts (chloride, phosphate, etc.) in accordance with the requirements of the organism.

3. The elimination of non-volatile end-products of metabolism, chiefly those of protein metabolism.

4. The elimination of certain foreign substances (foreign proteins, dyes, etc.).

5. The synthesis of hippuric acid and ammonia formation.

6. The retention of normal protein constituents in the blood plasma and the reabsorption, in the tubules, of substances necessary to the organism which pass in excessive quantities into the glomerular filtrate (glucose, chloride, etc.).

As a result of these functions the kidneys play an important part in:

1. The regulation of the water balance and the crystalloid and colloid osmotic equilibrium between the blood plasma and tissues.

2. The regulation of the "acid-base" equilibrium of the body.

3. The removal of toxic substances and waste products.

Considered in a broad sense, the chief function of the kidney is to eliminate solid substances in solution in water. Many of these substances exist in the urine in much greater concentration than in the blood, the ratio of the average concentration in the urine to its concentration in the blood during the same period (concentration ratio) varying greatly for each of the urinary constituents. This is illustrated in Table 74. Thus, in the normal performance of its excretory functions the kidney must concentrate the eliminated substances, the necessary degree of concentration at any moment depending upon the relative quantities of solids and water available at that moment in the blood passing through the glomerular capillaries. One of the most important characteristics of the healthy kidney is its ability to eliminate the required quantity of solids regardless, within wide limits, of the amount of water available for their solution. In other words, the normal kidney exhibits a remarkable flexibility in its concentrating ability. Consequently, the concentration of solid constituents of normal urine, as evidenced by the specific gravity, varies considerably during the day

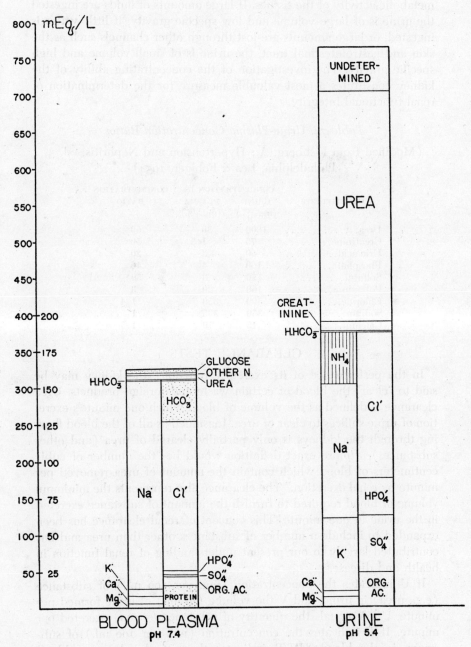

Fig. 135. Composition of urine compared with that of blood plasma (Gamble)

in accordance with the ingestion of fluids and solid food and with the metabolic activity of the tissues. If large amounts of fluids are ingested the urine is of large volume and low specific gravity; if little water is ingested, or large amounts are lost through other channels such as the skin and gastrointestinal tract, the urine is of small volume and high specific gravity. The investigation of the concentrating ability of the kidney constitutes a most valuable measure for the determination of renal functional integrity.

Table 74. Urine-Plasma Concentration Ratios

(Modified from Fishberg, A.: Hypertension and Nephritis, ed. 5, Philadelphia, Lea & Febiger, 1954)

CONSTITUENT	CONCENTRATION IN URINE (mg. %)	PLASMA (mg. %)	CONCENTRATION RATIO
Urea.............	1800	30	60
Creatinine.........	75	1.5	50
Uric acid..........	60	3	20
Phosphate.........	160	4	40
Sulfate............	150	3	50
Potassium.........	160	20	8
Chloride...........	500	350	1.4
Sodium............	350	335	1
Calcium...........	15	10	1.5

CLEARANCE TESTS

In the performance of its excretory functions, the kidney may be said to "clear" the blood of certain waste and foreign products. Urea clearance is defined as the volume of blood which one minute's excretion of urine suffices to clear of urea. Inasmuch as all of the blood flowing through the kidneys is only partially cleared of urea (and other substances), a more exact definition would be "the number of cubic centimeters of blood which contain the amount of urea removed per minute by renal excretion." The clearance also represents the minimum volume of blood required to furnish the amount of substance excreted in the urine in one minute. This concept of renal clearance has been expanded to include a number of substances other than urea and has contributed largely to our present understanding of renal function in health and disease.

If U indicates the concentration (mg. per 100 ml.) of substance (e.g., urea) in urine, and V the volume (in ml.) of urine formed per minute, U x V equals the quantity of substance (x 100) excreted per minute. If B indicates the concentration (mg. per 100 ml.) of substance in the blood, UV/B indicates the virtual volume of blood "cleared" of substance per minute, i.e., the "clearance." It is essential that plasma be used instead of whole blood for clearance determinations if the substance investigated is not distributed uniformly between plasma and corpuscles (e.g., inulin, Diodrast, phenol red).

Theoretically, a substance may be excreted by (1) glomerular filtration alone, (2) filtration plus tubular excretion, or (3) filtration plus tubular reabsorption. If a substance is completely filtered at the glomerulus and is subsequently completely reabsorbed by the tubules, its clearance will be zero (e.g., glucose). As the degree of tubular reabsorption diminishes, the substance appears in the urine and its clearance increases (e.g., urea), until, if there is no reabsorption (e.g., inulin), the clearance will be equivalent to the rate of glomerular filtration. If a substance, in addition to being filtered through the glomeruli, is also excreted by the tubular epithelium (e.g., phenol red, Diodrast), its clearance will exceed the rate of glomerular filtration by an amount equal to the extent of tubular clearance. Inasmuch as the kidneys cannot excrete more of a substance per unit of time than is brought to them in the blood, the upper limit of renal clearance is determined by the renal blood flow. For example, if a substance undergoes glomerular filtration and tubular excretion, and if all that is contained in the blood passing through the kidneys is removed and is concurrently transferred to the urine, its clearance will be complete (e.g., Diodrast clearance); i.e., it will be equivalent to the volume of plasma flowing through the kidneys per minute. These facts constitute the basis for quantitative determination of various aspects of renal function.

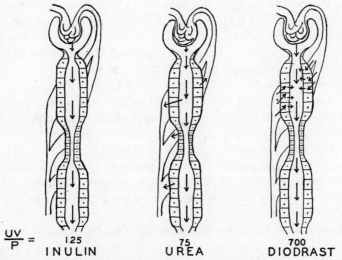

$$\frac{UV}{P} = \quad \underset{\text{INULIN}}{125} \qquad \underset{\text{UREA}}{75} \qquad \underset{\text{DIODRAST}}{700}$$

Fig. 136. Characteristic clearance values. Scheme to illustrate mechanisms of excretion: Inulin is excreted by glomerular filtration alone, with no tubular reabsorption. Urea is excreted by glomerular filtration and is partially reabsorbed by the tubule. Diodrast is excreted by both glomerular filtration and tubular excretion.

RATE OF GLOMERULAR FILTRATION. Inulin is a polysaccharide which is not metabolized in the body and, following its intravenous injection, is excreted quantitatively by the kidneys within a short time. It is excreted entirely by glomerular filtration and undergoes no reabsorption in the tubules. Inasmuch as inulin, being freely filtrable at the glomerulus, exists in the blood plasma and glomerular filtrate in identical concentration, and since the quantity of inulin excreted per minute in the bladder urine is equal to the amount entering the glomerular filtrate per minute, it follows that the inulin clearance (UV/P) represents the volume of glomerular filtrate formed per minute. Employing this procedure, it has been found that the average rate of glomerular filtration is 125 ml. per minute (about 70 ml. per sq. meter of body surface). Similar figures are obtained with other carbohydrates, viz., mannitol, sorbitol, and dulcitol. Lower values (by 25–45 per cent) may be obtained in elderly (70 to 85 years of age), apparently normal subjects.

Determination of the rate of glomerular filtration (inulin clearance) has several important physiological applications: (1) The glomerular filtration rate minus the rate of urine flow (bladder) equals the quantity of water reabsorbed in the tubules per minute. (2) The inulin clearance minus the clearance of another substance (X) divided by the inulin clearance equals the proportion of substance X reabsorbed in the tubules. For example: inulin clearance (125) minus urea clearance (75), divided by inulin clearance (125), equals 0.4, indicating that 40 per cent of the urea of the glomerular filtrate is reabsorbed during its passage through the tubules. (3) When a substance has a clearance higher than that of inulin, it is excreted partly or entirely by the tubules (p. 761). Such data have been found to be useful in studying the mode of action of diuretic agents and abnormalities in the excretion of such substances as glucose and uric acid.

A decrease in inulin clearance may result from (1) decrease in renal blood flow, (2) partial obliteration of or decrease in the number of functioning glomeruli (glomerulonephritis, glomerulosclerosis, destructive or suppurative lesions of the renal parenchyma), or (3) decrease in the effective glomerular filtration pressure. The last (p. 755) is the resultant of (a) the glomerular blood pressure, (b) the plasma colloid osmotic pressure, and (c) the capsular pressure. Diminution in the first or/and increase in the last two forces result in a decrease in effective filtration pressure.

Determination of glomerular filtration (inulin clearance) is obviously of enormous value in investigating the pathological physiology of urine formation. However, except under unusual circumstances, the determination of urea clearance is entirely satisfactory in the clinical study of renal function in patients with renal disease and for purposes of diagnosis and prognosis. The values for urea clearance usually parallel those for inulin clearance and the latter may usually be calculated from the former according to the following formula: Urea clearance/0.6 = Inulin clearance. The percentage of average normal inulin clearance may be calculated by dividing the inulin clearance value by 1.25.

RENAL BLOOD FLOW. Diodrast is excreted largely by the tubules, i.e., by transfer from the peritubular capillaries across the cells of the proximal tubule into the lumen of the tubule. It has been found that the removal of Diodrast from the plasma is nearly complete (80–90 per cent) at low plasma concentrations of Diodrast, and that the plasma Diodrast clearance is approximately equivalent to the "effective" renal plasma flow, i.e., the flow to active renal excretory tissue. The total "effective" renal blood flow can be calculated if the fraction of plasma present in the blood is known (hematocrit determination). Values for renal plasma flow in normal subjects have been reported ranging from about 325 to 920 ml. per minute per 1.73 sq. meters of body surface, with averages of 500–670 ml. (600). Reported values for total renal blood flow range from 520 to 1560 ml. per minute per 1.73 sq. meters of body surface, averaging 860–1115 ml. Lower values may be obtained in elderly subjects. The renal plasma flow is reduced in normal subjects by brief, strenuous exercise.

p-Aminohippurate is excreted by the same mechanism as Diodrast, identical values being obtained for the clearance of both substances. The former (PAH) has certain practical advantages over the latter (Diodrast) in this connection: (1) it does not penetrate the erythrocytes; (2) it is less extensively bound to plasma proteins; (3) its quantitative determination is a much simpler procedure. For these reasons, p-aminohippurate clearance is replacing Diodrast clearance in the estimation of renal blood flow.

Decrease in "effective" renal blood flow (Diodrast or p-aminohippurate clearance) may occur as a result of: (1) generalized circulatory stasis, as in congestive heart failure and shock syndrome; (2) local changes in the kidneys or renal circulation, e.g., (a) decrease in the mass of functioning renal tissue (hypoplasia and destructive renal lesions, as tuberculosis, malignant disease, suppuration, etc.), (b) decrease in the renal vascular bed (renal arteriosclerosis, arteriolosclerosis, glomerulonephritis, and (c) increased local resistance to the flow of blood resulting from constriction of the afferent or efferent glomerular arterioles. An absolute increase in renal blood flow may occur after administration of typhoid vaccine or other pyrogenic agents. Following unilateral nephrectomy the blood flow through the remaining kidney may increase as much as 70–100 per cent in a short time and may be temporarily increased also by a high-meat diet.

TUBULAR EXCRETORY MASS. Inasmuch as the process of tubular excretion is limited by the mass of functioning tubular tissue available for the transfer of any substance from the blood to the urine, the measurement of the maximal rate of excretion of a substance excreted by this mechanism constitutes a measurement of the "tubular excretory mass" of the kidneys. This value, designated T_m, is calculated from simultaneous inulin and Diodrast clearance determinations at high levels of plasma Diodrast according to the formula,

$$T_m = U_d V - P_d C_{in} WF = \left(\frac{C_d}{C_{in}} - WF \right) P_d C_{in},$$

where U_d is the concentration of Diodrast per milliliter of urine, V is the urine volume in milliliters per minute, P_d the quantity of Diodrast per milliliter of plasma, C_{in} the inulin clearance, C_d the Diodrast clearance, W the fraction of water in the plasma, and F the fraction of Diodrast free in the plasma. This value represents merely the difference between the total excretion of Diodrast per minute and the quantity excreted by filtration.

It has been suggested that the T_m may be calculated indirectly as follows:

$$T_m = \frac{Sp. \ Gr. - 3.4}{4.8} \sqrt{UC},$$

where Sp. Gr. represents the second and third decimal place figures of the maximum urinary non-protein specific gravity obtained by the concentration test (viz., 1.028 = 28.0) and UC is the urea clearance in terms of per cent of average normal.

The normal Diodrast T_m has been found to range from 36.6–72.0 mg. iodine per 1.73 sq. meters of body surface per minute, averaging 53.3 in men and 46.7 in women. The value of this determination lies in the fact that, at effective plasma Diodrast concentrations and with adequate but not necessarily normal renal blood flow, the Diodrast T_m is dependent of glomerular activity and reflects the amount of functioning renal tubular tissue. For example, if one kidney were removed, T_m would be diminished by 50 per cent; if a portion of the excretory tissue were destroyed (either tubular destruction or obliteration of circulation), T_m would be reduced in proportion to the extent of destruction. If the glomeruli were entirely obliterated without impairing the circulation to the tubules, T_m would be unaltered.

The ratio, C_d/T_{md} (Diodrast clearance/Diodrast tubular excretory mass), is an expression of the volume of plasma completely cleared of Diodrast per unit quantity of the excretory tissue effecting this clearance. Normal values range from 10.2 to 16.7, averaging 13.4.

TUBULAR REABSORPTION. If another substance as freely filtrable through the glomeruli as inulin has a clearance value lower than the latter, it has undergone reabsorption in the tubules. The extent of this reabsorption may be calculated as follows:

$$\text{Reabsorption} = \frac{\text{Inulin clearance (e.g., 125)} - \text{Clearance of X}}{\text{Inulin clearance (125)}}$$

By means of this calculation it is evident that about 40–50 per cent of the urea present in the glomerular filtrate is normally reabsorbed in the tubules.

$$\frac{125 - 75}{125} = 0.4 \text{ or } 40 \text{ per cent}$$

FILTRATION FRACTION. The ratio of plasma inulin clearance (i.e., volume of glomerular filtrate) to plasma Diodrast clearance (i.e., renal plasma flow) represents the fraction of plasma filtered through the glomeruli. Under normal conditions this is about 0.20 (i.e., $\frac{125}{600}$), indicating that approximately 20 per cent of the water of the plasma flowing through the kidneys is filtered through the glomeruli into the lumen of Bowman's capsule.

VASOACTIVE SUBSTANCES FORMED IN THE KIDNEYS

Hypertension can be produced experimentally by reducing the renal blood flow (ischemia), e.g., by placing a clamp on the renal arteries. It has been shown that this is due to the release into the blood stream of a proteolytic enzyme "renin," which is found normally in the renal tubular epithelial cells. Renin, which does not itself influence blood pressure, acts on a plasma globulin substrate "hypertensinogen" (also called "renin-substrate") to form "hypertensin" (also called "angiotonin"), which causes arteriolar constriction and increases cardiac output, with consequent rise in arterial blood pressure. Hypertensinogen is apparently formed in the liver. Under normal conditions, circulating hypertensin is destroyed by enzymes which have been called "hypertensinases." There has been considerable investigation of the relation of this "renin mechanism" to the pathogenesis of various types of clinical hypertension.

Another vasoexcitor principle, VEM, is formed in the kidneys, apparently only under anaerobic conditions. This substance, the exact nature of which is not known, enhances the responsiveness of the terminal vascular bed to epinephrine, augmenting constriction of the precapillary sphincters. This substance is inactivated in the kidney under normal aerobic conditions. The effect of VEM is counteracted by a vasodepressor principle, VDM, which has been identified as apoferritin (p. 618), produced in the liver, spleen, and skeletal muscles under anaerobic conditions. VDM, which is inactivated in the liver under normal aerobic conditions, causes dilatation of the pre-capillary sphincters in the terminal vascular bed. The possible relation of VEM : VDM imbalance to the pathogenesis of clinical and experimental shock and hypertension is under investigation.

NORMAL URINE COMPOSITION

The urine is the most important medium of elimination of non-volatile substances from the body. Under normal conditions these include non-utilizable metabolites (e.g., urea, creatinine, uric acid), and materials ingested or produced in the organism in excess of metabolic requirements (e.g., water, electrolytes, etc.). The quantitative composition of the urine reflects the function of the kidneys in preserving important aspects of homeostasis and of the normal equilibrium between the organism and its environment. It will therefore vary widely in normal subjects at different ages and under different conditions of diet and activity. Detailed consideration of quantitative aspects of urine composition is not very profitable in a text of this nature. Attention will be directed chiefly toward its significant characteristics and toward the general principles and physiological factors governing the excretion of the most important normal constituents of the urine.

COLOR. The color of normal urine varies from light straw to reddish-yellow, depending on the degree of concentration. This color is due largely to two pigments: (1) urochrome, a S-containing substance of unknown nature, an oxidation product (exposure to air) of the colorless urochromogen; (2) urobilin, an oxidation product (exposure to air) of the colorless urobilinogen, a product of the degradation of hemoglobin (p. 595). The color intensifies on standing.

Normal, freshly voided urine, acid in reaction, is clear and translucent. Alkaline urine may be turbid and turbidity develops on standing (ammoniacal fermentation), due to precipitation of phosphates which are relatively insoluble at alkaline reactions (p. 777). Turbidity may also be due to uric acid, urates, calcium oxalate (excessive amounts in highly acid urine), to precipitation of mucin or nucleoprotein (usually on standing), or to abnormally large numbers of cells (epithelial, leukocytes, erythrocytes).

Certain drugs and foodstuffs may impart rather characteristic colors: e.g., santonin (orange-yellow), senna, rhubarb, cascara (brown-red), methylene blue (green), phenol (brown-black, on standing).

ODOR. Normal, freshly voided urine has a slightly aromatic, rather characteristic odor, the origin of which is not known exactly. The odor is apparently contributed to by small amounts of certain volatile organic acids. On standing, urine develops an ammoniacal odor due to hydrolysis (bacterial) of urea to ammonia. Urine voided after eating asparagus has a rather typical odor, which has been attributed to the presence of methyl mercaptan. Certain drugs, which are not commonly administered, impart rather specific odors (e.g., turpentine, cubeb, copaiba, tolu).

VOLUME. The quantity of urine excreted daily by normal subjects varies widely and is determined chiefly by the fluid intake. Under ordinary dietary conditions it ranges from 1000 to 2000 ml. It is influenced somewhat by the protein and NaCl intake, the excreted urea and salt acting as diuretic agents. Excessive perspiration and strenuous exercise decrease the urine volume by prerenal deviation of water (skin, lungs) (p. 296) and, under abnormal conditions, the same is accomplished by vomiting, diarrhea, and edema. The amount excreted during the day (8 A.M. to 8 P.M.) is two to four times that excreted during the night (8 P.M. to 8 A.M.). The minimum volume required for excretion of a given quantity of solids is determined by the concentrating capacity of the kidneys (p. 758). Under conditions of average adequate food intake, it is about 300 ml./sq.M. body surface (i.e., about 500 ml. for a 70-kg. man) (p. 296).

SPECIFIC GRAVITY. The specific gravity of the urine is directly proportional to the concentration of solute and, therefore, with any given total solid excretion, varies inversely with the volume under usual normal conditions. The grams of solute per liter may be calculated roughly by multiplying the last two figures of the specific gravity (to the third decimal) by Long's coefficient, 2.6. This is only an approximation, particularly since all substances do not exert the same effect on specific gravity. For example, the specific gravity of a liter of urine is raised 0.001 by 3.6 grams of urea, 1.47 grams of NaCl, and 3.8 grams of NaH_2PO_4 (also 2.7 grams of glucose and 3.9 grams of albumin).

Under ordinary dietary conditions, the specific gravity of the mixed twenty-four-hour urine usually varies between 1.014 and 1.026. However, it may be as low as 1.001 on a very high water intake or as high as 1.040 if fluid is restricted or excreted in excess by other routes (skin, bowel, etc). In normal subjects it rarely exceeds 1.040, the maximum attainable osmotic concentration in man being about 1.4 osmolar.

Normal kidneys eliminate the required amount of solids regardless, within wide limits, of the amount of water available for their solution. When their function is impaired, the kidneys lose this ability to dilute and concentrate the urine, and, with increasing damage, the osmolar concentration and specific gravity of the urine approach values for protein-free blood plasma (glomerular filtrate). The maximum attainable specific gravity falls and the minimum rises, the urine specific gravity being relatively fixed within narrowing limits below and above 1.007. The importance of the urinary specific gravity arises out of these facts, determination of the concentrating ability of the kidneys constituting an important test of renal function.

ACIDITY. Urinary acidity may be expressed in two ways: (1) its H+ ion concentration (true acidity); (2) its titratable acidity. These two factors (and also urinary ammonia) are responsive to the same influences, but are not necessarily related quantitatively. The pH may be regarded as an "intensity" factor and the titratable acidity as a "capacity" factor. Secretion of ammonia into the tubular urine decreases its H+ concentration, playing an important role in the renal regulation of "acid-base" balance (p. 323).

pH OF NORMAL URINE. The extreme limits of urinary pH in health are 4.8 and 8.0, usually, under ordinary conditions, ranging between 5.0 and 7.0, averaging 6.0 in the mixed twenty-four-hour sample. The mechanism of acidification of the glomerular filtrate (pH 7.4) is discussed elsewhere (p. 321).

TITRATABLE ACIDITY. The titratable acidity of the urine is expressed as milliliters of N/10 alkali required to neutralize the twenty-four-hour output of urine. This usually varies normally from 200 to 500, averaging about 350. If phenolphthalein is used as the indicator, values below 250 usually indicate an actual alkalinity, since an end-point is attained at about pH 8.3. Because of the intimate relationship between urinary acidity and urinary ammonia (p. 323), the latter (usually 300 to 500 ml. of N/10 alkali) should be included with the former in studies of acid-base balance (i.e., titratable acidity plus ammonia).

The urinary acidity and pH are reflections chiefly of the ratio, $NaH_2PO_4:Na_2HPO_4$, which is 1:4 at pH 7.4 (blood plasma; glomerular filtrate), about 50:1 at pH 4.8, and 9:1 at pH 6.0. This transformation of the dibasic to the monobasic salt effects considerable conservation of Na, which is returned to the plasma (p. 321). Acid urine contains virtually no bicarbonate (HCO_3^-). In alkaline urine, however, this ion is present and the pH may be determined largely by the ratio, $H_2CO_3:NaHCO_3$. The urinary acidity is normally also contributed to, but to a minor extent, by organic acids (lactic, uric, hippuric, β-hydroxybutyric).

The acidity of the urine is normally influenced chiefly by the nature of the diet (i.e., alkaline or acid ash). Ingestion of large amounts of protein (meats, bread, cereals), which yields acids in the course of metabolism (sulfuric, phosphoric), increases urinary acidity and ammonia. Most vegetables and fruits (orange, lemon, grape, apple, peach, pear) contain organic acids (e.g., citrate, oxalate) which form bicarbonate in the body and hence decrease urinary acidity. Certain fruits (plums, cranberries) contain benzoic acid and quinic acids, which are metabolized to and excreted as hippuric acid, increasing the urinary acidity and ammonia. These are increased also by starvation or dietary carbohydrate restriction, owing to increased catabolism of body protein and fat, with increased urinary excretion of sulfate, phosphate, and ketone acid (β-hydroxybutyric and aceto-acetic).

Shortly after eating (within an hour) there is a decrease in urinary acidity and ammonia and [H$^+$] concentration. This "postprandial alkaline tide" has been attributed generally to the increased secretion of HCl by the stomach, temporarily increasing the plasma bicarbonate. It is said not to occur in subjects with achlorhydria. This explanation is not accepted by some. On standing, normal urine becomes alkaline and ammoniacal owing to the action of bacteria on urea (ammoniacal fermentation).

NON-PROTEIN NITROGENOUS CONSTITUENTS. The term "non-protein nitrogen" (NPN) is applied to nitrogen present in compounds not precipitable by the usual protein-precipitating agents. These substances, occurring in the blood (p. 745) and other body fluids and in the urine, consist chiefly of intermediary- or end-products of protein metabolism. They include urea, ammonia, amino acids, creatinine, creatine, uric acid, and a number of other compounds present in small amounts, not readily determined quantitatively, and referred to as "undetermined nitrogen" (peptides, hippuric acid, etc.).

The several components of this heterogeneous mixture have different origins and significance and are influenced by different factors; the amount of each excreted in the urine varies under different conditions of diet and metabolism. The most important features of the biogenesis and metabolic significance of these substances are considered in the section on intermediary metabolism of proteins (p. 508 ff.) and nucleic acids (p. 569). Attention will be directed here mainly to their excretion in the urine of normal subjects.

TOTAL NON-PROTEIN NITROGEN. Normal adults on an adequate protein diet are in a state of nitrogen equilibrium, the quantity excreted daily being equivalent to that ingested. This is not the case during periods of tissue growth (children, pregnancy, convalescence) (positive nitrogen balance, p. 492). Inasmuch as the amount of nitrogen excreted in the feces is relatively constant (p. 277) and that lost by other extrarenal channels is usually small and constant, the quantity in the urine may be regarded as reflecting the amount of protein ingested and the state of protein catabolism. It may vary from as little as 3 grams daily on a low protein intake (20 grams) to as much as 24 grams or more on a very high protein diet (160 grams); it ranges between 11 and 15 grams on usual protein intakes (70 to 80 grams).

UREA. Urea is the chief end-product of the catabolism of amino acids (p. 513) and is the substance in which is incorporated, for purposes of excretion, the bulk of the nitrogen provided to the organism in excess of its needs. Under usual dietary conditions it comprises about half of the total urine solids, and is therefore the most abundant urinary constituent (except water). Because of these facts, and because it is a metabolic end-product, virtually not utilizable, the quantity of urea excreted in the urine is the most significant index of the extent of protein catabolism and, consequently, is influenced more directly by the protein intake than are the other nitrogenous compounds.

The mechanism of excretion of urea is discussed elsewhere (p. 762). On a high protein diet, urea nitrogen (16–25 grams) comprises 80 to 90 per cent of the urinary NPN. On very low protein intakes it may fall to 60 per cent or less of the total NPN, since variations in dietary protein are reflected almost exclusively in urinary urea and ammonia (p. 512 ff.), the amounts of the other nitrogenous constituents remaining relatively constant (Table 75).

Table 75. Urinary Nitrogen Partition in Same Individual on High and Low Protein Diets
(After Folin, O.: J.A.M.A. 69:1209, 1917)

	HIGH PROTEIN (grams/24 hours)	(% of total N)	LOW PROTEIN (grams/24 hours)	(% of total N)
Urine volume	1170 ml.		385 ml.	
Total N	16.80		3.60	
Urea N	14.70	87.5	2.20	61.7
Ammonia N	0.49	3.0	0.42	11.3
Uric Acid N	0.18	1.1	0.09	2.5
Creatinine N	0.58	3.6	0.60	17.2
Undetermined	0.85	4.8	0.29	7.3

AMMONIA. Unlike the other non-protein nitrogenous constituents of the urine, preformed ammonia is not removed by the kidneys from the blood stream, in which ammonia is present in only minute amounts. It is formed in the renal tubular epithelium, chiefly (60 per cent) from glutamine (glutaminase), the remainder from other amino acids (p. 323). It is passed largely into the tubular urine where, acting as a base, it combines with H^+ ions, forming NH_4, thus serving to lower the H^+ concentration and permitting further passage of H^+ ions into the lumen in exchange for Na^+ (p. 321). This mechanism is an important factor in the renal regulation of "acid-base" balance.

Under usual dietary conditions, normal adults excrete about 0.3–1.2 grams (average 0.7 gram) of ammonium N daily (20 to 70 mEq.), comprising 2.5–4.5 per cent of the total NPN. Inasmuch as the urea and ammonia of the urine are both derived ultimately from amino acids, an increase in ammonia is accompanied by a corresponding decrease in urea, at any given level of NPN excretion. The quantity of ammonia in the urine of normal subjects is determined chiefly by the requirement for acidification of the urine. The chief immediate stimulus to its formation in the tubular epithelial cell is apparently a decrease in the pH of the plasma and, consequently, in that of the urine in the tubules (p. 323).

The output of ammonia increases with increasing levels of dietary protein, owing probably to the acid-producing properties of protein (oxidation of S and P) (p. 313). It is increased also by ingestion of acids or acid-forming substances (NH_4Cl, NH_4NO_3) and in association with acidosis (except renal), and is decreased by ingestion of alkalies or base-forming foods and in alkalotic subjects. As much as 10 grams of ammonia may be excreted daily by individuals with severe diabetic acidosis. Administration of ammonium salts of mineral acids (viz., NH_4Cl, NH_4NO_3) is equivalent to administration of corresponding amounts of the free acids, since the ammonium is converted to urea in the body ($2NH_4Cl + CO_2 \rightarrow$ Urea $+ 2HCl + H_2O$). These ammonium salts therefore increase urinary acidity and can induce acidosis. If urine is allowed to stand without a preservative, its ammonia content increases markedly as a result of hydrolysis of urea by bacteria ("ammoniacal fermentation").

CREATINE AND CREATININE. The metabolic origin and significance of these substances are considered elsewhere (p. 521).

Creatine is not excreted in significant amounts in the urine of normal adult males. This is apparently due to the fact that it is completely reabsorbed from the glomerular filtrate in the renal tubules at normal plasma creatine levels (< 0.6 mg./100 ml.). It is present in the urine (increased plasma level) of prepuberal children (4.2 mg./kg.) and certain normal women, periodically or constantly, and occasionally during pregnancy and the early puerperium.

Under normal conditions, creatine formed in or otherwise provided (food) to the organism over and above the requirements or capacity for storage in the muscles (as phosphocreatine, p. 413) is either transformed to creatinine or excreted as such. The creatine tolerance test is a measure of the capacity for utilization of creatine. Normal adult men excrete in the urine (in twenty-four hours) not more than 20 per cent and women not more than 30 per cent of a test dose (1.32 or 2.64 grams) of creatine hydrate. Urinary creatine is increased in association with conditions accompanied by muscle wasting, muscle dystrophies, and thyrotoxicosis.

Creatinine (creatine anhydride) is formed from creatine in quite constant amounts daily (men, 1.0–1.8 grams; women, 0.7–1.5 grams), corresponding to about 2 per cent of the body creatine (p. 521), practically all of which is eliminated in the urine. The excretion of creatinine is therefore constant from day to day under quite varied conditions, being relatively uninfluenced by diet or urine volume, and being determined chiefly by the muscle mass (creatine content of body). Because of this fact, the daily excretion of creatinine is determined commonly in balance studies as a check on the accuracy of twenty-four-hour urine collections. Endogenous creatinine is excreted in man by glomerular filtration and active tubular excretion, the value for creatinine clearance (about 145) exceeding that for inulin (p. 762).

The term "creatinine coefficient" is applied to the number of milligrams of creatinine (plus creatine, if any) nitrogen excreted daily per kilogram of body weight. Normal values are 20–26 for men and 14–22 for women. The corresponding values in terms of nitrogen are 7.5–10 for men and 5–8 for women. The creatinine coefficient may be regarded as an index of the amount of muscle tissue, and is therefore more directly proportional to the ideal than to the actual weight.

AMINO ACIDS. Amino acids are excreted in the urine in both free and combined form. The latter are present in peptide linkage, as in compounds such as hippuric acid (glycine). The free amino nitrogen ranges normally from 0.1–0.15 gram daily, comprising 0.5–1.0 per cent of the total nitrogen. The total amino nitrogen output is 0.5–1.0 gram daily (2–6 per cent of the total nitrogen). The organism conserves amino acids efficiently, the amount excreted by normal subjects varying but slightly with wide fluctuation in protein intake and even when amino acids are administered parenterally. Severe liver damage results in an increase in urinary amino acids and a corresponding decrease in urea (impaired deamination and urea formation).

URIC ACID. Uric acid is the chief end-product of the metabolism of purines. Its metabolic origin is considered elsewhere (p. 569). Normal values for urate clearance range from 11–15 ml. per minute; consequently, about 85–90 per cent of the urate filtered through the glomeruli is reabsorbed in the tubules.

In urine of average pH (6.0 or higher) uric acid is present largely as the soluble sodium and potassium urates, whereas in highly acid urine the relatively insoluble free acid may predominate and may precipitate from solution.

The amount of uric acid in the urine of normal subjects depends on the quantity of nucleoprotein ingested (exogenous) and that formed from tissue nucleic acids and nucleotides (endogenous). On purine-free diets, the urinary uric acid is of solely endogenous origin and is rather constant for the individual, usually 0.1–0.5 gram daily. This may be increased somewhat by strenuous exercise and by a high protein or high caloric intake (stimulating endogenous metabolism).

On a high purine diet (meat, liver, kidney, sweetbreads, leguminous vegetables, etc.) the uric acid output may be as much as 2 grams daily. In adults on the usual mixed diet the average daily excretion is about 0.7 gram, comprising 1–2 per cent of the total nitrogen. The urine of newborn infants contains relatively large amounts of uric acid (0.2 gram/100 ml.), comprising about 7–8 per cent of the total nitrogen. Crystals of free uric acid and ammonium urate may be present and urate "infarcts" of the kidneys are not uncommon. A sharp drop to normal adult levels occurs after seven to ten days. A considerable increase follows administration of cinchophen and salicylates. Caffeine and other methylpurines (in tea, coffee, cocoa) cause little or no increase, being either transformed largely to urea or undergoing more complete destruction in the body.

Urinary excretion of uric acid, reflecting nucleoprotein catabolism, is increased by 11-oxygenated adrenocortical hormones and by ACTH. It has been suggested that determination of the extent of rise in the urinary uric acid:creatinine ratio after administration of ACTH may be useful as a test of the reserve functional capacity of the adrenal cortex (p. 571).

ALLANTOIN. Allantoin is formed from uric acid in the liver by the action of the enzyme uricase (p. 569). In man and anthropoid apes, the livers of which exhibit little or no uricase activity, allantoin is excreted in very small amounts (5–25 mg. daily). In other mammals it is the chief end-product of purine metabolism, accounting for 90 per cent or more of the excretion of purine metabolites. It was formerly believed that the metabolism of purines in the Dalmatian dog resembled that in man and apes (differing from that of other mammals) in having uric acid as its chief metabolic end-product. Present evidence indicates that the urinary excretion of relatively large amounts of uric acid is due to its incomplete reabsorption by the renal tubular epithelium and not to a difference from other breeds of dogs in capacity for forming allantoin from uric acid.

OXALIC ACID. Small amounts of oxalate (10–25 mg.) are excreted daily in the urine of normal subjects. Its origin is not well understood. Calcium oxalate, which precipitates from neutral or alkaline urine in the presence of abnormally high oxalate excretion, is an important constituent of urinary calculi. Under normal conditions, the main source of urinary oxalate is probably dietary, it or certain metabolic precursors being present in many common foodstuffs (tomatoes, rhubarb, cabbage, spinach, asparagus, apples, grapes, etc.). Oxalate may also be one of the end-products of the metabolism of ascorbic acid and may also be formed, perhaps, in the intermediary metabolism of carbohydrate, presumably not significantly under normal conditions.

GLUCURONIC ACID (P. 16). Glucuronic acid occurs in normal urine conjugated with a wide variety of compounds in two types of linkage, (1) ester and (2) glycosidic. The carboxyl groups of such compounds as phenylacetic acid and benzoic acid form ester linkages, whereas the hydroxyl groups of such substances as aliphatic or aromatic alcohols (chloral, camphor, phenol, menthol, indole, skatole, morphine, pregnanediol, estriol, etc.), form glycosidic linkages. This conjugation apparently takes place in the liver, which is probably also the site of formation of glucuronic acid, the metabolic derivation of which is not clear.

The normal daily excretion of glucuronic acid is about 0.3–1.0 gram. This may be increased by administration of the substances indicated above, as well as acetylsalicylic acid, sulfonamides (except sulfanilamide), turpentine, antipyrine, and phenolphthalein. When present in relatively high concentration, the ester types reduce the usual copper reagents (e.g., Benedict's), probably owing to concomitant hydrolysis, and may therefore interfere with the interpretation of urinary tests for glucose. The glycoside types do not reduce these reagents unless previously hydrolyzed.

HIPPURIC ACID (BENZOYLGLYCINE) (P. 282). Hippuric acid is formed by the conjugation, in peptide linkage, of benzoic acid and glycine. In man, this occurs largely if not solely in the liver; in certain species (e.g., dog), it occurs also in the kidney.

Benzoic acid (or benzoate) is present, as such, in many vegetables and fruits (e.g., cranberries, plums) and addition of sodium benzoate, as a preservative, to certain prepared foodstuffs is legally permissible. Quinic acid, another constituent of vegetables and fruits, is converted to benzoic acid in the body; the latter may arise also from intestinal bacterial action on aromatic compounds, viz., tyrosine and phenylalanine.

Glycine is normally invariably present in amounts adequate to convert all of the benzoic acid formed to hippuric acid. The latter, formed in the liver cells, enters the systemic circulation and is excreted in the urine in amounts ranging from 0.1–1.0 gram (usually 0.5–0.7 gram) daily, depending largely on the dietary intake.

CITRIC ACID. Citrate is excreted in the urine in amounts of 0.2–1.2 grams daily. It is increased by administration of estrogen and decreased by androgen. Urinary citrate varies during the menstrual cycle, increasing during the first half (increasing elaboration of estrogen), persisting at a high level during the luteal phase (synergistic action of estrogen and progesterone), and falling in the premenstrual phase (drop in estrogen). The significance of these changes is not clear. Administration of alkalies or alkaline ash diets increases, and acidification decreases, urinary citrate.

Citric acid is formed in large amounts in the course of oxidative metabolism of carbohydrate. Whether or not this is the main source of urine citrate is not known. Citrate is present in the bones, apparently as a superficial deposit on the crystal lattice of apatite, which is the chief mineral complex in bone (p. 613). Citrate forms soluble and undissociable complexes with calcium, and these two ions exhibit certain interrelationships in their urinary excretion. Administration of parathyroid hormone or of very large doses of vitamin D, producing hypercalcemia, increases urine calcium and citrate (mobilization from skeleton?). Injection of citrate increases urinary excretion of calcium, perhaps by increasing its solution from bone.

OTHER ORGANIC ACIDS. Lactic acid, the end-product of glycolysis in muscle, passes into the blood stream, undergoing ultimate reconversion to glycogen or glucose in the liver (p. 386). About 50–200 mg. are excreted daily in the urine under ordinary conditions of activity. Much more may appear during periods of prolonged, strenuous muscular exercise or anoxia.

Minute amounts (up to 50 mg. daily) of fatty acids may be excreted in the urine. These are mainly short-chain acids (formic, acetic, butyric), which arise chiefly during intermediary metabolism and as a result of intestinal bacterial action (p. 272).

Certain aromatic hydroxyacids may appear in the urine of normal subjects in small amounts. The most important are p-hydroxyphenyl-acetic and p-hydroxyphenylpropionic acids, which are formed in the intermediary metabolism and intestinal putrefaction of tyrosine. Other aromatic hydroxyacids (p-hydroxyphenylpyruvic, p-hydroxyphenyl-lactic, dihydroxyphenylacetic acids) may be excreted in abnormal states (tyrosinosis, vitamin C-deficient infants, certain cases of mental deficiency, alkaptonuria) (pp. 550, 552).

KETONE BODIES. The substances designated "ketone bodies" include acetone, acetoacetic acid, and β-hydroxybutyric acid. These are formed in the liver in the course of metabolism of fatty acids (p. 450), and are conveyed in the blood stream to the tissues for further oxidation. Under normal conditions, on the usual mixed diet, less than 125 mg. are excreted daily in the urine. Larger amounts may be eliminated on high-fat diets, during starvation or severe carbohydrate restriction, and during normal pregnancy. Marked increases are encountered in a variety of abnormal states associated with excessive ketogenesis (p. 483), e.g., diabetes mellitus (p. 430).

SULFUR-CONTAINING COMPOUNDS. Sulfur appears in the urine as (1) so-called neutral sulfur and (2) sulfate, the latter in (a) inorganic and (b) organic (ester; ethereal sulfate) combination. The bulk of the urinary sulfur is derived from the metabolism of the amino acids, methionine, cystine and cysteine, the amount excreted by normal subjects therefore varying with the protein intake.

The total sulfur excretion usually ranges from 0.7–1.5 grams daily, averaging about 1.0 gram. The urinary N:S ratio is about 15:1. Neutral sulfur comprises about 5–15 per cent of the total (0.04–0.15 gram), and sulfate-S 85–95 per cent. About 5–15 per cent of the latter is organic (ethereal) sulfate (0.06–0.12 gram), the remainder inorganic (0.6–1.0 gram).

Neutral sulfur includes such substances as cystine, methionine, methylmercaptan, taurine and its derivatives (taurocholic acid), thiocyanate, thiosulfate, and urochrome.

Ethereal (organic) sulfate consists largely of phenolic sulfates, formed in the liver from aromatic compounds arising from intestinal bacterial action on tyrosine and tryptophan (indole, skatole, cresol, phenol) (p. 282) or from benzene or other phenolic compounds entering the organism (as under conditions of industrial or accidental exposure). Certain hormones, including estrone and androsterone, are excreted largely as sulfates and fall into this category (pp. 661, 667). Indole, which arises almost entirely from intestinal putrefaction, is converted to indoxyl in the liver, is conjugated with sulfate, and appears in the urine as potassium (and sodium) indoxyl sulfate (indican). This is a rough index of the extent of intestinal putrefaction (< 20 mg. daily normally).

Further details are considered in the section on sulfur metabolism (p. 605).

PHOSPHATE. The metabolism of phosphorus is considered in detail elsewhere (p. 609). Phosphorus is excreted (urine and feces) largely as inorganic phosphate, and to a small extent in organic form (< 4 per cent of total). Inasmuch as the phosphate is derived chiefly from the metabolism (oxidation) of phosphorus-containing organic foodstuffs (and tissue components), such as phosphoproteins, nucleoproteins, nucleotides, and phospholipids, the quantity excreted depends in large measure on the nature of the diet. It is therefore extremely variable.

The proportion of the total phosphorus excretion eliminated in the urine depends under normal conditions on dietary and intra-intestinal factors. On the usual mixed diet the daily urinary phosphorus excretion is 0.7–1.5 grams, averaging about 1.1 grams, almost entirely in the form of inorganic phosphate, comprising about 60 per cent of the total excretion (feces 40 per cent). If intestinal absorption of phosphate is diminished, as by high intake of calcium or magnesium (also aluminum, beryllium, iron), which tend to form relatively insoluble phosphates, unusually high intestinal alkalinity, and low vitamin D intake (in children), the amount and proportion of phosphorus eliminated in the urine decreases (increases in feces). Conversely, on a low calcium, moderately high phosphorus intake, about 75 per cent of the total excretion is urinary. The parathyroid hormone increases renal excretion of phosphate by diminishing its reabsorption in the tubules (p. 616). The "renal threshold" for phosphate excretion is about 2 mg. P/100 ml. plasma, excretion falling to a minimum at lower concentrations.

The phosphate ion appears in the urine in two forms, viz., acid phosphate, $H_2PO_4^-$, and basic phosphate, $HPO_4^=$. The ratio, $BH_2PO_4:B_2HPO_4$, varies with and largely determines the pH of the urine, since acid and basic phosphates constitute the major buffer system in that fluid (p. 321). Relatively insoluble phosphates tend to form in alkaline urine, and are often important components of urinary calculi. The turbidity which develops in urine on standing (ammoniacal fermentation) is contributed to largely by precipitation of phosphates, including $MgNH_4PO_4$ ("triple phosphate"), insoluble at alkaline reactions.

CHLORIDE. In normal subjects on an average diet (8–15 grams NaCl intake), the quantity of chloride in the urine is second only to urea, among the solid constituents, approximating the intake (5–9 grams chloride ion; 110 to 255 mEq.). The normal "renal threshold" for chloride is about 340 mg./100 ml. plasma; in normal subjects, as the plasma chloride concentration descends to this level, urinary excretion of chloride decreases (renal tubular reabsorption, p. 600). This is influenced by the level of adrenal cortical function (p. 678).

If the chloride intake is changed suddenly, some time may be required for the reestablishment of equilibrium between intake and output. For example, the sudden addition of a large amount of salt is usually followed by elimination of the excess within forty-eight hours. However, if the previous intake has been unusually low, the elimination of the increment may be delayed several days.

In conditions in which elimination of chloride through other channels is increased, e.g., excessive perspiration, diarrhea, vomiting, the urine chloride decreases correspondingly.

SODIUM; POTASSIUM. The kidney is the chief regulator of excretion, consequently of the body equilibrium of sodium and potassium, the chief cations of extracellular and intracellular fluids, respectively. Operation of these excretory mechanisms therefore plays an important role in the maintenance of water and "acid-base" equilibrium (pp. 321, 600). The daily urinary output of these elements by normal adults approximates their intake. Under usual dietary conditions, normal adults excrete in the urine about 3–5 grams (130–215 mEq.) sodium and 2–4 grams (50–100 mEq.) potassium daily (Na:K ratio about 5:3). During periods of fasting or inadequate protein intake, excessive tissue protein catabolism, with liberation of intracellular fluid components, results in an increase in urinary potassium and a change in the Na:K ratio.

Adrenal cortical hormones, under ordinary circumstances, stimulate reabsorption of sodium and depress that of potassium by the renal tubular epithelial cells (p. 678). Potassium enters the urine from the plasma by glomerular filtration and also by active tubular secretion, the latter mechanism apparently competing with that for urine acidification. Details of this process are considered elsewhere (p. 322). The amount of potassium in the urine is therefore influenced by the requirement for urine acidification, increasing when this requirement is low (e.g., alkaline ash diet; alkalosis) and decreasing when it is high (highly acid ash diet; acidosis).

Abnormal loss, through extrarenal channels, of sodium (excessive sweating, diarrhea, etc.) or of potassium (diarrhea) results in decrease in the urinary excretion of these elements.

CALCIUM; MAGNESIUM. Under usual dietary conditions in normal subjects, urinary excretion accounts for about 15–30 per cent of the total calcium and about 20 to 50 per cent of the total magnesium elimination, the remainder being excreted in the feces. At low or moderate levels of calcium intake (0.1–0.5 gram daily), about 30–50 per cent is eliminated in the urine, whereas at high levels of intake (1.0 gram) about 10–25 per cent is so eliminated. The dependence of the urinary excretion of these elements on their absorption from the intestine, and the factors involved (vitamin D, phosphate, etc.), are considered elsewhere (pp. 615, 616).

The "renal threshold" for excretion of calcium lies between 6.5 and 8.0 mg. per 100 ml. plasma, little being eliminated at lower plasma calcium concentrations. The influence of the parathyroid hormone in increasing urinary calcium is secondary to its action in increasing mobilization of calcium from the bones into the blood stream (p. 694). The effect of vitamin D in increasing urine calcium is a consequence of its enhancement of absorption of calcium from the intestine (p. 153).

CARBOHYDRATES (P. 428). Normal urine may contain reducing substances (< 1.5 grams/24 hours), up to 40 per cent of which are fermentable; concentrations over 0.25 per cent (Benedict's test) should be regarded as probably abnormal. A portion of this is glucose, the remainder being derived chiefly from the diet (galactose from lactose of milk; pentose from fruits; caramelized sugar and dextrins; proteins; products of intestinal bacterial action).

Glucose may appear in the urine in small amounts during normal pregnancy, particularly in the later months. In certain normal individuals, glucose may be excreted after ingestion of large amounts of sucrose, glucose, or, at times, starch (alimentary glycosuria). Lactose is excreted frequently during lactation. Pentose (L-arabinose) may appear in the urine of normal subjects after they have eaten large quantities of foods rich in pentose, e.g., cherries, grapes, plums, prunes (alimentary pentosuria). There is a chronic, familial type of pentosuria, in which L-ketoxylose is excreted independently of the nature of the diet. Galactose and fructose rarely appear in the urine of entirely normal subjects except after administration of supertolerance doses of these sugars.

MISCELLANEOUS. The urine of normal subjects may contain protein in amounts too small to be detected except by very sensitive procedures. The normal urinary protein does not exceed 75 mg. daily, and consists of serum albumin, which passes through the glomerular filter, enzymes (e.g., pepsin, trypsin, lipase, amylase), and nucleoprotein and "mucin" derived from the lower urinary tract.

The twenty-four-hour urine may contain minute quantities of iron ($<$ 0.3 mg.), arsenic ($<$ 0.5 mg.), copper ($<$ 0.1 mg.), zinc ($<$ 0.6 mg.), iodine ($<$ 0.07 mg.), and trace amounts of cobalt, nickel, fluorine, silicon, and lead.

A number of the water-soluble vitamins and their metabolites are excreted in the urine, usually in proportion to their intake. The quantities eliminated in the urine under controlled conditions have been employed as a basis for clinical evaluation of the state of vitamin nutrition, and are considered in the discussion of the individual vitamins (q.v.).

Certain hormones or their metabolites are excreted in the urine, e.g., gonadotrophins (p. 664), estrogens (p. 661), androgens (p. 668), pregnanediol (p. 664), adrenocortical hormones (p. 677). Determination of the quantities eliminated is employed in the clinical evaluation of the state of functional activity of the respective endocrine glands (q.v.).

Normal urine contains only minute amounts of lipids. Rarely, fat may appear in the urine after ingestion of unusually large amounts of fat, e.g., cod-liver oil ("alimentary lipuria").

BIBLIOGRAPHY

Annual Review of Physiology.

Berliner, R. W.: Renal excretion of water, sodium chloride, potassium, calcium and magnesium, Am. J. Med. 9:541, 1950.

Berliner, R. W.: Relationship between acidification of the urine and potassium metabolism, Am. J. Med. 11:274, 1951.

Cantarow, A. and Trumper, M.: Clinical Biochemistry, ed. 4, Philadelphia, W. B. Saunders Company, 1949, p. 336.

Goldblatt, H.: The renal origin of hypertension, Physiol. Rev. 27:120, 1947.

Macy Foundation Conferences on Renal Function, I, II, III. New York, Josiah Macy, Jr., Foundation, 1949, 1950, 1951.

Peters, J. P. and Van Slyke, D. D.: Quantitative Clinical Chemistry, Vol. I: Interpretations. Baltimore, Williams & Wilkins Company, 1931.

Pitts, R. F.: Renal excretion of acid, Fed. Proc. 7:418, 1948.

Shorr, E., Zweifach, B. W., Furchgott, R. F. and Baez, S.: Hepatorenal factors in experimental hypertension. Macy Foundation Conferences on Factors Regulating Blood Pressure, 1947, p. 32; 1951, p. 165.

Smith, H. W.: The Kidney. Structure and Function in Health and Disease, New York, Oxford University Press, 1951.

INDEX

Glyceraldehyde-3-phosphate, 390, 392, 404
  dehydrogenase, 392, 370
  oxidation, 392, 393
  structure, 22
Glyceric acid, 16
  structure, 17
Glyceric acid-2-phosphate, structure, 22
Glyceric acid-3-phosphate, structure, 22
Glyceric acid-1, 3-diphosphate, structure, 22
Glycerides
  autoxidation, 29
  chemistry, 28–31
  fatty acids in, 30
  hydrolysis, 29
  melting points, 29
  nomenclature, 29
  occurrence, 28
  saponification, 29
  solubility, 29
Glycerol
  in fat digestion, 264
  in fats, 28–31
  metabolism, 20, 405
  nature, 20
  solubility, 30
  structure, 21
Glycerophosphatase, classification and occurrence, 230, 231
Glycerophosphate dehydrogenases, 365
Glycine
  as source of "formate," 541
  bile acid precursor, 268
  conjugation, 282
    with benzoic acid, 282, 283, 520
    with bile acids, 520
    with cinnamic acid, 283
    with nicotinic acid, 283
  conversion to glyoxylic acid, 519
  from metabolism of betaine, 538
  in creatine synthesis, 521
  in detoxication, 282
  in glutathione synthesis, 521
  in porphyrin synthesis, 520, 587
  in purine synthesis, 520, 567
  interconversion with serine, 519
  metabolism, 519–522
  relation to "formate," 519
  structure, 49
Glycine dehydrogenase, 362, 364
Glycineamide ribotide in purine synthesis, 567
Glycocholic acid, 36. See also *Bile acids*.
  biosynthesis, 267, 268
  in bile, 267
Glycocyamine, 521
Glycogen
  action of salivary amylase, on, 259, 260
  bone formation, and, 614
  energy from, 395, 396
  functions, 2, 16
  in brain, effect of blood glucose, 721
    factors influencing, 721
  in cartilage, 614, 715
  in endometrium, 662
  in heart, 415
  in muscle, 409
  in nervous tissue, 720

Glycogen (*cont'd*)
  in skin, 717
  in vaginal epithelium, 662
  iodine reaction, 26
  liver
    after adrenocortical hormones, 432, 679
    after pancreatectomy, 691
    blood glucose from, 419
    content, 407
    effect of adrenocortical hormones, 679
      of epinephrine, 693
      of hyperglycemic factor, 693
      of insulin, 423, 691
    in diabetes mellitus, 691
    sources of, 406
  muscle, amount, 723
    effect of adrenocortical hormones, 432, 679
      of growth hormone, 701
      of insulin, 691
  occurrence, 16
  phosphorolysis, 16
  storage, 386
  storage disease, 407
  structure, 16
  synthesis, 386, 391
Glycogenesis
  effects of insulin, 691
  in nervous tissue, 720
  influence of blood glucose, 407
  liver, 385, 386, 390, 391, 406, 407
    effect of blood glucose, 419, 420
      of insulin, 419, 423
    factors influencing, 419
  muscle, 386, 390, 391, 408
Glycogenolysis, 385, 391, 406, 407
  effect of blood glucose, 407, 420
    of epinephrine, 391, 419, 424, 672, 693
    of exercise, 419
    of hyperglycemic factor, 391, 424, 693
    of insulin, 691
    of thyroxine, 419, 424, 685
  liver, 406, 407
Glycogenolytic factor, 693. See also *Hyperglycemic factor*.
Glycolaldehyde
  occurrence, 8, 403
  structure, 4
Glycolipids
  cerebrosides, 11, 34
  chemistry, 34
  classification, 28
  distribution in tissues, 442
  galactose in, 11
  gangliosides, 35
  in muscle, 724
  metabolism, 469
  occurrence, 11, 34
Glycolysis, 387, 388–396
  ATP in, 390–394
  definition, 388
  effect of epinephrine, 672
  energetics of, 393–396
  energy production, 374
  ethanol formation, 390, 393
  high-energy phosphate from, 393–396
  in bone formation, 614

Heparinase, 736
  occurrence in liver, 234
Hepatotoxic agents, fatty liver from, 477, 480
Hesperidin, 167
Heteropolysaccharidases, classification, 233
Heterosaccharides, 3, 14, 18
γ-Hexachlorocyclohexane, 650
Hexitols. See *Sugar alcohols.*
Hexokinase, 389
  classification, 247
  effect of adrenocortical hormones, 389, 423
    of anterior pituitary hormones, 423, 424
    of growth hormone, 423, 424, 700, 701
    of insulin, 389, 423
    of pituitary hormones, 389
  in brain, 394
  in glucosamine metabolism, 405
  in liver, 395, 406
  in muscle, 395
  reaction, effect of adrenocortical hormones, 680, 692
    of growth hormone, 680, 692
    of insulin, 692
Hexosans, 3, 14
Hexose diphosphate aldolase, classification, 242
Hexose phosphates
  conversion to trioses, 392
  in carbohydrate metabolism, 390
  structure, 22
Hexosediphosphatase, classification and occurrence, 230, 231
Hexosemonophosphatase, classification and occurrence, 230, 231
Hexoses. See also under names of individual forms.
  anaerobic metabolism, 390
  classification, 3
  definition, 3
  energy production, 401, 402
  glycolysis, 390–394
  in polysaccharides, 14
  interconversions, 387, 394, 395
  metabolism, 383–403
  occurrence, 10
  phosphorylation, 390, 395
  reducing properties, 8
  tests for, 23–26
Hippulin, 660
Hippuric acid, 282, 283
  in urine, 774
  structure, 51
  synthesis from glycine, 520
Histamine
  acetylation, 455, 526
  antagonists of, 647, 648
  formation, 526
  from histidine, 274
  gastric secretion and, 260, 261
  oxidation, 526
Histidase
  classification and occurrence, 239
  in histidine metabolism, 527
Histidine
  as source of "formate," 541
  bacterial action on, 274
  buffer action, 315

Histidine (*cont'd*)
  conversion to glutamic acid, 527
    to histamine, 526
  formation of anserine, 526
    of carnosine, 526
    of "formate," 527
  histamine from, 274
  metabolism, 526–527
  structure, 49
Histidine decarboxylase, classification, 242
Histones
  classification, 44, 45, 47
  composition, 80
  in nucleoproteins, 96
Holoenzyme, definition, 222
Homocysteine, 531
  in purine synthesis, 567
  methylation, 537
  pyridoxine action on, 192
Homocysteine desulfhydrase, classification, 241, 242
Homogentisic acid
  excretion in alcaptonuria, 552
  formation, 552
  oxidation, 553
Homopolysaccharidases, classification, 233
Homosaccharides, 3, 14, 18
Homoserine, 531
Hopkins-Cole reaction, 87
Hormones, 654–707. See also under names of individual hormones.
  adrenal, 670–681
    cortical, 673–681
    medullary, 670–673
  androgens, 665–670
  definition, 654
  enterocrinin, 264
  estrogens, 658–662
  fat-mobilizing, 680
  gastrointestinal, 705–707
  in carbohydrate metabolism, 422–424, 430–433
  in protein deficiency, 633
  in urine, 779
  influence on enzymes, 254–255
  neurohormones, 704–705
  pancreatic, 689–693
    hyperglycemic factor, 693
    insulin, 689–693
  pancreozymin, 262
  parathyroid, 693–695
  pituitary, 695–704
    anterior, 695–701
    melanophore-expanding, 703
    posterior, 701–704
  polysaccharides in, 18
  progesterone, 662–665
  secretin, 262
  steroid, 35
    adrenocortical, 673–681
    androgens, 665–670
    estrogens, 658–662
    nomenclature, 655–658
    progesterone, 662–665
  thyroid, 681–689
Houssay animals, 433
Hüfner factor, 289

17-Ketosteroids in urine, in ascorbic acid
    deficiency, 148
  neutral, 668
L-Ketoxylose
  from glucuronic acid, 406
  in pentosuria, 405
  in urine, 9, 779
  occurrence, 9
  structure, 9
Kidney(s)
  acid excretion by, 321–323, 327, 329, 331
    in acidosis, 323, 326, 327, 329
    in alkalosis, 323, 326, 330, 331
  acid-base balance regulation, 320–324,
    327, 329, 331
  adrenocortical hormone action on, 678,
    679
  ammonia formation, 323, 757
    in acidosis, 323, 326, 327, 329
    in alkalosis, 323, 326, 330, 331
  blood flow, 763
  carbon dioxide reabsorption, 323
  concentrating ability, 758–760, 767
  disease, blood creatinine in, 746
    blood urea in, 746
    blood uric acid in, 746
    globulins in blood in, 742
    glomerular filtration in, 762
  excretion of chloride, 600
    of potassium, 600
    of sodium, 600
  function, 754–779. See also Renal function.
  iodine excretion, 606, 607
  magnesium excretion, 608
  phosphate reabsorption, effect of para-
    thyroid hormone, 695
  potassium excretion, 322, 600
  renin from, 765
  sodium reabsorption by, 321–323, 327
  sodium-hydrogen exchange, 321–323, 327
  tubular excretory mass, 764
  tubules, ammonia formation in, 323, 757
    excretion by, 323, 757
    potassium reabsorption, 600
      excretion, 322, 600
    reabsorption in, 756, 764, 765
    sodium reabsorption, 600
  vasoexcitor principle, 765
Kinases. See Phosphokinases and under
    names of individual enzymes.
Kjeldahl method, 88
Krebs cycle, 397–401. See also Tricarboxylic
    acid cycle.
Kynurenic acid, 184, 185, 547
Kynureninase in tryptophan metabolism, 546
Kynurenine, 184, 185, 545, 546

Labile methyl groups, 536
Lactalbumin in milk, 727, 728
Lactase, 265. See also β-Galactosidase.
Lactation
  ascorbic acid requirement, 148
  basal metabolism, 341
  calcium requirement, 617
  iron requirement, 620, 625
  lactogenic hormone and, 699

Lactation (cont'd)
  protein requirement, 624, 625, 632
  riboflavin requirement, 182
  urine lactose in, 778
  vitamin A requirement, 140
  vitamin D requirement, 157
Lactic acid
  blood glucose from, 419
  energy level, 374
  formation in muscle, 413
    in blood, 414, 743
      effect of epinephrine, 424, 672
      in exercise, 414
    in muscle, 724
    in semen, 752
    in urine, 775
    utilization by heart, 408
  dehydrogenase, 365, 367, 394, 396
Lactobacillus bulgaricus factor, 170
  casei factor, 202
    acetate factor, 215. See α-Lipoic acid.
Lactogenic hormone, 699
  actions, 699
  assay, 699
  chemistry, 699
Lactoglobulin in milk, 727, 728
Lactose. See also Carbohydrates.
  digestion, 265, 384
  from galactose, 387, 395
  from glucose, 387
  in blood, 743
  in milk, 417, 418, 728, 729
    fermentation of, 729
    synthesis of, 729
  in urine, 228, 417, 778
  occurrence, 12
  structure, 12
  tests for, 23–26
Lactosuria, 417, 428, 778
  in lactation, 778
Lead
  effect on phosphate absorption, 155
    on porphyrin excretion, 596
  in blood, 747
  in urine, 779
  rachitogenic action, 155
Lecithin(s)
  chemistry, 31
  choline in, 31
  classification, 28
  in brain, 719
  in erythrocytes, 738
  solubility, 31
  structure, 32
Lecithinases (A and B), classification and oc-
    currence, 228, 230
    (C and D), classification and occurrence,
    230, 231
  in snake venoms, 33
Leucine
  metabolism, 544
  structure, 49
Leucine aminopeptidase. See Aminopep-
    tidase, leucine.
Leucoriboflavin, 178, 181
Leucovorin, 203
Leukemia, blood uric acid in, 746

Ovary (cont'd)
  estrogen formation, 660
  progesterone formation, 662
Oviduct, avidin in, 200
Ovomucoid, 18
Oxalacetic acid
  condensation reaction, 398, 399
  decarboxylase classification, 242
  decarboxylation, 400, 407, 408
  in pyrimidine synthesis, 571
  in tricarboxylic acid cycle, 398, 399
Oxalic acid from ascorbic acid, 141, 773
  in pentose metabolism, 403
  in urine, 773. See also *Urine, oxalic acid.*
Oxalosuccinic acid decarboxylase, 399
  classification, 242
  in tricarboxylic acid cycle, 398
Oxidases, 359, 361, 362. See also individual
  enzymes.
  electron transfer, 358
  prosthetic groups, 362
Oxidation(s)
  and phosphorylation, 378–380
  biological, 354–370. See also *Biological
  oxidations.*
  cellular, in mitochondria, 711
  coupled, 378–380
  coenzymes, 379
  definition, 354, 355
  energy production, 374
  enzyme systems, 358–370
  in detoxication, 279
  in tricarboxylic acid cycle, 398–401
  of alcohols, 279
  of aromatic hydrocarbons, 280
  of methyl groups, 280
  uncoupling, 381
Oxidation-reduction. See also *Biologica
  oxidations.*
  definition, 355
  reactions, ascorbic acid in, 145
    nicotinamide in, 187
    riboflavin in, 178, 181
    tocopherols in, 159
Oxidative chain phosphorylation, 379
Oxidative deamination, 509
Oxybiotin, 197, 198
  biotin activity, 197
Oxygen
  affinity, of myoglobin, 723
  caloric value of, 334, 335
  capacity of blood, 289
    of hemoglobin, 289
  combining capacity, 122
  consumption, effect of epinephrine, 672
    of thyroxine, 685
    normal, 340
  dissociation curve
    of hemoglobin, 289
    of myoglobin, 723
  exchange in lungs, 286, 287, 292
    in tissues, 287, 292
  in alveolar air, 286
  in atmosphere, 286
  in blood, 287, 289–292
  in expired air, 286
  in inspired air, 286

Oxygen (cont'd)
  partial pressure, hemoglobin saturation
    and, 289, 290
    in alveolar air, 286
    in atmosphere, 286
    in blood, 287, 289–292
    in expired air, 286
    in inspired air, 286
  saturation of hemoglobin, 289
  tension, and iron absorption, 619
  transport, 288–292
  uptake, in vitamin E deficiency, 160
  utilization, 287, 288
Oxyhemoglobin. See *Hemoglobin, oxy-.*
11-Oxysteroids. See *Corticosteroids, 11-
  oxygenated.*
Oxytocin, 701, 702
  assay, 702
  chemistry, 702
  structure, 81

PABA. See *p-Aminobenzoic acid.*
Pain
  effect on blood glucose, 416
    on glycogenolysis, 419
"Paludrine," as possible pyrimidine antagonist, 649, 650
Pancreas
  amylase
    action, 263
    nature, 263
  disease, blood amylase in, 747
    blood lipase in, 747
  hormones, 689–693. See also *Insulin;
  Hyperglycemic factor.*
  islets
    destruction by dehydroascorbic acid,
      148, 432
    effect of alloxan on, 432
      of dehydroascorbic acid, 432
      of hyperglycemia, 431, 432
  fistula, acidosis in, 327
  juice, 262–264
    amylase, 263
    bicarbonate in, 601
    carboxypeptidase, 263
    chloride in, 601
    chymotrypsin, 263
    composition, 262
    electrolytes in, 328, 601
    enzymes, 262
    lipase, 263
    nucleases, 264
    pancreozymin stimulation, 262
    potassium in, 601
    secretin stimulation, 262
    sodium in, 601
    trypsin, 262
    vagus stimulation, 262
  lipase, 263
    action, 264
    nature, 263
Pancreatectomy
  acid-base balance, 691
  blood cholesterol, 691
  blood glucose, 691

Phosphorylases, effect of epinephrine, 391,
424, 672, 693
of hyperglycemic factor, 391, 424, 693
in intestine, 266
occurrence, 245
Phosphorylation
and oxidation, 378, 379
coupled, 378, 379
coenzymes, 379
effect of thyroxine, 687
effect of phlorizin, 429, 434
in carbohydrate absorption, 384, 389
in glycolysis, 389–392
in renal reabsorption, 429
substrate, 378, 379
coenzymes, 379
uncoupling, 381
Phosphotransacetylase, classification, 248
Phosphotriose isomerase, classification, 242
Photosynthesis, 372
Phrenosin, 34
Phytic acid
and vitamin D, 153, 611
effect on calcium absorption, 212, 610, 611,
615
rachitogenic action, 153, 212, 610, 611
structure, 212
Phytin
inositol in, 21
structure, 212
Phytosterols, in feces, 277
pI, 62
Pigment
in skin, 717–719
in urine, 766
Pigmentation
adrenal hormones and, 718
androgens and, 718
effect of vitamins, 718
estrogens and, 718
in inflammation, 718
pituitary and, 703
Pimelic acid
biotin precursor, 198
structure, 198
Pincus reaction, 668
Pitocin, 701, 702. See also *Oxytocin.*
Pitressin, 701–703
antidiuretic effect, 702
assay, 702
chemistry, 702
functions, 702
structure, 81
Pituitary
anterior, effect of androgen, 670
of epinephrine, 671, 672
function and insulin tolerance, 421
hormones. See also individual hormones.
adrenocorticotrophic, 697
anterior, 695–701
gonadotrophic, 698–700
growth, 700, 701
pars intermedia, 703, 704
posterior, 701–703
chemistry, 702
effects of, 701
functions, 702

Pituitary hormones (*cont'd*)
posterior, melanophore-expanding, 703
nature of, 701, 702
thyrotrophic, 696
trophic, 696
Pituitrin, 701. See also *Pitressin; Pitocin.*
pK, 57
Placenta
carotenoids in, 131
chorionic gonadotrophin from, 699
estrogen formation, 660
progesterone formation, 662
Plasma. See also individual components and
Blood.
albumin. See *Albumin, plasma* and *Blood,
albumin.*
cholesterol, 472–473
and atherosclerosis, 473
influence of diet, 473
of thyroid, 473
globulins. See *Globulins in plasma,* and
Blood globulins.
lipids. See also *Blood lipids.*
influence of food and nutrition, 474–475
postabsorptive concentrations, 471–474
phospholipids, 473–474
in diabetes mellitus, 474
influence of thyroid, 474
proteins, 501. See also *Blood plasma proteins,* and individual components.
and estrogen transport, 660
carbamino compounds, 293
electrophoretic pattern, 501
fractionation by alcohol, 502, 503
fractionation by salting out, 502
functions, 505–507
identity, 501–504
in protein deficiency, 633
lipoproteins, 470, 503
metabolism, 504–505
physical properties, 501–504
thyroxine in, 684
triglycerides, 474. See also *Blood lipids.*
Plasmagenes, 256
Plasmalogens
classification, 28
occurrence, 33
structure, 32
Plasmapheresis, 496
Platelets. See also *Thrombocytes.*
composition of, 738
in blood coagulation, 735, 736
lipids in, 739
proteins in, 739
PNA, definition, 94. See also *Ribonucleic
acid.*
pO₂. See *Oxygen, partial pressure.*
pOH, 57
Polarized light and optical isomerism, 5
Polymers
of amino sugars, 18
of monosaccharides, 13
of sugar acids, 18
Polynucleotidases, classification and occurrence, 230, 231
Polynucleotides, structure, 102
Polyols, 3

Pregnanediol (*cont'd*)
  glucuronide, 663, 664
  structure, 663
  in urine, 16, 664
  in pregnancy, 661
Pregnanolone, 663
Pregnene, 663
Pregnenolone, 663
Proenzymes, definition, 224
Progesterone
  biological actions, 662, 665
  biosynthesis, 662, 664
    gonadotrophins and, 662
  chemistry, 663
  effect on hyaluronic acid, 714
    on oviduct avidin, 200
    on sodium balance, 665
    on water balance, 665
  from adrenal cortex, 675
  metabolism, 663, 664
  secretion
    effect of interstitial cell-stimulating hormone, 699
    of lactogenic hormone, 699
  solubility, 664
Prolactin, 699. See also *Lactogenic hormone*.
Prolamines
  classification, 44, 46
  gliadin, 46
  zein, 46
Prolidase
  classification, 235
  occurrence, 235
  specificity, 235, 236
Prolinase
  classification, 235
  occurrence, 235
  specificity, 235, 236
Proline
  effect of adrenal cortex on oxidation in kidney, 529
  metabolism, 528–529
  structure, 49
Propionic acid
  from isoleucine, 544
  from valine, 524
  glucogenicity, 453
Prostatic fluid
  acid phosphatase in, 752
  composition, 751, 752
Prostate, effect of interstitial cell-stimulating hormone, 699
Prosthetic group. See also *Coenzymes*.
  definition, 222
Prostigmine, 645, 646
Protamines
  classification, 44, 45, 47
  in nucleoproteins, 95
Proteans, classification, 47
Proteases. See also individual enzymes.
  definition, 234
  in digestion, 258
Protein(s)
  albumins, 44, 45
  amino acid content, 77
    table, 80
  amino acid sequence, 77, 81

Protein(s) (*cont'd*)
  anabolism, effect of adrenocortical hormones, 680
    of thyroxine, 685
  animal, 629–632
  as buffers, 65
  as charged particles, 63–67
  axial ratio, 73
  biological value, 495, 629–632
  biuret reaction, 88
  buffer action, 315
  caloric value, 332
  capillary permeability to, 302
  carbamino reaction, 87
  carbohydrate from, 385, 386
  catabolism, 500
    effect of adrenocortical hormones, 680
    of thyroxine, 685
    urine sulfur and, 605
  charged groups, 63–64
  chemistry, 42–93
  chlorophylloproteins, 44, 46
  classification, 44
  coagulation, 83
  colloidal properties, 67–72
  composition (table), 80
  conjugated, 44
  connective tissue, 712–714
  deficiency, 633
  definition, 42
  denaturation, 81–84
  denatured, 44, 47, 81
  deprivation, 497
  derived, 44
  detection of, 84–93
  determination of, 92–93
  dialysis, 71
  dielectric dispersion, 73
  dietary, amino acid composition, 630, 631
    animal, 629–632
    biological value of, 629–632
    caloric content, 623
    deficiency, 633
    functions, 628
    inadequate, 630, 631
    nitrogen balance and, 629–632
    quality of, 629–632
    quantity of, 624, 625, 632, 633
    requirements, 495–497, 624, 625, 629–632
    supplementary relationships, 631
    vegetable, 629–632
  digestion, 486–487
    aminopeptidases, 265
    carboxypeptidase, 263
    chymotrypsin, 263
    dipeptidases, 265
    effect of cottonseed oil, 628, 633
      of gossypol, 628, 633
      of soybean, 628, 633
    gastric juice, 261
    in stomach, 261
    pancreatic juice, 263
    pepsin, 261
    summary of, 270
    tripeptidases, 265
    trypsin, 263

Sulfonamides, competition with PABA, 204
  mechanism of action, 635–636, 640, 649
Sulfur. See also *Sulfates*.
  absorption, 604
  ethereal, 605
  excretion, 604–606
  in feces, 604
  in insulin, 690
  in urine, 775, 776. See also *Urine sulfur*.
  inorganic, conjugation, 605
    detoxication, 605
    excretion, 604–606
    formation, 604
  metabolism, 604–606
    general pathways, 534–535
    intermediary, 604
  occurrence, 604, 605
  organic, excretion, 604–606
    occurrence, 604, 605
    oxidation, 604
    utilization, 604, 605
Sulfuric acid
  conjugation, 282
    with indole, 282
    with phenol, 282
  in detoxication, 282
  production in body, 313
Suprasterols, 150
Sweat. See *Perspiration*.
Sympathetic nerves
    epinephrine formation, 671, 672
    norepinephrine formation, 671, 672
Sympathin in nervous tissue, 721
Sympatholytics, mechanism of action, 648
Sympathomimetics, mechanism of action, 648
Synovial fluid
    composition, 750
    glucose in, 416
    hyaluronic acid in, 714

TACHYSTEROL, 150
Tagatose, structure, 4
Talose, structure, 4
Tauber reaction, 24
Taurine
  bile acid precursor, 268
  conjugation with bile acids, 268
  synthesis from cysteine, 268, 533
Taurocholic acid, 36. See also *Bile acids*.
    biosynthesis, 267, 268
    in bile, 267
Tay-Sach's disease, lipid deposits in, 442
Teeth
  composition of, 715
  in vitamin A deficiency, 137
  in vitamin E deficiency, 160
  minerals in, 716
  proteins in, 715, 716
  vitamins and, 137, 716
Temperature and oxyhemoglobin dissociation, 292
Temperature regulation, by vaporization, 296
Tendomucoid, 713
Testane, 658

Testis
  androgen formation, 665
  effect of follicle-stimulating hormone, 698
    of interstitial cell-stimulating hormone, 699
  estrogen formation, 660
  progesterone formation, 662
Testosterone, 665, 666
  metabolism, 666–668
  vitamin A and, 133
Tetany
  after parathyroidectomy, 694
  in alkalosis, 617
  in hypocalcemia, 616, 617, 694
  in magnesium deficiency, 608
  in vitamin D deficiency, 155
  infantile, 155
  osteomalacic, 155
"Tetraethylammonium," 645, 646
Tetroses
  classification, 3
  definition, 3
Tetrahydromesobilanes, structures, 112, 113
Tetrahydromesobilenes, structures, 112, 113
Tetranucleotide hypothesis, 103
Thiaminase, 176
Thiamine, 170–177
  absorption, 173
  antilipotropic action, 477
  assay, 174
  biosynthesis, 171–173
  carbohydrate absorption and, 385
  catabolism, 173
  chemistry, 171
  destruction, 171
  excretion, 173
  functions, 175
  in blood, 173, 177, 748
  in cerebrospinal fluid, 173
  in feces, 174
  in foods, 174
  in milk, 174, 730
  in tissues, 173, 174
  in urine, 173, 174, 177
  inhibition of metabolism by pyrithiamine, 641, 642
  metabolism, 173
  occurrence, 174
  requirement, 177
    effect of thyroxine, 686
  solubility, 171
  storage, 173
  tests, 174, 175
  units, 174
Thiamine deficiency, 175–177
    beriberi, 175
    catatorulin effect, 176
    demonstration, 176
    edema, 176
    encephalopathy, 176
    lactic acid in blood, 176, 177
    occurrence, 176
    oxygen uptake by brain, 176
    paralysis, 176
    pyruvic acid in blood, 176, 177
    saturation tests, 177
    symptoms, 175

Thyroxine (*cont'd*)
  effect on cytochrome, 687
    on development, 686
    on electrolyte metabolism, 685
    on enzymes, 687
    on fatty acid oxidation, 685
    on gluconeogenesis, 685
    on glucose absorption, 420, 424
    on glycogenolysis, 419, 424, 685
    on growth, 686
    on lipid metabolism, 685
    on metamorphosis, 686
    on oxygen consumption, 685
    on phosphorylation, 687
    on plasma cholesterol, 685
    on plasma phospholipid, 685
    on protein metabolism, 685
    on thyroid, 688
    on thyrotrophin, 688
    on urine calcium, 686
    on urine chloride, 685
    on urine potassium, 685
    on urine sodium, 685
    on urine volume, 685
    on vitamin A, 686
    on vitamin requirement, 686
    on water balance, 685
  excretion, 608, 684
  formation, 556–557, 681–683
  in blood, 607, 684
  in thyroid, 608, 681, 683
  in uncoupling phosphorylations, 382
  influence on lipid metabolism, 481
    on protein metabolism, 508
  mechanism of action, 687
  metabolic effects, 684–687
  metabolism, 556, 557, 681–684
  secretion, 608, 683
  structure, 49
Tissue culture in study of intermediary metabolism, 347
Tissue factor in blood coagulation, 735
Tissue homogenates in study of intermediary metabolism, 348
Tissue mince in study of intermediary metabolism, 347
Tissue slic s n study of intermediary metabolism, 347
Tissues
  calcification after parathyroid hormone, 695
  chemical composition, 710–726. See also individual tissues.
  estrogen in, 660
  gas exchange in, 287, 292
  insulin combination, 691
  iodine in, 607, 608
  iron in, 619, 620
  water in, 299
Tocopherols, 157–161. See also *Vitamin E.*
  absorption, 159
  antioxidant action, 29, 38, 131, 132, 157, 158, 159, 160
    on fats, 158
    on vitamin A, 158
  chemistry, 157
  classification, 28

Tocopherols, excretion, 159
  forms, 157
  functions, 159–161
  in blood, 159
  in feces, 159
  in fetus, 159
  in foods, 158
  in milk, 159
  in oxidation-reduction reactions, 159
  in tissues, 159
  in urine, 159
  occurrence, 158
  solubility, 157
  storage, 159
  tests, 159
  vitamin A and, 138
Toxisterol, 150
TPN, 183, 184. See also *Triphosphopyridine nucleotide.*
Transacetylations. See *Transacylations.*
Transacylases
  classification, 248, 249
  coenzyme, 249
Transacylations, 454–456
  acetyl-CoA in, 195
  coenzyme A in, 195
  pantothenic acid in, 195
Transamidases, classification, 245, 246
Transamidination, 250
Transaminases
  classification, 246, 247
  coenzyme of, 246
  mechanism, 246
Transamination, 510
Transdeamination, 511
Transferring enzymes, 244–251
"Transforming substances" of bacteria, relation to nucleic acids, 580
Transformylases
  classification, 250
  coenzyme, 250
Transglycosidases, classification, 244, 245
Transimination, 250
Transmethylases, classification, 249, 250
Transmethylation, 536–540
  donors and acceptors of methyl groups, 536
  from "activated" methionine, 539
  from betaine, 537
  structures of donors, 537
"Transoxygenases," 250
Transpeptidases, classification, 245, 246
Transpeptidation and protein synthesis, 499
Transphosphorylases, classification, 247
Transphosphorylation, 377, 378
  enzymes, 377
Transthiolation, 250
Tricarboxylic acid cycle, 397–401
  decarboxylation in, 398–401
  dehydrogenation in, 398–401
  energetics, 401
  oxidation in, 398–401
"Triethyl" choline
  as inhibitor, 641, 642
  lipotropic action, 479
Triglycerides. See also *Fats* and *Glycerides.*